LIST OF SECTIONS

Numerical

ALPHABETICAL LIST APPEARS INSIDE BACK COVER.

ONE OF AN EXTENSIVE GROUP OF
REFERENCE BOOKS PUBLISHED BY
THE RONALD PRESS COMPANY

Sponsored by

The American Society of Mechanical Engineers

and the

American Material Handling Society

MATERIALS HANDLING HANDBOOK

Edited by

HAROLD A. BOLZ
PROFESSOR OF MECHANICAL ENGINEERING AND
ASSOCIATE DEAN, COLLEGE OF ENGINEERING
THE OHIO STATE UNIVERSITY

Associate Editor

GEORGE E. HAGEMANN
CONSULTING ENGINEER

NEW YORK
THE RONALD PRESS COMPANY
1958

Library of Congress Catalog Card Number: 57–11291

PRINTED IN THE UNITED STATES OF AMERICA

BOARD OF CONTRIBUTING AND CONSULTING EDITORS

FOREWORD

Development of modern manufacturing methods has necessitated parallel development in materials handling systems and equipment. As early as 1920, The American Society of Mechanical Engineers formed a Materials Handling Division to sponsor presentation of technical papers at meetings of the Society. This Division has actively cooperated with other Divisions of the Society, such as production engineering, management, railroad, aviation, and machine design, as well as with other societies and trade associations.

During World War II the stupendous problem of supplying American troops with munitions and supplies focused attention on military logistics and the problems of moving, packaging, warehousing, and shipping all kinds of materials. In order to profit by the experience in improved materials handling technology that had been developed for the war effort, several interested groups of materials handling engineers formed local societies, the first being the Material Handling Society organized in 1945 in Pittsburgh. The local groups joined forces in 1949 to form the American Material Handling Society.

Both the AMHS and the Materials Handling Division of ASME have been working in a common cause, dedicated to the advancement of the theory and practice of efficient materials handling in manufacturing, processing, warehousing, distribution, and transportation operations. They have striven to disseminate information regarding the best materials handling practices and to stimulate the development of better and more efficient materials handling equipment.

The art and science of materials handling is old in many respects. However, as most progress has been made in the past few years, comprehensive literature on the subject has been notably lacking. It was felt that much of the experience regarding materials handling principles, procedures, and techniques should be made available to students and to materials handling men in all types of manufacturing and processing industries and in other fields where materials handling is becoming increasingly important. There appeared to be an especially urgent need for a reference handbook in which all this material could be consolidated. Hence, the ASME Materials Handling Division and the AMHS jointly agreed to sponsor the MATERIALS HANDLING HANDBOOK.

The Joint Materials Handling Handbook Committee has made an outstanding contribution to the completeness of the HANDBOOK by developing the scope and coverage in the early stages of the work. After the Committee had accomplished this primary function, the work of examining, reviewing, and approving manuscripts, galley and page proofs for technical accuracy devolved on the Committee Chairman. Herbert H. Hall, with his broad and extensive experience in materials handling problems, has richly earned the appreciation of both Societies.

JAMES N. LANDIS, *President,* 1958
THE AMERICAN SOCIETY OF MECHANICAL ENGINEERS

WILLIAM E. KAPPLER, *President,* 1958
AMERICAN MATERIAL HANDLING SOCIETY

To determine the content of the proposed handbook, expedite the assembly of expert authors, and verify the technology, the two Societies formed the ASME-

vii

AMHS Joint Materials Handling Handbook Committee, most of whom were members of both Societies:

Herbert H. Hall, Aluminum Company of America, Pittsburgh—*Chairman.*
Robert C. Brady, W. B. McClelland Company, Cleveland.
James R. Bright, Harvard University, Boston.
Armand T. Gaudreau, Gaudreau, Rimbach & Associates, Pittsburgh.
H. L. Keely, Fiddes-Moore Company of Pennsylvania, Pittsburgh.
H. C. Keller, Lamson Corporation, Syracuse.
Harry J. Loberg, Cornell University, Ithaca.
Carleton Lord, Corning Glass Works, Corning.
Randolph W. Mallick, Westinghouse Electric Corporation, East Pittsburgh.
Donald W. Pennock, Carrier Corporation, Syracuse.
V. J. Reade, Whitehead Metal Products Company, Incorporated, New York.
Sidney Reibel, Jervis B. Webb Company, Detroit.
R. C. Sollenberger, Conveyor Equipment Manufacturers Association, Washington.
Jervis C. Webb, Jervis B. Webb Company, Detroit.

This Committee began its work in 1951, consulting, aiding, and assisting the Publishers' editorial staff. Meeting many times over a period of about two years, the Committee prepared and perfected specifications designating the scope and arrangement of the HANDBOOK. They developed a complete and integrated outline of the material to be covered by the HANDBOOK.

The untiring effort and energy put into the programming of the work by the Committee has resulted in a HANDBOOK of which the Societies are justly proud. With the aid of outstanding authors and competent staff editors, the HANDBOOK is the most complete and comprehensive treatise on materials handling ever produced.

HERBERT H. HALL, *Chairman*
ASME-AMHS JOINT MATERIALS HANDLING HANDBOOK
COMMITTEE

EDITORS' PREFACE

Addressed to all who have an interest in the efficient and economical handling of materials—whether in raw, in-process, or finished form—the MATERIALS HANDLING HANDBOOK brings together tested practical information on nearly every facet of this complex industrial problem. Organized into 47 coordinated sections, the HANDBOOK treats methods for analyzing handling problems; principles, procedures, and techniques for effective operation and control; systems design and installation; integration of materials handling activities with the manufacturing processes; and the design, selection, and classification of materials handling equipment. In compiling and editing this vast amount of information, it has been our constant aim to attain a clear, concise, and accurate form of presentation that will enable the HANDBOOK user to find the facts he seeks without time-consuming research. It is the hope of the Editors and Publishers that this HANDBOOK will make a significant contribution to the reduction of manufacturing and distribution costs through increased materials handling efficiency and that the information here presented will stimulate continued progress in the field of materials handling.

The HANDBOOK is an integrated treatment of accepted principles, practical procedures, tested data, and established facts drawn from the literature of the field and the experience of broad segments of industry. Its scope and organization were developed with the guidance of the distinguished members of the Materials Handling Handbook Committee of the American Society of Mechanical Engineers and the American Material Handling Society. The tremendous task of preparing the huge volume of material for the book was accomplished by a corps of contributing experts representing plant materials handling engineers, consulting engineers, educators, editors of technical publications, and manufacturers of materials handling equipment. With the objectivity and judgment born of experience, these men have collected significant information from books, journals, technical bulletins, reports, and the operating records of many companies. They have included a considerable selection of forms, tables, charts, diagrams, and photographs to insure a clear understanding of the subject matter.

The material thus collected was thoroughly reviewed and edited to assure an accurate and balanced treatment. Careful cross-referencing and thorough indexing provide quick access to related topics. Thus it is hoped that the user of this HANDBOOK will find it a convenient source of the information needed to answer the long-range policy questions and to solve the day-to-day operating problems of materials handling. It is further anticipated that from the successful experience of others, of which many examples are cited, he will find solutions that can be directly applied to the problems at hand.

The MATERIALS HANDLING HANDBOOK is the result of the thoughtful planning and coordinated effort of many men. The largest share of credit is due, of course, to the Contributing Editors, without whose efforts the HANDBOOK would have been impossible. They have given generously, not only in authorship, but in advice and counsel. While the writing and thinking of each are reflected through-

out the work, the sections to which they have made major contributions are listed
below:

Rodney R. Adler ....Elevators

John G. Anderson ....⎰Materials Positioning in Production
                                   ⎱Positioning Equipment

Alphonse F. Anjeskey ....Traveling Cranes and Towers

Charles B. Archibald ....Powered Industrial Trucks

G. H. Atwood ....⎱Fixed Cranes, Derricks, and Cableways
                               ⎰Traveling Cranes and Towers
                                ⎱Portable Cranes

G. H. Bannerman ....⎰Cable Conveyors
                               ⎱Fixed Cranes, Derricks, and Cableways

Curtis H. Barker, Jr. ....Industrial Tractors

Clarence M. Bartelme ....Powered Industrial Trucks

Herbert Bisen ....Powered Industrial Trucks

Frank M. Blum ....Traveling Cranes and Towers

Jack Breslav ....Auxiliary Crane Equipment

James R. Bright ....Communications Systems

James Francis Brown, Jr. ....Unit Handling in Manufacturing

Stanley E. Bryan ....Materials Handling and Production Control

J. F. Carle ....Training Personnel

Richard Carr ....Elevating Conveyors

David W. Chase ....Warehousing and Yard Handling

E. J. Clement ....Unit Handling for Various Shapes

A. E. Conover ....In-Process Handling of Bulk Materials

James Flett ....Scrap Classification and Handling

Herbert J. Flint ....Vibrating and Oscillating Conveyors

Irving M. Footlik ....⎰Industrial Hand Trucks
                                         ⎱Powered Industrial Trucks

Sherman W. Fountain ....⎰Fixed Cranes, Derricks, and Cableways
                                ⎱Traveling Cranes and Towers

Armand T. Gaudreau ....⎰Factory Planning
                                    ⎱Warehousing and Yard Handling

Saul Goldweitz ....⎰Palletization
                                        ⎱Pallets and Containers

Robert G. Hagemann ....⎰Uses of Containers in Industry
                                      ⎱Pallets and Containers

Herbert H. Hall ....Definition and Scope of Materials Handling

T. L. Harp ....⎰Cable Conveyors
                               ⎱Fixed Cranes, Derricks, and Cableways

O. R. Heidenrich ....Industrial Tractors

John B. Hulse ....Highway Trucks and Truck-Trailers

Burr W. Hupp ....⎰Railroad Terminal Handling
                                     ⎱Truck Terminal Handling

John R. Immer ....Air Terminal Handling

Robert W. Johnson ....Air Terminal Handling

Walter E. Johnson ....In-Process Handling of Bulk Materials

H. L. Keely ....Materials Handling Factors

H. C. Keller ....⎰Package Conveyors
                                 ⎰Unit Handling for Various Shapes
                                  ⎱Positioning Equipment

Lane C. Kendall ....Marine Terminal Handling

John H. Kincaid .... $\left\{\begin{array}{l}\text{Fixed Cranes, Derricks, and Cableways} \\ \text{Traveling Cranes and Towers} \\ \text{Elevators} \\ \text{Auxiliary Crane Equipment} \\ \text{Positioning Equipment}\end{array}\right.$

Jerome J. Kipnees ....Industrial Packaging

Edw. L. Lee ....Industrial Hand Trucks

John F. Meissner ....Handling Bulk Materials

J. W. Milliken .... $\left\{\begin{array}{l}\text{Railroad Terminal Handling} \\ \text{Railroad Freight Cars}\end{array}\right.$

Arthur F. Murray ....Unit Handling in Manufacturing

J. A. Nicols ....Pneumatic Conveyors

William L. Peck ....Positioning Equipment

Arthur M. Perrin .... $\left\{\begin{array}{l}\text{Scrap Classification and Handling} \\ \text{Pneumatic Conveyors}\end{array}\right.$

Charles J. Rausch .... $\left\{\begin{array}{l}\text{Air Carriers} \\ \text{Air Terminal Handling}\end{array}\right.$

R. W. Rausch ....Belt Conveyors

Sidney Reibel ....Trolley Conveyors

Ingram H. Richardson ....In-Process Handling of Bulk Materials

Eugene Richman .... $\left\{\begin{array}{l}\text{Unit Handling for Various Shapes} \\ \text{Unit Handling in Manufacturing}\end{array}\right.$

Henry J. Ritmeester, Jr. ....In-Process Handling of Bulk Materials

Charles L. Sauerbier .... $\left\{\begin{array}{l}\text{Marine Carriers} \\ \text{Marine Terminal Handling}\end{array}\right.$

Byron W. Saunders ....Analyzing Materials Handling Problems

H. S. Sayre ....Pneumatic Conveyors

B. G. Schneider ....Chain Conveyors

Fred Schneider ....Unit Handling for Various Shapes

John Drury Sheahan .... $\left\{\begin{array}{l}\text{Truck Terminal Handling} \\ \text{Railroad Terminal Handling}\end{array}\right.$

E. Ralph Sims, Jr. .... $\left\{\begin{array}{l}\text{Analyzing Materials Handling Problems} \\ \text{Powered Industrial Trucks}\end{array}\right.$

A. D. Sinden .... $\left\{\begin{array}{l}\text{Elevating Conveyors} \\ \text{Belt Conveyors}\end{array}\right.$

John C. Somers ....Powered Industrial Trucks

T. F. Stack ....Handling Bulk Materials

Robert J. Stoddard .... $\left\{\begin{array}{l}\text{Fixed Cranes, Derricks, and Cableways} \\ \text{Traveling Cranes and Towers} \\ \text{Portable Cranes} \\ \text{Winches}\end{array}\right.$

Jules A. Vichness ....Pallets and Containers

Jervis C. Webb ....Haulage Conveyors

R. Frank Weber ....Materials Handling Research

Norman E. Weinberg ....Industrial Tractors

Willard W. Wentz ....Portable Conveyors

J. W. Wunsch .... $\left\{\begin{array}{l}\text{Portable Cranes} \\ \text{Winches}\end{array}\right.$

The advice and counsel freely afforded us by the AMHS–ASME Materials
Handling Handbook Committee, and especially by its Chairman, Herbert H. Hall,

have been invaluable. From the planning of the outline to the final review of proofs the Committee has served tirelessly as an authoritative check point for accuracy and adequacy of coverage.

The Editors wish here also to express their thanks to the many others who, remaining anonymous, have generously contributed in ideas and material; to the organizations, companies, and associations who have given access to their experience and records; and to the publishers of books and magazines for readily granting permission to quote from their publications. Finally, special mention is made of Professors Henry A. Cozzens, Jr., Eugene Richman, and of the Technical Committee of the Conveyor Equipment Manufacturers Association for their assistance in reviewing and editing portions of this book.

HAROLD A. BOLZ
GEORGE E. HAGEMANN

CONTENTS

DEFINITION AND SCOPE OF MATERIALS HANDLING

CONTENTS

DEFINITION AND SCOPE OF MATERIALS HANDLING

THE ART AND SCIENCE OF MATERIALS HANDLING. During recent years, as the study of handling materials has progressed and broadened, there has emerged a better understanding of the scope of the art and science of materials handling. The reference to **materials handling as an art and science** is made advisedly, because the solution of most handling problems is not susceptible to a single definite answer but depends largely on the experience and judgment of the individual materials handling engineer. Although this fact indicates that modern materials handling is still an art, modern analytical methods are being perfected and engineering data, formulas, statistics, and standards, which are beginning to approach the stage of a science, are being developed. These factors are becoming increasingly helpful in arriving at more definite answers for the many aspects of the problem. Although materials handling will always remain to a large degree an art, it will become increasingly scientific as the principles of good materials handling become better understood and applied.

DEFINITION OF MATERIALS HANDLING. After considerable deliberation and searching analysis of the many definitions of materials handling that have appeared from time to time, the American Material Handling Society adopted the following short, simple, and all-inclusive definition, which has also been approved by the Materials Handling Division of the American Society of Mechanical Engineers: **Materials handling is the art and science involving the moving, packaging, and storing of substances in any form.**

Other Definitions. Other definitions that have been considered are:

1. Materials handling is the creation of time and place utility in a material.
2. Materials handling is the creation of time and place utility in material, excluding movement by transporter.
3. Materials handling is the movement and storage of materials at the lowest possible cost through the use of proper methods and equipment.
4. Materials handling is the lifting, shifting, and placing of material which effect a saving in money, time, and place.
5. Materials handling is the lifting, shifting, and placing of any material regardless of size, form, or weight.
6. Materials handling is the moving of material or products by any means, including storage, and all movements except processing operations and inspection.
7. Materials handling is the science and art of conveying, elevating, hauling, transporting, and handling materials from one location to another.
8. Materials handling is the art and science of conveying, elevating, positioning, transporting, packaging, and storing of materials.

TECHNICAL DIVISIONS OF MATERIALS HANDLING. The general field of materials handling may be divided into six distinct functional divisions or spheres of activity. These are, in the order in which they usually occur in industry:

1. Bulk handling.	4. Warehousing.
2. Unit handling.	5. Carrier handling.
3. Industrial packaging.	6. Handling operation analysis.

1. **Bulk handling.** Bulk handling involves the extracting, handling, and storage of all kinds of bulk materials, including gases, liquids, semiliquids, and solids. These processes apply particularly to such materials as ore, coal, aggregates, chemicals, bulk agricultural products, etc. The techniques of bulk handling have advanced rapidly in the past few years, as exemplified by the huge conveyor installations, the use of large earth-moving vehicles, and the extensive railroad and marine terminal installations of today.

2. **Unit handling.** Basically, unit handling involves the handling of unit loads of all kinds. In manufacturing operations, it covers the handling of formed materials in the initial, intermediate, and final stages of manufacture. More materials handling development has probably been accomplished in this field than in any other, involving the movement of an almost endless variety of products ranging from pins to locomotives.

3. **Packaging.** Packaging covers the design, selection, and use of in-process containers, and includes industrial packing and packing of semifinished and finished products.

4. **Warehousing.** The area covered by warehousing includes the receiving, storing, and shipping of unit materials in any form, and at any point in the process of manufacture and distribution.

5. **Carrier handling.** This designation covers the loading, securing, transporting, unloading, and transfer of all kinds of materials in highway trucks, railway cars, barges, ships, airplanes, and at carrier terminals.

6. **Handling operation analysis.** In this category are all the general analytical aspects of materials handling, such as surveys, plant layouts, organization, training, safety, maintenance, standardization, research, cost analysis, methods analysis, and other techniques for developing efficient materials handling procedures.

SCOPE OF MATERIALS HANDLING. History records many ingenious applications of materials handling methods dating back for centuries. The general recognition of the importance of improved materials handling methods is confined mostly to the last hundred years, however. Although considerable experience has been developed in bulk handling and transportation, much of the emphasis on materials handling and most of the literature on the subject was, up to a few years ago, confined largely to the lighter manufacturing industries.

In more recent years there has been a growing interest in, and recognition of, the importance of **bulk materials** handling, particularly in the processing, basic heavy industries, and in the mining and construction industries.

Similarly, in the transportation industry, a realization of the importance of improved materials handling methods and techniques has resulted in the recognition of **transportation** as a necessary factor in the materials handling field. The loading, securing, transporting, and unloading of transportation carriers, highway trucks, railway cars, barges, ships, and aircraft, and the movement of materials at carrier terminals, are now generally recognized as important integral parts of the vast materials handling activity. The design, dimensions, clearances, construction features, and standardization of truck bodies, railroad cars, barges, and the cargo spaces of ships and aircraft are being profoundly influenced by the new requirements for improved materials handling methods.

In the movement of materials of all kinds from points of origin to the ultimate consumers, there are many areas where material must be held in storage for indeterminate lengths of time. The **storage or warehousing** of material at each stage of processing or distribution is an integral step in the flow of goods from the raw materials stage to delivery as finished products to the consumer. The handling of materials going into and out of storage, together with the problems incident to storage and warehousing, constitute an important specific phase of materials handling.

Packaging, in its broadest meaning, may be divided into in-process packaging and semifinished- or finished-goods packaging. In-process packaging includes the use of a wide variety of shop containers and supports, such as shop boxes, tote pans, bins, tanks, racks, pallets, skids, and other equipment used during manufacturing or processing operations. The packaging of semifinished or finished products for later final assembly, or for delivery to dealers or ultimate consumers, may be further divided into two classifications—industrial packaging and consumer packaging.

Industrial packaging is functionally designed primarily to provide proper protection to the materials to be transported. **Consumer packaging,** on the other hand, is designed especially for customer sales-appeal and is characterized by special materials, often unique forms, and appealing decorations. Consumer packages or containers are also more elaborate and expensive than is required solely for protection of the contents against possible damage or deterioration in transit or in storage. The cigarette package, the face powder container, and the breakfast food box are typical consumer packages. The cartons and cases in which consumer packages are packed and shipped are industrial packages, intended for protection of products during transportation and storage. The strapping of lumber in bundles and the blocking of machinery on flat cars are important examples of the heavier kinds of industrial packaging.

There is an inseparable interdependence of in-process and industrial packaging with the various phases of materials handling during processing, manufacturing, warehousing, and transportation. The inclusion of in-process and industrial packaging as integral parts of the general materials handling field has recently been recognized and permits a more complete understanding of the over-all materials handling processes involved in the production and distribution of goods from point of origin to ultimate consumer.

ACTIVITIES COVERED BY MATERIALS HANDLING TECHNIQUES AND PROCEDURES. The broad scope of materials handling reaches into many industries and across many fields of engineering that are vitally affected by modern handling methods, procedures, and techniques.

In the **manufacturing industry,** the handling of all kinds of materials in the process of manufacturing represents probably the largest single field for the application of materials handling methods and techniques and extensive use of a wide range of materials handling equipment. The analysis of materials handling problems in a manufacturing plant—involving surveys, plant and equipment layouts, and the routing, packaging, and storage of material—is of vital concern to plant industrial and mechanical engineers, as well as those engaged in materials handling.

In the **processing industries,** the handling of bulk materials, such as gases, liquids, semiliquids, and bulk solids, involves many special materials handling problems—a fact that has had an important influence on the activities of the mechanical and chemical engineers who design and operate processing plants.

In the **building construction industry,** the architectural engineer must familiarize himself with the many aspects of building planning and construction that involve the proper receiving, sorting, storing, and moving of materials.

In the **heavy construction industry,** there has been a rapid development of materials handling methods and equipment for handling construction materials and for large-scale movement of earth in grading and road-building operations. These revolutionary materials handling methods, together with the ingenious handling equipment developed in recent years, have greatly influenced civil engineers in the planning and performance of heavy construction work.

In the **mining industry**—in both underground mines and open-pit operations —the advances made in materials handling methods, involving the use of many new kinds of equipment, have revolutionized the extraction, handling, and transportation of coal and ore. Costs of extracting the materials mined have been cut to a mere fraction of the former expenditures.

The **power industry,** particularly in coal-burning steam plants, employs many kinds of materials handling equipment for handling fuel. The mechanical engineer must keep abreast of the continual improvements in materials handling methods and equipment so he can reduce the cost of fuel- and ash-handling to a minimum.

In the **machine-tool manufacturing industry,** the design of many processing machines is influenced by the need for integrating various materials handling features or attachments into modern machine mechanisms. The tool engineer must be thoroughly familiar with the many kinds of materials handling equipment which may now be incorporated into the design of processing and production machinery. The use of materials handling devices as integral parts of conveyor ovens, car-type furnaces, continuous plating or cleaning machines, and feeding and discharging attachments on production equipment are typical examples of the influence of materials handling techniques on the machine-tool manufacturing industry.

Truck builders, the trucking industry at large, and automotive engineers are concerned with the improvement of the automobile truck and trailer as efficient materials handling vehicles, designed for ease and speed in loading and unloading, proper securement of cargo, and safe transportation of innumerable kinds of materials.

Railroad car builders and those who operate railroad systems are deeply interested in the design of improved railroad cars, development of terminal equipment, and improvement in materials handling procedures for loading and securing freight and transferring or unloading it at terminals.

Similarly, in the **barge and shipbuilding industry,** marine architects are working continually to develop new handling devices and improved kinds of marine carriers to simplify and reduce the cost of loading and unloading barges and ships, and devising safe stowage methods for cargo in transit. Many new materials handling techniques and procedures are being developed in the marine field.

In the **aircraft industry,** aeronautical engineers are likewise developing better cargo handling and stowage methods for air transportation. Radical changes in the conventional designs of aircraft have been developed to simplify the methods and cut the costs of handling cargo going into and out of aircraft. The problems here are often very special in detail but embody the basic operating fundamentals of good materials handling practices.

FIELDS CONTRIBUTING TO MATERIALS HANDLING PROGRESS. Designers in other fields of engineering have developed equipment and methods that can be applied to great advantage by materials handling engineers. **Hydraulic and sanitary engineers** have developed pumps and gravity-flow pipe lines for use in conveying the many kinds of liquids and semiliquids, or slurries, which are conveyed in pipe lines.

Heating and ventilating engineers, in developing equipment and methods for moving air in ducts, have also furnished much of the engineering data for the development of low-pressure duct-handling systems for conveying materials such as sawdust, tobacco, and cotton.

ECONOMICS OF MATERIALS HANDLING. In the process of converting raw material into useful and marketable goods and placing them in the hands of the ultimate consumer, **value** has been added by creating form utility, place utility, time utility, and ownership utility. Gathering of the raw materials, their movement through processing operations, and their final distribution to the consumer create **place and time utility** by having the raw, in-process, and finished materials at the place where they are needed and at the time they are needed. Processing during manufacture creates **form utility**; sale to the ultimate consumer creates **ownership utility.** The economist's conception of materials handling is the addition of **place and time utility.** The former concept that materials handling increased the costs of the materials moved but added nothing to their value has been converted into a far wider concept of the basic functions and economic importance of materials handling.

Classification of Equipment

PURPOSE OF CLASSIFICATION. In recent years there has been an increasing understanding and agreement among materials handling engineers regarding the scope of materials handling and the equipment that might be classified as materials handling equipment. The following classification was developed by Hall (Material Handling Equipment and Containers—AMHS) to establish logical groupings of the various types of materials handling equipment and to cover all equipment embraced by the modern concept of the scope and definition of materials handling as described above.

In order that this classification might be of maximum benefit as an outline and an index for filing materials handling equipment data, the classification was developed around the **decimal system.** This classification incorporates, with as little change as possible, several previously used partial classifications of various groups of materials handling equipment. In arranging this classification on the decimal system, all types of materials handling equipment have been divided into the following nine main divisions:

1. **CONVEYORS.** This classification includes "all fixed and portable equipment for conveying material between two fixed points with continuous or intermittent forward movement—continuous drive." This definition with some exceptions corresponds closely with the definition of conveyors covered in the Conveyor Equipment Manufacturers' Association pamphlet "Conveyor Terms and Definitions."

2. **CRANES, ELEVATORS, AND HOISTS.** This group covers "all equipment for moving material having a reversing vertical or lateral movement—drum windup and payoff or reciprocating plunger drive." This definition would include all hoists and elevators with a drum windup and payoff as contrasted to

the continuous-drive automatic elevating conveyors included under Conveyors. Also included under Cranes, Elevators, and Hoists are pneumatic and hydraulic plunger hoists as well as capstans and winches.

3. **POSITIONING, WEIGHING, AND CONTROL EQUIPMENT.** This classification includes most materials handling equipment that is neither conveyor, crane, elevator, hoist, carrier vehicle, ship, container, nor support. It includes equipment used for local positioning and transferring, for weighing, and for controlling material movement. This comprises such items as manipulators, up-enders, positioning platforms, and transfers, whether portable or fixed; also all types of scales and weighing equipment; and handling control devices such as float control devices, bin indicators, electrical and mechanical limit controls, counters, etc.

4. **INDUSTRIAL VEHICLES.** This classification covers all types of materials handling vehicles used in industry, excluding motor highway vehicles and public-carrier railroad cars. Included in this classification are all types of industrial trucks, rail cars, trailers, tractors, excavating and grading equipment, off-highway carriers and agricultural vehicles used in materials handling.

5. **MOTOR VEHICLES.** This classification covers all types of highway passenger and cargo vehicles including trucks, tractors, and trailers whose dimensions and capacities permit use on public highways.

6. **RAILROAD CARS.** This classification covers all standard and narrow-gage public carrier railroad rolling stock used on the country's railroad system. It does not include narrow-gage industrial rail cars used in interplant operations nor the industrial tractors or locomotives used for motive power. These are included under Industrial Vehicles.

7. **MARINE CARRIERS.** This classification covers all water-borne vessels, including ocean, lake, river, and canal boats, small craft, and other miscellaneous marine equipment used in the handling of materials.

8. **AIRCRAFT.** This classification covers all types of aircraft, including passenger and cargo airplanes, rotary-wing aircraft, gliders, and lighter-than-air airships.

9. **CONTAINERS AND SUPPORTS.** This classification covers all types of pressure, tight, loose, and open-top containers; also platform and coil supports, and all types of securements such as strapping, cinches, bulkheads, dunnage, etc.

These nine main subdivisions should account for all the various types of equipment used in handling materials. The classification which follows has been developed to three digits to make it suitable to serve as a convenient index for filing materials handling equipment data.

1. **CONVEYORS.**
    11. **Belt Conveyors.**
        111. Bulk material belt conveyors.
        112. Packaged material belt conveyors.
        113. Metallic belt conveyors.
        114. Closed belt conveyors.
        118. Belt conveyor components and auxiliaries.

    12. **Elevating Conveyors** (Capable of Vertical Lift).
        121. Bucket elevators.

122. Bucket elevating conveyors.
123. Mass-movement elevating conveyors.
124. Arm conveying elevators.
125. Suspended-carrier elevating conveyors.
128. Elevating conveyor components and auxiliaries.

13. **Carrier Chain and Cable Conveyors** (Load Carried on Moving Conveyor).
131. Apron conveyors.
132. Slat conveyors.
133. Crossbar conveyors.
134. Carrier chain conveyors.
135. Pallet conveyors.
136. Car conveyors.
137. Trolley conveyors.
138. Aerial tramways.
139. Carrier chain and cable conveyors not otherwise classified.

14. **Haulage Conveyors** (Weight of Pushed or Pulled Load Carried by Stationary Troughs, Surfaces, or Rails).
141. Drag conveyors.
142. Flight conveyors.
143. Tow conveyors.
144. Cable tramways.
145. Car hauls.

15. **Roller Conveyors.**
151. Straight roller conveyors.
152. Concave roller conveyors.
153. Herringbone roller conveyors.
154. Skewed roller conveyors.
155. Troughed roller conveyors.
156. Double conical roller conveyors.
157. Wheel conveyors.
158. Roller-conveyor components and auxiliaries.
159. Roller conveyors not otherwise classified.

16. **Screw Conveyors.**
161. Horizontal screw conveyors.
162. Vertical and inclined screw conveyors.
163. Screw feeders.
164. Screw-type mixing conveyors.
165. Rotating casing screw conveyors.
166. Load-carrying helical conveyors.
168. Screw-conveyor components and auxiliaries.
169. Screw conveyors not otherwise classified.

17. **Pipeline Conveyors.**
171. Hydraulic conveyors (liquid and semiliquid pipelines).
172. Gas pipeline conveyors.
173. Pneumatic bulk material conveyors.
174. Pneumatic package conveyors.
175. Air-jet hydraulic lifts.

18. **Vibrating and Reciprocating Conveyors.**
181. Electric vibrating conveyors and feeders.
182. Mechanical vibrating conveyors and feeders.
183. Oscillating conveyors and feeders.
184. Reciprocating conveyors and feeders.

19. **Special Conveyors and Auxiliary Equipment.**
191. Special feeders.

192. Screens.
193. Hopper-car shakeout unloaders.
194. Chutes.
195. Hoppers, troughs, and spouts.
196. Flumes and sluices.

2. CRANES, ELEVATORS, AND HOISTS.

21. Fixed Cranes and Derricks (Stationary Mount).
211. Pedestal cranes (hinged boom).
212. Pillar jib cranes (self-supporting).
213. Supported jib cranes.
214. Fixed revolving jib cranes.
215. Fixed revolving cranes (hinged boom).
216. Fixed bridge cranes.
217. Fixed loading and unloading towers.
218. Derricks.
219. Fixed cranes and derricks not otherwise classified.

22. Traveling Cranes (On Rail Runways).
221. Overhead traveling bridge cranes.
222. Traveling gantry bridge cranes.
223. Traveling gantry portal-type cranes.
224. Traveling gantry storing and reclaiming bridges.
225. Traveling gantry bulk cargo cranes and unloading towers.
226. Traveling low-carriage and wall cranes.
227. Overhead monorail or tramrail systems.
228. Crane components.
229. Traveling cranes not otherwise classified.

23. Portable Cranes.
231. Railroad cranes.
232. Crawler cranes.
233. Wheeled cranes.
234. Portable floor cranes.
235. Floating cranes and derricks.
236. Auxiliary cranes mounted on vehicles and ships.

24. Elevators.
241. Building elevators.
242. Self-supported low-lift elevators.
243. Dumb-waiters.
244. Construction elevators (hoists).
245. Mine elevators (hoists).
246. Skip hoists.
247. Inclines.
248. Auxiliary elevator equipment.
249. Elevators not otherwise classified.

25. Cableways, Drag Scrapers, and Cable-shifters.
251. Rope-trolley tautline cableways.
252. Man-trolley tautline cableways.
253. Slackline cableways.
254. Drag scrapers.
255. Logging yarding and loading cable systems.
256. Cable-shifters.

26. Hoists.
261. Cylinder hoists.
262. Chain hoists.

263. Cable hoists.
264. Rope hoists.
265. Elevator hoisting machines.
266. Crane-trolley built-in hoists.

27. **Winches.**
  271. Windlasses.
  272. Capstans.
  273. Single-drum winches.
  274. Multiple-drum winches.
  275. Auxiliary winches mounted on industrial and highway vehicles.

28. **Crane, Elevator, and Hoist Auxiliary Equipment.**
  281. Crane slings.
  282. Crane grabs.
  283. Crane buckets.
  284. Crane hook auxiliary equipment.
  285. Crane boom attachments.
  286. Crane, elevator, and hoist components.

29. **Special cranes, elevators, and hoists not otherwise classified.**

3. POSITIONING, WEIGHING, AND CONTROL EQUIPMENT.

31. **Manipulators and Positioners.**
  311. Manipulators.
  312. Positioning chargers.
  313. Positioning holding fixtures.
  314. Pantograph and similar holding devices.
  315. Auxiliary positioning attachments on production equipment.

32. **Up-enders and Dumpers.**
  321. Up-enders and turnovers.
  322. Car dumpers.
  323. Tilting truck dumpers.
  324. Box, barrel, and bag dumpers.

33. **Positioning Tables and Platforms.**
  331. Fixed positioning tables.
  332. Fixed positioning platforms.
  333. Automotive service lifts.
  334. Portable positioning tables.
  335. Portable lifters.
  336. Portable jacks.
  337. Positioning attachments on industrial and motor vehicles and cars.

34. **Positioning Transfers.**
  341. Transfer cars.
  342. Lorries.
  343. Turntables.
  344. Ball and caster transfers.
  345. Walking-beam transfers.
  346. Marine and aircraft transfers.
  347. Power car movers.

35. **Fixed Positioning Bridges and Ramps.**
  351. Movable crossover bridges.
  352. Railroad and truck dock leveling bridge ramps and platforms.
  353. Fixed marine and air dock bridge ramps and gangplanks.
  354. Fixed ships' bridge ramps, gangplanks, and ladders.

36. **Portable Positioning Equipment.**
    361. Portable dock bridge plates and gangplanks.
    362. Portable ramps, skid plates, boards, and rails.
    363. Ladders, portable step platforms, and scaffolding.
    364. Portable stands, trestles, horses, and shores.
    365. Hand positioning tools.

37. **Weighing Equipment.**
    371. Yard scales.
    372. Floor platform scales.
    373. Portable scales.
    374. Counter scales.
    375. Batch scales.
    376. Conveyor scales.
    377. Crane scales.
    378. Single lever and spring scales.
    379. Weighing equipment not otherwise classified.

38. **Handling Control Devices.**
    381. Float control devices.
    382. Bin indicators and control devices.
    383. Limit switches and mechanical limit controls.
    384. Electronic handling control devices.
    385. Counters.
    386. Magnets.

4. INDUSTRIAL VEHICLES.

41. **Powered Industrial Trucks.**
    411. Fixed-platform powered industrial trucks.
    412. Powered industrial inboard lift trucks.
    413. Powered industrial outboard lift trucks (fork-truck type).
    414. Powered industrial lift trucks with retractable forks.
    415. Straddle carrier powered industrial lift trucks.
    416. Powered industrial scooters.
    417. Powered-industrial-truck auxiliary attachments.
    418. Industrial-truck auxiliary power equipment.
    419. Powered industrial trucks not otherwise classified.

42. **Hand Trucks.**
    421. Two-wheeled hand trucks.
    422. Platform hand trucks.
    423. Hand lift trucks.
    424. Wheeled shop containers.
    425. Buggies and wheelbarrows.
    426. Dollies.
    427. Bicycles and tricycles.

43. **Industrial Trailers.**
    431. Industrial crawler trailers.
    432. Industrial wheeled shop trailers.
    433. Industrial semitrailers (fifth wheel).
    434. Industrial semitrailers (pintle hitch).
    435. Bogie trailers.
    436. Semilive skid platforms, boxes, racks.
    437. Drag trailers.

44. **Industrial Cars.**
    441. Mine and quarry cars.
    442. Side-dump construction cars.

443. Powered shuttle and monitor cars.
444. Industrial flatcars and rack cars.
445. Furnace and oven cars.
446. Industrial dump cars.
447. Hot metal and ladle cars.
448. Combination rail and rubber-tired vehicles.
449. Special industrial cars not otherwise classified.

45. Industrial Tractors and Locomotives.
451. Crawler tractors.
452. Wheeled tractors.
453. Industrial locomotives.
454. Underground mining locomotives.
455. Rack-and-pinion tractors.

46. Bulk Materials, Handling Vehicles, and Portable Equipment.
461. Single-bucket excavators.
462. Continuous-bucket, cutter, and auger excavators.
463. Self-feeding conveyor loaders.
464. Scoop loaders.
465. Dozers, graders, rippers, and plows.
466. Scraper carriers.
467. Dumping carriers.
468. Portable screening, mixing, and spreading equipment.
469. Special bulk materials handling vehicles and portable equipment.

47. Agricultural Vehicles and Attachments.
471. Plows and harrows.
472. Planters.
473. Cultivators.
474. Mowers.
475. Harvesting equipment.
476. Agricultural wagons and spreaders.

48. Special Military Vehicles (Not Including Motor Vehicles),
481. Armored tanks.
482. Wheeled armored cars.
483. Self-propelled artillery vehicles.
484. Crawler-type personnel and cargo vehicles.
485. Amphibious carriers.

49. Special Industrial Vehicles and Components.
491. Special animal-drawn vehicles.
492. Wheels, casters, and tires.
493. Industrial trailer and car couplings.

5. MOTOR VEHICLES.

51. Passenger Automobiles.
511. Coupes.
512. Sedans and limousines.
513. Station wagons.
514. Taxicabs (with special taxicab bodies).
515. Ambulances and hearses.
516. Military passenger cars.
517. Passenger-automobile chassis.
518. Passenger-automobile auxiliaries and components.
519. Special passenger automobiles not otherwise classified.

52. Motor Buses (Capacity for carrying 10 or more passengers).
521. City-type motor buses.

522. Suburban-type motor buses.
523. Intercity-type motor buses.
524. Sight-seeing motor buses.
525. School buses.
526. Trolley buses (includes combinations with engine-generator).
527. Bus chassis.
528. Bus auxiliaries and components.
529. Special buses not otherwise classified.

53. Trucks and Truck Tractors.
531. Motor trucks (commercial).
532. Military motor trucks.
533. Truck tractors (commercial).
534. Military truck tractors.
536. Truck bodies (commercial).
537. Truck and truck-tractor chassis.
538. Truck and truck-tractor auxiliaries and components.
539. Special trucks and truck tractors not otherwise classified.

54. Truck Trailers.
541. Truck semitrailers.
542. Full truck trailers.
543. Trailer converter dollies.
544. Pole trailers.
545. Military truck trailers.
546. Trailer bodies.
547. Trailer chassis.
548. Trailer auxiliaries and components.
549. Special truck trailers not otherwise classified.

55. Passenger-Car Trailers.
551. Utility trailers, Class A, SAE (capacity not over 2,000 lb.).
552. Passenger-car trailers, Class B, SAE (capacity from 2,000 lb. to 5,000 lb.).
553. Passenger-car trailers, Class C, SAE (capacity from 5,000 lb. to 10,000 lb.).
558. Passenger-car-trailer auxiliaries and components.

56. Motorcycles.
561. Motorcycles (one or more cylinders of 30 cu. in. or more piston displacement).
562. Powercycles (one cylinder of less than 30 cu. in. piston displacement).
563. Motor tricycles.
564. Motorcycle sidecars.
568. Motorcycle accessories and components.
For motor scooters see 416, Powered industrial trucks.

6. RAILROAD CARS.

61. Passenger Cars.
611. Passenger day cars.
612. Sleeping cars.
613. Dining cars.
614. Combination passenger and baggage cars.
615. Gasoline- or diesel-powered passenger and combination rail cars.
616. Electric rapid-transit cars.
617. Electric interurban cars and streetcars.

62. Baggage Cars.
621. Baggage cars.
622. Express cars.
623. Mail cars.
624. Combination baggage, express, and mail cars.

625. Gasoline- or diesel-powered rail express cars.
626. Electric express cars.

63. House Cars.
631. Boxcars.
632. Refrigerator cars.
633. Stock cars.
634. Bulk material house cars.

64. Flatcars.
641. Flat-deck flatcars.
642. Depressed-center flatcars.
643. Well-hole flatcars.
644. Skeleton-frame flatcars.
645. Rack and stake flatcars.
646. Container flatcars.

65. Gondola Cars.
651. Solid-bottom gondola cars.
652. Turnover dump high-side gondola cars.
653. Drop-bottom gondola cars.
654. Hopper-bottom gondola cars.
655. Side-dumping gondola cars.
656. Well-hole gondola cars.
657. Gondola container cars.

66. Hopper Cars.
661. Open-top center-dump hopper cars.
662. Open-top center- and end-dump hopper ballast cars.
663. Covered center-dump hopper cars.
664. Covered conveyor-unloading hopper cars.

67. Tank Cars.
671. General-service tank cars.
672. Acid-service tank cars.
673. Lined tank cars.
674. Aluminum tank cars.
675. Pressure tank cars.
676. Tank cars with wooden tanks.
677. Enclosed tank cars.
678. Tank cars for dry powdered or granular material.
679. Special tank cars.

68. Locomotives.
681. Electric road locomotives.
682. Diesel-electric road locomotives.
683. Steam road locomotives.
684. Gas-turbine road locomotives.
685. Electric switching locomotives.
686. Internal-combustion-engine switching locomotives.
687. Steam switching locomotives.
688. Miscellaneous types of switching locomotives.
689. Special locomotives not otherwise classified.

69. Special Railroad Cars.
691. Freight train service cars.
692. Maintenance-of-way service cars.
693. Side-dump cars.
694. Railroad testing cars.
695. Special personnel cars.
696. Special military railroad cars.

7. **MARINE CARRIERS.**
    71. **Ocean Vessels.**
        711. Passenger boats.
        712. Freighters (12 or less passengers).
        713. Bulk carriers.
        714. Tankers.
        715. Car ferries.
        716. Sailing vessels.
        717. Naval surface vessels.
        718. Submarines.
        719. Ocean vessels not otherwise classified.

    72. **Lake Vessels.**
        721. Passenger boats.
        722. Freight boats.
        723. Bulk carriers.
        724. Self-unloading bulk carriers.
        725. Tankers.
        726. Car ferries.
        727. Combination lake and canal boats.

    73. **River and Canal Boats** (Self-Propelled).
        731. River passenger boats.
        732. River packets.
        733. Vehicle and passenger ferries.

    74. **Barges and Lighters.**
        741. Harbor barges.
        742. Covered lighters.
        743. Car floats.
        744. Hopper barges.
        745. Deck barges.
        746. Covered dry-cargo barges.
        747. Tank barges.
        748. Self-unloading bulk barges.
        749. Barges and lighters not otherwise classified.

    75. **Towboats.**
        751. Ocean towboats.
        752. Harbor tugs.
        753. River and canal towboats.
        754. River pushboats.
        755. Integrated pushboats.
        756. Work boats.
        757. Marine tractors.

    76. **Small Craft.**
        761. Power cruisers, launches, etc.
        762. Outboard powered small craft.
        763. Landing craft, sweepers, chasers, etc.
        764. Fishing craft.
        765. Fireboats.
        766. Sailboats.
        767. Rowboats, skiffs, canoes, etc.
        768. Sweep boats or lighters.
        769. Small craft not otherwise classified.

    77. **Mobile Floating Equipment.**
        771. Floating drydocks.

772. Floating landings and stages.
773. Pontoons.
774. Scows.
775. Rafts.
776. Floating booms.

78. Suction Dredges.
781. Pumping suction dredges.
782. Self-loading and dumping suction dredges.

79. Special Marine Carriers Not Otherwise Classified.

8. AIRCRAFT.

81. Passenger Airplanes (fixed-wing airplanes—combination cargo).
811. Single-engine passenger airplanes.
812. Two-engine passenger air transports.
813. Three-or-more-engine passenger air transports.

82. Cargo Air Transports (fixed-wing airplanes).
821. Two-engine cargo air transports.
822. Three-or-more-engine cargo air transports.

83. Military Combat Airplanes.
831. Fighters.
832. Fighter bombers.
833. Medium-range bombers.
834. Long-range bombers.
835. Reconnaissance aircraft.
836. Military trainers.
837. Military transports.

84. Rotary-Wing Aircraft.
841. Gyros.
842. Helicopters.

85. Gliders.
851. Passenger gliders.
852. Cargo gliders.

86. Balloons and Airships (lighter-than-air aerostats).
861. Free balloons.
862. Semirigid airships (blimps).
863. Rigid-frame airships.

9. CONTAINERS AND SUPPORTS.

91. Pressure Vessels.
911. High-pressure gas cylinders (over 12 lb. per sq. in.).
912. High-pressure railroad and truck cylinders (over 12 lb. per sq. in.).
913. Compressed-gas cartridges and bottles (over 12 lb. per sq. in.).
914. Low-pressure fixed tanks (under 12 lb. per sq. in.).
915. Low-pressure portable tanks (under 12 lb. per sq. in.).
916. Low-pressure railroad and truck tanks (under 12 lb. per sq. in.).

92. Tight Containers (hermetically sealed or with breather).
921. Metal drums.
922. Barrels (tight), hogsheads, casks, kegs, tubes, etc.
923. Bottles, flasks, carboys, vials, ampoules, etc.
924. Sanitary and other sealed cans and canisters.
925. Sealed cargo containers (metal, rubber, plastic, etc.).
926. Tanks, portable and fixed.
927. Tanks built into trucks, cars, barges, and ships.

93. **Entirely Enclosed Containers** (loose).
    931. Loose barrels, kegs, drums, firkins, etc. (nonmetallic).
    932. Boxes, chests, cases, cargo containers, trunks, and hand baggage (wood, metal-bound, metal, fiber, paper, cloth, etc.).
    933. Crates (wood, wirebound, etc.).
    934. Cartons (corrugated-paper, fiber, etc.).
    935. Cans (with loose lids).
    936. Bags (burlap, canvas, cloth, mesh, paper, plastic, etc.).
    937. Wrappings (bales, bundles, rolls).
    938. Covered bins and silos.
    939. Entirely enclosed containers not otherwise classified.

94. **Open-Top Containers.**
    941. Shop boxes and containers (rectangular).
    942. Round shop containers.
    943. Tote boxes, pans, and baskets (rectangular).
    944. Pans.
    945. Open bins and silos, bunkers, hoppers.

95. **Platform Supports.**
    951. Pallets.
    952. Skid platforms.
    953. Tables.
    954. Trays and conveyor boards.
    955. Separators.
    956. Racks.
    957. Skids, runners, horses, cradles.

96. **Coil Supports.**
    961. Reels.
    962. Spools.
    963. Textile beams.
    964. Arbors, cores, poles.
    965. Tubes and drums.
    966. Bobbins.
    967. Cones.

97. **Securements.**
    971. Strapping (wire, metal banding, tape, cord, etc.).
    972. Cinches (chain, cable, or rope, with tighteners).
    973. Portable bulkheads used in trucks, railroad cars, airplanes, and ships.
    974. Securements permanently attached in trucks, railroad cars, airplanes, and ships.
    975. Bracing (temporary bulkheads, shoring, chocks).
    976. Dunnage (duckboards, loose lumber).
    977. Fastenings (bolts, screws, nails, staples, clips, clamps, etc.).
    978. Auxiliary equipment (strapping devices, staplers, tying machines, etc.).
    979. Securements not otherwise classified.

98. **Auxiliary Packaging Equipment.**
    981. Drum-filling equipment.
    982. Sanitary can-filling equipment.
    983. Sack-filling equipment.
    984. Car-loading equipment.
    985. Carton- and case-making, loading, and sealing equipment.
    986. Bottling equipment.
    987. Box-, jar-, and tube-filling equipment.

99. **Containers and Supports Not Otherwise Classified.**

ANALYZING MATERIALS HANDLING PROBLEMS

CONTENTS

CONTENTS (*Continued*)

ANALYZING MATERIALS HANDLING PROBLEMS

BASIC PRINCIPLES OF ANALYSIS. The analysis of materials handling problems is not essentially different from the analysis of any other engineering problem. Facts are needed and various techniques are presented to show how to get these facts. Intelligent judgment and planning must be applied to develop successful solutions to given problems. Experience with, as well as knowledge of, materials handling equipment is necessary to achieve practical solutions and bring about lasting profitable results to handling problems.

The analyst attempting to solve a problem concerning mobile equipment, for example, is at a distinct disadvantage unless he is also familiar with processing methods, techniques, basic elements of design, building construction, and other factors important to the solution. The use of the techniques herein presented, however, will not of itself result in improved materials handling. Bright (The Engineer, vol. 195) points out that some of the gravest errors are committed by inexperienced analysts who assume that the application of mechanized equipment to handling operations will automatically solve problems and result in better materials handling procedures.

Definite techniques are available for analyzing materials handling problems and indicating where improvements can be made. An improvement in the handling elements of a job, however, is no solution if it is possible to eliminate the operation itself instead of merely improving it. Metter (American Machinist, vol. 96) states that any materials handling analysis should always include the question "Is this trip necessary?" He further states that a major factor in any handling problem is the design of the manufactured part, because the design determines what shop operations are necessary, which operating sequences should be followed, and, on the basis of a fixed layout, which routes of travel should be adopted. Many times, slight product-design changes will considerably simplify handling problems.

The real problem facing the analyst is not, for example, merely answering questions such as: How should a certain part be handled? How many parts should be put on a pallet? How often should a particular truck make a trip? How high above the floor should a conveyor line be? Nor is it concerned with the "how's" confronting the general materials handling practitioner. Instead the analyst's **primary concern** should be:

1. What material is to be moved and why?
2. Where is the material to be moved and why?
3. When is the material to be moved and why?
4. What is the volume of the material to be moved?

If satisfactory answers are obtained to these questions, then the methods to be employed will be infinitely simplified. The "how" is a job of equipment selection, and the selector may be the analyst; but he must assemble other facts before he can determine the "how."

The techniques here presented will aid the analyst in securing answers to the "what, where, when, and why" of materials handling problems. Questions of "how," following the principles of proper equipment selection, will then be more readily solved.

BASIC KINDS OF HANDLING PROBLEMS. Materials handling problems are usually of three kinds:

1. Problems associated with new or untried handling situations.
2. Problems connected with existing handling situations where no basic change is anticipated in the materials being handled or in the environment in which they are found.
3. Problems associated with an existing handling situation where changes in the material and/or its environment must be considered.

The **first kind of problem** is not of such common occurrence as the other two, but if not given proper study, it in turn creates, or is the cause of, the other two. When a new product is being planned for manufacture, the time to study the handling problem is in the design stage, before final specifications for materials and manufacturing methods are determined. The same requirement applies when planning a new warehouse or laying out storage areas. The materials handling analyst should be a member of the group making the decisions concerning the new product, its ultimate design, and often, the ultimate layout of its warehouse. Otherwise handling problems of the second and third kind will soon arise. Many handling problems that do occur would not arise if the planning of new products, plants, warehouses, office procedures, inventory control systems, and other necessary provisions were recognized immediately as being complementary to materials handling.

The **second kind of problem** is perhaps the most common. A materials handling project may arise because, from observation or cursory analysis, the methods in use appear to be wasteful in labor and high in cost. An employee may make important suggestions for improving the handling methods and reducing the costs. The techniques available in such cases are constructive, and their selection is dictated only by the amount of time and money that the analyst can spend on the assignment.

The **third kind of problem** is one involving some combination of the other two. It may range from merely changing the area within which the material will be handled to the establishing of a whole new plant. The choice of analytical methods is unlimited, and their use will make the plan more readily acceptable to the management and be convincing evidence in securing the necessary financial appropriations.

Of these three kinds of problems, the first logically calls for the most creativity —making the plan visual by means of a drawing or a scale model of the proposed layout. The analytical methods and techniques employed must be those of synthesis, with economic analysis as each successive step is considered in relation to the total job. Operation analysis techniques are helpful in establishing the best methods and deciding on the best equipment for handling the materials. Check lists are practically imperative as assurance that important points will not be overlooked.

In the **second and third categories,** while synthetic methods are helpful in considering proposed changes, the techniques that record factual "on-the-spot" data based on observation of the job being done, and make existing information available to the analyst, are the most useful in getting to the fundamentals of the problem. Such techniques—using flow analyses, travel charts, cycle charts, density patterns, work sampling studies, and the like—are most helpful for assembling factual information. Synthetic methods are useful in evaluating proposals for the recommended changes.

Isolating a Materials Handling Project

IDENTIFYING A HANDLING PROBLEM. Many times the identification and isolation of a problem are more difficult than the analysis of the problem. Problem identification is the responsibility not only of the materials handling analyst but also of all those who may be concerned with some project. These handling problems are sometimes assigned to an analyst as the result of a cost study or a cost report. Frequently they may arise from another kind of investigation made by one of the engineers. A continuous and organized effort should be made to detect inefficiencies in materials handling and to work out methods for their elimination.

Some analysts have developed **standard questions** for use when making an over-all survey covering materials handling problems. The Material Handling Institute, in Booklet No. 2 of its "Library of Know-How" series, dealing with general rules, analyses, cost data, etc., lists key questions to be answered by the analyst making a survey to define and isolate a materials handling problem. These questions are as follows:

In Receiving Operations:

1. Are incoming materials unloaded by hand?
2. How often are the materials handled from the receiving dock to the start of production?
3. Are the units of proper size to facilitate easy and economical handling?
4. From the receiving dock to the first stage of production—which may or may not include warehousing—how can the materials best be handled: By chute? hoist? conveyor? power fork or elevating truck? tractor-trailer system (for long hauls)? hand lift trucks? pallet? crane? hand platform trucks? caster trucks (perhaps in conjunction with conveyors)? two-wheeled hand trucks? any combination of the above?
5. In handling materials from the receiving dock to the first stage of production, can weight control be installed as an integral part of the proposed or existing system, such as overhead track scales, suspension scales, crane scales, and conveyor scales, rather than a conventional scale platform?
6. Are materials received in one form, used in another? For example, are they received in cartons, then palletized for in-plant handling? Or are they received in barrels, then unloaded and handled in bulk?
7. Is the receiving container suitable for shipping the end product?
8. Are men idle, waiting for the "big jobs"?
9. How may the natural law of gravity be employed for transporting materials?

In Production:

1. Is straight-line production, which eliminates "back-hauls," in use?
2. Do skilled workers handle manufacturing materials, heavy dies, and the like?
3. Are materials deposited at a distance from the machine which uses them, because for example, aisles are too narrow for trucks?
4. Are delicate parts frequently damaged in transit?
5. Would rubber-tired truck equipment reduce wear on floors and cut down breakage of fragile parts in transit?
6. Would various individual kinds of conveyors, tote pans, stacking boxes, skids, pallets, or racks be more suitable, or would a combination of such equipment be desirable?
7. Would automatic and weight-recording or counting scales, installed as a part of the line-production system, regulate lot control of materials in process?

CHECK LIST OF QUESTIONS FOR TESTING MATERIALS HANDLING EFFICIENCY

Checks in the "Yes" column will indicate a need for studying and possibly improving your materials handling methods.

	Yes	No
Are your indirect labor costs high?	☐	☐
Do you have many employee accidents due to the handling of materials?	☐	☐
Is there much manual handling of materials weighing more than 50 lb. (by male employees) or 25 lb. (by female employees)?	☐	☐
Do you have many handling jobs requiring two or more employees?	☐	☐
Are skilled employees, such as machine operators, required to waste time handling materials to and from their machines?	☐	☐
Are there frequent delays in production time due to poorly scheduled delivery and removal of materials?	☐	☐
Can you make more efficient use of your storage space by mechanical high-tiering of stock to the ceiling?	☐	☐
Are your demurrage charges high?	☐	☐
Can you make more efficient use of "unit loads"?	☐	☐
Is much of your material damaged during handling?	☐	☐
Are the maintenance costs on your materials handling equipment continuously rising?	☐	☐
Are there many single handling jobs requiring two or more different types of handling equipment?	☐	☐
Do you load freight cars or trucks by hand?	☐	☐
Do your shop trucks operate empty more than 20% of the time?	☐	☐
Is the major portion of your materials handling equipment over ten years old?	☐	☐
Do you have many rehandling points along your production lines?	☐	☐
Are you performing too many different kinds of handling operations when fewer would do?	☐	☐
Do your lines of material travel overlap?	☐	☐
Are you using power arrangements when gravity could move the work more economically?	☐	☐
Are you trying to fit misfit handling devices to new production jobs just to use up old equipment?	☐	☐
Do you perform many unnecessary handling operations?	☐	☐
Have you been using special devices when standard equipment would suffice?	☐	☐
Can you combine operations to avoid repetitions of materials travel?	☐	☐
Do you try to make one kind of equipment do all kinds of handling jobs?	☐	☐

Fig. 1. Check list of questions for testing materials handling efficiency.

8. If the use of skids or pallets is indicated, can they be carried through to the end of production operations?
9. Does the storage of parts in process add appreciably to the handling costs?
10. Is the production area cluttered with parts and materials waiting to be used? If so, can a "continuous flow" be instituted?
11. Is scrap disposed of promptly?
12. How far back in the production line may the end product be put with or into the shipping containers?
13. How often is the finished product handled up to the time when it is shipped?
14. Can automatic and weight-recording or counting scales be used in connection with the handling equipment to improve the flow at the end of the regular production or packing line?
15. Can handling operations be reduced by having the "active" products conveniently located for packing and shipping?
16. What is the current sales unit? Can it be increased? Has the sales department been told of the "best" order size?
17. Can valuable warehouse space be saved by tiering products on pallets or in containers?
18. What traffic problems arise in connection with warehousing and shipping?
19. Will better layout and wider aisles facilitate handling operations by reducing or eliminating congestion of traffic?

In Shipping:
1. How is the finished product shipped—by railroad, by highway truck, by ship, or by a combination of these transportation media?
2. How can the receiver handle the products most economically?
3. If the products can be efficiently loaded, warehoused, handled, and shipped on skids or pallets, should the skids be expendable or returnable?
4. Can further economies be made by:
   a. Adopting glued pallet or skid loads?
   b. Eliminating pallets or skids entirely through use of unit loads with built-in space for handling by forks or rams?
5. Which kinds or combinations of the following materials handling equipment will be best suited for the shipping room:
   a. Conveyors?
   b. Hoists with efficient grabs?
   c. Two-wheeled trucks?
   d. Four-wheeled, flat-bed push trucks?
   e. Hand-lift pallet or skid trucks?
   f. Power industrial trucks: fork, elevating, platform, motorized hand lift truck, tractor-trailer system, and the like?
   g. Special trucks or racks equipped with casters for ready maneuverability?

Many analysts use check sheets as a guide to the isolation and identification of materials handling problems. Fig. 1 shows one such check sheet.

Whenever a "Yes" answer is given to any of the above questions—or an answer is given which appears to be at variance with efficient practices—a potential problem is raised in an area to which further study and attention should be given. Specific analytical techniques should be used in such cases. Questions or check lists are merely aids in identifying and defining existing problems. Answers to questions such as these, however, should in no sense constitute a solution of the problem proper.

Work Simplification Methods

WORK SIMPLIFICATION. The most successful kind of training to develop the "why, what, when, where, and how" questioning attitude in regard to materials handling problems is training in work simplification. Such training includes the use of analytical techniques to help secure adequate answers to the "why, what, when, where, and how" questions. In addition, it is necessary to recognize that there are both human problems and material problems connected with changing of methods and that both kinds must be properly considered, or else any attempted solution will fall short of its intended goal. Adequate training offers to every operator handling materials the opportunity to become a potential simplifier of work.

Work simplification applied to materials handling problems employs the charting techniques connected with the flow process chart, the operation process chart, and the left- and right-hand chart, which are the charts of greatest value. Additional techniques have been developed to satisfy particular needs, or to improve methods, where current analytical techniques have not been able to provide the data necessary for analysis. Once an analysis chart has been made, or the facts for analyzing a particular handling situation have been gathered, the questioning attitude must be adopted.

Basic Questions. The basic questions which the work simplification analyst must ask himself are:

1. Can the operation be eliminated?
2. Can it be combined?
3. Can the sequence be changed?
4. Can it be improved?

The analyst is concerned with the "why, what, where, when, how" of any job. He must take up these questions in the order given and ask for answers to each of the four primary questions about the material, the location, and finally the handling time.

In the case of the material:

1. What material is being handled and why?
2. Can this material or this operation be eliminated?
3. Does this material have to be used, or are other materials equally satisfactory?
4. What is the density of this material compared to other available materials?
5. In what other shapes or forms can this material be received?
6. Can this material, and the process that it is used for, be combined with other materials or processes?
7. Can the process be simplified to provide for the use of alternate or different materials, or the elimination of materials that are mandatory now solely because of current design?
8. Is the material in the proper form for handling, i.e., should it be handled in bulk, in cartons, in unit loads, or on pallets?

In regard to location:

1. Where is this material now?
2. Why is it there and how long has it been there?
3. Is this stopover location or temporary storage necessary?
4. Can this stopover or storage be eliminated?
5. Is this location the best available, or should a new location be provided?
6. Is the material to be used at its present location or must it be transported elsewhere?
7. Should not the location be on a high level to utilize the force of gravity in removing the material from storage?

Considering the timing involved:

1. Why must this material be moved now?
2. Could it be moved tomorrow, or could it have been moved yesterday without additional cost or at less cost?

3. Can the material be moved simultaneously with other material transported on the same trip, at either the same or at a different time?
4. Is the time allowed for this move flexible as to the time of actual transit? Will other operations be impeded if the material does not arrive at the stated times?

Even the simplest of problems is difficult to understand and analyze, prior to such an analysis.

Barnes (Motion and Time Study), in discussing this point in connection with operation analysis, suggests the following questions concerning materials handling:

1. Can the number of times the material is handled be reduced?
2. Can the distance moved be shortened?
3. Is the material received, moved, and stored in suitable containers? Are the containers kept clean?
4. Are there delays in the delivery of the material to the operator?
5. Can the operator be relieved of handling materials by supplying them on conveyors?
6. Can backtracking be reduced or eliminated?
7. Will a rearrangement of the layout or a combining of operations make it unnecessary to move the material?

Lowry, Maynard, and Stegemerten (Time and Motion Study) suggest checking on the following questions concerning operation analysis and relating specifically to materials handling:

1. Where should incoming and outgoing material be located with respect to the work station?
2. Is a conveyor justified?
3. Can a progressive assembly line be set up?
4. Is the size of the material container suitable for the amount of the material transported?
5. Should the material handling problem, in general, receive more intensive study in the immediate future?

Morrow (Motion Economy and Work Measurement) asks the following questions with reference to the analysis of materials handling problems:

1. What is the nature of material or parts handled?
2. What are the quantities being handled?
3. Is the handling in units or containers?
4. Is the flow continuous or intermittent?
5. Does the material travel set the pace of operations?
6. What operations are performed while the materials are moving?
7. What distances do the items travel while under operation?
8. What kinds of handling apparatus are used: cranes, hoists, trucks, conveyors, etc.?
9. Can operations be combined to reduce material handling?
10. Can the operator deliver the part to the next operation as he disposes of it?

Such questions are typical of the investigations which might be made during the **analysis of a materials handling problem** in order to determine the "why, what, where, when, and how" of the job. The list is not all-inclusive, and many of the questions suggested do not have universal application. Other questions will be suggested in practically all cases when the details and the characteristics of the job to be analyzed are assembled.

Additional details and characteristics are assembled through the use of one of the charting techniques, after the job has been defined. Then, as each activity is identified on the chart, the foregoing questions, or similar ones confronting the analyst, can be very effectively applied in pointing the way toward a solution.

Make Ready, Do, Put Away. One other factor of work simplification is valuable to the materials handling analyst: All jobs or operations may be divided into three principal elements:

1. Make ready.
2. Do.
3. Put away.

The "do" elements are those which represent the performing of an operation or an inspection. Something is actually being done to the material, either to change it from its existing condition or state, or to verify its condition or state. Value is either added directly to the job—as in the case of an operation, or it is being verified, as in the case of an inspection.

All other activities associated with this "do" element are either **preparatory** or **subsequent** to the "doing." The preparation is referred to as the "make ready," and the subsequent work of cleanup, or transporting the item away from the scene of the "doing," is termed the "put away." Often only the "do" elements are considered to add value to the product, while the "make ready" and "put away" elements add cost but not value. The latter elements are very significant from an economic standpoint. They may add place and time utility to the materials moved. The factors of most importance are those concerning the job, the "do" elements. In the first place, should they be performed at all?

Materials handling activities are associated with the "make ready" and "put away" elements of a job. If any "do" element can be eliminated or combined with another "do" element, then the associated "make ready" and "put away" elements, generally representing materials handling, are likewise eliminated or combined. As a result, a reduction in cost has been made, practically without any analysis of the materials handling proper by the analyst. He has concentrated on the "do" element alone to this point.

In summary, a materials handling analyst should be trying to **determine the answers** to questions such as the following:

> What is to be moved and why?
> Where is it to be moved and why?
> When is it to be moved and why?

To determine the answer the job must be identified according to:

> Make ready.
> Do.
> Put away.

Each "do" operation should then be challenged by the questions:

> Can it be eliminated?
> Can it be combined?
> Can the sequence be changed?
> Can it be improved?

Further questions should then be raised relating to the specific job being analyzed. Finally, the "make ready" and "put away" elements should be challenged by the same questions.

When a satisfactory and rational set of answers to these basic questions of analysis has been obtained, the necessity for the handling activity itself should be established. The final answer is then merely a matter of determining how the material is to be handled—this being mainly a kind of analysis that is more closely related to the equipment selection function than to the more basic analysis of the operating problems proper.

Symbols and Symbolization

ANALYSIS BY MEANS OF SYMBOLS. The analysis of any materials handling problem is considerably simplified—and its possible solution becomes more apparent—when the problem itself can be pictured or portrayed in some appropriate form. Because of the importance of portraying such problems, it has been necessary to develop a "shorthand" method of describing the various specific **types of activities and motions.** The importance of having a "shorthand" method available to the analyst, in order to record what is actually going on in any particular situation, has resulted in the development of certain symbols which are used to identify clearly the actual different activities which are taking place. Through the use of symbols a new method can be planned and checked for feasibility and possible improvements in order to justify the expense of actually installing the method.

To use symbols to the best advantage, the analyst must first **identify his problem** in accordance with the previous suggestions, decide which symbols he will use, and finally make sure that these symbols are adequately defined if they are nonstandard. This step is important because other analysts will then be able to use the analyst's work sheets and fully understand the nature and scope of the problem. Then, by actual observation at the scene of the activity, the problem should be diagrammed or charted in accordance with the symbols, using whatever further descriptive material is necessary. With the problem thus analyzed in the form of charts and diagrams, the questioning method so necessary in work simplification can be applied much more readily and with better concrete results than could otherwise be obtained.

The **principal symbols** useful for analytical work in solving materials handling problems were originated by a number of individuals, among whom were Frederick W. Taylor, Carl Barth, Frank B. and Lillian M. Gilbreth, Professor David B. Porter at New York University, Alan Mogenson, and later Robert L. Morrow, and Wendell Phillips and his associates at Eli Lilly & Company.

Therbligs. Therbligs are symbols developed by Dr. Frank B. and Dr. Lillian M. Gilbreth for particular use in the charting of activities associated with motion analysis. From a materials handling standpoint they can be used when studying the handling characteristics of an operation done by a worker at an individual or group work place. They are not so readily applicable for the broader kinds of materials handling problems.

Symbols. The symbols of the American Society of Mechanical Engineers, which established its Materials Handling Division in 1920, have been approved as an ASME standard. They were developed by a committee designated by the ASME to standardize the symbols that were then being used for process-chart work. The committee started with the original process-chart symbols developed by the Gilbreths, and modifications of these symbols as worked out for use by others. Based on certain criteria established by the committee, a report was published containing the symbols shown in Section 1 of the ASME standard for Operation and Flow Process Charts. It is reproduced in part here on pages **2·11** ff.

Yale & Towne Symbols. The Yale & Towne Manufacturing Company has added to the ASME list some symbols which are considered to be useful for analyzing problems associated with the operation of a fork truck or other kinds of mobile equipment. These symbols are shown in Fig. 2.

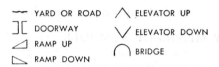

Fig. 2. Supplementary Yale & Towne process analysis symbols.

Handligs. A further set of symbols was developed and found useful by Wendell W. Phillips and his associates at the Eli Lilly Co. These symbols—called "handligs"—are used sometimes separately and sometimes in conjunction with other process-chart symbols. They are shown later in Fig. 28 as part of the discussion on Cycle Charts and are an extension of shorthand designations. Because of their complexity and number, however, they are used mainly where they definitely add to the analysis information which cannot be obtained except through the use of an extensive set of symbols. If a word or two can be substituted for the symbols and will convey the same meaning to the analyst, then the use of handligs would add little to any analysis. On the other hand, in cases where the symbols do add information that cannot be gained by simpler methods, they are a contribution to the available analytical techniques.

Techniques of Analysis

ANALYSIS TECHNIQUES. The specific techniques followed in making an analysis of a materials handling problem are the result of developments over many years by highly qualified management and industrial engineers. The basic mechanisms of analysis were developed through a process of evolution, and gradually many of them have become practically standardized. The ASME committee mentioned under the topic "Symbols and Symbolization" developed and published the **ASME Standard on "Operation and Flow Process Charts,"** which is the basis for the presentation here of operation process charts and flow process charts. Additional techniques have been developed in connection with particular types of problems in cases where the more standardized types of charts did not specifically fill the need.

The specific type of chart to use for any particular situation depends on the **problem facing the analyst.** Analysts should be thoroughly familiar with all the basic types of charting techniques, however, so that the best possible solutions can be worked out as the result of the thorough study of each particular problem.

Flow Diagram. A flow diagram is a chart indicating the **route or path** which a material or commodity should follow in passing through a plant, warehouse, or shipping center. Its primary purpose is to establish the flow path for the material, or the pattern of its movement.

The analyst must secure an accurate floor plan of the area through which the material is to pass, drawn to scale so that distances may be measured from the diagram. The floor plan should show the location of the machinery and equipment in the area, with obstructions indicated.

There are countless variations of the **flow diagram.** The simplest is one that shows merely a continuous line starting at the point where the material is first identified and indicates the precise path that that material takes until it reaches the end point of its travel. Arrows are drawn along the line to show the direction of travel. Fig. 23 (shown later) shows a flow diagram for a single product passing through a certain area and illustrates the simplest form of flow diagram. This diagram is not to scale and shows only direction of flow without any detail. Another type of flow diagram, presented in Fig. 24 (also shown later), shows a multiple-product flow through the same manufacturing area.

On some flow diagrams it is desirable to **indicate the processes or activities** that occur in the various areas by inserting the **process-chart symbols** in the flow line at the appropriate points. This procedure is illustrated later in Fig. 8. From a flow diagram drawn in this manner a flow process chart (as shown in Fig. 9) can then be constructed to explain details that cannot very well be presented on the flow diagram.

OPERATION AND FLOW PROCESS CHARTS. The operation process chart is a valuable tool by means of which to present the concept of ideal flow. While the chart itself does not show any materials handling activity, it does show the work flow of all manufactured parts and the relationships of those parts one to another in terms of where they enter the process and how they are assembled into the finished product. Materials handling is only a service function, but it must serve the processing operations. By means of an operation process chart, the complete processing can be shown in its entire form, and the ideal plan of work flow is presented. The closer the ultimate flow can be made to conform to the ideal flow shown on the chart, the more the handling will be minimized.

The following description concerning process charts is quoted directly from the report of the American Society of Mechanical Engineers.

ASME Standard Operation and Flow Process Charts

SECTION 1—PROCESS CHART.

Definitions.

1. Process Chart. A process chart is a graphic representation of events and information pertaining thereto occurring during a series of actions or operations.

2. Operation Process Chart. An operation process chart is a graphic representation of the points at which materials are introduced into the process, and of the sequence of inspections and all operations except those involved in material handling. It includes information considered desirable for analysis, such as time required and location.

3. Flow Process Chart. A flow process chart is a graphic representation of the sequence of all operations, transportations, inspections, delays, and storages occurring during a process or procedure, and includes information considered desirable for analysis such as time required and distance moved.

(a). The material type presents the process in terms of the events which occur to the material.

(b). The man type presents the process in terms of the activities of the man.

Process Charting Procedure.

4. For analytical purposes and to aid in detecting and eliminating inefficiencies, it is convenient to classify the actions which occur during a given process into five classifications. These are known as operations, transportations, inspections, delays, and storages. The following definitions cover the meaning of these classifications under the majority of conditions which will be encountered in process charting work.

Activities Defined.

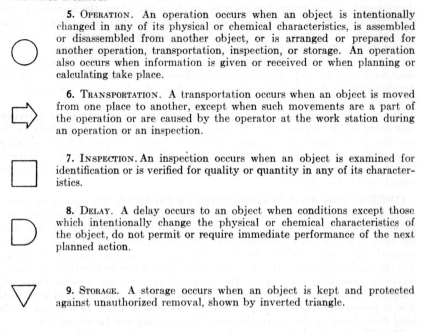

5. OPERATION. An operation occurs when an object is intentionally changed in any of its physical or chemical characteristics, is assembled or disassembled from another object, or is arranged or prepared for another operation, transportation, inspection, or storage. An operation also occurs when information is given or received or when planning or calculating take place.

6. TRANSPORTATION. A transportation occurs when an object is moved from one place to another, except when such movements are a part of the operation or are caused by the operator at the work station during an operation or an inspection.

7. INSPECTION. An inspection occurs when an object is examined for identification or is verified for quality or quantity in any of its characteristics.

8. DELAY. A delay occurs to an object when conditions except those which intentionally change the physical or chemical characteristics of the object, do not permit or require immediate performance of the next planned action.

9. STORAGE. A storage occurs when an object is kept and protected against unauthorized removal, shown by inverted triangle.

10. COMBINED ACTIVITY. When it is desired to show activities performed either concurrently or by the same operator at the same work station, the symbols for those activities are combined, as shown by the circle placed within the square to represent a combined operation and inspection.

11. When unusual situations outside the range of the definitions are encountered, the intent of the definitions summarized in the following tabulation will enable the analyst to make the proper classifications.

CLASSIFICATION	PREDOMINANT RESULT
Operation	Produces or accomplishes
Transportation	Moves
Inspection	Verifies
Delay	Interferes
Storage	Keeps

SECTION 2—PRINCIPLES AND PRACTICES FOR CONSTRUCTION OF OPERATION PROCESS CHARTS.

Form.

14. Operation process charts differ widely from one another because of differences in the processes which they are portraying. Hence, it is impractical to use a prepared form which will show anything other than identifying information. Operation process charts are therefore drawn on plain paper of sufficient size to accommodate the chart.

Major Conventions.

18. The sequence in which the events depicted on the chart must be performed is represented by the arrangement of process chart symbols on vertical flow lines. Material, either purchased or upon which work is performed during the process, is

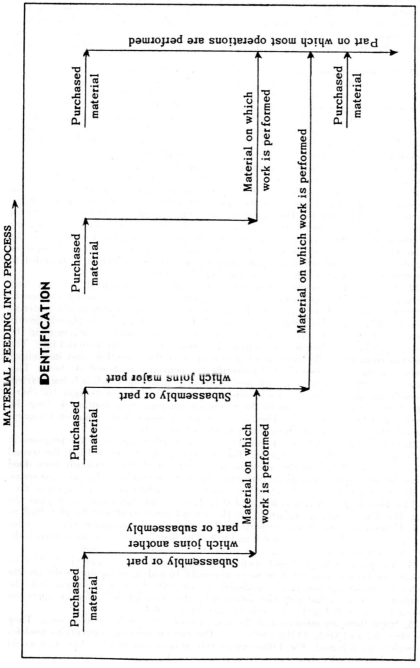

Fig. 3. Graphic representation of principle of operation process chart construction.

shown by horizontal material lines feeding into the vertical flow lines. Fig. 3 is a graphic representation of this principle.

19. One of the parts going to make up the completed product is selected for charting first. Usually a chart of the most pleasing appearance will be obtained by choosing the component on which the greatest number of operations is performed. If the chart is to be used as a basis for laying out a progressive assembly line, the part having the greatest bulk to which the smaller parts are assembled would be chosen.

20. When the component which is to be charted first has been chosen, a horizontal material line is drawn in the upper right hand portion of the chart. A description of the material is recorded directly above this line. The description may be as complete as is deemed necessary. Usually a brief description, such as "20 ga. Steel Sheet" or "⅝ in. Hex. Brass Bar" will suffice, since it is the purpose of the chart to give a picture of the process as a whole rather than the detailed specifications of the materials used. In order to identify the part itself, the name and identifying number are recorded in capital letters directly above the material description.

21. A vertical flow line is next drawn down from the right-hand end of the horizontal material line. Approximately ¼ in. from the intersection of the horizontal material line and the vertical flow line, the symbol is drawn for the first operation or inspection which is performed. To the right of this symbol, a brief description of the event is recorded, such as "Bore, turn, chamfer, and cut off" or "Inspect material for defects." To the left of the symbol is recorded the time allowed for performing the required work. Other pertinent information which it is considered will add to the value of the chart, such as department in which the work is performed, male or female operator, cost center, machine number, or labor classification, is recorded to the right of the symbol below the description of the event.

22. This charting procedure is continued until another component joins the first. Then a material line is drawn to show the point at which the second component enters the process. If it is purchased material, a brief identification of the material, such as "Wing Nut No. 18023" or "X and Y Co. No. 80 Filter" is placed directly above the material line. If work has previously been done on the component in the plant, a vertical flow line is erected from the left-hand end of the material line. The material from which the component was made and the operations and inspections performed on it are then charted following the conventions described above. This same procedure is repeated as each new component joins one which is being charted. As each component joins the one shown on a vertical flow line to its right, the charting of the events which occur to the combined components is continued along the vertical flow line to the right. The final event which occurs to the completed apparatus will thus appear in the lower right hand portion of the chart.

23. Operations are numbered serially for identification and reference purposes in the order in which they are charted. The first operation is numbered 0–1, the second 0–2, and so on. When another component on which work has previously been done joins the process, the operations performed upon it are numbered in the same series. If the first component on the chart has had four operations performed upon it, they will be identified as 0–1, 0–2, 0–3, and 0–4. If a second component then joins the first, the first operation performed on the second component will be identified as 0–5. If two more operations are performed on the second component before it joins the first, they will be numbered 0–6 and 0–7. The first operation performed after the two components have come together would then be identified as 0–8.

24. An operation number once used is never repeated on the same chart. If after a chart has been completed, it becomes necessary to add an operation to the process between two operations, it is permissible to identify the new operation with the number of the preceding operation followed by the subscript "a." Thus an operation inserted between 0–4 and 0–5 would be identified as 0–4a.

25. Inspections are numbered in the same manner in a series of their own. They are identified as INS-1, INS-2, and so on. The same numbering conventions used for operations are followed. Fig. 4 illustrates a typical operation process chart as it would appear when completed.

OPERATION PROCESS CHART
PRESENT METHOD

SUBJECT CHARTED Strip Type Thermostat Assembly   DWG. NO. 82103   ITEM 4
DATE CHARTED 5/29/–   CHARTED BY John Smith   DIVISION Small Parts

INSERT A-176   ADJUSTING SCREW A-253   CASING A-116
7/16" Hex. Cold Drawn Steel   1/4" Hex. Cold Drawn Steel   20 Ga. Cold Rolled Steel

0.0018   (O-9) 1st machine   0.0043   (O-5) Machine complete   0.0005 (O-1) Shear strips
                S. M. Dept.   S. M. Dept.   Pr. Dept.

0.0013   (O-10) Finish machine   (O-6) Tap   0.0013 (O-2) Emboss, pierce,
                S. M. Dept.   0.0032   D.P. Dept.   notch, form, and
                                                                                     cut off
                                                                                     Pr. Dept.

0.00005 (O-11) Nickel plate   0.00005   (O-7) Nickel plate   0.0020 (O-3) Finish form
                Pl. Dept.   Pl. Dept.   Pr. Dept.

D.W.   [INS. 3] Inspect   D.W.   [INS. 2] Inspect   0.0015 (O-4) Nickel plate
                  Pl. Dept.   Pl. Dept.   Pl. Dept.

                    SETSCREW M-70   [INS. 1] Inspect
                                                                                     Pl. Dept.
                                 0.0053   (O-8) Assemble   D.W.
                                                setscrew to
                                                adjusting screw
                                                Assemb. Dept.

                    LUBRICANT

STOP LUG W-133   (O-12) Cover thread with
1/8" × 3/32" REC. STEEL WIRE   0.0021   Lubricant and
                                                start in insert
                                                Assemb. Dept.

0.0005   (O-14) Cut to length   (O-13) Run down and set
                Pr. Dept.   0.0026   adjusting screw
                                                Assemb. Dept.

0.00005 (O-15) Nickle plate
                Pl. Dept.

D.W.   [INS. 4] Inspect
                  Pl. Dept

                                 0.0050   (O-16) Spot-weld lug to
                                                adjusting screw
                                                Assemb. Dept.

                                          0.0090 (O-17) Rivet insert
                                                         assembly to
                                                         casing
                                                         Assemb. Dept.

                                          D.W.   [INS. 5] Calibrate
                                                           and inspect
                                                           Assemb. Dept.

Fig. 4. Typical operation process chart.

2·15

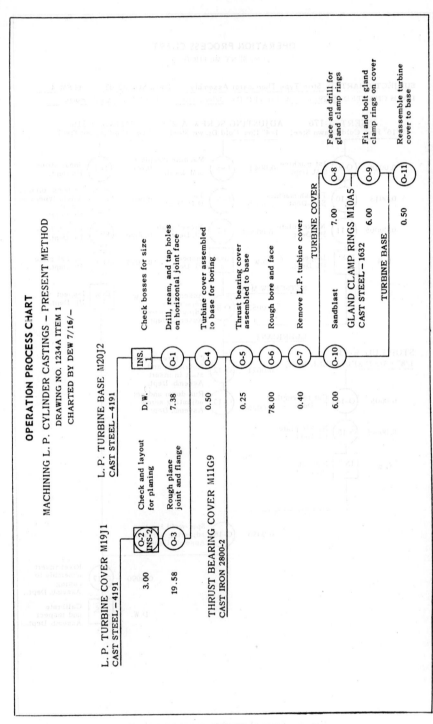

OPERATION PROCESS CHART

MACHINING L. P. CYLINDER CASTINGS – PRESENT METHOD

DRAWING NO. 1234A ITEM 1

CHARTED BY DEW 7/16/–

L. P. TURBINE COVER M19J1
CAST STEEL – 4191

L. P. TURBINE BASE M20J2
CAST STEEL – 4191

THRUST BEARING COVER M11G9
CAST IRON 2800-2

GLAND CLAMP RINGS M10A5
CAST STEEL – 1632

TURBINE COVER

TURBINE BASE

Op.	Value	Description
INS. 1	D.W.	Check bosses for size
O-1	7.38	Drill, ream, and tap holes on horizontal joint face
O-4	0.50	Turbine cover assembled to base for boring
O-5	0.25	Thrust bearing cover assembled to base
O-6	78.00	Rough bore and face
O-7	0.40	Remove L.P. turbine cover
O-10	6.00	Sandblast
O-2 / INS-2	3.00	Check and layout for planing
O-3	19.58	Rough plane joint and flange
O-8	7.00	Face and drill for gland clamp rings
O-9	6.00	Fit and bolt gland clamp rings on cover
O-11	0.50	Reassemble turbine cover to base

Fig. 5. Operation process chart showing convention for depicting a disassembly and subsequent reassembly.

Other Conventions—Portrayal of Disassembly Methods.

26. The conventions followed for portraying disassembly operations are quite similar to those used for assemblies. Material is represented as flowing from the process by a horizontal material line drawn to the right from the vertical flow line approximately ¼ in. below the symbol for the disassembly operation. The name of the disassembled component is shown directly above the horizontal material line. The subsequent operations which are performed on the disassembled component, if any, are shown on a vertical flow line extending down from the right-hand end of the horizontal material line.

27. If the disassembled component is later reassembled to the part or assembly from which it was disassembled, that part or assembly is shown as feeding into the flow line of the component. This practice moves the major vertical flow line always to the right. Thus, when disassembly operations are to be shown, the chart cannot be started in the upper right-hand corner of the form but must be started farther to the left.

28. In numbering the operations, it is the practice to number the operations performed on the disassembled component after disassembly before numbering the operations on the part from which it was disassembled. Then if the part later rejoins the disassembled component, the conventional numbering practices may be followed. This practice also applies to inspections.

29. Fig. 5 is an operation process chart which shows a disassembly and a reassembly. A study of this figure will make clear the charting practices followed in cases of this kind.

30. It sometimes happens that a part may follow two or more alternate courses during part of the process. For example, a partially processed part may be inspected at a certain point. If it is satisfactory in every respect, it may go directly to the assembly. If not, it may require one or more corrective operations, depending upon the nature of the defects.

31. When it is desired to portray a condition of this kind on an operation process chart, a horizontal line is drawn below the vertical flow line, the central point of the line being at the intersection of the vertical flow line and the horizontal line. Vertical flow lines are then dropped from the horizontal line for each alternative which it is desired to show. If no operations or inspections are performed during one alternative a vertical flow line only is shown. In all cases, operation and inspection symbols are added in the conventional manner. They are numbered serially beginning with the first unused number in the operation or inspection series. The symbols on the flow line furthest to the left are numbered first, then those on the next flow line to the right, and so on until all have been numbered.

32. When all of the alternative paths have been charted, a horizontal line is drawn connecting the lower ends of all of the alternate flow lines. From the midpoint of this line, a vertical flow line is dropped and the balance of the process is charted in the conventional manner. Fig. 6 illustrates an application of this convention.

33. In some cases, it will be found that the same component is used at two or more different points in the same process. If it is a purchased part, it may be shown in the conventional manner each time it enters the process. If it is a part upon which work has previously been done, however, it will add to the time and effort required to prepare the chart if the component is completely charted every time it enters the process, particularly if its own processing is extensive. To avoid unnecessary charting work, the second time a part is shown entering a process, it is represented by a horizontal material line above which is written the name of the part and a reference to the operation numbers which show the processing it has undergone, as "Hand wheel No. 851A, See 0–6 to 0–12 incl."

34. In general, an operation process chart should be so constructed that vertical flow lines and horizontal material lines do not cross. On charts of complicated processes, this is sometimes difficult to avoid. When it is necessary to cross a vertical flow line and a horizontal material line, the fact that no juncture occurs is indicated by the convention shown by Fig. 7.

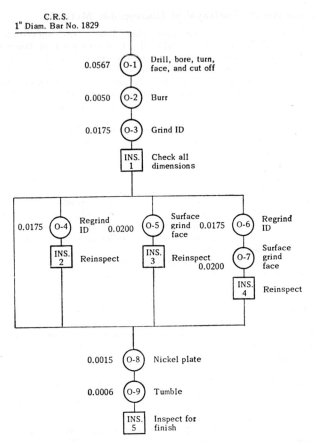

Fig. 6. **Convention for indicating alternate processes.**

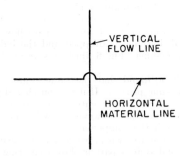

Fig. 7. **Convention for crossing vertical flow lines and horizontal material lines.**

35. In some cases, the unit shown by the chart changes as the process progresses. The chart might start out showing the operations performed on a long bar. The bar might subsequently be cut into short lengths so that the operations performed thereafter would apply to the short pieces rather than the long bar. Whenever it is desired to show the unit which is being charted, it is the convention to break the vertical flow line by drawing two parallel horizontal lines about 1½ in. long and ¼ in. apart centered with respect to the vertical flow line. Between these lines the unit which is to be followed during the subsequent operations and inspections is shown.

Summary—Presentation of Proposed Method.

36. When a proposed method is to be presented by an operation process chart, it is often desirable to show the advantages which it offers over the present method. This may be done by including with the information shown on the chart a summary of the important differences between the two methods.

37. This summary may take the form given in Fig. 8.

TOTAL YEARLY SAVING — DIRECT LABOR _____					
INSTALLATION COST OF PROPOSED METHOD_____					
ESTIMATED NET SAVING — FIRST YEAR _____ _____					
	Present Method		Proposed Method		Difference
Unit Cost — Direct Labor					
	No.	Time	No.	Time	No.	Time
○ . . . . Operations					
□ . . . . Inspections					

Fig. 8. Summary of important differences between present and proposed methods.

38. The summary should be placed in a prominent location on the chart. On a small 8½ in. × 11 in. chart, it will usually be in the lower left-hand corner. In the case of a folded chart, it will be on the outside when the chart is folded. It may also be desirable to show it on the inside.

Conclusion—Coverage of Situations.

39. It is recognized that the above description of principles and practices for construction of operation process charts may not cover every conceivable situation which it may be desired to show. Probably at least 95 per cent of the situations which are ordinarily encountered in industry are covered however. The balance may be charted satisfactorily by following the prescribed conventions as closely as possible, representing the unusual situations with the objective of clearness uppermost in mind. A process chart is a means to an end rather than an end in itself. If it performs its function and is reasonably clear to all who study it, it may be considered to be a satisfactory chart.

SECTION 3—PRINCIPLES AND PRACTICES FOR CONSTRUCTION OF FLOW PROCESS CHARTS.

Form.

41. Flow process charts differ widely from one another because of the nature or scope of the processes they portray. They are usually drawn on plain paper of sufficient size to accommodate them when they portray the events occurring to more than one item of material, the activities of more than one person, or the alternate routes or procedures followed by material or men. This condition applies to most flow process charts of office procedures, so that they usually must be specially designed for each procedure charted. When events occurring to a single item or the activities of a single person are charted, prepared forms may be used. These forms are usually printed in the following sizes: 8½ × 11 in., 11 × 17 in., and 17 × 22 in., which may be filed in the standard letter file, and 8½ × 14 in., and 14 × 17 in., which may be filed in the legal-size file.

Identification.

42. The flow process chart should be identified by a title placed at the top of the chart. It is the usual practice to head the identifying information with the words

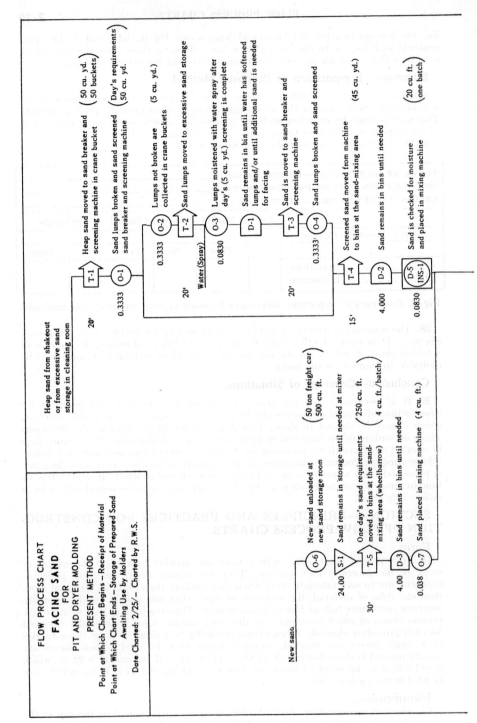

FLOW PROCESS CHART
FOR
FACING SAND
FOR
PIT AND DRYER MOLDING
PRESENT METHOD

Point at Which Chart Begins – Receipt of Material
Point at Which Chart Ends – Storage of Prepared Sand
Awaiting Use by Molders

Date Charted: 2/25/– Charted by R.W.S.

Heap sand from shakeout
or from excessive sand
storage in cleaning room

T-1   20'

O-1   0.3333

Heap sand moved to sand breaker and
screening machine in crane bucket   (50 cu. yd.)
                                        (50 buckets)

Sand lumps broken and sand screened   (Day's requirements)
sand breaker and screening machine   (50 cu. yd.)

O-2   0.3333   Lumps not broken are   (5 cu. yd.)
               collected in crane buckets

T-2   20'   Sand lumps moved to excessive sand storage

Water (Spray)

O-3   0.0830   Lumps moistened with water spray after
               day's (5 cu. yd.) screening is complete

D-1   Sand remains in bin until water has softened
               lumps and/or until additional sand is needed
               for facing

T-3   20'   Sand is moved to sand breaker and
               screening machine

O-4   0.3333' Sand lumps broken and sand screened

T-4   15'   Screened sand moved from machine   (45 cu. yd.)
               to bins at the sand-mixing area

D-2   4.000   Sand remains in bins until needed

D-5   0.0830   Sand is checked for moisture   (20 cu. ft.)
INS-1   and placed in mixing machine   (one batch)

New sand

O-6   New sand unloaded at   (50 ton freight car)
               new sand storage room   (500 cu. ft.)

S-1   24.00   Sand remains in storage until needed at mixer

T-5   30'   One day's sand requirements   (250 cu. ft.)
               moved to bins at the sand-   (4 cu. ft./batch)
               mixing area (wheelbarrow)

D-3   4.00   Sand remains in bins until needed

O-7   0.038   Sand placed in mixing machine   (4 cu. ft.)

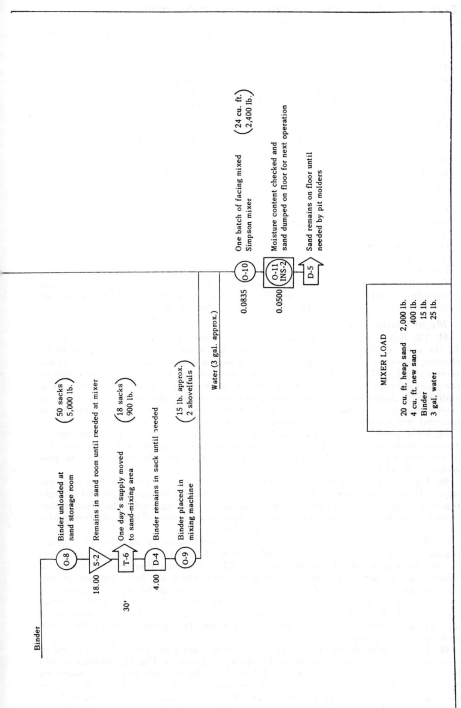

Fig. 9. Flow process chart of the material type showing manner in which several components are processed and brought together.

"Flow Process Chart." The identifying information which is always necessary is as follows:

Subject charted

Present Method or Proposed Method

Drawing number, part number, or other identifying number

Chart Span $\begin{cases} \text{Point in the process at which chart begins} \\ \text{Point in the process at which chart ends} \end{cases}$

Date Charted

Charted by

Additional information which is sometimes valuable for identifying purposes includes:

Plant $\qquad$ ⎫

Building $\qquad$ ⎬ Location

Department ⎭

Chart Number

Chart Type (Material or Man)

Sheet No. _____ of _____ Sheets

Approved by:

Quantity Information

Yearly Production

Cost Unit

43. If the chart is to be folded for filing in such a manner that the identifying information is on the inside, then sufficient identifying information for filing purposes should be repeated on the outside of the folded form.

Major Conventions.

44. The flow process chart is essentially an expansion of the operation process chart. In the case of charts drawn on plain paper where more than one item is to be charted, the same arrangement and conventions which are used for the operation process chart are likewise used for the flow process chart. Flow process charts contain the process operations and inspections shown on the operation process chart, and in addition the handling operations, transportations, delays, and storages. In the man type of flow process chart, there are no horizontal lines representing the entrance of material into a process, and the storage symbol is not used.

45. Flow process charts are usually drawn on plain paper of sufficient size to accommodate them when they portray the events occurring to more than one item of material, the activities of more than one person, or the alternate routes or procedures followed by material or men.

46. Fig. 9 is an example of a material type flow process chart drawn on plain paper. It shows the manner in which several components are processed and brought together to make the completed product, in this case facing sand. The arrangement is similar to that of an operation process chart, but because delays and transportations are shown, it is classed as a flow process chart.

47. When a flow process chart is made of a single item of material or a single person, usually only one column of symbols is needed, and no horizontal line is used to introduce material. There is enough similarity among flow process charts of single items to permit the use of prepared forms which are both convenient and time saving. The simplest of these forms provides headings for distance moved in feet, time, chart symbols, and process description. No vertical or horizontal rulings are provided. Thus the chart is stripped of all extra lines, so that the process data and symbols stand out clearly, as shown by Fig. 10. The symbols are usually drawn with the aid of a templet.

48. Vertical and horizontal rulings are sometimes used as aids in locating and in spacing the information recorded on the chart, as shown by Fig. 11. Rulings should be very light in weight in order not to detract from the symbols and their connecting flow lines. Where emphasis is placed on the time for each class of event for cost or analysis purposes, it is useful to subdivide the time column into five columns, one each for operation, transportation, inspection, delay, and storage times. Fig. 12 is a chart of this type.

PROCESS CHART

NAME OF PART OR PRODUCT   Requisition for Supplies — Rush Job

Chart Begins at Machine Shop Foreman's Desk, Ends on Typist's Desk in Pur. Dept.	CHART NO.

ORDER NO.	LOT SIZE	DEPT.	SHEET 1
CHARTED BY C.H.H.	DATE CHARTED 7/28/–	BLDG. M. E. Lab.	OF 1 SHEETS

Travel in ft.	Time in min.	Symbol	Operations	Remarks
		①	Written longhand by foreman.	
		1	On foreman's desk (awaiting messenger).	
1,000		1	By messenger to secretary of head of department.	
		2	On secretary's desk (awaiting typing).	
		②	Typed.	
15		2	By messenger to head of department.	
		3	On head of department's desk (awaiting approval).	
		O-3 INS-1	Examined, approved, and coded (signed and code stamped).	
		4	On head of department's desk (awaiting messenger).	
2,000		3	To purchasing department.	
		5	On purchasing agent's desk (awaiting approval).	
		2	Examined and approved.	
		6	On purchasing agent's desk (awaiting messenger).	
25		4	To typist's desk.	
		7	On typist's desk (awaiting typing of purchase order).	

SUMMARY

Number of operations 3

Number of delays 7

Number of inspections 2

Number of transportations . . . 4

Total travel in feet . . . 3,040

Fig. 10. Process chart with preprinted headings and captions.

2·23

| | | | SUBJECT CHARTED __Relief Valve Body__ | | CHART NO. __1021__ |

SUBJECT CHARTED	Relief Valve Body			CHART NO. 1021
DRAWING NO.	A-520612	PART NO. 16150		CHART TYPE
CHART BEGINS	Barstock Storage			CHARTED BY J. Smith
CHART ENDS	Assembly Department Storeroom			DATE 9/9/–

○ OPERATION   ▷ TRANSPORTATION   SHEET NO. 1 OF 1 SHEETS

□ INSPECTION   ▷ DELAY   COST UNIT 1 Valve Body

▽ STORAGE

Dist. in Feet	Unit Time in Hours	Chart Symbols	Process Description of __Proposed__ Method
		▽1	Stored in bar stock storage until requisitioned.
10	.0002	①1	Bars loaded on truck upon receipt of requisition from machine shop (2 men).
210	.0002	1▷	Moved to No. 301 machine.
10	.0002	②2	Bars unloaded to bar stock rack near No. 301 machine.
	4.00	D1	Delayed, waiting for operation to begin.
8	.0550	③3	Drill, bore, tap, seat, file, and cut off.
	2.00	D2	Delayed, awaiting drill press operator.
20	.00002	2▷	Moved to drill press by operator.
8	.0350	④4	Drill eight holes.
	2.00	D3	Delayed, awaiting moveman.
300	.0011	3▷	Moved to burring department.
	1.50	D4	Delayed, awaiting burring operation.
6	.0100	⑤5	Burr.
	2.00	D5	Delayed, awaiting moveman.
550	.0005	4▷	Moved to seat-lapping machine in detail department.
	6.00	D6	Delayed, awaiting operator.
6	.1700	O-6 INS-1	Lap seat, test, and inspect.
	2.00	D7	Delayed, awaiting moveman.
400	.0004	5▷	Moved to paint booth.
	6.00	D8	Delayed, awaiting painter.
15	.0380	⑦7	Mask, prime, paint, dry, unmask, and pack in box.
425		6▷	Sent by conveyor to assembly department storeroom.
	60.0	▽2	Stored until requisitioned.

Fig. 11. Chart using rulings as aids in locating and spacing data to be charted.

2·24

SUBJECT CHARTED ___ Relief Valve Body ___   CHART NO. ___ 1021 ___
DRAWING NO. ___ A-520612 ___ PART NO. _16150_   CHART TYPE _____
CHART BEGINS ___ Barstock Storage   CHARTED BY _J. Smith_
CHART ENDS ___ Assembly Department Storeroom   DATE ___ 9/9/–

○ OPERATION   ⬠ TRANSPORTATION   SHEET NO. _1_ OF _1_ SHEETS   COST UNIT _1 Valve Body_

☐ INSPECTION   ⬠ DELAY   ▽ STORAGE

Dist. Moved Ft.	Unit Oper. Time Hr.	Unit Transp. Time Hr.	Unit Inspect Time Hr.	Delay Time Hr.	Storage Time Hr.	Chart Symbols	Process Description of _Proposed_ Method
						▽1	Stored in bar stock storage until requisitioned.
10	.0002					○1	Bars loaded on truck upon receipt of requisition from machine shop (2 men).
210		.0002				⬠1	Moved to No. 301 machine.
10	.0002					○2	Bars unloaded to bar stock rack near No. 301 machine.
				4.00		⬠1	Delayed, waiting for operation to begin.
8	.0550					○3	Drill, bore, tap, seat, file, cut off.
				2.00		⬠2	Delayed, awaiting drill press operator.
20		00002				⬠2	Moved to drill press by operator.
8	.0350					○4	Drill eight holes.
				2.00		⬠3	Delayed, awaiting moveman.
300		.0011				⬠3	Moved to burring department.
				1.50		⬠4	Delayed, awaiting burring operation.
6	.0100					○5	Burr.
				2.00		⬠5	Delayed, awaiting moveman.
550		.0005				⬠4	Moved to seat-lapping machine in detail department.
				6.00		⬠6	Delayed, awaiting operator.
6	.1700					○O-6 INS-1	Lap seat, test, and inspect.
				2.00		⬠7	Delayed, awaiting moveman.
400		.0004				⬠5	Moved to paint booth.
				6.00		⬠8	Delayed, awaiting painter.
15	.0380					○7	Mask, prime, paint, dry, unmask, and pack in box.
425						⬠6	Sent by conveyor to assembly department storeroom.
					60.0	▽2	Stored until requisitioned.

Fig. 12. Chart showing subdivison of time column into each class of event.

2·25

SUBJECT CHARTED __Relief Valve Body__	CHART NO. __1021__	
DRAWING NO. __A-520612__ PART NO. __16150__	TYPE OF CHART__ Material__	
POINT AT WHICH CHART BEGINS __Receipt of requisition from machine shop__	SHEET NO. __1__ OF __1__ SHEETS	
_____ LOCATION __Bar stock storeroom__	CHARTED BY __J Smith__	
POINT AT WHICH CHART ENDS __Storing of finished product in storeroom__	DATE ____9/8/-__	
_____ LOCATION __Assembly Dept Storeroom__	APPROVED BY __J Jones__	
	DATE _____9/9/-__	

QUANTITY INFORMATION

I Bar makes 50 bodies	YEARLY
I Packing box holds 25 bodies	PRODUCTION __100,000 pieces__
	COST UNIT __I Valve body__

PRESENT METHOD

QUANTITY UNIT CHARTED	SYMBOLS	DESCRIPTION OF EVENT	DIST. MOVED IN FEET	UNIT OPER. TIME IN HR.	UNIT TRANSP TIME IN HR.	UNIT INSPECT TIME IN HR.	DELAY TIME IN HR.	STORAGE TIME IN HR.
I Bar		Bar loaded on truck upon receipt of requisition from machine shop (2 men)	10	.0002				
20 Bars		Moved to No. 301 machine	210		.0002			
I Bar		Bar unloaded to bar stock rack near No. 301 machine (2 men)	10	.0002				
		Bar waits for operation to begin					4.00	
I Valve body		Drill, bore, tap, seat, file, and cut off	6	.0550				
		Await moveman					4.00	
300 Valve bodies		Moved to burring department	300		.0011			
		Await burring operator					1.50	
I Valve body		Burr	6	.0075				
		Await moveman					2 00	
300 Valve bodies		Moved to drill press in machine shop	320		.0011			
		Await drilling operator					2.00	
I Valve body		Drill and countersink 8 holes		.0480				
		Await moveman					4.00	
300 Valve bodies		Moved to inspection department	100		.0001			
		Await inspector					1.50	
I Valve body		Inspect and gauge	6			.0085		
		Await moveman					2.00	
300 Valve bodies		Moved to storeroom No 2	3000		.0020			
		Storage until requisitioned by detail department						48.0
300 Valve bodies		Moved to seat lapping machine	2550		.0025			
		Await operator					1.50	
I Valve body		Lap seat and test	6	.1700				
		Await moveman					2.00	
100 Valve bodies		Moved to paint booth	400		.0004			
		Await painter					4.00	
I Valve body		Mask, prime, paint, dry, and unmask	10	.0350				
100 Valve bodies		Carried to packer by painter	125		.0001			
		Await packing					3 00	
I Valve body		Pack in box	12	.0100				
Box 25 Valve bodies		Sent by conveyor to assembly department storeroom	300					
		Storage until requisitioned						60.0

Fig. 13. Flow process chart with preprinted symbols showing

CESS CHART

SUMMARY

TOTAL YEARLY SAVING – DIRECT LABOR $ 2,200.00		PRESENT METHOD		PROPOSED METHOD		DIFFERENCE	
	UNIT COST – DIRECT LABOR AND INSP.	.300		.278		.022	
	DISTANCE TRAVELED IN FEET	7,383		1,843		5,540	
INSTALLATION COST OF PROPOSED METHOD $150.00		NO.	TIME IN HR.	NO.	TIME IN HR.	NO.	TIME IN HR.
	○ OPERATIONS	8	3250	7	.3084	1	.0175
	⇨ TRANSPORTATIONS	9	.0085	6	.00222	3	.00628
ESTIMATED NET SAVING – FIRST YEAR $2,050.00	☐ INSPECTIONS	2	.0085	1		1	.0085
	D DELAYS	12	31 5	8	25.5	4	6.0
	▽ STORAGES	2	108 0	1	60 0	1	78.0

PROPOSED METHOD

QUANTITY UNIT CHARTED	SYMBOLS	DESCRIPTION OF EVENT	DIST. MOVED IN FEET	UNIT OPER TIME IN HR.	UNIT TRANSR. TIME IN HR	UNIT INSPECT. TIME IN HR.	DELAY TIME IN HR.	STORAGE TIME IN HR.
1 Bar	①⇨☐D▽	Bar loaded on truck upon receipt of requisition from machine shop (2 men)	10	0002				
20 Bars	○①☐D▽	Moved to No. 301 machine	210		.0002			
1 Bar	②⇨☐D▽	Bar unloaded to bar stock rack near No. 301 machine	10	.0002				
	○⇨☐①▽	Bar waits for operation to begin					4.00	
1 Valve body	③⇨☐D▽	Drill, bore, tap, seat, file, and cut off	8	.0550				
	○⇨☐②▽	Await drill press operator					2.00	
100 Valve bodies	○②☐D▽	Moved to drill press by operator	20		.0002			
1 Valve body	④⇨☐D▽	Drill 8 holes	8	.0350				
	○⇨☐③▽	Await moveman					2 00	
300 Valve bodies	○③☐D▽	Moved to burring department	300		.0011			
	○⇨☐④▽	Await burring operator					1.50	
1 Valve body	⑤⇨☐D▽	Burr	6	.0100				
	○⇨☐⑤▽	Await moveman					2.00	
300 Valve bodies	○④☐D▽	Moved to seat lapping machine-detail department	550		.0005			
	○⇨☐⑥▽	Await operator					6.00	
1 valve body	⑥⇨①D▽	Lap, seat, test, and inspect	6	.1700				
	○⇨☐⑦▽	Await moveman					2.00	
100 Valve bodies	○⑤☐D▽	Moved to paint booth	400		.0004			
	○⇨☐⑧▽	Await painter					6 00	
1 Valve body	⑦⇨☐D▽	Mask, prime, paint, dry, unmask, and pack in box	15	.0380				
Box 25 Valve bod's	○⑥☐D▽	Sent by conveyor to assembly department storeroom	425					
	○⇨☐D▽	Storage until requisitioned						60.0
	○⇨☐D▽							
	○⇨☐D▽							
	○⇨☐D▽							
	○⇨☐D▽							
	○⇨☐D▽							
	○⇨☐D▽							
	○⇨☐D▽							
	○⇨☐D▽							
	○⇨☐D▽							
	○⇨☐D▽							

present and proposed methods with a summary of cost savings.

49. An example of a more complete development of a prepared flow process chart form is given in Fig. 13. This shows the inside of a 17 × 22 in. sheet which is folded twice into an 8½ × 11 in. size for filing. Features of this form are: The provision for showing both present and proposed methods; prepared symbols, which obviate the need for drawing them by hand with a templet; a summary showing cost data and savings; and more complete information under the identification heading. The reverse side is arranged to provide a cross section background for a sketch of a layout or flow diagram and basic information for identification which appears on the front cover when folded. (See Fig. 14a.) The two center pages are for a detailed explanation of proposed changes (see Fig. 14b), and the back cover provides for recording action taken on the proposed method (Fig. 14c).

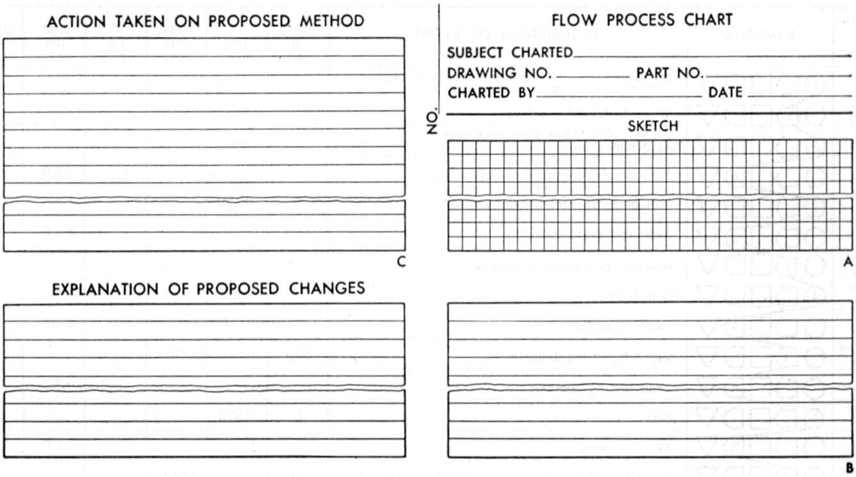

ACTION TAKEN ON PROPOSED METHOD

FLOW PROCESS CHART

SUBJECT CHARTED_____
DRAWING NO. _____ PART NO._____
CHARTED BY_____ DATE _____

SKETCH

C

A

EXPLANATION OF PROPOSED CHANGES

B

Fig. 14. The reverse side of Fig. 13.

50. When material is followed from the beginning to the end of a process, the unit being charted may change from time to time. When this occurs it is important to show what the unit is at any point on the chart, so that confusion will be avoided. In the illustration given, the chart shows the process of transforming an aluminum bar into relief valve bodies. The bars are loaded and unloaded singly, but are moved twenty at a time. At the third operation, each bar is machined and cut up to form fifty valve bodies. For all subsequent operations, one valve body is the unit, but the valve bodies are moved in quantities of one hundred or three hundred until they are packed. The unit then becomes twenty-five valve bodies contained in a packing case. This quantity information is entered in the spaces provided under that heading in the identification section of the chart.

51. It is customary to express all costs on the basis of the finished product. The cost unit may be one finished item, a dozen, or any number, being determined by the nature of the product. In any case, the allowed time information for operations, transportations, and inspections, which is to be recorded on the chart, should be given on the basis of the cost unit. If, for example, in the case given in Fig. 13, it requires 0.0100 hr. to load one bar onto the truck, because one bar makes fifty valve bodies, the time per valve body will be $0.0100 \div 50 = 0.0002$ hr. Similarly, if it takes 0.2000 hr. to move twenty bars 210 ft., the time per valve body will be $0.2000 \div (50 \times 20) = 0.0002$ hr. However, the time for delays and storages is not divided by the number of units in the bar or lot, for each unit is delayed or stored the full time. The same reasoning applies to recording distance moved. The distance the bar is moved is not divided by 50 because each unit within the bar must move the entire distance. By keeping all time figures which directly affect cost on the basis of the same unit, confusion is avoided and all figures on the chart are directly comparable. The cost unit chosen is recorded on the chart to complete the necessary preliminary information.

52. The chart proper is begun by recording in the first column under the head of "Present Method" the quantity unit being charted at the beginning of the process. A brief description of the event which first occurs is entered in the third column. In Fig. 13, this is "Bar loaded on truck upon receipt of requisition from machine shop (two men)." This is classed as an operation. It is the first operation which has occurred, so the numeral 1 is placed within the operation symbol in column two. The information concerning this first event is completed by recording the total distance the bar is moved and the unit time for moving it.

53. When the charting of the first event is completed, the information regarding the second event is entered. This is repeated until the process has been completely charted. All operations, transportations, inspections, delays, and storages are numbered serially in the order in which they occur, but each classification has its own series. To complete the chart, it is the usual practice to join all used symbols with short straight lines so that the flow of the process will stand out clearly. A study of Fig. 13 will show the conventions followed in constructing this type of process chart.

54. When writing the description of the events charted, it is preferable to use the passive voice when material is being followed. This is logical since the material is the object of all the actions taking place and, cannot of itself initiate action. It further helps the chart maker to keep his attention focused on the material being followed, instead of becoming sidetracked by following an operator or move man.

55. Examples of this practice are shown on Fig. 12, as T–1, "*Moved* to #301 machine," D–3, "*Delayed* awaiting move man," and S–2, "*Stored* until requisitioned." Similarly, operations and inspections may be described in the passive voice, although if it is desired for the sake of uniformity to adhere to the terminology used on shop and cost records, it is permissible to use the active voice. 0–6 and Ins.–1, "lap seat, test, and inspect" is an example of this alternative.

56. When writing the description of events on a man-type flow process chart, the active voice is used, because the man who is being followed is the one who initiates the action.

57. Whenever an activity outside of the scope of the investigation occurs, it is the convention to break the vertical flow line at the point where the interruption occurs by drawing two wavy horizontal lines about 1½ in. long and ¼ in. apart, centered with respect to the vertical flow line. An activity outside the scope of the investigation is an operation, transportation, inspection, delay, storage, or series of these which for any reason the investigator considers unnecessary or impractical to analyze during the current study.

58. The arrow which is used for the transportation symbol may be drawn as a straight line with arrowhead ($\rightarrow$) when not preprinted or drawn with the aid of a template. The symbol may be given additional meaning by changing its direction. When the arrow points to the right, the material is represented as progressing in the proper direction. When the arrow points to the left, backtracking is indicated. Upward movement of the material is indicated by pointing the arrow upward, and downward movement by pointing the arrow downward.

SUMMARY.

59. To bring out clearly the differences between the present and the proposed methods, a summary form is provided in the upper right-hand corner of Fig. 13. The summary provides space for recording the total yearly direct labor saving, the cost of putting the proposed method into effect, and the estimated net savings for the first year. This information is supported by a summary of the detailed changes in terms of unit cost, distance traveled in feet, and number and time of operations, transportations, inspections, delays, and storages under the present and proposed methods. No direct monetary savings are usually shown as resulting from reductions in distance moved or storage or delay time, as it is difficult to measure accurately savings emanating from these sources. Experience, of course, indicates that when distances moved or storage or delay times are decreased, the operation of the plant

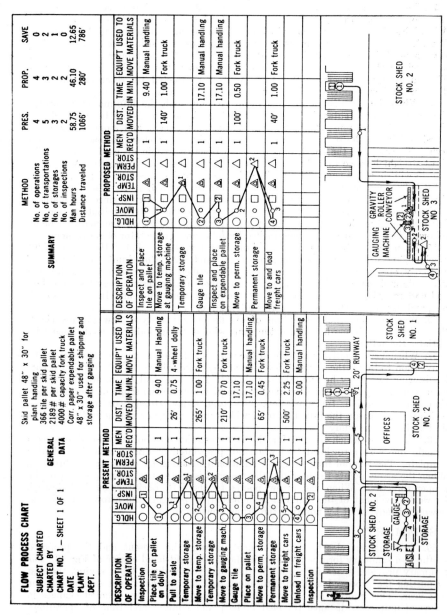

Fig. 15.   Flow process chart form which includes both present and proposed methods.

is more effective, so the results accomplished in this direction are recorded in the summary.

CONCLUSION.

60. A process chart is a graphic representation of events and information pertaining thereto occurring during a series of actions or operations. Its purpose is to present a picture of a given process so clearly that an understanding of its every step will be gained by all who study the chart.

61. The principles and practices described herein have been selected from all those in use in the past, because they appear to give a clear, practical portrayal of the kind of industrial activities in connection with which flow process charts are most commonly used. Although these principles and practices will probably apply satisfactorily to the great majority of processes charted, it is recognized that there may be cases in which it will be felt that the process will be made clearer if practices not covered by the standard procedure are introduced.

62. For example, in order to emphasize the symbols used, they may be filled in with solid black. The solid black symbol is sometimes reserved exclusively for the do or process operations. The filling in of the symbols prevents the practice of placing numbers within them. Therefore, if numbers are desired, it is necessary to provide a column for them.

63. Another variation from the type of chart shown by Fig. 13 uses letter symbols in place of geometric symbols. A column is provided for each classification of event and is headed by the initial letter of that event. A column is provided for the use of colors which are employed to differentiate among three major conditions. These and the conditions representing them are: do operations, white; storage and delay, red; make-ready and put-away operations, blue.

64. Because it is the purpose of a process chart to present a picture, it is recognized that at times such departures from standard practice may be permissible if clearness of presentation is gained. At the same time, in the interest of standardization, it is recommended that the principles and practices described under the head of Major Conventions be adhered to whenever possible.

CHARTING BOTH PRESENT AND PROPOSED METHODS. Fig. 15 shows a flow process chart form covering both present and proposed methods. The symbols used here are some of the original Gilbreth symbols. A flow diagram is included in the process chart proper, thus enabling the user to check on the work flow as well as on the process chart proper. (Booklet No. 2, Library of Know-How. Materials Handling Institute.)

Analysis and Summary Forms

TYPICAL FORMS FOR PROCESS ANALYSIS. Several kinds of basic forms, such as those here shown, have been developed by various companies and organizations for the study and analysis of work simplification problems. Certain of these analysis procedures are included here.

Vis-O-Graf Analysis. The Yale Vis-O-Graf System was developed by the Yale & Towne Manufacturing Company for work analysis procedures. Fig. 16a describes the nature and use of the methods presented. The chart used is shown in Fig. 16b. The methods employed are explained in Fig. 17.

Flow Process Charts. Charts of flow process operations are quite generally employed. They cover the five typical standard activities occurring in all handling procedures and are used at work simplification conferences, such as those conducted at Lake Placid, New York. Representative uses are shown in Fig. 18, which gives the "before" and "after" procedures employed and the reductions in distances traveled.

The Yale Vis-O-Graf makes it easy for you to write in in chronological order exactly what loading, moving, and unloading steps are now taken during the sequence of operations you select for study. Read the explanations and instructions below with the form fully unfolded.

How to Simplify Your Analysis. In many manufacturing activities the material handling and processing operations are highly complex. Parts or ingredients are rarely received, processed, stored, and shipped in a nonstop flow. Seldom is the same part received and put through the plant every day. All kinds of components—motors, castings, forgings, bulk materials—may arrive in a single day but are required in varying quantities in processing and assembling. Some parts or ingredients are stored, to be processed later; others are processed immediately, then placed in stores; still others are processed, assembled, and shipped the same day.

Because of these differences you may feel that a major handling problem exists only in one phase of your operations. Therefore, unless your plant is small and your handling steps are fairly simple, it is wise to confine your analysis to only a single phase. For instance, start first with RECEIVING, then follow with PROCESSING (by department, if numerous processes are involved), and finally take up STORAGE and SHIPPING. Or, you may decide that the easiest course is to select an average part, unit, or a definite quantity of bulk material and trace its travel through a single department or through the plant. Even with the analysis of only a single phase of your handling operations, you may find ways to effect improvements and to cut costs, which will indicate that a study of your *other* handling routine will prove invaluable to you. This approach avoids confusion and enables you to give more exacting attention to the analysis of each succeeding phase of your handling operations.

Meaning of Symbols. The five symbols described below are used by men responsible for planning plant layouts and keeping material on the move. They are printed in Column No. 2 of the Vis-O-Graf.

The *large circle* signifies a HANDLING OPERATION. The operation may be loading (lifting) or unloading (setting down) of material on a conveyance of one kind or another—on the receiving platform, in storage, at machines or processes, in the warehouse, and on the shipping dock.

The *small circle* signifies actual MOVEMENT of material—its transfer from one location to another.

The *square* signifies an INSPECTION or WEIGHING.

The *double triangle* signifies TEMPORARY STORAGE.

The *single triangle* signifies PERMANENT STORAGE.

Explanation of Terms. Most of the terms used on the Vis-O-Graf are self-explanatory, but all are intended to reveal information which has a direct bearing on the cost of handling operations. Each column is numbered for easy reference when reading the explanations below.

Description of Operation or Activity—Column No. 1. Write in this column what operation takes place, such as "Loading castings onto truck for move to grinder" or "Loading cartons on dolly for move to temporary storage." Be sure to *name* the material, part, or product.

Activity Symbols—Column No. 2. After the operation or activity is written in Column No. 1, draw a line from that operation or activity to the next, writing right over the symbols in Column No. 2. Thus as you proceed with the analysis, each operation, move, inspection or weighing, and storage will be indicated in Column No. 2 by a zigzag line. This gives you a step-by-step visual picture of the movement of material. To obtain the totals for each activity, operation, move, inspec-

Fig. 16a. Yale Vis-O-Graf instructions (continued on next page).

tion or weighing, temporary storage, and permanent storage, simply add the number of times the line passes through each symbol.

No. Men Required—Column No. 3. Write in the number of men required to lift the material onto the conveyance, the number who travel with it, and the number who unload it at each destination. Total all entries.

Distance Moved—Column No. 4. This means the distance in feet between the location where material is picked up and where it is next deposited. Total all entries.

Time Required—Column No. 5. In each case this should represent the number of minutes necessary to (1) lift the items in the load onto conveyance; (2) travel with the load from one location to another; and (3) to unload or set down the items in the load.

When more than one man does the handling operations, multiply the time by the number of men. Total all entries.

No time should be noted for activities which do not involve actual handling operations and moves.

Type of Equipment Used—Column No. 6. Write in this column whether manpower, a dolly, 4-wheeled hand truck, conveyor, hoist, hand lift truck, power truck, etc., is now used to move the material.

Load Capacity of Equipment—Column No. 7. Write in this column the rated capacity of the equipment now used to move the material. If manpower is used, leave the space blank.

Load Characteristics—Column No. 8. Load *shape* may be that of a single large part, a carton, bale, bag, reel, skid bin of many small items, pallet load, etc. Name it.

Number of Units in Each Load—Column No. 9. This means the number of cartons, bags, bales, parts, etc., moved *at one time.*

A figure should appear in this column each time a HANDLING OPERATION or MOVE occurs. You can obtain the total by adding all the figures in the column.

Do not put figures in this column for inspections, weighing, temporary or permanent storages.

Total Weight of Each Load—Column No. 10. To arrive at this figure, multiply the weight of each unit by the number moved at one time.

The total weight handled during the phase analyzed is obtained by following the procedure outlined above for total number of units handled (Column No. 9).

Do not put figures in this column for inspections, weighing, temporary or permanent storages.

Make a Diagram of Handling Steps. The right-hand section of the VIS-O-GRAF, when fully unfolded, provides graph paper on which to lay out the *route* taken during the handling steps analyzed.

To enable you to diagram your operations and to trace the route of materials, Yale provides with The How Book a special template rule containing the five activity symbols. Additional symbols are also included on the rule, so that you can indicate *where* ramps, doorways, yard or road, elevator or bridge are located en route.

Vis-O-Graf Summary. The Summary Folder provides a form on which to collect data from the VIS-O-GRAF chart or to record data you may have previously compiled, information about the physical characteristics of your plant, and the types of material handling machinery now used.

By completing your analysis, the diagram, and the summary, you can visualize what factors enter into your handling operations—visualize if your present material handling procedure and tools provide the best possible operation, or if changes in methods and equipment will reduce costs.

Fig. 16a. (Concluded.)

(1) Description of Operation or Activity (Name kind of material handled, such as castings, pipe, rods, liquids, cores, bulk materials, etc.)	(2) Handling Operation	Move	Inspection or Weighing	Temporary Storage	Permanent Storage	(3) No. of Men Required	(4) Distance Moved in Feet	(5) Time Required in Minutes	(6) Type of Equipment Used to Move Material from Location to Location (Manpower, conveyor, hoist, dolly, power truck, hand lift truck, hand truck, etc.)
	○	○	□	△	△				
	○	○	□	△	△				
	○	○	□	△	△				
	○	○	□	△	△				
	○	○	□	△	△				
	○	○	□	△	△				
	○	○	□	△	△				
	○	○	□	△	△				
	○	○	□	△	△				
	○	○	□	△	△				
	○	○	□	△	△				
	○	○	□	△	△				
	○	○	□	△	△				
	○	○	□	△	△				
	○	○	□	△	△				
	○	○	□	△	△				
	○	○	□	△	△				
	○	○	□	△	△				
	○	○	□	△	△				
	○	○	□	△	△				
	○	○	□	△	△				
	○	○	□	△	△				
	○	○	□	△	△				
	○	○	□	△	△				
	○	○	□	△	△				
	○	○	□	△	△				
	○	○	□	△	△				
	○	○	□	△	△				
	○	○	□	△	△				
	○	○	□	△	△				
	○	○	□	△	△				
	○	○	□	△	△				
	○	○	□	△	△				
	○	○	□	△	△				
	○	○	□	△	△				
	○	○	□	△	△				
	○	○	□	△	△				
	○	○	□	△	△				
	○	○	□	△	△				
	○	○	□	△	△				
Totals									X X X X X X X X X

Fig 16b. Yale Vis-O-Graf

(7) Load Capacity of Equipment (Pounds)	(8) Load Characteristics				(9) No. of Units in Each Load	(10) Total Weight of Each Load (Pounds)	USE TEMPLATE RULE WHEN DRAWING SYMBOLS
	Load Shape	Length	Width	Height			
							Number each symbol with a separate series of consecutive numerals, beginning with 1.
							Note change in route of horizontal travel by changing direction of lines when drawing diagram.
							◯ Handling Operation
							◯ Move
							△ Temporary Storage
							△ Permanent Storage
							☐ Inspection
							◺ Ramp Up
							◹ Ramp Down
							⊐⊏ Doorway
							∿ Road or Yard
							∧ Elevator Up
							∨ Elevator Down
XXXX	XXXX	XXX	XXX	XXX			∩ Bridge

analysis sheet.

2·35

YALE MATERIAL HANDLING VIS-O-GRAF SUMMARY

To be used to collect data from the Vis-O-Graf or to record data you may have previously compiled.

This form, plus the data on the Vis-O-Graf, will give you the information necessary to determine the extent that improved material handling methods or the adoption of modern material handling machinery will bring reduced costs and savings to you.

From the figures developed on the detailed Vis-O-Graf chart, transfer the totals to the Summary Record on the next page. These totals include the total number of operations, moves, inspections and/or weighings, storages, and men, and the total distance, time, and load weight.

Only two of the terms, Volume and Tonnage, require explanation:

Volume per Day means the total number of units handled during the steps analyzed (refer to total in Column No. 9 of Vis-O-Graf chart), multiplied by the total number of times per day the same type of load is handled and moved through the same steps.

Tonnage per Day means the total weight handled during the phase of handling analyzed. You will obtain this figure by multiplying the total entered in Column No. 10 on the chart by the number of times per day the same type of load is handled and moved through the same steps.

A Suggestion: Perhaps studies you have already made of your handling operations will provide sufficient information to complete this Vis-O-Graf Summary. If so, you need not work out the Vis-O-Graf chart, but the diagram of the *route* taken during handling operations will be particularly helpful, as it will picture your material flow.

If you use only total figures from your present records and not those obtained by filling in the Vis-O-Graf chart, remember that Tonnage per Day does not mean the tonnage received per day but actually the tonnage of material moved through the plant, department, or operation studied. It is the normal daily manufacturing tonnage multiplied by the number of times it is handled and moved per day. The same rule applies to Volume Handled per Day. It is essential that you state on the front of this form whether your total figures cover your entire plant, a certain department, or a part or group of parts traced through a department or the entire plant.

SUMMARY RECORD

Fill in data applicable to this handling analysis only

	TOTAL		TOTAL
No. of Operations (col. 2)	_____	No. of Men (col. 3)	_____
No. of Moves (col. 2)	_____	Distance Moved (col. 4)	_____
No. of Inspections and/or Weighings (col. 2)	_____		Feet
		Time Required for Operations and Moves (col. 5)	_____
No. of Temporary Storages (col. 2)	_____		Minutes
No. of Permanent Storages (col. 2)	_____	Weight Moved (col. 10)	_____ pounds

VOLUME HANDLED per Day .... _____ units

TONNAGE HANDLED per Day .... _____

HOURLY PAY RATE per Move-Man .... _____

Fig. 17. Yale Vis-O-Graf summary sheet (continued on next page).

GENERAL

Is your plant a single story building? ....Yes ☐ No ☐
If no, how many stories does it have? _____
What is the approximate floor capacity of your plant? _____
Overhead Structure: Clearance:_____feet. Capacity:_____lbs.
Outdoor Travel: ☐ Yard ☐ Road ☐ Bridge
Surface Construction: ☐ Wood ☐ Concrete ☐ Asphalt ☐ Brick ☐ Dirt
Condition: ☐ Smooth ☐ Rough
If "bridge," give capacity:_____lbs.

RECEIVING

Material received via: ☐ Rail ☐ Truck ☐ Ship
Unloading Dock(s): ☐ Yes ☐ No If "yes," give dimensions of each.
Length _____ _____ _____ _____
Width _____ _____ _____ _____
Height _____ _____ _____ _____
If via rail, give height from top of track to dock floor:_____

Dock Construction: ☐ Wood ☐ Concrete ☐ Asphalt ☐ Brick ☐ Dirt
Condition: ☐ Smooth ☐ Rough
Doorways in path of travel:
Width _____ _____ _____ _____
Height _____ _____ _____ _____
Aisle Width: Minimum_____ Maximum_____
Ramps:
Length _____ _____ _____ _____
Width _____ _____ _____ _____
Grade _____% _____% _____% _____%
Ramp Construction: ☐ Wood ☐ Concrete ☐ Asphalt ☐ Brick ☐ Dirt
Condition: ☐ Smooth ☐ Rough
Elevator: Width_____Height_____Depth_____Capacity_____lbs.

PROCESSING

Doorways in path of travel:
Width _____ _____ _____ _____
Height _____ _____ _____ _____
Aisle Width: Minimum_____ Maximum_____
Floor Construction: ☐ Wood ☐ Concrete ☐ Asphalt ☐ Brick ☐ Dirt
Condition: ☐ Smooth ☐ Rough
Ramps:
Length _____ _____ _____ _____
Width _____ _____ _____ _____
Grade _____% _____% _____% _____%
Ramp Construction: ☐ Wood ☐ Concrete ☐ Asphalt ☐ Brick ☐ Dirt
Condition: ☐ Smooth ☐ Rough
Elevator: Width_____Height_____Depth_____Capacity_____lbs.

STORAGE AREAS

Length _____ _____ _____ _____
Width _____ _____ _____ _____
Ceiling
Height _____ _____ _____ _____

Fig. 17. (Continued.)

Doorways in path of travel:
Width _____ _____ _____ _____
Height _____ _____ _____ _____

Aisle Width: Minimum_____   Maximum_____

Ramps:
Length _____ _____ _____ _____
Width _____ _____ _____ _____
Grade _____% _____% _____% _____%

Ramp Construction: □ Wood □ Concrete □ Asphalt □ Brick □ Dirt
      Condition: □ Smooth □ Rough

Floor Construction: □ Wood □ Concrete □ Asphalt □ Brick □ Dirt
      Condition: □ Smooth □ Rough

Elevator: Width_____Height_____Depth_____Capacity_____lbs.

SHIPPING

Material shipped via: □ Rail □ Truck □ Ship
Loading Dock(s): □ Yes □ No If "yes," give dimensions of each.
Length _____ _____ _____ _____
Width _____ _____ _____ _____
Height _____ _____ _____ _____
If via rail, give height from top of track to dock floor:_____

Dock Construction: □ Wood □ Concrete □ Asphalt □ Brick □ Dirt
      Condition: □ Smooth □ Rough

Doorways in path of travel:
Width _____ _____ _____ _____
Height _____ _____ _____ _____

Aisle Width: Minimum_____   Maximum_____

Ramps:
Length _____ _____ _____ _____
Width _____ _____ _____ _____
Grade _____% _____% _____% _____%

Ramp Construction: □ Wood □ Concrete □ Asphalt □ Brick □ Dirt
      Condition: □ Smooth □ Rough

Elevator: Width_____Height_____Depth_____Capacity_____lbs.

TYPES OF MATERIAL HANDLING MACHINERY NOW USED

	Number		Number
1. Conveyors	_____	8. Hand Power Lift Trucks	_____
2. Power Fork Trucks	_____	9. Tractor Trailers	_____
3. Power High Lift Platform		10. Tiering Machines	_____
Trucks	_____	11. Wheel Barrows	_____
4. Power Low Lift Platform		12. Push Trucks	_____
Trucks	_____	13. Electric Hoists	_____
5. Power Crane Trucks	_____	14. Hand Chain Hoists	_____
6. Power Load Carriers	_____	15. Other	_____
7. Hand Lift Trucks	_____	State Type	

Be sure to check instructions for arriving at figures for VOLUME and TONNAGE
handled per day

Fig. 17. (Concluded.)

ANALYSIS	
WHY?	

WHAT? WHERE? WHEN? WHO? HOW?

QUESTION EACH DETAIL

WORK SIMPLIFICATION CONFERENCES
LAKE PLACID, N. Y.

FLOW PROCESS CHART

NO. _3_
PAGE _1_ OF _1_

SUMMARY

	PRESENT		PROPOSED		DIFFERENCE	
	NO.	TIME	NO.	TIME	NO.	TIME
O OPERATIONS	10					
⇨ TRANSPORTATIONS	2					
☐ INSPECTIONS	0					
D DELAYS	4					
▽ STORAGES	0					
DISTANCE TRAVELED	40 FT.		FT.		FT.	

JOB : Pricing and Posting Orders

☐ MAN OR ☑ MATERIAL _Priced Orders_
CHART BEGINS_____ On A's desk
CHART ENDS_____ On A's desk
CHARTED BY _John Smith_ DATE _4/15/—_

POSSIBILITIES

	DETAILS OF { PRESENT / PROPOSED } METHOD	OPERATION	TRANSPORT	INSPECTION	DELAY	STORAGE	DISTANCE IN FEET	QUANTITY	TIME	ELIMINATE	COMBINE	SEQUE.	PLACE	PERSON	IMPROVE	NOTES
1	Placed on A's desk	O	⇨	☐	D	▽										By messenger
2	Time stamped	O	⇨	☐	D	▽										
3	Placed in OUT box	O	⇨	☐	D	▽										
4	Waits	O	⇨	☐	D	▽							✓			
5	Picked up by C	O	⇨	☐	D	▽										At least every 15 min.
6	To desk	O	⇨	☐	D	▽	20						✓			
7	Sorted into priced and unpriced	O	⇨	☐	D	▽					✓	✓	✓			
8	Waits	O	⇨	☐	D	▽							✓			
9	Posted	●	⇨	☐	D	▽										
10	To A's desk	O	⇨	☐	D	▽	20				✓	✓	✓	✓		By C
11	Placed on A's desk	O	⇨	☐	D	▽					✓					
12	Waits	O	⇨	☐	D	▽					✓					
13	Sorted	O	⇨	☐	D	▽					✓	✓	✓	✓		For inside and outside company
14	Placed in envelopes	O	⇨	☐	D	▽						✓	✓	✓		
15	Placed in OUT box	O	⇨	☐	D	▽						✓	✓	✓		
16	Waits	O	⇨	☐	D	▽										
17		O	⇨	☐	D	▽										
18		O	⇨	☐	D	▽										
19		O	⇨	☐	D	▽										
20		O	⇨	☐	D	▽										
21		O	⇨	☐	D	▽										
22		O	⇨	☐	D	▽										
23		O	⇨	☐	D	▽										
24		O	⇨	☐	D	▽										

Fig. 18a. Flow process chart on priced orders—present method.

ANALYSIS				
WHY?				
WHAT? WHERE? WHEN? WHO? HOW?				

QUESTION EACH DETAIL

WORK SIMPLIFICATION CONFERENCES
LAKE PLACID, N. Y.

FLOW PROCESS CHART

NO. __4__
PAGE _1_ OF _1_

SUMMARY

JOB __Pricing and Posting Orders__

	PRESENT		PROPOSED		DIFFERENCE	
	NO.	TIME	NO.	TIME	NO.	TIME
O OPERATIONS	10		8		2	
⇨ TRANSPORTATIONS	2		1		1	
☐ INSPECTIONS	0		0		0	
D DELAYS	4		2		2	
▽ STORAGES	0		0		0	
DISTANCE TRAVELED	40 FT.		14 FT.		26 FT.	

☐ MAN OR ☑ MATERIAL __Priced Orders__
CHART BEGINS ____On A's desk____
CHART ENDS ____On C's desk____
CHARTED BY __John Smith__ DATE __4/15/—__

POSSIBILITIES

DETAILS OF { ~~PRESENT~~ / PROPOSED } METHOD

	DETAILS	OPERATION	TRANSPORT	INSPECTION	DELAY	STORAGE	DISTANCE IN FEET	QUANTITY	TIME	ELIMINATE	COMBINE	SEQUE.	PLACE	PERSON	IMPROVE	NOTES
1	Placed on A's desk	O	⇨	☐	D	▽										
2	Time stamped and sorted	O	⇨	☐	D	▽										
3	Placed in OUT baskets	O	⇨	☐	D	▽										2 wire baskets
4	Waits	O	⇨	☐	D	▽										Shorter wait
5	Picked up by C	O	⇨	☐	D	▽										
6	To desk	O	⇨	☐	D	▽										
7	Placed on desk	O	⇨	☐	D	▽										
8	Posted and sorted	●	⇨	☐	D	▽										
9	Placed in envelopes	O	⇨	☐	D	▽										
10	Placed in OUT basket	O	⇨	☐	D	▽										
11	Waits	O	⇨	☐	D	▽										Picked up by messenger
12		O	⇨	☐	D	▽										
13		O	⇨	☐	D	▽										
14		O	⇨	☐	D	▽										
15		O	⇨	☐	D	▽										
16		O	⇨	☐	D	▽										
17		O	⇨	☐	D	▽										
18		O	⇨	☐	D	▽										
19		O	⇨	☐	D	▽										
20		O	⇨	☐	D	▽										
21		O	⇨	☐	D	▽										
22		O	⇨	☐	D	▽										
23		O	⇨	☐	D	▽										
24		O	⇨	☐	D	▽										

Fig. 18b. Flow process chart on priced orders—proposed method.

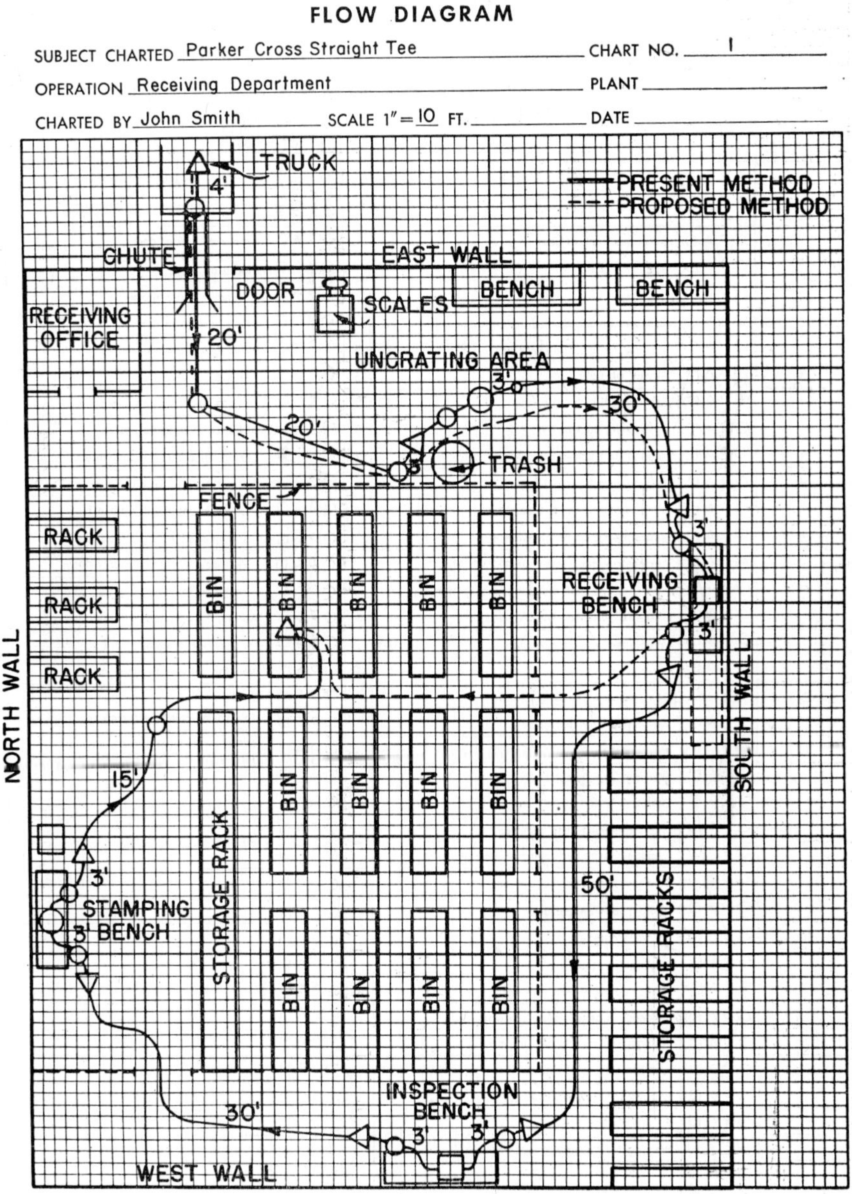

FLOW DIAGRAM

SUBJECT CHARTED _Parker Cross Straight Tee_____ CHART NO. ____I_____

OPERATION _Receiving Department_____ PLANT _____

CHARTED BY _John Smith_____ SCALE 1″= _10_ FT. _____ DATE _____

Fig. 19. Flow diagram including both present and proposed methods.

SUBJECT CHARTED	Parker Crosses St. Tee	PROCESS CHART			SUMMARY			
					METHOD	PRESENT	PROPOSED	SAVING
OPERATION	Receiving				NO. OF OPERATIONS	2	2	0
CHARTED BY	John Smith				NO. OF MOVES	11	6	5
CHART NO. 1	SHEET NO. 1	CAN I ELIMINATE?			NO. OF STORAGES	9	4	5
					NO. OF INSPECTIONS	2	1	1
DATE		CAN I COMBINE?			MAN HOURS	9.00	6.92	2.08
					DISTANCE TRAVELED	181	107	74
PLANT		CAN I CHANGE SEQUENCE?			P & L — MAN			
DEPT.	Receiving	CAN I SIMPLIFY?			MECH.			
					TOTAL COST			

Process chart detail:

DIST	TIME	PRESENT METHOD	DIST	TIME	PROPOSED METHOD
10		On motor truck at door	10		On motor truck at door
4'		Placed on chute	4'		Placed on chute
20'		Slid down chute-gravity	20'		Slid down chute–gravity
20'	10	Slid to storage and stacked up(1 crate at a time)	3'		Place on hand truck
	30	Waiting for uncrating of glass	20'	5	Move to uncrating area
3'		Placed on floor		5	Remove lid of crate
	5	Removing lid of crate and	30'	5	Move to inspection area by truck
		removing packing list		5	At bench waiting for unload
3'		Loaded on truck–(2 men)		20	Carton removed from box and
30'	5	To receiving bench–(2 men)			Opened, tees unwrapped and placed on
	10	At bench-waiting for unloading			bench, counted, checked off
3'		Boxes placed on bench–(2 men)			list, gauged, and stamped; parts
	15	Cartons removed from box and opened,			replaced in carton and carton
		tees unwrapped and placed on bench,			replaced in box
		counted, checked off list, and		5	Waiting for transportation
		replaced in carton; carton	30'		To distribution point
		replaced in box		360	Wait for delivery to stock room
3'		Box placed on truck–(2 men)			Brief:
	5	Waiting for transportation			This saving can be effected by: Combining two inspections and one
50'	10	To inspection table			operation and performing them at the bench at the south wall.
	10	Waiting for inspection			
	20	Carton removed from box;			
		carton opened, tees removed,			
		gauged, inspected, and replaced in			
		carton, carton replaced in box.			
	5	Waiting for transportation			
30'	5	To parts numbering table			
	15	Waiting for stamping			
	15	Carton opened–tees removed,			
		placed on bench, identified with			
		stamp, replaced in carton and			
		carton returned to box.			
	5	Waiting for transportation			
15'	5	To distribution point			
	360	Waiting for delivery to stock room			
181	**540**	**2 11 9 2** ◄—— TOTAL	**107**	**415**	**2 6 4 1** ◄—— TOTAL

Fig. 20. Flow chart for flow diagram in Fig. 19.

A combination of a work-flow diagram (Fig. 19), and a flow chart analyzing the corresponding operations and activities (Fig. 20), indicates how these two kinds of procedures are combined to reduce the distances traveled and the operating time lost when equipment layouts and production procedures are found to be inefficient. The saving in distance traveled in this latter case amounted to 41 percent.

Figs. 15, 16, 18, and 20 show further examples of flow process charts which illustrate the degree of variation found in their construction. The most successful charting technique is the one that fits the application and conveys the information necessary for the analyst to arrive at a desired improved work-flow procedure. Considerable detail, and one type of chart, may be necessary in certain situations. In other cases a simple chart may be adequate.

Operation Analysis Methods

OPERATION ANALYSIS. Another technique of analysis to be considered in analyzing materials handling situations is the broad general area referred to as "Operation Analysis." The terms "motion analysis" and "motion study" have been used to designate such analyses, but the term "operation analysis" is broader and more inclusive. There are many techniques used and classified under such a title.

Much of the early work of the Gilbreths was in this general area—then one of great inefficiency. In general, it has to do with the **analysis of operations performed by human effort at a single work place.** The tools of analysis are those that would single out the inefficiencies and aid planning for corrective action. Naturally, these studies would include inefficiencies in the handling activity at the work place, but they would also cover many other activities having to do with over-all methods analysis and methods improvement, including operations or processes themselves, and all tools, jigs, fixtures, etc., being used, as well as the location of machine controls and the tote boxes or conveyors for incoming and outgoing work, etc.

Of the many different mechanisms of analysis available, one type of chart is included here. It is the **operator chart,** commonly known as the **right- and left-hand chart.** Such a chart is very useful to the materials handling analyst when he is confronted with a job involving operations by a worker at a work station. The symbols used are the same as those used for process analysis, and the technique is merely to record what is done, first by the left or right hand during a complete cycle of work, and then by the other hand. The questioning attitude and challenging of each activity, which characterize work simplification, can be adopted. In cases of great existing inefficiency and real potential savings, the analyst would have to decide whether or not there is justification for adopting more detailed methods of analysis and more costly procedures in terms of time and equipment to make the analytical study. Such methods would cover simo charts, micromotion charts, and other kinds of detailed analytical techniques, including the many different types of film analysis.

Figs. 21a and 21b illustrate the right- and left-hand charts for analyzing materials movement by an operator at a work station, in this case, present and proposed methods of inspecting inlet and outlet pipes.

WORK SIMPLIFICATON CONFERENCES
LAKE PLACID, N. Y.

SUMMARY PER __4__ PIECES

	PRESENT		PROPOSED		DIFFERENCE	
	LH	RH	LH	RH	LH	RH
○ OPERATIONS	6	8				
⇨ TRANSPORTS	2	3				
▽ HOLDS	2	2				
D DELAYS	3	0				
TOTAL	13	13				

RIGHT- AND LEFT-HAND CHART

OPERATION __Inspect Inlet and Outlet Pipes__

PRESENT / PROPOSED } METHOD DATE __10/10/—__

OPERATOR _____ ANALYST __Fred Hindle__

LAYOUT

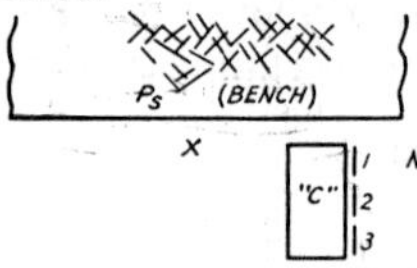

P_s - STOCK OF PIPES ON BENCH
C - PACKING CASE
X - NORMAL POSITION OF INSPECTOR

P_s (BENCH)

X

"C" |1 |2 |3

NOTE: PACKING CASE WAS
PLACED ON LOW BENCH
ABOUT 18" FROM FLOOR.

PACKED 3 ROWS WITH LENGTH OF CASE.

PARTS SKETCH

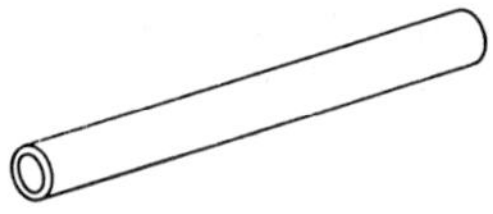

LEFT HAND	OPER.	TRANS.	HOLD	DELAY		OPER.	TRANS.	HOLD	DELAY	RIGHT HAND
To stock of pipes on bench					1					To stock of pipes on bench
Grasp two pipes					2					Grasp two pipes
To R.H. at X					3					To L.H. at X
Roll pipes to inspect					4					Roll pipes to inspect
Grasp two pipes					5					Grasp two pipes
Turn to one end					6					Turn to one end
Hold for inspection					7					Hold for inspection
Turn to other end					8					Turn to other end
Hold for inspection					9					Hold for inspection
Release to R.H.					10					Grasp four "pipes"
Wait					11					To case "C"
Wait					12					Release four pipes
Wait					13					Stack–position in layers
					14					
					15					
PRICE $.50 PER M.					16					
					17					
					18					
					19					
					20					
					21					
					22					

Fig. 21a. Inspect inlet and outlet pipes—present method.

WORK SIMPLIFICATON CONFERENCES
LAKE PLACID, N. Y.

NO. __00__
PAGE 2 OF 2

SUMMARY PER 4 PIECES

RIGHT- AND LEFT-HAND CHART

OPERATION __Inspect Inlet and Outlet Pipes__

~~PRESENT~~ PROPOSED } METHOD DATE 10/10 –

OPERATOR _____ ANALYST __Fred Hindle__

	PRESENT		PROPOSED		DIFFERENCE	
	LH	RH	LH	RH	LH	RH
O OPERATIONS	6	8	6	6	0	2
⇨ TRANSPORTS	2	3	3	3	-1	0
▽ HOLDS	2	2	2	2	0	0
D DELAYS	3	0	0	0	3	0
TOTAL	13	13	11	11	2	2

LAYOUT

HOPPER
CONVEYOR
"C" CASE - SAME HEIGHT AS LENGTH OF PIPE
"X"

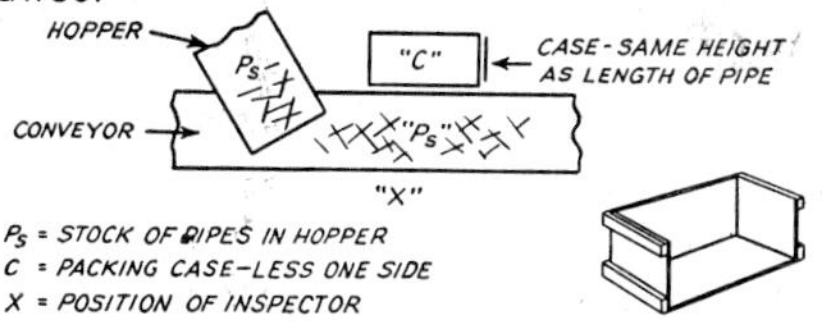

Pₛ = STOCK OF PIPES IN HOPPER
C = PACKING CASE–LESS ONE SIDE
X = POSITION OF INSPECTOR

PARTS SKETCH

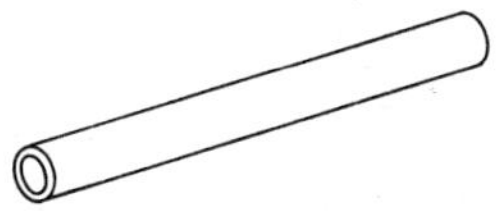

LEFT HAND	OPER.	TRANS.	HOLD	DELAY		OPER.	TRANS.	HOLD	DELAY	RIGHT HAND
To pipes on conveyor	O	⇨	▽	D	1	O	⇨	▽	D	To pipes on conveyor
Grasp two pipes	O	⇨	▽	D	2	O	⇨	▽	D	Grasp two pipes
To R.H	O	⇨	▽	D	3	O	⇨	▽	D	To L.H.
Roll pipes for inspection	O	⇨	▽	D	4	O	⇨	▽	D	Roll pipes for inspection
Grasp two pipes	O	⇨	▽	D	5	O	⇨	▽	D	Grasp two pipes
Turn to one end	O	⇨	▽	D	6	O	⇨	▽	D	Turn to one end
Hold for inspection	O	⇨	▽	D	7	O	⇨	▽	D	Hold for inspection
Turn to other end	O	⇨	▽	D	8	O	⇨	▽	D	Turn to other end
Hold for inspection	O	⇨	▽	D	9	O	⇨	▽	D	Hold for inspection
To case	O	⇨	▽	D	10	O	⇨	▽	D	To case
Release	O	⇨	▽	D	11	O	⇨	▽	D	Release
	O	⇨	▽	D	12	O	⇨	▽	D	
	O	⇨	▽	D	13	O	⇨	▽	D	
	O	⇨	▽	D	14	O	⇨	▽	D	NOTE: CASE NOW PLACED ON BENCH
	O	⇨	▽	D	15	O	⇨	▽	D	AT BACK OF CONVEYOR, AND AT
COST REDUCED TO $.30 PER M.	O	⇨	▽	D	16	O	⇨	▽	D	THE SAME HEIGHT –BUT IN FRONT
	O	⇨	▽	D	17	O	⇨	▽	D	OF INSPECTOR - TOP SIDE REMOVED.
	O	⇨	▽	D	18	O	⇨	▽	D	PIPES PACKED STRAIGHT IN
	O	⇨	▽	D	19	O	⇨	▽	D	
	O	⇨	▽	D	20	O	⇨	▽	D	
	O	⇨	▽	D	21	O	⇨	▽	D	
	O	⇨	▽	D	22	O	⇨	▽	D	

Fig. 21b. Inspect inlet and outlet pipes—proposed method.

MEMOMOTION ANALYSIS. Memomotion is a special type of micro-motion analysis developed by M. E. Mundel and is mentioned here because it has proved to be of considerable value of late in the analysis of materials handling problems. Memomotion uses the **film technique,** but instead of exposing film at the normal speed of 16 frames per sec., it exposes at the much reduced speed of 100 frames per min. In this way each frame represents 0.01 min. Some analysts prefer to use the technique with exposure at 1 frame per sec., while others choose 50 frames per min. The actual exposure time is dependent on the type of job on which it is being used and the available equipment. This particular technique is useful where a study is to be made over a long period of time, or where the cycles of work performed are long by themselves. It is also particularly useful when **analyzing activities of crews of workers** on either irregular or regular cycles of work. The technique results in a considerable reduction in the cost of analysis because of the reduced amount of film being used. The method of analysis and the charting technique to use are the same as for any other operation analysis.

Travel Charts

THE TRAVEL CHART. A travel chart, as the name implies, is a method of charting **material travel within a manufacturing area.** Devised, and explained here, by D. G. Cameron, its construction is very similar to the mileage chart found on the back of road maps. Unlike conventional flow diagrams, the travel charts show—in addition to the areas in which material is produced and the area in which it is used—**the degree of self-sufficiency of user areas** and **the degree to which each contributing area supports the user areas.** These charts also show where **inventory control problems** may exist because of the complexity of material movement patterns.

Travel charts are valuable aids in laying out the routing of material in a new plant or illustrating routing in an existing plant. In this connection, they are a useful source of information for the development of a general plan of manufacture previous to the making of elaborate and expensive layouts.

The conventional method of analyzing material flow is to show **route lines** on the chart connecting the areas through which the material passes. The route chart is simple when only a single product is involved, but, as the number of material items increases and the directions of movement multiply, such a chart eventually becomes a maze of lines which are meaningless to anyone except the person who made it.

Fig. 22 illustrates the method of showing material flow by flow lines for a single product. The flow plan is easily followed and analyzed, particularly when few areas and parts are involved. Fig. 23 illustrates the difficulty of analyzing material movement by the use of flow lines for multiproduct flow. A single chart has now become a maze of lines, which makes it difficult to locate waste motion. This method of charting material movement provides no convenient way of **evaluating the amount of material that is moved** between particular areas, nor does it show the **dependency of one area upon another.** Furthermore, this method is time-consuming, since each line must be individually traced and each path must be individually studied. Even after careful study of this chart, the user is still unable to visualize at a glance all the possible combinations of movements that may take place between areas being studied.

Since travel charts are based on the analysis of material movement in terms of total output of contributing areas, they frequently **disclose conditions that were not previously recognized.** For example, an analysis of material movement in a

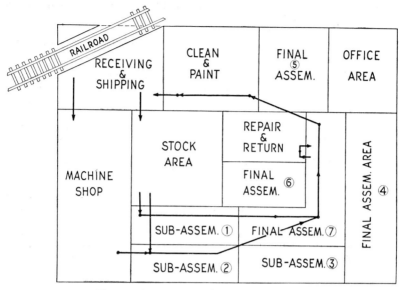

Fig. 22. Diagram of single-product flow.

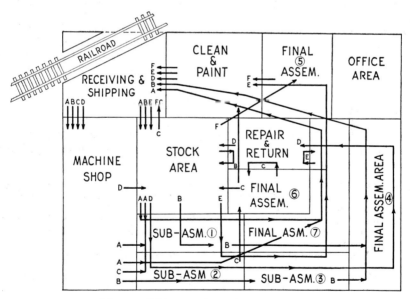

Fig. 23. Diagram of multiproduct flow.

multiproduct plant may show that one of the products, because of the growth of the business, has become the dominant product, and should actually be manufactured with the same manufacturing techniques as would be the case in a single-product plant. When such a case is discovered, the analysis of machine utilization, and the utilization of other manufacturing facilities by the use of the travel chart, will enable management to **allocate facilities to the dominant product line** in the proper manner.

Use of Travel Charts. For ready reference, the detailed uses to which travel charts can be put have been listed below:

1. To analyze material flow so that manufacturing facilities can be arranged to reduce material movement to economical minimums.
2. To show the amount of material movement between various manufacturing areas in terms of the output of contributing areas.
3. To supplement flow diagrams by providing a means of showing that portion of the material produced by a contributing area which is delivered to each user area.
4. To show the dependency of one manufacturing area upon another area by showing the source of material and its end use.
5. To show the self-sufficiency of each user area.
6. To determine, from the standpoint of material movement, which manufacturing areas should be combined and which should be located adjacent to one another.
7. To assist in determining the proper combination or segregation of product lines by showing the relationship between user areas and contributing areas.
8. To assist in developing a manufacturing plan which can readily be presented in visual form in two- or three-dimensional layouts.

The information in the foregoing outline is of assistance to the layout engineer in **weighing the advantages of assigning machines to product lines** in order to reduce work-in-process inventory and to shorten manufacturing cycle time. Comparisons can be made between this arrangement of manufacturing facilities and the advantages of grouping equipment in centralized machining areas. This sort of information becomes a valuable part of the presentation of the rearrangement program, or the new plant program, to top management. The fact that the advantages of the rearrangement can be expressed in numbers makes the presentation more understandable to members of the organization (such as accountants) who are not necessarily familiar with physical factory facilities.

DEFINITIONS OF TERMS USED ON TRAVEL CHARTS. Although the terms used on travel charts are in common use, they have special significance when employed to analyze material movement.

1. **Contributor.** The term "contributor" is applied to any area or machine whose output is being used by some other area within the confines of the facilities being studied.
2. **User.** The term "user" is applied to any area or production line that obtains material from any contributing area within the confines of the facilities being studied.
   a. A "user" may obtain material from a "contributor" and apply direct labor and incorporate this material in a finished product.
   b. A "user" may obtain material from a "contributor," apply direct labor to this material, and then transfer it to a second "user" area for use in a finished product. In this case, the first "user" becomes a "contributor" as far as the second "user" area is concerned.
   c. The travel chart automatically takes care of situations (a) and (b), since the total output of each area is fully accounted for on the chart.
3. **Customer.** The term "customer" is applied to any "user" outside the confines of the area being studied.
   a. A "customer" may be a company warehouse.
   b. A "customer" may be another department of the same company.

c. A "customer" may be another manufacturing section of the department that is making the study. In this case, however, the manufacturing section receiving the material will be outside the area of the study.

d. A "customer" may be the ultimate customer of the company.

4. **Measurement of material to be moved.** The amount of material to be moved from contributing areas to user areas must be expressed in some common denominator. Where the product lends itself to such measurement, the amount of material moved can be expressed in terms of **units or pounds.** However, in the case of multiproduct plants utilizing general-purpose machining areas which produce a great variety of parts or units, weight is not always a practical means of measuring material movement.

Where units or weight are not practical, **direct labor content of the material produced by contributor areas** has been found to be a simple method of determining the distribution of the output of contributing areas. Direct labor content of a product usually has a direct relationship to the utilization of machines and other manufacturing facilities, and, therefore, this factor is a direct means of determining that portion of a contributing area's facilities which is required to support each user area.

By definition, the **output of a contributor area** will be expressed in terms of 100% of the direct labor content of the output. The numbers shown on the travel chart under each contributor will then show the percent of the total output of the contributor, expressed in percent of direct labor, that is delivered to each user area. From the user viewpoint, the numbers opposite each user are those portions of the various contributors' output that are required to support the user area.

METHOD FOR CONSTRUCTING A TRAVEL CHART. By defining sources and end-use of material in the terms previously described, it is possible to construct a material movement chart which is much simpler than that of the method shown in Figs. 22 and 23. Fig. 24 shows a **hypothetical set of conditions** concerning an assumed travel of work in process in the course of manufacture, used here for illustrative purposes only. On this chart, areas being analyzed are designated by numbers from 1 to 10. The equipment in these areas can consist of either a variety of machines performing various manufacturing processes or a single group of standard machines, such as milling machines or screw machines.

To make the illustration shown by Fig. 24 as general as possible without being too confusing, it has been assumed that the areas being studied are located in Buildings A and B. Areas 1 to 5 are located in Building A, and areas 6 to 10 in Building B. It is conceivable that in an actual case all the areas might be in one large building, or they might be in several small buildings instead.

The first step in constructing the travel chart is to arrange the areas from 1 to 10 across the top of the chart. These areas are designated as "contributing" areas. The areas are next arranged down the left-hand side of the chart in exactly the same manner, but now they are designated as "user" areas.

By **analyzing the output of each contributor area** in terms of percent of the total direct labor, it is possible to determine the proportion of the output of each contributor that is delivered to each user. This amount of material, expressed in percent of the total output of the contributor, is then inserted on the chart opposite the user. By following this procedure for each contributor area, the total material provided by contributors (expressed in percent of direct labor) can be accounted for.

There will be some material produced by contributor areas that goes directly to a customer. Referring to the description of the term "customer," it will be recalled that this material may be delivered to any destination outside the area being studied.

After arranging the contributor output in accordance with the above instructions, the **numbers in each vertical column must total 100 percent,** because these numbers account for the entire output of the corresponding contributor. By reading across the chart opposite each user, the source of material within the area being studied can be determined.

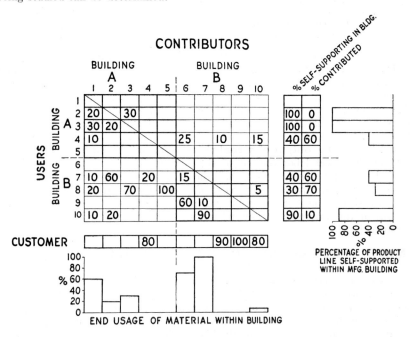

Fig. 24. Hypothetical set of conditions concerning travel of work in process— Case 1.

On Fig. 24 attention is called to the horizontal line between user areas 5 and 6 and to the vertical line between contributing areas 5 and 6. These horizontal and vertical lines separate the areas located in Building A from those located in Building B. Those numbers falling outside of these areas indicate conditions where material must be transported between Buildings A and B. For example, any number under Building A as a contributor and opposite Building B as a user shows where material is moved between buildings. The same is true for any number under Building B as a contributor and opposite Building A as a user. The objective of the analysis of material movement is to **eliminate as many of these numbers as possible** by placing the source of material in the building in which it is used.

Several other conclusions can now be drawn from the travel chart shown in Fig. 24. Reading vertically, the **amount of material produced by each contributor** that is used in each contributor's building is shown under each contributor area. For example, 60 percent of the material produced by Contributor 1 is used in Building A. Forty percent must be transported to Building B. In the case of Contributor 5, which is located in Building A, all the material must be transported to Building B. The material produced by Contributor 9 is delivered directly to a customer, which will be any "customer" defined by the description of terms used on the chart.

The conditions illustrated on the chart and described in the two preceding paragraphs can be referred to as "end usage of material within the building." To illustrate the degree to which the material is used in the building in which it is produced, a series of chimneys can be constructed at the bottom of the chart. Further reference to these chimneys will be made when analyzing the significance of Fig. 24.

Looking at the travel chart from the viewpoint of the user, it is seen that User 2 gets 20 percent of the output of Contributor 1 and 30 percent of the output of Contributor 3. It should be noted that User 2 and Contributors 1 and 3 are all located in Building A. Therefore, the **material is used in the building in which it is produced.** User 4 gets 10 percent of the output of Contributor 1, 25 percent of that of Contributor 6, 10 percent of Contributor 8, and 15 percent of Contributor 10. User 4, however, is in Building A, while Contributors 6, 8, and 10 are in Building B; therefore these portions of the output of these contributors must be transported to Building A. A similar analysis can be made of the **source of material consumed by each user,** and the self-sufficiency of the user areas can be shown by bar charts on the right-hand side of Fig. 24.

Further description of these bar charts will make their application more clearly understood. First, it must be realized that the numbers on the chart indicate those portions of a contributing area's output which are delivered to the various user areas. The material from the contributing areas may not represent the total amount of material required by the user. In other words, there may be other sources of material within the plant, or material may be received from outside vendors. The only factor that the chart is intended to show is the **distribution of material produced by those areas which are being analyzed.**

The statement just made is very important because it should be clearly understood both that the numbers opposite each user **do not necessarily total 100 percent** and, in order to determine the degree to which a product line is self-supporting within its own building, the material from all sources must be analyzed. For the purposes of the study illustrated by Fig. 24, it is assumed that this analysis has been made and that the analyst has determined the percent of the total material required by the user that is produced by the contributors being studied. Under this assumption, it is possible to construct the two columns to the right of the travel chart which show the percent of self-sufficiency of this product line within the building and the percent contributed from other areas included in the study. The bar chart on the right-hand side of Fig. 24 shows the degree of self-sufficiency within the user's building in a graphical form.

Using the chart as an example for the analysis of all material required by the users, it has been found that all the material required by User 2 is produced in Building A. Therefore, the self-sufficiency of User 2 is 100 percent. The same is true for User 3. User 8, on the other hand, receives from contributors within its own building only 30 percent of the material which it requires; 70 percent must come from other sources. When this stage of the analysis is reached, the layout engineer may find it advisable to initiate investigations into sources of materials outside the confines of this particular study.

ANALYSIS OF TRAVEL CHARTS. An analysis of Fig. 24—which is summarized by the chimney chart showing the end usage of material and the bar chart showing self-sufficiency of user areas—indicates that the arrangement of contributor areas in relation to user areas leaves something to be desired. A rearrangement which will provide vastly improved conditions is shown by Fig. 25. Contributors 1, 3, 5, and 8 have now been located in Building A, and Contributors 2, 4, 6, 7, 9, and 10 in Building B. This rearrangement was selected because it places most of the contributors in the same buildings as the users that take material from this particular group of contributors.

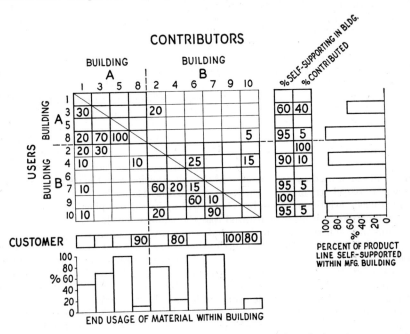

Fig. 25. Rearrangement of contributor areas, Case 1, in relation to user areas.

When the contributors are rearranged, as shown at the top of the travel chart in Fig. 25, the users must also be rearranged, since, by definition, users are arranged on the left-hand side of the chart in exactly the same order as contributors are arranged across the top of the chart.

It is evident, from an examination of the end-usage chimney chart and the percent-of-the-product-line self-sufficiency bar chart, that conditions have been substantially improved in so far as the movement of materials between Buildings A and B is concerned. There is, however, room for still further improvement. For example, Fig. 25 shows that 50 percent of the output of Contributor 1 is used in Building A and 50 percent in Building B. Fig. 25 also shows that 20 percent of the output of Contributor 2 is used in Building A, and 80 percent is used in Building B. An analysis of the facilities of Contributors 1 and 2 should be made to find out whether the facilities of these two contributors can be divided between Buildings A and B, thus eliminating the necessity for transporting material from these contributors into another building. On the assumption that these facilities can be economically divided, Fig. 26 shows the improvements that are realized. The new contributors that have been created by dividing the facilities of Contributors 1 and 2 have been designated as 1A and 2A. The end-usage chimney chart and the percent-of-product-line self-sufficiency bar chart now show better conditions than those illustrated by Fig. 25.

In making **rearrangements of facilities,** it is advisable, of course, to place the user areas as close to the contributing areas as possible, thus reducing the distances the material is moved within a building. Contributor 2, for example, should be placed adjacent to User 3, since 100 percent of the output of Contributor 2 is delivered to User 3. For the same reason, Contributor 5 should be placed adjacent to User 8. The output of Contributor 9, on the other hand, goes directly to a customer, so it may be advisable to place this area adjacent to shipping facilities.

From an **analysis of travel charts** similar to those shown by Figs. 24, 25, and 26, the layout engineer can determine the proper relationship between contributors and users, and can develop an economical plan of manufacture previous to starting layouts. The economies that can be derived from a reduction of material move-

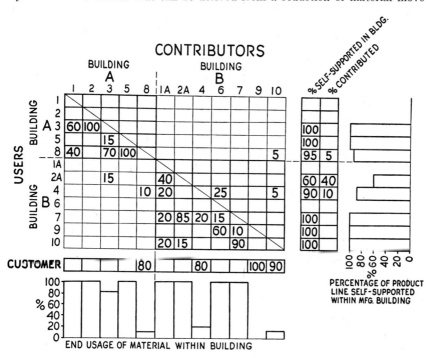

Fig. 26. Improvements realized by rearrangements made in Case 1.

ment can be calculated by the help of these travel charts, and the charts are a valuable aid when presenting to management proposed rearrangement of projects. The travel-chart approach is especially useful when explaining a project to persons who are not intimately acquainted with manufacturing equipment and methods, but who do understand an analytical approach to the solution of problems. After the analytical stage of the project is passed, the objectives of the visual two- or three-dimensional layouts will be evident.

Cycle Charts

OBJECTIVES OF CYCLE CHARTING. Phillips and Earle (Factory Management and Maintenance, vol. 111) describe cycle charting as a method of analyzing materials handling problems, because cycle charts can be made in 15 to

20 percent less time than is needed to make ordinary flow charts. The charts present maximum data in minimum space, graphically show up handling waste, provide a convenient form for calculating handling costs, give permanent records, and are a big help when recommending changes in methods to top management.

The **cycle charting technique** cited by the authors consists of three factors: the cycle concept itself, handligs (Fig. 27), and chart construction.

STANDARD INDUSTRIAL ENGINEERING SYMBOLS

D	Delay	O	Operation	⇨	Transport
☐	Inspection	▽	Storage		

YALE AND TOWNE SYMBOLS

∩	Bridge	V	Elevator down	◿◺	Ramp up-down
][	Doorway	∧	Elevator up	≈	Road

HANDLIGS

B	Bag	₆⌐	Highway truck — body type, holding 6 pallets (boxes, etc.)	Ⅲ	RR car — refrigerator
☐	Box or carton			0	RR car — tank
C	Carboy	‖	Highway truck—tractor trailer	H	Skid bin
₵	Conveyor — gravity			S	Supplier
⌐	Conveyor — powered	H	Hoist	₽	Tank
⚲	Crane — overhead	♀	Man	⊔	Tote box
⌐	Crane — yard	M	Monorail		Tractor trailer — with 4 trailers
⌐	Dock	⊓	Pallet or skid	↳	Truck — hand pallet or skid jack
X	Dolly	[1o]	Pallet — 10 packages on	L	Truck — high lift fork
♀	Dragline — floor	2000 ⊓	Pallet — 2000 lbs. weight	L¹	Truck — high lift fork with 1 trailer
⚲	Dragline — overhead	₂⊓	Pallets — two	⌊	Truck — high lift walkie
⊟	Drum	2000 ₂[1o]	Pallets—two—10 on—2000 lbs.	L	Truck — low lift
AⱯ	Elevator — automatic	⊓	Pallet rack	⌐	Truck — low lift fork
3rd	Floor designation	→	Pipe line	⌐²	Truck — low lift fork with 2 trailers
⌐	Gas cylinder	-⦿►	Pump	＼	Truck slide (from tailgate)
T	Hand truck — platform	Ⅱ	RR car — box		
/	Hand truck — two wheeler	I	RR car — flat		
⊥	Highway truck — body type	Ⅴ	RR car — hopper		

Fig. 27. Handlig symbols.

Cycles Covering Materials Handling. To identify the various actions that are involved, the authors have established "cycles" for the different units of a materials handling activity. These cycles are as follows:

1. **Basic cycle.** Materials handling tasks generally consist of four basic elements —pickup, move, putdown, and store. Sometimes other elements are intermixed

with these operations. The basic cycle is found wherever handling is done. Neither size, weight, nor shape of load affects the concept. The basic cycle can be completely mechanical. When a man picks up a box and puts it on a belt conveyor, he completes a basic cycle. When a machine picks up a part, moves it, and puts it down, it completes a basic cycle.

2. **Semicycle.** The man picking up a box and placing it on a conveyor performs a basic cycle. As the box moves along the conveyor, there is no "pickup" or "putdown" in this movement cycle. The box is, in effect, in storage while it is moving. This cycle, therefore, is identified as a semicycle because it does not have all the elements which a basic cycle must include. A fork truck or a crane, on the other hand, completes basic cycles because it inherently has ability to pick up, move, set down, and store objects.

3. **Mixed cycle.** The mixed cycle is really a basic or semicycle into which some other element or operation is introduced. For example, a man picks up a piece, inspects it, and puts it back on a tray. Introduction of the inspection element makes the activity a mixed cycle. An operator may perform some fabricating or assembly operation while moving the part. The result again is a mixed cycle.

Differentiating the cycles. Assume that an observer watches a man feeding pieces into a machine. The man picks up a piece, moves it to a chuck, and inserts it. After the piece is machined, the machine unloads itself and ejects the piece onto a conveyor. Then, at some point along the conveyor, a man removes the piece and puts it on a pallet. What kind of cycles are followed here? The following breakdown will help to identify them:

Man picks up piece, moves it to chuck and inserts it.	Pickup Move Putdown Store	BASIC CYCLE
After piece is machined, machine unloads itself and ejects piece onto conveyor.	Move Putdown Store	SEMICYCLE
At some point along conveyor, man removes piece, puts it on pallet.	Pickup Move Putdown Store	BASIC CYCLE

To utilize this cycle concept, consider a situation such as the following typical handling operation:

A low-lift fork truck picks up a pallet loaded with 20 bags of chemicals weighing 2,000 lbs. from a dock and moves it 125 ft. to an elevator. The truck lowers the pallet into the elevator. To describe this handling situation symbolically, the authors of the article have utilized for symbols both the Yale & Towne symbols and handligs. In applying them, the above statement becomes:

What—the pallet load—becomes $\frac{2\,0\,0\,0}{2\,0}$.

From where—the dock—becomes $\ulcorner$.

How—the low-lift fork truck—becomes $\_\lrcorner$.

To where—the elevator—becomes $\wedge$.

Hence the shorthand becomes $\frac{2\,0\,0\,0}{2\,0}$ $\ulcorner\lrcorner$ $\wedge$

There is one more consideration to be taken into account in making and using cycle charts. It is necessary to **differentiate between positive and negative moves:**

A positive move is one in which the load is moved in a direction approximating a straight line flow. Any real deviation from that approximation is a negative move.

Sometimes a move may be both positive and negative. If a fork truck, for example, must follow a devious route to reach its objective, some of the distance will be negative, some positive.

It is important to understand and use this idea because then one can identify moves as negative or positive, on a chart, along with distances involved. With that information it is easy to total up negative moves and positive moves. These totals can then be used to show how much excess handling is being done.

Fig. 28 illustrates a cycle chart with a typical handling situation. The situation is built around the receipt of a 30-ton load of bagged chemicals by rail from a supplier in another city. The loaded bags are not palletized, and weigh individually 100 lb. The facts that this cycle chart discloses are as follows:

Line 1.   Bags in boxcar are placed on pallet by man, 15 bags per pallet. 600 bags are handled this way (600 cycles, 40 pallets). Man travels 2 ft. each cycle.

Line 2.   Hand-pallet jack moves pallets from boxcar to highway truck. Truck holds 6 pallets. 40 pallets constitute 7 truck loads. So pallet jack must make 40 round trips. Distance involved is 20 ft.

Line 3.   Six pallets, each holding 15 bags, are moved from boxcar by highway truck to dock of Building 1. This semicycle is repeated 7 times. Each cycle covers 2,600 linear ft.

Line 4.   Pallet containing 15 bags is moved from truck by hand-pallet jack to dock of Building 1. This cycle is also repeated 40 times. Pallets are moved 20 ft. in the negative direction at this point.

Line 5.   Pallets are moved from storage on dock by hand-pallet jack to elevator and taken to second floor. Elevator holds 4 pallets, so 10 trips will be needed.

Line 6.   Four loaded pallets are moved from first to second floor by elevator.

Line 7.   Pallets are unloaded from elevator by hand pallet jack and moved to temporary storage area near elevator.

Line 8.   Pallets are moved from temporary storage by power fork truck to permanent storage. All distances for putting material in storage are negative distances.

Line 9.   Now material needed in production is requisitioned from storage. Pallets are taken from permanent storage by power fork truck to temporary storage near elevator.

Line 10.   Pallets are loaded on elevator.

Line 11.   Pallets go down to first floor by elevator.

Line 12.   Pallets are taken off elevator and put in temporary storage nearby.

Line 13.   Pallets are taken through Buildings 1 and 2 to "outgoing materials area." Pallets are placed in temporary storage in Building 2 until highway truck is available.

Line 14.   Building 2 has no truck dock, so pallets are tailgated on highway truck by fork truck.

Line 15.   Pallets are arranged in truck by hand pallet jack.

Line 16.   Truck loaded with 5 pallets moves from Building 2 dock to dock of Building 3.

Line 17.   Pallets are moved from truck to dock, from which they will shortly be moved into process.

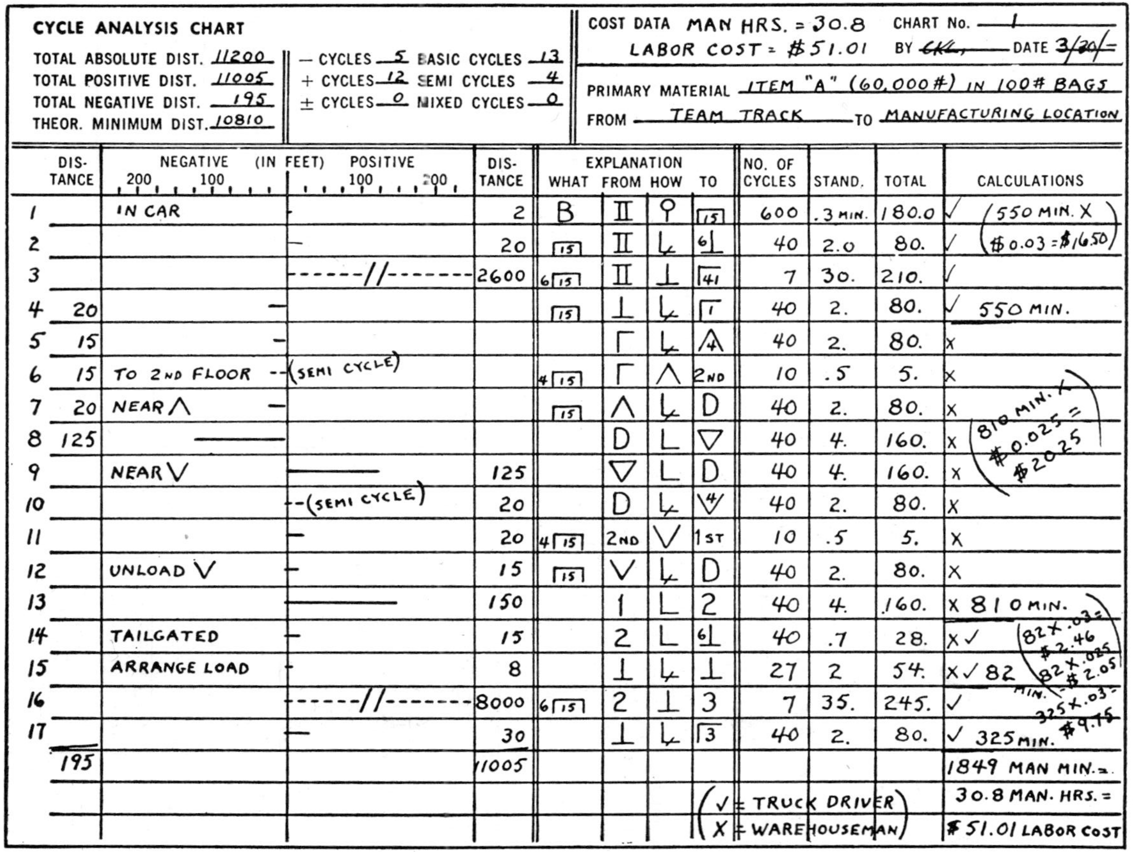

CYCLE ANALYSIS CHART

TOTAL ABSOLUTE DIST. 11200 — CYCLES 5 BASIC CYCLES 13
TOTAL POSITIVE DIST. 11005 + CYCLES 2 SEMI CYCLES 4
TOTAL NEGATIVE DIST. 195 ± CYCLES 0 MIXED CYCLES 0
THEOR. MINIMUM DIST. 10810

COST DATA MAN HRS. = 30.8 CHART NO. 1
LABOR COST = $51.01 BY 644 DATE 3/20

PRIMARY MATERIAL ITEM "A" (60,000#) IN 100# BAGS
FROM TEAM TRACK TO MANUFACTURING LOCATION

DIS-TANCE		NEGATIVE (IN FEET) POSITIVE	DIS-TANCE	EXPLANATION WHAT FROM HOW TO	NO. OF CYCLES	STAND.	TOTAL	CALCULATIONS
1	IN CAR		2	B II 9 15	600	.3 MIN.	180.0	(550 MIN. X) 550 MIN. X
2			20	15 II 4 6	40	2.0	80.	($0.03 = $1650)
3			2600	15 II 1 4	7	30.	210.	
4	20			15 1 4 7	40	2.	80.	550 MIN.
5	15			1 4 4	40	2.	80.	X
6	15 TO 2ND FLOOR (SEMI CYCLE)			4 15 1 4 2ND	10	.5	5.	X
7	20 NEAR			15 4 1 D	40	2.	80.	X
8	125			D 1 D	40	4.	160.	X
9	(SEMI CYCLE)		125	D 4 D	40	4.	160.	X
10	NEAR		20	D 4 4	40	2.	80.	X
11				2ND V 1ST	10	.5	5.	X
12	UNLOAD		20	4 15 V 4 D	40	2.	80.	X
13			15	15 1 2	40	4.	160.	X 810 MIN.
14	TAILGATED		150	2 4 6	40	.7	28.	X 81 × .3 $2.46
15	ARRANGE LOAD		15	2 4 1	27	2	54.	X 82 × .05 $2.05
16			8	2 1 3	7	35.	245.	82 × .05 $4.15
17			8000	1 4 13	40	2.	80.	325 × .03 325 MIN.
	195		30					1849 MAN MIN. =
			1005					30.8 MAN. HRS. =
				(√ = TRUCK DRIVER)				$51.01 LABOR COST
				(X = WAREHOUSEMAN)				

Fig. 28. Cycle charting with handligs.

Quoting further from Factory Management and Maintenance:

The last four columns provide space for finding costs by cycles and in total. In the column marked "Stand" put down the standard time for each cycle. (Stop-watch readings can also be used if standards are not available.)

Then multiply the standard time by the number of cycles to get the total time.

Once the total time is ascertained, it can then be multiplied by the wage rate of the person or persons involved. This calculation can be made in the last column in as much or as little detail as desired.

This information is then summarized at the top of the chart, and can show as much of the data as it is desired to present. With the completed cycle chart it is now possible to refer back to the basis of any analysis, asking the questions of "what, when, where," and especially "why" with the suggestions previously given in order to develop a better method.

Using Predetermined Standards in Analysis

MANUAL STANDARDS. The use of standard data, or of predetermined time standards, for measuring manual work performed in industry has become quite common. There are several different systems of standards in regular use. Each system requires somewhat different procedures in order to apply the available data properly. Tested time values for various machine operations have been compiled by Hadden and Genger (Standard Time Data); and Maynard, Stegemerten, and Schwab (Methods-Time Measurement) describe one analytical method. The use of standard data is not peculiar or unique to the analysis of materials handling problems: A synthesis of information pertaining to it can be

REACH — R

Distance Moved Inches	Leveled Time TMU				Hand in Motion		Case and Description
	A	B	C or D	E	A	B	
1	1.8	2.1	3.6	1.7	1.3	1.5	A. Reach to object in fixed location, or to object in other hand or on which other hand rests.
2	3.7	4.3	5.9	3.8	2.8	2.7	
3	5.0	5.9	7.3	5.3	3.8	3.6	
4	6.1	7.1	8.4	6.8	4.9	4.3	
5	6.5	7.8	9.4	7.4	5.3	5.0	B. Reach to single object in location which may vary slightly from cycle to cycle.
6	7.0	8.6	10.1	8.0	5.7	5.7	
7	7.4	9.3	10.8	8.7	6.1	6.5	
8	7.9	10.1	11.5	9.3	6.5	7.2	
9	8.3	10.8	12.2	9.9	6.9	7.9	C. Reach to object jumbled with other objects in a group so that search and select occur.
10	8.7	11.5	12.9	10.5	7.3	8.6	
12	9.6	12.9	14.2	11.8	8.1	10.1	
14	10.5	14.4	15.6	13.0	8.9	11.5	
16	11.4	15.8	17.0	14.2	9.7	12.9	D. Reach to a very small object or where accurate grasp is required.
18	12.3	17.2	18.4	15.5	10.5	14.4	
20	13.1	18.6	19.8	16.7	11.3	15.8	
22	14.0	20.1	21.2	18.0	12.1	17.3	
24	14.9	21.5	22.5	19.2	12.9	18.8	E. Reach to indefinite location to get hand in position for body balance or next motion or out of way.
26	15.8	22.9	23.9	20.4	13.7	20.2	
28	16.7	24.4	25.3	21.7	14.5	21.7	
30	17.5	25.8	26.7	22.9	15.3	23.2	

Fig. 29. MTM data for element Reach—R.

MOVE — M

Distance Moved Inches	Leveled Time TMU				Multiplying Factor		Case and Description
	A	B	C	Hand in Motion B	Wt.	Factor	
1	1.7	1.7	1.7	1.5	Up to 5#	1.00	A. Move object to other hand or against stop.
2	3.6	4.2	4.2	2.7			
3	4.9	5.7	5.7	3.6	10#	1.03	
4	6.1	6.9	7.3	4.3			
5	7.3	8.0	8.7	5.0	15#	1.05	
6	8.1	8.9	9.7	5.7			
7	8.9	9.7	10.8	6.5	20#	1.08	
8	9.7	10.6	11.8	7.2			
9	10.5	11.5	12.7	7.9	25#	1.11	B. Move object to approximate or indefinite location.
10	11.3	12.2	13.5	8.6			
12	12.9	13.4	15.2	10.0	30#	1.14	
14	14.4	14.6	16.9	11.4			
16	16.0	15.8	18.7	12.8	35#	1.16	
18	17.6	17.0	20.4	14.2			
20	19.2	18.2	22.1	15.6	40#	1.19	C. Move object to exact location.
22	20.8	19.4	23.8	17.0			
24	22.4	20.6	25.5	18.4	45#	1.22	
26	24.0	21.8	27.3	19.8			
28	25.5	23.1	29.0	21.2	50#	1.25	
30	27.1	24.3	30.7	22.7			

Fig. 30. MTM data for element Move—*M*.

GRASP — G

Case	Leveled Time TMU	Description
1A	1.7	Pick Up Grasp — Small, medium or large object by itself, easily grasped.
1B	3.5	Very small object or object lying close against a flat surface.
1C1	7.3	Interference with grasp on bottom and one side of nearly cylindrical object. Diameter larger than ½".
1C2	8.7	Interference with grasp on bottom and one side of nearly cylindrical object. Diameter ¼" to ½".
1C3	10.8	Interference with grasp on bottom and one side of nearly cylindrical object. Diameter less than ¼".
2	5.6	Regrasp.
3	5.6	Transfer Grasp.
4A	7.3	Object jumbled with other objects so search and select occur. Larger than 1" × 1" × 1".
4B	9.1	Object jumbled with other objects so search and select occur. ¼" × ¼" × ⅛" to 1" × 1" × 1".
4C	12.9	Object jumbled with other objects so search and select occur. Smaller than ¼" × ¼" × ⅛".
5	0	Contact, sliding or hook grasp.

Fig. 31. Typical analysis of a hand operation using MTM data.

SIMPLIFIED DATA

HAND AND ARM MOTIONS	BODY, LEG, AND EYE MOTIONS

HAND AND ARM MOTIONS

REACH OR MOVE   TMU
1"................ 2
2"................ 4
3" to 12" 4 + length of motion
Over 12" 3 + length of motion
(For TYPE 2 REACHES AND
MOVES use length of motion
only.)

POSITION

Fit	Symmetrical	Other
Loose	10	15
Close	20	25
Exact	50	55

TURN – APPLY PRESSURE
Turn............... 6
Apply pressure 20

GRASP
Simple 2
Regrasp or transfer... 6
Complex.......... 10

DISENGAGE
Loose 5
Close 10
Exact 30

BODY, LEG, AND EYE MOTIONS

                TMU
Simple foot motion 10
Foot motion with pressure 20
Leg motion 10

Side step case 1 20
Side step case 2 40

Turn body case 1 20
Turn body case 2 45

Eye time............ 10

Bend, stoop, or kneel on
   one knee 35
Arise 35

Kneel on both knees ... 80
Arise 90

Sit............... 40
Stand 50

Walk per pace 17

(All times on this Simplified
Data Table include 15%
allowance)

1 TMU = .00001 hour
     = .0006   minute
     = .036   second

Fig. 32. Simplified MTM data.

found in the Production Handbook under the topic "Time Study and Work Measurement." Forms in which the data are found are illustrated in Figs. 29, 30, 31, and 32.

The designers of the MTM (Methods-Time Measurement) system of predetermined time standards here shown have also published some simplified data so that the inexperienced analyst will have available information for establishing time values. The simplified data strike an average of the complete data. They are easier and faster to apply and are quite useful for making a quick check of a job or a short analysis of a special situation.

Standard data and predetermined time standards can be used in all phases of analysis where any manual effort is involved. Operating equipment controls, loading pallets, stacking material, small-part handling and packaging, and many other types of activity can all be analyzed more effectively with valid time standards.

DEVELOPMENT OF BASIC TIME DATA. Much less information has been made available about predetermined time standards for the operation of equipment, particularly of industrial trucks. A major contribution to the field of **predetermined time standards** was made in a research project conducted jointly by the Yale Materials Handling Division of Yale & Towne Manufacturing Company, and the Wharton School of Commerce and Finance, University of Pennsylvania. Technical principals in the study were Bruno A. Moski, Director of Industrial Engineering at Yale & Towne, and V. Donald Schoeller, Director of the Taylor Management Laboratory at the Wharton School.

Memomotion study was used to analyze **fork truck operations** in 18 different plants, and 195 students at the Wharton School participated in the analysis of the films, for the development of standard time data. A total of 21 basic truck motions were isolated and evaluated, and 27 variable factors were identified, with specific methods being developed for the evaluation of the variable factors.

The basic time data apply to a **typical 4,000-lb. electric fork lift truck,** covering a range of loads from an empty truck to a 4,000-lb. load in increments of 1,000 lb. In order that the standard time data may be of maximum practical value to industrial firms throughout the country, Yale & Towne has developed a standard technique for the application of the data. Several exhibits and examples have been prepared to illustrate the standard technique.

Standard Time Data for Basic Fork Truck Motion Elements. The analysis in Fig. 33 identifies and describes the 21 basic truck motions for a Yale K51AT-40 electric fork lift truck, indicates the element symbols for abbreviating the basic truck motions, and lists the basic time values. The **basic truck motion element symbols** are then summarized with corresponding basic time values. This summary is comparable to the cards and folders used in other systems of predetermined time standards, such as Methods-Time-Measurement (MTM). It is the basis for the application of all basic time values in the analysis of all materials handling situations involving this type of fork lift truck equipment.

APPLICATION IN ANALYSIS. In the analysis of materials handling cases, it is necessary to survey each plant to determine the representative materials handling conditions which exist.

Plant Layout. The section of a typical industrial plant shown in Fig. 34 includes a raw materials stores area, two machining departments (each of which contains a temporary storage area), and a finished goods stores area. All of the work is fully palletized on 4,000-lb.-pallet cubed loads 48 × 48 × 48 in., which are stacked three high at the raw materials stores, temporary storage, and

Basic Truck Motion	Load (lb.)	Unit	Element Symbol	Base Minutes
1. ACCELERATE, EMPTY OR LOADED Occurs each time truck moves from dead stop to full speed	Empty 1,000 2,000 3,000 4,000	Occurrence	AE AL	0.0300 0.0250
2. STRAIGHT RUN FORWARD Begins when truck has reached full speed at end of acceleration, and ends when truck begins to stop	Empty 1,000 2,000 3,000 4,000	Per foot	FE1F F1M1F F2M1F F3M1F F4M1F	0.0023 0.0024 0.0025 0.0025 0.0027
3. STRAIGHT RUN REVERSE Same as Straight Run Forward	Empty 1,000 2,000 3,000 4,000	Per Foot	RE1F R1M1F R2M1F R3M1F R4M1F	0.0023 0.0024 0.0025 0.0025 0.0027
4. STOP Includes application of brakes to bring truck to dead stop from full speed	Empty 1,000 2,000 3,000 4,000	Occurrence	SE S1M S2M S3M S4M	0.0200 0.0330 0.0340 0.0350 0.0360
5. STRAIGHT RUN-IN, 1st LEVEL Includes moving truck at slow speed from dead stop to insert forks into pallet or place a pallet after forks have been raised. Time includes starting and stopping. Horizontal distance through which truck moves is approximately 4 ft., the length of the pallet	Empty 1,000 2,000 3,000 4,000	Occurrence	1NE 1N1M 1N2M 1N3M 1N4M	0.0800 0.0800 0.0800 0.0700 0.0700
6. STRAIGHT RUN-IN, 2d LEVEL	Empty 1,000 2,000 3,000 4,000	Occurrence	2NE 2N1M 2N2M 2N3M 2N4M	0.0800 0.0900 0.1100 0.1000 0.1000
7. STRAIGHT RUN-IN, 3d LEVEL	Empty 1,000 2,000 3,000 4,000	Occurrence	3NE 3N1M 3N2M 3N3M 3N4M	0.1100 0.1200 0.1300 0.1200 0.1200

The Yale & Towne Mfg. Co.

Data are for Yale model K51AT-40 electric truck.

Fig. 33. Standard time data for 21 basic fork truck motions (continued on next page).

Basic Truck Motion	Load (lb.)	Unit	Element Symbol	Base Minutes
8. STRAIGHT RUNOUT, 1st LEVEL Includes withdrawal of forks from pallet, or removal of pallet. Time includes starting and stopping. Truck moves backward approximately 4 ft. when performing this motion.	Empty 1,000 2,000 3,000 4,000	Occurrence	10E 101M 102M 103M 104M	0.0600 0.0650 0.0650 0.0600 0.0600
9. STRAIGHT RUNOUT, 2d LEVEL	Empty 1,000 2,000 3,000 4,000	Occurrence	20E 201M 202M 203M 204M	0.0600 0.0650 0.0700 0.0600 0.0600
10. STRAIGHT RUNOUT, 3d LEVEL	Empty 1,000 2,000 3,000 4,000	Occurrence	30E 301M 302M 303M 304M	0.0600 0.0700 0.0700 0.0800 0.0800
11. TURN FORWARD LEFT Change in direction to the left, usually 90° and in minimum turning radius, while truck is running forward	Empty 1,000 2,000 3,000 4,000	Occurrence	TFL	0.0550
12. TURN FORWARD RIGHT Change in direction to the right, while truck is running forward	Empty 1,000 2,000 3,000 4,000	Occurrence	TFR	0.0550
13. TURN REVERSE LEFT Change in direction to the left while truck is running backward	Empty 1,000 2,000 3,000 4,000	Occurrence	TRL	0.0550
14. TURN REVERSE RIGHT Change in direction to the right while truck is running backward	Empty 1,000 2,000 3,000 4,000	Occurrence	TRR	0.0550
15. TURN FORWARD LEFT, STOP Change in direction to the left while truck is running forward, followed by dead stop. Motion usually followed by Run-In or Hoist	Empty 1,000 2,000 3,000 4,000	Occurrence	TFLS	0.0600

Fig. 33. (Continued on next page.)

Basic Truck Motion	Load (lb.)	Unit	Element Symbol	Base Minutes
16. TURN FORWARD RIGHT, STOP Change in direction to the right while truck is running forward, followed by dead stop	Empty 1,000 2,000 3,000 4,000	Occurrence	TFRSE TFRS1M TFRS2M TFRS3M TFRS4M	0.0700 0.0700 0.0700 0.0750 0.0750
17. TURN REVERSE LEFT, STOP Change in direction to the left while truck is running backward, followed by dead stop	Empty 1,000 2,000 3,000 4,000	Occurrence	TRLSE TRLS1M TRLS2M TRLS3M TRLS4M	0.0650 0.0750 0.0750 0.0650 0.0700
18. TURN REVERSE RIGHT, STOP Change in direction to the right while truck is running backward, followed by dead stop	Empty 1,000 2,000 3,000 4,000	Occurrence	TRRSE TRRS1M TRRS2M TRSS3M TRRS4M	0.0650 0.0850 0.0800 0.0800 0.0800
19. TILT BACKWARD Tilt fork carriage backward	Empty 1,000 2,000 3,000 4,000	Occurrence	LB	0.0250
20. TILT FORWARD Tilt fork carriage forward	Empty 1,000 2,000 3,000 4,000	Occurrence	LF	0.0250
21. HOIST UP Move fork carriage up while truck is at rest	Empty 1,000 2,000 3,000 4,000	Per Inch	UE1N U1M1N U2M1N U3M1N U4M1N	0.0028 0.0029 0.0030 0.0032 0.0033
22. HOIST DOWN Move fork carriage down while truck is at rest	Empty 1,000 2,000 3,000 4,000	Per Inch	DE1N EL1N	0.0030 0.0018

Fig. 33. (Concluded.)

finished goods stores areas, and one-high at the machines. In this example, all work on the pallets is of the same type, for which the first operation can be performed on any machine in Department *A* and the second operation on any machine in Department *B*.

To determine the representative materials handling situation which exists, an analysis of the minimum and maximum pallet travel has been prepared.

Minimum vs. Maximum Pallet Travel. The minimum motion path which a pallet can travel from raw materials stores through temporary storage, Department *A*, temporary storage, and Depatment *B* to finished goods stores, is indicated by arrows in Fig. 34. In this exhibit, minimum distances have been selected, and the pallets moved are stacked one-high at all locations. The motion path followed by the pallet load is from pallet location No. 32 through pallet location Nos. 43, 41, 42, 68, 66, 67, and 98. **Evaluation of minimum pallet travel** indicates the precise motion path followed by the pallet load and is expressed in element symbols together with the corresponding basic time values in minutes in Fig. 35. The total basic time for the minimum pallet travel is 3.9434 min.

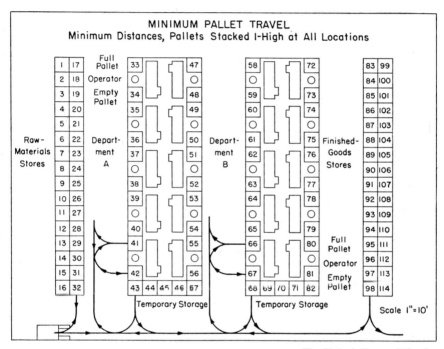

The Yale & Towne Mfg. Co.

Fig. 34. Plant layout showing minimum pallet travel.

Maximum pallet travel analyzed on a plant layout diagram, as in Fig. 34, indicates the maximum motion path which a pallet can travel to accomplish the same job. Maximum distances were selected, and the pallets moved were stacked three-high at raw materials stores, temporary storages and finished goods stores, and one-high at the machines. The fork lift truck started at a point at the maximum distance from the first pallet to be moved. The motion path followed by the pallet load was from pallet location No. 1 through pallet locations Nos. 57, 33, 34, 82, 58, 59, and 112. **Maximum pallet travel** described is evaluated in Fig. 36. The total basic time is 9.0183 minutes.

Evaluation of Average Pallet Travel. Fig. 37 summarizes the data of Figs. 35 and 36. The total basic time for the average pallet travel is 6.4809 min. On the basis of 32 pallet locations and 3 pallets per location, there are initially 96 pallets in raw materials stores. With 96 pallets, and 6.4809 min. per pallet, the basic time required to transport all pallets through Departments *A* and *B* to

Plant _____ Work Kit _____ Date _____ April 20, 19—
Materials Handling Case _____ Evaluation of Minimum Pallet Travel in Fig. 34
Analyst _____ Industrial Engineering Dept.

Element Symbol	Base Minutes	Element Symbol	Base Minutes	Element Symbol	Base Minutes
AE	0.0300	1NE#42	0.0800	1NE#67	0.0800
TFLSE	.0600	LB	.0250	LB	.0250
1NE#32	.0800	104M	.0600	104M	.0600
LB	.0250	TRLS4M	.0700	TRLS4M	.0700
104M	.0600	AL	.0250	AL	.0250
TRLS4M	.0700	F4M16F	.0432	F4M16F	.0432
AL	.0250	TFL4M	.0550	TFL4M	.0550
F4M16F	.0432	F4M31F	.0837	F4M32F	.0864
TFLS4M	.0600	TFLS4M	.0600	TFLS4M	.0600
1N4M#43	.0700	1N4M#68	.0700	1N4M#98	.0700
LF	.0250	LF	.0250	LF	.0250
10E	.0600	10E	.0600	10E	.0600
TRRSE	.0650	TRRSE	.0650	TRRSE	.0650
AE	.0300	AE	.0300		
TRFSE	.0700	TFRSE	.0700		
1NE#43	.0800	1NE#68	.0800		
LB	.0250	LB	.0250		
104M	.0600	104M	.0600		
TRRS4M	.0800	TRRS4M	.0800		
AL	.0250	AL	.0250		
F4M11F	.0297	F4M12F	.0324		
TFRS4M	.0750	TFRS4M	.0750		
F4M12F	.0324	F4M12F	.0324		
TFRS4M	.0750	TFRS4M	.0750		
1N4M#41	.0700	1N4M#66	.0700		
LF	.0250	LF	.0250		
10E	.0600	10E	.0600		
TRLSE	.0650	TRLSE	.0650		
AE	.0300	AE	.0300		
FE8F	.0184	FE8F	.0184		
TFLSE	.0600	TFLSE	.0600		
Total		Total		Total	3.9434

The Yale & Towne Mfg. Co.

Fig. 35. Summary in motion element symbols—minimum pallet travel.

Plant _____ Work Kit _____ Date _____ April 20, 19—

Materials Handling Case ___ Evaluation of Maximum Pallet Travel _____

Analyst   Industrial Engineering Dept. _____

Element Symbol	Base Minutes	Element Symbol	Base Minutes	Element Symbol	Base Minutes
AE	0.0300	F4M28F	0.0756	AL	0.0250
FE103F	.2369	TFR4M	.0550	TRRS4M	.0800
TFRE	.0550	F4M60F	.1620	AL	.0250
FE60F	.1380	TFRS4M	.0750	F4M28F	.0756
TFRSE	.0700	1N4M #33	.0700	TFR4M	.0550
UE96N	.2688	LF	.0250	F4M60F	.1620
3NE#1	.1100	10E	.0600	TFRS4M	.0750
LB	.0250	TRLSE	.0650	1N4M #58	.0700
304M	.0800	AE	.0300	LF	.0250
DL96N	.1728	FE8F	.0184	10E	.0600
AL	.0250	TFLSE	.0600	TRLSE	.0650
TFLS4M	.0700	1NE#34	.0800	AE	.0300
AL	.0250	LB	.0250	FE8F	.0184
F4M72F	.1944	104M	.0600	TFLSE	.0600
TFL4M	.0550	TRLS4M	.0700	1NE #59	.0800
F4M36F	.0972	AL	.0250	LB	.0250
TFLS4M	.0600	F4M64F	.1728	104M	.0600
U4M96N	.3168	TFL4M	.0550	TRLS4M	.0700
3N4M#57	.1200	F4M48F	.1296	AL	.0250
LF	.0250	TFLS4M	.0600	F4M62F	.1674
30E	.0600	U4M96N	.3168	TFL4M	.0550
DE96N	.2880	3N4M #82	.1200	F4M48F	.1296
AE	.0300	LF	.0250	TFLS4M	.0600
TRRSE	.0650	30E	.0600	F4M6F	.0162
AE	.0300	DE96N	.2880	TFLS4M	.0600
TFRSE	.0700	AE	.0300	U4M96N	.3168
UE96N	.2688	TRRSE	.0650	3N4M #112	.1200
3NE#57	.1100	AE	.0300	LF	.0250
LB	.0250	TFRSE	.0700	30E	.0600
304M	.0800	UE96N	.2688	DE96N	.2880
DL96N	.1728	3NE #82	.1100	AE	.0300
AL	.0250	LB	.0250	TRRSE	.0650
TRRS4M	.0800	304M	.0800		
AL	.0250	DL96N	.1728		
Total		Total		Total	9.0183

The Yale & Towne Mfg. Co.

Fig. 36. Summary in motion element symbols—maximum pallet travel.

```
 1. Minimum  pallet  travel.............................     3.9434 bin.
 2. Maximum  pallet  travel  ...........................     9.0183 min.
 3. Total minimum and maximum........................    12.9617 min.
 4. Average pallet travel ...............................     6.4809 min.
 5. Total number of pallets.............................       96 pallets
 6. Total base time.....................................   622.1664 min.
 7. Total  base  time  (622.1664 ÷ 60).....................     10.37 hr.
 8. Total pallet load  .................................    384,000 lb.
 9. Total  pallet  load  (384,000 ÷ 2,000)....................       192 tons
10. Total load per hour (192 ÷ 10.37)....................    18.51 tons/hr.
11. Variables affecting results are evaluated on the basis of
    specific conditions in individual plants.
```

Fig. 37. **Evaluation of average pallet travel.**

Variable Factor	Reason for Time Allowance	How To Measure the Allowance
A. HUMAN		
1. Skill	Actual operator ability and effort relative to normal operator	Estimate percent that your operator is above or below normal operator in skill or effort
2. Fatigue	Necessary rest and personal time for operator	Compare with plant fatigue allowances for similar work. Generally 10%, but local conditions may justify more or less
3. Carelessness	Effectiveness of supervision of truck operators, including observation of safety rules	Estimate or develop from time study, percent of time lost through fault of supercision, or safety rules
B. MECHANICAL		
4. Distance	Operation over distances too short to use capacity speed of truck	Adjust running time by ratio of capacity to usable speed
5. Tier height	Stacking above three levels requires additional time	Apply percent additional time to run-in and run-out, based on estimate or time study
6. Fork load	Basic time values are for 1,000 lb. increments, to 4,000 lb.	Add new time values for other loads as required
7. Direction	Different rates of forward or reverse speed, due to truck types	Add basic motion time values for different equipment

Fig. 38. **Table of operating variables (continued on next page).**

Variable Factor	Reason for Time Allowance	How To Measure the Allowance
8. Truck condition	Mechanical and electrical condition of truck affects lost time due to breakdowns.	By estimate, work sampling, or time study, develop percent of time lost because of breakdowns
9. Truck type	Make model of truck other than that designated	Establish separate tables of basic motion time values for different makes or models
10. Battery	Power ebbs with use, generally slowing truck after 5 hr. of constant operation	Adjust basic time values for acid-type batteries when excessive time between charges occurs, as follows:

Time Battery in Actual Use	Time Increment for Hour Named	Average Increment for All Hours
1–5 hr.	0.00	0.000
6 hr.	0.01	0.002
7 hr.	0.08	0.013
8 hr.	0.25	0.043

Variable Factor	Reason for Time Allowance	How To Measure the Allowance
11. Maintenance	Downtime for preventive maintenance during shift	Convert scheduled daily preventive maintenance time to percent of basic motion time per day
C. OPERATIONAL		
12. Traffic	Delays caused by pedestrians and other vehicles in truck operating area	By estimate, work sampling, or time study, develop percent delay time related to total basic motion time
13. Obstructions	Low headroom, narrow passages, and similar layout obstacles that prevent free truck operation	By estimate, work sampling, or time study, develop percent delay time related to total basic motion time

Fig. 38. (Continued on next page.)

Variable Factor	Reason for Time Allowance	How To Measure the Allowance
14. Pavement	Type and condition of surfaces over which a truck operates	Adjust basic motion time as follows: Pave- Incre- ment ment a. Asphalt, concrete .... 0.00 b. Brick, wood, ice, hard snow, macadam, poor concrete, granite, planking, tarvia.. 0.01 c. Soft snow, gravel, poor macadam.. 0.02 d. Clay .... 0.09 e. Sand road....... 0.12 f. Loose sand, 3 in. deep 0.14
15. Loading area conditions	Combination of traffic, housekeeping, and other factors	Apply adjustments to individual factors
16. Load size and type	Basic motion time values based on cubic load measuring 48 in. each way Larger dimensions may affect time	By estimate or time study, develop percent for other size loads, if necessary, applied to specific basic motions.
17. Lighting	Basic motion time values based on 5-ft. candles or more	Foot- Incre- Candles ment 5 or more 0.00 4 0.20 3 0.40 2 0.60 1 0.80
18. Housekeeping	Areas cluttered by poor housekeeping delay truck operations.	By estimate, work sampling, or time study, develop percent delay to necessary basic motion time
19. Scheduling	Time lost by trucks waiting for loads or work instructions	By estimate, work sampling, or time study, develop percent delay to basic motion time
20. Temperature	If operating temperatures are outside normal 32° to 90°, additional time must be allowed	Increase basic motion time by 10% for temperatures below 32° or above 90°
21. Weather	Precipitation generally decreases truck performance outside	Increase basic motion time by 10% on days when there is precipitation

Fig. 38. (Continued on next page.)

Variable Factor	Reason for Time Allowance	How To Measure the Allowance
22. Aisle width	Basic motion time values apply to aisle widths equal to truck specification width plus 1 ft. Narrower aisles slow down trucks	Increase basic motion time affected by 43% for each foot, or fraction of a foot, that aisle is narrower than specification width plus 1 ft.
23. One-or-two-way traffic	Basic motion time values apply to one-way traffic or to two-way traffic in aisles at least equal to width of two passing trucks plus 18 in.	By estimate, work sampling, or time study, develop percent delay to basic motion time
24. Doorways	Some doorways cause no delay, while others cause truck to slow down or stop	By estimate, work sampling, or time study, develop percent delay to basic motion time
25. Intersections	Basic motion time for turns affected if one or both aisles are narrow. Some intersections require truck to stop	By estimate, work sampling, or time study, develop percent delay to turning time
26. Angle of tiering	Angle at which pallets are placed in relation to aisle boundary affects turn and stop, run-in and run-out.	*(see table below)*
27. Grades	Upgrades reduce speed of trucks	For upgrades only, increase straight run basic motion time by 8% for each percent of grade

Basic Motion Numbers	Increment for Storage Angle		
	30 deg.	45 deg.	60 deg.
5–10	−0.69	−0.25	┃0.50
15–18	−0.34	−0.50	−0.67

The Yale & Towne Mfg. Co.

Fig. 38. (Concluded.)

finished goods stores is 622.1664 base min., or 10.37 base hr. This example completes the demonstration of the manner in which basic time values are applied.

EVALUATION OF VARIABLES. It is then necessary to evaluate the variable factors which affect the basic time values, on the basis of the specific conditions which exist in individual plants. Fig. 38 lists the 27 variable factors identified in **Fork Truck Operation,** the reason for each time allowance, and the specific method of measuring each time allowance.

Evaluation of variables at The Yale & Towne Manufacturing Company (Fig. 39) indicates the results of a study made to evaluate specific conditions recommended by its materials handling division. **Standard time data** for Yale Model:

STANDARD PERFORMANCE DATA FOR FORK LIFT TRUCKS

SUMMARY OF BASIC AND VARIABLE TIME

Plant _____ Work Kit _____ Analyst _____ Industrial Engineering Department _____ Date _____ April 20, 19—

Element Symbols	Total Basic Minutes	1. Skill	2. Fatigue	3. Careless.	4. Distance	5. Tier Ht.	6. Fork Load	7. Direction	8. Trk. Cond.	9. Trk. Type	10. Battery	11. Mainten.	12. Traffic	13. Obstruct.	14. Pavement	15. Load Area	16. Loads	17. Light	18. Housek'p.	19. Schedule	20. Temper.	21. Weather	22. Aisles	23. 1-2 Traffic	24. Doorways	25. Intersect.	26. Avg. Tier	27. Grades	Total	Total Variables	Total Minutes
1. FE, 1M, 2M, 3M, 4M			.15	.02							.04								.01	.05										.27	
2. RE, 1M, 2M, 3M, 4M			.15	.02							.04								.01	.05										.27	
3. AE, AL			.15	.02							.04		.02	.01					.01	.05					.01	.02				.33	
4. SE, 1M, 2M, 3M, 4M			.15	.02							.04		.02	.01					.01	.05					.01	.02				.33	
5. 1NE, 1M, 2M, 3M, 4M			.15	.02							.04									.05										.26	
6. 2NE, 1M, 2M, 3M, 4M			.15	.02							.04									.05										.26	
7. 3NE, 1M, 2M, 3M, 4M			.15	.02							.04									.05										.26	
8. 10E, 1M, 2M, 3M, 4M			.15	.02							.04									.05										.26	
9. 20E, 1M, 2M, 3M, 4M			.15	.02							.04									.05										.26	
10. 30E, 1M, 2M; 3M, 4M			.15	.02							.04									.05										.26	
11. TFR			.15	.02							.04								.01	.05										.27	
12. TRR			.15	.02							.04								.01	.05										.27	
13. TFRSE, 1M, 2M, 3M, 4M			.15	.02							.04								.01	.05										.27	
14. TRRSE, 1M, 2M, 3M, 4M			.15	.02							.04								.01	.05										.27	
15. TFL			.15	.02							.04								.01	.05										.27	
16. TRL			.15	.02							.04								.01	.05										.27	
17. TFLS			.15	.02							.04								.01	.05										.27	
18. TRLSE, 1M, 2M, 3M, 4M			.15	.02							.04								.01	.05										.27	
19. LB, LF			.15	.02							.04									.05										.26	
20. UE, 1M, 2M, 3M, 4M			.15	.02							.04									.05										.26	
21. DE, DL			.15	.02							.04									.05										.26	
22. Totals																															

Fig. 39. Evaluation of variables at Yale & Towne Manufacturing Company.

STANDARD PERFORMANCE DATA
FORK LIFT TRUCKS
APPLICATION OF BASIC TIME VALUES

Plant _____ Work Kit _____ Date ____ April 20, 19—
Materials Handling Case ____ Standard Time Data for Yale Model: K51AT-40 Truck at
Yale & Towne Manufacturing Company ____ Analyst ____ Industrial Engineering Dept.

Element Symbol	Base Minutes	Element Symbol	Base Minutes	Element Symbol	Base Minutes
AE	0.0399	3N4M	0.1511	TRRSE	0.0825
AL	.0332	10E	.0755	TRRS1M	.1080
FE1F	.0029	101M	.0819	TRRS2M	.1017
F1M1F	.0031	102M	.0819	TRRS3M	.1017
F2M1F	.0032	103M	.0755	TRRS4M	.1017
F3M1F	.0032	104M	.0755	LB	.0315
F4M1F	.0034	20E	.0755	LF	.0315
RE1F	.0029	201M	.0819	UE1N	.0035
R1M1F	.0031	202M	.0882	U1M1N	.0037
R2M1F	.0032	203M	.0755	U2M1N	.0038
R3M1F	.0032	204M	.0755	U3M1N	.0040
R4M1F	.0034	30E	.0755	U4M1N	.0042
SE	.0266	301M	.0882	DE1N	.0038
S1M	.0439	302M	.0882	DL1N	.0023
S2M	.0452	303M	.1008		
S3M	.0465	304M	.1008		
S4M	.0478	TFL	.0698		
1NE	.1008	TFR	.0698		
1N1M	.1008	TRL	.0698		
1N2M	.1008	TRR	.0698		
1N3M	.0882	TFLS	.0762		
1N4M	.0882	TFRSE	.0889		
2NE	.1008	TFRS1M	.0889		
2N1M	.1132	TFRS2M	.0889		
2N2M	.1386	TFRS3M	.0952		
2N3M	.1260	TFRS4M	.0952		
2N4M	.1260	TRLSE	.0825		
3NE	.1386	TRLS1M	.0952		
3N1M	.1511	TRLS2M	.0952		
3N2M	.1637	TRLS3M	.0825		
3N3M	.1511	TRLS4M	.0889		
Total		Total		Total	

Fig. 40. Standard performance data for fork lift trucks—application of basic time values.

DRIVE AXLE HOUSINGS STUDY

	Standard Minutes	Standard Hours
1. STANDARD TIME DATA		
a. Move (3) bins from spray painting conveyor to outside storage	7.4412	0.124
b. Move (3) bins from outside storage to incoming-material area of machining department	9.8721	0.165
c. Move (3) bins from out-going material area of machining department to finished stores	10.1192	0.169
d. Total standard time	27.4325	0.458
2. CONVENTIONAL TIME STUDY		
a. Move (3) bins from spray painting conveyor to outside storage	8.2570	0.138
b. Move (3) bins from outside storage to incoming-material area of machining department	8.3950	0.140
c. Move (3) bins from out-going material area of machining department to finished stores	8.9125	0.149
d. Total standard time	25.5645	0.427
3. VARIATION OF CONVENTIONAL TIME STUDY FROM STANDARD TIME DATA		−0.031
4. PERCENT VARIATION OF CONVENTIONAL TIME STUDY FROM STANDARD TIME DATA		−6.8%

Fig. 41. Comparison of standard time data with conventional time study.

K51AT-40 Truck (shown in Fig. 40) indicates the results of increasing the basic time values by the percentages listed in Fig. 39, to develop standard time values for a specific plant. When the procedure illustrated is properly completed, it should no longer be necessary to devote time to the evaluation of variable factors.

Comparison of **standard time data** with **conventional time study** of a drive axle housing indicates the results of an application of the standard time data in Fig. 40 to a specific example. In the development of Fig. 41, the transportation moves for 3 bins of drive axle housings were charted in the manner demonstrated above, using the standard time data in Fig. 40. After the standard time had been established on the basis of standard time data, a fork lift truck operator was instructed to perform the actual work. A conventional time study was taken with a stop watch for the full period of the example, with actual time values having been adjusted to compensate for the pace of the operator and with the addition of 15 percent for fatigue, to develop standard time on the basis of time study. The variation in standard time, from 0.458 standard hours on the basis of standard time data to 0.427 standard hours on the basis of conventional time study, was 0.031 standard hours, or 6.8 percent, which is considered an eminently satisfactory degree of correlation between the two methods of evaluating standard time.

It is noted that this body of standard time data not only provides a method of determining the **work load of fork lift trucks,** but it also provides a yardstick for the evaluation of **excess materials handling costs.** The careful analysis of variable factors in specific plants can result in the determination of excess costs resulting from poor pavements, inadequate aisles, poor lighting, poor housekeeping, aisle traffic, obstructions, grades, inadequate maintenance, and other factors contributing to high materials handling costs. It may be to the economic advantage of management to change operating conditions and capitalize upon the potential reduction of excess materials handling costs.

With this contribution to the field of predetermined time standards, and other bodies of standard time data, the problems of **methods planning** and **equipment selection** in the area of materials handling can be solved in precisely the same manner as they are solved in all other areas of manufacturing.

Specialty Techniques of Analysis

There are many specialty techniques of analysis which can be applied under certain conditions. Many of these techniques that can be used are not peculiar to materials handling analysis alone but are much more universally applicable in all phases of industrial operations. Because of this universality and nonuniqueness to materials handling, they are only mentioned rather than described in detail.

STATISTICAL STUDIES. Sampling techniques have come into common use when analyzing materials handling problems. **Work sampling,** more specifically, has been used to evaluate the proportion of activity assignable to either of two basic conditions. Such conditions can be checked by such work sampling comparisons as "Amount of Truck Use vs. Amount of Truck Idleness," "Amount of Time a Fork Truck Is Lifting vs. Amount of Time Not Lifting," or "Amount of Time Space Is Occupied vs. Amount of Time Space Is Unoccupied." Within the two basic conditions under study, additional breakdowns of activity can also be observed, recorded, and subsequently analyzed. Extreme care should be taken in drawing inferences from such subsidiary information, however. Work sampling studies are generally designed to evaluate the percent activity of two basic conditions that can be occurring. Such studies are designed for probabilities based on a binomial distribution. To infer subsequently that the subsidiary effects are correct with the same degree of precision, with only the observations required for the basic study, is to assume much more than was designed into the normal work sampling study.

The **queuing theory** or "waiting-line" theory, as it is more commonly known in this country, has also been applied in materials handling analysis. The usual situation concerns the use of the waiting-line theory to find the economic balance between the number or amount of service facilities, i.e., dock spaces, materials handlers, trucks, etc., and the cost of waiting time incurred from all causes because of the lack of such service facilities. Excess facilities represent high "idle" time costs and inadequate facilities cause waiting on the part of somebody or something waiting to be served. By studying the distributions of "arrivals" and the "rate of service" and by assigning proper costs to all pertinent factors, the situation can generally be described mathematically. Then, by simulating many possible combinations and conditions of operation with the aid of computers, it is possible to find the optimum arrangement of facilities and specify that particular one.

COST STUDIES. Cost analysis is naturally a very necessary part of materials handling analysis. The isolation and identification of costs associated with any receiving, producing, warehousing, or distribution system can not be neglected. However, caution must also be observed in drawing conclusions from cost figures. The cost system and method of collecting costs must be understood as well as the method of prorating and allocating costs to various departments and producing units. It is not intended here to outline any analytical methods for making cost studies but merely to advise caution in drawing the conclusions from such studies. To attempt to lower materials handling costs once they have been isolated, without regard to the effect such changes might have on the over-all system, is not good analysis or good engineering. To handle this portion of the analysis adequately, it is necessary to understand overhead costs and overhead rates, marginal costs, increment costs, standards and variances, and the many details found within the many different methods and types of costing. This is a complete subject by itself. The best the materials handling analyst can do is to determine what the costs really are—not based on some arbitrary rates and allocations, but the true costs, based on actual conditions of operation. Such costs can seldom be found in the cost records directly but must be synthesized from several sources. Then, for any changes that are being proposed, it is necessary to determine what **relevant costs** are being avoided and what **new costs** are being created. Again, this must be done without regard to existing overhead rates, bases of allocation, etc. Only by so doing can a realistic appraisal of the problem be made.

MATERIALS HANDLING FACTORS

CONTENTS

MATERIALS HANDLING FACTORS

Use of Factors in Analysis

STUDY OF MATERIALS HANDLING PROCESSES. An outline for the study of materials handling operations, while written in terms generally ascribed to a manufacturing process, can be applied to working out practically any project in which materials handling is involved.

The method of study is divided into three phases:

1. What elements of the total process constitute materials handling?
2. What factors affect the materials handling situation?
3. What kinds of equipment should be installed as indicated by the study?

A further division of the study into parts may be advisable when the following situations exist simultaneously:

1. Existing buildings and structures are to be utilized.
2. New facilities are to be constructed.

Revamping old facilities is largely a matter of adapting new or varying types of materials handling equipment to the existing physical environment. In **new planning,** with straight-line flow sheets as determined by production and planning, fullest advantage can be taken of modern equipment by suitable functional design of the new environment.

Materials Handling Elements. Materials handling has been defined as the art and science of moving, packaging, and storing of substances in any form. Materials handling elements are characterized by a **change of position or location.** Production elements are characterized by the addition of value through a **change in form or characteristic** of the substance being handled. By applying these tests, the materials handling elements may be distinguished from the production elements.

Materials Handling Factors. After the elements which constitute materials handling are identified, the first step is to find out what factors are operative in the situation. Any materials handling problem may be analyzed into its component parts by applying the factors presented in Fig. 1, which answer the following questions:

1. What is to be moved?
2. In what will it be moved?
3. Where does the movement take place (origin and destination)?
4. How often does the movement occur?
5. How far does the item move?
6. How fast does the movement take place?
7. Upon what does the movement take place?
8. By whom is the movement carried out?
9. With what equipment is the movement made?

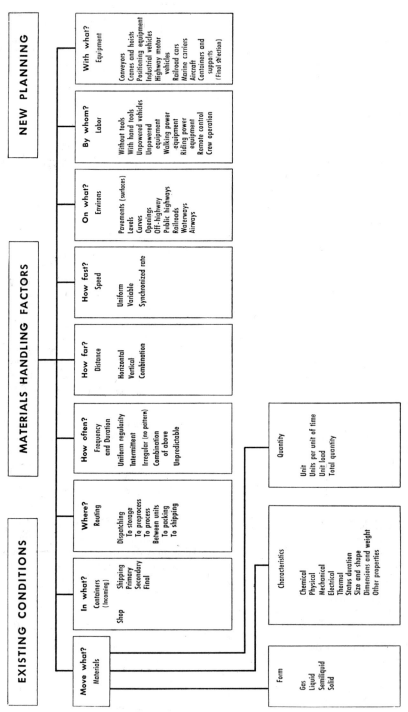

Fig. 1. Materials handling factors.

Materials

DESCRIBING MATERIALS. The answers to the first of the foregoing questions are important because they concern the remaining elements of the analysis. Since **materials** or substances are to be moved, the problems in this moving will be affected by the nature of such materials. Therefore compiling a complete description of each specific material involved in the problem is the first task. The three fundamental factors of the materials to be handled are:

1. Form.
2. Characteristics.
3. Quantity.

FORMS OF MATERIALS. Materials may be divided into four all-inclusive general classes (as tabulated in Fig. 2):

1. Gases.
2. Liquids.
3. Semiliquids.
4. Solids.

So that the exact nature of what is to be moved may be stated, each of these general classes may be divided into various subclasses. By use of the decimal system all the classifications can be made extremely flexible, and detailed expansions covering the different materials in question can follow, where needed. Fig. 2 gives the initial breakdown of forms of materials. Gases, for example, may be divided, in conformity with Interstate Commerce Commission regulations, into high pressure and low pressure—over and under 25 lb. per sq. in., respectively. In making a breakdown of material into these classifications, the aim has been to conform to as many existing standards and regulations as possible. By using as many subdivisions as are required, a detailed description of any combination of properties and characteristics can be made.

CHARACTERISTICS OF MATERIALS. Because of the wide variations existing among the myriad substances which must be studied, separate consideration must be given to the nature of each substance, as expressed by the following several properties and characteristics:

1. Chemical.
2. Physical.
3. Mechanical.
4. Electrical.
5. Thermal.
6. Status-duration.
7. Size and shape.
8. Dimension and weight.
9. Other.

The check sheet (Fig. 3) provides a largely self-explanatory list of items involved—to which other items may be added as required. Because all forms of material must be identified by their varied properties and characteristics, the use of the check sheet is important.

Since the nature of the material to be moved is the first factor to be taken into consideration, proper attention must be given to the physical, chemical, and special characteristics of the material. **Gases** can be handled only in tight or, where required, pressure-resisting containers. **Liquids** and **semiliquids** require tight containers. **Solids**—since they vary from bulk materials, which may be granular, powdery, lumpy, etc.; to formed solids of various shapes, dimensions, and weights; even to living things—represent a variation of the problem.

GASES AND LIQUIDS

1. HIGH PRESSURE GAS (over 25 lb. per sq. in. I.C.C. Reg.)
   a. Compressed gas under high pressure.
   b. Liquefied gas under high pressure.
   c. Absorbed gas under high pressure.

2. LOW PRESSURE GAS (under 25 lb. per sq. in.).
   a. Low pressure compressed gas.
   b. Liquefied gas under low pressure.
   c. Absorbed gas under low pressure.

3. UNSTABLE LIQUIDS.
   a. Volatile liquids (tend to evaporate).
   b. Foaming liquids (effervescent).
   c. Fuming liquids (fume on exposure to air).
   d. Supersaturated solutions (tend to precipitate).
   e. Molten materials (usually solid at normal temperatures).
   f. Liquid refrigerated gases (gas at normal temperatures).
   g. Chemically unstable liquids (changing chemical composition).

4. STABLE LIQUIDS.
   a. Water, salt and fresh.
   b. Aqueous solutions.
   c. Liquid petroleum products.
   d. Liquid chemicals and solutions.
   e. Paints, adhesives, liquid plastics, liquid coatings, etc.
   f. Liquid food products and beverages.

SEMILIQUIDS AND SOLIDS

5. SEMILIQUIDS.
   a. Emulsions.
   b. Slurry, sewage.
   c. Sludge, slime, mud.
   d. Pulp.
   e. Paste.

6. BULK SOLIDS.
   a. Mined raw materials—coal, ore, stone, etc.
   b. Earthy raw materials—gravel, sand, clay, loam, etc.
   c. Beneficiated and graded raw materials.
   d. Processed dry bulk chemicals—soda ash, chemical salts, etc.
   e. Agricultural bulk products—grain, flour, sugar, etc.

7. FORMED SOLIDS.
   a. Animal products.
   b. Vegetable products.
   c. Forest products.
   d. Mineral products (basic forms).
   e. Metal products.
   f. Manufactured articles and parts.
   g. Completely fabricated durable goods.
   h. Consumer goods.

8. LIVING THINGS.
   a. People (human beings).
   b. Beasts (four-footed mammals).
   c. Birds (feathered bipeds).
   d. Reptiles.
   e. Fish and marine animals.
   f. Insects.
   g. Plants.
   h. Microorganisms.

9. MATERIALS NOT OTHERWISE CLASSIFIED.

Fig. 2. Forms of materials.

The simpler problems are those that deal with **inert, noncorrosive substances** not affected by light and temperature—those in which chemical purity and outside contaminations do not enter. The more complex handling situations dealing with the need for air conditioning, light and temperature control, protection from contaminating influences, such as foreign matter—these require different approaches, but they all come under the designation of materials handling.

During the handling process **conditions may change** from a combination of liquids and solids to a semisolid, or paste (for example, asphalt emulsion or toothpaste), or to a liquid end product (paint, for example).

Granulated sugar and soda ash are, in certain respects, somewhat similar materials, but they present entirely different problems from a materials handling standpoint because of the corrosive nature of the soda ash.

Different **properties** may be listed under a number of classifications. Most of those listed in Fig. 3 are self-explanatory, such as acid or alkaline under "chemical," hardness and porosity under "physical," abrasive or fragile under "mechanical," conductivity and resistance under "electrical," heat conductivity and boiling point under "thermal." The size, shape, dimension, and weight, together with a **description** of the unit, will apply to nearly all substances. **Other properties** are listed embracing such items as affinities, such as silica-gel for water and asphalt for rubber; repulsions such as acids against alkalies and oil against water; aging-curing reactions from catalysts, and dispersion agents such as colloids. All of these characteristics may have a bearing on the choice of containers, environs, and equipment and should be duly recorded on the survey sheet.

When the **form or nature** of the substance handled changes during processing or transportation, another check sheet is required. For example, molten steel cannot be handled in the same manner as the charging of scrap into a cupola or an open-hearth furnace. Photographic film becomes sensitive to light at particular stages in the production process. Ice cream, a compound of cream, flavoring, etc. —largely liquid—becomes a solid during manufacture, and thus presents an entirely different handling problem. Some processes consist mainly in removing impurities. In copper mining, 10 percent ore is very desirable, with 90 percent waste. In contrast, raw cane-sugar yield usually averages 96 percent, leaving only 4 percent of impurities to be eliminated.

Handling of materials is often complicated by the nature of the product or substance which is being handled and which may be undergoing a **chemical or physical change** because of the lapse of time, changing thermal conditions, or mechanical operations, such as agitation or other irregularities. Additional problems arise, such as the setting of cement after it is poured and the production of synthetic resins and similar materials where, when the desired consistency is arrived at, the process must abruptly terminate.

Many **special conditions** call for attention, such as items which cannot be properly placed among the specific properties as listed. For example, certain chemical reactions, such as the "pot life" of glue, are affected by the passing of time.

Aging and curing may be necessary for materials intended for human consumption which require a period of inactivity, such as the aging of cheddar cheeses. In contrast, butter, cream, eggs, and other products of a related perishable nature are more desirable the sooner they are received from the source. Curing refers to the treating of hams, bacon, and other meat products; it also refers to the setting of cement. There are many other products and materials to which this classification applies, and all should be duly tabulated in proper order to obtain a full comprehension of the classification problem.

OUTLINE CHECK SHEET FOR

MATERIALS

PROBLEM: _____ EXISTING CONDITIONS _____ NEW PLANNING _____ DATE _____ LOCATION _____

DEPT. _____
SECT. _____

SUITABLE HEADINGS

REFER TO DRAWING NUMBER _____

QUANTITY

UNIT _____
UNITS _____ PER UNIT OF TIME _____
UNIT LOAD _____
TOTAL QUANTITY _____

FORM

1. HIGH PRESSURE GAS (over 25# psi)
2. LOW PRESSURE GAS (under 25# psi)
3. UNSTABLE LIQUIDS
4. STABLE LIQUIDS
5. SEMILIQUIDS

6. BULK SOLIDS
7. FORMED SOLIDS
8. LIVING THINGS
9. OTHER MATERIALS

CHARACTERISTICS

Indication of degree   H = High   M = Medium   L = Low

A. CHEMICAL PROPERTIES

1 ☐ Acid
2 ☐ Alkaline
3 ☐ Corrosive.
4 ☐ Soluble
5 ☐ Explosive
6 ☐ Noxious or poisonous
7 ☐ Odorous.
8 ☐ Light sensitivity
9 ☐ Perishable
10 ☐ Volatility

D. ELECTRICAL PROPERTIES

1 ☐ Conductivity
2 ☐ Resistance
3 ☐ Magnetic
4 ☐ Capacity
5 ☐ Radioactive
6 ☐ Affected by static
7 ☐
8
9

G. SIZE AND SHAPE

1 ☐ Dust or powder
2 ☐ Paste
3 ☐ Granular
4 ☐ Lumpy
5 ☐ Mixed sizes
6 ☐ Uniformity of particle size
7 ☐ Nonuniformity of particle size
8 ☐ Simplicity of shape or form
9 ☐ Complexity of manufactured form

B. PHYSICAL PROPERTIES

1 ☐ Hardness – Rockwell scale
2 ☐ Density – Lbs. per cu. ft.
3 ☐ Specific gravity
4 ☐ Compressibility
5 ☐ Elasticity
6 ☐ Ductility
7 ☐ Porosity
8 ☐ Permeability

C. MECHANICAL PROPERTIES

1 ☐ Abrasive
2 ☐ Slippery
3 ☐ Sticky or tacky
4 ☐ Rugged or tough
5 ☐ Fragile or brittle
6 ☐ Viscosity – Baumé
7 ☐ Free flowing – Angle of repose
8 ☐ Pressure psi or inches MG
9 ☐ Moisture content – Relative humidity

E. THERMAL PROPERTIES

1 ☐ Heat conductivity
2 ☐ Expansion coefficient
3 ☐ Specific heat   °F. or °C.
4 ☐ Boiling point   °F. or °C.
5 ☐ Melting point   °F. or °C.
6 ☐ Latent heat (boiling) °F. or °C.
7 ☐ Latent heat (melting) °F. or °C.
8 ☐ Deteriorates on exposure to heat
9 ☐ Deteriorates from lack of heat

F. STATUS DURATION

1 ☐ Life
2 ☐ Aging, curing
3 ☐ Style life
4 ☐
5 ☐
6 ☐
7 ☐
8 ☐
9 ☐

H. DIMENSIONS AND WEIGHT

1 ☐ Length
2 ☐ Width
3 ☐ Height
4 ☐ Diameter
5 ☐ Cross-sectioned area
6 ☐ Surface area
7 ☐ Volume
8 ☐ Weight
9 ☐ Screen size

I. OTHER PROPERTIES

1 ☐ Affinities
2 ☐ Repulsions
3 ☐ Catalytic action
4 ☐
5 ☐
6 ☐
7 ☐
8 ☐
9 ☐

Fig. 3. Outline check sheet for materials.

QUANTITY FACTORS. Although it is treated as a basis factor in its own right by many people engaged in handling materials, quantity also covers the factors of form, physical nature, and other characteristic properties of the materials handled. The **quantity** of material to be moved is an integral property of the material itself, but merely stating that X quantity must be moved is not sufficient. Under the "quantity" classification are included the unit, the total units, the number of units per unit of time, the unit load—all of which are pertinent parts of any handling problem. The total quantity to be moved within a given time will, in most cases, determine the kind and amount of equipment required.

Containers

TYPES OF CONTAINERS. There are two general classes of **containers** —those used in **manufacturing** and those used in **transporting** products. Fig. 4 shows a classified list of containers and supports used in industry, broken down into subdivisions which may be still further broken down. Certain shipping containers consist of primary, secondary, and final or shipping cases. A notable example is the packaging of cigarettes, which are put up in packs of 20, ten packs to a carton, many cartons to a case. Certain kinds of production containers used during manufacture may be used in production lines in the course of manufacture and accompany the products to their final destinations. An example is a skid on which a load of flat paper has been wire-strapped: when it comes from the cutter, the paper is deposited on the skid, and the skid usually goes with the paper to its final destination—from the mill, to the jobber, and finally to the consignee. Another common example is a skid on which an electric refrigerator is assembled, the skid becoming the bottom of a crate in which the refrigerator is shipped. Some steel window sashes may be crated around the edges, ready to be set into a wall without removing certain portions of the crate.

In many instances the type of incoming container is beyond the control of the recipient, particularly when the shipment has been received from a common carrier. In some industries, however, consultation with suppliers can often bring about desired changes in shipping containers which will substantially reduce handling and perhaps transportation costs. Some manufacturers of machinery now often specify how incoming raw materials, component parts, and subassemblies shall be packed for shipment, and in some instances the purchaser pays the additional cost of packing and transportation, because substantial savings may thereby be made in the recipient's own materials handling operations.

Routing, Scheduling, and Dispatching

CONTROL OF MOVEMENT. Routing (see Fig. 5) tells where movement takes place. Scheduling sets the timetable for carrying on production. Dispatching—often referred to as communications—is directive contact with the flow of work. Dispatching may be achieved through either direct personal contact or remote contact. Examples of means of remote contact are written communications; verbal communications by telephone, loud-speaker, or two-way radio (the last of which has proved especially effective in directing the movement of vehicles over large areas from a central point); and audible or visual signals. Audible signals such as whistle blasts and bells are used for hoists, logging operations, and construction elevators. Visual signals—specifically, here, signals by hand—are used in the operation of cranes and similar equipment. A well-organized dispatch-

SHOP OR MANUFACTURING AND SHIPPING: PRIMARY, SECONDARY, AND FINAL

1. PRESSURE VESSELS.
   a. High pressure gas cylinders (over 25 lb. psi I.C.C. Regulation).
   b. High pressure railroad and truck cylinders (over 25 lb. psi. I.C.C. Regulation).
   c. Compressed gas cartridges and bottles (over 25 lb. psi. I.C.C. Regulation).
   d. Low pressure fixed tanks.
   e. Low pressure portable tanks.
   f. Low pressure railroad and truck tanks.
2. TIGHT CONTAINERS (sealed or with breather).
   a. Metal drums.
   b. Barrels, hogsheads, casks, kegs, and tubes.
   c. Bottles, flasks, carboys, jars, vials, demijohns, and ampules.
   d. Sanitary and other sealed cans.
   e. Sealed shipping containers.
   f. Tanks (fixed and portable).
   g. Tanks built into cars, trucks, and ships.
3. ENTIRELY ENCLOSED CONTAINERS (Loose).
   a. Loose barrels and kegs (nonmetallic).
   b. Boxes and cases (wood, metal, fiber, and paper).
   c. Crates.
   d. Cartons, corrugated paper, etc.
   e. Bags (burlap, canvas, cloth, mesh, paper, and plastic).
   f. Wrappings, bales, bundles, and rolls.
   g. Weatherproof shipping containers.
   h. Cans with loose lids.
4. OPEN TOP CONTAINERS.
   a. Shop boxes, rectangular.
   b. Round shop containers.
   c. Tote boxes, pans, and baskets, rectangular.
   d. Pans.
   e. Bins.
   f. Silos, bunkers, and hoppers.
5. PLATFORM SUPPORTS.
   a. Pallets.
   b. Skid platforms.
   c. Tables.
   d. Trays.
   e. Separators.
   f. Racks.
   g. Skids, runners, horses, and cradles.
6. COIL SUPPORTS.
   a. Reels.
   b. Spools.
   c. Textile beams.
   d. Arbors, cores, and poles.
   e. Tubes and drums.
   f. Bobbins and shuttles.
   g. Cones.
7. SECUREMENTS.
   a. Strapping (wire, metal banding, tape, rope, and cord).
   b. Cinches (chain, rope or wire, with tighteners).
   c. Bulkheads (portable) for trucks, railroad cars, ships, and planes.
   d. Securements attached to trucks, railroad cars, ships, and planes.
   e. Bracing (temporary bulkheads, shoring, and chocks).
   f. Dunnage (duckboards, loose lumber).
   g. Fastenings (bolts, clamps, clips, nails, and screws).
   h. Auxiliary equipment (staplers, strapping devices).
8. AUXILIARY PACKAGING EQUIPMENT.
9. OTHER SPECIAL CONTAINERS.

Fig. 4. Containers and supports.

ing system, particularly where a large fleet of equipment is in operation, offers many opportunities for substantial savings.

ROUTING. Routing may involve the movement of materials from the outside source of supply, to the point of original receipt at a plant, through all the subsequent various stages of production—between steps in manufacturing processes, between buildings and plants, and perhaps into and out of temporary storage. It may involve carriers not directly under the control of those authorizing the movements. In every instance, however, routing should be broken down to cover each movement with a separate analysis. Because of the economies which may be effected through efficient use of materials handling equipment, previous routings and handling of materials may sometimes be considerably changed to take advantage of the cost-reducing opportunities offered by the introduction of newer methods, such as those made possible by means of industrial lift trucks, cranes, conveyors, and other materials handling equipment.

---

1. DISPATCHING.
   a. Personal contact (verbal).
   b. Written orders.
   c. Telephone (including loud-speaker.)
   d. Radio (two-way).
   e. Signals.

2. To STORAGE (Raw or incoming material).
   Stacking, piling.
   Unpacking.
   Palletizing or other similar handling.

3. To PREPROCESS.
   This classification required in only a few types of industry.

4. To PROCESS.
   Details as required.

5. BETWEEN PRODUCTION UNITS.
   Details to suit local conditions.

6. To PACKING (PRIMARY, SECONDARY, AND FINAL ENCLOSEMENT).
   This movement probably classed as part of production when machines do all or part of packing function.

7. To WAREHOUSE STORAGE (END PRODUCT).
   Piling, tiering, and other warehouse functions.

8. To SHIPPING AND SHIP (MAY INCLUDE PACKING).
   Weighing, marking, loading, bracing, etc.

Fig. 5. Routing procedures.

SCHEDULING. The function of scheduling is to set up the timetables for operations to be carried on in the manufacturing departments of a company. In some industries there is a **prepreparation step** in the process, which may take place long before the final or principal manufacturing activities are planned. Examples of such prepreparation are the aging and sandblasting of castings before putting them in storage prior to machining, and the peeling of logs in the manufacture of paper and plywood, which is often done weeks or months in advance of the actual manufacture of the paper or the cutting of the veneers. Such a step is designated as a preprocess. Usually the first process is one which initiates the particular manufacturing cycle.

DISPATCHING. Where there is a division of labor betwen production and materials handling, usually the materials handling engineer's **responsibility** for movement terminates with the delivery of the incoming material to the first step in the process. The engineer is not concerned primarily with the functioning of the automatic machines used in manufacturing, or with the hand operations of workers engaged in fabricating or otherwise changing the nature of the materials; he is vitally concerned, however, with the movement of the materials through the production operations and into any area where the materials may be temporarily stored.

It is important to determine where **production** ceases and where **transportation** begins. In some industries, the transporting of material between steps in the process is a function assigned to the production staff. When material is moved from one production unit to another, it sometimes passes into temporary storage. In some industries, those responsible for production also have charge of the movement of material between units. It is assumed here that the materials handling function is under the direction of an individual responsible solely for that movement. **Inspection** is not included in the transfer because inspection and quality control are usually the responsibility of the manufacturing and standardization departments.

After the product has been produced, it must be packed for shipment. In many industries there may be a divergence of operations at this point, particularly when automatic machines that may be used in the packing are considered part of the manufacturing and processing equipment and are under its supervision. The materials handling engineer, however, is concerned not only with the internal movement of the product but also with its arrival at its destination in good condition. Because of this fact, he can contribute to the design, methods of operation, and upkeep of the packaging machinery.

STORING. Storage comprises all the problems of warehousing, including receiving, piling or stacking, unpiling, palletizing, and recording; and in many instances it may involve planning for first-in, first-out, or first-in, last-out situations. The next step after recording usually is moving the ready-to-ship materials to the warehouse, then from warehouse to the loading and shipping area, where they are finally loaded on outgoing carriers. Related procedures are carried on in varied forms in the handling, warehousing, and shipping of agricultural products, and in earth-moving, mining, and many other bulk materials handling operations.

FREQUENCY OF MOVEMENT OF MATERIALS. The frequency of movement of materials (see Fig. 1) is of particular importance. In analyzing this factor it is necessary to answer questions such as the following:

1. Is the movement of uniform regularity?
2. Is it intermittent or irregular?
3. Is it a combination of the above two kinds?
4. Is it a one-time job?

Where occasional movement or movement only at long or irregular intervals exists, entries may be listed under the blank spaces provided on the analysis form. Less frequent movement and handling of larger loads may result in considerable savings in the handling procedures. Such an unpredictable and irregular materials handling task as snow removal, which includes many necessary preparations, occurs with appreciable frequency in colder regions, and the services of a considerable fleet of materials handling equipment may be required to keep the roads and yards open for traffic.

DISTANCE AND DIRECTION OF MOVEMENT. The distances over which materials may have to be moved (see Fig. 1) and the direction which the moving must take are likewise important considerations. First, what horizontal movement may be necessary? Is it from one machine to another, from one building to another, or from one plant to another? Or is it on more than one horizontal level? Movement may also be vertical (from one floor to another) or it may be a combination of horizontal and vertical (moving across the floor, for example, and descending or ascending to another level). Distance of movement may include transportation, even to other plants. It may require transportation by an outside carrier, even a waterway carrier. Within the plant, the choice between conveyors, fork lift trucks, and tractor-trailer trains is influenced principally by the distances to be covered.

SPEED. How fast does the movement take place (see Fig. 1)? Is the speed uniform or does it vary? And is it necessary to synchronize the movement, such as from one conveyor belt to another belt, so that the products on the first belt will arrive at the time and place required for incorporation into another part of the product? Intermittent storage may possibly be considered at this point, where a storage reservoir is needed to insure continuity of operations.

The present speed and the required, or desired, speed in moving materials must be ascertained. **Synchronism** may be brought about by the addition of another production unit, thus increasing the output capacity and stepping up the movement of the material from one point to another. Speed and time are interrelated. The number of units which can be handled per unit of time, as analyzed under the materials (quantity) factor in Figs. 1 and 3, brings up consideration of the time element at this step of the analysis.

ENVIRONS. In assembling the data collected in a materials handling survey —particularly in an older plant, although equally applicable in the case of certain kinds of new plants—it is necessary to check on the physical conditions and surroundings, which greatly influence the selection of the materials handling equipment to be used. An example is that of a machine shop in which the floor might not lend itself to the operation of fork trucks as readily as to other kinds of equipment. Among the many **elements of environs** which must frequently be taken into consideration are the nine included in Fig. 6.

Consideration must be given to the movement of agricultural and forest products and earth and construction material—much of which is transported over **off-highway terrain,** dirt roads, or trails—and to topographical features, such as hills, flats, and marshes, and **railroads** from which sidings into company property may be laid.

Waterway transportation is of great importance because by it vast loads can be moved over long distances. Shipping methods and types of vessel vary for different uses. There are four kinds of waterway transportation: ocean, lake, river, and canal. Ponds and basins can be used for channels of transportation, particularly in logging and timber industries. Occasionally the logs are tied together into rafts and transported on rivers and other larger bodies of water. Flumes, sluices, and ditches are also employed in the lumber industry. In some instances certain agricultural products, particularly melons, are collected and transported in large irrigation ditches, where the water carries them for considerable distances. Shipping conditions differ materially in the case of many products coming under these classifications.

Air travel has become vastly important in the transportation of freight as well as in passenger traffic and the transportation of mail. The advent of the "pod," a separate body attached under the cargo plane, has added another facility for air cargo transportation.

1. PAVEMENTS.
    a. Inside pavements (surfaces, etc.)
    b. Outside pavements (roads, etc.).
    c. Floors (surfaces, load limits).
    d. Aisles and turnouts (widths).

2. LEVELS.
    a. Ramps (grades).
    b. Loading docks and cross-over bridges.
    c. Ceiling heights.
    d. Overhead supports.

3. CURVES.
    a. Horizontal.
    b. Vertical.
    c. Combined or with gradient.

4. OPENINGS.
    a. Doorways (width, headroom, type of door).
    b. Elevator openings (width, headroom, type of door).
    c. Hatches.
    d. Column spacing.

5. OFF-HIGHWAY TERRAIN.
    a. Surfaces (smooth, rough, rocky, sandy, marshy).
    b. Grades (flat, hilly, mountainous).
    c. Trails.
    d. Ice and snow conditions.

6. PUBLIC HIGHWAYS.
    a. Improved highways (State roads, turnpikes, freeways).
    b. Hard-surfaced roads.
    c. Unpaved secondary roads.

7. RAILROADS.
    a. Standard gauge.
    b. Narrow gauge.
    c. Industrial.
    d. Cog roads.

8. WATERWAYS.
    a. Oceans.
    b. Lakes.
    c. Rivers.
    d. Canals.
    e. Ponds and basins.
    f. Flumes, sluices and ditches.

9. AIRWAYS.
    a. Scheduled flights.
    b. Nonscheduled flights.

Fig. 6. Environs in the plant.

Men and Equipment

LABOR FACTORS. While many kinds of equipment and devices for handling exist, there is still a significant demand for **labor, skilled and unskilled,** in the area of transportation. Materials practically always require a certain amount of hand handling; there is no cheaper or better means for loading, transporting, unloading, and stowing many kinds of materials. The movement may be carried out by the various means listed in Fig. 7.

Further study of this problem, and the working out of widely acceptable definitions and terms, will be useful in setting down the data describing new and old operations. In most cases, **time and motion studies** may be required to ascertain the best layout for optimum production, and, where taken care of by men other than those engaged in the materials handling survey, the closest coordination is required for satisfactory results.

EQUIPMENT FACTORS. Except where a radical departure from present practice is contemplated, the general type of equipment needed to effect the desired economies will conform to standard practice in the industry in question, thus reducing the choice of types to a minimum. The major classifications of materials handling equipment are given in Section 1.

With complete data assembled and flow sheets and time studies completed, **selection of equipment** can be undertaken to answer the question, With what

1. LABOR WITHOUT HAND TOOLS.
   a. Sitting.
   b. Standing.
   c. Combination of sitting and standing.
   d. Walking.
   e. Combination of standing and walking.
   f. Carrying.
   g. Rolling round objects.

2. MANUAL LABOR WITH HAND TOOLS.
   a. Using shovels, picks, etc., for digging, loading, and unloading.
   b. Using hooks, for turning or dragging.
   c. Using pusher blades or scoops for moving soft materials.
   d. Using rakes, hoes, brooms, etc.
   e. Using bars, wedges, drift pins, wrenches, etc.
   f. Using power hand tools.

3. MANUAL LABOR OPERATING UNPOWERED VEHICLES OR CRANES.
   a. Pulling or pushing hand trucks.
   b. Pushing two-wheeled hand trucks, buggies, and wheelbarrows.
   c. Operating hand lift trucks and portable lifters.
   d. Using dollies and rollers.
   e. Operating hand cranes, hoists, and winches.
   f. Operating bicycles, tricycles, and roller skates.

4. MANUAL LABOR OPERATING OTHER UNPOWERED EQUIPMENT.
   a. Lifting and pulling with hand jacks and pullers.
   b. Adjusting positioning tables and equipment by hand.

5. LABOR WITH WALK-ALONG POWER VEHICLES AND CRANES.
   a. Operating cranes with pendant floor controls.
   b. Operating walk-along industrial trucks with handle controls.

   c. Operating drag scoops with handlebar controls.
   d. Walking, driving animal-drawn equipment.

6. LABOR RIDING POWER VEHICLES AND CRANES.
   a. Cab-operating power cranes and monorails.
   b. Cab-operating power elevators.
   c. Driving power industrial trucks and tractors.
   d. Operating bulk material handling vehicles.
   e. Driving power agricultural vehicles.
   f. Driving animal-drawn vehicles.
   g. Driving motor vehicles.
   h. Operating rail cars.

7. LABOR OPERATING POWER EQUIPMENT BY REMOTE CONTROL.
   a. Remote control of gravity conveyor switches.
   b. Remote control of trolley conveyor systems.
   c. Remote control of monorail crane and conveyor systems.
   d. Remote control of industrial truck systems.
   e. Remote control of robot vehicles.
   f. Remote control of car-loading devices (including TV operation).
   g. Remote control of fixed materials handling equipment.
   h. Remote control of mobile materials handling equipment.

8. CREW OPERATION OF LARGE OR MULTIPLE EQUIPMENT.
   a. Crew operation of industrial vehicles.
   b. Crew operation of bulk materials handling vehicles.
   c. Crew operation of agricultural vehicles.
   d. Crew operation of railroad equipment.
   e. Crew operation of ships, boats and marine carriers.
   f. Crew operation of air transports.
   g. Crew operation of fixed handling equipment.
   h. Crew operation of equipment not otherwise classified.

Fig. 7. Labor.

equipment is the movement to be made? A **new summary sheet** listing different kinds of materials handling equipment should next be prepared, with the final selection of the equipment depending on a comparison not only of the different types but also of individual makes of each type, and the conclusion being arrived at by a process of elimination. A form of summary sheet such as that in Fig. 8 can be used—first in the selection of types of equipment in comparison with other types and later for comparison by makes of each group or type of equipment. Such a sheet is exceptionally valuable in presenting the salient features and recommendations to those who will make the final selection.

In such a sheet, the main items to be considered are the initial delivered **cost of the equipment,** the delivered **cost of auxiliaries,** such as pallets when fork trucks are to be used and palletization is to be adopted, and the **installation cost,** which should include all building alterations and any additional expense involved through the adoption of the new equipment. This summation gives the total invested cost of making the changeover, from which a deduction of the recoverable value of any replaced equipment can be made. This amount is the **initial total capital investment** required for making the changeover.

Under **operating costs** will appear depreciation, based on the period which the industry has found to be the average normal useful service life of the equipment and including an allowance for obsolescence from any cause, whether it be the development of better kinds of equipment or any other factor.

Other items of operating costs are the **estimated cost of maintenance,** including repairs and supplies; interest on the investment; taxes and insurance; license fees for trucks, where required; garage rent when equipment must be stored in rented quarters; power, direct labor, indirect labor, supervision, and burden not covered by maintenance.

Certain other items should be recorded which may not have a direct financial bearing on the case but are still worthy of consideration. Some of the most important items are those which will furnish intangible benefits, such as an **increase in productivity** through reduction of fatigue, labor turnover, or better housekeeping and improved accident prevention. Many cases are on record where the **intangible benefits** are of sufficient importance to warrant installation of equipment which did not return much in the way of savings.

EQUIPMENT COMPARISONS. In comparing one type of equipment with another, data on existing conditions should be listed in the column captioned "Present," and in the remaining columns comparative data associated with each type of equipment considered should be listed. **Routing** may or may not be changed. **Frequency** might be increased or decreased under certain conditions. It might be decreased where larger unit lots are transported and increased when another type of equipment, such as a belt conveyor, is installed. **Distance** may or may not be affected; the same is true of **speed. Environs** would probably change with any changes in the physical condition of the plant. **Labor** presents an important comparison in hours required for the different proposals. **Equipment and containers** are also listed under each column for comparison.

The total **cost** of each of the proposed operations under consideration would then be compared with the present costs, the difference being the savings to be expected. The **length of time** required for amortization of the expenditures, through savings made under the proposed new methods, should then be estimated.

After making comparisons between various types of equipment which might be installed, the same procedure should be followed in **selecting the manufacturers** from whom to purchase the new facilities. At this point the purchasing agent and

SUMMARY SHEET

Capital Equipment Expenditures	Proposed Operations		
	A	B	C
Initial delivered cost of equipment			
Delivered cost of auxiliaries			
Installation cost (Including alterations, etc.)			
Total			
Less recoverable value of replaced equipment			
Total capital investment			
Intangible benefits – Good housekeeping, reduced labor turnover			
Increase in productive capacity expected			
Increase in storage capacity expected			
Expected reduction of fatigue			
Increased safety factor			

Equipment Operating Cost	Present	Proposed Operations		
		A	B	C
Depreciation				
Maintenance—Repairs, supplies, etc.				
Taxes and insurance				
Interest on investment				
License fees (Trucks, etc.)				
Rent (Garage, etc.)				
Power				
Direct labor				
Indirect labor				
Supervision				
Burden				
Total annual cost				

COMPARISON OF PRESENT AND PROPOSED OPERATIONS

Factors	Present Operation	Proposed Operations		
		A	B	C
Materials				
Quantity				
Routing				
Frequency				
Distance				
Speed				
Environs				
Labor				
Equipment				
Containers				
Cost				
Savings				
Amortization period				
Remarks:				

Fig. 8. Summary sheet.

the engineer should combine their efforts to find out which kinds of **equipment** are best for performing the required operations under the conditions which must be met.

Methods Improvements. Materials handling problems usually involve most of these factors. The objective in each case is to improve the methods presently in use. The **engineering survey** will show conditions as they exist. The expected volume of production, the physical layout of the terrain, the total floor area required will to a large extent govern the methods used in improving the handling of materials and in a large measure will influence the kinds of materials handling equipment to be used under the circumstances.

When the project reaches the **drawing-board stage** the whole plan can be thoroughly reviewed. The layout finally adopted should be designed for the minimum movement of material—if possible, for **straight-line production.** **Flow sheets** must be prepared, preferably on a comparable basis, one showing the existing conditions and the others the proposed or alternate methods.

This analytic study illustrating the proper applications of the so-called materials handling factors in actual installations is not presented as a complete solution to any particular case, but rather as an important aid in analyzing practically any kind of materials handling problem, in arriving at constructive conclusions, and in installing proper methods and equipment. If this basic method is followed, it should be of substantial importance and value in solving a wide range of materials handling problems and in selecting the most suitable and economical equipment.

SECTION 4

FACTORY PLANNING

CONTENTS

CONTENTS *(Continued)*

FACTORY PLANNING

INDUSTRIAL MATERIALS HANDLING. Materials handling in manufacturing industries includes all movement and storage of material from the time it enters the plant until it leaves as a finished product. It does not include handling materials in transportation by public carriers, such as railroads, highway trucks, cargo vessels, or cargo planes, because such transportation is beyond the control of the manufacturing plant, except in cases where manufacturers own and operate these outside facilities.

Materials handling within the plant may be defined as the transportation and progression of materials—whether raw, worked, or finished—on the plant premises. The number of times a material unit is handled during the course of a manufacturing cycle varies with each type of unit and with each system of materials handling. Often, as many as 150 handlings are required for relatively simple units in some plants.

Flow of Material Through the Plant. In a representative flow, the material may be handled as follows:

1. Unloaded from a freight car or motor truck.
2. Placed on skids.
3. Moved by fork truck to an inspection point.
4. Unloaded for inspection.
5. Reloaded onto the skid.
6. Lifted by fork truck.
7. Trucked onto an elevator.
8. Transported to another floor.
9. Lifted by fork truck.
10. Trucked to a storeroom.
11. Unloaded from the skid.
12. Stored in bins.
13. Reloaded later onto a skid.
14. Trucked to a work station.
15. Unloaded from the skid.
16. Placed on a machine.
17. Fed into the machine.
18. Removed from the machine.
19. Reloaded onto a skid.
20. Moved to the next operation.

A similar number of handlings may be involved at each processing and assembling operation, inspection point, packaging point, temporary storage point (awaiting shipment), and finally on the shipping platform, where the finished product is loaded into a freight car or motor truck for outward shipment to customers.

Tons Handled per Ton Shipped. Recent studies reveal that for every ton of finished product shipped in metalworking industries, the equivalent of 50 to 65 tons of materials is handled, and that, in traveling through a plant, materials generally are actually worked on about only one-third of the time, the other two-thirds being taken up by materials handling or temporary storage. The speed of production is therefore confined to only one-third of the time that the material is flowing through processing. Experience has shown that, by setting the pace of materials handling through a well-engineered plant layout—as notably achieved in the meat-packing, automobile, chemical, and food industries—the manufacturing cycle can usually be shortened to eliminate much of the two-thirds of the time during which the material is not being worked on.

Recent surveys indicate that the **total weight of material received** in a plant is 20 percent higher than the **total weight shipped out.** The excess in receipts over shipments is attributable to shrinkage in processing, to scrap and waste, and to consumption of materials and supplies in maintenance activities. Before materials can be processed in a plant they must be received, tallied, inspected, stored, and rehandled out of storage for release to the manufacturing cycle. After the material has been processed, assembled, and packed, it must again be received, tallied, inspected, stored, and rehandled out of storage for release to outbound shipping.

Influence on Plant Construction Outlays. The trend of capital outlays for industrial plant construction and equipment in the United States since 1915 follows closely the major cyclical swings in industrial output. Over this period, these outlays were expended at the rate of 28 percent for plant buildings and 72 percent for equipment—2½ times as much for equipment as for new factory buildings. Since materials handling systems influence structural design, construction engineers today must study all the loads to be handled before they actually start designing a building.

Fundamental Factors

MORE TIME IN HANDLING THAN IN PROCESSING. As already indicated, surveys conducted in several industries have revealed that, on materials being processed, as much as two-thirds of the duration of the process is spent for handling the materials at the work station, and only one-third of the total process time is used for doing the actual work. In addition to the handling cost at the work station proper, there are costs involved in moving materials to and from work stations, receiving and storing raw materials, and storing and shipping finished products.

Materials Handling Adds to Cost but Not to Sales Value. When 50 tons of material weight are handled in manufacturing 1 ton of finished product, only this 1 ton of material brings in a return in the form of sales value. The other 49 tons handled only add cost to the ton of product shipped. Materials handling operations do not change the form or otherwise convert the material in the cycle of making the finished product. These handlings occur mostly while transporting and positioning the material for processing and assembling operations.

In so far as processing and assembling are concerned, many handlings can be dispensed with as long as the material is found at the right place, in the right position, at the right time, and in the right quantities. The planning required to fulfill these requirements is done by designing appropriate materials handling systems during the laying out of the plant.

Cost of Materials Handling Generally Not Revealed in Accounting. The amount of money being paid to skilled operators for portions of their time spent in materials handling at work stations is, in cost-accounting practice, classified as—and buried into—**productive-labor cost.** How much of this labor exists in a plant will remain unknown unless special studies to ascertain its amount are made at each work station. Ordinarily much of the time thus spent by skilled labor could be eliminated through the use of proper materials handling equipment, or at least the tasks could be performed by unskilled labor.

Simple changes in the arrangement of machinery that improve materials handling operations and keep machines under production can result in significant savings in operating cost without large investments in materials handling equipment. High-speed semiautomatic machines are frequently **slowed down** by such trivial matters as:

1. Improper stationing of machine operators.
2. Awkward positioning of materials, thereby occasioning unnecessary reaching.
3. Lack of coordination between production and shipment.
4. Irregular flow of materials brought to, and taken from, the machines.

In many cases hand operations can be entirely eliminated and manufacturing can be carried on exclusively by conveying the material automatically from operation to operation. In certain kinds of machinery, notably those for making incandescent lamps and for bottling beverages, roughly 90 percent of this goal has already been reached. This new science of manufacturing is called "automation," and it has already revolutionized many of the methods in manufacturing.

Portion of Payroll Spent for Materials Handling. The share of the wage dollar spent for materials handling has been variously estimated for certain different industries, the average figure generally used for all industries being 40 percent. Thus a very sizable percentage of the manufacturing plant's labor payroll is spent for materials handling alone. This expenditure adds nothing to the sales value of the product, and can price some products—or even entire plants—out of the market. Many executives who have been able to determine the total of their handling costs have found them far greater than expected. Once uncovered, those costs can often be slashed by a comparatively small investment in new materials handling equipment or in better utilization of the old equipment.

Labor is the most costly item in materials handling. A leading automobile manufacturer has been spending approximately $42,000,000 a year for materials handling labor alone. This cost amounts to about 30 percent of the plant's total labor cost—in a plant where mechanized handling has already undergone considerable development and application. The figure of 40 percent of the total labor payroll for materials handling labor alone in industry at large does not seem too much out of line when such a highly mechanized industry as that of automobile manufacture is spending 30 percent of its production dollar for its materials handling labor alone.

Remaining Sources of Major Savings. Cutting down the large proportion of the plant payroll expended in materials handling and instituting the revolutionary improvements that can be made in materials handling methods through the wide variety of materials handling equipment now available combine to offer industry a virtually unexplored opportunity for major cost reductions. By applying sound principles of materials handling analysis and plant layout engineering, this opportunity poses a tangible challenge to the progressiveness of present-day management.

No further major materials handling savings are foreseeable in the already highly developed techniques of the production machinery itself until the state of full automation is reached; that is, the stage where material will automatically be fed to and removed from these machines without the assistance of materials handling labor. In the meantime, only through the gradual mechanization of present forms of materials handling can management substantially lower plant operating costs.

Management often views materials handling as merely a nonproductive service and considers the purchase of mechanized handling equipment as being an unnecessary expense. An effective handling system need not be costly or elaborate. Most businesses can afford capital investments which pay for themselves within one or two years out of savings in operating costs—as frequently happens in materials handling modernization projects. The production of goods in large quantities for expanding markets, despite constantly rising wages and diminishing working hours, is made possible primarily by labor-aiding mechanical methods, on which the present standard of living is definitely based.

INFLUENCE ON MANUFACTURING CYCLE AND COSTS. Improved materials handling methods are consistently increasing production output and at the same time cutting costs. In the manufacture of an internal-combustion engine cylinder head, by way of illustration, from receipt of casting until assembly into the finished product, the total manufacturing cycle amounts to 121 standard hours for the 55 operations. Out of these operations only eight represent processing, the balance all being materials handling processes. In terms of time, processing amounts to 47 hours, representing just 39 percent of the total cycle. When individual materials handling operations can be eliminated or expedited, the manufacturing cycle can often be considerably shortened. Furthermore, when handling costs exceed processing costs, as illustrated in the representative case above, greater potential savings may exist in improving methods of handling than in simplifying machine operations.

Influence on Plant Inventories. Plant inventories can usually be held down to reasonable reserves of raw materials and semifinished and finished products when a plant has well-organized storage areas and has set up adequate records of raw, semifinished, and finished stocks. Close contact with both the plant storeroom on the one hand and the work in process and the finished-stock rooms on the other hand, can adequately protect against shortages.

MOVING MATERIALS, MEN, AND MACHINERY. To manufacture a product the three factors of materials, men, and machinery must be brought together before the fabrication operations can be performed. In some industries only one of these three factors is mobile and must therefore be brought to the other two, which occupy a fairly fixed position. In other industries two of the factors are mobile. Sometimes all three factors are mobile and must all be brought to the point where the product is to be processed and assembled. These various conditions are illustrated in Fig. 1.

Of all seven basic types of movement in industry (as shown in Fig. 1), the one which is the most prevalent in manufacturing, and the one which incurs the most material handling, is beyond question the first shown: **moving material** to men and machinery. In many ways the broad applications of this movement also exist in Type 6, where the two-factor movement of material and men to machinery characterizes the continuous transformation processes of distilling and refining. The main concern in the present case, however, is Type 1—hence the title "Materials Handling."

MOVEMENT OF MATERIAL, MEN, AND MACHINERY IN INDUSTRY

Basic Types of Movement	Factors Moved	Destination of Movement	Representative Industries
A. MOVEMENT OF ONE FACTOR			
1.	Material ⟶	{ Men / Machinery }	{ Metalworking / Woodworking }
2.	Men ⟶	{ Material / Machinery }	{ Gasworks / Waterworks }
3.	Machinery ⟶	{ Material / Men }	{ Railroad / Shipping }
B. MOVEMENT OF TWO FACTORS			
4.	{ Men / Machinery } ⟶	Material	{ Mining / Fishing }
5.	{ Material / Machinery } ⟶	Men	{ Garment homework / Bench assembly work }
6.	{ Material / Men } ⟶	Machinery	{ Distilling / Refining }
C. MOVEMENT OF THREE FACTORS			
7.	{ Material / Men / Machinery } ⟶	Product	{ Building construction / Shipbuilding / Farming }

Gaudreau, Rimbach & Associates

Fig. 1. Basic kinds of movement in manufacturing industries.

4·5

Mechanization of Processes and Materials Handling

MECHANIZED HANDLING. Since the beginning of the twentieth century, there have been three distinct turning points which have established the present revolution in industry through the application of mechanized handling. These three milestones are:

1. Henry Ford's mechanical conveyor assembly line in 1913.
2. The powering of trolley conveyors and industrial trucks in World War I.
3. The mechanization of materials handling in the functions of storage and shipping by the armed services during World War II.

Mechanizing Work in Process. There is a fourth milestone, which is still in the embryonic stage. It is the mechanization of materials handling on the shop floor while the work is in progress. This kind of handling accounts for approximately 75 percent of all materials handling costs in a plant, whereas storage and shipping account for the other 25 percent of plant handling costs. Within the next decade it is conceivable that this fourth stage in the present era of full mechanization may be attained, that is, **mechanized handling** as well as **mechanized processing** at the processing machines in many industries, commonly known as **automation.**

For the purpose of reducing the rising cost of handling material and of expediting the flow of material through the successive stages of manufacturing, various mechanical devices have been developed since 1920. A variety of some 300 major types of mechanical handling equipment are on the market, many of which have overlapping applications.

It is not always necessary to mechanize a handling operation so that costs may be reduced. Often a well-planned rearrangement of the plant layout uncovers savings which may be obtained without investing in materials handling equipment. A plant may be overconveyorized or overequipped to the point where the new equipment requires more additional maintenance cost than can be saved in materials handling cost. Such situations have developed in some plants largely as the result of the lack of a proper layout design, or of arbitrary decisions made under force of circumstances, or of well-intentioned but overzealous salesmanship by equipment suppliers' representatives.

DEVELOPMENT OF MASS PRODUCTION. Mass production as developed in the United States may be divided into three stages of development:

1. **Plant expansion.** In the first stage, industry built tremendous plants, designed enormous machines, and developed line-and-staff organizations to promote progressive expansion of operations under one roof.
2. **Processing methods.** In the second stage, attention was concentrated largely on improved methods of processing through the development of time and motion studies.
3. **Mechanized handling.** Now, in the third stage, emphasis is being placed on scientific methods of handling materials with the aid of mechanical devices.

High-Speed Processing but Antiquated Handling. Much has been written about the Industrial Revolution, which was ushered in on a practical scale with the factory system around 1840. Little has ever been said, however, about the fact that the mechanization of processing operations greatly outdistanced that of handling operations in the succeeding years. Yet, materials handling labor today accounts for roughly 40 percent of the labor payroll in manufacturing industries, in general.

Present-day automatic and semiautomatic machines are beginning to lose some of their superior production values because of the mounting problems of transporting materials to and from these highly developed fabricating units. Scarcely a processing or assembly operation is performed today that has not been minutely time-studied in terms of man-hours expressed in four decimal places. But this searching analysis, in most instances, seems to have completely bypassed materials handling operations, which amount in cost, as already indicated, to about 40 percent of a plant's wage dollar. In analyzing metalworking manufacturing operation costs, attention has been centered largely on such **machine operations** as milling, drilling, cutting, grinding, turning, finishing, stamping, and most kinds of assembly operations. Comparatively little thought has been given to materials handling operations such as picking up, laying down, lifting, carrying, reaching, feeding, hauling, moving, pushing, pulling, heaving, dragging, and storing.

Slow Acceptance of Mechanized Handling. Engineering design of materials handling equipment over the past fifty years has not lagged behind the improvement made on processing machinery. The deficiency in improving materials handling systems is attributable mainly to four basic weaknesses in industry's modernization programs as they existed before World War II, namely:

1. Unfamiliarity with the materials handling equipment available.
2. Lack of proper application of such equipment.
3. Failure to design the plant layout to permit this equipment to reduce or eliminate materials handling operations.
4. Neglect to mechanize the materials handling operations remaining after eliminating the unnecessary operations.

Little, if any, attempt was made to appraise these weaknesses and to make recommendations to overcome them. Nor were any improvements made in terms of specific measurements of the amount of materials handling work involved in manufacturing operations. Nor was a sound comparison made of operating costs and the relative savings obtainable through use of the different kinds of handling equipment recommended for the tasks to be performed. This haphazard, piecemeal approach to materials handling problems caused the hidden opportunities for reducing operating costs to be overlooked for a long time in many attempts at modernization.

Materials Handling in the Automobile Industry. Even though plant equipment mechanization did not begin to reach other industries until 1930, it began to expand rapidly in the automotive industry in 1915. It has been calculated that a 1947 automobile selling for $1,500 would have cost more than $50,000 if built with the tools in use forty years earlier. Walter Chrysler, well-known automobile manufacturer, once said that if his company discontinued the use of its conveyor systems alone, the manufacturing cost of the cars produced by the company would triple in amount.

Gains to be made by studies leading to organized mechanized flow of material in operational sequence, by the elimination of bottlenecks in this flow, by utilizing heretofore empty air space above shop floors and warehouse areas, and by expediting the travel time of material through the manufacturing cycle are of far greater importance than the gains to be made from further improvement in processing operations by merely installing new and faster process machinery. Attention has swung from the processing unit to the **handling unit** in an effort to keep the processing unit in continuous operation.

Analysis of Materials Handling Problems Through Planned Layouts

MAIN KINDS OF OVER-ALL PROCESS FLOWS IN A PLANT.
The movement of material to men and machinery in a plant may be made according to three plant-wide flows, namely:

1. **Job-lot flow.** This flow is in variable quantities at irregular times.
2. **Continuous flow.** In this case the flow is in uniform quantity on a steady basis.
3. **Combination flow.** The majority of plants have a job-lot flow in some departments and a simple, continuous flow in others.

These flows constitute the main kinds of over-all process flows in a manufacturing plant. All other side variations are usually subservient to the plant's main process flow.

Job-Lot Flow. In the job-lot, or intermittent, flow, material undergoes changes in size, shape, dimensions, and finish without losing its basic characteristics. Sheet steel, for example, may be stamped into different designs on punch presses, and bar stock may be fabricated into products such as roller bearings or motor shafts on screw machines. Metalworking plants and furniture factories are representative of industries laid out on the job-lot system.

Such plants may use many rather than few raw materials, which may often be the finished products of other plants. The type of plants using the job-flow system vary in size from the small machine shop up to the mass-production enterprise, as shown in the following:

1. **Small machine shop** with little or no assembly. Work moves in small lots from machine to machine according to the varying operation sequence of each lot.
2. **Between two departments** in a small plant where the foundry output is moved into a machining department, or where machining flows into assembly.
3. **From machine group to machine group** in mass-production plants. Often designated as **process control** or **functional method,** this flow signifies the movement of work from department to department. In plants so laid out, there may be a general rough-machining department, a general punch-press department, a general screw-machine department, a general buffing-and-plating department, an assembly department, etc. For years this was the generally accepted method of manufacture in the larger plants. It seemed to constitute the logical flow because it gave the greatest amount of production for the least number of productive machines. This method, however, introduces the need for **weighing, counting,** and **inspection** in each department coming under different supervision.

Continuous Flow. In the continuous, or product-basis, flow, raw materials flow consecutively through a series of machines or processes which are laid out to operate as a completely coordinated unit. These continuous processes may carry a standardized product from machine to machine through repetitive operations, or combine raw materials into a synthetic product, or break down a natural product into several finished products and by-products.

The continuous system is often organized by setting up small factories within the plant, each one making a certain product. A plant set up on a continuous-flow basis possesses many advantages in the handling of materials, notably in the

reduction in the distance traveled by the various parts. The three kinds of process flows falling into the category of continuous flow are as follows:

1. **From machine to machine** in mass-production industries. The high degree of work specialization in the automotive and other highly modernized metal-working industries requires extensive layout planning. This kind of flow is usually adopted for standardized products.
2. **Synthetic process** of combining ingredients from separate processing departments. This process is a continuous building up of several materials into products by successive processing operations, usually resulting in a product of characteristics different from those of the ingredients.
3. **Analytical process** of refining a material into one or more products finished separately. This process is a continuous refining or conversion of a basic material into one or more finished products or by-products.

Combination Flow. The process flow in the majority of plants is usually made up partly of a job-lot flow in some departments and a continuous flow in others, thus producing a combination flow. For example, a plant performing a number of different operations on a job-lot basis—such as on punch presses, screw machines, boring mills, etc.—on a variety of small metal parts may eventually move these parts to a plating department. In this department the parts flow through a continuous process of washing, rinsing, and plating. As they emerge from plating, the various parts may again be separated into job lots and moved as such to various finishing departments of the plant.

Decentralization of Continuous Operations. Few plants can justify the setting up of a number of separate, complete processing units, such as, for example, plating or heat-treating units. Many plants, however, today install a number of separate washing units and spray-painting booths, the operations of which for many years were considered more efficient when centralized in one spot.

New and more effective equipment has often made it possible to decentralize certain departments and distribute the equipment at strategic points in order to eliminate the transportation of all the work to the one area. Such decentralized equipment units may be located close to either the preceding or succeeding operation in order to eliminate the former handling of material between departments.

Plant Layout as the Key to Materials Handling Problems

PLANT LAYOUT APPROACH TO MATERIALS HANDLING. Until such time as materials handling problems are analyzed and solved by means of a thorough engineering approach, and plant layouts are designed from factual information derived from this approach, many plants may continue to handle thousands of tons of material unnecessarily each day. Throughout planning, the plant layout engineer must keep foremost in his mind the axiom that the time required and distance traveled in the course of manufacturing a product directly affect its cost of production.

In many plant layouts primary consideration is given to the proper integrating of manufacturing processes, while only secondary attention is paid to the requirements of receiving, shipping, and warehousing operations. Such layouts are found to be impractical in actual operation because of delays, confusion, "bottlenecks," and excessive rehandling occurring at the receiving and shipping ends of the plant. The flow of materials through the plant should be the core of the entire plant layout, and there must be both an intake and an outlet at strategic points if a smooth internal flow is to exist. All materials flowing through processing and assembling operations must pass through first the receiving and finally the shipping ends of the plant. These two areas require the same careful study while making a plant layout as that given to the process flow itself.

In a plant where the **layout has been properly arranged,** either before or after the plant was built, many of the materials handling requirements may have been altered or minimized. What remains of materials handling operations is usually that portion which could not justifiably be eliminated in the course of layout planning. For this reason, materials handling may be considered as being, in part, a **by-product or offshoot problem of plant layout.** A first step in analyzing a materials handling situation is, therefore, to make a close analysis of the plant layout.

Influence on Production Planning. Production planners in a certain plant manufacturing electric power motors get an over-all, integrated view of all flows of material through the entire 2,238,000 sq. ft. of production floor area on a mural plant layout board. Measuring 11 ft. × 24 ft., the board shows every storage area, machine, production line, material-flow line, aisle, conveyor, and crane in the plant. This exhibit clearly reveals unnecessary handling, backtracking of material, excessive distances in material travel, and possibilities of mechanizing handling as production lines are being shifted to meet changing requirements. Because of the influence of materials handling on production planning, plant layout engineers analyze the materials handling requirements before they decide on the ultimate plant design.

Integrated Materials Handling. Executives in many cases fail to realize the necessity for a broad materials handling program that cuts across all operational functions. Still fewer recognize that the responsibility for carrying out this program must be fixed at the management level. Integrated materials handling requires close **supervision.** It cannot be left to the discretion of the various departments and cannot be expected to function haphazardly; instead, it requires continuous attention.

The responsibility for developing a modern materials handling program could be vested in the hands of a **transportation manager** responsible for the handling and movement of materials throughout the plant. This plan would help to avoid the overlapping and duplication which are so often found in a job of "face lifting" in plant operations. If a transportation manager is assigned to report directly to the production manager, he can give the same degree of emphasis to materials handling as has been given in the past to inventory control, work scheduling, tooling, and supplies—all of which are related functions of production control.

Future Opportunities in Materials Handling. During the past few years, many equipment manufacturers have developed, and are now building, numerous kinds of materials handling equipment to meet many different handling needs of industry and transportation, and to reduce handling costs. The conclusion of these equipment manufacturers, as well as of the industries they serve, is that the surface has merely been scratched regarding what can be done in materials handling.

The materials handling engineer has one of the most important jobs in modern industry, with great responsibility for all productive materials and inventories within the plant. To meet this extensive responsibility, he should have complete authority to receive, transport, store, package, and ship his company's materials and products, using the most modern equipment and methods available. It is his responsibility to maintain an ever-constant flow of material from the time it enters the plant until it leaves in the form of finished products. He can improve the company's methods and procedures of both internal and external materials handling, and on the basis of knowledge and experience he can improve his own activities. In many cases a capable materials handling engineer can mean the difference between profit and loss.

Laying the Foundation for a Handling Modernization Program

TRACING THE OVER-ALL FLOW OF MATERIAL.

In making a diagnosis of the materials handling conditions in a plant, the flow of material should be traced from the point where raw materials are received; followed through all storage points, processing operations, and assembly; and not terminated until the flow has reached the point of outgoing shipments of finished products. The course so obtained provides an over-all flow from which an integrated, plant-wide materials handling program can be developed. Not until this over-all flow has been fully determined should it be broken down into individual projects.

Piecemeal attack permits only of substitutions of one materials handling method for another within a limited section of the plant or warehouse. Any one of countless specific improvements can be made in existing materials handling methods with temporary justification. Unfortunately, a great many so-called improvements have at times been made hastily in this manner by simply substituting new materials handling devices for existing equipment or for manual methods, all in limited areas. As time went on, it was discovered that these new pieces of equipment, although admirably suited for a specific department at the time of purchase, did not lend themselves to interdepartmental coordination of flow or to interchange of use. Furthermore, the piecemeal development was found to have denied the plant the much larger savings attainable under an over-all coordinated materials handling system.

Because of the endless ramifications which exist in materials handling operations throughout a plant, the materials handling modernization program should be developed for a coordinated over-all process flow **without limitations of departmental lines.**

Once a modernization movement gets under way in a plant, the temptation soon develops to install more mechanical equipment than is actually needed. A given materials handling device may improve only one part of a plant-wide process. When too many such devices are installed, a plant becomes a mass of machines, requiring a crew of mechanics for maintenance alone. Sometimes more of these mechanics are needed than the number of materials handlers who have been transferred to other jobs since the introduction of mechanization.

To guard against overmechanization through piecemeal changes, it behooves management to pattern its materials handling improvements from a **plant-wide process-flow study.** Through such an over-all program, a plant is most likely to achieve larger and more permanent savings in its materials handling costs.

Preplanning by a Leading Electric Appliance Manufacturer. Case histories of successful modernization programs launched in leading industries invariably possess one characteristic in common, namely, **over-all preplanning.** These programs have usually been preceded by exhaustive studies of plant layouts and complete process flows, such as are described in the following case example.

When it became apparent to a leading electric appliance manufacturing company that its production of washing machines had to be moved to a new site, a preliminary survey of the flow of products to be handled and of the layout of the building to be occupied was conducted. This survey clearly revealed that scientific preplanning of potential materials handling problems in the over-all process flows would yield significant economies. Accordingly, it was decided to lay out the building with just as much emphasis on economical materials handling as on the placement of production machines and equipment.

Approach Made by a Tractor Manufacturer. When a leading farm-tractor manufacturing company began studying its supply lines and the problem of improving mechanical handling, an initial survey was made of plant-wide process flows. Following this preview, the company decided to make an exhaustive study of its entire materials handling problem. It was decided to defer the purchase of any and all materials handling equipment until specific recommendations for an over-all program could be made. Six months' time was taken to complete this study and to formulate the foundation for a modern mechanized handling program.

Materials Handling Charts, Layouts, and Diagrams

BASIC DATA FOR A MATERIALS HANDLING PROJECT. A check list of the various factors to be considered in developing a materials handling project is given in Fig. 2. The four main categories of factors consist of:

1. Material and container (in upper left-hand box).
2. Equipment operating cost (in upper right-hand box).
3. Building characteristics (in the next box below). It is in this category that most of the factors of physical building limitations are encountered; these can largely be overcome by proper engineering in the plant layout.
4. Handling activity and cost analysis (in lower half of chart).

All the factors that affect materials handling are fundamentally related to plant layout. The facts revealed by this check list should be analyzed and coordinated as accurately as the basic data that determine machine loads and processing sequences. The application of these basic data is demonstrated later in the section.

Area Allocation Diagram for Developing Materials Flow. The chart presented in Fig. 3 is a schematic plan of preliminary allocations of area and of work flows through a plant. It is primarily a basic guide for determining the logical relationships of departments. It also provides an outline of the flow of materials and products through these departments. The ultimate use of materials flow charts is to develop this area-allocation diagram, as shown in Fig. 3. This diagram is a preliminary allocation of floor areas to the various departments and manufacturing activities involved.

The usual practice is to trace on this rough schematic diagram a graphic flow line of the product through the plant. The diagram itself is only a guide for planning the actual plant layout, and it does not contain any detailed machinery or equipment data. When the proper plant-wide flow has been determined, this rough diagram of plant areas serves as the nucleus from which the floor layouts may be planned.

EXISTING PLANT LAYOUT OF A FOUNDRY AND MACHINE SHOP. The over-all flow of material through a plant is illustrated on the floor plan shown in Fig. 4, which presents the actual plant layout of a foundry and machine shop. The various courses followed by the material through this foundry and machine shop are traced by heavy flow lines superimposed on the layout drawing. As indicated in boxed numerals, the flow shows:

1. Incoming raw materials (in top right section).
2. Dispersion of material through work in process (in center, near bottom).
3. Outgoing shipments (in top left section).

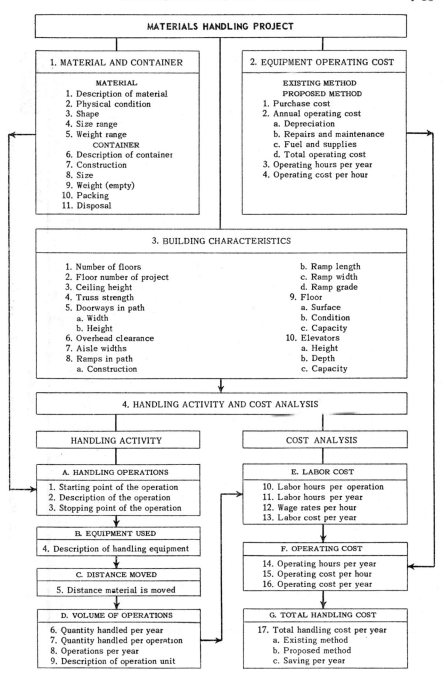

Fig. 2. Analysis of a materials handling project.

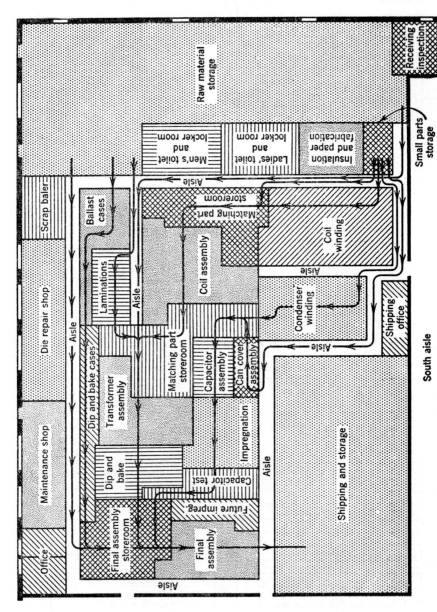

Fig. 3. Plan of preliminary area allocation and product flow through a plant.

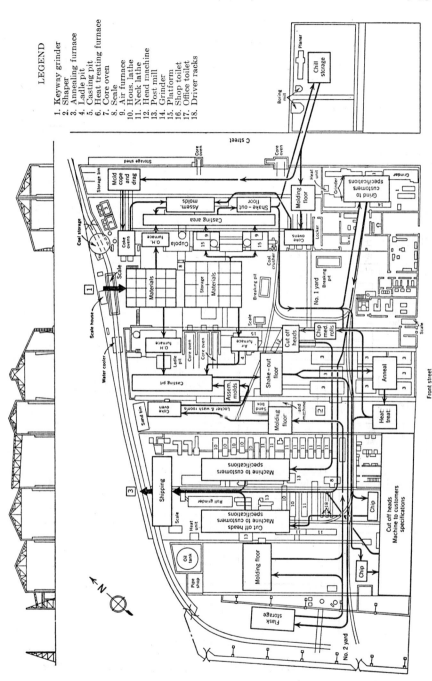

LEGEND

1. Keyway grinder
2. Shaper
3. Annealing furnace
4. Ladle pit
5. Casting pit
6. Heat treating furnace
7. Core oven
8. Scale
9. Air furnace
10. Hous. lathe
11. Neck lathe
12. Head machine
13. Post mill
14. Grinder
15. Platform
16. Shop toilet
17. Office toilet
18. Driver racks

Fig. 4. Layout diagram of a foundry and machine shop.

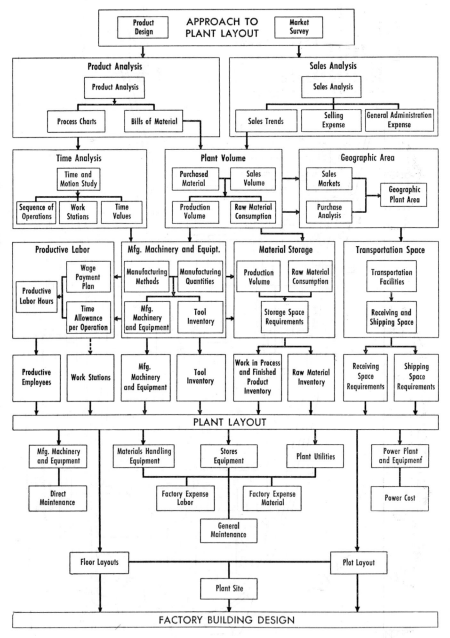

Fig. 5. Diagram of a plant layout integrating plant-wide handling.

This plant-wide plan provides the basis for integrating and shortening the existing flow lines. It also points to those areas where backtracking, lengthy travels, and roundabout paths offer obvious opportunities for improvement in materials handling activities.

Along the top margin of this plan are the elevations of the various adjoining buildings included in this layout. These elevation sketches show truss clearances and column supports for cranes, monorails, and overhead conveyors. They also show the obstructions caused by intervening walls as the material progresses from receiving dock to shipping platform.

Evolution of a Plant Layout Integrating Plant-wide Handling. The analysis of an existing plant layout or the planning of an entirely new project entails a succession of ideas and considerations originating in practically all the departments of an organization. This concept is graphically illustrated in Fig. 5. Because of the broad range of separate management activities affected by plant layout, the inefficiency of a layout is usually not so obvious to the average operating executive as to a trained observer.

At the root of the plant layout are the **product design** from the engineering department and the **market survey** of the product from the sales department. The product design forms the basis for developing **process charts** from which methods studies are made to determine the kind and sequence of processing operations, expressed in time values. These **methods studies,** in turn, lead to the selection of proper machinery and equipment suitable for the desired production volume. The production volume, on the other hand, is based upon the sales volume, as determined from the sales trends. These sales volumes are indicated in the **sales analysis** made from the market survey. The sales analysis marks the second of the two starting points in the evolution from product design to the point preparatory to the selection of machinery for carrying on manufacturing.

Manufacturing methods form the basis for determining the proper wage-payment plan, which, coupled with the time allowance per operation, determines the number of productive employees and **work stations** required in the plant layout. Paralleling this development, the similarly **interrelated factors** of geographic location, material storage requirements, and receiving and shipping space to be provided are determined. Other correlating information, such as quantity and size of necessary **inventories** of tools, raw materials, work in process, and finished products, is also required.

The manufacturing layout proper does not begin until all these factors have been carefully weighed and reconciled. Failure to reconcile all these factors **before shuffling templates or models** on the floor plan accounts for the ineffectiveness of many layouts. Planning a plant layout is thus something more than the widespread conception of merely positioning templates or scale models of machinery and equipment within wall boundaries on a floor plan.

Functional Chart for a Plant Layout Organization in Headquarters. The entire field of plant layout engineering, as it applies within a national manufacturing organization, is broken down in the chart shown in Fig. 6 into 73 key activities grouped into five major sections, namely, survey section, planning section, field section, layout section, and drafting section. These 73 activities provide an indication of the scope of preparation necessary in layout work alone before an integrated materials handling system can be developed from existing or projected production and handling requirements.

Mural Layout Boards of Different Departments in a Materials Flow. When a number of material flows of different departments and areas are being

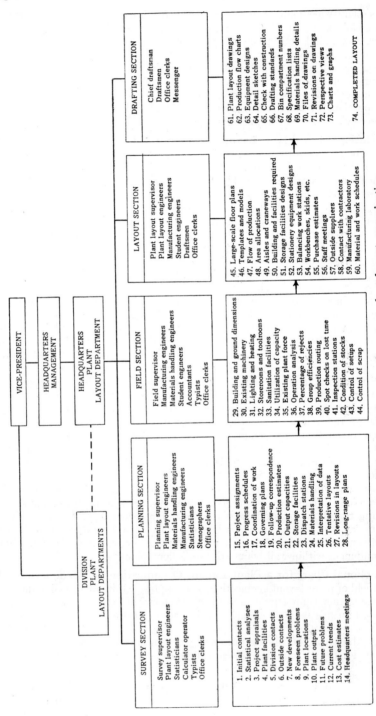

Fig. 6. Functional chart for a headquarters plant layout organization.

used to coordinate plant-wide flows, the layouts are frequently placed on boards which can be mounted on walls for convenience of reference. To facilitate the use of large numbers of such layout drawings, the boards on which these drawings are mounted may be affixed to one or several walls. This arrangement provides uninterrupted continuity from one layout board to another. Layout engineers use these mural boards to plan machinery and equipment layouts and to develop integrated materials flow plans.

Three-dimensional Scale Models. In making alternate rearrangements of departments, machine groupings, and material flow lines representing the layout of specific portions of an existing plant, the construction of miniature models of the projects has become a widely accepted **medium of presentation.** These models give the nontechnical men as well as the engineers a fair opportunity to visualize the project in a realistic way and to offer constructive suggestions as to improved layouts. Additional floors or buildings, and rearrangements of existing facilities, are often set up on this kind of planning model years ahead of actual construction.

For purposes of discussion at conferences, entire floor layouts from any of the building's models may be lifted intact and carried to the conference room. Each of these floor layouts is fully equipped with scale models of machinery and equipment placed in proper position according to the plant layout and the flow of material under an integrated plant-wide plan. Individual sections of these floors can be removed and brought to the conference room when it is not convenient to use the entire model or when the complete model is kept at some other plant.

Physical Survey of Materials Handling Projects

MAIN STEPS IN DEVELOPING A MATERIALS HANDLING PROJECT. Among the main successive stages of development common to most materials handling projects are the following survey points:

1. Recognizing the problem.
2. Tracing test flows of material.
3. Studying the building limitations.
4. Analyzing the handling activity.
5. Selecting the handling equipment.
6. Determining the total handling cost and savings.

For the purpose of analyzing and solving handling problems, this sequence of survey points brings into focus the intangible as well as the physical and economic factors and provides a basis for the formulation of final recommendations.

Understanding the Problem. A preliminary review of the operating conditions surrounding a materials handling problem usually discloses that certain handling activities require the use of improved methods. The manual handling of incoming materials should be analyzed at the stages of receiving, unloading, delivery to storage, and piling in storage in order to determine the possibilities for handling by power equipment. The delivery of materials from storage to production operations, and thence through processing, brings up possibilities of handling improvements during such operations as work positioning at the machines, setup time, flow from operation to operation, storage of work in process, movement from machining to assembly, scrap disposal, and storage and shipping of finished products.

Unsuitability and inefficiency of existing handling equipment often hold the key to the handling problem. A telltale criterion frequently exists in a **cost**

analysis made to determine the number of man-hours required in handling materials by skilled direct labor and by service labor. The existence of major potential economies in materials handling costs may go undetected for years until trained observers and analysts undertake the task of reviewing the current operating conditions. Unless soundly analyzed and planned, the solutions proposed may lead to false economies by giving rise to overlooked **hidden costs** well in excess of the more obvious savings claimed in direct costs.

Tracing Test Flows of Material. One of the most practical ways of discovering hidden problems in materials handling operations is to select representative items of raw materials for test flows through the plant. Such items may be bar stock or sheet metal in a metalworking plant, bales of rags or rolls of paper in a paper-mill, or logs of wood in a furniture factory.

As each such selected item goes through processing operations, its progress should be followed and recorded at every handling, movement, and point of stoppage, including machining and assembly operations, inspection points, and packing and shipping procedures. The observations should not end until the material reaches the point where the resultant finished product has been loaded and properly braced inside an outbound car, truck, ship, or airplane. Not until this over-all flow has been fully traced and recorded should it be broken down into piecemeal projects.

Studying the Building Limitations. Upon receipt of a request to analyze a materials handling problem, the materials handling engineer needs a set of drawings that show the construction of the building. He should start with these drawings in order to familiarize himself with the **structural characteristics** of the building in which the handling problem has arisen. Every square foot of floor space involved should be studied before final plans are prepared. The location of the floor in question and its surface condition and load-bearing capacity should be ascertained. Aisle widths, ramp construction, overhead clearances, ceiling heights, and walls and doorways should likewise be clearly noted on these drawings. Structural obstructions in the path of material travel may be a deciding factor in the ultimate selection of suitable handling devices.

Where the operations concerned extend into more than one building a plot plan of the plant premises should also be consulted. This plan will provide the engineer with information about relative locations of the structures and distances between buildings. It is also advisable for the engineer to secure building construction drawings and details plus a detailed plant layout of the operating area being studied. This plant layout should show the exact location of all machines and the flow of material from machine to machine, thus providing the engineer with the exact **geographical factors** of the existing layout.

Analyzing the Handling Activity. For the purpose of properly analyzing the handling activity under consideration, a **survey form** covering all the materials handling operations in the existing method should be prepared, as well as a similar form for the proposed method, as shown in Fig. 10. One or more lines should be allotted across the form for each operation. The columns on this form should begin with an identification number for each operation and continue across the sheet to show the starting point of the operation, description of the operation, its stopping point, the distance traveled, the number of pieces handled per year and the number per handling, the number of operations per year, and a description of the handling-operation unit, such as a piece, a trip, a load, etc. This information provides the physical data forming the basis for calculating the handling costs and the projected savings.

Selecting the Handling Equipment. For each materials handling operation involved in analyzing a given handling activity, another set of columns should be provided on the previously mentioned survey form for the determination of the resultant **equipment operating cost**, as shown in Fig. 9. These columns might carry such information as equipment description and purchase cost and total equipment operating cost per year for the particular equipment used for each operation. This cost usually includes depreciation, maintenance, power, fuel, and supplies, but does not cover any labor.

Determining the Total Handling Cost and Savings. A final set of columns on the survey form (see Fig. 10) may contain the following data for the purpose of determining the total handling cost for each existing and each proposed handling operation:

1. Labor hours per operation and per year.
2. Wage rates per hour to enable calculation of labor cost per year.
3. Equipment operating hours per year to determine equipment operating cost per year.

The addition of labor cost to equipment cost yields total handling cost per year for each operation. Finally, the total handling cost per year for all the operations in the existing method, when compared with the total cost of the handling operations for the proposed method, indicates the prospective annual saving anticipated under the proposed method through use of the equipment recommended.

Basic Data for a Materials Handling Project. The various factors to be considered in developing a materials handling project, from both a physical and an economic standpoint have been shown in Fig. 2. The 42 factors listed here fall into the following four major categories:

1. **Material and container** (11 factors). This category covers mainly the description, size, and weight of the merchandise handled and of the package or container in which it is received and stored, Such information is needed for each significant commodity or line carried in stock in order to select the most suitable equipment and storage racks or other facilities.
2. **Equipment operating cost** (4 factors). The savings to be realized from different kinds of materials handling equipment can be determined only by a comparison of operating costs under the existing method with those estimated under a proposed method. These data are also helpful when analyzing and deciding on the amount of investment justifiable for new equipment.
3. **Building characteristics** (10 factors). The structural characteristics of the building itself will greatly influence the selection of the proper kind of mechanical equipment most suitable for handling the material. Ceiling heights, floor-load capacities, and structural obstacles all have a significant bearing on the mechanization of handling operations.
4. **Handling activity and cost analysis** (17 factors). Under "Handling Activity" are the four subdivisions of handling operations, equipment used, distance moved, and volume of operations. "Cost Analysis" is then expressed in terms of labor cost, operating cost of equipment, and total handling cost. With all these factors properly analyzed, significant potential savings may be revealed, and the risk of making an improper investment in equipment is generally greatly reduced.

Tables of Data on Buildings, Materials, and Equipment. Perhaps the quickest way to visualize the application of these factors in actual practice is to demonstrate their use in the case example of an actual problem which calls most of these factors into play. This schedule, shown in Figs. 7, 8, 9, and 10, illustrates some of the tables of basic data for a specific materials handling problem. Expressed in terms of statistical tables, the basic data required in approaching the problem are illustrated on this schedule. The first three tables shown here consist of:

1. **Building characteristics.** The information in Fig. 7 is needed to determine what the structural strength of the building can support in the way of new materials handling equipment and what structural alterations might become necessary to permit the proper modernization of handling methods.
2. **Material and container.** The data in Fig. 8 specify the type and size of loads being carried in the materials handling operations involved in the project.
3. **Equipment operating cost.** Information on the equipment operating cost (Fig. 9), covers data on the existing materials handling equipment, consisting of a fork truck and a tractor. The project at hand calls for the acquisition of an overhead conveyor at a purchase cost of $23,000. The annual operating cost of each piece of equipment takes into account depreciation, repairs and maintenance, power and fuel, and supplies. Based on 4,000 operating hr. per yr., the operating cost per hour is determined in the last column. The overhead conveyor in this case will cost $1.01 per operating hour for the equipment alone, in addition to which the labor cost must be included.

NUMBER OF FLOORS ___3___ FLOOR NO. OF PROJECT ___1___

CEILING HEIGHT ___20 ft.___ TRUSS STRENGTH ___Not involved___

DOORWAYS IN PATH OF TRAVEL ___None___

WIDTH:

HEIGHT:

OVERHEAD CLEARANCE: ___14 ft.___ AISLE WIDTHS: MIN: ___12'___ MAX: ___15'___

RAMP CONSTRUCTION: ___None___ LENGTH: ___ WIDTH: ___ GRADE: ___ %

FLOOR SURFACE: ___Cement___ CONDITION: ___Smooth___ CAPACITY: ___(Ground)___ LBS.

ELEVATOR: WIDTH: ___None___ HEIGHT: ___ DEPTH: ___ CAPACITY: ___ LBS.

Fig. 7. Building characteristics.

DESCRIPTION OF MATERIAL: ___Steel Tanks___

PHYSICAL CONDITION (Fragile, Wet, Explosive, etc.): ___Painted___

SHAPE: ___Basically round, with protrusions___

SIZE RANGE: ___12" diam. × 24" long to 22" diam. × 42" long___

WEIGHT RANGE: ___20 to 130 lb.___

CONTAINER (Box, Carton, Keg, Reel, Roll, etc.): ___Pallet___ CONSTRUCTION: ___Wooden___

SIZE OF CONTAINER: ___48" × 66"___ WT. OF EMPTY CONTAINER: ___70 lb.___

CONTAINER PACKING (No. of Pieces and Total Wt.): ___7 tanks, 22" diam.: 20 tanks, 12" diam.___

DISPOSAL OF EMPTY CONTAINERS: ___By power trucks and trailers___

Fig. 8. Material and container.

DESCRIPTION OF EQUIPMENT (D)	Purchase Cost of Equipment (a)	ANNUAL OPERATING COST					COSTING RATE	
		Depreciation (b)	Repairs and Maintenance (c)	Power and Fuel (d)	Supplies (e)	Total Operating Cost (f)	Operating Hours per Year (g) (2 shifts)	Cost per Hour (T)
5-A. EXISTING EQUIPMENT								
Fork lift truck	$5,600	$560	$480	$1,060	$180	$2,280	4,000	$.57
Tractor	4,500	450	360	570	100	1,480	4,000	.37
5-B. PROPOSED ADDITIONAL EQUIPMENT								
Overhead conveyor	$23,000	$2,300	$1,200	$240	$300	$4,040	4,000	$1.01

Fig. 9. Equipment operating cost.

Identification and Structural Data for a Project

BASIC FACTORS IN MATERIALS HANDLING. From a practical standpoint, the six groups of basic factors to be analyzed in developing a materials handling project fall into two principal categories, as follows:

A. IDENTIFICATION DATA	B. MEASUREMENT FACTORS
Remaining fixed for all handling operations in a project.	Varying with each handling operation making up a project.
1. Materials handling project (Fig. 10).	4. Handling activity (Fig. 10).
2. Building characteristics (Fig. 7).	5. Equipment operating cost (Fig. 9).
3. Material and container (Fig. 8).	6. Total handling cost and savings (Fig. 10).

By using this approach, the varying factors of production quantity and handling cost may be developed into a sound basis for determining the best handling method to fit a particular project.

Identification Data for a Project. The three groups in category A, "Identification Data," as shown in Figs. 7, 8, 9, and 10, apply in general to all the various handling operations constituting a process-flow or handling problem.

In companies operating several manufacturing divisions in different cities, or in plants with several process and assembly departments on the premises, or in small plants handling job lots running into several weeks of continuous production, materials handling projects arise at various times. Each project should therefore be clearly identified at the outset for future reference whenever similar problems arise. Furthermore, materials handling statistics soon become meaningless unless directly identified with a specific project. The identification of the materials handling project should invariably be made clear in the file of work papers developed for the project.

Building Characteristics. In an existing plant it is of primary importance to study the **structural limitations** of the building involved before proceeding too far afield with the development of the handling methods for a given process, or even for a single materials handling problem. Ceilings, walls, doorways, aisles, ramps, floors, superstructures, and elevators limit to a large extent the handling alternatives which may be considered for a project, as shown in Fig. 7.

Material and Container. The material flowing through a given process frequently covers a range of sizes and weights for a specific type of product or for a specific class of products. This material may be handled in containers (as illustrated in Fig. 8), in which case the material and the container combined become the item to be handled. When the containers have reached the end of their function in a process flow, the empty containers themselves present a handling problem in returning them to the starting point for reuse.

Equipment Operating Costs. To have control over the activities of equipment operation, it is advisable to keep records of the cost of operation of the many kinds of mobile equipment used in the plant. The form already shown in Fig. 9 indicates how such information can be recorded for reference and control purposes.

Measurement Factors. A process usually involves a number of separate handling operations in transporting a product from one location to another for further processing. For example, in the comparatively simple flow of transporting small steel tanks from machining to assembly, the following eight handling operations may be encountered as shown in Fig. 10:

1. Load trailers.
2. Transport trailers.
3. Unload trailers.
4. Stack pallet loads.

5. Unstack pallet loads.
6. Transport pallet loads.
7. Unload pallets.
8. Return empty trailers.

The distances, quantities, frequencies, and comparative handling costs of these various handling operations vary considerably with different types of handling devices. It is therefore of paramount importance to evaluate the cost of material movement on alternative types of devices before arriving at recommended handling methods in a project. The three groups of basic variable factors which must be duly weighed and synchronized in a project are as follows:

1. Handling activity.
2. Equipment operating cost.
3. Total handling cost and savings.

The factors included in these three groups of measurement factors are discussed in detail under "Economic Factors To Be Considered" and illustrated in Figs. 10 and 12.

BASIC FACTORS OF HANDLING ACTIVITY AND MECHANICAL REQUIREMENTS. As previously indicated, the first of the three groups falling into the category of Measurement Factors is identified as "Handling Activity." This is the group of factors which includes the mechanical requirements of a materials handling project. The principal functions served by each of the five factors making up this particular group will now be considered briefly.

1. **Volume handled per year.** A fairly reliable gage of the volume of activity of handling to be considered is frequently best obtained by using a period of time which is sufficiently long to span the four seasons of the year. In other words, the volume of materials handled is usually best measured in terms of a period covering the last twelve months for which the information is available, regardless of which is the first month of that span. This information should be expressed in quantities of pieces or units handled per year, units per ton, and tons handled. This volume also should be identified by the number of working days per year for each material item under study.

2. **Travel speeds.** The statistics on volume handled per year provide a sound basis for determining the handling volume per working day, per operating hour, and per minute. These figures form the basis for determining the average rate of speed at which the material must travel on its path through the manufacturing cycle.

3. **Carrier trips.** When material is transported from one place to another on mobile handling equipment such as industrial trucks, flatcars, or cranes along the line of production, the precise load carried and frequency of trips must be known if the proper kind of carrier is to be selected. For this purpose it is necessary to determine the quantity of material items handled per carrier, such as the number of newsprint rolls on an industrial truck or flatcar. The number of carriers per trip, such as the number of flatcars per shunt, also must be known. Lastly, data on the number of carrier trips per day, such as car trips or crane trips, are likewise necessary for subsequent calculations.

PROJECT NUMBER _____ S-3164 _____

MATERIALS

DIVISION ___Tank___   WORKS ___Cleveland___   COMPILED BY ___C. L. n.___

BUILDING NUMBER __8__   SECTION NUMBER __B-30__   DATE COMPILED __6/12/X2__

PROBLEM AND OBJECTIVES: Transportation of 188% increase in volume of steel tanks to assembly

HANDLING ACTIVITY

	HANDLING OPERATIONS			EQUIPMENT USED	DISTANCE	VOLUME OF	
Operation Number	Starting Point (A)	Handling Operation (B)	Stopping Point (C)	Materials Handling Equipment (D)	Distance Moved (E)	Quantity of Pieces Per Year (F) ÷	Per Oper. (G)
							EXISTING
1	Floor	Load trailers	Trailer	Trailer (12 pcs.)	30'	125,591	1
2	Bay F-20	Transpt. trailers	Bay A-90	2 trls., 1 tractor	1,630'	125,591	24
3	Buggy	Unload trailers	Pallet	Pallet (7 pieces)	5'	125,591	1
4	Floor	Stack pallets	6-7 high	Fork lift truck	50'	125,591	7
5	6-7 high	Unstack pallets	Floor	Fork lift truck	50'	125,591	7
6	Bay A-90	Transport pallets	Bay B-30	Fork lift truck	1,020'	125,591	14
7	Pallet	Unload pallets	Floor	None	10'	125,591	1
8	Bay A-90	Return trailers	Bay F-20	2 trls., 1 tractor	1,630'	125,591	24
		Actual Totals—Year, 19X1			4,425'	125,591	1
							FORECASTED
		Forecasted Totals — Year, 19X4			4,425'	362,400	1
							PROPOSED
1	Roller conv.	Load conveyor	Ovhd. conv.	Rope hoist	10'	362,400	1
2	Bay F-20	Transport pieces	Assy. stores	Ovhd. conveyor	600'	362,400	1
3	Ovhd. conv.	Unload conveyor	Pallet	Pallet (7 pieces)	10'	362,400	1
4	Floor	Stack pallets	6-7 high	Fork lift truck	50'	362,400	7
5.	6-7 high	Unstack pallets	Floor	Fork lift truck	50'	362,400	7
6	Assy. stores	Transport pieces	Bay B-30	Ovhd. conveyor	50'	362,400	1
7	Pallet	Load conveyor	Ovhd. conv.	None	6'	329,800	1
8	Bay F-20	Transport pallets	Bay A-32	Fork lift truck	300'	32,600	14
9	Palt. or con.	Unload pieces	Floor	Rope hoist	10'	362,400	1
10	Bay A-32	Return pallets	Assy. stores	Fork lift truck	300'	32,600	42
		Forecasted Totals — Year, 19X4			1,386'	362,400	1
						SAVING (')	MINUS (")
		Total Saving			3,039'		
		Percent Saving			69%		

Fig. 10. Typical handling activity and

HANDLING PROJECT

REVISED BY ____ ᵟC. ____   APPROVED BY ____ J.B.S. ____

DATE REVISED ____ 7/15/X2 ____   DATE APPROVED ____ 7/28/X2 ____

HANDLING COST AND SAVINGS

OPERATIONS		LABOR COST				OPERATING COST			TOTAL COST
Number of Operations per Year = (H)	Operation Unit (K) ×	Labor Hours per Operation (M)	Labor Hours per Year = (N)	Wage Rate per Hour × (P)	Labor Cost per Year = (R)	Operating Hours per Year (S) ×	Operating Cost Per Hour (T)*	Per Year = (U)	Total Handling Cost per Year (V)
METHOD (')						(N')			(R' + U')
125,591	Pieces	.018	2,261	$ .90	$ 2,035	None	None	None	$ 2,035
5,233	Trips	.460	2,407	.90	2,167	2,407	$ .37	$ 891	3,058
125,591	Pieces	.018	2,261	.90	2,035	None	None	None	2,035
17,942	Loads	.063	1,130	.90	1,017	1,130	.57	644	1,661
17,942	Loads	.063	1,130	.90	1,017	1,130	.57	644	1,661
8,971	Trips	.254	2,279	.90	2,051	2,279	.57	1,299	3,350
125,591	Pieces	.018	2,261	.90	2,035	None	None	None	2,035
5,233	Trips	.460	2,407	.90	2,167	2,407	.37	891	3,058
125,591	Pieces	(.1285)	16,136	$ .90	$14,524	9,353	($.467)	$4,369	$18,893
ACTIVITY (')						(.0745	Operating hours per piece)		
362,400	Pieces	(.1285)	46,568	$1.08	$50,293	26,999	($.467)	$12,609	$62,902
METHOD (")						(N")			(R" + U")
362,100	Pieces	.010	3,624	$1.08	$ 3,914	None	None	None	$ 3,914
362,400	Pieces	None	None	None	None	3,624	$1.01	$3,673	3,673
362,400	Pieces	.010	3,624	1.08	3,914	None	None	None	3,914
51,771	Loads	.063	3,262	1.08	3,523	3,262	.57	1,859	5,382
51,771	Loads	.063	3,262	1.08	3,523	3,262	.57	1,859	5,382
362,400	Pieces	None	None	None	None	737	1.01	744	744
329,800	Pieces	.004	1,319	1.08	1,425	None	None	None	1,425
2,329	Trips	.180	419	1.08	453	419	.57	239	692
362,400	Pieces	.008	2,899	1.08	3,130	None	None	None	3,130
776	Trips	.180	140	1.08	151	140	.57	80	231
362,400	Pieces	(.0512)	18,549	$1.08	$20.033	11,444	($.739)	$8,454	$28,487
IN PROPOSED METHOD									(W)
			28,019		$30,260	15,555		$4,155	$34,415
			60%		60%	58%		33%	55%

*See Fig. 9.

handling cost and savings data form.

4. **Distance traveled.** Information such as the following is useful in regard to distance traveled:

   a. Number of carriers moved per day.
   b. Number of feet traveled per round trip.
   c. Number of carrier-miles per day.
   d. Number of carrier-trips per hour.
   e. Number of carrier-miles per hour.

This set of statistics gages the kind of equipment best suited for carrying the stipulated loads of material over given distances to keep up with the rate of production and shipping. This information is particularly important when the mill or plant operates on more shifts than do the shipping warehouses.

5. **Lifting operations.** When unit loads of material must be stacked in temporary storage and later detiered for shipping purposes, the amount of lifting and lowering of material should be measured. This information is needed to determine the amount of crane time or truck time and attendant labor effort involved for these functions alone, apart from the traveling operations.

When these five factors of handling activity have been duly analyzed, a determination of the **relative economic advantages** of the crane, conveyor, industrial truck, or other handling device can then be made for each handling stage along the plant-wide flow of material.

6. **Equipment work loads.** The basic data secured in the foregoing set of five major factors set up a measure of the work load which will be required from whatever kind of handling equipment is finally selected. This work load is, of course, expressed in terms which apply interchangeably to a crane, a conveyor, an industrial truck, or any other kind of equipment. An illustration of how this work load may be developed and summarized from the data supplied in the foregoing five major factors is given below for the handling of newsprint rolls in the finishing room of a paper mill. The materials handling operation consists of picking up a 1,400-lb. newsprint roll, one roll at a time, from the scale on which the roll lies on its bilge after it leaves the paper machine.

The roll must then be upended, transported to a flatcar which has its bed on a level with the shipping platform and which is located 70 ft. away from the scale. The roll is deposited in an upright position on the car bed, and the handling device returns to the scale for another load.

Handling Newsprint Rolls. In the following example, the handling device considered is an electric lift truck equipped with a 90° rotating hydraulic clamp capable of engaging one newsprint roll at a time. The basic figures used here are equally applicable to a crane or conveyor:

Tons of paper produced per year in the mill........................	236,333 tons
Number of working days per year...................................	÷305.7 days
Tons of paper produced per 3-shift day...........................	773.1 tons
Number of newsprint rolls per 3-shift day........................	1,118 rolls
Number of truck trips per 3-shift day carrying one roll per trip......	1,118 trips
Number of feet traveled per round trip............................	×139 ft.
Total feet traveled per 3-shift day................................	155,402 ft.
Total truck-miles traveled per 3-shift day........................	29.42 mi.
Number of truck-miles traveled per mill-hour......................	1.23 mi.

Minutes of work load per truck hour:

Travel time: 1.23 mi. ÷ 5 mi. × 60 min. = 15 min.
Lifting and lowering time:
  1,118 rolls ÷ 24 hr. = 46.6 rolls per hr.
  46.6 rolls × 6 ft. up and down ÷ 27 ft. per min. = 10 min.
Total work load per truck hour.................. 25 min.

It is evident from this calculation that there is work for one truck only, and for only 25 min. out of every mill-hour for that one truck to take care of this handling operation. When all the subsequent handling operations along the way to storage into the wharf sheds have been measured, as was done in this example, it may well be that an overhead chain conveyor running from the mill to the wharf sheds would absorb the truck handling considered not only in this example but also at other points along the way. This example also illustrates the importance of viewing the handling problems of a plant from an integrated, plant-wide standpoint rather than on a piecemeal basis at each handling point.

TABLE OF DATA ON HANDLING ACTIVITY. Expressed in the language of a statistical table, Fig. 10 shows the factors included in the groups captioned "Handling Activity" and "Handling Cost and Savings." This is a standard survey form for a plant manufacturing small steel tanks for housing power transformers. The schedule portion in question appears in the upper left corner under the caption "Handling Activity." This heading encompasses the following ten columns:

Operation number.   Distance moved (E).
Starting point (A).   Quantity of pieces per year (F).
Handling operation (B).   Quantity of pieces per operation (G).
Stopping point (C).   Number of operations per year (H).
Equipment used (D).   Operation unit (K).

This is the information which ultimately indicates how much handling work has to be done by the contemplated project. The next, and final, group of survey factors has to do with a determination of the cost and resultant savings involved in acquiring the specific materials handling facility, which is revealed thus far as being the desirable one to consider as a solution to the problem at issue. These factors are discussed later under "Economic Factors To Be Considered."

Selection of Proper Kinds of Handling Equipment

COMPARING SAVINGS IN SELECTING MATERIALS HANDLING DEVICES. The following study shows the methods by which savings with several alternate methods of handling may be compared.

Moving 2,000 Cartons of Canned Goods 150 Feet. A comparison of the several types of handling which are suitable for moving 2,000 cartons of canned goods over a distance of 150 ft. provides a simple illustration of a positive approach to analyzing, planning, and selecting materials handling systems. The relative advantages, costs, and savings in transporting this load are analyzed by the following four representative methods for doing this kind of work:

  1. Carrying each carton by hand.
  2. Wheeling 5 cartons at a time on a hand truck.
  3. Pushing 20 cartons at a time on a platform truck.
  4. Handling 40 cartons at a time by fork truck.

Carrying Each Carton by Hand. By carrying the load by hand, carton by carton, the worker has no piling to do at the starting point, where the cartons are located. He merely lifts one carton, carries it over the distance of 150 ft. in about ¾ min. and piles it at its destination at the rate of approximately 180 cartons per hr. The time taken for carrying the 2,000 cartons by this method is therefore:

Piling time: Hr.
   2,000 cartons piled at destination at 180 per hr............................ 11.11
   Unpiling floor storage for next movement............................... 11.11

Travel time:
   2,000 trips to the pile at ¾ min. per trip, 1,500 min...................... 25.00
   2,000 return trips for stock at starting point............................. 25.00
      Total man-hours for the task 72.22

The only conceivable advantage in this method is the total absence of investment for materials handling equipment. This factor is more than offset, however, by the space wasted by storing on the floor, for floor space in a building in itself represents a large investment. As for other disadvantages, none can be detected until a comparison is made with some other materials handling methods which lend themselves to this kind of movement.

Wheeling 5 Cartons at a Time on a Hand Truck. The nearest alternative to the completely manual method is handling by the use of a 2-wheel hand truck. The handler can carry 5 cartons per trip, thereby reducing his travel time to 400 trips each way, as against 2,000 trips when carrying only one carton at a time. However, the hand truck introduces an added operation in that the handler must now pile the cartons on the truck before he can transport them to the pile. The cost of this method may be summarized as follows:

Piling time: Hr.
   Piling on truck at source... 11.11
   Piling at destination 11.11
   Unpiling for next movement 11.11

Travel time:
   400 trips to the pile at ¾ min... 5.00
   400 return trips to starting point 5.00
      Total man-hours for the task 43.33

Under this method, the travel time of 10 hr. is less than one-third of the piling time of 33.33 hr. As a rule, when travel time is less than piling time, it is frequently considered unnecessary to seek further economy by introducing more materials handling equipment. The fallacy of this generalization, as reflected in the figures given in the illustration, lies in the fact that the material is piled three times, thereby causing the travel time to appear low in comparison.

Pushing 20 Cartons at a Time on a Platform Truck. A further alternative to the problem under discussion is to provide the handler with a push-type platform floor truck. He can then haul 20 cartons per trip and thereby further reduce the number of trips to 100 each way. The piling time remains unchanged, however, since he must still load the truck, unload it at the destination, and unpile it again for the next movement. The floor-truck method may be summed up as follows:

Piling time: Hr.
   Piling on truck at source 11.11
   Piling at destination 11.11
   Unpiling for next movement... 11.11

Travel time:

100 trips to the pile at ¾ min. 1.25

100 return trips to starting point 1.25

Total man-hours for the task. 35.83

Travel time has been reduced again, but piling time, which now accounts for 33.33 hr. of the total of 35.83, has been left unchanged. It is evident from these figures that the investigation must now be directed toward a reduction in the piling time.

Handling 40 Cartons at a Time by Fork Truck. Under the preceding two methods, the entire 2,000 cartons are piled or unpiled on three separate occasions, namely, at the source, at the destination, and in preparation for the next movement. If the pile is made at the source by loading it on pallets, the entire pile can be moved as a pallet load to its destination without necessitating further piling or unpiling. The pallet handles 40 cartons per trip, and the fork truck travels at least twice as fast as the push-type floor truck. The piling and travel time have thus been reduced to the figures summarized below:

Piling time: Hr.

Piling on pallet at source. 11.110

Travel time:

50 trips to the pile at 0.375 min. per trip 0.315

50 return trips to starting point 0.315

Total man-hours for the task. 11.740

If the material movement were continuous, in a steady direction, and planned to last over a sufficient period of time, consideration might also be given to the use of a conveyor.

COMPARISON OF COSTS AND SAVINGS UNDER THE FOUR DIFFERENT METHODS. In comparing the four methods presented thus far, no allowance has been made for the depreciation, maintenance, and fuel cost of the trucks used in each case. A summary of these operating costs, and of the labor cost incurred in each of the four methods, is made in Fig. 11.

Allowing $2.00 per hr. for labor, plus the amount for depreciation, maintenance, and fuel cost of the trucks used, the total materials handling cost of moving the 2,000 cartons over a distance of 150 ft. ranges from $144.44 in Method A to $24.39 in Method D.

Using the hand-truck method as a basis, the saving realized under the platform push-truck method amounts to 17 percent, whereas by using a fork truck the saving becomes 71 percent, or $62.29, for this particular task. By calculating the savings to be realized from all the materials handling work which could be appropriately assigned to the fork truck over one month's time, a simple division of this monthly aggregate into the cost of the truck will indicate readily how many months it will take for the equipment to pay for itself.

The powered industrial lift truck is a typical materials handling device which is bringing about remarkable changes in industrial operations. Palletization, which was developed extensively by the U. S. Army and Navy into the "unit-load" idea during World War II, has already gained tremendous industry-wide acceptance. The savings to be realized from this system alone offer vast cost-reduction potentialities to industry.

Description of Materials Handling Performance	METHOD A Carrying Each Carton by Hand	METHOD B Wheeling 5 Cartons on a Hand Truck	METHOD C Pushing 20 Cartons on a Platform Truck	METHOD D Handling 40 Cartons by Fork Truck and Pallet
Piling time in hours..............	22.22	33.33	33.33	11.11
Travel time	50.00	10.00	2.50	0.63
Total time	72.22	43.33	35.83	11.74
Total labor cost at $2.00..........	$144.44	$86.66	$71.66	$23.48
Total equipment cost for depreciation, maintenance and fuel cost..	–	0.02	0.07	0.91
Total materials handling cost for method	$144.44	$86.68	$71.73	$24.39
Comparative Savings				
Saving over Method B..........			$14.95	$62.29
Percent saving over Method B..			17%	71%

Gaudreau, Rimbach & Associates

Fig. 11. Comparison of materials handling methods and costs of transporting 2,000 cartons of canned goods over a distance of 150 ft.

Economic Factors Influencing the Ultimate Choice of Equipment

ECONOMIC APPRAISAL OF THE PROJECT. The statistical information presented in the earlier paragraphs of this section under the heading "Basic Factors of Handling Activity and Mechanical Requirements" provides a definite measure of the range of advanced materials handling developments which are taking place at present, or are projected for the future. The quantity, weight, speed, frequency of movement, and distance traveled—all concerning materials handled, from raw stage to finished product—provide the basic information for the selection of the best available kinds of materials handling equipment. This information removes most of the guesswork from the solution of materials handling projects.

At certain points along the line of production, specifications may point strongly in favor of a particular kind of equipment, for example, a crane. At other points, the weight of the factors analyzed may point more definitely in favor of some other device, such as a conveyor, for example, in preference to a crane or to an industrial truck. Throughout these comparisons, however, only the **physical aspects** of the handling problems and devices have been considered. Although a crane may appear to be the ideal kind of equipment to use from a mechanical angle, it may not be justifiable from an **economic standpoint.** A crane perhaps would perform a physical job better than other types of equipment, but the savings or other economic benefits accruing from its use might not be sufficient to pay for its purchase cost as quickly as the savings from a conveyor or truck would pay for them. To guard against such pitfalls in choosing between optional types of handling devices, the major factors classified under the heading of "Economic Appraisal" should be taken into consideration before a selection of equipment is made. These factors are six in number, and a brief description is given here.

1. **Equipment work loads.** The amount of work in terms of tons, trips, and miles required from whatever kind of handling device is ultimately selected for a particular handling operation, is obtained from this factor, as was illustrated earlier under the heading "Basic Factors of Handling Activity and Mechanical Requirements."

2. **Number of men required.** The composition and size of the materials handling crews for each materials handling operation along the line of production, storage, and shipping are the data secured under this heading. They include the number of payroll-hours per year per occupation, and the number of men per occupation for each kind of handling device considered.

3. **Annual cost of labor.** This cost can then be calculated for each kind of handling device under consideration.

4. **Annual cost of fuel, maintenance, and depreciation.** This particular economic yardstick eliminates many devices which cannot pay for themselves out of savings within a favorable period of time, especially when depreciation is taken into account.

5. **Capital investment required.** This figure should reflect such considerations as the purchase cost of the contemplated device, its transportation and installation costs, the cost of dismantling and retiring present equipment and accessories, the net book value of existing equipment to be written off the ledgers, the cost of making necessary building alterations, and the cost of training operators to run the contemplated handling device.

6. **Amount of savings.** Barring extraneous factors which preclude making a choice (such as the mandatory installation of equipment which provides safety for process workers), the ultimate measure which perhaps exerts the most influence in the selection of a specific type of handling device is in the relative amount of savings involved. This savings figure is made comparable for different kinds of equipment by expressing it uniformly in terms of **yield** on the full capital investment required for each device. The yield is usually based on the savings in the annual cost of labor, fuel, maintenance, and depreciation, plus any other direct costs affected by the proposed installation.

Selection of the Proper Kinds of Handling Equipment. As gaged by their respective sales volumes per year, cranes, conveyors, and industrial trucks rank as the **three largest groups** of materials handling equipment in use today. The remaining groups consist mainly of lifts and hoists, monorail systems, pneumatic systems, tractors and trailers, rail cars, stackers, and miscellaneous storage facilities and process-handling accessories.

Cranes and conveyors transport material along fixed paths whereas industrial trucks are self-propelled units, free to travel in any direction. **Economical traveling distance,** however, is longer for conveyors than for trucks and longer for trucks than for cranes. The travel speed is generally faster for trucks than for cranes and faster for cranes than for conveyors. As another general rule for the corresponding amount of two-way ton-miles of work performed, cranes cost more than trucks, and trucks more than conveyors.

The methods of handling raw materials, work in process, and finished products in a plant vary almost as much as the processing operations which they serve. Distillation operations require tanks, pumps, and pipe lines for handling materials. Machining operations in metalworking plants require numerous kinds of cranes, conveyors, and industrial trucks.

Continuous-process operations—such as in making paper, textiles, rubber, and glass—give rise to different handling problems at various stages along the flow of production as the material in process changes in form. In a **newsprint paper mill,** for example, the manufacturing cycle may begin with long logs of wood floating in a mill pond, the logs being later cut into short blocks, which eventually are ground into a fibrous pulp suspended in water. The pulp is formed into a continuous sheet of paper which ultimately is wound into newsprint rolls averaging 1,400 lb. each, measuring about 36 in. in diam. and generally 64 in. in height when standing on end.

To keep the material flowing through the paper-making cycle, the mill uses several distinct kinds of materials movers. For example, logs are moved on conveyors; groundwood blocks travel by gravity chutes, conveyors, and straddle trucks; newsprint rolls are handled at various points on powered conveyors, fork trucks, flatcars, dollies, cranes, ship's booms, industrial trucks, and highway trucks. Each kind of materials handling equipment used is chosen for its specific mechanical features, coupled with economic advantages over competitive kinds of equipment.

The problem of **selecting the most suitable type** of materials handling equipment for each of the various handling requirements in a given industrial plant has become increasingly complex in recent years for two reasons in particular. The first reason is that the **variety** of mechanical handling devices has grown to the point where there are now over 300 major kinds of such equipment on the market, and many of them have overlapping applications. As for diversity within main groups of equipment, there are fully 50 distinct kinds of cranes alone, about 90 different kinds of conveyors, and at least 40 separate kinds of industrial trucks—and the list is growing every year.

The second reason is the **broad range** of handling operations which increasingly lend themselves to mechanization as new handling devices continue to appear. A prospective user must therefore take into consideration not only the mechanical aspects of a particular handling device but also the entire economic appraisal of the various other devices that are likewise capable of performing the same handling operation.

ECONOMIC FACTORS TO BE CONSIDERED. In the calculation of handling costs and savings incidental to a given handling operation, or to a sequence of handling operations as already illustrated in Fig. 10, definite values are usually applied to a number of economic factors. These factors relate to **distance, quantity, speed, time,** and **cost.** They vary with each handling operation involved in a project and with each different kind of handling device considered for one or more of these operations. A simple formula composed of these factors then provides a ready medium for determining the handling cost and savings for each handling operation.

The quickest way to visualize the application of these economic factors is to demonstrate their use in a case example similar to the one illustrated earlier in Fig. 10. Such a standard survey form may be used for evaluating a complete handling project from the statistical data constituting the economic factors of the particular project. The following points regarding the form should be noted:

1. The evaluation columns are confined to three factors (as shown in Fig. 12), namely, Handling Activity, Equipment Operating Cost, and Total Handling Costs and Savings.

2. Each column caption under these three sections in Figs. 9 and 10 is identified by a letter symbol, such as *E, F, G, H,* etc. Except for the purely descriptive

columns in the Handling Activity and the Total Handling Cost and Savings columns, the letter symbol in each column becomes a component factor in evaluating operating costs and savings as evidenced by the mathematical signs also registered in the column headings. For example, in the Handling Activity section, **volume of operations** appears as:

Column F (quantity of pieces per year)
$\div$ Column G (quantity of pieces per operation)
$=$ Column H (number of operations per year)

Under Handling Activity, the **distance moved** and the **volume of operations** are recorded for each handling operation. Over to the right, under Total Handling Cost and Savings, the factors of **labor cost** and **equipment operating cost** are brought together in final form for determining the **total cost** of each handling operation involved in the project. As previously indicated in Fig. 9, the **equipment operating cost** is calculated separately for each type of handling device, whether the equipment be already in operation or contemplated for the project.

Classification of Economic Factors. Expressed in terms of statistical data, these economic factors may also be classified into the following three separate categories, as shown previously in Figs. 9 and 10.

---

1. Handling Activity

E. Distance moved.
F. Pieces per year.
G. Pieces per handling operation.
H. Operations per year ($F \div G$).

2. Equipment Operating Cost

a. Equipment purchase cost.
b. Annual depreciation.
c. Annual maintenance and repairs.
d. Annual power and fuel.
e. Annual supplies.
f. Annual total operating cost:
  ($b + c + d + e$)
g. Operating hours per year for **all** projects served by this equipment.
T. Operating cost per hour.
  ($f \div g$)

3. Total Handling Cost and Savings

M. Labor hours per operation.
N. Labor hours per year ($H \times M$).
P. Labor wage rate per hour.
R. Labor cost per year ($N \times P$).
S. Equipment operating hours per year on this operation.
T. Equipment operating cost per hour.
U. Equipment operating cost per year ($S \times T$)
V'. Total handling cost per year: existing method ($R' + U'$)
V''. Total handling cost per year: proposed method ($R'' + U''$)
W. Annual savings in proposed method (total V' less total V'')

Handling-Cost Formula

Total handling cost per year for each handling operation $= V$

$$V = \frac{FMP}{G} + \frac{S(b + c + d + e)}{g}$$

Gaudreau, Rimbach & Associates

Fig. 12. Economic factors for evaluating a materials handling project.

Measurement of Handling Activity. In the body of the schedule in Fig. 10, each line represents a separate materials handling operation. Each operation is identified by an Operation Number in the very first column on the left. The first eight operations in the top lines constitute the **existing method** of handling the tanks in the project, and the ten operations listed in the bottom section of the schedule represent the **proposed method** developed as a solution to the problem at hand.

Under the existing method, Operation 1, for example, consists of loading the tanks onto trailers. Column A shows that the tanks are standing on the floor at the start of this operation. Column C indicates that the tanks have been placed on a trailer as the stopping point of this first operation. In Operation 2, the trailers are transported from Bay F-20 to Bay A-90, a distance of 1,630 ft., as recorded in column E.

The remaining six operations under the existing method consist of (1) unloading the trailers, (2) stacking palletized loads, (3) unstacking these loads, (4) transporting the palletized loads, (5) unloading the pallets, and (6) returning the trailers to their original starting point, in Bay F-20. The total distance traveled for the existing eight operations, as shown in column E, is 4,425 ft. The equipment used for these eight existing operations is described in column D, and consists of tractors, trailers, and fork lift trucks.

EVALUATION OF SAVINGS UNDER THE PROPOSED METHOD. The next step is to see what happens when the handling job is conveyorized, as analyzed under the proposed method in the ten operations listed in the lower half of the table. The equipment used in this case, as also described in column D, proposes to substitute an overhead conveyor for the tractors and trailers but retains the fork lift trucks for storing the tanks in palletized loads. The total distance traveled when using a conveyor is now only 1,386 ft., as shown in column E. This shorter distance constitutes a reduction of 69 percent in the distance involved under the existing method.

The labor cost per year for both methods is shown in Fig. 10 at the right, in the column heading identified by R. For the forecasted quantity of 362,400 steel tanks per year, the labor cost under the old method is over $50,000 as compared with $20,000 under the proposed method. The indicated reduction of 60 percent in labor cost alone under the conveyorized method yields a saving of over $30,000 per year.

The **saving in the operating cost of the equipment**, as shown in column U, amounts to a further reduction of over $4,000 per year, after making due allowance for depreciation, repairs and maintenance, power, fuel, and supplies, as previously analyzed in Annual Operating Cost in Fig. 9. All told, therefore, the combined saving accruing from partly conveyorizing this job, as shown in column V, amounts to $34,415 per year, marking a net reduction of 55 percent in total cost. Since the new overhead conveyor required for this project costs but $23,000 (Fig. 9), this investment fully pays for itself in 9 months, out of the $34,415 saved in the handling cost for the first year alone. Thereafter, the proposed installation will continue to yield a $34,000 saving year after year—an amount which will go directly into net profit without any further capital investment.

SOLVING MATERIALS HANDLING PROBLEMS. The solution to the foregoing problem was not obtained by isolating one kind of materials handling equipment and then developing costs and projecting savings on that particular kind of equipment. Attention was not focused on one kind of equipment at a time, such as tractors, to the exclusion of the other kinds in use. In order to present an integrated picture without omitting any relevant factors, all the different pieces of equipment involved in this localized area were considered as parts of a unit.

What really happened in this survey may be summarized as follows in terms of distance moved by each type of equipment. Tractors and trailers were completely eliminated in the new method. The distance moved by fork lift trucks was reduced 37 percent, and that of loading and unloading vehicles of all types, 20 percent. The total distance moved in all handling operations was reduced 69 percent. Even though the overhead conveyor completely replaced the tractors and trailers, it also partly reduced the work of the fork lift trucks, which remained as a part of the proposed system under review.

The survey of a handling system should not be limited to the point of merely comparing one type of equipment with another. All the various types involved in a selected area should be surveyed. By carefully **listing, evaluating,** and **comparing** all the basic data on handling activity and handling cost for each handling operation involved in a given area, or for a given method, many alternative solutions which might otherwise escape detection will inevitably suggest themselves.

Intangible Factors Not Revealed in Statistics. Most survey forms do not include any provision for the many intangible factors that cannot be entered in tabular form but which must nevertheless be considered by the materials handling engineer in arriving at his recommendations. For example, no mention is made of the possible interference of plant service lines (such as water pipes and electric conduits), structural obstructions, or crucial processing characteristics. Any of these and other limiting factors not specifically listed on the survey form may affect the final decisions regarding a materials handling proposal. For these factors, the engineer must refer to other sources of information and draw on his knowledge of materials handling engineering. The most economical handling system, from the standpoint of savings reflected in the proposal on the survey form, may be totally eclipsed by the cost of the building changes required to allow for the use of the proposed equipment.

The life of a plant layout in job-lot (or intermittent) manufacturing operations may range from a few months to 3 or 4 years. Materials handling equipment may last from 1 to 20 years. It is necessary in recommending the purchase of handling equipment to consider the **adaptability** of this equipment to periodic changes in plant layout. Powered conveyors, for example, are usually engineered for a particular layout and cannot be reused for another layout without making prohibitive changes in power lines, etc. Gravity conveyors, on the other hand, are easily adaptable to layout changes and may therefore be more economical for a given materials handling project even though the indicated immediate savings may be smaller.

FORTHCOMING PROBLEMS. With the introduction of self-powered machine loaders and unloaders on process machines and of automatic conveying equipment from machine to machine, industry is now concerned with the automatic handling of component parts in production, known as **automation.** In some industries assembly work has already been placed entirely on conveyors which serve as the pace setters for assembly operations. In a spark-plug plant, for example, all assembly work is being paced by a powered conveyor, although machine-tool operations are individually estimated by means of standard time values. In the processing end of manufacturing activities in some plants, however, **automatic handling** has already been incorporated in the design of several varieties of machine tools, presses, parts washers, and heat-treating furnaces.

In several recently constructed plants, machine operators are being paid on a day-work basis rather than on the basis of standard time values. Standards are not a substitute for good management planning. In many of these newer plants, the flow of production is under **timed control.** The pace setter may be powered conveyor equipment which transports work in process from work station to work station, or some other handling device which helps to provide continuous flow of work through the plant. A group bonus for better performance often supplies a simple but effective wage incentive for the employees working on these **mechanized production and assembly lines** and may dispense with the necessity of standard time values for pay purposes.

MATERIALS POSITIONING IN PRODUCTION

CONTENTS

MATERIALS POSITIONING IN PRODUCTION

MECHANIZED MATERIALS HANDLING. The development of modern industrial machines has resulted from the trend established by the Industrial Revolution of substituting mechanical power for the inadequate power of the individual manual worker. Today's industrial plants use thousands of units of mechanical horsepower to supplement the individual worker's efforts and to increase production.

As the trend in productive mechanization continues, with factories producing more and better goods at lower cost, there appears to be a limiting factor in the progressive mechanization. This factor is the **physical inability of the machine operator** to load, position, and unload his machine fast enough to permit the maximum available machine production. While the need for particular muscular strength on the part of the operator has almost vanished from the job requirements, a need for superhuman speed and dexterity has arisen that cannot be attained with human hands. To meet this need there has developed the new science of mechanized materials handling dealing with the problem of **loading, positioning, and unloading** production equipment with speed, accuracy, and safety. There are few industries that have not utilized some kind of mechanized materials handling equipment on their production equipment.

As in all cases concerning the addition of new equipment, however, the basic economic consideration of **return on investment** must be impartially determined. Primarily, there must be a definite need for increased production, a decrease in scrap, or the elimination of some hazardous condition. Materials handling equipment should be treated in the same manner as are the basic kinds of production equipment in the plant. When savings, both tangible and intangible, resulting from the use of the equipment can repay the initial investment and accompanying expenses in conformance with established accounting procedures, then such equipment should be considered.

This section deals with representative types of mechanical means of loading, positioning, and unloading production equipment in representative American industries. Basic types of equipment have been selected to illustrate the principles used in solving particular problems. An improved method that cuts costs under one set of conditions will not necessarily reduce operating expenses under different kinds of management conditions. Nor will the fact that the problem exists in a totally different industry preclude the use of the improved method in this other industry. The ingenuity of the materials handling engineer is the key to the successful application of sound principles and practical methods to the problems at hand.

POSITIONING DEVICES FOR LOADING AND UNLOADING. Mechanisms in this category are those which are either separate units which are attached as accessories to production machines, or are designed integral to machines to position units undergoing processing. Representative mechanisms in this classification which are to be discussed are:

1. Hopper feeding devices.
2. Indexing fixtures.
3. Continuous material feeders.
4. Fillers and sealers.

5. Carton setup and loading devices.
6. Mechanical press unloaders.
7. Gaging and sorting mechanisms.

Many of these devices are not new, having been used in certain industries for many years. Their value as illustrations lies in the possibility of adaptation of the principles involved to solve problems in other industries. Most of the mechanical mechanisms have existed in the past. The application of these basic mechanisms to perform required actions will here be explained.

HOPPER FEEDING DEVICES. The **application of gravity** in materials handling operations has been practiced since prehistoric times. The principle is used extensively in the industries moving vast quantities of bulk materials. Cereal-processing plants, the beverage industry, the chemical industry, and innumerable other users of dry or liquid materials that will flow have made **extensive** installations of gravity-feed devices.

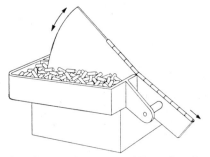

Fig. 1. Mechanism for loading automobile wrist pins into a chute.

In the case of bulk materials, where large quantities must be stored prior to processing, the primary receiving and storage unit is usually a silo or a similarly enclosed structure, generally located at a height sufficient to allow the material to flow by gravity to the first processing operation. In industries where the raw materials must be mixed, the use of gravity-feed hoppers to bring the materials to a central batch-weighing device is common practice. The hoppers may be manually or mechanically operated by direct or remote controls.

Hopper feed is used in loading automatic and high-production machines. Many different kinds of hoppers and feeding mechanisms are installed for such purposes. Primarily, such hoppers serve as bulk storage stations, where materials can be delivered in sufficient quantity to last throughout a major portion of an operation period. This plan of bulk feeding eliminates down-time of production machines and cuts down the number of trips which the materials handling stockman must make to keep the equipment in productive operation. Hoppers are designed to contain a normal production run of material or a standard unit load of parts, under the unit load method of plant materials handling.

Another function of the hopper is to prearrange the items contained into the **proper position for delivery** through the feed chute to the work fixture. This prearrangement is accomplished in most instances by one of two methods. The first method is the use of a mechanical device designed specifically for the part to be handled and operating in sequence with the operating cycle of the production machine. Fig. 1 shows a mechanism for loading automobile wrist pins into a chute for delivery to a centerless grinder. This example illustrates a corollary principle that there are few general-purpose devices that can handle a considerable variety of parts. Careful study should be made to find out what the expected time and cost savings may be from the use of a proposed automatic loading device. The cost of designing and building such special equipment may be greater than the anticipated savings which may be made by the automatic mechanism.

The second frequently used means of prearrangement of parts to be processed makes use of kinetic energy in the form of **induced vibration.** The vibratory hopper itself must be designed for handling the parts to be processed, although such hoppers have a wider range in certain classifications than the mechanical feeder. The design utilizes the motive power of induced vibration to move the contained parts along a predetermined path in a required position to the point where they are loaded into the production machine. Vibration is induced by the attachment of a rotating eccentric to the hopper in such a position that the

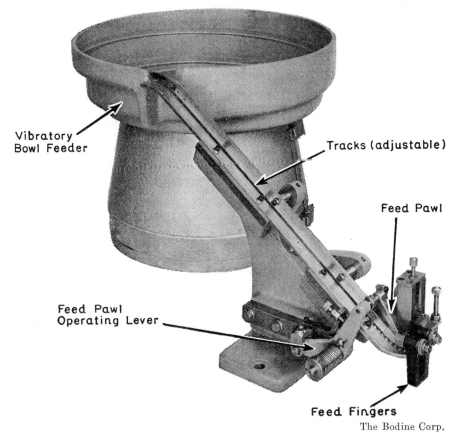

The Bodine Corp.

Fig. 2. Vibratory bowl-type feeder with mechanical transfer device.

induced vibration is of the proper frequency, and the vibratory plane is properly adjusted to produce the required movement. The mechanical type of vibrator is usually powered by an electric motor. Electromagnetic vibrators are also used in such applications. Fig. 2 shows a vibratory bowl-type feeder. Screws are fed by vibration down the track and are then mechanically transferred to feed fingers by a feed pawl and automatically driven into the work.

A third type of hopper in use in industry is the **static storage-type hopper** with a tray and door, or a bottom dumping arrangement, which allows the machine operator to select a part for manual loading into the production machine. While this type of hopper does not automatically load and position a part in a machine, it does allow savings to be made in unit handling and improves the efficiency of the operator's manual handling. In many cases the part to be loaded is of such shape that it cannot be positioned effectively by automatic means. Also, it might be found by a cost analysis that the operation in question will not justify the investment in a completely automatic device.

The static storage hoppers are of varying design, construction, and size. In a plant where their use is general, an attempt should be made to use a standard hopper plant-wide to allow for flexibility in over-all materials handling operations. For small parts, such as screws and nuts, the hoppers are usually of small table-mounted types, which are easily moved for filling or for plant layout rearrangements. Hoppers used in heavy stamping operations are larger and require power equipment to move and position them. A special type of hopper used in "between-press" operations is mounted on a castered base frame to allow manual positioning or moving.

Drop-bottom hoppers are another kind of special container which is used for movement of materials between departments. They provide a convenient and time-saving means for unloading by a subsequent production operator. In some cases movable storage hoppers are permanently stationed at operations. Like fixed hoppers, such hoppers are kept filled by dumping of parts into them by means of special rotary devices on the fork trucks delivering the materials.

INDEXING FIXTURES. In the operation of many production machines, the time consumed in loading a part into the holding fixture is often greater than the machining time. In such cases an indexing fixture may be used to improve

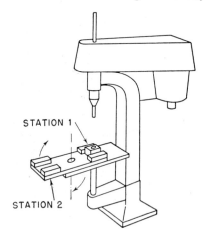

STATION 1

STATION 2

Fig. 3. Simple two-station indexing fixture.

the productivity of the machine. This device is simply a **multipositioned holding fixture** with a considerable number of stations that are mechanically moved into position and automatically loaded and unloaded.

A simple two-station indexing fixture is shown in Fig. 3. While a drill is operating on the part held in Station No. 1, the operator will remove a finished part from Station No. 2 and load a new part into this station. If the time used in unloading and loading equals the time used in drilling the hole, the machine is working at its maximum productivity, and its rate has been doubled. More machine time can be obtained if the simple two-station fixture is rotated 180° by some mechanical means. This procedure is termed "indexing." In addition to two sta-

Warner & Swasey Co.

Fig. 4. Automatic indexing fixture.

tions, three, four, or more stations may be provided. The angularity of the index is obtained by dividing 360° by the number of stations. Usually indexing fixtures contain an even number of stations. The mechanical means of rotation is provided by a number of different means.

The simplest mechanism for rotating an indexing mechanism is the **ratchet and pawl.** The fixtures are mounted on a plate rotating on a vertical shaft. The ratchet connected to the lower end of the shaft is moved a predetermined number of degrees by the pawl. The pawl is connected to a reciprocating member of the production machine in the case of a punch press or to an adjustable crank connected to a rotating member in a different type of machine. This mechanism, while relatively simple and inexpensive, is not used in many of the newer indexing mechanisms, because of its jerky motion and lack of definite positioning.

A more positive indexing mechanism is the Geneva drive, Fig. 4. This device is used extensively and provides a positive locating feature in addition to a smoother rotation. The mechanism imparts a constantly increasing acceleration and deceleration to and from the work station, which eliminates jerking and the possible dislodging of parts in a fixture.

Indexing fixtures are used not only in single-operation machines but also in **multiple-operation machines.** A representative example of this kind of fixture is found in vertical multistationed milling machines and in some kinds of chucking lathes. In the automatic screw machine the indexing fixture is the multitubed bar-stock holder. The machine automatically cuts off and ejects the finished part. Machines of this kind can be run in groups operated by but one attendant, who services the machines and removes the finished parts. Other multistation, multiple-operation machines have one position open for loading and unloading at each indexing, the stations moving progressively around through a sequence of operations. In the case of very heavy parts, mechanized loading is usually restricted to a well-planned work station with work-level hopper feeds. Unloading is usually manual, but the receiving containers are conveniently placed.

Indexing mechanisms are nowadays designed and **built** integral to most modern machines. Again the details of the design and the degree of automaticity are determined by the economics of the situation. When complete machines or lines of machines are designed for cycles of operations, as is the case where the principle of automation is adopted, very special indexing fixtures are used.

CONTINUOUS MATERIAL FEEDERS. The principle of feeding material continuously to a production machine is one of the older forms of mechanized materials handling at the work station. This method is used on machines that have a means of cutting off a required amount of material, determined by the size of the part being produced. **Coil-stock roll feeders,** which automatically deliver wire and strip materials to metal forming machines, are presently used extensively in industry. Basically, such devices consist of a reel of sufficient strength and capacity to hold a coil of stock. The reel is usually equipped with a rotating device, either an electric motor drive or a mechanical ratchet operated by the stroke of the press. The precision of feed of the coiled stock is usually controlled by a feeding device mounted on the press. This device is adjustable for scrap control and is usually activated mechanically by the stroke of the press. The small press installation in Fig. 5 includes a stock straightening device.

The use of coil stock raises the problem of length of stock per coil to reduce machine down-time while reloading. This factor becomes more acute with heavier gages and wider stock, which reduces the linear footage as the limit of the weight of the coil is reached. In continuous processes, provision is made for uninterrupted stock by means of duplicate reels, festoons of stock, and a butt welder to join the stock. Unloading of parts from presses using stock feeders is usually accomplished automatically by air ejection or mechanical means, and the part is conveyed by chute or conveyor to the next operation.

Another kind of material that lends itself to mechanized loading is **rod and tube stock.** The smaller size rods and tubes are usually shipped in coils. The means of feeding coiled rods and tubes to a production machine is similar to that used with coiled strip except that a straightening operation must be performed. This is done in special straightening machines placed between the coil reel and the production machine.

Wittek Manufacturing Co.

Fig. 5. Typical small press installation.

Large-size bar and tubing stock is usually straight as received, and can be fed to a press by means of a gravity rack and pusher rail. The stock is loaded into the gravity rack by means of an overhead crane. The pusher rail is aligned with the feed tube of the production machine. As most lathes and screw machines have automatic feeding mechanisms built into the unit, it is necessary only that the pusher device move the stock into the feed tube far enough to insure engagement with the feeding mechanism. Shorter bars or tubes can be fed to machines by means of inclined troughs or special hoppers.

FILLERS AND SEALERS. In the food industry one of the problems solved was the filling of cans, jars, bottles, boxes, or bags with the correct amount of material, usually by weight, and sealing the containers with the proper kind of closure. Obviously, all parts of the equipment in contact with the food require positive freedom from contamination and ease in cleaning. Mechanization of the packing procedure is accomplished in many ways, depending on the material to be packed. Fig. 6 shows a machine used in the bottling industry for filling and capping operations. The liquid to be bottled is fed to the machine by pipeline, and the bottles are automatically filled and volumetrically weighed. The bottles then continue to the capper. The capper mechanism is fed from a hopper, the caps being conveyed in proper position through a feed chute. The capping operation seals the bottles. They then proceed by conveyor to a device that loads them automatically into the shipping containers.

Blatz Brewery

Fig. 6. Filler machine used in the bottling industry.

Flour and cereals also are packed automatically on special machines designed for the particular type of material to be packed. Because materials such as sugar vary in volume for a given weight, it is necessary to apply a slight packing pressure to reduce the filled bag to size. Some machines bring about this reduction by means of a screw which retracts as the bag is loaded. Other machines use vibrating tables for this packing effort. Correct weight is brought about by either preweighing batches or weighing them as the bag is being filled. When the bag is filled it passes through a device which performs the closing operation. Many kinds of closures are employed, such as stitching, taping, and stapling.

Figs. 7a and 7b show equipment installed for packaging powdered milk. It makes a double package with glue-sealed glassine liner. Here a machine for forming the package, a filling machine, and a closure machine are joined by conveyors. Note that the conveyor between the filler and closure machines not only transports the filled package but also settles the contents. This line of equipment, run by two operators, can produce 85 uniform, lined packages per minute.

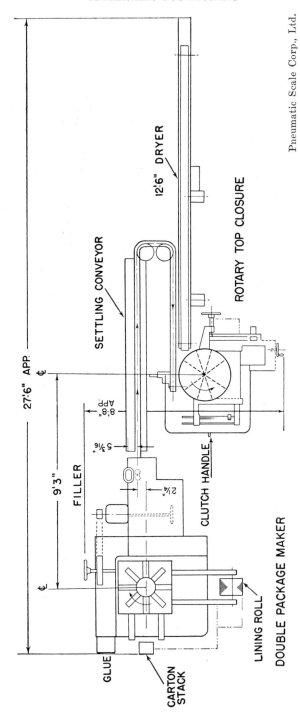

Pneumatic Scale Corp., Ltd.

Fig. 7a. Plan view of the packaging-line setup shown in Fig. 7b.

Pneumatic Scale Corp., Ltd.

Fig. 7b. Packaging line consisting of package-maker, two-head filled, and rotary top closure.

CARTON SETUP AND LOADING MECHANISMS. In many industries the product to be sold to the individual consumer is packaged in small cans, bottles, bags, or boxes. For economical shipment and distribution it is necessary that these small individual units be packed in larger containers. This task of loading the larger containers is another instance where mechanized materials handling at a work station lowers production costs and eliminates a production bottleneck.

Glass bottles and jars are usually purchased from the maker in corrugated shipping cartons that are designed to be re-used for the filled bottles. The process of unloading prior to filling leaves the carton set up, ready for reloading. When the bottles are filled and sealed it is necessary only to move the original set-up cartons to the loading point and allow the loading mechanism to load the carton. In the case of cans, bags, and boxes, however, the final shipping container is received in a flattened, knocked-down condition. The stacks of flattened cartons are fed into a set-up machine, which opens the carton, bends and seals the bottom flaps, and conveys the carton to the loader.

Loaders are designed to handle particular containers. Fig. 8 shows a type of loader which pushes an assembled load of cans into a set-up carton. From this point the loaded cartons pass through a carton sealer, which either applies a liquid adhesive to the flaps, uses staples to close the flaps, or tapes the flaps shut by means of special closure tapes. Another kind of carton set-up and loading mechanism is the one used to open and set up the individual cartons in which butter, lard, and similar products are packed and shipped. Like the larger shipping containers, these smaller boxes are shipped flat. Manually setting up these boxes is costly and slow, so that mechanization is again employed. Such machines, one of which is shown in Fig. 9, are complex and are designed to set up a par-

Fig. 8. Machine loading an assembled load of cans into cartons.

Bartelt Engineering Co.

Fig. 9. Machine used for setting up and loading individual packages of grated cheese.

ticular size and type of box. The set-up machine is usually a complete-cycle unit. In this type, after the carton is shaped the produce is automatically placed into it, and the machine finishes the operation by closing the carton.

Another mechanized unit employed in the packaging industry is the **wrapping machine,** which is used in packaging such products as bread, butter, and cheese. Wrapping of cartons is also a common practice. Fig. 10 shows a typical wrapping machine. These machines are usually designed to wrap particular sizes or types of commodities and to use particular sizes and types of wrappings. The extremely high production of the commodities wrapped, however, usually warrants the installation of a special wrapping machine.

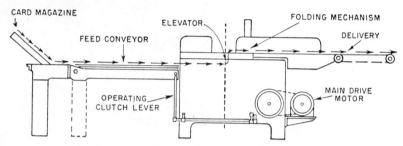

"Continuous flow" chart of the Battle Creek Model 43.

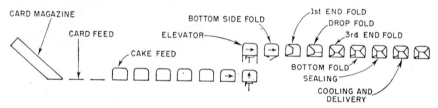

Battle Creek Packaging Machines

Detail of the wrapping functions performed during the smooth "continuous flowing" action.

Fig. 10. Wrapping machine.

MECHANICAL UNLOADERS. In the pressed-metal industries the loading and unloading of the large presses has been time-consuming and arduous. Even though the rate of production is relatively low because of the size of the presses and the work done by them, the over-all productivity of a press plant can be increased if mechanical means are employed to unload the **presses.** Smaller stampings are sometimes ejected from presses by the use of an intermittent jet of compressed air impinged on the underside of the finished stamping. The force of the air causes the part to rise out of the die, and if the air jet is properly directed, the stamping can be blown into a receiving hopper or box. Mechanical ejectors are also used to unload sheet metal from presses. Pivoted arms, which knock the parts out of the die air-operated punches, and spring-loaded strippers are used as conditions warrant.

A recent development in the mechanization of individual presses in a progressive forming line is the "iron hand." This device is a highly mechanized grab so designed and installed that unloading is done quickly and safely. Fig. 11 shows an iron hand in action. Not only does this device reduce the unloading time; it also

Ford Motor Co.

Fig. 11. The "iron-hand" mechanized grab device.

can be designed to drop the pressed shapes in a predetermined position on a take-away slot conveyor or on a feeding mechanism for the next press operation. The iron hand is also used extensively in the die-casting industry to remove hot castings from the machine. Here the device eliminates a hazardous hand operation.

GAGING AND SORTING MECHANISMS. Close inspection of mass-produced parts has frequently presented serious problems which have been costly and time-consuming. Manual **inspection operations** formerly in use are gradually being superseded by the use of automatic devices. In many cases it is not simply a question of which parts are acceptable and which must be rejected but rather the problem of **segregating the parts** into groups in which tolerances are within the accepted limits.

In the most modern automobile-engine assembly plants, the piston pins—a precision part—are selectively fitted to the pistons. This operation requires that a 100-percent inspection be made both for hardness and for diametrical limits. An **electronic gaging machine** quickly and accurately performs this task by first checking each pin for hardness and then for size. The hardness checker is an adaptation of a Rockwell hardness-checker and is set to reject all pins whose hardness is below a specified limit. Pin diameter is measured by movable gage blocks that read in increments of one-half of a ten-thousandth of an inch. The gaging device, on reading the diameter, energizes electronic devices that sort each pin into its proper size group as it is discharged from the machine. Segregation by weights, color, and texture can also be done automatically in high production industries by means of **optics, photometry,** and **electrical, pneumatic,** and **mechanical devices.** Such sorting devices can be incorporated as part of the production machine and function as mechanical unloaders as well as sorters.

In many highly integrated production machines with several separate work stations in a unit, separate inspection stations are incorporated in the unit to check accuracy or completeness of certain critical operations. Failure of a work station to perform its operation will be indicated by the automatic inspection unit; a signal will be given, and the whole unit will be stopped.

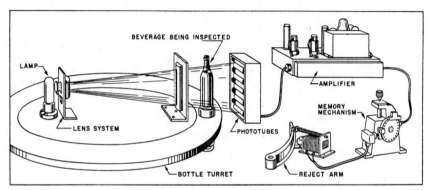

Radio Corporation of America

Fig. 12. Electronic beverage-inspection device on bottle turret conveyor.

Fig. 12 shows an electronic beverage-inspection device which scans the contents of bottles as they are conveyed from the pasteurizer to the labeler. Minute transparent bits of foreign matter, such as particles of glass or cellophane, will cause the scanning phototubes to trigger a memory circuit controlling a reject arm. When a bottle containing such impurities reaches the outfeed of the machine, this arm will divert it to a reject table. In order to guard against a failure in the inspection process, a built-in automatic device checks all functional features of the machine after each bottle is inspected. Up to 150 bottles can be inspected per minute.

MATERIALS HANDLING RESEARCH

CONTENTS

MATERIALS HANDLING RESEARCH

DEVELOPMENT OF MATERIALS HANDLING RESEARCH. As a general rule, economies effected as the result of materials handling research will approximate **$3 to $4 for every dollar spent.** In some industries, this proportion might be dollar for dollar and yet be considered favorable and well worth the investment. At the end of the first year of operation, a small packing and shipping research department was able to show an approximate cost reduction of $45,000 in its company's materials handling operations, mostly in materials.

The success of materials handling research depends in large measure on what is expected from it. Factors other than immediate financial returns may outweigh all other considerations. These factors include reduction of labor turnover, improvement of the quality of products, making the work more interesting to employees, and helping the sales department give better service to customers.

Expansion of the Handling Function. As an outgrowth of materials handling reduction projects, research work usually brings about improvement in methods of handling.

In the course of supplying new methods of packing replaceable tractor engine sleeves and pistons, the research department of one company helped plan a roller-conveyor line for applying corrosion preventives and for wiring the sleeve containers. Assistance was likewise given in working out a method of packing export tractors on a progressive roller-conveyor line. The research department also brought about the use of **small lift trucks** to handle pallet loads of interworks production items from packing floor to the loading platform.

Many handling operations are often originally performed only with great difficulty. In one case large engine crankshafts were originally manhandled and trucked through at least eight production departments, moved up and down on elevators, and finally dipped into a hot grease which coated them with a heavy, black mass. They were then dropped into large wooden boxes, of approximately the same weight as the shaft itself. Employees were burdened with constant hoisting, hauling, and pushing by hand, which was exceedingly fatiguing. The handling problem lay in the entire production cycle, from the receipt of the raw material to its final fabrication.

In any program of materials handling research, attention should be concentrated on those departments which have the most **involved handling problems** and are handling the largest volume of products, such as rough forgings, castings, sheet metal stampings, finished gears and shafts, screw machine parts, and complete assemblies. In the foregoing case it was determined that items such as these should be palletized for transfer between production departments to storage areas and the shipping platform. The company's research laboratories developed pallets for comprehensive initial tests, most of which were conducted on available platform lift trucks.

Company-wide Materials Handling Research

WIDENING THE RESEARCH ACTIVITY. Full-time materials handling and packaging research should be undertaken on a company-wide basis. In multiple-plant organizations each plant should be visited and plans made for the coordination of materials handling activities with the findings of the company's materials handling research laboratory.

CENTRALIZED MATERIALS HANDLING RESEARCH. Materials handling research may be carried on by a section of a centralized manufacturing research department, a department that should be headed by an executive or engineer of wide experience. A large midwest manufacturer's materials handling research, for example, is so organized; the general functions of its materials handling research section are shown in Fig. 1.

Materials handling research includes, besides materials handling, the functions of **loading, packaging and packing, storage,** and **warehousing.** The organization of such a section is shown in Fig. 2. Under this plan of organization, the general supervisor of the materials handling research section reports to the manager of manufacturing research. The manager, in turn, is responsible to the vice-president of manufacturing under the president. Relations with operating plants should be consultative in nature, and the research section should act in an advisory capacity. The principal points of contact with any plant are through the particular works manager and his materials handling engineer (see Fig. 3).

An adequate amount of floor space should be allotted for materials handling research. This area would be used for originating and developing palletizing, handling facilities, foreign and domestic packing and packaging, loading methods, and storage and warehousing systems.

Facilities for testing containers and pallets should include a range and variety of equipment. One installation includes an incline-impact machine, called the Conbur, for impacting the container or pallet at speeds from 4.5 to 8 mi. per hr. against a heavy wood and steel backing. Two shakers are provided to test the containers or pallets under vibrations up to 300 cycles per min. One of these shakers has a capacity of 5,000 lb. and the other of 1,000 lb. A 30,000-lb. capacity compression machine is used mainly for pallet and container testing. Standard instruments for testing papers are set up in the paper room. These include a General Electric puncture tester, an Elmendorf tear tester, Tabor stiffness tester, serigraph tensile tester, scuff tester, and a Mullen bursting tester. For the production of experimental paperboard containers and pallets, this laboratory has a board rack and a carton-making machine. Other testing equipment might include a weather-o-meter for simulating weather effects on small samples, a salt-spray cabinet, humidity cabinet, freezing cabinet, heating cabinet, and a moisture meter for determining free moisture in wood (Fig. 4).

A materials handling manual and a packing and packaging manual are necessary guidebooks covering manufacturing operations and should be prepared by the research staff. Some of the procedures written into these books would be the results of developments in the research laboratory. Specifications, bulletins, and manufacturing briefs should be issued to keep the plant staff informed of current materials handling data and other factual information.

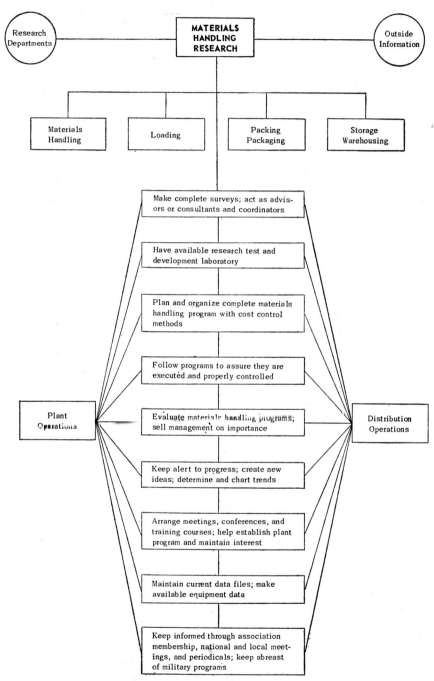

Fig. 1. General functions of the materials handling research section.

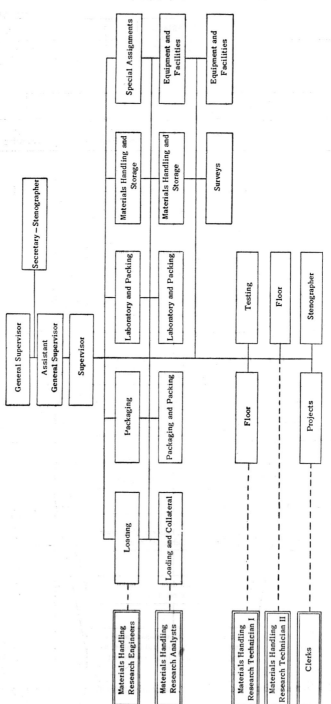

Fig. 2. Manufacturing research—materials handling section organization.

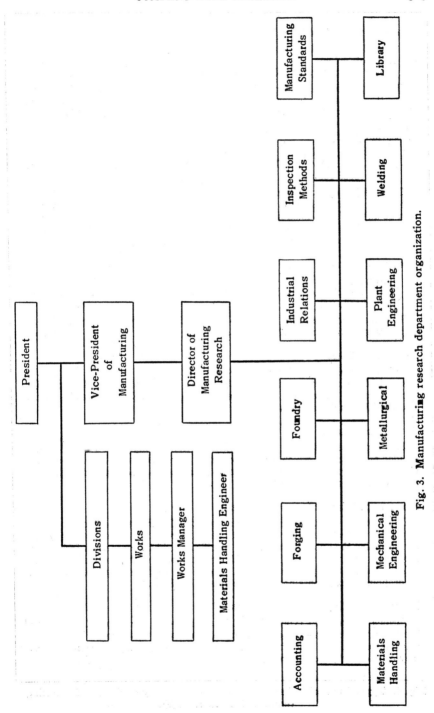

Fig. 3. Manufacturing research department organization.

INCLINE-IMPACT UNIT

Capacity: 5,000 lb.
Angle of incline: 10°.
Motor data: 220/440 volts, 60 cycle, 3 hp., equipped with reducer.

This machine simulates switching and bumping impacts received in railroad cars. It is adjustable to speeds up to 8 mi. per hr., equivalent to 12 mi. per hr. in railroad cars equipped with draft gears. It is approved by A.S.T.M.

VIBRATION TESTER

Capacity: 5,000 lb.
Motor data: 220/440 volts, 60 cycle, 3 phase, 7.5 hp., equipped with a variable speed reducer.

This testing machine simulates the vertical and horizontal action or movement that containers would receive in railroad or highway truck shipments. It can be adjusted to a maximum speed equivalent to 55 mi. per hr. on a railroad car. The time a package is subjected to vibration determines the length of trip; i.e., 30 min. of testing is equivalent to a 500-mi. trip.

VIBRATION TESTER

Capacity: 1,000 lb.
Motor data: 220/440 volts, 60 cycle, 3 phase, 3 hp., equipped with a variable speed reducer.

This machine is similar to the 5,000-lb. vibration tester except that its capacity is limited to 1,000 lb. Adjustment and test correlation are the same.

FLOOR DROP PLATE

This device consists of a movable chain hoist on a monorail and special device hooks which are used to hoist boxes and cartons to specified heights for drop testing on a steel plate. Containers loaded to 1,000 lb. gross weight can be tested with this piece of equipment.

ACME DROP TESTER

This drop tester consists of a wooden platform, hinged on two sides and divided at the center, which can be located at a desired distance from the floor. Containers placed on the platform can be positioned to drop on a corner, edge, or side when the stops are released.

SUPPORT FOR TESTING LARGE CONTAINERS

Large export containers of excessive weight (5,000 lb. or more) can be drop tested by resting one end of the container approximately 8 in. from the floor and dropping the opposite end from a specified height by means of a fork truck. A support has been devised on which one end of a container can be placed when dropping the opposite end. It is capable of withstanding stresses caused by dropping heavy containers from heights up to 24 in.

MACHINE FOR MAKING SAMPLE CARTONS

Various weights and types of corrugated and solid fiberboard stock are on hand for use in developing all types and sizes of containers. The above machine cuts, scores, and slots the material for making sample cartons so that they can be fabricated for any specific use.

Fig. 4. Typical materials handling research laboratory equipment for testing (continued on next page).

Spray Booth

This booth is capable of holding large export boxes as well as smaller waterproof cartons. Overhead nozzles can be regulated to produce water streams of various pressures and temperatures. It is used to determine the effect of rain and moisture on waterproof papers, cartons, etc. The sprays are so arranged as to provide 2½ gal. of water per hr. per sq. ft. of floor.

Weather-O-Meter

230 volts, 30–34 amps, 60 cycle.

This unit is used to simulate heat, sunshine, and rain. Steel panels coated with various types of corrosion preventives are placed in the weather-o-meter to test the durability of the coatings. Paints, metal alloys, and virtually any material exposed to weather conditions can be tested. Thirty 24-hr. cycles are equal to one year outside storage.

Salt Spray Cabinet

115 volts, 60 cycle, 8.7 amps.

This unit atomizes a 20% salt solution into a fine spray in a tightly sealed cabinet for testing coatings to be used for export shipment or outdoor storage. It is an accelerated test with temperatures at 100° F. and air pressure at 14½ lb.

Humidity Cabinet

115 volts, 60 cycle, 70 amps.

This is a gravity-type humidity cabinet with temperature set at 100° F. and 100% humidity. It is used as an accelerated test on all types of protective coatings.

Heating Cabinet (small)

This cabinet is used for testing corrosion preventives, paper, etc., that may be subjected to temperature up to 180° F.

Oven (large)

This oven is used for larger items that require testing to determine their resistance to heat. The temperature in this cabinet can be raised to 300° F.

Refrigeration Unit

This unit is used for the purpose of testing corrosion preventives, paper samples, and small packaged parts in subzero temperatures. This unit is capable of lowering the temperature to −40° F.

Blast Cleaning Unit

One of the uses of this unit is for cleaning parts by the soft grit method developed by the U. S. Department of Agriculture for utilizing waste farm products. This cleaning medium consists of a combination of ground corn cobs and rice hulls. Dimensional limits are unchanged by this process.

Solvent Dip Tanks

These are used for cleaning parts of corrosion preventives using a petroleum solvent.

Fig. 4. (Continued on next page.)

MULLEN TESTER

Capacity: 0 to 800 lb. per sq. in.

This machine is used to test the bursting strength of corrugated board, solid fiberboard, paper, and other materials. Resistance to pressure is recorded in pounds per square inch.

SERIGRAPH

Capacity: 120 lb. tensile strength.

This machine is used for testing the tensile strength of paper, corrugated board, wrapping material, and other items whose tensile strength does not exceed the capacity of the machine.

ELMENDORF TEAR TESTER

This testing unit measures the tearing strength of packaging material in grams. A test sheet of paper, tape, or wrapping material is placed in the machine and a knife released to make an initial cut. The force required to tear the remaining length of the sample is then measured.

SCUFF TESTER

The scuff test consists of sliding the corresponding outside surfaces of two identical test specimens by means of a power-driven testing machine having a reciprocating arm. The test samples are required to withstand excessive wear or scuffing over a specified time.

pH METER

This meter is used to determine the amount of acid or alkaline content of various types of packaging papers. Packaging papers having a high acid or alkaline content are detrimental to finished surfaces, with a reaction similar to corrosion.

MOISTURE METER

This meter tests the moisture content of lumber. Some specifications state that the moisture content of lumber must not exceed 19%. Lumber which has excessive moisure will shrink and sometimes warp when drying.

CONTAINER COMPRESSION TESTER

Capacity: 30,000 lb.

This machine is used to compress shipping containers between platens to simulate static loading in storage. The motion of the upper platen can be regulated from ½ to 1 in. per min. while testing. The platens are 54 × 48 in., and boxes up to 72 in. high can be placed between them. It is also possible to test the compression and recovery characteristics of various cushioning materials.

BASIS WEIGHT SCALE

Range: From 2 to 200 lb. per ream.

This instrument measures the weight of paper in the standard paper terms.

Fig. 4. (Continued on next page.)

G.E. Puncture Tester

Range: From 0 to 1,600 in.-lb.

This machine measures the energy required to puncture sheet materials, such as paper and corrugated board. The puncturing point is formed to simulate the corner of a box.

Taber Stiffness Gage

Range: From 0 to 5,000 gm.-cm.

Capacity: Up to ⅛-in.-thick material.

This instrument measures the force required to bend a strip of sample paper through 15°.

Wind Tunnel

Motor: ¼ hp., 220 volts.

This machine consists of an electric fan set in a tube 12 in. in diam. In the exhaust end of the tube a rack is fixed for supporting coated articles while drying. The flow past the rack averages 600 ft. per min.

Vapometer

This instrument is for testing vapor permeability of thin sheets. It consists of a flanged cup in which water is placed and weighed. The sample is clamped over the cup. The vapor transmission is indicated by the loss in weight over a period of time.

Fig. 4. (Concluded.)

Materials Handling Projects. Projects undertaken by materials handling sections originate from three main sources:

1. The company organization as a whole. A materials handling project may come from sales departments within the company in the form of customer suggestions, from manufacturing plants, or from other internal research groups.
2. The research department, which itself should propose projects when it sees opportunities for making improvement.
3. Other industries, technical literature, schools and universities, and outside research organizations.

Classification of projects over a recent period of five years in a typical multiplant manufacturing group revealed the following assignments: 112 in materials handling, 174 in packaging and packing, 45 in loading and shipping, and 15 in storage and warehousing.

Materials Handling Committee. A materials handling committee, consisting of plant materials handling engineers and general office staff members, is especially useful in multiple-plant or division operations. Such a committee should hold periodic meetings, usually alternating between different plants and the manufacturing research department. The general supervisor of the materials handling research section should act as chairman. Close liaison should be maintained between the committee and the materials handling research laboratory so that they can assist, and supplement the activities of, each other. **General handling methods** of interest to individual plants and the company as a whole should be discussed. The committee can act as a clearing house for advanced handling ideas and help maintain interest in progressive materials handling in all plants. Committee meetings will engender a spirit of cooperation in working out closely related interworks handling problems.

PRACTICAL CONCEPTIONS OF MATERIALS HANDLING RESEARCH. There are many factors to be taken into consideration in the original development of any **research program and facilities,** and still others to be **considered on a periodic basis.** Those of concern in the early stages may include size of company, whether large or small; manufacturing experience, an old or new company, research experience, extensive or very little; type of product, fabricated item or processed material and complexity of manufacture; and the company's competitive position.

Not every research investigation turns out successfully. Although the success or failure of a particular investigation is more technical than administrative, the development and authorization of a well-balanced research program is definitely an administration problem of great importance.

The administrator must have sufficient foresight to plan his program and resourcefulness to carry it out in such a way as to **provide the best over-all return.** In so doing, he must consider the proper balance between fundamental and applied research.

A properly balanced industrial program should be basically "applied" but supplemented by some "fundamental" activity. Most fundamental research activities can be best operated if taken over by universities or special laboratories, where the best talent and facilities are available.

A research program should be flexible. Only with a dynamic program capable of being adjusted to immediate needs can success be assured. As problems of immediate importance come up, or as the need or probability of success of current investigations becomes apparent, the original program must be altered. A rigid program tends to restrict progress toward even greater goals. Periodic program review should be established to guarantee flexibility of action.

Another problem of concern in industry is that of **selling the product of research effort.** There are times when the results are outstanding and sell themselves. In other instances, it is necessary to create enthusiasm and sustained interest in those who must put a recommendation or change into effect.

The **techniques and channels** which permit the administrator to accomplish the best results would unquestionably vary with each and every concern. Such factors as attitude toward research, degree of participation, method of reporting, organization relationships, and amount of cooperation within a specific company would have considerable influence on the choice of method.

The ideal research worker is thought of as one having highly specialized training and possessing more than normal curiosity, imagination, and individual initiative. The organization should be built up of a combination of practical know-how and scientific comprehension. Men trained in the fundamentals of engineering and science and familiar with the procedures of scientific experimentation can readily review and evaluate the results of fundamental research within their specialized fields. They can supplement fundamental results by further experimental investigation where necessity demands. On the other hand, there are men who, by virtue of a background of practical experience and acquaintance with the technical and operating problems in the field, can recognize practical implications of tremendous value in achieving goals. Thus, the merger of the two tends to keep activities within practical bounds and results in balanced man power among a group working primarily in the applied research area.

Research requires that those engaged in technical activities be familiar with management principles and have scientific training. Often the technical man lacks management experience, and special efforts must be made to supplement his training or to bring in people who have had such training.

Nature and Extent of Research

TYPICAL ORIGIN OF PROJECTS. One of the first project suggestions at International Harvester came from the depot operations department. The materials handling research laboratory was asked to develop a pallet for shipping service parts from plants to depots. The requirement was that these pallet containers were to have a feature that would make it possible to remove the parts while the pallets were stacked four and five high. They were to be constructed of light lumber to reduce weight, and to be collapsible for return for re-use. No nails could be used in the assembly of the panels.

Several models were developed and tested, but each had features that were objectionable to depot operations personnel. After ten or eleven designs had been submitted and rejected, an idea was worked out which incorporated not only all the original requirements but also a few that were added to improve the handling methods and facilities for depot operations. The initial laboratory tests proved acceptable. The actual shipping tests and depot tests also were approved. Approximately 100,000 of these pallet containers are now in use throughout the Harvester depot operations.

Extent of Materials Handling Research. Recently a national survey was made to determine how many research laboratories were actively engaged in materials handling research. Although it was learned that packaging research laboratories were numerous and had been well established, it was also learned that very few industries had, to any extent, actually included the development of materials handling in their research activities. Plans were being made in some plant operations to organize and equip such research units, but not on a very broad scale. Still, many executives recognized the economic need for conducting materials handling research and were delegating the task as a general engineering or development function. Suppliers of materials handling equipment facilities were making noteworthy research and engineering strides in their endeavors to bring out new machines and special features for the betterment of materials handling. There is evidence, therefore, that the need for materials handling research is gaining far wider recognition and that industries are giving increasing attention to the potential benefits and economies possible through instituting such programs.

The survey pointed out that liberal contributions to the compilation of information on materials handling research are being made throughout industry. Among the types of surveyed industries whose experiences have been most useful are the following, classified by area of contribution:

Industry	Classification
Air freight	Shipping
Auto frames and pipe lines	Production and shipping
Automobiles and trucks	Production
Box shooks	Fabrication
Chain restaurants	Service
Chemicals	Processing
Dairy products	Processing
Docks	Shipping

Industry	Classification
Electrical apparatus	Production
Flour	Processing and storage
Food products	Processing
Fractional hp. engines	Production
Heavy machinery	Production
Hotels	Service
Household appliances	Production and shipping
Logging operations and sawmills	Fabricating
Mail order	Service and storage
Meat packing and stockyards	Processing and shipping
Mechanical handling equipment	Production
Merchandising	Sales and warehousing
Ore, coal, and grain	Processing and storage
Overseas packing	Processing
Paper cartons	Production and service
Paper-mills	Processing and storage
Plate glass	Processing
Plumbing and heating supplies	Production
Publishing and newspapers	Processing
Radio and television	Production
Railroad freight yards	Shipping
Railroad passenger traffic	Transportation and service
Railway express	Shipping
Road machinery	Production
Rubber tires	Processing
Self-service food stores	Sales and distribution
Shoes	Production
Steamship docks	Shipping
Steel	Production and fabrication
Terminal warehouses	Storage

A great deal of thought should be given to the problem of determining how materials handling research can be made to pay in any industry. Sources within the individual company may resist any expenditures for research and may scrutinize every dollar spent. And because there are certain limitations to how far any type of research will go, initial results may not be so great as anticipated. It is essential, therefore, that the promoter of the program be thoroughly sold on the research idea. His belief in its fundamental importance must not be easily shaken. He should have a well-grounded knowledge of what it will and will not do for his plant. He must gather his data, analyze it thoroughly, sell the idea to his company, and be willing to start in a small way.

One capable man assigned to start materials handling research in a small industry can accomplish results commensurate with those brought about by a staff of research men in a large company. Small packaging and materials handling laboratories have been operated with excellent results by one or two men. But, whether or not they are in large or small industries, because the entire materials handling field is one of **constant change and progress,** the need for additional laboratories for materials handling research is becoming more and more imperative.

Research in Small Companies

OPPORTUNITIES IN SMALL COMPANIES. The question of whether materials handling research can be made to pay in a small company often arises. Investigation of industrial research laboratories devoted to handling and packaging shows that most of the materials handling research in industry starts in a small way. The outlay is nominal for equipment, for laboratory space, and for personnel required for conducting the initial research activities.

The decision on the continuance of a small laboratory must be made by the plant or other parent organization. Where the program has been well planned, the trend for continuance has been favorable in small companies which have started materials handling research laboratories. For some industries the services of the numerous **outside consulting laboratories** available for carrying on handling and packaging research have advantages.

Following are suggestions for **setting up** a materials handling research program in small industries.

1. **Top management** must be active in support of the materials handling research program and maintain its support. The executive in charge of plant operations must let his staff know how vital materials handling is in production.

2. **Responsibility** should be placed in one man, properly trained in materials handling research. His first task should be to make an analysis of the entire plant and determine what plant areas will be most benefited by research. Going back over past history is not a waste of time in establishing a new program. Since a one-man or part-time research staff cannot take on all possible activities at once, spotting the plant's worst materials handling problems helps determine where the least effort will produce the most results. As big problems are taken care of, those less pressing can be considered.

3. The materials handling research man should have the **help of a committee.** No matter who the materials handling man is or what his background may be, he is certain to get important suggestions and realistic advice from a working committee.

4. Setting up a **simple cost-control record system** is the next step. This system should be based on the costs per ton of handling in individual departments. This cost system should be kept simple. Often the best source of information for setting up a cost system in a smaller company is the company's own auditor or cost man.

5 Regular meetings of supervisors keep interest high and provide a forum for discussion not only of materials handling research but also of related problems in the fields of production. Common sense dictates that supervisors must be the main vehicles of interest and enthusiasm in such a program.

6. A materials handling research program works down to the individual handler. He also should be taught to think in terms of improved handling. Some companies get valuable suggestions through plant-wide employee suggestion systems. Foremen should pass on their knowledge of materials handling to the handling personnel in their departments in order to stimulate cooperation.

Selecting Men for Research Activities

IMPORTANCE OF WORKING WITH OTHER SPECIALISTS. A successful materials handling engineer always is willing to seek counsel of other research specialists. When there are no such specialists available, he should discuss the research projects with the departmental personnel directly concerned. Experience has shown the advantages of working closely with other research or industrial engineers having positions that qualify them to speak with authority on specialized work connected with the handling of research projects being surveyed. This type of consulting is of great aid to a materials handling research engineer in arriving at the proper answers to his problems quickly and effectively.

Two general sources should be considered in **selecting men for materials handling research work**: practical factory men trained in industrial operations, and technically trained men with a college background. In an analysis of personnel in typical materials handling laboratories, it has been found that there is a very close balance between the two sources.

The most generally accepted classifications of the personnel in a materials handling research section are materials handling **research engineers**, materials handling **research analysts**, and materials handling **research technicians**. Their duties are described in Figs. 5, 6, and 7.

GENERAL STATEMENT OF DUTIES AND MANAGERIAL RESPONSIBILITIES

As a managerial representative of the materials handling section, he is held directly responsible for analyzing, developing, and carrying out materials handling projects and programs such as movement of material, transportation equipment, storage, protection, packaging, packing and loading, and training of company personnel on new methods and procedures affecting materials handling.

He directs, disciplines, instructs, and assigns work to the employees under his supervision and initiates the hiring, promoting, discharge, lay-off, transfer, and rates of pay of such employees, with the aid of service departments.

He is responsible for carrying out company policies, formulates rules necessary for the efficient performance of the activities under supervision, receives and acts on employees' grievances in the first step of the grievance procedure, and performs related duties as assigned.

His work involves the performance of responsible nonmanual duties directly related to management policies or general business operations and of a specialized nature, requiring special training and experience, and the exercise of discretion and independent judgment.

TYPICAL DUTIES

1. Make recommendations and carry out programs, developing methods and procedures which will result in the more efficient and economical handling of materials.
2. Determine and initiate the establishment of specifications and standards for all phases of materials handling.
3. Develop and recommend designs of materials handling equipment, containers, pallets, and allied accessories.
4. Develop experiments and tests for determining the efficiency and adequacy of materials handling methods, devices, and accessories for all phases of materials handling.
5. Originate and develop new methods, procedures, and manuals for packing, loading, and storing of materials and end products.
6. Make layouts for packing and loading operations.
7. Conduct experiments and tests, compiling data for protecting material and product against corrosion and deterioration.
8. Keep informed on latest developments in equipment, methods, procedures, and testing in the materials handling field.
9. Make surveys of new designs, methods, and materials, developing recommendations designed to improve packaging procedures and reduce cost.
10. Arrange shipping tests and follow-up results.
11. Train personnel in the techniques of all phases of materials handling.
12. Supervise and instruct technicians in all phases of operations in the materials handling laboratory.

Fig. 5. Materials handling research engineer—duties.

General Statement of Duties

Under supervision, to investigate, survey, and analyze company's materials handling methods and problems, making recommendations designed to improve materials handling methods and procedures.

Typical Duties

1. Make survey of existing materials handling methods and procedures, collect and analyze data, and recommend improvements to the end of effectively improving materials handling and storing practices.
2. Prepare and develop progress reports of investigations and surveys.
3. Plan and lay out programs for developing new materials handling methods, procedures, and manuals.
4. Develop and recommend new or improved designs of materials handling equipment, including packaging, storing and loading, product protection, and other related items.
5. Compile data and assist in the establishment of standards and specifications for all phases of materials handling.
6. Follow up recommendations of investigations and surveys for most efficient results.
7. Guide and instruct technicians in processing techniques to be employed in the execution of materials handling activities.
8. Perform related duties as assigned.

Fig. 6. Materials handling research analyst—duties.

General Statement of Duties

Under direct but intermittent supervision, to execute a wide variety of the more difficult materials handling assignments involving development and layout work, operating tests, and actual manual operations required in the construction of devices and accessories for such purposes.

Typical Duties

1. Originate and make, for the purpose of improving design and effecting more economical handling, a wide variety of accessories and devices, such as cartons, crates, cases, boxes, bales, bundles, pallets, wrapping, coatings, and related devices.
2. Set up and operate fatigue-testing machines, drop-testing machines, weather-o-meters, water-testing machines, and other related equipment, conducting tests on materials handling devices and containers.
3. Collect data and develop progress reports of projects and operations being performed in the laboratory.
4. Suggest and recommend new designs, devices, equipment, tests, and testing equipment.
5. Originate and make layouts for packing, loading, receiving, storing, and shipping installations.
6. Instruct others in the proper use of testing materials and equipment storing and handling facilities.
7. Maintain testing and laboratory equipment in good working order.
8. Assist in developing methods, procedures, and manuals for proper handling of materials and end products.
9. Perform related duties as assigned.

Fig. 7. Materials handling technician—duties.

EQUIVALENT QUALIFICATIONS OF FACTORY-TRAINED AND COLLEGE-TRAINED MEN. Two selections have been made from the company's industrial materials handling research staff to show that factory- and college-trained men have an equal opportunity for success in research.

The factory-trained research man was selected from several manufacturing-plant prospects. His occupation was that of welder and he had had several years of loading experience at his particular plant. After a few months of training, including industry and transportation contacts, he was assigned several loading research projects. His ideas and manner of dealing with people enabled him to accomplish these tasks successfully, and it was established that he had qualities which were essential for a materials handling research man. He gradually took on additional responsibilities and made excellent progress.

Later he was given a very important assignment in the interest of the sales department. This research task covered the handling and storage of disassembled implements in district sales warehouses. The job was completed during the following year and had the full approval of the sales department. He was then promoted to the position of materials handling research engineer. He continued in a wide range of materials handling research developments and studied for an engineering degree at night in an accredited college.

The technically trained college man received his B.S. degree in mechanical engineering and spent 10 yr. in engineering, personnel, public service, industrial research, and machine and foundry work, both in the United States and abroad.

During his recent years in materials handling research, he had both laboratory and operational assignments. His training in the fundamentals of materials handling, packing, warehousing methods, equipment, factory layouts, costs, compilation of data, and presentation of systems and reports has been very extensive, including experience in:

1. Coordination of materials handling research laboratory test procedures.
2. Basic research in volatile corrosion inhibitors industry specifications and usage guide.
3. Fork truck survey analysis and data system.
4. Cooperation in a survey to establish a standardized service parts layout and location system.
5. Development of an improved warehousing procedure involving 9,000 production items, which will have wide application in industry operations.

REQUIREMENTS FOR THE POSITION OF MATERIALS HANDLING RESEARCH ENGINEER. Men succeeding in materials handling research seem to possess qualities making them what might be termed **"research minded."** Usually these men have more than average imagination, a determination for accomplishment even under many obstacles, the facility to judge people and consider their ideas, and the ability to analyze and coordinate facts that have a bearing on potential research progress. Some of this knowledge is inherent in the individual, but a great deal must be acquired. A good practical approach to a new development is also essential.

A materials handling research engineer should be:

1. An idea man and have a good imagination.
2. Able to look at projects from a broad viewpoint.
3. Able to meet and work with all kinds of people from executives to the men actually doing this handling.
4. Willing to consider ideas even though they may appear to be impractical.
5. Possessed of a sound knowledge of national materials handling programs and able to contribute something to make these programs successful.

MONDAY 9:30–11:30 A.M.

Organization

1. History.
2. Functions.
3. Difference between plant materials handling and materials handling research.
4. Qualifications of a materials handling research engineer.
5. Scope of materials handling—trends.
   a. Project and program system.
6. Relation to other manufacturing research sections.
7. Ideas and imagination.
8. Library references.
   a. Periodicals.
   b. Engineering training.
9. Materials handling cost reduction program.
10. Objectives.
11. Cost analysis.
    a. Tonnage costs.
    b. Weekly budgets.
12. Control charts.

TUESDAY 9:00–11:30 A.M.

Materials Handling Research

1. Basic objectives.
   a. Reduction of handling costs.
   b. Increase of capacity.
   c. Improvement in working conditions.
   d. Improvement in distribution.
2. Layouts.
   a. Over-all planning before the layout is started.
   b. Layout of originating departments.
   c. Layout of operating departments.
   d. Flow of materials.
3. Plant organization for materials handling.
4. Materials handling equipment.
5. Preventive maintenance of materials handling equipment.
6. Collateral handling.
7. Bundling program.
8. Vendor program.
9. Materials handling committee and subcommittee.

WEDNESDAY 9:00–11:00 A.M.

Warehousing and Storage

1. Systems.
2. Production storage.
3. Yard storage.
4. District sales warehouse storage.
5. Parts storage.
6. Outside rented warehouses—parts.
7. Outside rented warehouses—production items.

Fig. 8. One-week training course in materials handling research (continued on next page).

Loading and Transportation

  1. Methods.
  2. Loss and damage reduction.

Freight Increases

  1. How to overcome.

THURSDAY 9:00–11:00 A.M.

Packing

  1. Domestic containers.
  2. Export containers.
  3. Construction and fabrication.
  4. Reinforcements.
  5. Testing: laboratory and field tests.

Packaging

  1. Cartoning.
  2. Specifications.
    a. Corrosion prevention and volatile corrosion inhibitors.
    b. Protection.
  3. Sales appeal program.
  4. Equipment.
  5. Identification.
  6. Marking.

Summary—General discussion.

Suggestions

  1. Continuation of specific training.
  2. Materials handling equipment and attachments.
  3. Warehousing and storage.
  4. Collateral.
    a. Light pallet.
    b. Depalletization.
  5. Surveys and layouts.

Materials Handling Subcommittees

  1. These committees also need training.
  2. Their efforts should be directed toward a better understanding of their duties.
  3. Subjects should be presented for discussion at each committee meeting.
  4. Training outlines for each committee will be available when they meet.
  5. Training in the special subjects for each committee is essential for their continued progress. It will coordinate with the materials handling research section training activities.

Fig. 8. (Concluded.)

6. Filled with an unlimited enthusiasm for his job and willing to extend extra effort to succeed.
7. Continuously growing with materials handling research progress.
8. Last, but not least, able to sell himself and his ideas to the rank and file of men in industry.

A typical **one-week training course** for materials handling research personnel is outlined in Fig. 8.

VALUE OF ADVANCED RESEARCH. The experience gained in the materials handling research laboratory has provided a sound basis for applying planned research thinking to other present problems and to future progress. Without planned thinking, any research program of the future will lose much of its value. In the competitive economy existing today, no research group can carry on successfully without a real basis of planned thinking.

One phase of planned thinking is to **map or chart a course for future guidance:**

1. What should be accomplished in the years to come?
2. What are the important objectives?

A plan, to be successful, should provide a long-range look ahead—and this requirement is particularly true of research. Sometimes, through desire to concentrate on present assignments, sight is lost of the fact that the principal job of a research group is to initiate and develop ideas that are in advance of present practices.

Research in Materials Handling Costs

CONTROL OF COSTS. Materials handling cost control should be part of every materials handling research program. In most industries materials handling costs range from 25 to 40 percent of the cost of production. Without a plan for controlling this cost, a great deal of the effort of a materials handling research laboratory might be lost. The problem is one requiring a thorough study to set up the best possible cost system, with the help of the company's accountants. Reductions in excess of 10 percent of total handling costs have recently been made in several large manufacturing operations through the adoption of a system initiated by the company's research group.

It is advisable to allocate handling costs through established accounts into a **tonnage cost statement.** These reports should be submitted monthly or quarterly, from each plant operation, to the materials handling research laboratory. By comparison with experience in a like period during the previous year, it is possible to calculate cost trends (Fig. 9). Those plants showing cost increases can then be assisted by the materials handling research department to establish proper control.

Recently the materials handling research department of a large manufacturer was asked to develop a **cost reduction plan** for a triplant division with an unfavorable handling cost factor. The program planned by the research staff was based on:

1. A cost control budget.
2. Maintaining continued interest of plant personnel.
3. Plant movement and flow surveys.
4. Analysis of methods and equipment.
5. Continued coordination with the materials handling research laboratory.

MATERIALS HANDLING COST, WAGES ONLY, ADJUSTED TO CURRENT WAGE LEVEL

Plant	Tonnage	Cost per Ton	Change per Ton		Value
MACHINES					
A	51,669	$11.22	$.25	Increase	$12,917
B	150	22.09	3.99	Decrease	599
C	72,147	7.51	.07	Increase	5,050
SERVICE PARTS					
A	–	–	–		–
B	5,213	$63.80	$15.42	Decrease	$80,384
C	43,596	30.67	.39	Increase	17,002
COLLATERAL					
A	29,263	$12.11	$.34	Increase	$9,973
B	77,752	10.19	.21	Increase	16,328
C	25,365	10.85	.19	Decrease	4,819

Plant	Net Value (Cumulative this season)	
A	$22,890	Increase
B	64,655	Decrease
C	17,233	Increase
Net Decrease	$24,532	Decrease

Data for a one-year period compared to previous year.

Fig. 9. Materials handling tonnage costs.

The program developed is shown in Fig. 10. After this program had been in effect for about one year, costs showed a favorable downward trend.

RECOMMENDATIONS
1. Establish cost control budget.
2. Maintain continued program activity.
3. Survey plant to determine handling methods improvement.
4. Develop additional plans to keep materials handling costs on a downward trend.
5. Coordinate program with manufacturing research section.

NOTE: A divisional plan of this kind, involving all manufacturing operations, might well be guided and kept active by a divisional head appointed by the manager of manufacturing.

1. Cost control budget.
   a. Review present tonnage cost statements.
   b. Outline weekly departmental cost system.
   c. Appoint a budget control supervisor.
   d. Coordinate the plan through a staff assistant.
2. Maintain continued follow-up of program.
   a. Through staff meetings.
   b. Through foremen's meetings and training.
   c. Through department heads assisting materials handling engineers, including plant engineer, mechanical engineer, planning engineer, methods engineer, etc.
   d. Through maintaining interest of all handling personnel in better handling methods.

Fig. 10. A materials handling cost reduction program planned by a materials handling research section (continued on next page).

3. Plant survey to improve materials handling.
   a. Begin with departments or operations requiring immediate improvements.
   b. Volume items should come first.
   c. Flow of material and routings.
   d. Relocation of machine tools for straight-line production.
   e. Analyze over-all movement throughout plant from incoming to outgoing; this will bring out necessary handling operations.
   f. Increase mechanical and decrease manual handling.
   g. Replace collateral pallets and boxes in production with permanent handling facilities.

NOTE: Department foremen are an essential part of the success of these surveys. Their efforts and ideas will control their costs and their methods and at the same time help the entire plant in a better over-all handling system.

4. Additional developments.
   a. Make better use of materials handling equipment now available for movement of materials. (The preventive maintenance program for lift trucks will be of benefit.)
   b. Coordinate with suppliers to reduce incoming handling and unloading costs.
   c. Improve loading methods for cost reduction.
   d. Load in depot or standard pallet boxes at last production operation.
   e. Improve use of floor space, in storage, to reduce length of hauls, store more material in space available, install location system, and reduce inventory.

NOTE: An appraisal of the materials handling engineer and his duties and how organized might be advisable. His position has a great deal to do with the success and progress of materials handling in his plant.

5. Assistance from manufacturing research.
   a. By studies in the application of methods developed through the materials handling section.
   b. Applying ideas from other industries.
   c. Assisting in surveys and cost control system.
   d. Through ideas in manufacturing research section bulletins.
   e. Periodical review of materials handling developments.
   f. Through help from other sections of the manufacturing research section pertaining specifically to their fields of work.

6. Specific suggestions.
   a. Collateral shipments to first operation in original pallet.
   b. Finished material in shipping pallet at last operation.
   c. Use materials handling facilities (racks, chutes, conveyors, etc.) for intradepartment purposes in place of collateral pallets.
   d. In-process handling is the biggest item of handling; it can be improved, as is done at other plants.
   e. Improved storage practices to reduce handling cost and conserve floor area.

NOTE: The majority of recommendations made in this outline are the result of actual developments now effective in other plants and closely coordinated with the materials handling research section of manufacturing research.

The most effective plans carried out by the materials handling section have been made directly with or through the works managers. Their active interest has made it possible to gain the best results in the shortest time.

Fig. 10. (Concluded.)

Of special significance in this research cost control plan were the weekly departmental cost allocations. Each foreman was held accountable under this system for his portion of the program. The plant budget controller was assigned the task of maintaining the budget (Fig. 11).

TYPICAL WEEKLY DEPARTMENTAL MATERIALS HANDLING COST RECORD—M PLANT

	Weight Handled (lb.)	No. 41—Packing Dept.		No. 43—Shipping Dept.	
		Wages	Per Cwt.	Wages	Per Cwt.
Budget (Season)	150,000,000	$60,000	$.0400	$270,000	$.1800
Weekly Costs					
First Week	2,000,000	1,260	.0630	5,600	.2800
Second Week	3,000,000	1,260	.0420	5,600	.1866
Third Week	4,000,000	1,260	.0315	5,600	.1400
Fourth Week	3,110,000	1,260	.0400	5,600	.1800
Fifth Week	2,000,000	800	.0400	3,600	.1800
Total	14,110,000	$ 5,840	$.0410	$ 26,000	$.1840
Balance	135,890,000	$54,160		$244,000	

Note: The budget established at the start of each year is based on objective cost reduction which usually averages about 10 percent under the showing for the prior year. In this case, the 4 cents per cwt. in Dept. 41 and the 18 cents per cwt. in Dept. 43 are the goals for the current year. In the previous year, the costs per cwt. were respectively 4.4 cents and 19.8 cents.

Fig. 11. Materials handling department cost budget.

Cost Reduction. Experience has shown that research developments in most phases of materials handling bring out **many different methods of action** to arrive at similar solutions. The type of research organization, the kind of industry, the product, and the method of distribution—all have a bearing on the research study and the final decision for the particular problem.

This condition applies especially to materials handling cost systems. The objective is to control costs. Any practical method that through a research study will meet this goal will be acceptable. The solution might be based on materials handling costs under a **weekly or monthly per ton method, a net product cost plan,** or the **man-hours required per ton of materials handled.** Research men studying cost programs plan their thinking to anticipate every known contingency.

Substantial savings, mostly in materials, also are made through projects developed in the materials handling research laboratory. A **wooden interworks pallet** was recently redesigned, tested, and approved in the laboratory, reducing lumber in thickness from ⅞ in. to ⅝ in. Costs were reduced by approximately 20 percent—all in materials.

A **corn picker shipping skid** was changed from a fabricated support to two bolted runners. Lumber savings exceeded 50 percent.

Industry, through research in materials handling, has before it many opportunities. Sufficient progress has been made by those laboratories already established to assure management that the time and effort expended in this type of research constitute a very profitable investment.

Materials Handling Research Surveys

PLANT HANDLING STUDIES. A materials handling research engineer must understand the **handling operations and flow of materials within the industrial plant.** His position as a consultant among industry personnel is recognized by his general knowledge of handling processes. He should know something about the product being manufactured, type of plant, flow of material, and plant layout. His knowledge of plant materials handling is a measure of the service he can render.

An industry having several manufacturing plants under the same central management can profit by interchange of ideas among the plants. Materials handling research develops new ideas which can be applied profitably in many materials handling operations.

Factory materials handling surveys usually are requested of the materials handling research group when materials handling costs are high or production processes need improvement. Surveys are planned, organized, and carried on through materials handling research. These plans call for a study of the **manual handling operations, safety features, quality control, and cost reduction possibilities.**

Proper planning of materials flow in plant operation sometimes makes the difference between success or failure in a materials handling system. Materials handling research surveys indicate what can be done to improve **layouts for straight-line production.** It is not uncommon to find that distance of travel of material in typical operations can be reduced one-half to one-third. New layouts of production machines, rearrangements of poorly planned departments, and the installation of better handling facilities almost invariably help to correct this condition.

The execution and control of the **equipment layout program** rest fundamentally with the plant engineering staff and are carried out under the direction of the **materials handling engineer,**

A materials handling control system supervised by materials handling research engineers is used as a guide in the initial survey of entire plants or of individual departments.

Materials handling surveys planned by materials handling research have covered, among numerous other projects, a large tractor plant, a rehabilitated collateral plant, a heavy machinery plant, and a group of domestic sales warehouses.

The **tractor plant survey** was made by two materials handling research engineers over a 1-yr. period. Working with the plant staff, the engineers were able to secure acceptance of improvements in the flow of material, in redesign of handling equipment, in rearrangement of operations, and in training of personnel. Materials handling cost reduction exceeded 10 percent during the first year of the survey. Other benefits included improved quality of product, greater tonnage stored and handled in the floor space available, and improved inventory control.

Surveys of this kind sometimes embrace a number of plants in the same industry, shipping collateral items. For instance, a large foundry may produce the castings for a group of plants; a sheet metal stamping operation may provide stampings for additional plants; a plant having a modern forge shop may be required to furnish forgings for five or six other plants. The amounts of materials thus moved in some industries may constitute a large percentage of the total output of such corporations.

A domestic sales warehouse survey was made as a cooperative project between the materials handling research laboratory and sales research. Some of the advantages realized were as follows:

Increased Space. Warehouses probably handle more merchandise now than ever before. A great deal of space can be saved through the use of "air rights." A product which can be stacked twice as high will save half the floor space formerly required. Additional space can be acquired through a better warehousing arrangement.

Better Warehouse Appearance. A warehouse that has been kept in a neat condition will always reflect directly on its supervision. Improved handling facilities will further insure clean and neat appearance.

Better Service to Customers. Quicker delivery of goods is appreciated by all dealers. Improved handling methods cut down time of loading dealers' trucks, and provide greater accuracy.

Better Product Protection. The quality and appearance of products are definitely not improved when they are subjected to carelessness and abuse within the warehouse. Better storage and less handling will do a lot to protect a product.

Reduced Inventory Time. If all items within the warehouse are palletized or unit bundled in standard quantities, it is a simple matter for anyone to count the number stacked and have an accurate record. This obviously relieves warehouse employees of a tedious job, and, in addition, cuts the labor needed at inventory time.

Improved Safety. With mechanized handling there is very little heavy lifting. According to one study, 25 percent of all industrial accidents happen when employees handle material manually. Palletizing reduced this percentage very materially. Lifting is confined to short lifts to the pallet, and hand-high lifting from floor to overhead is virtually eliminated.

Reduced Fork-Truck Time. Under a palletizing program, fork-truck equipment will spend less time in the movement of material. By reducing the truck time on one job, that truck is made available for other work.

INTEGRATION OF MATERIALS HANDLING AND PACKAGING.

Materials handling engineers have long known that both materials handling and packaging, to be fully effective, should be coordinated throughout the entire manufacturing and distribution cycle. With rising labor and materials costs and with other areas for cost reduction fully exploited, management is increasingly accepting this concept.

The Integrated Program. According to Weber (Modern Materials Handling, vol. 12) such a program is defined as the coordination of all phases of materials movement from the originating source to delivery of the finished product to the customer. The integrated handling and packaging program does the following:

1. Puts all responsibility under one head.
2. Ties in with the over-all company operations.
3. Initiates programs for all departments of the business concerned with improved handling, packaging, shipping, storage, and distribution.
4. Obtains the cooperation of outside facilities: vendors, common carriers, warehouse operators, overseas forwarders, and related services.
5. Challenges all handling personnel to new interest in every movement within the company.

Under an integrated program, the **coordinator**, preferably a materials handling engineer on the staff level, must be able to visualize the complete operation. He should keep abreast of three things: the degree of integration as it is at the time, the material flow system from vendor to customer, and the goals, throughout the system, toward which he is moving.

The **integration chart** (Fig. 12) provides the over-all viewpoint and is the coordinator's basic tool. First, it lists the 15 major materials handling and packaging functions and the departments where they occur. Placed horizontally across the top of the chart in their natural order, these may vary according to the company using the chart. Second, listed vertically at the left are the various aspects of coordination including communications, direct flow of materials, space utilization, utilization of handling equipment and facilities, quality improvement, cost control, and research and development.

As a trouble spotter, the **integration rating graph** at the bottom tells at a glance how well each of the 15 specific functions are integrated. It tells which departments need additional attention. In actual practice, the chart shown is a composite of many detailed charts. Studies of handling and packaging methods are undertaken, in most cases, to bring costs into line. Frequently, attention is focused on a given product line. Work sheets showing the costs of all operations by department are prepared.

Careful studies are then made of the methods used in each department for the parts or subassemblies of the product under study. From these studies it is possible to rate the effectiveness of current methods. This is a direct comparison with other methods that could be used. Ratings are made for each of the objectives listed along the left side of the integration chart.

Composite ratings for the product line can then be prepared for listing on the **master integration chart.** These ratings can be used as a guide in determining where the greatest need for improvement lies.

The chart approach to integration can be applied to any manufacturing plant, distributor, or service organization of reasonable size having material movement.

The Chart Objectives. In using the typical chart it is essential that all objectives be clearly thought out and considered in terms of every item that moves through the handling cycle. The chart approach reveals many areas for cost reduction previously unsuspected.

Weber describes the points to consider under each major objective as follows:

Communications is broken down into personnel coordination, training, and communications aids. This objective is of vital concern in direct proportion to the size of the company or the diversification of its activities. From the supervisors' viewpoint, instructions must be communicated to help initiate and maintain the program. —possible through meetings, directives, standards, charts, and training programs.

Under both personnel coordination and training, the handling personnel require training in the operation of handling equipment, understanding of the system, and motivation to help improve operations and carry out established procedures. Under the communications aids, the physical facilities of communications come under consideration. [See section on Communications.]

Under **direct flow of materials** are included coordinated layouts and mechanization —areas where the greatest savings can be found. This objective may demand big outlays for equipment and calls for re-appraisal of current operations, packaging systems, building uses and locations, storage areas, and loading and unloading docks. Its application should eliminate the majority of manual handling operations and also reduce distances of travel.

Space utilization must be made to maximum benefit. Companies that have coordinated their cycle of movement have been able to save sufficient space to make substantial increases in production without adding to building requirements.

Integration Chart for Export Industrial Tractor							
	Incoming Material		In-plant Operations				
			Initial Storage				
Major Functions ▶	1. Operations at Source	2. Initial Shipping	3. Indoor	4. Outdoor	5. Production	6. Assembly	7. Inspection
What Each Function Includes: ▶	Preparation of Materials for Shipment (RI in %)	Vendor to Receiving Plant (RI in %)	Interim Storage of In-coming Materials (RI in %)	Same as No. 3 (RI in %)	Operations To Prepare Materials for Fabrication and Service (RI in %)	Erection of Complete Machines and Components (RI in %)	Testing and Approving for Operation and Shipping (RI in %)
Major Objectives							
Communications	60	75	92	92	67	67	75
Direct flow of materials	70	67	75	75	68	80	83
Space utilization	80	90	92	92	67	60	75
Utilization of handling equipment and facilities	40	50	83	83	83	85	83
Quality improvement	70	50	100	100	60	60	100
Cost control	75	67	100	100	75	75	67
Research and development	40	50	100	100	50	50	75
Coordination rating — RI = Ratio of integration (a measure of the effectiveness of the present system)	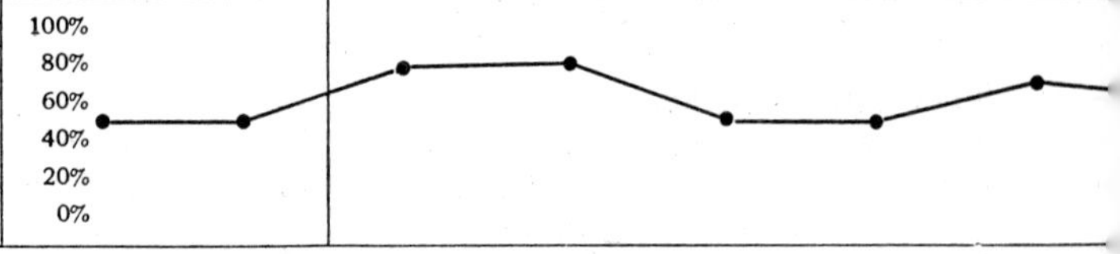 100% 80% 60% 40% 20% 0%						

Fig. 12. Typical

Full utilization of handling equipment and facilities is a must in the coordination program. After standards of operation are established they should be followed faithfully. Preventive maintenance enters strongly into the utilization picture.

Quality improvement results because coordination reduces the number of times that an item or product is moved or handled and reduces, by that number, the factor of error. Mechanical operations better protect items than can manual handlings.

The coordination program achieves better **cost control** by maintaining a consistently decreasing cost level. The experience of one company shows that cost reduction objectives of 10 to 15 percent per year can usually be met.

Research and development is important. A coordination program will not advance under its own power. Although the coordinator will provide the staff function, he needs the help of a good laboratory as a source and testing ground for the necessary continual improvement. Research provides the best answer, based on facts, and is not the result of guesswork.

Coordination ratings plotted on the graph, at the bottom of the chart, make it easy to visualize results throughout the company. It also tells the coordinator which functions or departments are out of line, where interdepartmental relationships are failing, and it forms the basis for management's evaluation of any progress made.

Integration Chart for Export Industrial Tractor							
In-plant Operations						Out-going Products	
Packaging, Crating, Bundling							
8. Domestic	9. Overseas	10. Unitizing	11. Plant Warehousing	12. Loading and Securement	13. Shipping	14. Sales & Parts Warehousing	15. Distribution
Containeri-zation and protection for Shipment or Storage (RI in %)	Same as No. 8 plus Added Precautions for Overseas Hazards (RI in %)	For Like Quantities of Items—Secured as a Unit to Pallet or Base (RI in %)	Finished Machines or Components for Interim Storage (RI in %)	Loading for Minimum Weights and Safe Transit (RI in %)	Via Rail, Truck, Express, Air, or Steamship—Domestic and Overseas (RI in %)	Finished Products and Service Parts for Distribution (RI in %)	Delivery of Products to User (RI in %)
–	92	–	–	83	83	50	50
–	83	–	–	53	53	40	40
–	70	–	–	67	67	40	45
–	50	–	–	67	67	20	20
–	78	–	–	67	67	50	50
–	50	–	–	67	70	10	10
–	100	–	–	78	65	0	0

integration chart.

The Coordinator. The duties of the coordinator are inclined to be administrative rather than operational. This is the man who does the planning and organizing for the system. He acts as a consultant to all departments of the business which affect the phases of the materials handling cycle. His duties might include —in addition to those already mentioned—consulting with construction engineers designing new buildings, helping the sales department warehouse finished products, working with purchasing personnel on specifications for packaging supplies and equipment, and planning special-device cars with the traffic department. These duties are ·typical of those which coordinators are handling in companies where such programs now exist.

Advantages of the Integrated System. The ten major benefits of integrated packaging and handling are:

1. Reduction of handling costs. Well-planned cost systems are set up to allocate costs by department for better control.

2. Savings in materials and supplies. Containers of all kinds, skids, blocking and bracing materials, wrapping supplies, strapping, tape, and allied packaging and shipping make up these savings.

3. Reduction in transportation costs. Reductions in weight of packaging and blocking materials, greater concentration of loads (more tons per car), more direct shipments from source to distribution point (bypassing user plant if no operations are needed), and greater use of special-device cars.

4. Better use of storage space. Unitization and palletization of materials under the coordination program, starting from vendor's operations, permit high stacking and narrow aisles with modern handling equipment; also, greater concentration of storage space.

5. Complete product protection, facilitating quality control. The integration program eliminates many handling operations, reducing the damage hazard. Reduced loss and damage in transportation is also a big factor under this plan. Quality is emphasized to a greater degree.

6. Safer working conditions. Most of the heavy handling is mechanized, and other facilities are provided under the program to improve the safety factor and make for better personnel relations.

7. Reduction of inventories. Through improved control of all materials from source to distribution, companies can operate with lower inventories and benefit from quicker turnover.

8. Greater emphasis on mechanized handling. Materials handling equipment, utilized to full advantage, does much to provide faster handling at lower cost. This factor is responsible for much of the savings achieved under integration.

9. Reducing time between receiving and distribution. Many handling operations are bypassed.

10. Standardization of materials, equipment, facilities, and communications results from research and development.

Research in Equipment and Facilities

SELECTION OF EQUIPMENT FOR HANDLING OPERATIONS. An important function of a materials handling research laboratory is to provide a basic continuing program devoted to the **study and evaluation of all types of mechanical handling equipment.** Recommended methods of use and allocations for selected manufacturing or service areas also are well within the range of research.

A broad-range **research program for power lift trucks** by one company has proved advantageous. The survey covered 970 lift trucks in operation in 20 manufacturing plants, 19 in sales warehouses, and 45 in service parts depots—a total of 1,034 lift trucks.

These trucks performed every kind of industrial handling task. They range in lifting capacity from 2,000 to 7,000 lb. Power is electric, gas-electric, and gas. Tires in use are solid rubber, cushion type, and pneumatic. The oldest truck was bought in 1918, the newest very recently.

The study revealed that each make of truck has some features preferred for definite requirements, that preventive maintenance and cost records reduce operating expense, that the choice of gas vs. electric power has an important bearing on the work to be performed, and that operators' training courses are of definite benefit.

In a research study of this nature, current data on new designs of lift trucks and attachment features is screened and evaluated for decision as to applicability in the long-range program. Thus, the research study has available at all times the latest data to aid in specifying the most desirable trucks for each type of service.

A method for realignment of lift trucks already in use also developed from this survey. In some operations this selective method of use undoubtedly has resulted in sufficient additional daily operating hours of service to reduce the requirement for new trucks.

While the original intent of this survey was to make cost and operating comparisons, additional advantages have resulted from the program:

1. Establishing a formula for obsolescence of lift trucks.
2. Finding out whether certain types or makes of trucks are adapted to special requirements.
3. Determining relative merits of gas, gas-electric, and battery types.
4. Improving safety features.
5. Comparing the service features of the various makes of power units.

The research activity is naturally divided into two categories. First, in materials handling, the attempt is made to explore the **basic principles of moving and storing goods.**

For this type of activity, it is considered that a good practical engineer, who has experience and knowledge pertaining particularly to the lift-truck phase of handling, rather than a detailed knowledge of developing mechanical devices, will accomplish the best results. It is the function of this activity to indicate what type of mechanical device should be developed for each of the various kinds of handling problems. After this information has been assembled, a corps of technical mechanical engineers work on the problem of producing devices that will be mechanically sound and economical of manufacture to satisfy these handling requirements.

There is no doubt that such a group of engineers will come up with a lot of fantastic ideas, but if only a small percentage of success is attained in this field, the efforts will be worth while. The basic attack is on the cost of pallets, skids, or other bundling devices for handling unit loads. This is a major project, but when it is realized that about 60 percent of the cost of the materials handling installations is represented by the pallets, and the other 40 percent by the machinery, it is obvious that great savings can be effected if the need for pallets is reduced.

In addition to the above type of research, it is advisable to devote considerable time to the **problem-child elements of handling present products—** for example, products such as hydraulic packing, pumps, motors, fluid drive transmissions, electric transmissions, etc. Eventually, a company with many and varied materials handling problems should be well equipped to make intelligent studies.

Mechanization of materials handling is expanding to very large proportions. A properly organized materials handling research laboratory must give a great deal of thought and attention to all varieties of handling equipment and facilities. Every progressive industry is keenly aware of the necessity of mechanization and looks to the research engineers to keep the company informed on important new developments.

Where volume of production justifies shipping devices, the railroads and truck lines (also the airlines) will provide **special returnable equipment** considered part of the transportation vehicle.

At a large manufacturing operation producing motors for truck plants, **special shipping and storage racks** were developed. These racks of tubular welded construction with hold-down features provide for six motors each. They are handled in and out of trucks or cars by lift trucks. At the motor truck plant the loaded racks are stacked, two or more tiers high in storage, and when needed, are delivered to the assembly line in the same racks.

Much of this type of special equipment for transportation is constantly under study by materials handling research laboratories in industry and by the railroads and truck lines. Under this classification also are the **special highway trailers, special-device flatcars,** and **railroad gondola cars,** with many attachment features for the large variety of machines and items shipped.

Loading Research

LOSS AND DAMAGE IN SHIPMENTS. One of the first problems faced during the earlier period of research concerned loss and damage to products in shipment and handling during transportation. The railroad associations issued bulletins showing large sums of money paid to American industries in settlement of loss and damage claims. This loss ran in excess of $100,000,000 annually.

In working with the general traffic department, plant management, and common carriers, it was learned that the principal causes were improper handling (mostly manual), incorrect packing, and poorly regulated loading methods. Surveys of company loading and handling practices also indicated that loading costs at the manufacturing plants were high.

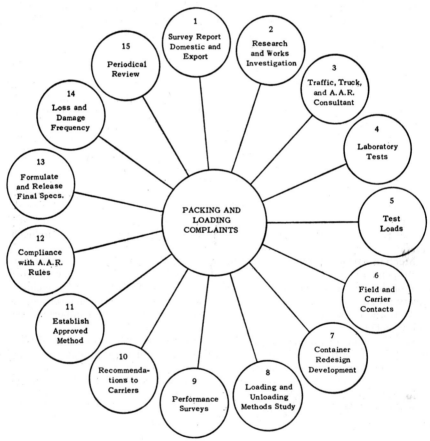

Fig. 13. Packing and loading complaint procedure chart for **research review.**

A concentrated effort was made to improve the situation in all company operations. Plant traffic supervisors, superintendents, shipping and loading foremen, and handling foremen were asked to help.

Frequent trips were made to company plants to maintain continued interest in reducing loss of, and damage to, shipments. Occasionally, unusual damages to a product were referred to the company's handling and packing research laboratory, then located at Milwaukee. The Association of American Railroads claim prevention department also cooperated. Visits to other industries permitted an exchange of information on damage prevention (Fig. 13).

A few case histories will illustrate how the materials handling research staff initiates and develops loading projects.

Floating-Load Depot Pallets. Because of loss and damage claims received from service-parts depots on parts shipped in depot pallets, this project was developed at the materials handling research laboratory. The old method was to load and secure depot pallet boxes, loaded with service parts, by using wooden blocks and braces nailed to the sides and bottom of the closed car.

A new method was proposed and tried out successfully whereby these **depot boxes were bound together as a mass** with wire or band without fastening the boxes to the inside of the car, thus constituting a free floating load. Shipping tests indicated that this method was superior to the rigid blocking procedure, and parts were received in much better condition. A reduction in cost also resulted from the floating-load method of shipment.

Template Loading of Tractors. When the smaller sizes of tractors were started in production, the problem of loading them efficiently and mechanically was referred to the materials handling research department. At least 20,000 lb. of tractors were required per flatcar so as to obtain the minimum freight rate. Ordinary methods of blocking were inadequate.

Through the research study, **a crosswise method of tractor loading** to minimum weight was agreed upon. The difficulty, however, was to place and secure the blocking and hold-down wires. The loading research engineer originated a template which permitted blocks and wires to be fastened to car floors in exact locations before loading the tractors by overhead crane. This template method proved very successful. The cost of loading was reduced and loss and damage were no longer a problem.

Loading Cotton Pickers. The cotton picker, a very large, heavy machine, offered a number of problems in safe loading for shipment to the cotton-growing areas. The original method of loading two pickers per flatcar was quite expensive and did not utilize carrier equipment to the best advantage.

Loading research engineers from materials handling research developed a procedure for loading which allowed three of these pickers to be loaded on a car in place of two. By disassembly of minor equipment and packing in wire-bound crates, the cost of loading also was reduced. The first large shipment of cotton pickers to southwest points loaded under research procedures was personally followed by the research engineers. Additional carloads were followed and inspected by these engineers en route as well as at destination. After minor blocking changes were made, this loading method was approved.

Wiring Tractors to Car. In connection with a study of bracing of tractors for shipment, a group of industrial and railroad men witnessed the first testing of a flatcar loaded with tractors. A unique method of wiring the tractors to the car— a radical departure from heavy blocking—was to be tried out.

The first impacts at 5 mi. per hr. against a heavy, stationary gondola car loaded with stone indicated no bad effects. The next impact at 8 mi. per hr. showed the same results. At 10 mi. per hr. the tractors blocked by the former method, which was very costly, showed evidences of loosening on the car. The final shock at 12 mi. per hr. gave the new procedure a "clean bill of health." The tractors blocked by the formerly acceptable system became dangerously loose and required reblocking.

The new idea, considered very radical, proved a principle—that mounted machines loaded on cars could be wired to the car in place of cradling in multiple blocking. Two cars loaded by this new method were shipped to the Northwest, coupled next to the caboose, for observation in transit. This trip further proved that the wiring idea was acceptable. The method was approved by the Association of American Railroads loading rules committee and is still the general practice for tractor securement. Loss and damage in transit is at a minimum and shipping costs have been substantially reduced.

After World War II, loading research became of national importance. It was one of the first assignments at the International Harvester Company's materials handling research laboratory. The Association of American Railroads a few years later set up its research testing laboratory in Chicago. A large strapping company has had a loading-test track in Chicago for a number of years. Other industries and suppliers have been developing testing procedures to improve loading practices. Many of the household appliance manufacturers have testing laboratories in which they are carrying on extensive work in connection with packing and shipping research, as part of the **National Safe Transit Program**. All these activities have been a big factor in reducing loss and damage claims. The **Farm Equipment Institute** organized a loading committee on problems within its own group. They coordinate their work closely with the **Association of American Railroads** loading rules committee.

Research in Packing and Packaging

LABORATORY STUDIES OF PACKING PROCEDURES. Packing and packaging research are considered functions of a materials handling research laboratory. The relationship between such research and plant operations, laboratory procedures, and the packing personnel management is very close. A materials handling research section, established to study research in materials handling, packing, and packaging, is in a strategic position to render maximum service to industry. To illustrate a typical research project in the export packing of a major machine, a wirebound box for the export shipment of twin engines has been selected.

The accepted practice had been to pack the twin engines in a heavy, nailed wooden container, with heavy bracing holding the motors in place. The research project of designing a wirebound container was a coordinated project between the laboratory, the plant, and the wirebound equipment suppliers. A number of designs were rejected through laboratory tests until a final design which met all laboratory test requirements was developed. Approval was received from the foreign-operations staff to make trial shipments to various overseas distributors. Acceptance of the new container was given, following this shipping experience, by export authorities and steamship and marine-insurance interests.

The wirebound box reduced cubic displacement by about 15 percent, reduced tare weight about 25 percent, and the total cost reduction was approximately 20 percent. Exporters highly recommended this type of container because of the additional safety to the product and the fact that the wirebound feature gave protection against pilferage.

In export shipping, space economy is as important as weight economy. The ideal cube ratio is 56 lb. per cu. ft. of displacement. This ratio is based on 40 cu. ft. per long ton of 2,240 lb. Shipments exceeding this ratio are assessed on a weight basis. In export packing projects, one of the objectives of research is to have a continuing program to reduce cubic displacement of containers, consistent with product protection.

One of these research developments concerned a medium-size tractor. Regular practice with this type of machine was to pack and ship one in a solid, sheathed crate with a cube ratio of 30 lb. per cu. ft. Working with the foreign operations department, the research laboratory designed a container for two tractors. By careful nesting and placing of disassembled parts, and packing all items except the rear wheels in the solid box, a cube ratio of 40 lb. per cu. ft. was arrived at. Initial laboratory testing procedures indicated the need for some design, blocking, and reinforcement changes before approval by research, foreign operations, and plant personnel. Extensive trial shipments were reported on by overseas distributors. Final cost comparison showed reductions of 15 percent in first cost, 10 percent in freight charges, and 25 percent in steamship charges as a result of the research developments.

MANUFACTURING RESEARCH, MATERIALS HANDLING SECTION
30 Lb. Kraft Single Ply

USE: For use as an inner wrap around parts containing iron or steel to protect against corrosion. An additional outer wrap or container is recommended to prevent undue loss of chemical vapor.

PROPERTIES OF VCI PAPER

Coverage:	1 sq. ft. of paper to 1 sq. ft. surface of item por year of packaging life.
Paper:	30 lb. minimum Kraft, pH 6.0 to 8.0, Mullen 20 lb., Tear 12 lb.
Rubbing:	No appreciable loss of inhibitor from normal handling.
Blocking:	No tearing of paper or transfer of inhibitor when sheets are unrolled or separated.
Volatility:	25% minimum loss in weight of active inhibitor from the treated carrier, under accelerated test.
Application:	Place paper with treated face toward—and not more than one foot from—article, in such a way that fumes may reach all surfaces of the article. Seal container to increase life of package. Machining oil need not be removed.
Protection:	When in commercially sealed packages, 1 yr. in outdoor sheltered storage, 2 yr. indoor storage.
Odor:	The VCI chemical treatment used shall not have an obnoxious odor.
Marking:	The following information shall be printed every 6 in. on the paper: 1. Name of manufacturer. 2. Active face of paper.
Approved Sources:	Furnished by purchasing department.

Fig. 14. Specifications in the use of volatile corrosion inhibitors.

Another research project was related to the shipment of **unpainted automotive sheet-metal stampings** for fabrication in overseas assembly plants. Painting or other corrosion preventive coatings were undesirable because of the subsequent assembly and painting operations to be performed overseas. The results of this project solved corrosion prevention problems in other handling activities as well as the one studied.

Volatile corrosion inhibitor papers had been undergoing research laboratory tests for a sufficient period to be released for trial shipments. They were considered a probable answer for this type of overseas shipment. Managers of foreign assembly plants were highly pleased at the suggestion and gave their approval. The proposed method was tried and proved successful, at the same time bringing about a net cost reduction. Additional research progress in the use of VCI paper indicates that such protection has a wide field of application for precision parts and assemblies in both domestic and export shipping. Specifications as to the use of VCI paper are listed in Fig. 14.

A packing research project goes beyond container design and method of packaging. A study must also be made of **all handling operations involved** to carry out research findings at the lowest cost and with a minimum of manual handling. Under ordinary procedures, it was found that 24 handlings were required for an export tractor from initial packing operation to foreign distributor delivery (Fig. 15). Service replaceable engine-sleeve sets, for domestic demand, required 26 separate handlings through packaging, shipping, and delivery to customer (Fig. 16). Such projects require study to see if better methods cannot be developed which will at the same time reduce costs.

---

1. Deliver from final production to packing department.
2. Provide box panels and blocking.
3. Assemble export box and place on conveyor.
4. Remove parts or assemblies of tractor to reduce cubic displacement.
5. Complete final packing operations.
6. Inspect.
7. Close box, nail, and apply reinforcements.
8. Stencil destination identification.
9. Deliver to shipping platform.
10. Load in cars.
11. Block boxes in cars.
12. Unload at port of embarkation.
13. Unload from car to dock.
14. Rehandle from dock to lighter.
15. Unload from lighter onto ship.
16. Stow in ship's hold.
17. Unload at port of debarkation, or unload onto lighter where no dock facilities are available.
18. Rehandle for delivery to distributor.
19. Unpack from box.
20. Reassemble and test.
21. Inspect.
22. Load on car or trailer.
23. Unload.
24. Deliver to customer.

Fig. 15. Loading, materials handling, and packaging research handling operations for export tractor.

1. Deliver from final production to packing department.
2. Dip piston with rings in neutralizer and assemble in sleeve.
3. Clean in hot alkaline solution.
4. Dip in corrosion preventive.
5. Drain and permit set of corrosion preventive.
6. Inspect for packing.
7. Convey to packing station.
8. Set up container.
9. Deliver containers to packing station.
10. Place dividers in containers.
11. Pack assembled sleeves in container in sets of 4 or 6.
12. Place envelope with rubber rings in container.
13. Close container.
14. Apply reinforcements with tension tools.
15. Stencil shipping data.
16. Provide shipping pallet.
17. Load packed containers onto pallet.
18. Secure packed containers to pallet with mechanically applied reinforcements.
19. Transport loaded pallet with lift truck to shipping platform.
20. Stencil name of consignee and destination on pallet.
21. Load in car or trailer with fork lift truck.
22. Secure in car or vehicle.
23. Make final loading inspection.
24. Unload at destination.
25. Store at distribution point.
26. Deliver to customer.

Fig. 16. Loading, materials handling, and packaging research handling operations for a set of pistons and cylinder sleeves.

Another research project covered the substitution—in place of a wire-bound container—of a 350-lb. test **carton with an inner liner** coated to resist cutting compounds and oil on hardware items. At the same time, a method of automatically loading and sealing the cartons was developed. These cartons are palletized 18 or 27 (100 lb. each) per pallet for shipment to collateral plants. Benefits from their use include cost reduction, improved storage, and better inventory control.

One of the functions of a materials handling research laboratory is to **keep abreast of advances** being made country-wide and even abroad. New methods and materials that will improve present practices may be under development in other companies, and the research laboratory engineers should have sources of information that will keep them in touch with progress along such lines.

To illustrate, the materials handling research staff of one company was informed that an automotive plant was having a southern mill fabricate export box panels using dimensional lumber which reduced packing costs up to 20 percent. After a tour of southern lumber sources, made with the cooperation of suppliers, it was learned that by specifying ⅝-in. thick lumber for sheathing, resawn from 6/4 cuttings, the price could be reduced. Former designs called for ¾- or ¹³⁄₁₆-in. thickness.

Laboratory and shipping tests of large export machine boxes with the ⅝-in. lumber were highly satisfactory. A few minor design improvements in the containers were the only changes required. The net lumber savings approximated

15 percent, which, at average crating prices, reduced the cost of each million board feet of lumber about $11,000.

Armed Forces Materials Handling and Packaging Research

FOREST PRODUCTS LABORATORY. The Forest Products Laboratory, a branch of the United States Forestry Service, at Madison, Wisconsin, with its excellent research facilities, has made rapid strides in carrying out a packaging and handling research program that proved of inestimable benefit to the armed services as far back as World War I. Efforts were directed toward providing better and safer methods of protection, handling, and shipping of military supplies; in training a vast number of persons, both military and civilian, in these fields; in research to set up new methods; and in developing techniques to use container materials for the armed forces to best advantage.

This laboratory has carried on an extensive cooperative research packaging program for the Ordnance Department. To carry out this program, a research staff was organized at the laboratory to handle special design and development problems, to prepare packaging manuals and specifications, and to establish performance standards for packaging materials.

About 17 billion bd. ft. of lumber were originally being used for packing, and therefore a far-reaching research program was set up to make sure that the vast quantity of lumber consumed was used to the best advantage.

An analysis of a large number of **redesigned containers** showed an average saving of about 10 percent in lumber. This saving indicated a possible reduction of over 1 billion bd. ft. of lumber per year. Economy in shipping space was estimated at about 20 percent, meaning that the saving in shipping space was equivalent to one cargo in five.

The Forest Products Laboratory was primarily interested in packaging research because of the large amount of wood and wood-base materials employed. Through research, savings were made by utilizing low-grade lumber, improving strength and serviceability, and reducing loss and damage claims. Many industries having armed forces contracts have also received help in improving their packaging through the research work of the laboratory.

NAVY DEPOT. The Navy Depot at Bayonne, New Jersey, has made substantial progress in research in materials handling and packaging. Its Naval Research Laboratory has carried on many commendable research projects in handling methods which have been of great value to the armed forces in shipping the many varieties and large tonnage of items used in naval operations.

U. S. ENGINEERING TESTING AND DESIGN LABORATORY. The U. S. Engineering Testing and Design Laboratory, at Fort Belvoir, Virginia, has a very complete packaging and handling laboratory. Here research is conducted for the packaging, processing, and shipping of something like 230,000 different items. This research laboratory is probably the most typical in its field in the armed forces service. With each project for the development of a container also goes the responsibility for working out the proper handling methods and facilities. The aims of this laboratory are twofold (Modern Materials Handling, vol. 7): (1) to prevent material from being damaged in shipment because of faulty containers, and (2) to prevent it from being damaged internally by corrosion, fungi, or because of improper processing before shipment. Containers must be designed to be transportable by truck, rail, ship, or air. All new container designs are subjected to a **vibration test.** This testing device causes vertical accelerations simulating the actual vibration encountered during transportation and caused by resonance, flat wheels, rail joints, rough roadbeds, car sidesway, etc. Containers of all kinds—boxes, crates, barrels, drums, kegs, pails, etc.— whether made of metal, wood, fiberboard, or a combination of these materials, can be tested with this apparatus.

These containers are then subjected to a **revolving hexagonal drum test** which determines the ability to withstand rough handling. The device simulates shocks and impact stresses which may be expected in handling and shipment. If the original design proves to be impractical, differently designed containers of the same size, and carrying the same load, are tested and compared until one is found that will hold up in service.

The **incline-impact test** comes next. Speeds up to 8 mi. per hr. can be obtained at the point of impact.

Another important consideration at the Fort Belvoir laboratory is the **maximum utilization of materials** going into the design and construction of the container. By using a new, improved, nailed wood, sheathed crate for shipping material in the 500- to 3,000-lb. weight range instead of the one formerly used, the same protection was given with a 17 to 30 percent saving in lumber. At times the weight of the crate had excedeed that of the equipment shipped in it.

Tests also are made to determine the **deterioration of materials by corrosion, fungi, and other sources** during shipment or in storage. The ability of the container to cope with these conditions is checked by submerging it in a 160-cu.-ft. tank. This tank is used to determine the effect of prolonged submersion at various depths and under various pressures on protective wrapping, sealing materials, and preservative coatings. It is illuminated at the 4-ft. level by lights recessed in the four sides.

To solve other packaging problems there is a complete processing line including:

1. Facilities for rust removal.
2. A number of preservative compound tanks.
3. Tanks for dipcoat sealing.
4. Complete facilities for wrapping, packing, and packaging, including a fiberboard box-making machine.

This engineers' development laboratory can duplicate almost any condition met in the field. Testing is also carried on in the field under actual handling and storage conditions. A typical example is a test, conducted with other Army services and with the Navy, of a shipment to Japan and the Philippines consisting of approximately 1,400 containers of various types, sizes, weights, loads, etc., to determine, among other factors, the need for **revision of existing container specifications.**

Besides the cooperation that is maintained with other government agencies, **this packaging laboratory works very closely with industry.** In fact, as a result of many practices established during wartime operation and insistence on their use with favorable results, there has been an increasing interest on the part of industry in preservation, packing, and packaging, both for domestic and overseas shipment and storage.

SPRINGFIELD ARMORY. The Springfield (Massachusetts) Armory carries on research in packaging and processing of **small arms and parts.** Research developments are conducted on a very high scale and of value to both the armed forces and industry, and especially to the contractors producing and packing small arms. Research of this kind, when performed in the right environment, with a qualified staff and proper testing facilities, is conducive to the best results.

Each armed forces establishment has its special problems of packaging and handling research. The armed forces need specialists in these particular fields of service to be able to arrive at the best decisions. The sum total of all of these research developments gives the answers to many projects which it would be difficult otherwise to work out.

KELLY AIR FORCE BASE. At the Kelly Air Force Base, San Antonio, Texas, a considerable range of materials handling research is carried on, of which the following developments have been typical (Modern Materials Handling, vol. 7):

Proof of the success of mechanization at the Kelly Base, beginning in 1948, under Major General McMullen, rests in the fact that, within a period of 3 yr. Kelly reduced its staff of materials handling employees by 25 percent while the work load on the base doubled.

Versatility is the most adamant demand made on Air Force handling of goods. Kelly Field receives an average of millions of pounds of property a day, ships half a million, with items ranging from instrument jewels to B-36 air foils. Kelly's physical inventory has listed over 365,000 different items. Such a situation demands a flexible handling plant.

Incoming merchandise, brought in by commercial freight lines, is unloaded at a central location onto pallets at the freight dock. Truck manifests are checked at this point, and property is broken down into Air Force classifications for storage purposes.

Pallets are placed on roller conveyors and guided, gravity-assisted, to loading doors where the complete load is rolled onto a waiting crash truck, also equipped with roller conveyors on its bed. Once loaded, the truck delivers the shipment to screening and inspection lines in one of three large supply areas. Simple chocks stabilize goods on roller beds during transit.

At screening lines, materials are unloaded onto a "chain-booster"—an inclined power conveyor—which raises them to work height where boxes are opened for processing. This operation necessitates only one fork-lifting—at the point where property leaves the commercial truck—as compared to four fork-lift handlings under previous methods. This system is infinitely faster than the one it replaces. It enables a roller-bed truck to be loaded or unloaded in less than a minute.

Kelly is key storage point for the Air Force's world-wide supply of oil drums. The principle utilized in operating amusement park roller coasters was adapted in designing a machine to unload drums from cars and pile them neatly in stacks of twelve. The device operates in the manner of a ditch digger, with an endless chain conveyor on a boom. Suitable arms hold the drums onto the conveyor, releasing them on a track at the top of the stack. From there, drums roll freely to their final destination.

The machine unloads, lifts, and stacks drums at the rate of 12 drums per min., cutting the time required to unload a boxcar of 300 drums to less than 30 min. The same number of men as before do the same job in less space, and three times as fast as by crane-stacking, which was the previous method used.

A system conceived by General McMullen has been regarded as the most efficient method for the automatic loading and unloading of aircraft cargoes. The **conveyor device** automatically moves cargo directly from the interior of the air freight terminal at Kelly Field, or vice versa.

When first put into operation the conveyor, in a trial run, unloaded 4,774 lb. of freight in 8 min.—an operation that normally would require an hour or longer with conventional methods.

Control of the system rests in a portable three-position switch box which can be carried onto the taxi apron or into the airplane by an operator.

The type of conveyor used in loading and unloading aircraft is reversible and is limited to a 21° angle of incline to provide **delivery of cargo at a height of 10 ft.** above ground level. Aircraft are towed into position for handling of cargo by conveyor. Where a plane can best be loaded or unloaded is indicated by painted stripes on the concrete apron outside the air freight terminal.

The powered conveyor rides on fixed rails. There is no lateral adjustment, and very little tolerance between the aircraft hold and the conveyor. Airplanes cannot be taxied to a position for handling, and towing takes time.

A big limitation in mechanical loading of cargo craft is the allowable **angle of incline.** If this angle exceeds 21°, cargo tumbles. This limitation could be overcome by extending the conveyor, but as airplanes become larger, this extension could become expensive.

Because of Kelly Field's immensity, its storage functions have been **segregated into three vast, separate areas.** In the north area, there is a **tow conveyor** which links six huge warehouses with one another and with receiving and screening lines, the packing area, and the shipping area. This conveyor is 5,415 ft. long, making it the **world's longest monoveyor setup.** It crosses a railway track in two places. A "drawbridge" was therefore designed so that the conveyor line could be hoisted when necessary to make way for trains.

The system was conceived to eliminate tug and trailer-train methods in transporting materials. In two other supply areas, tow conveyors provide a continual flow of goods throughout the operation of receiving, to warehouse, to packing, to shipping. End results are reduced processing time and release of fork lifts for other duties. The cost of the conveyors was $87,500, and the system, it is believed, paid for itself through savings within a year and a half.

Keeping a strict accounting of 365,000 stored items under a detailed location system becomes quite complex. Besides this, there is an immense handling job involved. During one month alone, after the system was well set up, the number of packages handled totaled 355,149. Within three months the number handled per month had jumped to 460,336. Despite this almost 30 percent increase in the number of packages handled, neither transportation nor material facilities—the division that is charged with materials handling duties at Kelly Field—had to employ a single extra person to accommodate the increased work load.

QUARTERMASTER RESEARCH DEPOT. At the quartermaster research depot, Chicago, a very complete testing and research division functions in the testing of all types of containers. This laboratory is prepared to do research work and testing on the widest variety of packaging, processing, and handling, because every type of equipment and subsistence material is furnished by this service. These items either are submitted by industry or originate in the armed forces.

The purpose of the testing is to establish **performance standards for containers and methods for testing containers** to determine whether they meet the requirements of the established performance standards. The testing division laboratory is equipped to perform all required tests, evaluate containers, and establish performance standards on all kinds of containers and container materials. The equipment is of the finest, and the variety of facilities exceeds that of most other testing laboratories.

The armed services recognize that they need materials handling and packaging research laboratories just as much as they need product engineering laboratories. The large production demands for the armed forces cannot be met with out-of-date handling and packaging methods and equipment. Modern war equipment manufacturing plants are built around handling systems. Handling research engineers play an important part in these military installations.

Planned Research

EVALUATION FACTORS. A planned materials handling program requires frequent evaluation. This evaluation is a function of the research staff. Outstanding factors in evaluating the program include:

Economies and Improvements. Results produced are the real tests of a research program. Among such results the following are of major importance:

1. **Economies in handling operations,** evaluated under the cost control plan. Weekly or monthly budget analysis by the plant staff for cost trends and progress toward carrying out assigned objectives. Continued interest and enthusiasm of the plant supervisory force.
2. **Improvement of quality of product** under the materials handling system. Reduction of handling lessens the possibility of damaging precision surfaces. Facilities for better protection of the product are provided under planned handling methods. These are factors also in cost reduction because of smaller amounts of rejected materials.
3. **Eliminating most of the manual effort of lifting and handling material** in a plant operation and establishing better personnel relations. Physical fatigue in handling is minimized, and the result is better workmanship.
4. **Availability of additional floor space.** In a large thresher plant, 27,600 sq. ft. of floor space were saved by controlling flow of materials in the incoming storage area and using "air rights" with the aid of steel stacking boxes, yet maintaining full production.
5. **Storage and warehousing of the finished product** as part of the materials handling plan. Through better methods of control, many improvements are being made in the storage of machines and parts, making them more quickly available for sales distribution.

Trends. Studying trends in materials handling comes under a research program. The art and science of materials handling exhibits an ever-changing picture; materials handling engineers must be alert to these trends. They denote progress, and without progress industry stagnates. Some of these trends are:

1. **Depalletization.** The tendency is to eliminate the use of pallets in favor of unit loads for shipping and storage. The original cost of pallets, including maintenance and replacement, is becoming relatively high.
2. **Expendable pallets.** Where still required for shipping, the light, expendable type is preferred. If properly designed, this type of pallet will carry heavy loads successfully. Reduced first cost, lower freight charges, and elimination of repairs result from its use.
3. **Equipment improvements.** Manufacturers of materials handling equipment, working with industries, are doing a great deal to improve fork trucks, attachments, and other mechanical handling facilities to economize further in handling operations. Among these improvements are considered the narrow-aisle lift trucks, many types of grabs and roll-over devices, forkless grabs, improvements in conveyors, better racks for storage, and special device transportation equipment. The trend is toward more mechanization in handling operations. The ultimate goal is the elimination of all fatiguing manual handling operations.
4. **Research in industrial storage and warehousing methods.** Probably up to 50 percent of storage space is now wasted in many storage areas. Many improvements in storage practices are imperative to conserve the large areas now wasted through antiquated practices.

Coordination and Advancement. During the past several years, professional societies have shown considerable interest in organizing technical groups for the advancement of materials handling and packaging. **The American Society of Mechanical Engineers, Society of Industrial Packaging and Materials Handling Engineers, American Material Handling Society,** and other professional organizations are carrying out effective programs through national conferences and at local chapters. Many colleges have established excellent **training courses** in materials handling and packaging which are of significant value to thousands of men in industry and students in college.

The combined efforts of these organizations, of educational institutions, of those in industries—both users and suppliers—and men in the armed forces are needed to help set the course for materials handling progress.

Those who are engaged in materials handling research will find it to their best interests to participate actively in these **group conferences and meetings.** To succeed in this field of research requires reliable data in all of the newest phases of materials handling methods and facilities. Ths research engineer should be able to evaluate this information and determine if it merits research investigation. He usually emphasizes research in the unknown factors, rather than in those that are apparent.

By serving on worthwhile **committees** related to materials handling and packaging, research men are able to obtain data on specific subjects. In turn, they can promote better materials handling and widen the knowledge in this field by giving talks on the engineering and operating phases of handling, and assisting in training courses.

A materials handling engineer's job is one of **constant training and investigation.** A materials handling laboratory must always be a little in advance of the general trend. The more comprehensive the researcher's "know-how" of what is being accomplished in his profession, the more valuable he will be to his industry and the more he will advance the adoption of improved materials handling methods and equipment.

Much of the progress in the field of materials handling will depend on how thorough a job is currently done in materials handling research laboratories. A coordinated effort and exchange of ideas between these materials handling and packaging laboratories will do much to accelerate progress.

The materials handling research engineer has an important function to fulfill in professional and training activities. Because of the wide scope of the materials handling field, which is still only in the initial stages of development, there should be a never-ending search for something new and better. This knowledge cannot be acquired by laboratory procedures alone. Every outside source that can contribute to a more modern method or improved piece of equipment will be of value in obtaining the best answer. Research must have that answer to justify its existence.

MATERIALS HANDLING AND PRODUCTION CONTROL

CONTENTS

MATERIALS HANDLING AND PRODUCTION CONTROL

OBJECTIVES OF PRODUCTION CONTROL. Production control is the regulation of production according to plan. This function is performed informally in some companies, other companies have large production control departments, and some companies operate successfully without a department known as the production control department. To insure effective production operations, however, the **function** must be performed in some way at some time, and somewhere in the organization.

Effective production control minimizes the investment needed in materials handling equipment. It maximizes the use of such equipment, regulates the use of equipment and personnel, and evens up fluctuations in their use. Production control activities are determined largely by the type of production and the kind of equipment which is most feasible for that type of production. Materials handling equipment and materials handling procedures have an important influence upon the **type of production control** necessary. The equipment and procedures necessary for a particular type of production probably have more influence upon the need for formal recognition of production control than does the size of the company.

The **objectives** of production control, as the function is found in various companies, are:

1. To maintain the proper time-sequence relationships between the various phases of a production project.
2. To assure the best possible utilization of machine, manpower, plant, and equipment capacity.
3. To maximize the successful completion of delivery promises.
4. To minimize delivery failures and their adverse effects on production.
5. To provide a source of accurate, useful, up-to-date information concerning production progress and production delays.
6. To furnish operating information for the processing, fabrication, and assembly of the product.
7. To plan work routing which will minimize materials handling and eliminate unnecessary delay in work flow.

The objectives of production control, in general terms, are to insure the receipt of proper materials at the proper place in the proper condition at the proper time. Production control usually includes elements of **production planning.**

General Procedures, Actions, and Evaluations

RELATION TO MATERIALS HANDLING. There are general procedures, actions, and evaluations used in production control which relate directly to materials handling:

1. The executive memorandum (or verbal request) for service or information.

2. The production control move order or shop order in the form of a routing sheet.
3. The predetermined program for materials handling by operator-controlled mobile units, such as lift trucks and tractor trains.
4. The predetermined layout of materials handling and use of fixed installations of materials handling devices, such as conveyors and chutes.

The **executive memorandum** or verbal request for service is used in situations where formal orders are not feasible. The use of memorandums or request procedures is indicated in operations which utilize centralized materials handling facilities and when need for service is not sufficiently frequent to warrant the use of specific move orders.

```
                                    MOVE TICKET
                                              NO.  246543
NOTE: ATTACH
TAG SECURELY   PART NO. 123876 Pin    OPERATION NO. 14   MACHINE NO.  36
TO MATERIAL
               OPERATION   Mill       DATE  2/15/-       SHIFT  No. 1

               DEPARTMENT  256        OPERATOR  75        ORDER NO.  8765
               - - - - - - - - - - - - - - - - - - - - - - - - - - -
               MOVE TO: Department 287  OPERATION NO. 20   MACHINE NO.  45

               DISPATCHED BY _____ DATE _____ REMARKS _____

               MOVED BY _____ DATE _____ NO. OF PCS. _____

               REMARKS _____
```

Fig. 1. Move order.

The **move order** (and the **shop order** used for routing) indicates a formalized procedure which is part of the larger system for production control. A common form of move order is illustrated in Fig. 1. These move-order tickets may be made up in advance of production operations or may be filled out by persons in the shop at the time the materials handling is to take place. Where duplication of orders and records is performed mechanically before production operations, time can be saved by preparing the move-order tickets along with the other papers used in production control.

A production order in the form of a **route sheet** is shown in Fig. 2. Materials handling is not specifically called for on the order. The sequence of operations, however, determines the handling. The production order is usually a duplication of the **master operation sheet,** described later, which is prepared in production planning.

In some operations the movement of materials into, through, and out of the plant may become highly routine. Where the routine is standardized and continuous, it is possible to integrate materials handling operations into the process without the use of formal orders. A **program** is set up in advance. The operators of materials handling equipment are given **standing orders** to move materials without specific orders or to keep up certain **banks** of parts at specified places.

CHANGE LETTER "B"
ORDER DATE 2/15/-
NO. OF PCS. 285

PART NO. 276565
PART NAME Block-support
ORDER NO. 26583

PRODUCTION ORDER

Operation No.	Operation	Symbol	Machine	Machine No.	Dept. No.	Tools	Begin Date	Finish Date	Operator Signature	Inspection Stamp	Remarks
1	Turn	18	P & W	25	256		2/20	2/23			
2	Mill	25	S	31	284	MF #1	2/24	2/28			
3	Drill	20				DF #1	3/2	3/8			
4	Ream	20	R	48	284	DF #2	3/9	3/11			
5	Clean	10			290		3/12	3/15			
6	Deliver							3/16			Note

DELIVER TO Dept. 346 Stores
PREPARED BY Brown
APPROVED BY Johnson

MATERIAL 1020 CR Bar Stk
FINAL INSPECTION REPORT

(PERCENTAGE COMPLETE)
(10 ' 20 ' 30 ' 40 ' 50 ' 60 ' 70 ' 80 ' 90 ' 100 'INSPECT')

(Part No.)
276565
(Finish Date)
Date 1 5• 9 13 17 21 25 29

Fig. 2. Production or work order in form of a route sheet.

The calculation of bank size is an industrial engineering problem, but control in maintaining it becomes a materials handling function.

Where materials handling is built into the plant equipment, in the form of conveyors and fixed materials handling devices, control is also mechanized and materials flow from place to place with no particular aid from materials handling personnel. Much of the production control is designed into the fixed equipment when it is planned. The management of production control finds the bulk of its day-to-day activities in the type of production which is not largely mechanized. Where operations are not based upon special-purpose fixed equipment, more production control activity is required in the proper issuance of shop orders and move orders.

In any kind of production there are **common actions** which must be performed. These actions include:

1. The provision of "conditions-precedent" to the specific handling of materials.
   a. The necessary factors, including materials handling equipment, must be available.
   b. There must be a "make-ready" function to insure the use of such factors, including materials handling equipment, being prepared for specific assignments.
2. Initiation of production control action.
   a. Receive orders for products or parts from the sales department.
   b. Receive some kind of executive memorandum which will authorize production.
   c. Receive an authorized program for production approved by top management.
3. The planning and routing of production.
   a. Determination of materials requirements.
   b. Estimates of costs of new jobs.
   c. Determination of tool and equipment requirements.
   d. Determination of operations required.
   e. Determination of sequence of operations.
   f. Determination of other planning and routing factors.
4. The scheduling of actions and facilities.
   a. Make up production schedules.
   b. Preparation of production orders.
   c. Make adjustments necessary to balance production operations.
5. The dispatching of specific orders and instructions.
   a. Assignment of jobs to particular men and machines.
   b. Issuing work orders.
   c. Control of materials handling.
   d. Issuance of materials and tool requisitions.
6. The supervision and direction of operations, including materials handling.
7. The necessary expediting and corrective action needed, including necessary adjustments in materials handling.
   a. Receipt of progress information and evaluation of progress.
   b. Provide remedial measures where planned progress is not achieved.
8. The completion of necessary records and action.
   a. Filing or destruction of production control papers.
   b. Report of performance, tabulation, and evaluation of action.

Part of the production control function is the assurance of later success of action. The needed equipment, materials, personnel, procedures, and other factors should be in reasonable readiness. Production control is not the function of actually furnishing the conditions necessary but rather the job of seeing to it that such conditions are provided by those responsible for the job. Action has to be initiated by some authorized means. Planning is normally considered as separate from control. Some planning of a more immediate nature, however, is necessary in carrying out the control function. This planning is recognized in the **routing** function.

Scheduling is the timing of operations. **Dispatching** is the release of orders to meet the times scheduled. The orders—written or verbal—carry necessary information and **directions** for carrying out the planned action. Proper **supervision** insures control. Shop orders which are not being completed or moved according to schedule require special action. **Expediting** and other corrective actions are often needed. Control is implemented by providing for specific **completion** of any particular action.

In plants utilizing **production lines,** some of these actions are "built in" during the planning and layout stage, but they are greatly telescoped. Fixed equipment, such as conveyors, and determined **rates of movement** largely determine the route and schedule. The large problems are met in the planning stage—the furnishing of proper equipment and later balancing and supplying the production line.

In plants which make a diversity of products to specific orders, the production-line technique may not be practicable. Most modern production operations, as a matter of fact, use production lines and jobbing operations intermingled.

FITTING PRODUCTION CONTROL TO PLANT NEEDS. No one system of production control can possibly be used for any and all production. The production control system installed must meet the needs of the particular plant. Even systems in operation in a particular company may not work from one plant to another within the same company. Systems should be checked from time to time.

Production control should:

1. Provide whatever means are necessary to accomplish the needed results.
2. Eliminate all unnecessary means.

Production control is a facilitative function. Its contributions are of great value, but they consist of enabling primary production to be accomplished more economically and effectively than would have been possible without the aid of a production control department. The cost of production control—in time, energy, and money costs—must be offset by the greater savings resulting from primary operations. Production control is not itself a frill or a luxury, but sound production control must be built upon the needs found in a particular plant.

Basic Production Control Factors

INTERMITTENT AND CONTINUOUS PRODUCTION. The basic factors which determine the type of production control needed are shown in the form of a table in Fig. 3. **Intermittent production** is the type of production in which the machinery and tools utilized are employed for only a relatively short period of time between setups. A setup is made for each new job. Intermittent production usually requires mobile materials handling equipment operated by workers; it requires careful scheduling and maximum utilization of equipment.

In **continuous production, or mass production,** machinery and tools are utilized for relatively long periods between production setups. Materials are handled by conveyors, chutes, and other devices which do not require an operator.

	OPERATION		MOVEMENT	
	Continuity	Nature	Pattern	Handling
PRODUCTION FACTORS	Intermittent	Fabrication	From work center to work center	Manually
	Continuous	Processing 1. Analytic 2. Synthetic	By production flow and production line	Manually directed mobile equipment (like trucks)
		Assembly, of 1. Like materials 2. Unlike materials	Assembly line	Automatic fixed equipment (like conveyors)

	PRODUCTION CONTROL		MATERIALS CONTROL	TYPE OF DEMAND
	Type	Concentration		
CONTROL FACTORS	Job-Order Control	Decentralized Control	Bill of Materials Control	Specific — To contract or to order
	Batch or Load Control		Executive Analysis Control	Limited — To program
	Flow Control	Centralized Control	Maximum-Minimum Control	General — To stock

Fig. 3. Production and control factors.

CHARACTERISTICS OF INTERMITTENT PRODUCTION. The characteristics of intermittent production are these:

1. A **variety** of different kinds of materials are handled in filling orders, but relatively few parts or products are made on each order.
2. Factory production operations on various kinds of work are usually **out of balance** in intermittent production.
   a. It is difficult to control the type of orders received, and many will require the same routing at one time.
   b. Some equipment usually has to be worked overtime at the same time that other equipment is idle for lack of work.
3. **General purpose equipment** is more likely to be used in intermittent production than are machines specially designed for specific work.
4. **Work centers** are set up in which similar kinds of machines are grouped together into specific departments.
   a. These departments are often named for the kinds of machines grouped together (milling department, punch press department, etc.).

    b. The movement of work is usually by specific order calling for a move from one department to another.

5. Foremen and machine operators in the specialized work centers or departments are usually **more highly skilled** than those supervising or running the same kinds of machines or equipment in a continuous operation.
    a. Operations on particular machines normally are more numerous and complicated.
    b. Foremen or operators in the work centers usually schedule the movement of materials from machine to machine.

6. Numerous written job instructions, work orders, move orders, and other **paper work forms** are required in intermittent production which are not necessary in continuous operations.

7. Material for each job is kept in one work center or department until the particular operation is completed, then the order is moved as a **complete unit.**
    a. Inventory-in-process is necessarily larger than it would have to be in continuous production.
    b. Materials are moved to machines in lots and removed after being worked on. Materials handling equipment is often used for moving materials into temporary storage.
    c. Materials handling equipment must be flexible in design so as to handle varying quantities at intermittent intervals.
    d. The movement of a particular order through its sequence of operations is necessarily slower than if it were processed on a continuous production line.

8. The need to move and store material on a bulk basis throughout the plant is reflected in **plant layout.**
    a. Storage space within departments, and wider aisles for storage, are characteristic.
    b. Manually operated materials handling equipment is used, such as industrial trucks, hoists, and elevators. Space is required for operating such equipment.

These characteristics are almost universal where production is intermittent in nature.

CHARACTERISTICS OF CONTINUOUS PRODUCTION. The characteristics where production is continuous are usually quite different:

1. Continuous production is characterized by **large volume** but **small variety** of product.
    a. Production lines are set up and materials are moved along these lines.
    b. Machines required for successive operations are placed in the sequence of operations needed to complete a unit of product.

2. An attempt is made to **balance** the capacities of various machines placed along the production lines.
    a. There is normally a fairly even flow of material from machine to machine or operation to operation.
    b. Some banks of materials may be in evidence to assure continuity of flow along the production line.
    c. No excessive amounts of materials are stored around work centers.

3. Machines used are likely to be **special-purpose machines,** including the equipment used in materials handling.

4. The foremen and machine operators are usually **less skilled** than the average foreman and machine operator in intermittent operations.
    a. The operations on any one machine are likely to be specialized but simple.
    b. The foremen and operators do not schedule the movement of materials but work on material which is sent down the production line.

5. **Few job instructions** are necessary because the production line enables the jobs to be broken down into simple elements, the route and sequence to be automatically set, and the schedule to be controlled mechanically.
6. Since materials move quickly through the plant the **materials-in-process inventory** is low compared with output.
7. Materials can be moved along **fixed conveyors.**
   a. The conveyor paces the work and controls the schedule.
   b. Where mobile units are used for handling in continuous production, their jobs are easily defined.
8. Aisles are narrower, less storage space is required in production areas, fewer elevators are needed, and flow of work is more easily controlled.

The continuity of production depends largely upon the **type of demand** which faces the particular company. Some types of production develop from **specific orders** or contracts. Although contracts can be let for orders of great quantity, the pattern in most companies working on specific orders is to have many smaller orders coming in which must be integrated into the production operations. In other cases the company may not get specific orders but forecasts the possibilities of getting specific orders in the future. If such is the case, the top executives may develop a program spelling out the type of production to be completed. Companies making **standard products** in wide demand are fortunate in being able to supply a constant market and to forecast it as well. Such companies, which are typically mass-production companies, can proceed to manufacture their product to stock before actual orders are secured.

TYPES OF MATERIAL CONTROL. The type of demand facing the particular company for particular products also largely determines the kind of material control it utilizes in the production of such products. Three general types of material control are recognized. They are:

1. Bill-of-materials control.
2. Executive-analysis control.
3. Maximum-minimum control.

Bill-of-materials control is used in the kind of manufacturing which depends upon individual orders. It is not always profitable to stock materials in such cases. As the work is planned, a bill of materials is prepared. In some instances the materials are furnished for specific orders in the plant from materials which are stocked in a central warehouse. The bill of materials provides for accumulation in such cases (Fig. 4). The bill of materials in some instances also serves as a **move order.** In other instances the materials handling equipment itself is designed specifically to allow for the accumulation of the items in a particular bill of materials.

Executive-analysis materials control is used as a materials control technique in manufacturing to a predetermined program which might require modification as the operations are carried on. Executive analysis may be applied with the other kinds of materials control as a check upon their effectiveness. They aid all materials control methods. They aid in determining in advance periods of high and of low activity for materials handling.

The **maximum-minimum kind of materials control** is used where the production operations require a stocking of materials, and materials orders are made up from the standard material so stocked. A type of maximum-minimum control is directly related to materials handling wherever the handling function is responsible for supplying certain kinds of materials for work banks. Materials banks at the beginning and end of production lines are often controlled by statements of the

MASTER PARTS LIST		
Item	Part Name and Number	Number per Assembly

Item	Part Name and Number				
1	42659 Assembly — Lock	1			
2	65132 Key		1		
3	53265 End — Shackle		1		
4	41920 Front — Lock		1		
5	42411 End — Keyway Assembly		1		
6	33421 Keyway			1	
7	43264 Assembly — Shackle			1	
8	52612 Spring — Shackle			1	
9	72653 Assembly — Back		1		
10	44321 Spring — Back			1	
11	53618 Post — Back			1	
12	56234 Back			1	

Fig. 4. Bill of materials for an assembly.

maximum and minimum quantities allowable. The **maximum** is usually determined by cost and space considerations; the **minimum** is usually determined by the time necessary to obtain replacement quantities.

Basic Types of Production Control

THREE VARIETIES OF CONTROL. There are many varieties of production control. For general analysis, however, they can be divided into three main categories. These three are:

1. Job-order control.
2. Flow control.
3. Batch or load control.

Job-Order Control. Job-order control is self-descriptive. A specific job order is created for each job because of the number and variety of jobs. Job-order control is usually the predominant type of control in intermittent production. A job order is created because each order requires a distinctive sequence of operations for its completion. The order may represent a specific contract with a specific customer, or it may be one of a series of like orders which are issued periodically to provide parts or materials for the production lines of the company's own plant. A similar contract for a supply of parts may or may not be issued at some subsequent date. The specific nature of the order requires a detailed statement of what is to be done, where it is to be done, who is to do it, how it is to be completed, and all other pertinent information that must be known in order to complete the job order satisfactorily.

In job-order control the differences in orders make it necessary to give specific instructions to the materials handling department as to what is to be moved, where it is to be moved, and when it is to be moved. Coordination of operations is achieved largely through the control of such movement. Companies using job-order control find it important to **coordinate production control** carefully with materials handling.

Flow Control. Flow control implies some type of continuous operation along a production line. Control is exercised by regulating the flow of material passing a particular point or moving along a particular production line. The production line is laid out according to the sequence of operations to be performed and represents a fixed pattern of movement for materials. With certain exceptions, the products coming off the end of the production line will all be alike.

Flow control is achieved largely by regulating the amount of materials moving over a production line. Specific orders may be evidenced even though the over-all operation is typified by control of production flow. Standing orders may be issued to materials handling personnel to keep an adequate bank of materials at the head of a particular production line at all times. Such an arrangement means that adequate **short-run production control** and **inventory control** must be operating. Adequate control is necessary to assure the materials handling personnel of having access to the proper amount of stock in stockrooms so as to supply the work banks. Even with flow control, a system of paper forms and controls is usually necessary if only to facilitate the ultimate flow of production along a mechanized production line.

Batch or Load Control. Types of production control vary in particular companies from the extreme job-order type of control to the extreme flow type of control. Between these extremes are many modifications. One modified type of control is batch or load control. Certain operations are uniquely suited to a movement of batches through a predetermined sequence of production operations. The operations themselves may be quite fixed in nature. The product, however, is made in batches of different size, color, or some other characteristic. Each batch moves as a unit. There are variations because of the unique nature of particular batches or styles.

Batch control needs some kind of paper order to accompany the batch. The problem of handling materials becomes one of moving particular batches of materials as a unit. The nature of the batch process makes the use of fixed equipment, such as conveyors, less effective than using mobile units. At the same time the sequence of operations is so fixed that there is usually no great problem in giving materials handling personnel proper directions. Materials handling personnel can be made available on a program basis. Materials are moved on the verbal instructions of department foremen or supervisors. The department may operate its own handling equipment, or the services of a materials handling department may be used. In either case certain problems peculiar to production control exist.

In the movement of batches where a production department has its own handling equipment, such equipment is usually not used to its maximum capacity. The **idle time** which must be assessed to cost of materials handling is often unwarranted. Production supervisors might prefer not to be charged with this materials handling cost. Problems of scheduling and control develop where the production supervisors and foremen depend upon a **central pool** of materials handling equipment. The problems include scheduling the requests of various departments. To justify the separate materials handling department as an independent operation, requests for service must be met promptly. Characteristic problems of production planning and control which arise include maximizing the use of equipment and at the same time performing an effective job of moving materials at the time required by persons requesting service.

In production control of the batch type it is difficult to exploit fully the advantages of either fixed materials handling or mobile materials handling equipment. Batch production requires a close **informal cooperation** between production control and materials handling.

Degree of Concentration of Production Control

INFLUENCE ON PRODUCTION AND MATERIALS HANDLING.
The degree of production control exercised in a particular plant has great influence upon the operations of materials handling equipment. The better the production control, the more effectively can the materials handling system serve the needs in manufacturing.

The two extremes in production control are: (1) centralized production control, and (2) decentralized production control. **Centralized production control** is characterized by the existence of a central production control department which plans and controls production operations in great detail. **Decentralized production control** is normally exercised through a production control department which allows other departments to participate in the control function. The latter gives foremen and other shop personnel considerable latitude in scheduling, dispatching, and supervising the follow-up of their particular operations.

Centralized production control affords a direct line of communication and control between the point of performance and central control authority. It implies speed of decision and promptness of action. Centralized control:

1. Insures more direct coordination. This coordination exists because all orders, information, and decisions emanate from the same control point.
2. Is designed with the objective of achieving better planning and greater unity and coherence in the orders issued.
3. Has certain advantages which are found to be important where production must be completed on a rigorously exact time schedule.
4. Is desirable when time or use of costly equipment has to be carefully apportioned.

Decentralized production control places more reliance upon contributions to the control action by other departments than does centralized control. The manufacturing departments and the materials handling department perform some of the control functions. Decentralized control:

1. Utilizes materials movement as one of its media for final control.
2. Must depend for its effectiveness upon proper training of the operating personnel.
3. Is apparently most effective in situations where schedules are not rigorous.
4. Is advantageous where equipment can be scheduled easily by the foremen and supervisors without resulting in bottlenecks in production.
5. Is also more effective than centralized control in situations where operating decisions and modifications can be made more efficiently and correctly at the point of performance.

As more personnel are involved in production operations, centralized production control decisions are likely to become less prompt. As the plant increases in size, **communications** between the central control authority and the point of performance are likely to become slower and less exact. Guides which might be used in determining the most satisfactory degree of production control centralization include the following:

1. **Centralization** increases in effectiveness if standardization is increased proportionately.
2. Centralization depends largely for its effectiveness upon the accuracy, speed, and adequacy of communications methods.
3. Centralization is proportionately more effective as production control facilities, organization, and personnel are better chosen and become more efficient.

4. **Decentralization** becomes more practicable as size and complexity of operations increase.
5. Decentralization is desirable as operations become more dispersed geographically.
6. **Flexible decentralization,** to maximize its effectiveness, must provide for quick shifting to centralized control in an emergency.

Centralized control lends itself particularly well to **continuous production** of homogeneous products controlled by rate of flow. When used for intermittent production, centralized control requires a wide diversity of paper or verbal orders. These orders must be dispatched, reports have to be returned, and the information must be transformed into production control data. Materials handling **move orders** are specifically dispatched. Reports are required when the move is completed. The effectiveness of the centralized operations depends upon knowledge of the actions taken and completed.

COMMUNICATIONS DEVICES. As companies grow in size, and their products become more diverse, and their operations become physically dispersed, the problem of proper functioning of communications becomes increasingly great. Intercommunication in a plant is important to correlate and control materials handling services. Certain developments in communications have kept up with the increase in size and extent of modern production operations. These faster communications methods are described in Section 8.

Layout, Mechanization, and Production Control

LAYOUT PLANNING. Some production operations lend themselves to the fabrication or assembly of a relatively **few standardized products** on a continuous basis. Layout and mechanization are more important in the control of such production than in diversified production. The pattern of movement is normally by flow down a **production line.** Plant layout is important.

Planning and control in such situations represent "before the fact" control. When a group of operations is to be executed continuously under standardized conditions, certain phases of production control can be performed at one time for all such operations. In highly continuous manufacturing, the layout and equipping of the production line is a major operation. Production processes and conditions are not likely to be changed to any extent until new models are designed and scheduled for production. Mechanization of the production line involves selecting the proper **equipment,** including materials handling devices, balancing the line, and work planning and routing. The pattern of movement is determined by the product.

In **other kinds of production** the mechanization of the plant plays a different role in determining the layout of the plant and pattern of movement. Where no one product dominates the operations to the extent that it pays to set up a production line for it, the pattern of movement is more likely to be determined by the grouping together of particular kinds of machines or equipment into respective departments or **work centers** to which any work, requiring that particular kind of equipment, will be sent. Thus there develops a layout pattern for milling departments, drilling departments, punch press departments, etc., with layout determined largely by the best placing of groups of like equipment or machines.

This type of layout is in contrast to the production line layout in Fig. 5. In the upper plant layout the **product** determines the layout and flow of orders. In the lower plant layout the equipment and functional operations are located with no

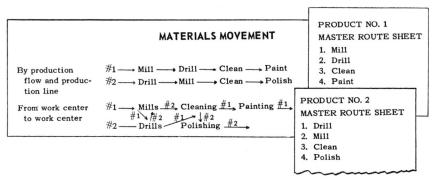

Fig. 5. Pattern of materials movement as a production factor.

specific attention to product. Work is routed to the departments in the sequence required by a product order.

Departments Related to Materials Handling

PLANT DEPARTMENTS SERVED BY MATERIALS HANDLING

Departments associated with materials handling are scattered throughout the organization. Certain departments associated with materials handling activities, either directly or indirectly, are:

1. Traffic.
2. Receiving.
3. Purchasing.
4. Inspection.
5. Materials control.
6. Production control.
7. Manufacturing departments.
8. Materials handling.
9. Stores.
10. Shipping.
11. Plant layout.
12. Expediting.

The **purchasing and materials control departments** are concerned with the ordering, delivery, recording, and control of materials. Material is usually delivered to the particular plant by common carrier, received, checked for quantity, inspected for quality, and moved to storage.

Production control, expediting, and **manufacturing departments** are all interested in having materials moved to the manufacturing departments or production lines according to schedule. The **materials handling department** and **plant layout department** are charged with moving materials as efficiently as possible. **Shipping departments** handle the finished materials and send them out into the channels of distribution.

Perhaps nowhere in the industrial organization is there a more complete **lack of uniformity** than in materials handling and storage. In the General Motors Corporation, for example, the management and control of industrial trucks, shop tractors, and other mobile equipment are found to fall variously as the responsibility of the (1) maintenance division, (2) materials handling division, or (3) individual production divisions. Reasons for such diversity are not difficult to find. There are **conflicting criteria** of association in the organization for materials handling. The "criterion of departmental use" places the control of such equipment and personnel near to, or in, the particular production department which finds most use for the required services. The "criterion of functional specialization" indicates that such equipment should be operated by a specialized department organized specifically for that purpose.

Valid reasons exist for setting up a **special materials handling department**:

1. Lower handling costs are possible through more complete and effective use of equipment.
2. More accurate cost accounting is possible when one department is assigned the transportation function.
3. More efficient maintenance and replacement policies and procedures can be adopted.
4. The development of newer and better methods is made possible.
5. Responsibility for materials movement and adequate supervision over such movement is definitely assigned.
6. Materials handling becomes recognized by top management as a definite function, with the benefits derived from such recognition.

No two plants are necessarily organized alike for purposes of materials handling, and there is no uniformity in assigning the responsibility for carrying on this work.

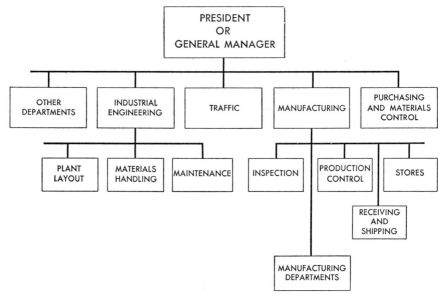

Fig. 6. **Relationships between materials handling and other departments (showing only functions associated with materials handling activities).**

Materials handling, however, is not likely to be a function of the production control department. Production control, although intimately associated with materials handling operations, is usually located in a different division of the management organization. In one company, for example, the production control department is located in the manufacturing department, and the materials handling department is located in the industrial engineering division. In a second company, however, production control is a part of the industrial engineering function, and materials handling is a department in the manufacturing division.

One arrangement in partial organization form which eliminates unrelated functions is shown in Fig. 6. In some of the electronics, aircraft, and other newer industries where the pattern of organization has not been established by years of tradition, there has developed a **materials division** which incorporates all the ordering, inventorying, storing, and moving of materials. The concept upon which such a division is based is that of delegating the responsibility of having the required materials at the proper place at the proper time, and deciding whether top management or technical management is to be given the responsibility for materials. All necessary functions for carrying out such a purpose are combined into a single division managed by a top-ranking executive who is given the necessary authority to carry out his responsibility (Fig. 7).

No matter how a particular company is organized, however, a close interrelationship must continue to exist between production control and materials handling. Both functions are auxiliary to actual manufacturing. Each must justify its

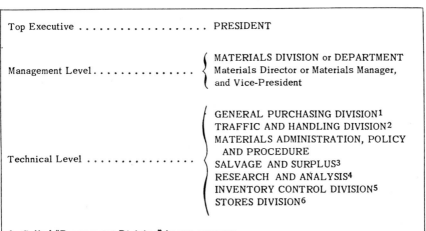

Top Executive . . . . PRESIDENT

Management Level. . . . . ⎰ MATERIALS DIVISION or DEPARTMENT
⎱ Materials Director or Materials Manager,
and Vice-President

Technical Level . . . . ⎰ GENERAL PURCHASING DIVISION[1]
TRAFFIC AND HANDLING DIVISION[2]
MATERIALS ADMINISTRATION, POLICY
AND PROCEDURE
SALVAGE AND SURPLUS[3]
RESEARCH AND ANALYSIS[4]
INVENTORY CONTROL DIVISION[5]
STORES DIVISION[6]

1. Called "Procurement Division" in one company.
2. Called "General Traffic Division" in two companies.
3. Variously called "Salvage Sales," "Surplus Disposal," and "Surplus Coordination."
4. Includes Market and Commodity Research and Component Cost Analysis.
5. Includes Materials Planning in two of the companies.
6. Includes Receiving, Shipping, Warehousing, and Materials Handling in various of the companies. In one case, Stores is not included in the Materials Division.

Adapted from a chart by Bryan, Purchasing, vol. 29

Fig. 7. Composite table showing the materials organization of five different companies in five different industries.

existence by making the manufacturing function more effective. Often they must sacrifice their own effectiveness so as to maximize the **effectiveness of manufacturing.**

With limitations imposed by manufacturing conditions, production control **regulates production.** It indicates what is to be done, where it is to be done, how it is to be done, and when it is to be done. Production control can be compared to the nervous system of the human body, whereas materials handling is more like the bloodstream of the body. Materials handling, within the limitations created by production problems, creates time and place utility in the materials which are to be moved by carrying out the requests of production control and manufacturing. To meet the requirements of directions and schedules from these departments, it may have to sacrifice certain of its own planned effectiveness.

The **traffic function** is closely allied to materials handling. In some companies the two functions are logically combined into a traffic and materials handling department, particularly if the company operates its own fleet of trucks and is engaged in moving materials from one plant to another for processing. An example of this kind is shown in the materials division organization charted in Fig. 7.

Traffic in general is associated with bringing in materials in advance of the time when the plant production control system is to make use of them. Production control **expediters** and purchasing **follow-up men** work closely with traffic personnel on delayed shipments. On specific shipments it may be necessary to coordinate closely the activities of traffic, materials handling, and production control. In most cases, however, the relationships between production control departments and materials handling activities begin with the arrival of materials at the plant receiving department.

Receiving, Inspection, and Storage

RECEIVING. The receiving function is in large measure a materials handling operation. The work of receiving materials has a direct connection with the work of the materials handling department and the production control department. Some **functions** of receiving are:

1. To check the number of packages, examine for the broken seals, evidence of tampering, shortage, external damage, water stains, and other indications of unacceptable materials.
2. To check identifying symbols, such as packing slips, car numbers, or other information pertinent to the preparation of receiving reports.
3. To unload and to unpack shipping cases.
4. To keep records of expected incoming deliveries, complete receiving reports, and distribute receiving reports to the proper departments.
5. Where damage or discrepancies occur, to note type of damage or discrepancies on shipper's bill, and to dispose of material temporarily until proper executives or department can deal with problem.
6. To keep receiving area clean, reasonably clear, and to enforce approved safety methods in handling materials.

Receiving departments vary in method and scope of operations. Some of the **policies** on receiving include: (1) receiving materials at any time materials are delivered, (2) receiving materials only during specifically stated hours, and (3) carefully scheduling receiving operations.

The receiving function is usually an operation of tremendous peak loads followed by periods of distinct idleness. **Production control techniques** applied to receiving operations offer promise of modifying such variances. Scheduling receiving operations is not feasible in most companies, but any move in that direction results in better utilization of manpower and equipment. By a study of **peak loads** in receiving, schedules can sometimes be planned, forecast, and controlled to correlate with periods of idleness in the shipping operations or materials handling activities, thus enabling handling equipment and personnel to be used on a rotation basis. The lag caused by purchasing lead time and delivery of shipments allows the receiving department to plan and prepare for the receiving activity to come, including provision of the needed pallets, trucks, and other handling equipment.

Quantity information may or may not appear on the receiving copy of the purchase order. It is frequently omitted so that the material must be counted in order to prepare the receiving report, thus forcing an actual accurate count.

Where quantity information is deleted, however, the receiving department cannot estimate in advance its activity load. Where the importance of scheduling delivery and receiving activity is emphasized, the quantity purchased should be known in advance by the receiving department, particularly if delays in handling will cause excessive demurrage charges.

INSPECTION. To implement **production control,** procedures should be provided for checking incoming shipments promptly and disposing of incomplete, damaged, substandard, or otherwise unacceptable materials. Some possible actions are:

1. To impound damaged, incomplete, or otherwise nonroutine receipts of materials.
2. To notify the proper persons or departments of the arrival and condition of materials.
3. To record discrepancies from specifications.
4. To provide for issuing orders to salvage, return, destroy, or otherwise dispose of such materials.

Adjustments with vendors in regard to materials rejected by the receiving or inspection departments are usually negotiated by the purchasing department. Work in process which has been rejected by the inspection department requires proper disposition. In either receiving inspection or work-in-process inspection the production control department is involved. Orders for the disposition and handling of rejected or spoiled materials are written or processed by the production control department. Rejections have to be considered for their possible effects upon present production schedules.

Inspection methods have direct relationships to materials handling. Handling is minimized if the inspector is brought to the materials but is maximized if the materials are taken to a central inspection area. Where materials must be moved to inspection it is possible to combine the move order and inspection report on one production control form.

STORAGE. Materials which are received and inspected usually then go into storage as does also a large percentage of materials which are first fabricated for later use in other manufacturing departments. Time lags exist between the time the material is received or finished and the time it is needed for production. Other materials are moved to storage in bulk and then issued from storage in small quantities.

Functions performed by the storage department include:

1. Receiving and recording the receipt of material.
2. Storing material in such ways as to minimize loss.
3. Filling orders and requisitions for materials.
4. Reconciling discrepancies between materials control records and actual material count.
5. Taking inventory of materials in storage.
6. Promoting better use of space, identification, location symbols, and other improvements in storage.

Most plants can improve storage procedures. Many executives do not fully appreciate the need for close control over receipt and issue of materials. Materials storage contributes to production control by increasing the economy and effectiveness by which materials are provided. Well-operated **materials storage:**

1. Provides more efficient storage.
2. Reduces to a practicable minimum the per-unit cost of storage.

3. Provides the type of information which will enable top management to develop sound materials storage policies.
4. Reduces the loss attributed to storage, including loss from such causes as:

a. Dust and dirt.
b. Rust and oxidation.
c. Must and dampness.
d. "Bust" and breakage.
e. Light.
f. Fire or water.
g. Heat or cold.
h. Evaporation or spillage.
i. Vermin or insects.

5. Insures maximum possible safety of persons involved in storage operations.

In achieving such goals, certain storage policy decisions develop which characterize the type of storage in a particular company. These **policies** include decisions as to:

1. Whether or not storerooms should be geographically centralized or decentralized.
2. Whether or not storerooms should be closed to personnel who are not members of the stores department.
3. Operating policies regarding standardization of storeroom layout, facilities, procedures, and methods.
4. Other policies directly concerned with minimizing storage loss.

Storeroom Location—Decentralized. Some of the above policy decisions are of direct concern to the persons responsible for materials handling. The location of storerooms has a direct relationship to the work of moving materials. There are certain distinct **advantages** to locating storerooms decentrally, placing them around the plant at various points:

1. Paper work in issuing material to manufacturing departments can usually be decreased because of the nearness in location of the two departments and the mutual understanding developed.
2. Closer relationships create the possibility for closer cooperation.
3. Time lags between requisitioning materials and issuing materials can be minimized.
4. Materials handling is performed on a less formal basis.

Decentralized storerooms vary from strictly controlled closed storerooms to open bins and banks of materials located on the production floor.

Storeroom Location—Centralized. Centralized stores operations require formal requisitions, move orders, and transportation from stores to the manufacturing areas as needed. The **advantages** gained include:

1. Possibilities for more effective supervision and better control.
2. Justification for having better materials handling equipment assigned to the storeroom because it will get more concentrated use than it might in smaller decentralized storerooms.
3. The nature of the operation justifies better storage facilities of all kinds, and layout can be more carefully considered.
4. Centralized storerooms are much easier to maintain as closed storerooms than are decentralized storerooms.

Closed storerooms implement closer control over materials, storeroom personnel do their work with fewer outside interruptions, supervision is more effective, and closed storerooms are necessary for high-cost materials. Questions are raised about materials handling, however, when storerooms are closed. Are materials handling personnel to be barred from closed storerooms? If so, how are the materials to be handled when received or issued? Some companies therefore have combined stores and handling operations into one department.

Open storerooms avoid certain materials handling problems. They may expedite production by minimizing the handling of materials by storeroom personnel; permit production personnel to locate materials, and possible substitutes for out-of-stock items; result in less material hoarding by production departments; allow a more even flow of work materials; and are particularly adapted to low-cost materials and supplies.

Standardization within storerooms aids materials handling. Standardization includes:

1. Standardization of facilities, layout, location, and other aspects of storerooms.
   a. This includes bin sizes, bin arrangements, pallet sizes, materials handling equipment, etc.
   b. Standardization of this style is of particular significance in companies operating many storerooms in many plants.
2. Standardization of methods of handling, stacking, piling, counting, and inventorying materials.
3. Standardization of issuing and receiving materials, storeroom location of materials, classification, and identification of materials.

Classification and identification of materials are properly parts of the larger function of production control. Distinct color codes, identification stampings on materials, and other marking help to insure the use of the right materials in production.

Materials Characteristics and Identifications

MATERIALS CLASSIFICATION. Classifications of materials are made on various bases. They include classification on the basis of (1) completion in process, (2) accounting charge, (3) form, (4) composition, and (5) identification system used.

A classification by **state of completion** in process usually uses a portion or all of the following groupings·

1. Raw materials.
2. Materials in process.
3. Finished goods.
4. Supplies.

5. Component parts.
6. Parts purchased finished.
7. Salvage.
8. Unclassified materials.

Accounting statements may consolidate several of these classifications. The classifications furnish a key to the relative degree of care to be used in the handling of materials. The nearer materials approach the finished state, the greater is the amount of cost invested in them. Component parts and parts purchased finished are higher per-unit cost items than raw materials. Materials in process may have to be protected carefully until they are assembled. General knowledge of the accounting classifications make materials handling personnel more aware of distinctions among materials.

When materials are charged to a job, an **accounting charge** is made to the job number for cost accounting purposes. For this accounting charge, materials are classified, according to Fig. 8, as: (1) **direct materials,** which are charged directly to the particular job, or, as (2) **indirect materials,** which are included in the burden or overhead charge assessed to the job.

Factory burden includes those items which are capable of being allocated, such as indirect materials, waste, repairs, taxes, insurance, indirect labor, power, heat, supplies, salaries of factory supervisors, depreciation, clerical workers' wages, etc. Burden is allocated on some such basis of distribution as proportional to direct material, direct cost, direct labor, number of machine hours used, or some other reasonable basis.

Direct material is usually controlled carefully in books of account. Thus it is logical for materials handling personnel to give more attention to its proper handling.

Classification of material by **form** is used because it provides a fairly easy method of identification. Material divides itself into standard shapes, special shapes, and a miscellaneous classification.

Overhead		Direct Labor	Direct Material
Selling and Administrative	Factory Burden	Direct Costs	
	Factory Cost		
Total Cost			

Fig. 8. Cost and expense charges.

Standard shapes are those which can usually be ordered directly from stock, and include: (1) channels, (2) angles, (3) T's, I's, H's, etc., (4) standard "hat" sections, (5) plates and sheets, (6) rods and wire, (7) tubes and bars, (8) standard extrusions, etc.

Selective shapes are found in the form of forgings, castings, stampings, upsets, special extrusions, etc. A company which uses sufficient quantities of any one of these types of materials can often design, or secure from manufacturers, efficient special materials handling equipment such as grabs to improve its handling operations.

Classification by **composition of material** also is of significance in planning materials handling procedure so as to guard against loss or breakage. Classifications by material include:

1. Metal.
   a. Ferrous—wrought iron, steel, cast iron, etc.
   b. Nonferrous—aluminum, copper, zinc, etc.
2. Nonmetal.
   a. Wood products.
   b. Plastics.
   c. Other products, including rubber, glass, etc.

Identification Systems. Identification systems for materials represent short-hand symbolization, and usually use numbers or letters. Identification systems are either unclassified or classified. **Unclassified systems** rely largely upon straight numbering. Numbers for particular parts and materials are chosen at random from unassigned numbers. **Classified identification systems** rely upon numbers and letters which carry particular significance.

One of the classified numbering systems is the **mnemonic system,** in which letters which aid the memory are employed. GT-1-CAL-1023, for example, might refer to a size No. 1 "grinding tool" which is used for cutting a part No. 1023 composed of cast aluminum. The same system can be used for raw materials. The classification system should be known and understood by all materials handling personnel.

Materials Control and Production Planning

MATERIALS CONTROL. Materials handling is affected by materials control in various ways. Orders may be issued to move materials which are not available. Materials may be moved by a **combined requisition and move order.** Production control departments often issue **work orders** on the assumption that certain materials will be available when the requisition for materials is submitted to the stores department. This assumption is not always valid. Requisitions coming directly from manufacturing departments or other operating departments may have depleted the stock of materials on hand in storerooms. Materials control departments exist for the purpose of better regulating the supply of materials. They also exist because the complexities in materials accounting warrant **control of materials** separate from storeroom operations.

BALANCE OF STORES RECORD							
Date	On Order	Received	Unit Price When Received	Withdrawal	On Hand	Apportioned	Available
1/1	4,900#	0#		0#	0#	0#	4,900#
1/4	3,300	1,600	$0.10	0	1,600	0	4,900
1/5	3,300	0		0	1,600	1,000	3,900
1/7	1,000	2,300	0.11	0	3,900	1,000	3,900
1/14	1,000	0		2,200	1,700	1,000	1,700
1/20	1,000	900	0.11	0	2,600	1,000	2,600
1/21	1,000	0		1,000	1,600	0	2,600

The transactions on this ledger were as follows: (a) 1/4, 1,600 lb. of material received. (b) 1/5, a requisition for setting aside for delivery to production 1,000 lb. was received in the materials control department, but delivery of the materials called for was not to be made until approximately 1/21. (c) 1/7, 2,300 lb. were received. (d) 1/14, a requisition for the immediate delivery of 2,200 lb. was received and since the material was available, it was issued. (e) 1/20, 900 lb. of the material issued on 1/14 were returned. (f) 1/21, 1,000 lb., which were set aside on 1/5, were issued on the production control order dispatched on this date. An internal audit is always available in this ledger because the amount "on hand" plus that "on order" should always equal the amount "apportioned" plus that "available."

Fig. 9. A materials control ledger.

Production control problems related to materials control have led to the design of **materials control ledgers** and **accounting devices** for handling such problems. One such ledger allows for recording specific materials as "mortgaged," "allocated," or "apportioned" in advance of the issuance of the actual requisition for their delivery to the proper production area. When the production order is written, a **preliminary requisition** is sent to the materials control department. The required amount of materials is "apportioned" on the proper materials ledger sheet or card by subtracting that amount of material from the "available" account and adding it to the amount "allocated" for the specific production order. The essential parts of the operation of such a ledger are shown in Fig. 9. This is the most effective, but also the most expensive, method and is particularly adaptable to operations which combine job-shop and order control with production line operations. The apportioning of materials before they are actually to be delivered allows accumulation to be completed properly before assembly.

Other methods of posting materials control records include: (1) withdraw and deduct, (2) prededuction, and (3) schedule. Under the **withdraw and deduct** method the materials control ledger is adjusted when the materials are withdrawn. It is perhaps the most widely used method, being simple, direct, easy to understand, and not requiring additional paper work. It is particularly adaptable where most of the production operations are manufacturing to stock. The **prededuction** method is a simple method in which the material is deducted from the stock record as soon as the requirement is known, even though it may not be physically withdrawn from the storeroom for some time. It works well with operations based on manufacturing programs and in operations where the manufacturing cycle is short. The **schedule** method is in reality the keeping of no stock records at all. Materials are ordered according to some predetermined schedule, with no attempt to control individual deliveries. **Periodic checks** on physical inventory are taken to avoid costly overages and shortages wherever possible.

Where **materials control records** are maintained, most manufacturing companies keep the records in a department separate from the physical stores department. Maintaining the materials ledger is an office-type activity, best done in such surroundings. The stores department performs largely a **materials handling operation.** A minimum of record keeping should be done in the stores department. In most cases, for control purposes, all that is needed in the storeroom—other than a file showing location of materials—are **bin tags** on the bins. These bin tags show the amount of materials in the bins and the records are adjusted on these tags whenever stock is added or withdrawn. The balance on the bin tag should be the same as the balance shown in the materials ledger when adjustments are made for entries which have not been physically completed.

The materials control accounting system should be understood by the materials handling personnel. **Procedures for receiving and withdrawal** of materials should be well defined and observed by the materials handling department. No materials should be moved from stores except upon a valid **materials requisition** properly entered in the materials control ledger. Where materials handling personnel help fill such requisitions from bins with bin tags attached, they should make the proper adjustments on the bin tags.

PRODUCTION PLANNING AND MATERIALS HANDLING. Production planning has direct influence upon subsequent materials handling. Production planning, as the function is here considered, is confined largely to some considerations of **production routing and layout.** Routing is necessary in any manufacturing operation which requires a sequence of operations. In manufacturing in which there is anticipated a repetition of orders for the same material or part, it is customary to develop a master routing. This **master routing**—which might be called a manufacturing outline, master route sheet, or be referred to in other similar terms—is a semipermanent record to be kept filed for reference. **Master route sheets** have the following functions:

1. To formalize the sequence of operations.
2. To provide the basis for plant layout of production lines where material is to be processed on such a basis.
3. To provide the basis for writing production orders where material is to be processed in various departments.
4. To aid in planning for the needed equipment, tools, handling fixtures, and other facilities.

5. To provide a basis for scheduling production orders or to plan production flow.
6. To incorporate in one place all pertinent information which will aid in the manufacturing of the particular part, or in processing the particular material, including:

a. Economic lot size.
b. Standard time per operation.
c. Setup time.
d. Part-number references.
e. Type and size of material.
f. Other significant information.

A master route sheet is shown in Fig. 10. Master route sheets may not contain any direct information as to the actual method to be used in materials handling. If special handling fixtures are to be used, however, these are recorded. Routine moves are omitted, although they are implied by the sequence of operations.

Where fixed materials handling equipment is to be used, or where production is to be continuous, specific movement of materials is determined by **plant layout.** Under mass production, plant layout is determined by the sequence of operations listed on the master route sheets, modified by conditions which exist in the plant. Where the plant is arranged in departments or work centers or according to kinds of equipment, and the materials are routed to the particular **work centers,** however, some special provision must be made for handling the materials between operations. Master route sheets do not normally show this fact. **Routing to inspection** is also often considered as a matter of common routine, the material being routed to inspection automatically after each operation and before it is moved to the next operation.

The relationships between production control, plant layout, and materials handling should be clearly understood. After the **blueprints and specifications** have been developed for the product, necessary changes have been made, cost estimates and sequence of operations developed, parts lists and bills of materials prepared, the **master route sheet** is worked out. The master route sheet may be translated into a **process flow chart** as the first step toward layout. The process flow chart is used to prepare a layout diagram. **Three-dimensional models** may be used to present the layout. It is during this stage of planning that many of the policy questions in the matter of materials handling must be determined. The particular layout, of necessity, will have a fundamental effect on the amount and type of materials handling equipment required. **Effective layout** should result in:

1. A provision for definite lines of work travel.
2. The determination of the most direct movements feasible between operations.
3. A reduction in cost of materials handling.
4. A minimizing of work-in-process time.
5. A maximum utilization of floor area.
6. A more effective utilization of production equipment.
7. An increased efficiency in labor output.

The **mechanization of the flow of work** by proper layout has certain advantages as related to production control. These advantages include:

1. Elimination of delays in manufacturing.
2. Shorter distances between operations, resulting in less material to be controlled in process.
3. Mechanical determination of sequence of operations.
4. Fewer possibilities of materials being lost in process.
5. Less need for banks of materials throughout the production area.
6. Less inspection because of the set pattern of production.
7. Replacement, through visual control, of much of the paper work necessary to control materials which do not follow set patterns.

MASTER OPERATION SHEET

CHANGE LETTER "B"
RELEASE DATE 2/10/-
ECONOMIC LOT SIZE 285

PART NO. 276565
PART NAME Block-support
NEXT ASSEMBLY 345982

Operation No.	Operation	Symbol	Machine	Machine No.	Dept. No.	Tools Used	Running Time per Pc.	Schedule Time	Setup	Cutting Speed	Feed	Remarks
1	Turn	18						8 hr.				
2	Mill	25	P & W	25	256	MF #1	5.50		1 hr.			
3	Drill	20	S	31	284	DF #1	.75		½ hr.			
						DF #2	.50		½ hr.			
4	Ream	20	R	48	284		.50		¼ hr.			
5	Clean	10						8 hr.				
6	Deliver							8 hr.				

DELIVER TO Dept. 346 Stores
PREPARED BY White
APPROVED BY Jackson
PROD. APPRVL. ack   ENGNRG. APPRVL. soy

MATERIAL 1020 CR Bar Stk
REFERENCE PRINTS 167865, 875043
REFERENCE SPECS. AN 163

Fig. 10. Master route (or operation) sheet.

The development of **work process charts** to show the layout, either as it is at the moment or as it is proposed it should be, helps to facilitate improved layout. Work process charts show in analytical form the amount of movement, the number of operations, and other information which is valuable in studying a layout. The symbols used help to spot the various activities quickly. A partial work process chart is shown in Fig. 11.

FLOW PROCESS CHART

SUBJECT CHARTED: Flow of Block Support   DATE: 2/11/–
                 No. 276565 Production Line   CHART NO. 7

PRESENT ___✓___)   SHEET 1 OF 1
                  METHOD
PROPOSED _____)   CHART BY mhb

SYMBOLS: O – Operation;   U – Transportation;   □ – Inspection,   ▽ – Storage;
          D – Delay

TOTALS: No. Oper. 10 , Total Time ____ ; No. Moves 5 , Total Dist. 75'

Operation No.	Symbol					Distance in Feet	Time in Minutes	Process Description
	O	U	□	▽	D			
1			□				1	Twenty pieces of stock in tote box are inspected and placed on conveyor.
2		U				15	1	Material moves to milling machine.
3				▽				Operator stacks tote box by his machine.
4	O						110	Operator places each piece on machine, one at a time, then back in box.
5			□				1	Operator checks count and places box on chute.
6		U				10	1	Chute carries box to drill operation.

Fig. 11. Work (or flow) process chart.

In the planning and production engineering for **continuous line production** there are **standard procedures and factors** which are commonly used. Some of these are:

1. Preparation of engineering drawings and specifications.
2. Product analysis and requests for engineering changes where improvements can be made or changes are necessary.
3. Forecast, estimate, or program for rate and volume of production and the additional engineering changes which such procedures warrant.
4. Bills of materials and equipment lists.
5. Production routing sheets, operation times, and manpower tables.
6. Layout planning, flow process sheets and diagrams, layout boards, models and templates, and installation drawings.

7. Tooling blueprints, installation of fixed handling equipment, and equipment procurement and fabrication.
8. Production line tryout and balance, manufacturing cycle time, and bank-size determination.
9. Pilot period in which operational changes are requested, materials handling is checked for adequacy, and time studies are made.
10. Continued improvement and rebalancing.

Forms and devices used in facilitating the completion of the procedures for planning and production engineering for continuous line production include:

1. Specifications.
2. Change request.
3. Cost estimate.
4. Bill of materials.
5. Parts list.
6. Master route sheet.
7. Process flow chart.
8. Layout diagram.
9. Tool and equipment order.
10. Line balance chart.
11. Time study observation sheet.
12. Master schedule.
13. Production order.

PRODUCTION SCHEDULING AND MATERIALS HANDLING.

The master route sheet often incorporates the schedule time necessary to complete a particular routing, and should state the **time** necessary to move the material from one operation to another, based upon time study or experience. The time indicated is normally a total time and includes the time necessary for the material to be placed at the point from which it will be picked up, tagged, and moved until it is received and placed at the machine which performs the next operation. In reality it comprises the **time lag** between one operation and another.

The master route sheet is a standing plan for a series of possible future production orders which might be written from time to time. It is therefore a **permanent or semipermanent guide.** Individual orders, however, must be scheduled as conditions warrant. The **scheduling problem** on individual orders is a particular problem in intermittent job-shop operations. Scheduling time for materials handling between operations may be secured from the master route sheet if it is included in that basic data sheet. If not, such time must be determined from experience or by approximation. In either case the scheduled time for materials handling should include time for all normal delays in movement.

As a basic data sheet the master route sheet should incorporate **accurate operation times.** These times should be the **basis for scheduling;** and all operations, including materials handling, should adhere to the schedules. Often the operation times can only be approximated. This condition is often true in job shops which operate on a decentralized job-order system of production control. In such instances due dates rather than hourly schedules are used. In all events, however, materials handling time should be sufficiently consistent to be counted upon when scheduling is done.

Careful **coordination** must be worked out between materials handling and production control so as to deliver materials on schedule. Some job shops have sufficiently large operations to enable the use of definite **scheduled trips** by materials handling trucks over distinct routes, practically on "train schedules." Some provisions should be made for taking **corrective action** when the schedules are not being adhered to, such as notifying the production control department of the completion of each move. Methods have to be designed which allow for coordination without too much paper work on the part of those not directly delegated with production control functions.

Devices which aid scheduling by presenting a visible record are numerous. These are prepared by the production control department but should be understandable

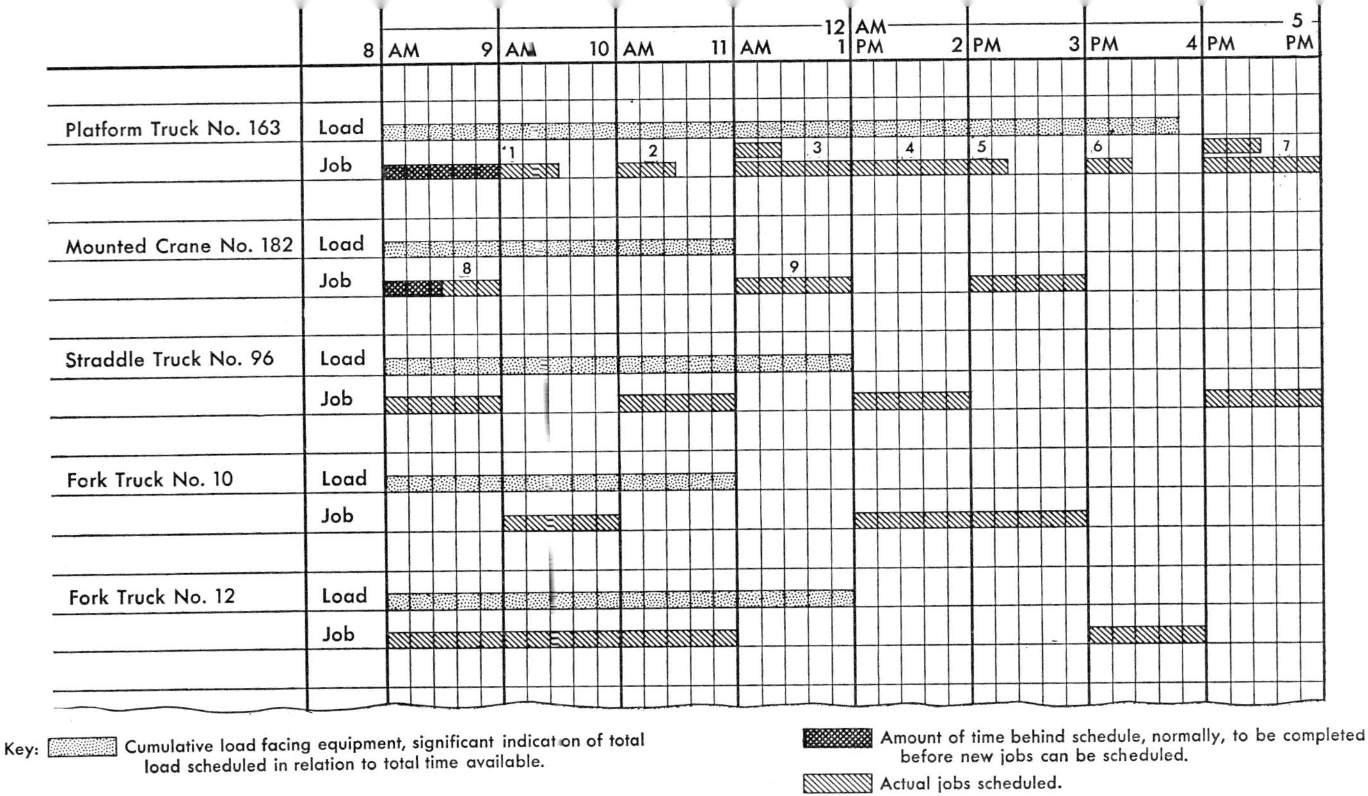

Fig. 12. Scheduling materials handling equipment by means of a Gantt chart (using basis of an 8-hr. day).

Key: ▓ Cumulative load facing equipment, significant indication of total load scheduled in relation to total time available.

▒ Amount of time behind schedule, normally, to be completed before new jobs can be scheduled.

░ Actual jobs scheduled.

CHART SHOWING SCHEDULING AS OF 8 A.M.: Platform truck No. 163 shows a load approximately 85% of capacity. It is 1 hr. behind schedule. Job 1 and Job 2 are half-hour jobs. Job 3 is a 1½ hr. job. It cannot be completed by 12 A.M. The work must be handled starting at 11 A.M. Probably the platform truck No. 163 will be worked overtime into the lunch hour. Job 7 will require similar treatment, probably resulting in the equipment and operator being required to work overtime after 5 P.M.

Mounted crane No. 182 is scheduled only to about 38% of capacity at the present time. It is about ½ hr. behind schedule. It has free time available between 9 A.M. and 11 A.M. At 11 A.M. it has a job, Job 9. It is free at 1 P.M. and from 3 P.M. to 5 P.M.

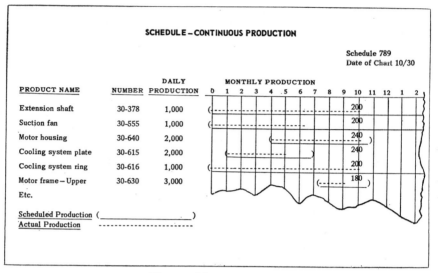

Fig. 13. Master schedule.

This schedule indicates the beginning and ending dates for the production of various parts. A control mechanism for indicating need for corrective action is added in the charting of actual production against the schedule. Interpreting the chart on 10/30, it will be noted that Part No. 30–378 is being produced according to schedule (200,000). Part No. 30–555 is behind schedule (approximately 130,000 produced on a schedule calling for 200,000). Part No. 30–640 is on schedule, etc.

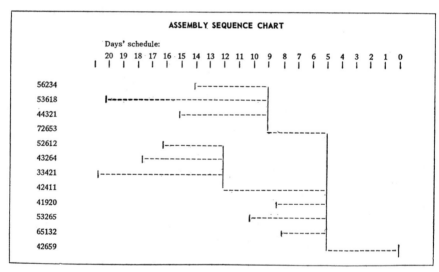

Fig. 14. Assembly sequence chart.

This chart shows the total time necessary to fabricate and assemble all the parts necessary to make No. 42659. The lines indicate the time necessary to manufacture a stated amount of each part and then to assemble the parts into the completed product. This time can easily be translated into a calendar schedule of due dates.

to all persons involved in carrying them out. Some of the types of **scheduling devices** used are (1) Gantt charts, (2) assembly sequence charts, and (3) commercially developed patented systems. All these devices are modifications of Gantt charts, which are forms to represent activities by relating the activities to time. Time is represented by horizontal distances across such charts.

A **Gantt chart** used for scheduling materials handling equipment is shown in Fig. 12. The same kind of chart can be used for scheduling any kind of activity. A **master schedule** for planning a continuous production operation is shown in Fig. 13. **Assembly sequence charts** are developed by charting the time necessary to fabricate and assemble the parts in the master parts list. An assembly sequence chart is shown in Fig. 14; this chart is constructed on the principle involved in the Gantt chart.

PRODUCTION DISPATCHING AND MATERIALS HANDLING. In production control, dispatching is the process of actually **issuing the orders** according to schedule. In highly continuous and mechanized operations, such as one might find in a refinery or chemical plant, dispatching might consist primarily of turning switches or valves as the schedule requires. In centralized order control of an intermittent nature, the usual procedure is for a central dispatcher to issue all necessary orders. In the case of materials handling a specific order is issued, which is normally returned after the handling is completed. Centralized production control depends upon specific orders issued followed by reports to indicate that such orders are carried out.

In decentralized order control, the dispatching function is much more informal. In the case of materials handling in **decentralized dispatching,** the dispatching is completed by someone attaching a move tag to the materials and placing the material on an outgoing pallet or shop truck. If the parts or materials are too large to place on the outgoing pallet or truck, the move man is directed to the tagged material and will then have it transported by motor truck or railroad car.

There are many variations in amount of centralization and of decentralization of dispatching and in the general methods used. Two methods are illustrated by simplified sequence charts in Figs. 15 and 17.

Centralized dispatching is represented in Fig. 15, as typified by a central dispatch booth which performs all dispatching. Basically, the system uses as many paper control forms as are necessary. Copies are made up simultaneously when routing and scheduling are done. The system revolves around the central dispatch station or booth. Control is exercised directly to the machine. The shop foreman does not bear the major responsibility for production control. There is a relatively large amount of control action taken in the dispatching booth. In the illustration, Fig. 17, departments have been combined to save space in the presentation.

Some of the other aspects of the particular system of central dispatch shown in Fig. 15 are as follows:

1. Central dispatch clerks work closely with schedule clerks who have prepared workable schedules.
2. Scheduling is directly to specific machines or work centers.
3. The operator receives his production orders or work orders by presenting his completed production or work order when one job is finished. The dispatch clerk assigns the new job to him by issuing the new order.
4. Before issuing a production or work order, the dispatch clerk has made sure that all materials, tools, facilities, and papers (including blueprints and instruction cards) are waiting at the machine or available immediately at the dispatch booth.

SEQUENCE \ DEPARTMENTS	Routing,* Scheduling	Central Dispatching Department or Booth	Stores* Department and Tool Department	Handling Department	Department A and Inspection	Department B and Inspection
Material Requisition sent to Stores Dept. by Central Dispatching, filled and returned.	#1	#1 ... #1	#1			
Move Ticket No. 2 is sent to Handling Dept. Handling Dept. moves material to proper production machine, returns completed ticket.	#2	#2 ... #2		#2	#2	
Tool Requisition sent to Tool Dept. by Central Dispatching, filled and returned.	#3	#3 ... #3	#3			
Move Ticket No. 4 is sent to Handling Dept., which moves tools to proper production machine and returns ticket.	#4	#4 ... #4		#4	#4	
Work Order No. 5 (including inspection) issued to machine operator when he reports for next job assignment. Operator completes job and returns order.	#5	#5 ... #5			#5	
Inspection Report No. 6 is received by Central Dispatch.		#6			#6	
Move Ticket No. 7 is sent to Handling Dept., which moves materials to next operation, returns unneeded tools, and picks up any additional tools needed.	#7	#7 ... #7		#7	#7	#7
Work Order No. 8 (including inspection) issued to machine operator when he reports for next job assignment. Operator completes job and returns order.	#8	#8 ... #8				#8
Inspection Report No. 9 is received by Central Dispatch.		#9				#9
Move Ticket No. 10 is sent to Handling Dept., which moves materials to correct location and returns tools to Tool Dept.	#10	#10 ... #10	#10			#10

* Departments combined to save space in presentation.

Fig. 15. A simplified sequence chart of a centralized control system with centralized dispatching (showing only two production departments).

5. To insure the presence of all needed materials, tools, etc., the dispatch clerk maintains some type of visible control dispatch board which shows the conditions of all aspects of the needed facilities.

    a. A route sheet, which serves as a check sheet and is marked as each needed item is ordered and secured.

    b. A "three-peg" or "three-pocket" arrangement to keep shop orders. Each work or production order is kept on one of three pegs or in one of three pockets. These three pegs or pockets are (1) On Machine, (2) Waiting at Machine and (3) Ahead of Machine.

6. The use of a series of orders to move materials and tools to the machine, secure the needed blueprints and specifications, etc. These orders are:
   a. Time ticket.
   b. Scheduling department form.
   c. Move order—materials.
   d. Materials identification.
   e. Materials requisition.
   f. Tool withdrawal requisition.
   g. Move order—tools.
   h. Inspection report.
   i. Move order—shop.
   j. Operation completion notice.
   k. Blueprint and specification request.
   l. Production order.

As is shown in Fig. 15, each order goes out from central dispatch and returns when the particular order is completed. All orders for shop activity revolve around the central dispatch station.

Where production is continuous in nature the **flow of work**, rather than the issuance of particular production orders, determines dispatching procedure. Some methods of dispatching for continuous flow are:

1. Issuance of orders simultaneously to all parts of the plant.
2. The use of positions or stations to determine elements of work flow, with work to move from station to station at definite times indicated by a dispatch signal.
3. The use of loading orders which indicate the sequence in which production lines should be loaded.

Fig. 16 shows a composite routing, scheduling, and dispatch diagram.

TelAutographs are used to dispatch the orders to various parts of the plant. For each car built, specific instructions are given as to types of accessories, color, type of upholstery, trim, etc.

Automobile plants are noted for their **moving conveyor lines,** which are synchronized. Some production, such as aircraft, may lend itself better to production lines which are not mechanized. Definite stations are used for specific operations. **Intermittent movement of production** takes place. The line might move each hour, which means that at a given signal, the product (such as a wing assembly) will be pushed to the next station. The work of every station must be planned so that operators at every station will have their work completed before the dispatch signal indicating the next "move" is given. The product must be on **handling fixtures** which enables the moves to be made easily.

Where specific synchronizing of the various production lines is too difficult, the dispatching problem may be resolved by using a **master loading order,** which indicates the sequence of work on each of the various lines. Thus, if a "blue" accessory is needed for a particular final assembly, it will be loaded on the accessory line on that basis. After it has been finished on the accessory line, the "blue" accessory may be stored as part of a bank of accessories at the point of assembly until needed.

Dispatching where flow is continuous depends largely upon careful scheduling of all parts and assemblies in relation to the schedule time for the completed product. Dispatching is represented by issuing the proper **instructions** to various parts of the plant to allow feeder lines to be loaded so as to synchronize with the main production line. TelAutograph or Teletype stations can be used for this purpose. Where lines all move at the same rate, the synchronizing of the various lines can be accomplished by carefully **planning** the positions on various lines to

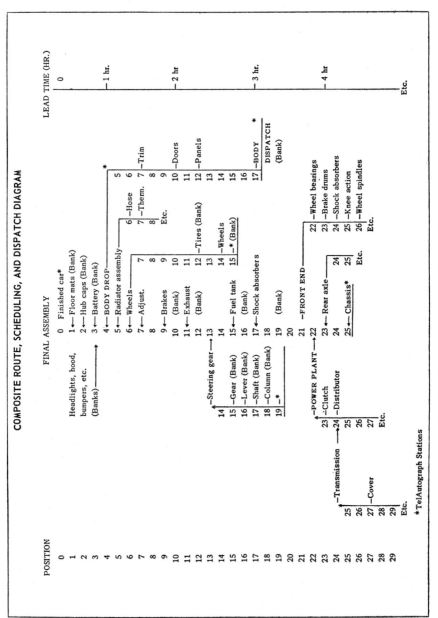

Fig. 16. Dispatching for continuous flow.

coincide in lead time. Thus, in Fig. 16 it is necessary for the body to be dispatched at the proper time from position No. 17 on the body line in order to meet its properly mated chassis at position No. 4. Where lines cannot be synchronized so closely, dispatching can be accomplished by issuing orders indicating the sequence of loading. The needed parts and assemblies can be dispatched in time to be placed in banks near the point of final assembly so as to be there when needed.

Decentralized dispatching, as is illustrated in Fig. 17, represents a particular system which has the following characteristics:

1. Schedules are worked out in advance but are loose schedules rather than tight ones.

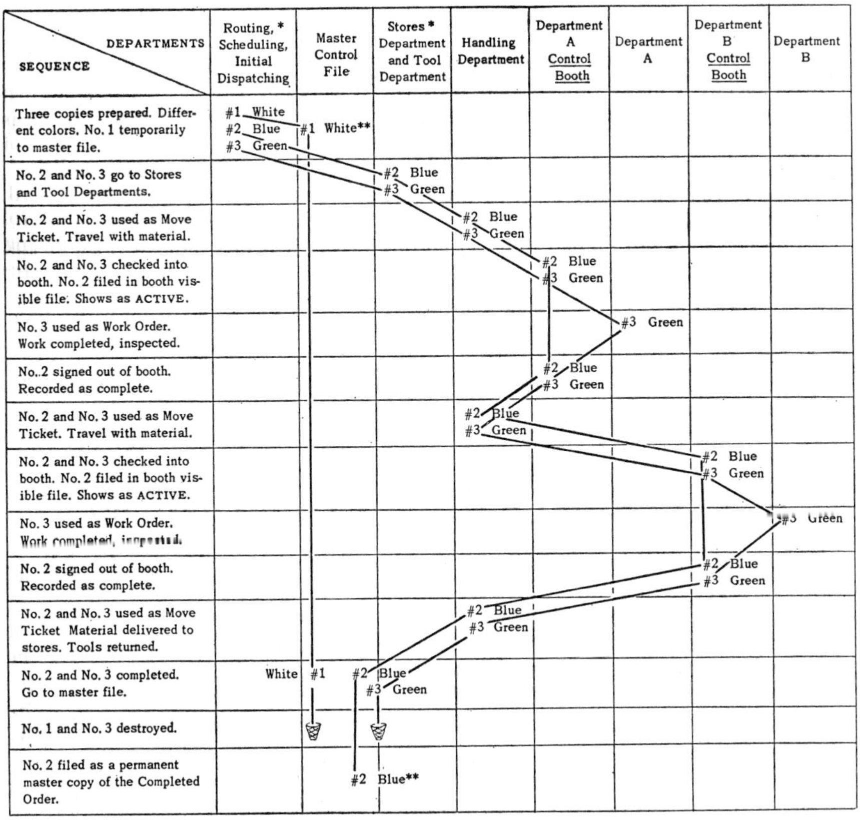

SEQUENCE \ DEPARTMENTS	Routing,* Scheduling, Initial Dispatching	Master Control File	Stores* Department and Tool Department	Handling Department	Department A Control Booth	Department A	Department B Control Booth	Department B
Three copies prepared. Different colors. No. 1 temporarily to master file.	#1 White #2 Blue #3 Green	#1 White**						
No. 2 and No. 3 go to Stores and Tool Departments.			#2 Blue #3 Green					
No. 2 and No. 3 used as Move Ticket. Travel with material.				#2 Blue #3 Green				
No. 2 and No. 3 checked into booth. No. 2 filed in booth visible file. Shows as ACTIVE.					#2 Blue #3 Green			
No. 3 used as Work Order. Work completed, inspected.						#3 Green		
No. 2 signed out of booth. Recorded as complete.					#2 Blue #3 Green			
No. 2 and No. 3 used as Move Ticket. Travel with material.				#2 Blue #3 Green				
No. 2 and No. 3 checked into booth. No. 2 filed in booth visible file. Shows as ACTIVE.							#2 Blue #3 Green	
No. 3 used as Work Order. Work completed, inspected.								#3 Green
No. 2 signed out of booth. Recorded as complete.							#2 Blue #3 Green	
No. 2 and No. 3 used as Move Ticket Material delivered to stores. Tools returned.			#2 Blue #3 Green					
No. 2 and No. 3 completed. Go to master file.		White #1	#2 Blue #3 Green					
No. 1 and No. 3 destroyed.								
No. 2 filed as a permanent master copy of the Completed Order.			#2 Blue**					

* Departments combined to save space in presentation.
** In the master file a white copy indicates an ACTIVE order, a blue copy a COMPLETED order.

Fig. 17. A simplified sequence chart of a decentralized control system with decentralized dispatching (showing only two production departments).

Basically, this system uses three copies of the production order. The blue copy is a traveling master copy, filed in production control booths to show an order active in departments while so filed. The green copy is the shop order copy and goes to that department. The white copy is a temporary copy used in the master file to show that the order is active somewhere in the shop. Production control schedules orders and exercises control to the control booth. The shop foreman controls orders within his department. Only a relatively small amount of control action is taken in the dispatching and control booths.

2. Scheduling is to departments rather than to machines within departments.
   a. **Due dates** rather than hours are used.
   b. The foreman of the particular department schedules his own department's machines.
3. The operator receives his production orders or work orders from the foreman or his representatives. The blueprints and needed papers are secured by departmental clerks.
4. The production orders have served as traveling orders to secure materials and needed tools for the operator before they become his working orders.
5. Control is maintained by reports to the production control office of orders which are not leaving particular departments on the dates stated as due dates.
6. The production or work orders serve a number of purposes, eliminating the need for many special orders of various kinds.

As is shown in Fig. 17, the orders are "dispatched" initially from a production control dispatch desk. The orders then travel through various departments as they are processed. They are returned when they are completed and filed in a completed file.

There are other ways in which dispatching can be done. However accomplished, it should have a legitimate place in the **relationships** between production control and materials handling. As the "bloodstream" of industry, the materials handling function will soon put an end to effective production if it does not keep the materials and tools flowing according to schedule.

A typical set of the **forms** used includes the following copies:

1. Central production control form.
2. Departmental production order.
3. Traveling production order.
4. Parts requisition.
5. Raw materials requisition.
6. Cost department form.

Production Control, Follow-up, and Materials Handling

THE FOLLOW-UP FUNCTION. If production control is to exist, follow-up becomes required in direct proportion to any realization in the other phases of control. Close follow-up is important to close production control. Variables of mechanical, economic, and an accidental nature require follow-up to maintain the smoothness of operation necessary to successful manufacture and materials handling. Materials which are **not moved as scheduled,** or materials **moved to the wrong location,** or materials **moved in an improper manner** all require follow-up and corrective action.

Records aid follow-up. Recording the sequence of moves in the route which a particular part might take is a costly process in terms of a materials handler's time, and it is disliked and avoided in most materials handling operations. The problem of records becomes one of securing sufficient information to aid subsequent follow-up, if it is needed, without resorting to tedious and costly recording of moves.

Identification tags, which can be prepared in advance by duplicating processes, can provide for markings and subsequently for records. Identification tags, move tags, production orders, and other pertinent information can be filed and kept until the order is complete.

Education of materials handlers regarding the problems of follow-up enables the production control function to be performed more effectively. **Periodic inspection** of mobile units, docks, storage points, and other areas where materials might accumulate prevents material from getting stranded. Loose tags and production control records should be forwarded quickly to the production control department.

Cooperation on follow-up enables the production control department to carry out its assignment. Special equipment may have to be held in readiness by the materials handling departments to provide service on emergency requests and systems of priority in materials handling may be required. Some means for providing cooperation on follow-up include:

1. The establishment of a special section or department to handle **special requests for materials handling.**
2. The creation within the normal system of materials handling of **recognized priorities,** which will enable certain orders to be given precedence over others.
3. The determination of policies, procedures, and controls within the materials handling function which will harmonize the needs of production control follow-up and corrective action with the requirements of **sound materials handling practices.**

A balance should be maintained between providing too much special service and not providing enough in the matter of production control follow-up and corrective action. Points of variance between good handling and good control which require consideration include:

1. The **procedure and priority** in the issuance of orders for materials handling.
2. The proper **place of the materials handling function** in the process of receiving and issuing materials.
    a. Procedures for receiving and issuing materials in the stores department should be planned to correlate with good materials handling practice.
    b. Procedures for receiving and issuing materials in the transportation operation between operating departments should be checked for proper relationships.
3. The types of **production control records** which are appropriate in indicating the materials handling activities performed should be consistent with the needs of the company for simplicity and adequate control.
4. **Inventory procedures** should be considered for their relationships to materials handling.
    a. The problem of accounting for materials in transit is increased as more material is involved. The type of production control has a direct relationship to the amount of material to be found in movement between departments.
    b. The place of the materials handling department as related to the inventory process should be considered.
5. The **need and use of damage information** and figures should be consistent with the needs of both materials handling and production control.
6. **Housekeeping procedures** should be provided in such a manner as to be consistent with the control of materials as planned in the production control system.
7. **Variances** in production control and materials handling procedures relating to **minimizing movement, maximizing space use,** and **standardization of facilities** should be eliminated where practicable.

Points where production control procedures are at variance with materials handling procedures can be investigated by a specific review of (1) routing, (2) scheduling, (3) dispatching, (4) operations, (5) recording, and (6) follow-up. Some of the questions other than those above are listed in Fig. 18.

Factors	Information at Hand?		Get Information from
	Yes	No	
1. Do routing procedures include consideration of handling problems?	( )	( )	Production Planning, Industrial Engineering
2. Are the kinds of materials, parts, and products handled in the plant generally known?	( )	( )	Purchasing, Department heads, Engineering, Production Control
3. Is the form in which materials are moved standardized and known? (Tote boxes, pallet loads, cartons, bulk, etc.)	( )	( )	Department heads, Purchasing, Materials Handling
4. Are plant layout and equipment consistent with the needs of handling?	( )	( )	Industrial Engineering, Department heads
5. Are difficulties encountered in meeting handling schedules?	( )	( )	Production Control, Materials Handling, Department heads
6. Is amount known of each type of material (in number of units or weight) handled each hour, day, or week?	( )	( )	Production Planning, Production Control, Department heads, Materials Handling
7. Are the number of times each handling job recurs known?	( )	( )	Production Control, Department heads, Materials Handling
8. Are handling orders definitely dispatched so the handling department has a specific order to initiate handling action?	( )	( )	Production Control, Department heads, Materials Handling
9. Are handling orders specific enough to prevent misunderstandings?	( )	( )	Materials Handling, Production Control
10. Are actual handling costs (in dollars per ton-ft., or some other figure) tabulated?	( )	( )	Accounting
11. Are the responsibilities of the handling department clearly spelled out?	( )	( )	Organization Analysis, Top Management
12. Are the relationships between handling and other departments known and understood?	( )	( )	Stores, Receiving, Production Control, etc.
Etc.			

Fig. 18. Check list on handling and control procedures.

EVALUATION OF PRODUCTION CONTROL AND MATERIALS HANDLING.

Methods of evaluating materials handling as a part of production control consist of the following:

1. Department audits which include an analysis of materials handling equipment, organization, and procedures.
2. Review of significant cost figures.
3. The use of performance ratios.

Department audits can be either informal or formal. The **informal audit** can be very simple, consisting of no more than casual observation. Checks can be made to see if materials move reasonably free from bottlenecks, or without too many complaints. **Formal audits** rely largely upon the preparation of a list of aspects which are to be checked. Questions such as the following might be significant in a formal departmental audit:

1. Are materials handling policies in writing?
2. Are standard practice instructions available for materials handling?
3. Is there a standard practice manual available?
4. Are definite maintenance schedules maintained for equipment?
5. Has physical handling been eliminated on handling assignments requiring the lifting of more than 50 lb.?
6. Where practicable, is material moved in a straight line?
7. Is the material handling equipment used in such a manner as to maximize the proportion of used time to idle time?
8. Is equipment utilized at the maximum safe speed at all times?
9. Are unit loads being increased sufficiently to decrease cost of movement of materials per unit?
10. Are all practicable measures being used to protect finished surfaces of materials, including accurate dimensions and other product characteristics?
11. Have production control procedures and devices been adequately explained to materials handling personnel?

The departmental audit usually is designed to seek these types of questions for all phases of the production control and materials handling operations. Questions are designed to check objectives, policies, procedures, organization structure, executive leadership, training, facilities, maintenance, control, and other factors in materials handling.

Performance Ratios. There are numerous performance ratios which are useful in evaluating the services performed by materials handling personnel and by the many different kinds of materials handling equipment used in industry, transportation, and kindred lines of activity. The following five ratios are among those which find the widest application:

1. Materials handling cost:
$$\frac{\text{Cost of materials handling}}{\text{Weight of materials moved}}$$

2. Scheduling effectiveness:
$$\frac{\text{Number of moves not made per schedule}}{\text{Number of moves scheduled}}$$

3. Labor utilization:
$$\frac{\text{Weight of materials moved}}{\text{Number of persons engaged in handling}}$$

4. Equipment utilization:
$$\frac{\text{Weight of materials moved}}{\text{Number of pieces of handling equipment}}$$

5. Storeroom effectiveness:
$$\frac{\text{Dollar value of discrepancy in count of actual count and inventory count}}{\text{Dollar value of average inventory}}$$

Over a period of time, ratios provide a pattern. The pattern shows **trends** and provides standards by which to judge operations. Trends in actual figures are also valuable aids in evaluating performance. Some actual figures include:

1. Dollar value of material issued from stores.
2. Number of requisitions put through in a particular period.
3. Demurrage charges (per period).
4. Damage charges assessed to handling (per period).
5. Weight of material moved.
6. Total cost of materials handling.

The procedures, actions, and evaluations used in controlling the movement of materials provide strong tying links between the functions of materials handling, production operations, and production control. Evaluation is a fundamental part of control. The purpose of evaluation, in a positive sense in the handling field, is to encourage improvement in the effectiveness and economy of materials handling.

COMMUNICATION SYSTEMS

CONTENTS

SECTION 8

COMMUNICATION SYSTEMS

IMPORTANCE OF COMMUNICATION SYSTEMS. Communication devices are powerful tools for expediting production and distribution activities. A large part of production is physical movement between work stations. The mechanization of communications offers industry the same advantages that it has given to the railroads, truck, air, and marine transport systems, namely, the efficient control of the movement of loads.

Industrial communication systems mechanize the transmission (and, sometimes, the recording) of information to or from remote points. Recently they have been developed to transmit information to a more remote time, thus eliminating the need for simultaneous presence of a sender and receiver.

Maximizing Materials Handling Efficiency. Each production sequence, no matter what the activity, reflects:

1. A decision **to move** materials.
2. A decision **to place** these materials at a given location.
3. A decision as to the **time** these materials are to be moved.
4. Often, a decision as to the **amount** of materials to be moved.
5. Knowledge of the **status** of these materials, that is, where they are and what processing stages they have passed through.
6. In most production sequences, **special decisions** as materials are moved from one operation to another, because of unforeseen delay, drastic emergencies, and numerous "on-the-spot" problems.
7. Frequently, **special alerts** to receiving work stations, departments, or plants concerning the kind, quantity, amount, and timing of materials about to be delivered.

A conveyor installation, an automatic dispatch monorail system, or some other transportation device may eliminate many of the above activities and decisions; therein lies one of the principal services of each. In nonautomatic operations, on the other hand, the movement of materials through a plant has inherent opportunities for wastefulness and inefficiency:

1. Delays occur while information about materials is being transmitted.
2. Delays occur because information about materials has not been transmitted.
3. Paper-work systems installed to provide this information are in many cases inefficient or costly or both. Paper work:
   a. Takes time to do.
   b. Takes time to transmit.
   c. Is often a presentation of history, not current events.
4. Vocal communications are completely inadequate under many conditions and expensive under most.

Mechanization of communications holds two great possibilities:

1. Information regarding materials movement may be transmitted from an initiating point to a distant delivery point, or vice versa; or this information may be transmitted to a central headquarters.
2. Information concerning materials received, delivered, or in process may be recorded and transmitted mechanically.

AIM OF COMMUNICATIONS. The aim of communications is to **regulate materials handling operations** so that they will accomplish the following results:

1. Save time:
   a. Mobile equipment can be dispatched promptly to the succeeding handling job.
   b. Time lost waiting for instructions when difficulties are encountered in the field can be eliminated.
   c. Precise timing can be provided for delivery or pickup of materials transferred from department to department or from receiving or shipping area to production area or transportation carrier.
   d. Transmitting information much more quickly from any materials handling activity area to a centralized headquarters.
2. Increase equipment utilization:
   a. Experience at many industrial truck installations proves that the tonnage of output per man-hour can be increased by 25 to 100 percent through the use of a communication system, with the turnover of truck time correspondingly reduced. (Most installations now average nearly 50 percent more output per hour than under previous methods.)
   b. Work loads on different pieces of equipment can be equalized.
   c. Output of a given piece of equipment can often be increased.
3. Eliminate paper work:
   a. Many production control operations can be conducted verbally instead of being reduced to writing.
   b. In-process time is reduced by faster movement of materials and products through a plant; correspondingly fewer status reports have to be made up and less follow-up of "paper work" is needed.
4. Reduce personnel requirements:
   a. Less clerical help is needed for recording data.
   b. Less supervisory help is needed for control.
   c. Less operating help is needed, because handling activities are faster or are remotely controlled.

Systems and Equipment

LIGHTS. Lighting devices are used for:

a. Signaling for attention by lighting alone or in combinations or by blinking.
b. Indicating the location of objects as they pass down conveyor lines, etc.
c. Indicating the level of materials in bins, vats, tanks, etc.
d. Indicating materials flow by activating them through limit switches, micro-switches, photoelectric relays, etc., as materials reach or leave their respective points around the plant.
e. Transmitting special information by code in combinations of lights or by colored lights or by blinking in code.
f. Signaling breakdown or overload for a materials handling device.

Simple lighting systems can be designed and installed with the help of a competent electrician. Complex lighting systems probably are best designed by electrical-control engineers.

BUZZERS AND BELLS. Sound-producing devices are widely used to signal for the attention of a particular person by code or to call the operator of a particular kind of equipment, such as a fork truck or crane operator. The bell or buzzer code is used by a department which needs fork truck or other service at that time. Systems of bells, buzzers, and lights have been installed in numerous plants. Bells, in particular, have been used quite widely for industrial communications. Although they are helpful for certain kinds of signaling, they have limitations. For example, they tell who is wanted but not *what* is wanted; and because the number of practical code combinations is limited, the number of people who can be called is not large. Also, in the mechanical "repeater" type of coded systems, it is necessary to wait for one call to clear before making another. Therefore coded bell and light systems are not particularly adaptable for materials handling work, and intercommunication devices are replacing them.

On the other hand, the bell as an "alarm" signal is particularly helpful. Wherever a dangerous movement—such as the movement of a gate or lift in the floor, the overflow of a tank, the excess delivery or the cessation of the flow of a material—must be signaled, the immediate attention-getting qualities of a bell or gong are highly valuable.

TELEPHONES. The **public telephone** is the basis of the vast majority of materials handling systems. Many companies set up a dispatcher's control point with telephone connections to message centers or materials control points around the plant. The dispatcher receives calls from department foremen when they are ready to release jobs or when their departments may need more work. Operators of industrial vehicles call in to the central communications system as they complete hauls and receive new movement orders from the dispatcher.

The advantage of the telephone system is that literally anyone in the plant can be contacted through it. Disadvantages are: the telephone line may be busy when needed; the dispatcher often cannot locate equipment without making many calls or until the driver calls in; and, conventionally, it is possible to speak to only one party at a time.

Private telephone systems are designed to augment and relieve the public telephone circuits in a plant. They operate by dial. They are installed at necessary points, and, since conversation is limited to this small circuit, there is little interruption or delay in transmitting movement messages. An additional major advantage is that "conference" circuits are incorporated so that a number of stations can talk or listen simultaneously.

PUBLIC-ADDRESS SYSTEMS. Basically, the public-address system consists of a microphone speaker connected to one or more loud-speakers. It is equivalent to a simplified or "homemade" version of the central-control system described later under "Intercommunication Systems" and should be considered from that standpoint. Occasionally, PA systems are installed on shipping and receiving docks to control movement of vehicles and to dispatch workers to various dock locations.

INTERCOMMUNICATION SYSTEMS. There are five basic intercommunication systems.

1. The **central-control system** (Fig. 1), the simplest of the arrangements, consists of one master station that can contact a number of staff stations, either individually or collectively. The staff stations, however, cannot talk to one another. As many as eighty stations can be reached from the single master station.

Where conditions are noisy, trumpets can be added. These devices give volume to the spoken message for noisy indoor or outdoor areas. Also, the staff station

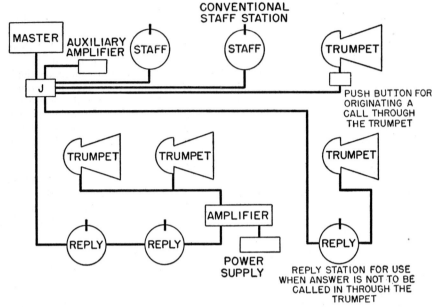

Fig. 1. Central-control system for two-way communication.

personnel can call into the trumpet without walking over to speak into a mouth-piece. Trumpets are therefore timesavers well adapted to production operations where it is not desirable to call employees away from their work. If privacy is required for the conversation, it is necessary to use the conventional microphone type of speaker.

2. Under the **dual-control type** of intercommunication, two master stations can speak over one set of wires to any number of staff stations, as in the central-control system previously described. Its major feature is that one of the master stations has a "right of way" over the other. Thus, the main master station can interrupt the conversation of the subordinate master station. It can so control the circuits that the conversation over the principal master station will be completely private. The subordinate master station also can be arranged as a screening point to monitor the calls coming in to the main master station (Fig. 2).

The dual-control system also features privacy switches, which make it possible for either unit to have a discussion with any station without being overheard by any other station or by the other master station. This kind of intercommunication system is extremely useful where an executive and a secretary want to speak to staff stations or where operating personnel must use this system subject to over-riding calls from a policy-making manager.

Numerous installations of the dual-control communication system have shown its superiority to the central-control system, which has only one master station. The dual-control arrangement provides considerably more privacy for users of the master station and is much more flexible than the central-control system.

3. With cental-control and dual-control systems, operatives at master stations can talk to any staff station, and vice versa. The staff stations, however, cannot

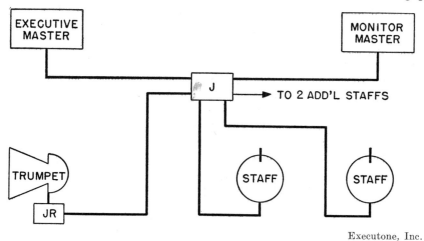

Executone, Inc.

Fig. 2. Dual-control system, by which executive and monitor stations can converse.

talk to one another unless a **multiple-master system** is installed. The basic value of the multiple-master system is that every station can talk to every other station (Fig. 3). Staff stations can be attached to the master-station system, and paging systems can also be tied in.

4. With the **conference system** of intercommunication, a number of stations can be linked together so that all can listen to and talk in the same conversation. Such a system can be tied in with staff stations and paging systems if desired. This arrangement holds great possibilities for expediting production control and materials handling.

5. **Straight paging systems** are merely devices to enable a call to be broadcast from a master station to the various paging stations that may be located around the plant.

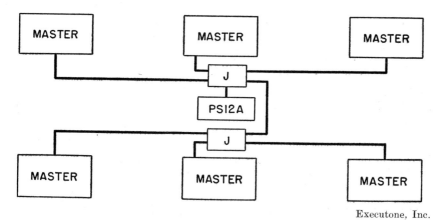

Executone, Inc.

Fig. 3. Multiple-master system, by which operators can converse with one another privately.

Special Features Available. There are many special features which can be added to some or all of these systems. For example, with "remote reply" staff stations, people can remain at their work, since the calls can be answered from across the room without even approaching or touching the station. Privacy-type staff stations, or a combination of both privacy and remote staff, may be installed. To communicate with personnel or locate equipment, all stations can be called at one time. Trumpet stations with auxiliary amplifiers can be added for paging to large, high-noise-level areas.

Uses of Intercommunication Systems. An intercommunication system offers not only most of the advantages of the telephone but also a number of special and important features that make it especially useful in industrial work.

1. An intercommunication system is faster, since speaking directly to the point in question without going through a switchboard is possible.
2. The listener does not have to pick up a receiver to hear a message; therefore, he can keep on working at his job.
3. With a "remote reply" station, individuals can answer the master station without leaving their work.
4. Conferences "on the air" can be arranged, and this technique can be applied to great advantage in straightening out materials handling and production problems.
5. Messages spoken at one spot can be repeated at a number of other spots simultaneously.

Applications of Intercommunication Systems. The intercommunication system can be applied for many purposes, as demonstrated by the following situations:

In one case it was applied to **expediting in-process handling.** Each department of a manufacturing plant had been using its own materials handling personnel to move work in process to the next department by industrial trucks, which then were returned empty to their own departments. A great deal of time was wasted waiting for loads to be assembled. Production workers lost many man-hours each week awaiting delivery of materials.

A central materials handling dispatcher was appointed and given a master station that was connected by staff stations to all departments in the factory buildings. All materials handlers were instructed to report to the central materials handler.

Now, when a department is ready to have materials moved, the **central dispatcher** is called directly through the local staff station. Over the staff station he directs a **materials handler** to go to the department and report his presence to the central dispatcher. The truck operator then picks up the load, proceeds to the department to which he has been directed, and delivers the material. From that location he calls the central dispatcher and remains there until directed to another location where work is waiting. Any materials handler can call the central dispatcher from any part of the plant for instructions.

The company is now moving 50 percent more material in a given time with no increase in the number of materials handlers. Lost man-hours per week through production delays has been cut more than 50 percent.

Checking for shipping operations at most shipping and freight terminals tends to put both a checker and an unloader in the trailer, truck, or other vehicle to be unloaded. The **unloader** sorts the packages by consignees, and the **checker** checks each lot against a copy of a bill of lading or a waybill. Each shipment is then marked, indicating whether it is to go to an outbound vehicle or to a spot location in the terminal or warehouse. After the contents have been sorted and checked, the checker or loader calls for a **materials handler.**

One checker is required for each vehicle being unloaded. Checking is often inaccurate. Shipments are frequently directed to wrong locations. Shipping papers are often lost. Movement of goods is delayed because there is no quick method of communicating with materials handlers or releasing vehicles.

Modern checking rooms are heated in winter and comfortable in summer. Master intercommunication stations are designed especially for centralized checking. There must be one master station for each checker when the organization is working at peak hours. A checker checks six to eight trucks simultaneously. A communication line is installed from the master station to each freight terminal floor or shipping dock location. Each **communication line** ends in an electric socket into which portable trailer speakers can be plugged, each having a cable and a switch for calling the central checker and for lighting a "call light" in the immediate loading station vicinity.

When a vehicle is to be unloaded, the dispatcher turns over to a **central checker** copies of all bills of lading or waybills covering all shipments in the trailer. These are coded and sorted to show the disposition to be made on each shipment as it is unloaded. The **unloader** takes a trailer speaker, hangs it in the vehicle, and plugs it into the line connecting him to the master station. As he sorts the different cartons or packages, he calls the shipments in to the central checker at the master station, who compares the items reported with the copies of the respective waybills or bills of lading. If the reports check, the unloader is told where to send the various lots. He then turns to his trailer speaker and presses another switch button, which turns on a red signal light, which summons a hand truck or power truck operator, who picks up the particular shipment and moves it to the proper shipping location. As he passes under the signal light, he jerks a cord, turning out the light.

Advantages of a centralized checking system are (1) trailers are unloaded in half the former time; (2) one checker can now check six or eight trailers simultaneously, compared to one checker for each vehicle under the old method; (3) waybills and bills of lading are kept in one office, so errors in loading shipments are vastly reduced; (4) shipments start to their destinations much more quickly; and (5) claims for lost shipments are held to a low minimum.

Other applications of intercommunication systems are installations (1) between floors of multistory buildings to facilitate discussions relating to the flow of materials between floors, (2) at points along conveyor lines so that jams or delays at any point can be quickly discussed with operators and cleared up at other points, (3) on shipping docks to tie in various loading stations with a dispatcher or a supervisor or with the person controlling conveyor lines feeding these points, (4) in production control rooms to tie in various departments of a plant with the production floor. Through such systems it is possible to hold conferences on the air and to eliminate a great deal of paper work by substitution of verbal reports.

MOBILE TWO-WAY RADIO SYSTEMS. Industrial radio users have **two bands of wave lengths** available to them. The first is the 152–174 mc. band. The other is the 25–50 mc. band. The latter has more frequencies and thus theoretically provides a greater choice of channels for communication in regions where there are many units on the air. The 152–174 mc. band, however, has no "skip" frequencies. Because of the particular wave length and the curvature of the earth, the radio waves of the 25–50 mc. band sometimes blank one another out. Locations some miles apart may have areas in which signals are not received. This blanking out does not occur with the 152–174 mc. band, and the latter is in more common use.

The following are three **types of units commercially available** for materials handling work:

1. The **hand carriage set**, known as the handie-talkie, weighs about 10 lb. The output is less than 1 w., sufficient to receive and transmit messages over a distance of one to five mi. in open country, down to a minimum of a few hundred feet inside a building (depending upon the steel structure and other materials that absorb or interfere with the radio wave transmission). Such a unit will operate for a day of continuous duty without a change of batteries. "Continuous duty" means the power on the receiver is on all the time, the transmitter is turned on so that the tubes are warmed up, and the two communicators can talk instantly at any time.

2. The **pack set** weighs 20 lb. and is in a pack that contains the larger batteries and additional equipment necessary to operate a loud-speaker. It has the same power output and range as the handie-talkie and will operate for approximately a week of continuous duty before needing recharging. It has the advantages of a loud-speaker.

3. A **self-contained unit** is usually mounted on fork trucks, yard cranes, locomotive cranes, overhead cranes, and other materials handling equipment. It includes transmitter and receiver. Two power ratings are common: less than 3 (about 1½ w. actual output) and 10 w. In lower-power industrial service, regulations of the Federal Communications Commission restrict the user to 1½ w. input and reception. The unit weighs 30 lb. The range is 1 to 10 mi., depending on the location of the transmitter and the height of the base-station antenna. The higher the antenna, the greater the range.

Mounting Two-Way Radios. Improvements are constantly being made in two-way radio equipment. For efficient materials handling operations, the receiver should be turned on all the time and the transmitter should always be warmed up. This operation takes 12 amp. at 6 v. or 6 amp. at 12 v. Usually the power requirements are expressed as approximately 15 amp. at 6 v.

With **gas-powered vehicles,** the usual procedure is to add a generator of extra capacity which can supply the necessary current to the radio set while the vehicle's motor is running. Additional capacity must be provided in the battery of this vehicle to operate the radio when the motor is not running.

On an **electric-powered vehicle,** there are three possibilities:

1. The **radio power terminals** can be hooked across the battery. Since the terminals must be connected across only a portion of the cells to get the proper voltage, they will discharge at a higher rate than those in the remainder of the battery. Accordingly, this rate of discharge must be compensated for by "differential charging" across those particular cells when the vehicle's battery is recharged. This operation is sometimes an awkward undertaking.

2. A **generator** with an electrical or mechanical drive from some moving part of the power train can be mounted on the vehicle. A separate battery can store the current from this generator and feed the radio set as required.

3. A **separate battery** may be used to operate the radio and for removing and recharging at proper intervals.

Mechanical shock does not raise any problem. The set should be bolted firmly to the vehicle, and mounted so that the chassis can be removed quickly and easily for servicing. In noisy areas the loud-speaker should be mounted close to the operator's ear rather than raising the output of the speaker.

Maintenance. For systems of 20 units or less, one spare set is sufficient for servicing. The entire chassis can be quickly replaced. Companies operating over 40 units often employ their own maintenance men. Other organizations often contract with a service organization to keep their equipment in operating condition for a fixed rate per month. These contracts usually include replacement of all parts and tubes as required.

Uses of Two-Way Radios. The two-way radio was originally used for switching locomotives and similar intraplant rail vehicles. Its application has spread to mobile cranes of both locomotive and rubber-tired or crawler types, to conventional motor trucks used for yard handling and other intraplant hauling, and to fork trucks, industrial tractors, overhead traveling cranes, tractors, and straddle trucks. A few installations based on the use of a handie-talkie or walkie-talkie—carried by the foreman or clerk of a labor crew, or by a checker, order-picker, or inventory-taker—have also been experimented with, although not yet widely adopted.

Substantial improvement of performance results when a two-way radio is used on handling vehicles. There is a striking reduction in deadheading in most operations. Equipment utilization is much higher; fork truck output, for example, often goes up by 30–200 percent. Emergencies are dealt with promptly, and far less time is wasted waiting for orders or for supervisory decisions at the point of action.

The less a materials handling activity conforms to a regular pattern of timing, distance, and location, the more significant this control problem becomes. Use of a two-way radio is one of the most effective ways to **keep equipment working** at the most important handling jobs, in the most economical sequence, with the least amount of lost time. It enables one to:

1. Reach the operator instantly no matter where he is working.
2. Give detailed verbal instructions.
3. Allow a two-way exchange of information.
4. Do the above without disturbing other workers.

In the following example two-way radios were used to **speed job-shop handling.** A 160-acre plant manufacturing heavy machine parts had built up a 14-mi. intraplant railroad system using 100 units of railroad equipment. This system was used in conjunction with overhead cranes in the shops. Study showed that the cost of moving one car was 75 cents per handling, but to spot a car required the movement, on the average, of four or five cars on a siding, totaling eight car handlings. The cost of this operation was $6, assuming no other cars interfered with the delivery.

As the first step a truck-trailer system appeared practical to replace railroad cars and platform trucks in making these transfers of heavy parts between shops. A series of trailers with a 35,000-lb. capacity and trucks capable of moving them was designed. The following cost comparisons resulted:

Locomotive Vs. Truck Trailers

Average cost to move and spot a loaded railroad car	$ 6.50
Cost to move the same load by truck trailer	1.30

Platform Truck Vs. Truck Trailers

To make 120 stops (average) platform trucks required 80 truck-hours at $3.25 per hr.	$260.00
To move equal amounts of material, truck trailers required 40 truck-hours at $4 per hr.	160.00

Finally two truck tractors and eight trailers were purchased and operated for 6 mo. without using a two-way radio. The performance of the equipment fell alarmingly below prediction. Trailers were "lost" after several moves and could be located only after numerous telephone calls or excursions to the shops. Truck drivers had to check each trailer to see if it was loaded and ready to move. They had to leave their trucks to call up dispatchers regarding new pickup orders. The two-way radio system was then installed and performance almost immediately came up to expectation.

The new radio installations cost about $50,000. Net savings through reduced railroad-car usage and greater utilization of equipment amounted to approximately $18,000 annually. Waiting time was greatly reduced in all the shops. Over-all simplification of the operation was brought about. Deliveries that at one time had to be scheduled days in advance could now be scheduled in hours. In this plant additional vehicles have since been equipped with two-way radios.

When used in **warehousing,** two-way radios not only offer the usual advantages of increasing equipment utilization and reducing deadheading but also have the extra advantage of providing better space control. With two-way radio, it is possible for a truck operator to immediately advise the central dispatch office (where space-control plans are usually kept) of an action taken or intended. By this means space-control records can be kept up to date without any paper work and without any appreciable time lag. Similarly, the space-control man can instruct the materials handler without any delay, advising him where to go for material or where to place a load.

Yard handling operations may be improved, as in the following case. In order to improve the handling of billets and steel products to and from the rolling mills, a steel manufacturer adopted a system based on straddle carriers and the use of a number of storage yards located several hundred feet to as much as 3 mi. from the mill.

Straddle carriers were installed to transport the bars, which range from 10 ft. to 40 ft. in length, in loads weighing up to 30,000 lb. About 10 trips per hour or approximately 700 trips per day, are now made by nine carriers. Often 125 tons per hour are handled per vehicle. It takes only 6 min. for a trucker to move in a load from storage yards as distant as 1½ mi. Two-way radio communication makes it practical to keep this equipment moving efficiently and to report all actions taken as fast as they occur. The two-way communication equipment has now been mounted on some 30 vehicles in this yard.

An **in-process handling** application is illustrated by the two-way radio system installed in a certain metalworking plant to speed the movement of materials between operations and improve production control. The central control room is equipped with 20 production control boards, each listing 100 key job orders in process. Information is brought into this plant over 6 two-way radio loudspeakers and a 90-station intercommunication system. Radio contact is maintained with fork trucks and two "roving reporters" equipped with walkie-talkie radios. The intercommunication system is connected with every important office in this 2,000-man plant. A wire recorder can be switched in to record the conversation over any loud-speaker.

The operation is as follows: A roving production reporter walks through his shop area observing the progress of key jobs, picking up the actual production count at particular machines, and calling the data in to the central control room, where the control-board record is changed accordingly. He reports all difficulties of any sort—tooling, materials, maintenance—to the control room. Through the intercommunication system, a "conference" with all interested parties is immediately arranged over the wire. No one has to leave his workplace or office. The decision reached is then communicated at once by radio to the roving reporters or the truck operators.

If more than one radio report comes in at any time, the control-room men (there are two) switch them over to the wire recorder. Then they are played back to the control room at the convenience of the control-room operators.

The total cost of this system was approximately $20,000. Work in process was reduced 20 percent. The in-process inventory total, approximately only 1.5 times the monthly sales, is expected to go as low as 1.2 times the sales. A tremendous amount of paper work has thus been eliminated.

In addition to such elaborate production control systems, many manufacturing plants are beginning to introduce two-way radios on fork trucks which deliver supplies to production machines. These applications generally show the same result—greatly increased effectiveness of the equipment and much greater production output. Production time lost and paper work are both greatly reduced.

TRANSCRIBING AND RECORDING EQUIPMENT. The conventional dictating machine, such as that used in the average office, has proved to be exceedingly useful in connection with materials handling work. This kind of equipment has many time- and cost-cutting applications. The wire or magnetic tape recorder can be used in a similar manner. All communication devices transmit information from one point to another, but the recording machine can also transmit information at a remote time simply by playing back the recording. Because recordings can be heard at convenience, it is often unnecessary to have a person at each end of such a communication system. Also, a permanent record is prepared without any manual attention.

Experience has shown that with recording and transcribing equipment, one can:

1. Minimize checking operations, thus releasing checkers for other duties while still increasing efficiency.
2. Do away with much paper work, thus eliminating an expense and a source of possible error.
3. Have a reliable, permanent, immediate, and unchangeable record of shipments, inventory, and messages of all kinds.
4. Speed handling operations, thus saving on overtime, reducing damage to perishable products, and providing better service and speedier delivery.
5. Automatically record at one location information which is reported into a telephone or speaker at a distant spot.

Application on a Freight Transfer Dock. A certain motor-truck freight operator cut operating costs $1,000 per month by installing dictating machines to speed checking. Instead of a check of incoming and outgoing shipments against the bills of lading and loading schedules on the docks, the work has been consolidated at a central control tower. Six recording machines are located in this tower, and one employee uses a playback machine to compare freight tallies with the records. When a shipment arrives on the docks, the break-out man hooks a microphone on the truck, the microphone being connected to the central control tower. The break-out man then communicates the information regarding the load into a speaker, which plays into one of the six recording machines in the tower.

One employee now does tally work for six unloading operations at once; no time is lost waiting for checkers. The trucks are able to get away from the dock 1 to 2 hr. sooner than under the former, conventional method. And since checking is done directly from the recordings, an extra typing operation has been eliminated.

Mechanizing Order Make-up. Recording machines have proved economical by reason of the fact that they eliminate the necessity of having operators at both ends of the communication system simultaneously. The technique was first developed by the U. S. Department of Agriculture for application to the wholesale warehousing operations in the food field.

Under the **old system** the driver-salesman made up a recapitulation of all his orders and invoices and then telephoned this information to the office. The office workers computed the tonnage for each load, checked price extensions and totals, and then made a list of items. A copy of this recapitulation for each truckload was sent to the shipping floor. The order pickers then took the merchandise for each load from stock and, by means of mechanical handling equipment or manual devices, moved the merchandise to the loading area and into the carrier.

One checker was required for each truck, or sometimes two trucks. He called the orders, and workers in the stock area picked up the material and dispatched it—by whatever means used—to the vehicle, where the worker in the truck stacked it. Invariably, one or the other worker would be idle, and frequently both workers were idle when the checker was having difficulty in interpreting the quantities as written on the invoices.

Under the **new system**, after the salesman's recapitulation is called into the office, and as a separate recapitulation of all the orders is being made up, a clerk calls off into a dictating machine the items from the invoices for the particular truckload. The split-item sheet is made up concurrently, thus taking very little time. No more than 5 min. are necessary to record all items for even the heaviest load. Any special information regarding an item or order is also recorded at this time.

When the recording is completed, the clerk writes the number of the motor truck, the weight, the number of the load, and the date on the dictating machine record and carries it with the "recap" and invoices to the shipping floor. The same handling equipment and the same assembly method and order-picking method are used as in the original operation. The main revision is in the actual loading of the motor trucks. The introduction of transcribing equipment makes it possible to reduce the loading crew from three to two men. The checker is no longer necessary, since the transcribing machine can now broadcast the record that was previously prepared.

The **communication equipment** needed for this work is a transcribing machine which serves the two loading points; four speakers, two at each loading area; a microswitch; and a finger-touch repeat switch.

The **operating procedure** is as follows: A record is slipped into a transcribing machine. The worker who loads stock onto the handling equipment, when ready to load the vehicles, pulls the cord that is strung along to the transcribing machine. This operation engages a microswitch and starts the transcriber. When several items that he has remembered have been called out from the transcriber record over the microphone he releases the rope to stop the machine. He then places on the conveyor belt the items which he has heard called. This procedure is continued until the truck is loaded.

One loud-speaker is located at each assembly area so that messages can be heard clearly at any point along the loading section. Also, the speaker is pointed toward the motor truck, thus enabling the loader in the truck to know what items are coming down to him so that he can plan the best arrangement of the load. If an item is missed, the conveyor loader presses a repeat switch, and the machine moves back a few grooves to repeat calling of the item.

The large **savings in costs** made under this system are as follows:

1. Each loading crew has been reduced from three to two men. This saving alone has repaid the cost of the installation in about 6 mo.
2. Starting time, or time required to prepare the load, has been reduced considerably. There is no waiting for a checker to get invoices and orders, no delay while he checks many invoices to find out where the particular items are entered.
3. Because one speaker is beamed at the worker in the truck, he can select whichever items he wishes to load in turn and can build a better load pattern in the truck, thus reducing damage to the material in transit.
4. A special worker is no longer required to check loads and read invoices. Anyone can locate and identify items and place them on the materials handling system.
5. Special instructions for any specific item can be given by an office clerk before the item is recorded on the belt or disc. During the daytime, instructions for the work of the night crew can be made up.

Inventory Control Work. Transcribing equipment has been especially adapted to inventory work. The key to the system is a standard dictation machine with a 300 ft. cable connecting it to the station of the person taking stock. The inventory man wears a chest microphone and carries in one hand a pistol-grip flashlight control that stops and starts the machine. The light on this control enables him to read labels in dark corners and warns him, by growing dim, whenever it is necessary to put a new record into the machine.

Method of Taking Inventory. The stocktaker, with the above equipment, starts at an aisle in the warehouse. Speaking into his **chest microphone,** he first identifies himself according to date, aisle, letter, and load number. Then he calls off the information and the number of items in each load. The **pistol-grip control** enables him to record when he is ready to give total quantities. He has complete freedom of action; he can climb safety ladders, turn corners, or double back on his route.

When the record is full, the stocktaker signs off, giving his position and referring to the next record number. The completed record is then delivered to the stock-control station, where the inventory card file is maintained.

A file clerk in the stock-control station has a standard **transcribing machine** before him. He simply inserts the completed record into the machine and listens to the data that was called off a few minutes earlier. With the foot pedal, he can start or stop his machine, control speed, volume, tone, and playback. Thus he can allow himself ample time to find each item on its correct file card and make the proper entry.

Time studies indicate that a file clerk, using this transcribing machine on an actual job, enters more than 100 items per hour without fatigue.

Results in a Particular Case. In one actual application, in a paper company warehouse, the annual inventory job involved 33 people and consumed 751 man-hr. of time. The warehouse occupied 60,000 sq. ft. and held 2,500 tons of stock, consisting of 6,700 items. Using the recording system, the inventory can be completed in 67 man-hr., a saving of more than 600 man-hr. over the former method.

Errors were drastically reduced; the number of dubious totals that had to be recounted was cut down 50 percent. Improper stock location was easily detected by the file clerk. Auditors were highly receptive to this dictating machine method, since it made their own jobs quicker and easier. As a check on the system they took just 10 percent of the completed records and transcribed the numbers and location of the items on them. Then they visited the warehouse and made an actual count to confirm this transcribed inventory with a master card file.

TELESCRIBER. The TelAutograph or telescriber is an intercommunication device duplicating the basic action of the "intercom" but using written instead of vocal messages. The person sending a message grasps the **mechanical pencil** and writes the message on the slot immediately beneath the pencil. The reproducing stylus writes the message on a piece of paper in the upper window of the machine. The reproducing stylus of similar machines to which this particular machine is connected will reproduce this message exactly as it shows in the window of the originating machine, on one or more receiving machines at locations up to 25 mi. from the originating machine.

Another type of telescriber can be used to fill out a form at one point and duplicates of the form wherever additional connected telescribers are located. As the message is written, the paper in the machine moves up and out of a slot, and the form can be torn off and disposed of as desired.

The chief limitation of a telescriber as compared with an intercommunication system is that the former is not practical for holding lengthy multistation "conversations."

Basic Advantages. Telescribers have two distinct advantages: (1) A permanent written message is instantly provided, and (2) it is not necessary to have a person at the other end of the communication system in order to have the message go through.

Telescribers are used for:

1. Expediting movement of incoming materials and parts into waiting production departments.
2. Minimizing time spent waiting for materials in manufacturing departments.
3. Lessening the need for stock chasers, messengers, and other clerical personnel.
4. Notifying various manufacturing departments and shipping, receiving, and purchasing departments of cancellation of orders, revisions, corrections, and rush jobs.
5. Providing centralized control over maintenance of materials handling equipment.
6. Aiding in fast and accurate handling of incoming items in very large storage yards.

When materials are received in a plant, the receiving department by telescriber instantly notifies the supply department about the arrival of incoming materials or parts and also indicates which of such materials have been sent to the inspection department for tests. Frequently the supply department must check on the receiving yards to ask whether urgently needed materials have arrived. Such reports and queries are handled by telescriber.

A "follow-up" section of the supply department concentrates on delayed deliveries, checks constantly with the receiving department regarding the arrival of these materials, and gives instructions for rapid handling after arrival.

After the inspection department has properly tested newly arrived material, it notifies the supply department by telescriber that it has approved and shipped the material to the department waiting for it or that the material is not up to specifications, and instructions are necessary as to its disposal.

TELETYPEWRITER. The teletypewriter is used in much the same way as is the telescriber. The distinction is that the teletypewriter produces a printed message. One big advantage is that messages can be sent across many miles, even across the country, by teletypewriter. This equipment can also be used to initiate simultaneous shipping instructions from widely separated warehouses and distribution points. Teletypewritten messages can be sent at roughly one-third to one-fourth the cost of telephone service. The teletypewriter, however, cannot duplicate the action of the telescriber in enabling the message center to use symbols not given on the conventional keyboard, nor can it transmit sketches.

In general, the large automotive companies with large plants and distant assembly points, order collecting centers, etc., have benefited most by this equipment. A General Motors survey showed the following:

> Cost of long distance telephone calls........ $2.50
> Cost of commercial telegrams.............. .92
> Cost of teletype messages.................. .37

The same company also reports that one of its assembly plants, using teletype for assembly control, gained these **advantages**:

1. Legibility of orders and records.
2. Completeness and uniformity of information and simultaneous reception at all key points.
3. Uniformity in the size of all forms.
4. Simplicity of operation (any typist can use a teletypewriter).
5. Reduction of the number of typing operations on all orders.
6. Minimization of "floats" of material in process.
7. Elimination of line-up sheets and avoidance of unnecessary handling of materials.
8. Elimination of "change notices."
9. Simplification of the entire operation.

The teletypewriter is also used for the transmission of sales orders, receiving reports, shipping reports, production reports, inspection reports, and car orders.

Producing Perforated Tape Records. A feature of the teletype system is that perforated tape records can be produced. These records can then be fed back into the machine for relaying to other stations without the necessity of again keyboarding them.

The teletypewriter can print copies at distant points and have the receiving printer prepare stencils for additional reproductions. It can be interoperated with business machines and can even provide the telegraphic link required for the remote automatic control of slug line-casting machines.

The teletypewriter has been widely used by railroads for all general communication purposes, such as for expediting car and train movements, for dispatching consist reports, waybills, and other information essential for advanced preparation of classification yard and terminal switch lists, for unloading instructions, invoices, etc., as well as for train make-up and passenger reservations and diversions in orders.

Typical Applications. Steel mills have used teletypewriters for interplant transmission and instructions covering **process control** and heavy **materials handling.**

An automobile plant uses telescribers and teletypewriters as a background for **production planning, scheduling,** and **control.** Twenty-six telescriber units and two sending and ten receiving teletype machines are linked together. The heart of the system is the main teletype sending station in the production scheduling department.

Orders received in the plant are forwarded to the sales distribution department, which prepares an official factory sales order. From this sales order a master framing schedule is prepared. Several days before the actual manufacture begins, copies of the schedule are issued to the sheet-metal, materials control, inspection, roughing-in lines, traffic, and other departments. When the teletype broadcasts the starting orders on the actual day of building, the master framing schedule becomes the car-building schedule.

Assembly and production data on the framing schedule are coded and stamped on a metal plate attached to the body of the dash line shortly after assembly begins. As the body moves down the line, the information is taken from the plate, and a telescriber sends it ahead to the next station, thus insuring that all special materials required for the particular body will be ready.

PNEUMATIC TUBE SYSTEMS. The pneumatic tube system is used in many places to aid materials handling communications. It is essentially a materials handling device, and, as such, it is the fastest means of dispatching papers, blueprints, and small objects around a plant.

Pneumatic conveyors have several major **advantages**:

1. They move very rapidly (25–50 ft. per sec.).
2. They deliver the original item to the receiver; thus there is no possibility of error.
3. They can transmit actual samples, small parts, etc. Thus inspection and other checks, such as laboratory analyses, can be completed quickly, and movement of the main body of material need not be delayed because of slow delivery of a sample.

Types of Pneumatic Tube Conveyors. There are three types of pneumatic tube conveyors: (1) the **conventional type,** which requires tubes between a central "mailing point" and each of the points to be served; (2) the **selective station type,** in which a single loop of tube joins all stations. (With this type, special carriers are "dialed" to drop out at the desired stations through automatic switches); (3) the **paper-sending pneumatic tube,** which sends a standard size of paper through the tube without a carrier. These tubes are rectangular in cross section (about 3″ × 1″), and the messages are written on a special piece of paper. After writing, the sender folds down the end of the paper to form a flap which acts as a "wing" to catch the air in the tube. Messages can be sent as far as 300 ft. in a few seconds.

Applications of Pneumatic Tubes. The principal use of pneumatic tubes is to transmit blueprints, job orders, bills of materials, requisitions, laboratory samples, reports, etc., to key points.

INDUSTRIAL TELEVISION EQUIPMENT. Industrial television is composed of a **camera,** which is installed where the desired scene can be recorded, and a **viewing screen or monitor** placed at the point where the observer is stationed. In some cases, an auxiliary unit is added to provide additional power. The camera and the viewing screen are connected by a cable. Industrial television is not a wireless transmission system; the picture signals are transmitted over the connecting coaxial cable.

Today's industrial television units operate from ordinary lighting circuits, that is, they can be plugged into any 105- to 125-v., 60-cycle circuit. The complete units, including camera and screen, weigh between 70 and 140 lb. The observation angle of the screen is approximately 150°.

The scene to be observed must be illuminated to a minimum of 60 ft.-candles. For certain special applications, such as guarding a warehouse, a moving figure would be detectable but not recognizable with as little as 25 ft.-candles. No technicians are needed to operate the equipment.

The distance between the camera and the power unit can be as great as 100 ft. The power unit can be separated from the viewing screen by as much as 1,500 ft. With special booster application this distance can be increased. The ambient operating temperature limitations of the camera are from 0 to 150° F.

Typical Applications. One of the applications of such equipment is to **control from a distance the transfer of materials** from handling devices to processing operations. Probably the largest and most elaborate industrial television system in the world is located at the Columbia-Geneva Steel plant at Geneva, Utah. At this plant four television cameras make it possible for one operator to feed steel slabs into three reheating furnaces. Before the television was installed, the operator had an assistant to spot the slabs as they moved along the conveyor in front of the furnace. When the slabs were in line, the assistant would signal the operator to start pushing them into the furnace. The new approach by central-ized control has reduced operating costs and avoids errors by placing the entire operation in the hands of one competent man.

Television equipment can also be used for **improving safety** and **controlling quality.** It has been applied successfully to the pouring of molten steel in which the problem is to get billets without spongy spots or air inclusions. This require-ment means that the mold must always be kept full to a precise level. Formerly it was necessary to station a man directly at the mold top to watch the pouring so that he could signal the operator 50 ft. away. There was always the possibility of a misunderstanding, and discomfort from the heat became unbearable.

The solution, based on industrial television, was to mount a camera with a long-focus lens above the mold. The camera transmits the picture to a viewing screen placed in the control panel. This application has saved manpower, pro-moted safety, and improved the control of quality in the continuous casting of steel billets.

Improving Equipment Performance. A 45-cu.-yd. power shovel representing a tremendous investment is involved in another application of television. If the shovel is not completely filled, this capacity is obviously partially wasted. Yet it is impossible for the operator to see whether or not he has obtained a full scoop because the shovel is so far from his cab.

A method of improving this procedure is to mount a television camera on the tip of the boom. The image is relayed by wire to a screen mounted in the operator's cab, making it possible for the operator to manipulate the machine with much greater effectiveness.

Other Applications. Industrial television has been used to control the feeding of sugar cane from a conveyor into the crushing machinery, to observe storage areas and production-line trouble spots, to watch for jams in coal tipples, and to provide vision for remote control in filling gondola cars with baled scrap. It has provided a rapidly increasing range of controls in a wide variety of other in-dustrial applications.

Comparison of Communications Systems

ADVANTAGES AND LIMITATIONS OF DEVICES. Fig. 4 shows a tabular comparison of principal types of communication devices. Examination of the individual items emphasizes the advantages and limitations of each device. To develop a system appropriate for a given application, it is necessary to decide on the result desired and then check it against the characteristics of the various systems.

	Characteristics of the Message					Characteristics of the Transmittal				
	Enables Two-Way Discussion	Provides a Record	Provides a Record at Both Ends	Provides Visual Picture of Conditions	Provides Original Document	Can Send to a Moving Point	Can Send from a Moving Point	Can Send to More Than One Point Simultaneously	Can Be Understood Even Though Recipient Is Not in Close Proximity to the Device	Special Comments
Lights	No[1]	No	No	No	No	Yes[6]	No	Yes	Yes	Can be very disturbing to others.
Bells and gongs	No[1]	No	No	No	No	Yes[7]	No	Yes	Yes	Almost any person and any place can be reached.
Public telephone	Yes	No	No	No	No	No	No	No[10]	No	Can be disturbing to others.
Industrial telephone systems	Yes	No	No	No	No	No[7]	No[9]	Yes	Yes	
Public address systems	No	No	No	No	No	Yes[7,8]	No[9]	Yes	Yes	
Intercommunication systems	Yes	No	No	No	No	Yes[7,8]	No[9]	Yes	Yes	
Two-way radio	Yes	No	No	No	No	Yes	Yes	Yes	Yes[11]	Extremely flexible, because sender and recipient can be moving.
Transcribing and recording machines	No	Yes	No	No	No	No	No	No	No	
Telescribers	Yes[2]	Yes	Yes	No[4]	Yes[5]	No	No	Yes	No	Up to 25-mi. range.
Teletypewriters	Yes[2]	Yes	Yes	No	Yes[5]	No	No	Yes	No	Unlimited as to distance.
Pneumatic tubes	Yes[2]	Yes	No	Yes[3]	Yes	No	No	No	No	Also can send small objects.
Industrial television	No	No	No	Yes	No	No	Yes	No	No	Only device to send visual picture.

1 Signals for attention only or provides very limited code.
2 Limited in speed of exchange as contrasted to vocal discussion.
3 Only to the extent that the item sent in the tube reflects what the recipient wants to see.
4 Can draw simple sketches showing general shapes, dimensions, etc.
5 Only to the extent that the message sent can be considered as the document for the information transmitted.

6 As long as recipient is within reasonable visual distance.
7 As long as recipient is within reasonable hearing distance.
8 Provided it is hooked up to play through loud-speaker.
9 An amplifying microphone can be installed to pick up conversation from across a room, etc.
10 Special "conference circuits" can be arranged.
11 If loud-speaker is hooked up to receiver.

Fig. 4. Comparison of communication devices for expediting materials handling movements.

Combinations of Systems. Usually no one system provides all the desired features, therefore combinations of systems must be planned. Typical examples are given in the following cases.

1. Industrial telephone systems have been arranged so that one can dial a number to speak over a two-way radio system or can record on a recording machine.
2. Two-way radio receivers have been wired to record on a machine at a distant point. The same thing can be done with telephones and intercoms.
3. Teletypewriters can be wired into control devices to start or stop machinery or to program machinery many miles away.

Many such combinations are in use. Thoughtful planning enables their users to obtain the **speed, coverage, record-making** and **record-transmitting** characteristics desired.

The scientific planning and application of composite communication systems is only in its infancy, and the use of two-way radio, industrial television, and recording machines is increasing at a rapid rate.

TRAINING PERSONNEL

CONTENTS

CONTENTS (*Continued*)

SECTION 9

TRAINING PERSONNEL

IMPORTANCE OF TRAINING. Materials handling training programs, although not yet widely adopted, have proved valuable in terms of financial returns. One program, conducted for Westinghouse Electric Corporation over a period of three months, is estimated to have saved that firm $53,000 during the first year. Changes in procedures and worker attitudes effected by one short training program for workers, are estimated to have exceeded the cost of the program by a wide margin. A general program available to management trainees, middle- and top-management executives, and sales personnel has resulted in establishing new positions in materials handling, in upgrading men to supervisory posts, and in helping sales personnel to render materials handling service and advice in addition to selling equipment. A middle-management materials handling training program has favorably affected attitudes, work habits, and techniques in motor manufacturing to the extent that an advanced program is conducted. In each instance two results were definitely gained—greater economy of operation and employee attitudes conducive to continuing economy.

Fundamentals of Training

FACTORS IN A TRAINING PROGRAM. Training has often been confused with education, but the connotation attached to training is quite different. The Training-Within-Industry Service of the War Manpower Commission's Bureau of Training (T-W-I Report) has drawn the following distinction: "**Education** is for the rounding out of the individual and the good of society; it is general, provides background, increases understanding. **Training,** in industry, is for the good of plant production—it is a way to solve production problems through people; it is specific and helps people to acquire skill through use of what they have learned." This definition, even though restricted to job-skill training, clearly distinguishes training from education.

A similar but not so limited definition is given by Haas and Ewing (Tested Training Techniques): "Training may be defined as: helping trainees acquire new knowledge and skills. Training consists mainly of telling, showing, and guiding people in the performance of tasks, then checking results." The following definition by Halsey (Training Industrial Personnel) expresses the training concept as it should exist: "Employee training is defined as the process of aiding employees to gain effectiveness in their present or future work through the development of appropriate habits of thought and action, skills, knowledge, and attitudes." The objectives cover not only job skill and knowledge, but also attitudes and action. As applied to materials handling training, the **definition** can be more specifically stated as: "A planned and coordinated procedure, tailored and conducted to help trainees develop an appreciation, know-how, and application of materials handling for the purpose of meeting specific plant and personnel objectives." The implications are clear: the emphasis is on plant economy, the

9·1

necessity for changing attitudes, planning for the application of training-program content, and on identifying the benefits of plant economy with those accruing to the trainee. No mention of follow-up is made, although follow-up is a vital part of all training.

FOUNDATIONS OF TRAINING. Training programs, to be successful, should be developed and conducted by those executives or others who have a keen appreciation of the fundamentals of training and a realization of its proper place in industrial management. As carried on for those engaged in materials handling work in a plant, warehouse, storeroom, transportation division, or other related industrial unit, a training program should be founded on the following basic concepts:

1. Training is an intelligently planned, conducted, and controlled function performed best by those who understand it fully.
2. Training is the most important medium for applying materials handling techniques to reduce costs and improve the efficiency of handling operations.
3. Those responsible for materials handling must be trained in materials handling before they can be expected to apply it advantageously.
4. To insure that gains made are perpetuated, a good materials handling training program must be followed up by short refresher training sessions.
5. If the trainee has not learned, effective training has not been given; positive learning must be one major outcome of materials handling training.
6. The training process is a direct adaptation of the psychology of learning.
7. The complexity of industry requires that employees be trained in skills and techniques for developing job competence and encouraged to cooperate and get along with fellow-workers.
8. The materials handling training job is not a simple trainee-trainer arrangement but rather a matter of using the best training techniques for the training need at hand.
9. Training in materials handling should start with those in the top management ranks and proceed along to the workers.
10. The content of the materials handling training program is no longer only a medium for development of knowledge and skill but is based on a need from which materials handling consciousness develops.
11. One of the major objectives of materials handling training is both to help the trainee develop his ability to think creatively, his power to reason, and his latent ability to lead others, and to stimulate his desire to do more on his job than he would otherwise do.
12. Training in materials handling is necessary if maximum benefits are to be derived from the vast potential for economy which is latent in industrial and transportation operations; few plants can afford to neglect training in materials handling.

The foundations of materials handling training are based on the best fundamental philosophy and educational objectives found in all successful training. In the foregoing statements are also found the bases for the specific objectives of each materials handling training program.

Why Train? The prime reasons for which a company will underwrite a materials handling training program are:

1. To make sure that the necessary knowledge and job skills required are transmitted to the employees and supervisors who will man a new materials handling installation.
2. To improve the efficiency of operators who are to run specific equipment and/or train new operators.

3. To improve the profit position of the plant by reducing materials handling costs.

The facts established from a study of plant operating and financial records point to these opportunities as valid reasons for organizing and conducting a training program.

Specifically, the reasons for training members of the plant personnel in materials handling operations are:

1. To develop a consciousness of materials handling in all personnel to be trained.
2. To insure successful operation of all materials handling installations serving production operations.
3. To develop the personal skill and ability of all employees engaged in handling materials.
4. To reduce costs of:
   a. Equipment operation and maintenance.
   b. Idle man and idle machine time in the production processes.
   c. Handling time and space in receiving, distribution, in-plant handling, production handling, storage, shipping, in-transit handling, and accompanying paper work.
   d. Human relations, working conditions, plant morale, union-labor relations.
   e. Sales, product distribution, and plant maintenance.
5. To help the company maintain its competitive position in its particular industry.

While the above factors are apparent as the general objectives of comprehensive and, to some extent, specific materials handling training programs, each program must be developed to attain its own specific objectives.

In the sales field, materials handling training is being utilized to give sales trainees a wide concept of the whole materials handling field. It is a foregone conclusion that equipment salesmen can sell their products better when they know how, where, and why these products fit into the entire range of a plant's operations. Advantages accrue to the equipment maker when (1) his product is properly applied and used and therefore performs best; (2) the customer realizes that he has purchased a materials handling unit which will reduce his operating costs; and (3) the performance record of the equipment proves the expenditure was amply justified, thus encouraging future purchases from the salesman, in whose integrity the purchaser now has full confidence. The training given should cover plant layout, management, plant operation, warehousing, transportation, and packaging.

Organizing Materials Handling Training

IN-PLANT TRAINING. In-plant training is a direct responsibility of the training director and his department, which in large companies is usually a part of the personnel department. In such organizations, specific training-program requests must be made to the training departments by the materials handling manager. There is close liaison between the materials handling manager and the training officer assigned to the task. Decisions on matters such as personnel to be trained, training content, methods of training, evaluation of results, application of the training to the solution of materials handling problems, and follow-up of results are handled between them. There should be a definite understanding that the materials handling manager is the technician who knows the field of materials handling and the training director is the man who knows the training field. Under such a setup and plan, the best results are likely to be attained.

In a small plant, it is probable that the materials handling training officer must conduct the training program with the aid and support of the plant superintendent, plant manager, production manager, chief engineer, or other executive assigned to supervise such training. Should the training program be under the direction of a high executive, especially one who is training-minded, the best results are likely to be secured.

In some cases no one within the plant may have the time or the background to conduct training in materials handling. It is then necessary to secure the services of someone outside the organization who is both widely experienced in materials handling and able to organize a worthwhile course and properly conduct the instruction. Where the company is located near a college or university which offers such courses, either the men who are to be trained can be enrolled in such classes or the company may arrange to have an instructor conduct the course at the company's plant. The best results are secured when the instructor has had practical experience in materials handling—perhaps as a consultant—and is also a capable teacher. If there are objections to taking men from their work during operating hours, the course may be given in the evening.

Two or more adjacent small plants may combine to give such training. The training sessions, if separately conducted can be scheduled to fit in with the operations of each plant or they may be held jointly in the evening. The best results for the individual company are secured, however, when the training is given separately for each company, so that the methods and procedures presented may be more closely related to each plant's particular materials handling needs.

Techniques and Materials for Training

METHODS OF TRAINING. The skill with which any method of training in materials handling is applied contributes significantly to the success of the training. While orderly procedure is necessary, the method used must be adapted to the background and experience of the trainees concerned.

Lecture Method. The lecture method is often used in industrial training and is at its best when the presentation is carefully planned. Essentially, it is an organized method for giving information orally and quickly. Thus it is helpful in materials handling indoctrination—telling the "how" and "why" and explaining fundamentals.

When to use it:

1. With a larger-than-average group.
2. When the trainees are easily motivated to carry on discussion.
3. When time is valuable and must be saved.
4. When it is necessary to establish a fundamental background.
5. When the group has a common background.
6. As a last resort, when there is doubt as to the best training method applicable.
7. When necessary to arouse enthusiasm or to reinspire trainees.

When not to use it:

1. On a problem-solving situation.
2. Where job skills are involved.
3. When group participation is planned.
4. When no skilled trainer is available.
5. When no survey or test is to be used.

Conference Method. The conference method is the best training method when the lecturers are also the industrial trainers. It is often used in small groups limited to 20 or fewer trainees. Essentially, it is (1) a method by which two or more persons each bring their experience, opinions, and thinking to focus on a common problem; (2) an informal situation conducive to voluntary discussion and participation on a common basis.

When to use it:

1. To correct materials handling trouble spots, technical or human.
2. To set up a standard materials handling practice or policy.
3. To develop new materials handling procedures or installation.
4. When all the personnel connected with materials handling are to work on the same materials handling problem.
5. When group morale needs a boost.
6. When a problem about which there is little available knowledge must be tackled.

When not to use it:

1. When a formal trainer-trainee environment exists.
2. When a skilled conference leader is not available.
3. When a new kind of information or a change in method is to be introduced.
4. When training time is running short.

Formal classroom environment should be avoided; the trainer must be a guide and an active participant in a constructively critical and analytical discussion. Trainees must be guided into not only the belief in but also the act of arriving at **sound conclusions** of their own volition without being told or taught.

Case Study Method. The case study method, as the title implies, utilizes a **hypothetical** or particularly adaptable **actual** case as the focal point for discussion. Through the discussion, both critical and analytical, the trainees are instructed in how to arrive at a conclusion which is acceptable and satisfactory, to both trainer and trainees. One version of this method has been called the Harvard Case Study.

What it is:

1. A combination of the conference and lecture discussion methods.
2. A means of training by example.

How to use it:

1. Prepare the selected case for discussion.
2. Present the case clearly, concisely, illustratively, and briefly.
3. Discuss the case thoroughly, noting facts, specifications, data, procedures, human attitudes, and conclusions.
4. Develop a method, technique, solution, and alternatives if possible, or a set of basic guiding principles.
5. Review the newly developed solution in terms of practical use, ready for application, or work out a new method which follows the basic guiding principles developed.
6. Put the results to work.

When to use it:

1. When a highly controversial problem is present.
2. When an example of an actual situation is needed to clear up a trouble spot.
3. When group acceptance of a specific practice or procedure is wanted.
4. When it is desirable to show the difference between theory and practice.

When not to use it:

1. When the case is not familiar to all trainees.
2. When the case has not been carefully prepared.
3. When the case is either too artificial or not sufficiently specific.

Trainees favor using the case study method if the formal classroom approach is omitted. A skilled trainer can make the project realistic, hold it within constructive channels, and **keep it simple.**

Individual Study Method. The individualized study method is used to help individual trainees in tackling the subject matter by providing skilled guidance in accomplishing the stated objectives. There are two ways in which it can be used effectively: the **in-plant method,** by which the company supplies a competent instructor or practical subject matter or both; and the **home study method,** by which the instruction, guidance, and subject matter are supplied by a competent source acceptable to the trainee and to the company.

Essentially, the individual study method is a job-related program utilizing a textbook, tests, a printed training guide, and competent personal direction. Retention of information is greater with this method than in most of the other methods outlined here.

When to use it:

1. When the number of trainees in the group does not exceed ten.
2. When training closely related to the job is necessary.
3. When personnel are being prepared for new materials handling responsibilities.
4. When carefully prepared training materials and a competent trainer and guide are available.
5. When a special group is to be trained in a given subject.
6. When time and speed are not critical factors.
7. When one of a group of materials handling specialists is to be trained in one or more phases of materials handling, that is, when it is desirable to develop a member of a materials handling team.

When not to use it:

1. When the trainee does not care to apply himself.
2. When the company has no adequate material or guide and cannot get either.
3. When time and speed are essential.
4. When the company does not keep a close check on trainee progress and is not prepared to help and encourage the trainees until completion of the training program.

Other Methods. Materials handling training projects can also make good use of other methods. **College, university, and technical institute classes** offer excellent sources of training under competent instruction. Several such classes have been in operation since 1947, and enrollment in them is increasing. The **institute method** consists of a 1-, 2-, or 3-day program of selected topics in materials handling given on a prearranged schedule, similar to a lecture series. Lecturers present materials handling information, and audience participation is encouraged. As many topics in materials handling as possible are presented, usually in either 1- or 2-hr. sessions. Copies of the proceedings are usually made available when the institute program is over.

The **research project method** is used when a group is assigned to a special materials handling project. While final results count, each trainee-researcher has the opportunity to make individual contributions to the final results and can be judged on such performance. This method is most effective when technically competent specialists are used as trainees.

Present-day training methods are successful when they are used under conditions suited to their individual advantages. **Tailoring training methods** to the training-session objectives usually results in combining methods, shifting from one to the other smoothly. Training methods should be skillfully correlated and used where they can be best applied.

Aids to Training

IMPORTANCE OF EFFECTIVE AIDS. Materials handling training makes use of every audio, visual, and special aid known to the industrial training field. The skill in utilizing training aids or materials determines how effective they will be. A training aid is a device which assists the trainer to develop appreciation and understanding and transmit knowledge, data, ideas, and facts. It is not a substitute for either teaching or training. The adage, "One picture is worth more than ten thousand words," can be taken too literally by the unskilled trainer. In reality, illustration is an impressive means of conveying ideas and proportion, but it is not a substitute for other effective training methods.

Motion Picture Films. The most common training aid, outside of text material, is the motion picture film. Through its realistic appeal, an appropriate film can help motivate trainees and develop a new and desirable attitude. Materials handling procedures, equipment operation and application, indoctrination of materials handling fundamentals, materials handling motions, and standard times and movements can be illustrated effectively by both motion picture films and film strips.

The skillful materials handling trainer should use the following reliable five-step procedure in presenting each film:

1. Introduce the film, telling trainees what to look for, not what the film is all about.
2. Show the entire film.
3. Discuss the subject matter as it relates to the objectives.
4. Use comments and facts as interest leads into the major objectives of the training session.
5. Proceed into full use of the selected training method, resorting to reshowing of the film only if absolutely necessary. (Reshowing film strips is often done, however, without danger of sacrificing a free-flowing, two-way discussion.)

Projectors. A basic rule in industrial training which applies particularly to materials handling is: Do not try to build up a mind-picture with words; show actual illustrations. The fact that explanations are necessary should not rule out the use of a picture. An **opaque projector** (often called a Balopticon) can project enlarged pictures of glossy photographs, mimeographed or printed copy, blueprints, ozalid prints, tabulated data, plant layouts, equipment-parts sketches, detailed data and directions, magazine illustrations, manual or book pages, pictures—in fact, almost any illustration.

The **overhead projector** is used when transparencies of the illustrated part, layout, equipment, data, sketch, or form are available. The transparency is placed on the projector table and reflected onto the screen. This method permits the instructor to write on the transparency, his notes being fully legible to the viewers. Materials handling flow, plant layout, location of receiving, shipping, and storage areas, and layout of the different production lines are easily pointed out. The use of colors and overlays makes it possible to show factors such as consecutive steps in product development, manufacture of in-process parts, different routes for trucks, work stations for personnel, and many other important items. Both the opaque projector and the overhead projector can be used in a lighted room, allowing the trainees to make notes and the trainer to maintain rapport during the conference session.

Because of its ability to add depth to illustrations, the **stereo projector** is effective. It is particularly useful in showing illustrations of "before" conditions, thus presenting the actual problem to be analyzed or solved as it really exists. Stereo cameras are used in many plants to take critical "spot" and "over-all" three-dimensional "shots" of conditions and installations. Materials handling layouts and distances, storage layouts, and unit load sizes are among the most adaptable to three-dimensional illustration. Viewing three-dimensional illustrations reduces trainees' uncertainties and avoids mistaken impressions. In-process handling methods, where space perception is vital, are thus better understood and interpreted in discussing layout changes or planning new procedures.

Field Trips. Field trips, which give trainees "the chance to see how somebody else does it," are popular and profitable training aids. Such a trip is made not in order to satisfy curiosity but rather to supplement training procedures. A field trip is the closest approach to reality where training objectives are concerned. The same five-step procedure followed in presenting films is applied to field trips:

1. Tell the training-group members what to look for, giving them enough information only to satisfy their natural curiosity.
2. Explain the purposes, features, merits, faults, etc., of what they will be seeing.
3. Discuss, in relation to training, what the group members have seen.
4. Use what has been seen and the comments made about it as "interest leads" for attaining the training objectives.
5. Proceed into full use of the preselected training method, using any other training aids applicable to the case under study.

Three-dimensional Models. A near approach to actual reality in the materials handling training program is the reduced-scale, three-dimensional model or mock-up. The addition of space and depth lends adequate realism to materials handling installations, storage planning, plant layout, packaging, production assembly, and materials handling, so the transition from the training group study to the actual planning and layout job is smooth and efficient. Component parts that can be disassembled, truck-operator models and mock-ups that can be handled by trainees, and parts that are cross-sectioned show proportional relationships, effectively visualizing the problem for those in the training group. Cost, space requirements, and difficulty of moving models and storing them for future use are important factors to consider in planning and conducting the training program.

Charts. Graphic presentation by means of charts—single, in groups, or in flip-chart form—is a very effective way to make layouts vivid. Such charts should be developed simultaneously with the planning of the training program. The objective of the chart is to highlight vital facts, procedures, material flows, equipment flows, specifications, standard times, plans, and other important data, taking full advantage of the aid given by the use of colors and sketches. The size and scale of such charts depend on the need for readability and ease of interpretation. Charts are helpful interpreters of facts and conditions if they present information truthfully and in a manner to be properly interpreted and applied.

Blackboards, Bulletin Boards, Flannel Boards. The old-fashioned blackboard is not only the most widely used training aid but also the most essential one. It is also an aid to other training devices, such as films, printed matter, personal demonstrations, models, and graphic portrayals. Bulletin boards also fall into this classification. Their use, though limited to announcements, posters, and training data, is most effective. Flannel boards, however, add flexibility, interest, and re-use to the advantages already credited to the other two boards. A materials handling layout, a production flow, some handling method, an equipment operating procedure—all can be developed on a flannel board, step by step, allowing full discussion at any and all times plus the privilege of going back to any previous point in the process. Each step in building up the "flannel-board story" is shown in relation to other steps clearly, legibly, and neatly.

Printed Material, Photographs. The most common training aid is printed matter that is both well illustrated and understandably written. The **textbook, manual, syllabus, training guide, pamphlet, handbook,** and **catalog** are among the most common; they are essential to successful materials handling training. **Photographs,** especially taken and strategically used, are very good alone and excellent when used with an opaque projector.

Personal Demonstrations, Trainee Participation. A very effective aid used in equipment-operator training is the personal demonstration. Trainee participation, the logical follow-up, is a training aid necessary to the completion of performance training.

The materials handling training methods presented here are those most commonly used. Industrial trainers have used other types, such as **understudies, role-playing, workshops, brainstorming,** and **buzz sessions.** Training aids are limited only by the imaginations of the trainer and the program-planners, but nothing can take the place of a skilled trainer with the personality, confidence, and ability to impart his own knowledge to others. Neither the best training method nor the skillfully selected and applied aid can supplant hard work by both trainer and trainee. On the other hand, oral discussion alone can never bear the full training load successfully; it needs the help of visual and other strategically placed training aids.

Kinds of Materials Handling Training

DIFFERENCES IN KINDS OF TRAINING. In view of the possibilities for cost reduction inherent in materials handling, it behooves every economy-minded management to train all plant personnel connected with either the operation or the administration of materials handling. But desirable as this training is, differences in organizational and job status and the educational background of trainees dictate differences in kinds of training. Differences in company objectives also call for differences in materials handling training-program content.

Generally, the training of personnel in materials handling will be undertaken by a plant to foster improvements which are **job-related** or **personnel-related.**

KINDS OF TRAINING. Actually, two kinds of materials handling training are available: **job-related training** and **personnel improvement training** which includes economics training, worker training, and management training.

1. **Job-related training.** The objectives of job-related training point specifically to materials handling operations training:

    a. Training of lift truck operators or operators of other materials handling equipment.

    b. Training of personnel to operate a materials handling installation, which includes equipment, work-flow procedures, and production units.

2. **Personnel-related training.** This is more often called personnel improvement training. Its objective is to increase the trainee's knowledge, technique, and

application of materials handling for economic purposes. Three types of personnel improvement training are in use.

- a. **Economics training.** Economics training sets up the specific goal of reducing costs. Such training programs are not restricted to management personnel but involve any personnel whose part in the materials handling area under economic scrutiny is an active one. The scope of materials handling training for cost reduction is restricted to the materials handling problem; therefore, it is a brief program in so far as time is concerned.
- b. **Worker training.** In this area the members of the worker personnel are given an abbreviated form of management training. The purposes are to develop an understanding of materials handling and of their job as it relates to the overall plant function and to encourage worthwhile suggestions for time-savings, effort-savings, and dollar-savings.
- c. **Management training.** Top and middle management participate in this training. The objective is to develop an appreciation and knowledge of materials handling activities, and a technique for applying, maintaining, and improving economic situations.

WHOM TO TRAIN. All plant personnel, from the top down, with the exception of clerical and other distantly related personnel, should be trained in at least the fundamental elements of materials handling operation and economy. Not every manager nor every worker represents a good training investment; materials handling training must be organized to improve the worth of personnel connected with materials handling.

Top Management. Materials handling training must start at the top; there should be no exceptions. While for most top-level executives a formal materials handling training program is not necessary, a deep appreciation of materials handling and its economy potential in almost every phase of industry must be developed. Top management so trained is "sold" on materials handling, and so it becomes easier to "sell" the idea to all plant personnel. Top management will not undertake materials handling changes, purchases of equipment, procurement of personnel, and other cost expenditures without a full understanding of the importance of training to get the best out of the materials handling operations. Progress in materials handling in a given plant is directly proportional to how well trained its top management is, from president or owner-manager down to and including functional executives.

Middle Management. Middle-management training in materials handling emphasizes management and human relations to help reduce costs by eliminating unnecessary handling, developing new handling methods and standards, and encouraging materials handling suggestions. Functional performance, which brings supervisors closer to production problems, is the factor which accentuates the difference between top and middle-management materials handling training. Middle-management trainees develop a concept of their position in the materials handling picture and of ways processes can be improved technically and professionally.

Workers. Training workers in materials handling is one of the least understood and most neglected industrial activities. What little has been done in industrial plants has been related only to materials handling jobs. To assume that workers can be trained only on the level of job-skill training is to take a narrow viewpoint. If given opportunities to learn, many employees become productive sources of supervisory leadership. A large proportion of employees welcomes the opportunity for training which offers a broader coverage than mere job-related training.

A worker looks at training as an opportunity to gain recognition from his management and the members of his immediate working group. It satisfies his need for new and different skills and at the same time improves his present skills, thus opening to him an avenue to increased earnings. He desires training because by it he learns about ways and means by which the effort needed to do his job can be reduced. As a result, worker satisfaction and morale rise toward maximum production levels. Fewer accidents occur because of the attention given to more intelligently thought-out work procedures. In addition, management can logically look to trainees for future leadership and supervisory personnel.

Materials Handling Sales Personnel. Sales personnel who are trained in materials handling activities supplementary to their regular sales training are better salesmen and may later qualify as sales executives. They are better able to explain to a customer how to apply materials handling equipment correctly and most advantageously. They can also give valuable information regarding the checking and maintenance of the equipment.

REFERENCE TO LEARNING CURVES, PERSONNEL RECORDS.

Knowles and Bell (Factory, vol. 108) point out that the question of whom to train, regardless of job status, can be answered by the use of learning curves. Learning curves of trainees can be plotted against a **standard learning curve,** thus showing the comparison of their actual learning time against the standard rate of learning. Learning curves are based on sound training methods and help to **reduce training time and cost.** They reveal mental, as well as manual, aptitudes. No standard curve has yet been set up showing how long it takes a trainee to learn how to carry on materials handling operations. A method recently developed by Smyth (Factory, vol. 101) for repetitive jobs may shed light on further development of learning curves in materials handling.

Whom to train, irrespective of job classification, is also determined in part by reference to personnel records. Results of aptitude, intelligence, attitude, interest, and occupational tests are used as criteria. Opinions and recommendations from superiors, though not considered absolutely reliable, may indicate patterns of behavior of individuals that bear on trainee selection. Very often, trainee selection is not a factor for concern, since it may be necessary to train or retrain each person engaged in or hired to do materials handling work. The objective in any case is to increase the rate of production and reduce operating costs.

TRAINEE RESISTANCE TO CHANGE.

Training personnel in the techniques and concepts of materials handling and in the operation of materials handling equipment involves changes, and resistance to these changes, is encountered. Lawrence (Harvard Business Review, vol. 32) points out that trainee resistance arises when the trainer is preoccupied with the technical aspects of training changes and overlooks the operator's or trainee's know-how. Operator-trainees, supervisor-trainees, and staff-trainees frequently have a vast storehouse of practical up-to-date experience superior even to the technical knowledge of the executive trainer and can readily spot and overcome operating difficulties in a new materials handling installation.

The following are steps the materials handling trainer can take to reduce or eliminate trainee resistance:

1. Examine and evaluate the trainee's social relationships which revolve around his job. Plan to continue customary work relationships.
2. Broaden the range of changes resulting from the training program. Eliminate preoccupation with, or complete engrossment in technology when it interferes with the human factors involved.

3. Take advantage of trainee know-how when planning and conducting the training program. Use the skill and technical experience of operating people, altering training and technical details when and where advantageous.
4. Give the results of the training enough time to show their value. If present, technological and social trouble spots will show up; if given time, they will correct themselves.
5. Broaden his own interests to the extent that all aspects of the total plant objective are identified in the materials handling training program. Avoid extreme and isolated identification with only one or a few departmental or functional interests.
6. Present the details of the training plan in understandable, everyday terms. Trainees must be able to interpret details readily and pass them along to untrained personnel if over-all efficiency is to result.
7. Interpret trainee resistance to change as a danger signal. Realization of the significance of trainee resistance induces easier correction of trouble areas as they occur, with positive results on the spot.
8. Develop the respect of trainees to the extent that they will cooperate readily and freely. Ask for ideas and suggestions in a straightforward manner and act upon them seriously. No threat to trainee work relationships must enter the picture.
9. Go about his own job, coordinating efforts and facilitating communication and understanding between people with different points of view. Conciliation and ease of understanding between such departments as production and engineering should be brought about by discussing experiences and answering questions frankly and tactfully, yet in terms of positive progress interpreted as an honest effort to achieve the major objectives of the plant.

The problem of trainee resistance to change is real. It can be handled successfully by positive action and careful pretraining planning. New ideas, changes in operations, and economic results can be assured when—and only when—the resistance problem is eliminated from the materials handling training program.

Setting Up the Personnel Improvement Training Program

ORGANIZING THE PROGRAM. Organizing the materials handling training program is simply a matter of logical progression. **Cooperation** should be sought from the plant management, and reports on the progress of the training should be made as the work progresses. The following steps, in logical order, are necessary for bringing about the best results.

1. Secure top management's approval and active participation.
2. Determine the real materials handling training needs. Put them in writing.
3. Establish whom to train and where and how to train.
4. Develop the training program to meet the real needs.
5. Pretest the trainees.
6. Put the training program into action.
7. Test the trainees during the training program.
8. Test the trainees at the end of the training period.
9. Evaluate training results in the light of actual needs.
10. Plan follow-up action and training.
11. Revise the training program for use in future training.

Training objectives evolve from plant problems. Plant needs are not always recognized by company executives as training needs because members of the managerial reorganization seldom have a practiced trainer's knowledge of what training can actually accomplish. The alert materials handling executive can be aware that materials flow is bottlenecked and that present equipment, though new, does not help his materials handling problems; but he does not necessarily view these trouble spots as indicating the need for training.

Developing a training objective from a plant problem is done to determine whether or not training can solve the problem, and how it can be solved as a training objective. Talking with men on the job, asking questions of a constructive nature, and showing interest in employees' materials handling problems is one way to discover real problems. Such **personal contact** encourages help, understanding, and cooperation from possible trainees.

MATERIALS HANDLING TRAINING CHECK LIST. A most effective means of spotting plant problems on which training objectives or needs are built is the Materials Handling Check List developed by Footlik and Carle (Industrial Materials Handling) and frequently used to make a materials handling analysis. Process-flow charts are likewise helpful as checks on personal comments from operating personnel. Check charts such as those prepared by Carle (Developing an Effective Materials Handling Program) and illustrated in Fig. 1 are also of considerable aid.

How and Where To Spot Training Needs

1. Presently troublesome spots.
2. Recurring trouble spots.
3. Worker surveys.
4. Plant records: cost, safety, quality, scrap, salvage, storage, shipping, receiving, personnel turnover, etc.
5. Pressure points in production flow.
6. Decrease in skilled machinists' production.
7. Current trends in materials handling techniques and equipment.
8. Use of experimental and control groups on new or old installations.
9. Steering committees to find training needs.
10. The suggestion box.
11. High grievance occurrence.
12. Top management conferences.
13. Middle management conferences.

Who and What Can Help Spot Training Needs

1. Worker personnel.
2. Middle management.
3. Top management.
4. Department heads.
5. Accounting department.
6. Safety engineer.
7. Production manager.
8. Production control.
9. Materials control.
10. Plant layout engineer.
11. Current periodicals.
12. Current books.
13. Manufacturer's brochures.
14. Training department.
15. Outside training specialist.
16. Suggestions system officer.
17. Any individual or department where information is located or developed.

Fig. 1. Materials handling check list for spotting training needs.

Whom to train and where and how to train are problems that must be solved. The suggestions and procedures already outlined will help get the program started. The materials handling executive will have had contact with the probable materials handling trainees during the preprogram research and planning; he should invite, rather than order, selected trainees to attend and take part in the materials handling training program. Available space, suitable equipment, and a proper training environment are necessary for success in the training.

TRAINING AREAS. To simplify the presentation of materials handling know-how and thereby develop a practical program, materials handling may be divided into training areas, as shown in Fig. 2. Since the individual learns by first gaining an appreciation of what he is to learn, all materials handling information relative to the **appreciation area** is listed. The materials handling trainee must also learn basic knowledge concerning materials handling; therefore, a **technical information area** is developed. Materials handling techniques demand a specific training method and are also "how-to-do" phases of materials handling, so the **technique area** is shown. The **application area** lists the subdivisions of materials handling which are usable in training for materials handling applications. The terms under each area-heading do not by any means pretend to exhaust the possible materials handling items that should be listed.

Building a materials handling program based on good teaching techniques is facilitated by reference to the materials handling training areas chart (Fig. 2). The chart shows in detail, by title, the discussion, lecture, or case-study content of the training session. By selecting from each area, beginning with "Appreciation," the materials handling program content can be tailored to fit both the trainees' and the plant's objectives.

A training program for worker personnel might assume an outline such as that shown in Fig. 3. Training must be tailored to fit plant needs. This outline is merely suggestive of what a program for ten weeks or less could be; it includes selected methods and audio-visual aids. Figs. 4, 5, 6, and 7 outline programs for other phases of training.

The materials handling training program takes shape as the training needs dictate. Each session is developed to satisfy one or more stated (written) needs or objectives. The chart is a guide only, simplifying the selection process and clarifying the make-up of the materials handling training program as a professional trainer would organize it.

CARRYING ON THE TRAINING PROGRAM. The **initial meeting** is an indoctrination session. A top management executive should be present to show that the company is supporting the training program. He should also attend subsequent sessions, making positive contributions to the discussion and the attainment of the objectives.

A **survey-type test** which covers the desired training results should be given. No time limit is set. The "survey" can be done at home. It indicates the employees' pretraining level of materials handling appreciation, knowledge, technique, and application and shows how much materials handling technique is known before the training is given.

Planned training methods should be followed, but the trainer must be prepared to shift from method to method as necessary. He must prepare a detailed "session plan" before each session and adhere to it. Constant reference to "our jobs," "our training needs," is vital to make the training program personal.

Testing during training can be done by (1) frequent short tests to determine how well the subject matter of foregoing sessions has been learned, and/or (2) by a "survey" test at the halfway point.

I Appreciation	II Technical Information	III The Technique	IV Application
1. Background	1. The equipment	1. Materials handling in production processes	1. Case studies
2. What it is	2. Time and motion studies	2. Materials handling in supply operations	2. Active problems
3. What it can do	3. Packaging	3. Materials handling in storage, warehousing	3. A typical solution
4. Where it fits	4. Shipping, receiving	4. Materials handling in transit	4. Potential handling economies
5. How it affects the engineer	5. Storage, warehousing	5. Selling materials handling to top management	5. Materials handling organization
6. How it affects the company	6. Plant layout	6. Making a materials handling analysis	6. Materials handling maintenance
7. Why it is worth knowing	7. Factors affecting materials handling operations	7. Selecting proper equipment	7. Materials handling and you and your company
8. The "cost" angle	8. Inter- and intraplant handling	8. Materials handling in the individual's company	8. Materials handling and your work force

Fig. 2. **Materials handling training areas.**

Unit	Area	Content	Estimated Time	Method Aids
1. Development and scope	I 1, 8	Brief history. What is materials handling? The objectives of materials handling. Basic definitions. Present status.	2 hr.	Lecture, Opaque projector
2. Fundamentals of materials handling	I 2, 3, 4	Necessity for fundamentals. Possible economies.	2 hr.	Lecture, Discussion, Opaque projector
3. Basic materials handling equipment	II 1, 4, 5, 6, 7	Various types of available equipment. Present, best, and possible applications.	2 hr.	Lecture, Opaque projector
4. Potential handling economies	IV 2, 4 III 6	Utilization of labor, space, equipment. Practical cases.	2 hr.	Discussion, Film
5. Time, motion, methods in materials handling	II 2	Work simplification survey. Analysis. Techniques.	2 hr.	Lecture, Film, Discussion
6. Materials handling in production processes	III 5, 6, 7	Where is materials handling in production? Extent of materials handling in production. Positioning materials for processing. Production equipment in use.	2 hr.	Discussion, Opaque projector
7. Shipping, receiving, warehousing	II 3, 4, 5, 6, 7	Utilizing cube. Unit loads. Coordinating warehousing, shipping, receiving, carriers. Codes, laws, regulations.	2 hr.	Lecture, Opaque projector, Discussion
8. A typical materials handling solution	IV 2, 4	The plant layout. Handling incoming materials, work in process, production items, finished product. Product handling and its cost.	2–3 hr.	Discussion, Case study, Opaque projector
9. How to make a materials handling survey	III 5, 6, 7	Why? How to spot a problem. The check list. Securing costs. Flow charts. Cost comparisons. Selling materials handling to top management. Applying the solution. Follow-up.	2–3 hr.	Lecture, Opaque projector, Discussion
10. Materials handling and you	IV 4, 5, 7, 8	Where do you fit in? How you use materials handling effectively. Cooperation. The economics of business. What helps the company helps you.	2 hr.	Discussion, Opaque projector
Total training time			20–22 hr.	

Fig. 3. Training program for worker personnel.

Unit	Content	Estimated Time
1. Development and scope	Brief history. What is materials handling? The objectives of materials handling. Basic definitions. Present status.	2 hr.
2. Fundamentals of materials handling	Necessity for fundamentals. Possible economies.	2 hr.
3. Basic materials handling equipment	Various types of available equipment. Present, best, and possible applications.	3 hr.
4. Factors affecting materials handling operations	Selection of equipment. Equipment characteristics. Product and production characteristics. Plant characteristics. Integration of equipment. Determining economical methods.	3 hr.
5. Industrial packaging	Objectives. Utilization of cube. Applications.	2 hr.
6. Potential handling economies	Utilization of labor, space, equipment. Practical cases.	2 hr.
7. Time, motion, methods in materials handling	Standards. Motion and methods work simplification. Analysis technique.	2 hr.
8. Materials handling in production processes	Where is materials handling in production? Extent of materials handling in production. Positioning materials for processing. Production equipment in use.	3 hr.
9. Plant layout	Present layout. Seeking materials handling economy. Developing and installing new layout.	2 hr.
10. Shipping, receiving, warehousing	Utilizing cube. Unit loads. Coordinating warehousing, shipping, receiving, carriers. Codes, laws, regulations.	2 hr.
11. A typical materials handling solution	The plant layout. Handling incoming materials, work in process, production items, finished products. Product handling and its cost.	3 hr.
12. How to make a materials handling survey	Why? How to spot a problem. The check list. Securing costs. Flow charts. Cost comparisons. Selling materials handling to top management. Applying the solution. Follow-up.	3 hr.
13. Materials handling organization	Why? Emphasis on responsibility. Centralization. Efficient management.	1 hr.
14. Materials handling and you	Where do you fit in? How you use materials handling effectively. Cooperation. The economics of business. What helps the company helps you.	2 hr.
15. Case studies and plant problems	Solution of actual and present plant problems. Where are materials handling problems in your job or department?	3 hr.
Total time		35 hr.

Fig. 4. Training for middle management, supervisory personnel.

Session	Content
1.	Introduction: Plant objectives, purposes. What stake trainees have in training. Instructor's objectives, procedure. Administer survey outline (½ hr.) Distribute textbook; assign reading.
2.	Development, scope of materials handling: What it is, what it is not. Where it exists in plant operations. Where it fits into future plans—yours, plant's. Visit operations.
3.	Fundamentals of materials handling: Guiding principles (develop materials handling consciousness). Recognizing good, bad materials handling practices.
4. and 5.	Materials handling equipment: Recognition, uses, application. Application to plant operations. Selected operations analysis for equipment application. Look for opportunity to assign materials handling problems to individuals or groups.
6.	Building layout principles: Basic principles. Practice with emphasis on storage operations at plant.
7.	Materials handling receiving operations: Present plant operations, equipment. Methods, equipment, supports, containers, securements, facilities, personnel, supplier relations, unit loads, LCL loose loads. Work simplification proposals.
8.	Materials handling storage techniques: Basic factors in good storage practice. Storage plans, techniques. Floor load calculations. Unit, loose loads.
9.	Materials control: Receiving, routing, storage, issue inventory, record-keeping. McCaskey, Remington-Rand, Productrol, Visitrol.
10. and 11.	Plant handling problems: Work simplification proposals checked, encouraged for completion.
12.	Final cleanup session: Check work simplification proposals. How to work in materials handling. Give final survey. Collect proposals for presentation.

Lincoln Extension Institute, Inc.

Fig. 5. Materials handling training for a plant engaged in warehousing.

Session	Contents	Comments
1.	Introduction to training program: Indoctrination (plant). Present training objectives. Pretraining survey. (*No. 1*)	Present: Why training advantageous. Give survey.
2.	Introduction to materials handling: Development of materials handling. Scope of materials handling in plant operations. Definition of materials handling (what it is, is not).	Develop definition of materials handling. Review, discuss survey. Discuss shop operations.
3.	Basic fundamentals of materials handling: Guiding principles.	Discuss 11 basic principles. Discuss photos, shop operations.
4. and 5.	Materials handling equipment: Recognition, uses, application. Application to plant operations. Operations analysis for equipment application. Assign materials handling problems if possible.	Emphasize equipment applicable to plant operations. Review all plant operations with the mechanical application in mind.
6.	Plant layout: Basic principles, flow chart, layout diagram. Job shop, product layouts. Plant problems. Assign materials handling problems if possible.	Emphasis on job shop layout. Review total plant layout with respect to related operations.
7.	Time, motion, methods in materials handling: Review of plant operational time studies. Apply work simplification principles. Assign materials handling problems if possible.	Review operations with time study figures. "How to do it better, simpler, faster, cheaper."
8.	Materials handling storage techniques: Basic factors in temporary, permanent storage. Storage plans, facilities. Floor load calculations. Unit, loose loads.	Fix basic principles. Examine present practices. Analyze for economy and possible change.
9. and 10.	Materials handling analysis: Analyzing the operation. The check list. Flow process charts. Layout diagram. Selecting, applying equipment. Training personnel. Selling materials handling to top management.	How to make an analysis. What to look for. What to start. What to do. How to sell it to top management.
11.	Plant materials handling operations: Final analyses of materials handling at plant. Review materials handling solutions for presentation to top management. Materials handling organization (if desired). Give final survey (No. 2).	

Specifications:
a. Sessions 2 hr., minimum 24 hr.
b. Selected personnel (supervisory).
c. Training on plant premises.
d. Training survey made.
e. Field trips supplementary to 24 hr. training time.
f. Plant executive selected as advisor to trainer.

Lincoln Extension Institute, Inc.

Fig. 6. Materials handling training for metalworking operations.

Session	Topic
1.	Introduction, development, scope, definition of materials handling.
2.	Fundamentals, guided principles in materials handling.
3.	Materials handling equipment review.
4.	Selection of materials handling equipment.
5.	Application of floor-operated materials handling equipment.
6.	Application of miscellaneous materials handling equipment.
7.	Application of power industrial trucks—yard handling.
8.	Application of overhead materials handling equipment—conveyors, hoists, etc.
9.	Application of fork trucks.
10.	Pallets, pallet system, unit loads—storage.
11.	Plant layout materials handling standards.
12.	How to make a materials handling analysis.
13.	Selling materials handling to top management.
14.	Developing an effective materials handling program. Materials handling organization.
15.	Seminar—all personnel.

Cleveland Engineering Society

Fig. 7. Educational program, materials handling course schedule.

Early in the program the men being trained should be encouraged to reveal their own ideas, suggestions, and plans for materials handling improvements. Trainees usually come into a training program with time-, work-, or man-saving suggestions of their own and should be encouraged to work them out in the training program with the aid of the instructor. These suggestions, if worthwhile, should ultimately be submitted to top management for serious consideration. Constant help in fully developing their suggestions by the end of the training program should be given the trainees.

The final training "survey" is given at the last session in the presence of the trainer. If a period of 10 to 12 wk. has elapsed, the pretraining survey can be given without fear that the "remembering" factor will affect results. Results established by comparing the pretraining and posttraining surveys not only help in evaluating the materials handling training program but also point to changes, additions, and deletions which should be made in similar programs planned for the future.

Evaluating the Personnel Improvement Training Program

ATTAINING THE OBJECTIVES. A training program is judged on the basis of the results it is supposed to have made, or will make, within an estimated period of time. The evaluation is often made solely in terms of dollars and cents. Such evaluation is good, but as the sole criterion it is not completely fair to the training efforts. Additional evaluation criteria include improvements made in morale, increase in product output, reduction in waste of materials, lowering personnel turnover, and other factors which contribute measurably to the tangible and beneficial end results.

In industrial training programs, an adequate **evaluation plan** is not only the last active step but also, unfortunately, often the last factor of the entire program to be considered. A reliable **evaluation procedure** must be an integral part of the initial planning phase of the training program. While planning how to train men to meet plant and personnel needs, it is important also to provide a means for measuring how well the training objectives are being met.

Evaluation of a training program may be undertaken in the traditional manner (1) after training is done, or (2) using a control group. The most effective method, however, involves the use of valid measures before, during, and after training, plus the "before" and "after" checks supplied by specific significant plant records designated during the "needs-determining" period. All such methods of measurement cover changes in ability, skills, attitudes, performance, and costs or economy factors.

The use of prepared subject matter, information sheets, plant problems, diagrams, prints, manuals, and textbooks with advance assignments promotes two-way discussion. A mere printed training program listing the topics for each session is not sufficient. Trainees who study and are given the opportunity to think through problems and subject matter prior to each session are most likely to contribute the most to the training objectives.

Programs of formal industrial training often have their foundations deeply imbedded in the formal classroom organization—the teacher-pupil relationship. An atmosphere of this kind is not conducive to obtaining the hoped-for results. It is likely that the **educational experiences and social environment** of most of the trainees (who to a large extent will be men with both considerable practical experience and responsibility for plant activities) will combine to arouse a resentment to training if a formal classroom atmosphere is evident. This avenue of failure has little reason to exist in a highly academic atmosphere, since the informality of free discussion, use of audio visual aids, ability to move out of the training room into the plant, and freedom to ask questions and make suggestions are well known to every experienced trainer and trainee.

Setting Up the Job-related Training Program

JUSTIFYING THE TRAINING. A materials handling machine that is either not operating or not operated at its peak efficiency cannot be fully justified as a sound capital investment. The best materials handling machines built are no more economical than the service they give. The lift truck is no exception. The extent of service rendered depends on the operators who control them. To justify the capital investment in a materials handling machine, it is necessary that the operator be fully trained. Lift trucks will operate as efficiently as they are directed; the more skilled the direction, the more efficient the handling.

Training operators of lift trucks or any piece of materials handling machine is an economic necessity. The size of the company or its budget is not an influencing factor in the decision to organize and administer a lift truck operator's training program. The presence and use of a lift truck is sufficient evidence that losses due to (1) down time, (2) damage to materials, (3) injuries to personnel, (4) repairs of damage to lift truck and facilities, are present. These losses do not always reflect the negative effect of inefficient operation on plant personnel—an intangible but vital factor which affects the balance sheet.

Specific Advantages from Training. The specific advantages accruing from a well-organized training program for lift truck operators, for example, include the following:

1. **Increased lift truck efficiency.** Trained operators get more volume per trip and more trips per unit of time, thus reducing costs of handling and of damage to materials being handled.
2. **Increased efficiency of plant operation.** Movement of materials between production area and shipping or storage areas is better coordinated with production rate and cube capacity.
3. **More effective use of time.** Time expended in loading, stacking, and maneuvering per handling is at its minimum with trained operators. Skillfully operated lift trucks operate longer with less down time, less maintenance cost.
4. **Safer operations.** Trained lift truck operators are closest to the operation and vehicle and aware of possible losses to life and limb, as well as financial losses. A properly trained operator is a safe operator.
5. **Minimized human problems.** Properly trained operators are more satisfied with their jobs, do them better and more safely. They inspire confidence of co-workers, help reduce turnover, transfers, quits, and supervisory problems.

Making the Decision To Train. A training program for lift truck operators arises out of definite needs determined either by a top management decision or through a survey. Even one lift truck in daily operation is sufficient reason for carrying on a training program to cut down bottlenecks in lift truck operations and conduct a survey of costs related to the operations. Excessive costs in any of these areas warrant training of lift truck operators.

Eidson (Modern Materials Handling, vol. 9) reports that one company compiled the following cost records, then made the decision to train its lift truck operators:

Damage to materials	$ 15,000
Injuries (including one death)	80,000
Vehicle damage	5,000
Damage to facilities	10,000
Total	$110,000

In another case, the company based its decision to train lift truck operators on out-of-line costs to maintain each vehicle, stating: "Our primary reason for this driver training program was to cut down excessive maintenance costs. Personnel injuries were not a particularly serious problem. Our drivers . . . had developed driving habits which caused wear and tear, often because of lack of training."

Another company reported the following instance:

An inexperienced operator engaged a pallet load and attempted to place it in a box car. Within 30 sec. he was hopelessly fouled up against the car bulkhead because of too sharp a turn on the bridge plate. He tried both backing up and going forward in an effort to extricate himself from the jam, but succeeded only in wedging his truck more tightly against the side of the box car and in rattling the steel bridge plate between the car and the loading platform. Minutes later he was persuaded to get off the truck and let someone else try to run it. A skilled woman mounted the truck, spun the steering wheel sharply, and a moment later had deposited the pallet load inside the car and was on her way back to the warehouse for another load.

Data concerning excessive maintenance costs as a basis for deciding whether or not to train truck operators should be assembled by setting up records giving the complete history of each lift truck and the work it performs on a day-to-day basis. The information needed is listed (Modern Materials Handling, vol. 7) under these headings: Date, type of truck, truck number, driver number, cost of parts, description of repairs, and cost of labor-hours. Executive decision on whether to train lift truck operators should be based on this information.

HOW TO TRAIN. Developing capable lift truck operators requires a carefully planned training program, skilled trainers, high-grade lift trucks, capable trainees, and suitable training environment. The training program should be developed from a well-grounded knowledge of the techniques which should be imparted to the trainees.

The training program Know-how Sheet shown in Fig. 8 is one example of such a program-planner's guide. It is used to aid in planning the respective classroom sessions and practice area sessions. In this Know-how Sheet, the program content is listed almost exactly in the order in which each skill is learned.

What the Trainee Must Learn	Where Taught
1. Why the program is being conducted (reasons, facts, figures).	Classroom session
2. Why the lift truck is used.	Classroom session
(a) Principle of the lift truck; the unit load; types of pallets, pallet patterns; skids; types of attachments.	
3. Operating responsibilities.	Classroom session
a. Safety. e. Dependability.	
b. Efficiency. f. Care.	
c. Skill. g. Plant rules.	
d. Neatness. h. Personal behavior.	
4. Safety responsibilities.	Classroom session
5. Maintenance responsibilities.	Classroom session
6. Operating reports responsibilities.	Classroom session
7. Inspection procedures and reports.	Classroom session
8. Nomenclature of lift truck parts.	Practice area
9. Function of lift truck and its parts.	Practice area
10. Basic operations know-how.	Practice area
a. Starting the engine.	
(1) Procedure before starting.	
(2) Procedure after starting.	
b. Moving the lift truck.	
Procedure before moving away.	
c. Driving forward and backward.	
(1) Procedure before each.	
(2) Steering explained.	
d. Turning right or left.	
Procedure for turning.	
e. Stopping the lift truck.	
Procedure before starting.	
11. Maneuvering with no load, with load.	Practice area at
a. Starting. e. Loading.	obstacle courses
b. Shifting. f. Positioning	
c. Steering. g. Stacking.	
d. Traveling. h. Stopping.	
An obstacle course for each is utilized.	

Fig. 8. Program know-how sheet.

A. STRAIGHT RUNS. The basic concept: All forward or reverse motions of the truck moving in a straight line.

1. **Forward**	This is a basic motion, with the truck running in a straight line of lateral travel.
2. **Reverse**	This is a basic motion, with the truck running in a straight line of lateral travel.
3. **Acceleration**	This is a basic motion and occurs when the truck moves from a dead stop to full speed.
4. **Stopping**	(Straight stop.) This is a basic motion and occurs when bringing the truck to a dead stop from a forward or reverse speed.
5. **Run-in**	This is a basic motion and occurs when moving the truck forward to insert forks into the pallet or when placing the load (after the fork carriage has been raised to the desired level). This includes Acceleration and Stopping.
6. **Run-out**	This is a basic motion and occurs when moving the truck backward to remove the forks from the pallet or removing the load.

B. TURNS. The basic concept: All forward or reverse motions of the truck not moving in a straight line (making turns).

7. **Right**	This is a basic motion and occurs when moving the truck forward or backward and negotiating a change of direction (right-hand) from a straight run.
8. **Right and Stop**	This is a basic motion and occurs when moving the truck forward or backward and negotiating a 90° right-hand turn while coming to a complete stop. This basic motion is used when approaching a materials storage area which is at a 90° angle to the straight line of travel. Note: This motion is usually preceded by a straight run and followed by a hoist and/or Run-in or Run-out.
9. **Left**	This is a basic motion and occurs when moving the truck laterally (left or right) and negotiating a change of direction from a straight run.
10. **Left and Stop**	This is a basic motion and occurs when moving the truck (forward or backward) and negotiating a left-hand 90° turn while coming to a complete stop. This basic motion is used when approaching a materials storage area which is at a 90° angle to the straight line of travel. Note: The motion is usually preceded by a straight run and followed by a hoist and/or Run-in or Run-out.

C. STACKING. The basic concept: All up or down vertical motion of the fork carriage on the channel.

11. **Tilt**	This is a basic motion and occurs when the channel moves forward or backward from a vertical position of 90°.
12. **Up**	This is a basic motion and occurs when the fork carriage moves up in a vertical direction on the channel. Note: This motion usually occurs when the truck has come to a complete stop.
13. **Down**	This is a basic motion and occurs when the fork carriage moves down in a vertical direction on the channel. Note: This motion usually occurs when the truck has come to a complete stop.

O. C. Carliss, "Standard Performance Times for Fork Trucks," Yale & Towne Mfg. Co., Philadelphia, Pa. A study performed by industrial engineering classes at Wharton School, University of Pennsylvania.

Fig. 9. Basic motions of the lift truck.

Fig. 9, another guide for the program-planner, is a study of basic motions necessarily performed by means of the lift truck in operation. This study lists basic motions which can be used in determining accurate standard performance times. The data can also be used by the program-planner to develop the basic know-how of the lift truck operator training program. Excellent training handbooks and guides are also available from lift truck manufacturers.

Organizing the Training Program. The training program for lift truck operators is a combined chronology of (1) classroom lectures and demonstrations and (2) practice-area instructions and applications. The learning period is followed by the practice and application period; the trainee learns theory, then puts what he has learned into actual practice.

Classroom periods usually consist of lectures supplemented by charts, photographs, film strips, films, model demonstrations, handouts, and short written tests. **Practice periods** include demonstrations and actual operation of the lift trucks to be used. Trainees are instructed by being told how, shown how, and by being allowed to perform the operations under guidance until they are thoroughly learned. Actual plant equipment is used wherever possible.

The program is conducted on an all-day, every-day basis until completed. Operators selected for one program (Modern Materials Handling, vol. 9) were thoroughly trained in a total of 16 hr., including both classroom training and actual practice. Inexperienced men usually require about 32 hr. of training. Sessions were run consecutively on a full-day basis. The General Electric Company at Lynn, Massachusetts, has set up a period of from one to three weeks for training operators to do their jobs properly, operators with some previous experience requiring the least amount of time.

Classroom sessions should be held in the lecture room of the plant training department or in some other area where the sessions can be conducted without disturbance. The practice area should be located immediately outside the classroom or within a short walking distance.

Selecting the Trainers. Trainers are selected on the basis of ability. The classroom instructor can be selected from the supervisory staff, preferably from those members with sound safety training backgrounds and lift truck know-how. A safety department executive is also recommended. The practice-area instructor should be an expert lift truck operator, preferably of the supervisory group. He should have definite teaching ability as well as know how to operate a lift truck skillfully. Technical ability alone does not make good instructors; they must be able to teach, to explain, and to make themselves easily understood.

Selecting the Trainees. With the exception of those who will assist the trainer, the current operators should be the first selectees for a training program. Sometimes operators from other companies can be added to the training group. The Automatic Transportation Company (Industrial Truck Operators Are Trained— Not Born) reported that women of thirty-five or over, especially those with families, make careful, steady operators.

Trainees should be tested on the following counts: (1) vision, (2) steadiness, (3) field of vision, (4) reaction time, and (5) distance judgment. The Hawaiian Pineapple Company uses a similar battery, which includes tests of (1) visual acuity, (2) field of vision, (3) distance judgment, (4) foot reaction, and (5) ability to distinguish red, yellow, and green. These tests are individually outlined in the company's truck-driver training-program manual. A complete physical examination is likewise specified. Prospective members of a plant training course should also be screened by the company's personnel department with respect to incidence of absenteeism, length of service, loyalty, desire to stay with the company, interest in advancement, enthusiasm for the job, dependability of personal action, maturity, and literacy.

Experience has demonstrated that the maximum group size in training lift truck operators is five members. Increasing the size of the trainee group reduces the individual attention which is necessary for developing skillful operators, especially in the practice area, where mistakes are corrected on the spot. Instruction sessions can be briefer and more effective when trainee groups are small enough to afford this individual attention.

ORGANIZING THE INSTRUCTION. The training-program content is developed chronologically from the basic know-how sheet. Preparation for each of the components of a training program (as shown in Fig. 10) will be necessary.

---

1. **Lectures on driving techniques.** Subjects of these lectures include types of hazards encountered and ways to avoid them.
2. **Conference periods.** These sessions are devoted to discussion of foregoing lectures, to quizzes, and to discussions on experiences of the operators and on questions raised by the operators.
3. **Written quizzes.** These quizzes should be given before each lecture to discover weaknesses in the instruction and to provide subjects for discussion (see Fig. 1).
4. **Obstacle course driving sessions.** These sessions consist of a series of driving tests given on obstacle courses set up for the purpose (see Fig. 12).
5. **Problem driving sessions.** These periods are devoted to situations which arise under actual driving conditions. They will present the driver with potentially hazardous situations which he is required to analyze and solve (see Fig. 13).
6. **Verbal coaching.** This method is used during driving sessions.
7. **Mimeographed training guide lessons, safety check lists, and handout sheets.** These items are distributed to all students at carefully predetermined times during the training schedule. (Examples are shown below; see also Figs. 14 and 15.)

Fig. 10. Components of a training program.

Sample Training Forms. Sample forms of the above-mentioned components of the training program for lift truck operators are shown in Figs. 11–17, inclusive. These forms have been taken from several functioning training programs. They can serve as guides in developing various components of a training program.

Testing, Classroom, and Practice Area. While the progress of each trainee can be checked by observing how well he applies what he learns, it is still necessary to develop a written testing program to accompany the practice problems and obstacle courses. The purpose of the testing program is to determine progress of learning and to supply a basis for discussion of what is important in safety, operation maintenance, plant rules, personnel responsibilities, and possibly work simplification. Tests prepared for classroom sessions should be brief and objective in type. They should not be "tough" tests. They are not meant to be hurdles in the path of the trainee; rather, they should fairly test the trainee on the facts, appreciations, safety precautions, and operating rules that he must know. Figs. 18–26, inclusive, are examples of such tests taken from several training programs.

OPERATION OF AN INDUSTRIAL TRUCK

1. Yes_____ No_____   Is it allowed to park on an incline without putting blocks under wheels?

2. T _____ F _____   The key does not have to be removed when the driver is leaving the truck.

3. T _____ F _____   The forks can be used to jack up other machines.

4. T _____ F _____   It is all right to push another machine to get it started.

5. Choice _____   When overtaking someone from the rear, you should:
a. Continue on as long as he is not right in front of you.
b. Go around him.
c. Sound horn and steer clear of him.

6. Choice _____   To cross railroad tracks you should:
a. Drive straight ahead.
b. Drive on a slant.
c. Turn and back across.

7. T _____ F _____   Regular traffic rules in the plant do not apply to fork trucks.

8. Choice _____   When entering or leaving a building, you should:
a. Stop and drive out.
b. Drive right out.
c. Stop, sound horn, and go out slowly.
d. Slow down.

9. T _____ F _____   It is all right to tow railroad cars or large trucks.

10. T _____ F _____   If you come to a stop, you may back up right away without looking behind you, because you have just covered that area and know it is clear.

11. Yes_____ No_____   If you are carrying a load, does it make any difference whether you stop slowly or stop suddenly?

12. T _____ F _____   A gasoline motor lift truck can be driven in gas areas.

13. T _____ F _____   An electric lift truck can be driven in gas areas.

14. Yes_____ No_____   Is it dangerous to drive through an oil puddle?

15. T _____ F _____   It is safe to let someone stand under a high load.

16. T _____ F _____   Loads that project beyond the truck need a red flag.

17. T _____ F _____   When parking you can get out of the truck and let it coast to a stop provided you take the key out.

The Industrial Truck Association

Fig. 11. Example of a classroom session quiz.

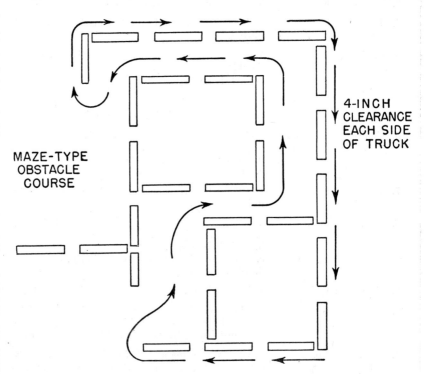

Fig. 12. Typical obstacle course of the maze type.

Practice Problem No. 1—Aisle Problem.

General Description

Use pallets to form an aisle with two turns, as shown in diagram. Aisle width depends upon size of truck used. Clearance in the aisle should be adequate for making the turns. Operator starts at one end, drives forward, makes the turns, drives out of the other end of the aisle, turns around, and returns to his starting point. He then repeats the problem, driving backward.

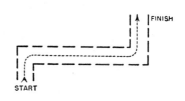

Practice Problem No. 2—Aisle Problem.

General Description

(This setup can be used as an alternate for Problem No. 1.) Make two parallel lanes about 30 ft. long, formed by pallets on end, as shown in diagram. Clearance in each lane should be adequate for making the turns. Operator drives truck down one lane, turns, and goes down the other. He returns backward over the same route.

Practice Problem No. 3—Truck Handling Problem.

General Description

Form a circle 30 ft. in diameter out of ten pallets placed on end, as shown in diagram. Suggested space between pallets is 5 ft. 4 in. Operator weaves his truck in and out of circle until he completes one full trip around the course.

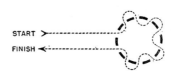

Yale & Towne Mfg. Co.

Fig. 13. Examples of practice problems (used in practice area application sessions).

(Bank Mfg. Co.)

What: 1. Approaching, Stacking, Backing Up, Stopping.

Where: Practice Area B.

Obstacle Course No. 4.

Practice Problems No. 4, 4A.

How: 1. Approaching for load—carrying away

- Face direction of travel.
- Set forks properly for entry to pallet.
- Coast in under load with forks correctly aligned.
- Run forks under load as far as possible.
- Pick up load in center; maintain balance.
- Tilt load against back rest before moving.
- Keep load low while traveling.
- Avoid jerky operation, sudden stops or starts.
- Use low gear up inclines, over crossings, with heavy loads.

2. Approaching with load—stacking.

- Face direction of travel.
- Approach at right angles.
- Stop; raise load with lift mechanism.
- Avoid excessive tilt when high lifting is done.
- Allow hoist lever to return to neutral.
- Move truck forward to base of stack.
- Place load on stack; lower slowly, continuously.

Caution:

- Do not leave truck in gear while stacking.
- Return shift lever to neutral; disengage clutch.

(Lincoln Extension Institute, Inc.)

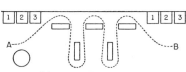

Obstacle Course No. 4

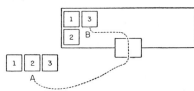

Practice Problem No. 4

Obstacle Course No. 4	Practice Problem No. 4
This practice problem will show how well you are able to maneuver with a load and stack it. You will pick up a load at point A, follow a course through the upright pallets, and stack the load in the other area. You will stack three columns each two loads high, the center column last. Be sure you set forks properly before approaching a pallet. Coast under the load once your forks are aligned. Pick up loads in the center, making sure they are properly balanced. Tilt your load against the back rest before moving your truck.	This next practice session will acquaint you with the problems of loading a boxcar. You will pick up a load at point A, carry it over to the boxcar door, dismount and test the bridge plate, and then stack the load at location 1. You will stack three columns each two loads high, starting with location 1, next 2, and then 3. Remember to use the correct methods of approaching, lifting, and carrying the load. Before you start, the instructor will show you a diagram of the course you will follow.

(Yale & Towne Mfg. Co.)

Fig. 14. Training guide lesson issued to all trainees prior to the practice area session.

Outside Safety

1. Be sure bridge plates are strong enough.
2. Inspect floors of street trucks and railroad cars before entering.
3. Stop, look, and listen at railroad tracks.
4. Go slow when descending ramp.
5. Don't ride on soft ground.

The following rules might be stressed again:

1. Follow standard procedure whenever leaving truck.
2. Don't lift or lower loads while traveling.
3. Keep load against carriage for extra support.
4. Don't speed on rough floors.

Safety to Others

1. Don't haul riders.
2. For better vision with bulky loads, drive backward.
3. Never travel with forks raised.
4. Watch blind corners and stop signs.
5. Watch rear-end swing.
6. Place forks flat on floor when truck is parked.
7. Don't use truck as a personnel elevator.
8. Don't daydream.

9. Face direction of travel.
10. Watch for unstable loads.

Safety to Self

1. Avoid sudden stops.
2. Observe floor load limits.
3. Watch overhead clearance.
4. Report faulty truck performance.
5. Keep clear of edge of loading docks.
6. Use care when stacking high.
7. Operate at safe speed.
8. Go slow around corners.
9. Don't speed on rough floors.
10. Don't descend ramp with load in front.
11. Only authorized drivers should operate trucks.

Fire Safety

1. Keep away from open flames when refueling.
2. Don't block fire-fighting equipment from use by parking or storing material in front of it.
3. Don't stack material in front of fire doors.
4. In case of fire in building: first, call fire department; then drive your truck slowly and carefully outside. Don't abandon your truck unless you are personally endangered.

Yale & Towne Mfg. Co.

Fig. 15. Examples of handouts on safety.

Neatness	Do not stack material in aisles or roadways.
	Allow ample room for passageways.
	Properly align loads stacked one above the other.
	Clear obstacles from your working area.
	Report slippery conditions on ramps and platforms at once.
	Report leaky containers or broken packages to supervisor.
Efficiency	Space stacks closely to conserve space.
	Place quick-turnover material in most accessible locations.
	Store the loads in stacks when safe to do so.
	Suggest changes to improve storage procedures.
	Suggest changes to improve ways of handling materials.
Skill	Perform work with minimum maneuvering.
	Work safely in confined quarters.
	Center load on forks at first approach.
	Avoid jerking of machine that may topple loads.
Speed	The type of load determines speed.
	Condition of roadway determines speed.
	Never exceed speed of 6 mi. per hr.
	Proceed slowly when backing.
	Work as rapidly as conditions safely permit.

Fig. 16. Handout on operating responsibilities.

Trucks on battery charge with brakes not set may roll and damage charging machine.
Loads being carried can fall and be damaged.
Damage can occur when poorly stacked material topples over.
Trucks may crash into doors, windows, etc. with poor handling.
Weak floors may break under heavy machine.
Trucks parked with brakes not set may roll and hit something.
Boxcars and trucks with weak springs may be damaged by heavy weight of machine unless braced or jacked up.
Warehouse floors can be overloaded with material.
Overhead pipe, wires, etc. can be struck as load is elevated.
Explosions can result from operating in gaseous areas.
Collisions with other vehicles can occur.
Pushing loads that cannot be lifted may cause damage.

Fig. 17. Handout on damage to other equipment.

1. T _____ F _____ Racing the motor keeps it warmed up and is good for it.

2. T _____ F _____ Fork trucks should be operated at full speed in order to get the work done.

3. Yes_____ No_____ After filling the tank with gasoline, is it safe to start the motor immediately?

4. T _____ F _____ It is permissible to start, turn, or stop a fork truck abruptly.

5. T _____ F _____ When a truck is crossing railroad tracks, the wheel should be held firmly.

Underline the correct answer to each question.

6. If an operator cannot start his truck immediately, he should:
   a. Fix it himself.
   b. Call the mechanic.
   c. Report the trouble to his foreman.

7. If mechanical trouble develops, the operator should:
   a. Fix it himself.
   b. Keep on driving.
   c. Report the trouble to his foreman.

8. Forks on an empty parked truck must always be:
   a. Two in. from the floor.
   b. Four in. from the floor.
   c. On the floor.

9. Forks on a moving truck, whether it is empty or loaded, must always be:
   a. Two in. from the floor
   b. Four in. from the floor.
   c. Reasonably low to miss any floor obstruction.

10. Another person may ride the forks of a fork truck:
    a. If absolutely necessary.
    b. Absolutely in no case.
    c. If the operator approves.

11. Fork trucks may be driven with the forks elevated:
    a. If considered necessary.
    b. Never in any case.
    c. At any time.

12. Explain the procedure you would follow if you were to leave the seat of your fork truck.

    a. c.

    b. d.

Modern Materials Handling, vol. 9

Fig. 18. Example of a classroom session quiz.

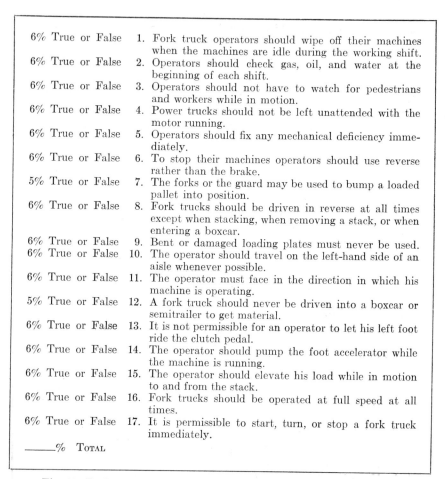

6% True or False	1. Fork truck operators should wipe off their machines when the machines are idle during the working shift.
6% True or False	2. Operators should check gas, oil, and water at the beginning of each shift.
6% True or False	3. Operators should not have to watch for pedestrians and workers while in motion.
6% True or False	4. Power trucks should not be left unattended with the motor running.
6% True or False	5. Operators should fix any mechanical deficiency immediately.
6% True or False	6. To stop their machines operators should use reverse rather than the brake.
5% True or False	7. The forks or the guard may be used to bump a loaded pallet into position.
6% True or False	8. Fork trucks should be driven in reverse at all times except when stacking, when removing a stack, or when entering a boxcar.
6% True or False	9. Bent or damaged loading plates must never be used.
6% True or False	10. The operator should travel on the left-hand side of an aisle whenever possible.
6% True or False	11. The operator must face in the direction in which his machine is operating.
5% True or False	12. A fork truck should never be driven into a boxcar or semitrailer to get material.
6% True or False	13. It is not permissible for an operator to let his left foot ride the clutch pedal.
6% True or False	14. The operator should pump the foot accelerator while the machine is running.
6% True or False	15. The operator should elevate his load while in motion to and from the stack.
6% True or False	16. Fork trucks should be operated at full speed at all times.
6% True or False	17. It is permissible to start, turn, or stop a fork truck immediately.
——% Total	

Fig. 19. Fork truck operator's questionnaire (true or false questions).

Name _____

Clock No. _____

Date _____

Scope _____

1. When entering an elevator should you drive in: ___ cab first? ___ load first?

2. Do you sound the horn when approaching pedestrians, doors, corners, exits, etc.? _____Yes _____No.

3. Do you avoid bumping into objects or materials? _____Yes _____No.

4. Do you report bad brakes or poor mechanical conditions of your truck to your foreman? _____Yes _____No.

5. Do you look in the direction of travel? _____Yes _____No.

6. Is it proper to carry a load several inches away from the mast? _____Yes _____No. Why?

7. Is it ever permissible to lift a load with the mast tilted slightly forward? _____Yes _____No.

8. While traveling, should the load be carried: _____high? _____low? Explain.

9. Should you ever push a load with the truck? _____Yes _____No.

10. Do you come to a complete stop before reversing direction of travel? _____Yes _____No.

11. Should the wheels of highway trucks and trailers be blocked and the brakes set when the truck is being loaded or unloaded? _____Yes _____No.

A   B

12. Which illustration shows the correct approach for a right-hand turn in close quarters? _____A _____B.

International Harvester Co.

Fig. 20. Test for power truck operators (continued on next page).

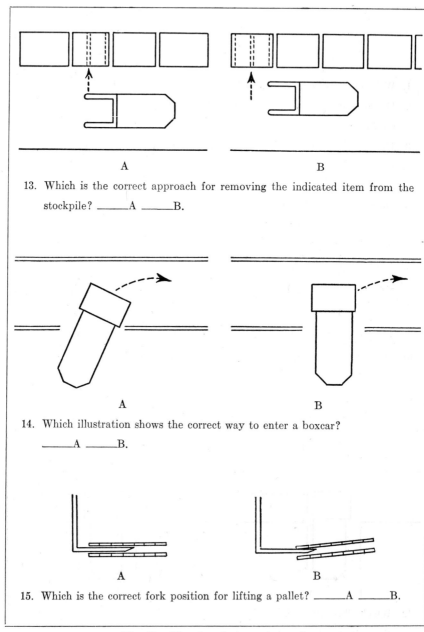

A B

13. Which is the correct approach for removing the indicated item from the stockpile? _____A _____B.

A B

14. Which illustration shows the correct way to enter a boxcar? _____A _____B.

A B

15. Which is the correct fork position for lifting a pallet? _____A _____B.

Fig. 20. (Continued on next page.)

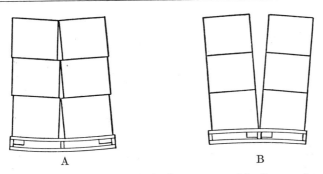

A   B

16. In which illustration are the forks in the correct position? _____A _____B.

17. The method shown here is the (correct, incorrect) way to pile bags on a pallet? Explain.

18. Are these drums loaded properly? _____Yes _____No.

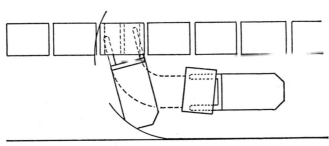

19. Is this operator correct in carrying this load at an angle?

_____Yes _____No.

A   B

20. Which is the safer way of stacking coils? _____A _____B. Why?

Fig. 20. (Concluded.)

Each classroom test is prepared directly from the content of the training guide lessons. Trick questions or statements are discouraged; only forthright questions which can be answered simply and which will form a sound background for class discussion should be asked. Fig. 21 illustrates a classroom test developed from Fig. 14.

TRAINING QUIZ

Approaching, Stacking, Backing Up, Stopping

Answer the statements below as directed by each statement. Be sure of your answers; keep your instruction and practice in mind as you answer each statement. Stop when asked to.

_____ 1. A skillful operator does not need to face the direction of travel; only a learner does. (T or F.)

_____ 2. If forks are not "all the way in" under a load, it is better to (a) stop and put them all the way in, (b) keep on going, because time is valuable. (Select best answer.)

_____ 3. If your first entry is not centered up, should you back up and get it centered whether it takes time or not? (Yes or No.)

_____ 4. The load is always tilted against the back rest before moving. (T or F.)

_____ 5. If you forget to lower the load before you start, you can always lower it safely while traveling. (T or F.)

_____ 6. If you can "make the incline" in high gear regardless of load, go ahead. (T or F.)

_____ 7. The load is started upward while you are approaching the stack (T or F.)

_____ 8. Before raising load (a) stop, (b) tilt uprights back, (c) avoid excessive tilt when stacking high, (d) use excessive engine speed to hurry lifting. (Select wrong answer.)

_____ 9. Is it so very important to shift to neutral and disengage clutch when raising or lowering loads? (Yes or No.)

_____10. List six "safety risks" in the lift truck operations outlined in the guide lesson for approaching, stacking, backing up, and stopping.

a. _____   d. _____

b. _____   e. _____

c. _____   f. _____

Score: Rights × 6⅔ = _____%

Lincoln Extension Institute, Inc.

Fig. 21. Simple classroom session training test (to accompany the training guide lesson, Fig. 14; used as a basis for discussion).

The obstacle course shown in Fig. 22 consists of pallets or boxes set on edge in a straight line with just sufficient space to permit passage of the truck. The trainee learns to zigzag through this maze in free, easy curves. The operator must be trained in the beginning to avoid sudden stops and turns.

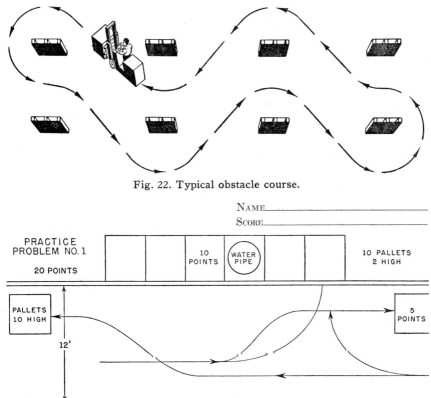

Fig. 22. Typical obstacle course.

International Harvester Co.

Fig. 23. A practice problem which includes description of the problem and method of scoring.

PROBLEM: Pick up pallets one at a time from stack and place two high next to wall. Pick up pallets two at a time from wall and place at opposite end of white lines from original stack.

Two-inch limit on spacing or straightness.
If both pallets line up together but are not square with line—1 point lost.
If first pallet is crooked and second lines up with line—2 points lost.
If first pallet lines up and second pallet is crooked—1 point lost.

One point penalized for each time operator moves pallet or changes direction to facilitate stacking pallets.

Tests to determine the extent of the truck driver's skill of operation are set up in the practice area. These are the obstacle courses and practice problems. They are tailored to represent the maneuvers that will need to be made in actual daily operations. Fig. 24 illustrates such tests.

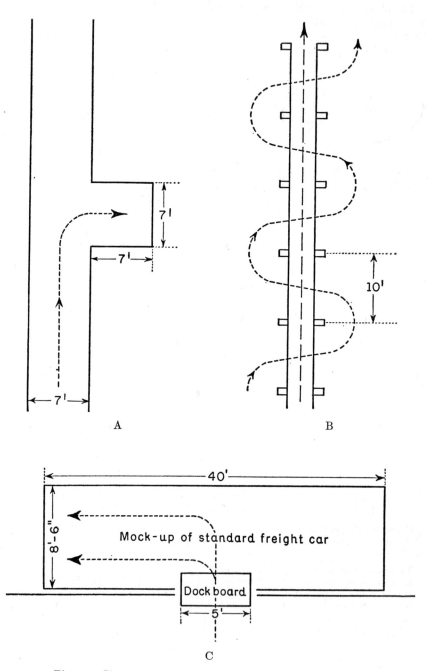

Fig. 24. Charts showing typical driving test requirements.

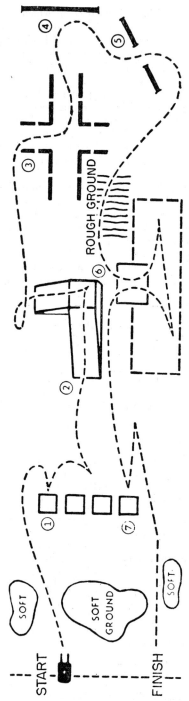

This practice problem will give the trainee an opportunity to show how well he has absorbed the rules of safe driving. He will encounter seven specific safety problems as he drives over this course. How he handles his truck in each case will demonstrate his knowledge of safety rules.

Fig. 25a. Safety practice problem.

Fig. 24a is a mock-up of an aisle with a space in which to place a pallet at right angles. The operator is required to drive into the aisle, place the load squarely in the space without touching the sides, and back out. Then he comes in at the other end and removes the load. Platform trucks use a 7-ft.-wide aisle; fork lift trucks use a narrower aisle, depending upon turning radius and over-all size.

In **Fig. 24b** the operator must first travel approximately 50 ft. between rows of objects (in this case, empty pallets) without striking them. Then he must drive backward and forward in a serpentine route around the objects.

Fig. 24c is a mock-up of a standard freight car. The fork lift truck operators are required to enter the area over a dock board and stack their loads at the ends of the car to simulate loading. Then they retrieve their loads to simulate unloading.

Testing in a training program for lift truck operators must include, in addition to the information covered here, tests in maintenance, put-away, ways of getting more work out of a truck, plant rules, safety rules, and other data which the company training objectives demand. All test results are shown to, and thoroughly discussed with, each operator in a personal interview, before the results are entered in the trainee's personnel record.

The Safe Driver Test is a logical follow-up or adjunct of the safety practice problem. The examples in Figs. 25 a and b show each in detail.

PERFORMANCE TEST FOR FORK LIFT OPERATOR
EXAMINER'S TEST SHEET

NAME OF TEST_____
ERROR SCORE_____
FINAL RATING_____

NAME_____ DATE_____

Operating Errors

___ 1. Started jerkily, overcautiously; unfamiliar with controls.
___ 2. Did not give proper signals when turning.
___ 3. Did not slow down at intersections.
___ 4. Did not sound horn at intersections.
___ 5. Did not obey signs.
___ 6. Did not look where he was going.
___ 7. Made too wide a turn on corners.
___ 8. Cut corners too sharply.
___ 9. Drove recklessly.
___10. Approached load improperly.
___11. Lifted load improperly.
___12. Maneuvered unnecessarily.
___13. Traveled with load too high.
___14. Lowered load too fast.
___15. Stopped too suddenly.
___16. Load not balanced properly.
___17. Forks not under load all the way.
___18. Struck pallet or floor with fork while loading.
___19. Failed to check bridge plates.
___20. Did not place load within marked area.
___21. Did not drive backward when required.
___22. Number of pallets displaced (or lines crossed).
___23. Number of unnecessary stops made.
___24. Did not follow instructions.
___25. Did not complete problem.

Yale & Towne Mfg. Co.

Fig. 25b. The safe driver test.

The obstacle course illustrated in Fig. 26a is a final performance test to measure the trainee's learning progress; normal operation time is 20 min. The test consists of running through the entire course three times, once (forward and backward) with each type of load shown in the right-hand figures. The instructor checks the operator's mistakes on a score card (Fig. 26b), totaling all deductions at the end of the third run.

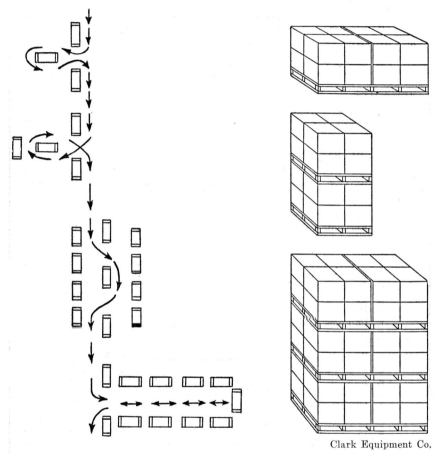

Clark Equipment Co.

Fig. 26a. Fork truck obstacle-course test layout.

A final written test (see Fig. 20) is given immediately after the obstacle course is completed. Such a test should be designed to determine the trainee's knowledge of proper operation procedures and safe practices in approaching, handling, and stacking loads.

An analysis of test results in addition to checking the trainee's learning also serves a vital purpose in measuring the effectiveness of the training program and of the instructional personnel. Instructors and those concerned with the planning and administration of the program should be apprised of the analysis of test results and should participate in its appraisal. This participation on their part, if carried on regularly, insures a dynamic program and an alert staff.

NAME:_____ DEPARTMENT:_____ EXPERIENCE:_____

TYPE OF TRUCK:_____

Test 1—10%
  Pallets displaced   Deduct
    a. Forward .... ( )   0.5_____
    b. Reverse .... ( )   0.5_____

Test 2—16%
    a. Pallets out of line........................... ( )   2.0_____
    b. Excess backing, etc. .... ( )   2.0_____

Test 3—14%
    a. Pallets displaced .... ( )   1.0_____
    b. Encounters difficulty .... ( )   4.0_____

Test 4—10%
  Pallets displaced
    a. Forward .... ( )   2.0_____
    b. Reverse .... ( )   2.0_____

Test 5—10%
    a. Pallets displaced .... ( )   2.0_____
    b. Encounters difficulty .... ( )   4.0_____

Test 6—20%
    a. Improper approach .... ( )   0.5_____
    b. Improper leaving .... ( )   0.5_____
    c. Quality of tiering .... ( )   10.0_____
    d. Cases lost .... ( )   2.0_____
    e. Improper approach for placing pallet........ ( )   2.0_____
    f. Improper direction to remove pallet.......... ( )   2.0_____

General Test 7—20%
    a. Poor starting technique..................... ( )   1.0_____
    b. Poor driving position .... ( )   1.0_____
    c. Rides clutch .... ( )   2.0_____
    d. Stalls engine .... ( )   1.0_____
    e. Clashes gears; reverses controls for brake.... ( )   2.0_____
    f. Races motor .... ( )   1.0_____
    g. Operation too—fast—slow .... ( )   4.0_____
    h. Careless operation .... ( )   4.0_____
    i. Inefficient operation .... ( )   4.0_____

Total deductions_____

Final grade_____

Below 65%   Not passing.
65– 75%   Fair.
75– 85%   Good.
85– 95%   Very good.
95–100%   Excellent.

Clark Equipment Co.

Fig. 26b. Score card for fork truck obstacle-course test.

A Typical Training Program for Lift Truck Operators

FITTING THE PROGRAM TO THE COMPANY'S NEEDS. The most effective and successful training program for lift truck operators for a company is one which is tailored to fit the particular company's needs, functions, objectives, and personnel. The "typical" training program presented in Fig. 27 is a composite of several successful programs embodying what are believed to be the best practices of each. The alterations necessary to fit it to any specific situation are left to the trainer or the executive having this responsibility.

In the planning phase of the training program for lift truck operators, it is advisable to keep the procedures **simple and easy to understand.** The most comprehensive training program may fail if the fact is overlooked that operators learn best when instruction and demonstration are simplified and logically presented. In addition, the training program must be conducted alternately in the classroom or lecture room and in the practice course or practice area, so that instruction can be followed by application. At the last classroom session, drivers' certificates and drivers' badges are given to successful trainees.

Such necessary training aids as discussion outlines, do's and don'ts sheets, handouts of plant rules, safety rules, tips to good operators, and union-manage-

Session	Content	Training Aids	Who
	CLASSROOM (C) AND PRACTICE AREA (P) SESSIONS		
1C	INTRODUCTION a. Discuss basis for training program. Cite examples with facts and figures. b. Discuss company objectives. c. Discuss personal benefits to operators. d. Explain fully how training is to be conducted. e. Hand out training guide lesson No. 1, safety check list No. 1. Proceed to practice area.	Opaque projector Photos, graphs, cost sheets Training program sheet Training guide Pretraining survey	Head of department, foreman, top-level executive, chief engineer, or training director
1P	BASIC APPRECIATIONS, INSTRUCTION PRACTICE a. Discuss principle of the lift truck, the unit load, various types in use. b. Give types, descriptions of pallet, skids. c. Explain basic operation of the lift truck; nomenclature; basic moves of starting, shifting, steering. d. Practice maneuvering with no load. e. Practice maneuvering with load. f. Run through practice problem No. 1. g. Run through obstacle course No. 1. Return to classroom.	Training guide (manual) Lift truck and operator Pallets, unitized loads Obstacle course No. 1 Practice problem No. 1	Trainer Skilled operator(s)

Fig. 27. **A typical training program for lift truck operators (continued on next page).**

Session	Content	Training Aids	Who
2C	INSTRUCTION QUIZZES a. Give quiz on practice area instruction and discuss answers. b. Give quiz on safety check list No. 1 and discuss answers. c. Discuss training guide lesson No. 2. d. Hand out safety check list No. 2. Proceed to practice area.	Training guide Opaque projector Film on safety Safety booklet	Trainer
2P	OPERATION PRACTICE a. Review briefly, if necessary, practice area session No. 1. b. Practice traveling with no load, traveling with load. c. Run through obstacle course No. 2 (close clearance with load). d. Perform practice problem No. 2. Return to classroom.	Lift trucks Obstacle course No. 2 Practice problem No. 2	Trainer Skilled operator
3C	INSTRUCTION, QUIZZES a. Give quiz on practice session, 2P; discuss answers. b. Give quiz on safety check list No. 2; discuss answers. c. Discuss training guide lesson, No. 3. d. Hand out safety check list No. 3. Proceed to practice area.	Opaque projector Charts Training guide Plant rules Do's and don'ts, etc.	Trainer Skilled operator
3P	OPERATION PRACTICE a. Review practice area session No. 2, if necessary; discuss answers. b. Practice loading, unloading. c. Run through obstacle course No. 3. d. Give practice problem No. 3. Return to classroom.	Opaque projector Charts Training guide	Trainer Skilled operator
4C	INSTRUCTION, QUIZZES a. Give quiz on practice session 3P, if necessary; discuss answers. b. Give quiz on safety check list No. 3; discuss answers. c. Discuss training guide lesson No. 4. d. Hand out safety check list No. 4. Proceed to practice area.	Opaque projector Film Booklets Plant handouts	Trainer Skilled operator
4P	OPERATION PRACTICE a. Review practice session 3P, if necessary; discuss answers. b. Practice approaching, stacking, backing up, stopping. c. Run through obstacle course No. 4.	Lift trucks Pallets, etc.	Trainer Skilled operator

Fig. 27. (Continued on next page.)

Session	Content	Training Aids	Who
	d. Give practice problem No. 4. Return to classroom.		
5C	INSTRUCTION, QUIZZES a. Give quiz on practice session 4P, if necessary; discuss answers. b. Give quiz on safety check list No. 4; discuss answers. c. Discuss training guide lesson No. 5 (final test on all lift truck operations). d. Hand out safety check list No. 5 (comprehensive coverage). Proceed to practice area.	Opaque projector Film Operating rules	Trainer Skilled operator
5P	OPERATION PRACTICE a. Make directions for test obstacle course clear. b. Run through test obstacle course No. 6. c. Take tally score sheet. Return to classroom.	Lift trucks Pallets, etc. Score sheets	Trainer Skilled operator
6C	INSTRUCTION, QUIZZES a. Discuss test obstacle course. b. Review and discuss score sheets individually. c. Discuss training guide lesson No. 6. d. Hand out safety check list No. 6. Proceed to practice area.	Opaque projector	Trainer Skilled operator
6P	OPERATION PRACTICE a. Instruct, discuss, demonstrate maintenance of lift truck. b. Fully discuss lift truck operator's total responsibility. c. Discuss, demonstrate records and forms to be used for lift truck. d. Discuss company matters as they relate to lift truck operators. Return to classroom.	Lift trucks Maintenance forms Models Forms, records	Trainer Skilled operator
7C	FINAL TEST—GRADUATION a. Give final test (brief) and discuss answers. b. Discuss any unanswered questions or refer to proper plant executive. c. Issue lift truck operators' handbook. d. Graduate trainees; confer "Authorized Operator" or "Skilled Operator" buttons and certificates.	Opaque projector Film on safety Union—management rules	Trainer Foreman Top executives

Fig. 27. (Concluded).

ment regulations must be developed to fit the program. Other useful aids are safety and stacking-pattern charts; illustrations of various lift truck attachments and their use; daily operations, inspection, and report forms; manuals or handbooks on the operation of lift trucks; and leaflets on the economies of an operator's job. All handouts, operating procedures, rules sheets, etc., should be standard in size so that the lift truck operator can keep them together in the form of a manual, which he can use for his own reference and retraining during his employment. Additional handouts issued after the original training program has been completed should likewise fit in the operator's manual.

Following Up Materials Handling Training

REASONS FOR FOLLOW-UP. Because training of lift truck operators is job-skill training, it might be thought of as training which requires little or no follow-up. Quite the contrary; a follow-up plan should be devised for (1) comparing new lift truck operation with pretraining operations, and (2) permitting close control of lift truck operations from day to day.

The Hawaiian Pineapple Company, Ltd., (Truck Driver Training Program) has a positive follow-up program. It states that the effectiveness of a training program may be ascertained through comparison and analysis of pretraining and posttraining data covering the following factors:

1. Promptness with which trouble calls are answered and completeness with which troubles are cleared up.
2. Number and nature of accidents adjusted.
3. Number and nature of operational disciplinary actions taken.
4. Reduction in cost of maintenance and repair of trucks.
5. Upward trend in general efficiency of machines repaired.

Follow-up training is pointed directly at the "weak spots" in the lift truck operation program. The training content and procedure used in the initial training program is utilized again to reinforce the prior instructon. While it is, in a sense, a review, it is effective.

Periodic driving re-examinations over obstacle courses and specially prepared problem courses must be planned. Drivers are graded or rated on each re-examination, and the results are discussed with them individually. Discussion sessions are held in which plant safety rules for accident prevention are fully explained. Photographs, charts, facts and figures, and other displays are shown during the training. The use of three-dimensional slides is very effective in showing how violations of safety rules result in accidents.

The "lift truck rodeo" is likewise a successful medium for training. The Connecticut Valley Materials Handling Society (Modern Materials Handling, vol. 8) has made use of it in truck-operation contests. Each driver contestant is given 6 min. to traverse a ten-obstacle course carrying a 4,000-lb. load of wet sand. Truck drivers are judged on (1) ability to stack loads, (2) gage distances, and (3) load freight, all scoring being based on factors of safety and skill. Worthwhile prizes are given to encourage the best effort from each contestant. The manner of staging the events and the methods for scoring are given in Figs. 28 and 29.

FORMS OF FOLLOW-UP TRAINING. Materials handling training of any kind is a repetitive undertaking. As long as human beings have the faculty for forgetting, training must be a continuing process. Training programs of the same kind, with the same trainees, are seldom repeated; but those who have been trained must be checked continually and additional training given whenever necessary.

Follow-up training may take one or more of several forms. In **job-related training** frequent performance testing on obstacle course or with laboratory layouts using full-scale materials handling equipment will quickly show up the need for, and type of, retraining necessary to maintain efficiency. **Observations of on-the-job performance** in materials handling installations reveal the level of operating practice as well as the efficiency of the operator, both of which factors will (1) determine the kind and extent of retraining needed and (2) affect the planning of future materials handling training.

Management training efficiency is determined from plant records, in which the materials handling performance of the trainee is directly incorporated. Continual checks on records of production costs, safety, quality, scrap, volume of flow, and personnel turnover, and frequent comparisons of performance serve as guides in the advisory, retraining, and future program-planning functions of the materials handling division. Follow-up training for management personnel can be accomplished by a few well-planned case-study discussions supplemented by adequate visual aids.

Economic training efficiency depends almost entirely on the story told by materials handling cost records. Costs of materials handling normally represent from 15 percent to 40 percent, or more, of production costs, depending on the kind of product, nature of materials, and methods of manufacture. The kind of manufacturing carried on and the relative cost of the materials used indicate the extent and, ordinarily, the method of retraining necessary.

Follow-up training itself differs from initial training only in emphasis and program length. The content of follow-up training depends mainly on the performance records made after the initial training is over. Follow-up is necessary and must be continuous, otherwise good training programs may lapse into insignificance performancewise, and the advantages obtained in the beginning will gradually be lost.

AVOIDING FAILURES IN THE TRAINING. There are numerous reasons why a materials handling training program may fail to attain its anticipated results. A badly selected group of trainees, lack of qualified prospects, an inefficient trainer, antiquated and inefficient equipment, an unsuitable meeting place, a poor season of the year—these are some of the most common causes of failure of a training program. Trainees who are "sold" on materials handling training and are kept interested by a capable leader do not cause program failure. Failures are usually the result of actions or omissions, or both, on the part of the training director, or a weakness in management policy in regard to the training function.

A management that fully believes in training may, by negligence, cause the training program to fail. Executives who appreciate the need, value, and possibilities of the program should take some active part in it. The man in charge of materials handling, if he is not functioning as the trainer, should at least help to launch the program and then should attend several subsequent training sessions and, if possible, become an active participant.

The following summary of the reasons why training programs sometimes fail is given primarily for its value as a check list during the period of program building. Many unforeseen factors, both technical and human, may crop up. Yet careful adherence to the constructive results of experience can ease the materials handling training program through hazards which otherwise might wreck the plans and defeat the purposes of the trainer who is developing his first course outlines.

1. Failure to appreciate the basic concept of training as an industrial and personnel function.
2. Failure to understand that industrial training is 'an art distinct from formal education.
3. Failure to develop a training program individually tailored to existing needs, both basic and auxiliary.
4. Failure to apply proper techniques of program building.
5. Belief that any man can be trained merely by telling him how to do what he should do.
6. Ignoring the trainee's social and technical needs.

EVENTS AND SPECIFICATIONS

1. **Preliminary Safety Check.** This is the driver's daily check of his equipment, such as horn, brakes, oil, water, and general check of the lifting and tilting mechanisms.

2. **Zigzag Maneuver.** Drive forward and backward through three pallets spaced 10 ft. apart in a row inside an 18-ft. aisle. To be done without touching the pallets.

3. **Pallet Pickup.** Travel along 12-ft. aisle and make a 90-deg. turn into rows of loaded pallets and pick up center of three pallets. Smoothness of operation throughout important, including one approach with forks centrally placed.

4. **Offset Pallet Drop.** Travel down aisle for 12 ft. and place pallet centrally in a 50 × 50 in. offset on one approach.

5. **Obstacle Course.** Balls on dixie cups are placed in two parallel rows 49 in. apart, five balls per row with each ball placed 4 ft. apart. Pallet load driven through obstacle with pallet 2 in. off ground. Stopping fork truck during run disqualifies contestant for this event.

6. **Rack Stacking.** Stack pallet on second tier of standard rack at the end of a 25-ft. run. Clearance is to be 3 in., and pallet is to be centered with one lift and one tilt.

7. **Pallet Stacking.** Stack pallet on second tier of loaded pallet at end of a 25-ft. run. Pallet to be centered with one lift and one tilt.

8. **Boxcar Maneuver.** This event simulates boxcar loading. Drive through 8-ft. door, make a left turn, and place pallet centrally within two rails 49 in. apart and within ½ in. from end rail. Overall distance from door edge to end of car to be 10 ft. The maneuver is to be performed with one approach and one drop.

9. **Offset Aisle Maneuver.** Drive through two parallel sets of pallets on end, each set being 6 ft. wide. The second set of pallets is 4 ft. from the first set and offset by 1 ft. This maneuver is to be performed without touching pallets while going through at a constant speed.

10. **Over-all Time.** The average time for all drivers in both classes (gasoline and electric) will be determined. Drivers completing the course in less time will receive up to ten points in bonus score; those taking more than average time will be penalized up to ten points on a graduated schedule.

Fig. 28. Fork truck rodeo specifications: events, how to score them, and individual events specifications (continued on next page).

HOW TO SCORE EVENTS

1. Preliminary Safety Check

   Possible Points

   a. Horn 3
   b. Brakes—backward and forward 3
   c. Oil, water, and gasoline check; battery connector check (electric). 2
   d. General check of tilt lift 1
   e. Check forks—positioned securely 1
   ___
   10

2. Zigzag Maneuver

   a. Two points for each pallet not touched........ 6
   b. Not touching side rail or end rail 2
   c. Smooth operation...... 2
   ___
   10

3. Pallet Pickup

   a. Centering of pallet forks 2
   b. One approach, one lift; tilt of forks........... 3
   c. Smoothness of operation; not hitting load.. 3
   d. General efficiency; not touching stacks at either side 2
   ___
   10

4. Offset Pallet Drop

   a. Maneuverability — one approach 3
   b. Centered load—within 1 in. sides and end...... 3
   c. Smoothness of operation (starting and stopping). 3
   d. General efficiency...... 1
   ___
   10

5. Obstacle Course—Balls on Dixie Cups

   Possible Points

   a. One point per ball standing 10

6. Rack Stacking

   a. One lift 3
   b. One tilt 3
   c. Centered pallet with 1½ in. each side....... 2
   d. General efficiency 2
   ___
   10

7. Pallet Stacking

   a. One lift 3
   b. One tilt 3
   c. Centered pallet—within 1½ in. each side........ 2
   d. General efficiency...... 2
   ___
   10

8. Boxcar Maneuver

   a. One approach.......... 3
   b. Within ½ in., three sides 3
   c. One drop 1
   d. Not touching pallets or side rails 2
   e. General efficiency 1
   ___
   10

9. Offset Aisle Maneuver

   a. One point for each pallet not touched. Lose two points for each pallet knocked over 4
   b. Constant speed 2
   c. One approach.......... 2
   d. General efficiency 2
   ___
   10

10. Over-all Time

    a. Time over or under average 10
    Plus or minus up to ten points.

Fig. 28. (Concluded.)

7. Ignoring the trainee's educational background.
8. Reluctance of management to finance fully an adequate materials handling training program.
9. Ignorance of or failure to appreciate and apply the psychology of learning to the training procedure.
10. Inability of trainees to put training into practice because of weaknesses in the teaching phase.

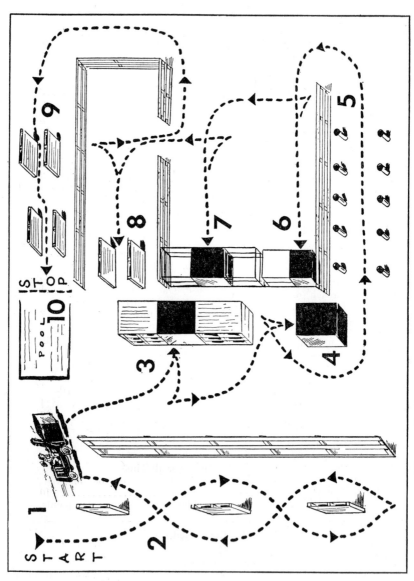

Fig. 29. Typical layout of a rodeo practice area, perspective view.

11. Belief that anyone in the plant who knows the job can do the training.
12. Failure to "sell" the training to trainees.
13. Poor selection of training methods. The media used are often the reason for failure.
14. Completely eliminating the need for trainees to contribute to the success of the program.
15. Failure by management to take an active part in the training program.
16. Failure to include basic materials handling fundamentals in the materials handling training program.
17. Failure to eliminate the "classroom atmosphere" carried over from formal education.

It is difficult to evaluate a training program to obtain a realistic measure of its success. Savings in materials handling costs, where they can be determined, constitute a valid criterion of success. All too often, however, management's conclusions, based upon inadequate data, are the criteria employed. More objective measures certainly should be sought through studies of actual plant operating records yielding comparative figures on production costs, accident reduction, quality improvement, shipping and receiving movement, personnel turnover, and other factors pertinent to the plant in question.

HANDLING BULK MATERIALS

CONTENTS

HANDLING BULK MATERIALS

Handling and Storage of Bulk Solids

FUNDAMENTAL FACTORS OF STORAGE. The storage of large quantities of material, which may amount to hundreds of thousands of tons, requires the most careful study of all facts so that in each case a proper choice can be made of the method and kind of storage best suited to the purpose and to the material. By describing and illustrating the purpose and general usefulness of many currently employed methods, an approach may be suggested which can lead to the solution of particular problems. Because of the complexities of most storage problems, a solution can be reached only through painstaking study. The solution may not lie in the mere adaptation of one method described but may be in the combination of several ideas derived from many sources.

Underlying Requirements. There is hardly a bulk solid which fulfills some important industrial need or serves some useful purpose that will not at one time or another go into storage, even though only temporarily, as part of a process step. Before the solution of a storage problem is attempted, underlying requirements must first be determined, together with the pertinent information related to the commodity itself which is under consideration. As an example:

1. What is the weight, size, and character of the material?
2. Is the material sticky or free flowing, wet or dry, hot, dusty, abrasive, corrosive, or combustible?
3. In what quantity should the material be stored?
4. Is the storage "standby" or reserve, or subject to frequent in-and-out turnover?
5. Is the supply seasonal while the demand is steady, or is the reverse true?
6. Will the commodity weather well when stored out of doors in open stockpiles, or will it deteriorate and consequently need to be stored under cover or placed in receptacles?
7. At what rate should the material be handled, both into and out of storage?
8. What is the source of the commodity to be stored?
9. Is the commodity produced within the plant, or is it received in railroad cars, trucks, or ships?

There are so many factors bearing on the solution of such a problem that no rule of thumb can be suggested. It may not even be practical to duplicate a method whereby a similar material will be stored under apparently identical conditions, because the proposed site, the nature of the ground, and the climate may differ radically from the area used as a pattern. Local regulations or ordinances may require changes. Quantity, in itself, may be a poor criterion in regard to method, because a large stockpile of material which is held in reserve for many years may not economically justify any investment for equipment either to store or reclaim the pile; whereas a small stockpile arrangement, which is subject to very frequent turnovers, and where work is to be accomplished at a substantially high hourly handling rate, may require a highly mechanized handling system for economical operation.

BINS. A bin is a large container or receptacle, used singly, in pairs, or in large groups, for holding any one of many bulk materials. It is the most versatile storage means at hand and may be built cylindrical or rectangular, or the shape may be modified for structural reasons or to favor or combat the behavior or the peculiar characteristics of a material. For sticky materials the bottom slopes may be made steeper, discharge openings may be enlarged, poke holes may be provided, and auxiliary helps, in the form of inside agitators or outside vibrators, may be installed. The auxiliaries may not only provide a measure of assistance but may, in fact, make it possible to carry on under otherwise impossible operating conditions.

Delivery of the material to a bin or bins may be by belt conveyor, bucket elevator, screw conveyor, or possibly by a combination of these kinds of handling equipment. Pneumatic conveyors are frequently used, especially for the finer and more pulverous materials. Many materials may be handled by continuous-volume elevating and conveying units, these being especially effective in making greatly simplified layouts, where one piece of equipment does the work of several units.

For the **recovery of the materials,** one of several well known kinds of feeders may be needed at the bin discharge opening, either to regulate the material flow or to provide an accurate volumetric or weight-determined feed. One such unit, the **apron feeder,** is suitable for use on coarse, abrasive, also hot, materials. The **belt feeder** serves many similar uses but is better suited to the less severe conditions. Both kinds provide a constant volumetric feed with practically no variations due to differences in moisture content or changes in the size of particles.

Reciprocating feeders and **electric vibrating feeders** are applicable over a wide range of materials and under varied conditions. They are reliable equipment, but they are more noticeably affected by variations in moisture and changes in the size of materials. **Screw feeders** and **vane feeders,** the latter also called star and pocket feeders, are used for fine, pulverous, and dusty materials and are usually part of a closed handling system, that is, one not open to the atmosphere. Weight-determining feeders or continuous-weighing feeders may be needed. The **horizontal rotary table feeder** is especially suited to the withdrawal of sticky materials, because the bin discharge outlet can be made large to avoid bridging and blocking, while a very small amount of material can be removed from the table by the adjustable plow blade. For any given blade setting, the volume of material removed is constant.

A study of the conditions in relation to the material under consideration will influence the choice of equipment and the procedures to be followed. The engineer, through his experience and specialized knowledge in dealing with material in a particular field, is best equipped to make the proper decision with respect to a given problem.

The names and purposes of bin installations may vary greatly. There are storage bins, surge bins, supply bins, bins for mixing or proportioning, and other bins to serve automatic weighing, bagging, or packaging operations. Bins are unquestionably the most commonly used, the most versatile, and the most important means of storage.

Bins, however useful, are not without some faults. Because they are frequently constructed to a considerable height in order to obtain sufficient capacity, there is a long fall of the material being stored, which is responsible for much breakage and degradation. Such falling is often a serious problem when handling carefully screened and sized materials, and the problem may be further aggravated if the commodity is of a friable nature. **Spiral chutes** or "ladders" are sometimes installed to lower the material and to reduce the direct fall. In many cases material removed from a bin must be rescreened before it is again acceptable for use.

Segregation of material particles is still another problem, and it is a condition that is propagated within bins. The cone-shaped pile which is formed inside every bin compartment has a natural tendency to classify granular materials with respect to particle size. The fine particles remain at the center of the cone, while the large particles travel toward the perimeter. When a bin of such segregated or classified material is emptied, the finer material will be withdrawn at first, especially when the center of the cone is directly over the centrally located bottom discharge gate. The downward mass movement will be in the relatively small vertical column of material directly over the gate opening, while the material which surrounds this downward moving column will remain relatively static. When enough material has been withdrawn through this central column to form a crater at the surface, the material will flow from the perimeter toward the center on its own flow surface and also move on down this central "pipe." When this point of the withdrawal operation is reached, a reclassification or reassembly of the different-size particles begins to take place. Special devices and methods have been proposed to lessen segregation within bins, but they have not always been successful. In an active bin, where, except for surges, the input and output are about equal, little segregation occurs, because the material merely moves down through the "pipe," with little disturbance in the mass itself.

BUNKERS. Individual attention should be given to a few important kinds of bin storage installations. Among these is the bunker, a large bin such as that used for the storage of coal in large electric-power plants.

Bunkers for coal storage are often many hundreds of feet in length, with only an occasional bulkhead, and will hold thousands of tons of coal, thus providing a boiler fuel supply for a full day or more. Many bunkers are of the catenary or suspended type, but other conventional designs are common. Coal may be received at the plant by means of a railroad-car dumper or from a coal storage pile and be transported by a belt-conveyor system to the point of delivery or distribution. The coal will be crushed and extraneous material and tramp iron removed. **Automatic trippers** which distribute and discharge the coal into the bunker may be provided with special floor-slot arrangements so that the escape of coal dust can be completely avoided if a small negative pressure is maintained in the bunker compartment. From the bunker the coal goes to the coal pulverizers and is blown into the combustion chamber of the boilers.

MIXING BINS. Elaborate conveyor systems handle coal from the railroad-track hopper or barge unloader to the storage pile and/or to the crushers and pulverizers and into the mixing bins at the coal carbonizing plants. For at least a part of the time during the handling process, the coal must be retained in the mixing bins. Several thousand tons of high- and low-volatility coal are temporarily stored in a succession of separate bin compartments, where large belt feeders, sometimes equipped with weighing devices, withdraw the coal in the desired proportion to formulize the coke-making mixture. The coke-making mixture is conveyed to large storage bins at the coke ovens, each of several thousand tons capacity, to provide a 16- or 24-hr. supply for the coke ovens.

STOCKHOUSE BINS. Such bins may be found at every blast-furnace plant. The so-called stockhouse is actually a number of somewhat conventional bins grouped in an elevated structure, over which railroad cars and transfer cars travel and into which they directly deposit various grades of iron ore and other commodities, such as fluxing stone, scrap metal, sinter, and coke. Special mechanical bin gates, operated from an electrically propelled scale car, work together, weighing out the batches or charges which are to be delivered to the blast furnace **skip hoist.** Several variations of this rather conventional stockhouse bin arrangement are in use. The railroad tracks may be replaced by a conveyor system for the distribution of coke, ore, and fluxing stone to the respective bin compartments.

ORE-POCKETS. The docks of the Lake Superior region which load iron ore aboard ship are still another unique arrangement of multiple bins. The ore pockets are high, massive bin structures more than 600 ft. in length, served by long approach trestles to permit trains of ore cars to drop the ore into the bins beneath. A multiplicity of discharge chutes on the water side of the ore pockets, spaced to correspond with the hatch spacing of the ore boats, make it possible to load a 15,000-ton cargo of ore in a matter of minutes.

SILOS. Another important storage facility is the silo. It is a tall, cylindrical structure, usually formed of reinforced concrete, built singly or in large clusters. Such silos, sometimes called tanks, are used to store enormous quantities of wheat, corn, and similar commodities in the large grain storage and flour milling centers. These installations are often served by special railroad car dumpers and are equipped with large-capacity conveyor systems, high-speed elevator legs with appropriate distributing conveyors above and collecting belts underneath the silos. Cleaning and milling plants, as well as oil-extraction plants, are usually important additions to these installations, which have a storage capacity of several million bushels. Plants built adjacent to waterways usually receive grain from barges or other vessels and reload it into bulk-cargo ships.

Another important use of the silo is in the bulk storage of Portland cement. Here, too, large groups of concrete silos are used to store the finished cement during the testing period as well as to effect some reasonable balance between a uniform daily production and the varying seasonal demands. Storage capacities range from about 200,000 bbl. to 500,000 bbl. Pneumatic conveyor systems are most frequently employed to elevate and distribute the cement to the cluster of silos, although elevators and screw conveyors, and the relatively new Airslide, are not uncommon.

The **Airslide** is a new kind of conveyor which successfully handles cement and many other pulverous materials. It has no moving mechanical parts and consists only of a 2-compartment enclosed metal trough placed on a downward slope of 5 to 20°. The division between the upper and lower compartment is a specially woven fabric which has a known porosity. Cement is fed to the upper compartment, while the lower compartment is supplied with a steady volume of low-pressure air. The air escapes through the fabric and into and through the layer of cement to fluidize this mass and cause it to flow down the slope in the upper trough compartment. The cement is recovered from the outlets at the bottom of the silos and conveyed pneumatically, by Airslide or other means, to the packhouse section of the storage plant. There the cement is automatically put into paper sacks by multiple-spout filling machines or loaded into railroad cars and trucks which are specially designed for this purpose.

To a lesser degree, silos are employed for bulk storage of cement at distribution centers and in areas of large consumption which lack the raw material for manufacture. Silos are also used in connection with the large centralized concrete mixing plants in metropolitan centers. Cement-plant operators are faced with the problem of storing large quantities of the basic raw materials used in cement manufacture, solid fuel, and cement clinker which is later ground into finished cement. The storage of these commodities, however, follows other conventional methods and is described later.

The **concrete silo** is not always of monolithic concrete construction. In many cases silos are assembled from precast concrete stave sections and are held together with outside steel reinforcing bands. Such silos, in individual units or in small groups, are in use throughout all industry for the storage of commonly used commodities, such as crushed stone, gravel, sand, coal, coke, ashes, salt, clay, and gypsum to mention only a few representative products.

SHEDS. Many commodities which must be stored under cover for one reason or another but which do not lend themselves to bin storage methods are frequently stored in buildings or sheds. Some of these materials may be classified as noncaving for all or for part of the time they are in storage, while others may be free-caving and even free-flowing for some of the time. Handling methods will vary for the different materials, especially with respect to the reclaiming process, as will be explained.

Sheds for the most part are tent-shaped structures, many with fan-shaped ends. They may be up to 300 ft. in width and about 1,000 ft. in length. The height of the sheds will vary with the width dimensions, but it is subject to some modification because of roof pitch. Sometimes the trussed frames are set on piers or foundations at grade level; at other times they are set on buttressed retaining walls. Retaining walls will add height and provide greater storage capacity for a shed of narrower width. Truss frames span the full width of the shed to provide a clear, unbroken storage area for the unhampered stockpiling of materials (Fig. 1).

The materials are almost invariably brought to the shed by a conveyor system. If the approach is from one end of the shed, the distributing means is usually an **inclined belt conveyor** which delivers to a horizontal distributing conveyor equipped with a self-propelled tripper. A reversible self-propelled **shuttle conveyor** can be used to good advantage where the delivery conveyor approaches the shed at right angles to, and at the midway point in, the length of the building. In either case, the distributing conveyor will be housed in the lantern, or monitor, at the ridge of the roof.

Storage sheds have one or sometimes two reclaiming conveyors which are housed and operated in a tunnel located just below the storage floor level. Frequently spaced feed openings are provided in the tunnel roof slabs, which are fitted with some well-known kind of conveyor-loading chute and make possible simple gravity reclamation of free-flowing materials. That part of the stored material mass which lies outside of the gravitational flow lines on each side of the tunnel can be moved toward the tunnel openings with a bulldozer, a power hoe, or a drag scraper.

The **more troublesome commodities**, which include those high in moisture content or those with an affinity for moisture, those with sticky, tacky, or cohesive characteristics, or any that are definitely in the noncaving classification during a part of their time in storage, are all in the group that require some extra or extraordinary means to effect their recovery. In many cases a **drag scraper** is the ideal means for attacking a stubborn pile, as a supplement to the reclaiming conveyor. For troublesome material the application and operation of a drag scraper differ greatly from its use with free-flowing materials. When used on a stubborn pile, the bucket is not worked along the toe of the pile but, with its tail sheaves mounted high, is effectively used for breaking down the pile as well as for moving the material toward the conveyor feed opening.

When handling free-flowing materials, a fairly regular volumetric flow can be expected with a well-designed tunnel belt-loading gate. **Mechanical feeders** are necessary when a constant volume is required, and even more so when the feed must

International Minerals and Chemical Co.

Fig. 1. Storage and curing shed showing rubber-tired scoop loaders used to reclaim material.

be accurately determined or when a sluggish material is being handled. The feeder may be of the belt or of the apron type. It may be made part of a feeder car that straddles the tunnel conveyor and can thus be moved about for withdrawing material from any one of the tunnel openings.

Tunnel conveyors are, on occasion, dispensed with altogether. Mobile equipment may be used to deliver material to a centralized receiving hopper equipped with a feeder, and a conveyor may carry the material from storage to the process plant or to cars for shipment. The **reclaimed material** may be caked or lumpy and must first be fed to scalping grizzlies or screens and then through disintegrators or lump crushers before it is again in suitable condition for conveyor transportation and further processing.

Rubber-tired or caterpillar-tread **tractors** equipped with scoop buckets (Fig. 1) are used to good advantage in reclaiming materials which have become consolidated during storage in a shed. Full-revolving crawler-mounted **electric shovels** are sometimes used in the more stubborn situations or for large-capacity operations. The rates at which the material must be recovered greatly influence the choice of the reclaiming unit.

Among the more important materials stored in sheds in large volume are bauxite ore, superphosphate, potash, gypsum, clays, salt, raw sugar, cottonseed, and cement clinker, but this is merely a representative list. A few large sheds have been built for the storage of grain, although this kind of grain storage is a departure from the conventional and more commonly used silo storage. Shed storage, when used for grain, is considered to lack many of the advantages and much of the flexibility of silo storage and may contribute to grain spoilage.

Cement plants almost universally use some form of shed for the storage of raw materials and for cement clinker. A belt conveyor may be used to deliver the different raw materials into storage, but drag conveyors and cranes are commonly used for handling clinker. The sheds are relatively narrow, with high vertical walls and, usually, traveling-crane runways below the roof truss level. Cranes that have clamshell bucket-equipped trolleys are able to cover the shed area fully and can distribute or recover material from any point and deliver it for use to any other point.

Storage sheds, in general, are admirably suited to the solution of many varied storage problems. They can combine the daily in-and-out requirement with the reserve storage requirements and also satisfy the need for cooling, curing, tempering, and the like. Obviously, such a handling system must be carefully planned to meet all the storage requirements and the other peculiarities of the material to be handled.

OPEN PILE STORAGE. Bulk solids are very frequently stowed in open storage piles. The number of materials so stored is not quite so great as in the case of other methods because some commodities cannot be placed in open storage. The variety of storage facilities available, however, and the numerous possible combinations and variations in types and methods of storage present an amazing number of opportunities for the solution of particular problems. Almost any method is applicable to several commodities, although some one method may be particularly well suited to the needs of a specific material.

When the use of an open storage pile is being considered, it is usually assumed that the broken bulk solid under consideration will weather satisfactorily, that it must be stored in large quantities, and that it must be stored and/or reclaimed at a substantial hourly capacity rate. All these conditions, however, are relative. A 5,000-ton stockpile may be too much material for one user, a 50,000-ton pile may be just about average for another, and a 500,000-ton pile may be hardly sufficient for still another. The same condition applies also to handling rates; they may be 100, 500, or possibly 2,000 tons per hr. These important factors influence the selection of the type and size of the plant to be constructed and the materials handling equipment to be installed.

CRAWLER CRANE. The crawler crane with a clamshell bucket is used universally for both stockpiling and reclaiming. Cranes can transfer the material directly from railroad cars or barges to open stockpiles as it is received, or they can transfer the material from a small surge pile, which may have been built up by a boom conveyor or a dump truck, to a large stockpile. Because of their extreme mobility, cranes very ably serve in restricted places and can stockpile and reclaim in odd-shaped areas poorly adapted to the use of some other, perhaps more elaborate, means.

While the crawler crane is so well able to solve both ends of the problem—that is, stocking and reclaiming—and to fill so many lesser requirements, it does not follow that it is limited in usefulness to smaller open storage needs. Many large operations depend on crawler cranes equipped with 3- to 5-cu.-yd. buckets and use them in combination with very elaborate conveyor arrangements.

SCRAPERS AND BULLDOZERS. The practice of building open storage piles with mobile earth-moving equipment and reclaiming by the same means is becoming more common. This is particularly the case with materials that are not harmed by degradation from tires and crawler tracks and which can be efficiently stockpiled by mobile equipment. Enormous reserve storage piles of bituminous coal have been laid down by means of load-carrying scraper units and rubber-tired dozers at many modern electric generating plants, at steel plants, cement plants, and other large fuel-consuming plants.

Scrapers are self-loading vehicles and are thus able to pick up loads from small initial piles specially formed for this purpose. In modern coal-handling systems there are strategically placed loading bins equipped with quick-acting power-operated gates that enable the scraper units to receive a full load of 15 tons or more of coal in less than a minute. The load is automatically dumped while the scraper is in motion and the coal is actually spread in layers about 6 in. thick.

Degradation is often a serious problem, but it is of no consequence in storing coal which is to be subjected to crushing and pulverizing for use as powdered boiler fuel or as the pulverized carbonizing charge in cooking ovens. On the contrary, some very worthwhile advantages are obtained by the scraper-layering method of building stockpiles. The large rubber tires, under the weight of the heavily loaded scraper units while hauling and spreading, will compact the coal by as much as 25 percent of its original loose or broken volume, consequently making it possible to store greater quantities in a given space. More significantly, the layering and spreading largely **overcome segregation** and **eliminate voids** in the mass; this, combined with the high degree of compaction, diminishes oxidation to a point where the hazards of spontaneous combustion are practically eliminated.

The danger of **spontaneous fires** in coal storage piles cannot be ignored. Tests and experiments lead to the conclusion that the hazard of self-generated fires can be lessened in two ways. In one way coal is thoroughly compacted in the pile, thus reducing the voids and "squeezing" out the air which is so essential to the oxidation process. Oxidation, although slow, may in time cause a pile to catch fire. In the other way, which is not suited to the scraper-layering storage method, the coal must be thoroughly screened to eliminate all fine coal particles. The fine particles are currently consumed and the coarse or lumpy screened coal is then carefully stockpiled with conveyor and gantry bridges to form, in effect, a **ventilated pile.** In a pile of screened coal with a relatively high percentage of voids, the heat created by the oxidation will be carried off. Scraper-layered, compacted coal piles are effective in preventing fires if the layering and compacting is properly done. The ventilation method, which is less frequently used, is more costly, although storage piles of a quarter million tons are in existence.

Scrapers very ably reclaim material from stockpiles, but in this work they must frequently receive assistance from bulldozers until they have gathered a full load, especially when reclaiming coal from a compacted pile. The loaded scraper will travel at high speed to the plant and there deliver the coal to a below-ground receiving hopper. The hopper may be provided especially to serve the scrapers, or the railroad-car hopper, in which the coal was originally received, may be used to empty the scraper. In either case, the hopper is provided with a coarse grating designed to support the loaded scraper and on which the unit can quickly discharge itself during a brief stop.

The number of mobile units needed for a specific job can be determined from the unit capacity of the size of scrapers selected, their speed characteristics, the haulage distance, and the quantity of material that must be either taken to or returned from storage during a given period of time. Piles can be built to about the same average height with scraper units as with other means.

A variation of the highly mobile load-carrying, self-powered scraper operation is that wherein only **bulldozers** are used. The difference in choice of equipment is largely one of economics, indicated by the size of the operation. Bulldozers are usually used for moving a small quantity of material over a short distance. Bulldozers are also used to supplement or augment the scraper operation, to push-load the units when reclaiming them from compacted piles (as already referred to), to spread the material, or directly to reclaim material in close proximity to a receiving hopper.

DRAG SCRAPER. The mechanically powered drag scraper is another means for stockpiling and reclaiming broken bulk solids. A **scraper system** is comprised of an electric double-drum haulage engine from which cables lead to sheave blocks on a headpost or mast and around a sheave block on the tailpost some distance away, and a crescent-shaped scraper bucket which is spliced into one of the cables. Material for storage is usually delivered by a conveyor to an initial pile in front of the headpost, where the scraper bucket, which is self-loading, picks up its load and moves it toward the tailpost. The bucket works along radial lines to spread the material gradually in a fan-shaped pile. Various tailpost arrangements are in use. Some require periodic manual relocation as the pile is fanned out. The larger, fully mechanized installations have remotely controlled, movable towers which operate on a radial track at the perimeter of the pile. The height of the tail sheave on the tail tower will, in general, control the height of the storage pile.

The **scraper bucket** is completely turned about in the cable and operated in the reverse direction for the purpose of reclaiming material. The bucket returns the material close to the headpost, where a receiving hopper is ordinarily located and which, as part of a conveyor system, transports the material to the plant.

Drag-scraper storage piles are not necessarily pie-shaped. Many odd-shaped areas, as well as rectangular or parallel areas, can be worked. The conveyor which delivers to the storage system and the conveyor receiving the reclaimed material must be located in such positions as to suit the available storage site most advantageously. Scraper buckets and their related hoist engines are built in many sizes for a wide range of hourly handling rates and ground storage capacities.

CONVEYORS. Conveyor stockpiling and reclaiming systems, which have as their basic elements (1) a conveyor for stocking out and distributing and (2) a tunnel conveyor for the gravity recovery of the material, are numerous and are built in several distinct styles and in many variations.

Open storage piles, which are centered or built around conveyor operations, are frequently a related or an integrated part of the entire processing-plant function. Some large iron-mining operations have such storage piles as do the large limestone plants which produce many sizes of chemical and fluxing stone in large volumes, as well as large commercial crushed-stone and gravel plants which produce a variety of sizes for concrete aggregates.

A comparison of two quite similar plants will serve to explain the open pile conveyor storage in principle and at the same time illustrate essential differences in the design of the storage facilities and differences in the choice of equipment.

The two plants under discussion are alike in many respects. Both produce high-grade, high-calcium limestone for chemical and metallurgical purposes in essentially the same number of product sizes and in about the same size range. In both instances almost the entire plant production is loaded into large lake vessels of 10,000- to 20,000-ton capacity, mostly of the self-unloading type, for shipment to the lower Great Lakes ports, where the stone is consumed in steel plants, alkali plants, carbide plants, cement plants, and other industries. Bulk-cargo steamers

Michigan Limestone Div., United States Steel Corp.

Fig. 2. Limestone crushing, screening, storage, and shiploading plant with overhead conveyor system.

operate on somewhat irregular schedules; in consequence, their arrival may occur at any hour of the day or night, so each plant must be ready at all times to provide a full cargo of any size commodity. Smooth and continuous operation of these large plants is absolutely essential, especially so for a production rate of 2,000 to 4,000 tons per hr. These requirements demand that a storage space in which the equivalent of a cargo or more can be accumulated must always be ready and waiting for each and every size of material. Invariably, only full cargoes of any one size are loaded. Alike as these two plants appear in function and purpose, notable differences exist, in their storage systems.

In one plant, each size, as it is produced, is carried off by its own belt conveyor to a storage pile (Fig. 2). The **distributing conveyors** are located overhead and are housed in conveyor truss structures, which are supported above the storage piles by steel arches or A-frames. The overhead conveyors are equipped with self-propelled trippers to distribute the stone throughout the length of each storage pile. Each conveyor is designed to handle its proportional part of the full hourly plant capacity.

A concrete tunnel and tunnel conveyor are located under each pile. Recovery of the stone is by gravity through gate openings in the roof of the tunnel. Specifically designed conveyor loading gates and/or mechanical feeders are used to regulate the material flow to the tunnel conveyors. They deliver the material to other conveyors, which transport the stone to the elevated ship-loading belts, which in turn discharge the stone into the ship's cargo hold.

The other plant, in contrast, is marked by the absence of all overhead conveyor truss structures and A-frames over the stockpiles (Fig. 3). Instead, each distributing conveyor line is at ground level and parallel to its respective storage pile. The distributing belt is served by a traveling boom conveyor stacker which deposits the product into its respective pile.

Inland Lime and Stone Co.

Fig. 3. Limestone crushing, screening, storage, and shiploading plant employing stacker system.

The **gravity flow recovery** to the tunnel conveyors is the same in principle, differing only in arrangement. All tunnel conveyors are linked to the conveyor system which delivers the stone to the ship-loader, which has a combination shuttling and luffing boom. The relative merits of the two systems—the overhead conveyor system and the stacker distributing system—as exemplified by the two plants described, will be discussed later.

These two representative, yet different, open storage systems have their counterparts elsewhere, although not without variations. A similar large limestone plant, of recent construction, uses the traveling stacker but features luffing boom conveyors for stockpiling each of the many sizes. It also features a ship-loader designed to travel the length of the dock instead of remaining in the usual fixed location. This newer plant has the striking loading-out rate of about 4,500 tons per hr., but the ship-loading time is further shortened because the ship itself remains in one position while the traveling ship-loader quickly moves from one to another hatch opening during the loading operation. In other installations, with fixed ship-loaders, the ship is obliged to move back and forth along the dock with the aid of its own lines.

Trunk-Line Stocking-out Conveyor and Traveling Gantry Bridge. Among the newest iron-ore storage plants—and perhaps the largest—is one located in Venezuela. The system is a combination of a trunk-line stocking-out conveyor associated with a traveling gantry bridge. The bridge itself carries the cross-pile distributing tripper conveyor, which builds up a pile of great width. Two parallel tunnel reclaiming conveyors are used to recover by gravity a large portion of the ore in storage, for a combined loading- out rate of 6,000 tons per hr. Here, too, a traveling ship-loader, equipped with a shuttling and luffing boom, not only lowers the material into the ship but also compensates for the difference between the light and loaded ship and for the differences in water level caused by tidal and flood variations.

In another variation of the open storage pile put down by belt conveyor which is common to the design of many smaller plants, the overhead tripper conveyor and truss structure are carried on **steel towers** standing in the pile of material. In still another and more desirable variation, the tripper conveyor structure is supported on **concrete pylons or piers.** These latter arrangements are usually chosen for reasons of economy. When the supports for the overhead truss structures are permitted to become buried in the material itself, the steel towers usually incur considerable damage, but whether steel towers or concrete piers are used, the supports in the piles of themselves interfere with and restrict the gravity flow recovery of the material.

The practice of placing structural steel supporting towers in the pile of material is one that should be avoided, unless the towers or bents can be located at the ends of the piles, or between adjacent piles, where no material is reclaimed and where the material in the pile will always remain static. Where towers are set in active piles, column bents will become twisted, and cross-braces will be torn from their gusset plates by the flowing, shifting action of material.

A single distributing conveyor line carried on pylons or piers is often used to form two adjacent stock piles. This arrangement will locate the conveyor-supporting tower structure outside of the active portion of the storage pile. It calls for the use of an open-truss span, with the conveyor and its traveling tripper carried on top. The tripper is special in so far as instead of having the usual discharge chute, which merely drops the material directly underneath, the tripper is provided with a pair of wing conveyors, which discharge the material at some distance to each side of the distributing belt. This style of tripper is often referred to as an airplane tripper. It is actually a form of boom conveyor stacker and was, in fact, a forerunner by many years of the now popular boom stacker.

STACKERS. The stacker in combination with distributing conveyors is today one of the most useful and most frequently installed stockpiling means. The large limestone plant described earlier makes use of a number of stackers for handling each one of several sizes of the material. That the principle is not at all new is evident from the fact that one plant which uses the combination was constructed about 1935.

Stackers can be very versatile in application. They are constructed as **single-boom stackers** or **double-boom stackers.** The boom may be held at a fixed angle, or it may be hinged and of the luffing type. **Luffing booms** are preferred because of their more gentle handling of materials that have been prepared, screened, or sized, or are friable in nature. In the stocking-out operation the boom is lowered to the remainder of the existing pile, to reduce as greatly as possible the drop of the material from the end of the boom to the pile. As the pile grows, the boom is raised, a little at a time; and after the pile is again at its full height, the stacker is advanced only a few feet at a time, so the material can roll down on its own slope, thus avoiding both degradation and, particularly, the shattering that occurs with the free fall from high overhead belts.

Barber-Greene Co.

Fig. 4. Aggregate plant with radial conveyor stackers.

The luffing boom has another advantage when handling dusty or fine material. It is then important that the discharge end of the luffing boom be kept within inches of the crest of the pile and that it be raised only a very little at one time to avoid any fall whatsoever, thus keeping down dust and avoiding wind losses of the material.

Fixed and luffing boom stackers, which are mounted on turntables and constructed to revolve, are not uncommon. Such revolving stackers will turn through an arc greater than 180° and have conveyor booms up to 150 ft. in length. A stacker of this design can build two piles, one on each side of the distributing conveyor, and the boom can also be used in spreading and trimming the piles.

A **distributing conveyor** and a **traveling boom stacker** form an economical combination for the handling of bulk materials. Only the simplest kind of steel supports are needed to carry the belt conveyor along the pile, close to ground level. Such simple conveyor supports are far less costly than high overhead conveyor truss spans and their high steel arches or A frames. Stackers are more costly than small simple trippers, but the great difference is in the cost of steel structures, which tips the balance in favor of the stacker method.

The overhead tripper conveyor drops the material vertically for a great distance, but this condition is practically eliminated with the boom stacker. **Free fall** may be a matter of grave concern where avoidance of degradation or breakage of the material is an important consideration. Either plan will otherwise provide an unobstructed storage area, and in this respect the two methods are on a parity.

In addition to the revolving stacker, which is a boom that is turntable mounted, there are other types which are properly called **radial conveyor stackers.** The latter types are usually constructed in the form of an inclined conveyor truss, pivoted at the tail-end loading point with intermediate supporting legs, which are provided with powered trucks or journaled wheel outfits and thus move around a radial track (Fig. 4). This form of stacker is especially useful in the smaller plants producing crushed stone or sand and gravel for concrete aggregates, because light standardized structural units of this kind, complete with machinery, are readily available in several sizes and provide storage at low cost. However, large-capacity, specially designed, and otherwise substantial installations of this kind have also been made. Such installations are useful for handling a variety of broken bulk solids. A variation of this type is also in wide use for the storage of pulpwood logs.

TUNNELS. Stockpiles formed by any one of the several variations of the distributing conveyor, as described in the foregoing paragraphs, are invariably combined with a tunnel for gravity recovery of the material.

An ordinary tent-shaped pile, with a longitudinal tunnel at grade, will yield less than one-half its volume to gravity recovery. The material which lies outside of the gravity flow lines is "dead" storage and in most cases is permanently nonrecoverable, although in other cases a part or all of the dead storage can be turned into reserve storage through the use of bulldozers which push the material to within the flow range of the reclaiming tunnel.

A **cut-and-fill arrangement** can be employed when an all "live" or recoverable storage is essential. The tunnel excavation is then made at a considerably lower depth, below grade. The sides of the excavation above the tunnel roof line are flared at an angle which is a little less than that on which the material will flow on itself. The excavated material is piled on each side to conform to the side slopes of the excavation. The effect is to have one tent-shaped pile on top of an inverted tent-shaped pile which is over the reclaiming tunnel.

Tunnel gate openings are seldom spaced according to any hard and fast rule; they are generally about 16 ft. on centers, often much less, sometimes more. By elaborate calculation it can be shown that the net loss of recoverable material constitutes a very small percentage if gates are spaced farther apart, say 25 ft. or even more. But a practical point to consider is that the material will very often arch in the pile; and when this arching occurs, the material ceases to flow through the opening. If the nearest gate on one or the other side is opened, withdrawal from that point may quickly collapse the arch that had formed, and the mass will again flow freely. This treatment is less effective with large spaces between gates; furthermore, an increase in the distance between gates increases the lost-time element. In this matter the tendency is to follow good practice as determined by experience.

Some very excellent conveyor-belt-loading gates have been devised for tunnel conveyors. Some are raised and lowered with small hand winches, while others are of a counterbalanced design for easy manual operation. Such gates will load the belt with a well-formed load cross section, while the **troughed tunnel belt,** in that case, acts as its own feeder. The belt can be stopped and restarted while the gate remains open, without overflow at the loading point or disturbance in the load or volume. High-capacity tunnel belts, which handle material at the rate of 3,000 to 4,000 tons per hr., use mechanical feeders to control the volume going to the belt. The feeders, part of a traveling car, have powered operating mechanisms for opening and closing the tunnel-roof gates.

Reinforced concrete box-section tunnels are most commonly used. Non-reinforced gravity arch tunnels are of less common occurrence. The economical parabolic concrete arch section should not be ignored, especially for tunnels of sufficient length to justify the use of slip forms. In some instances tunnels have been built of large-diameter sewer pipes or culvert sections. Such tunnels are less costly but have the disadvantage of an unsymmetrical arrangement and provide only a one-sided, cramped conveyor attendance aisle. The **parabolic steel-arch tunnel,** built with preformed steel plate sections and obtainable from commercial sources, is coming into favor. Installed on a simple concrete slab, it is a vast improvement over other so-called prefabricated tunnel sections, and it offers practically every advantage of the formed concrete tunnel at a great saving in first cost.

GANTRY BRIDGES. Literally hundreds of gantry bridges are in use for both stocking and reclaiming bulk solids. There is perhaps no other single equipment unit that is capable of performing so many varied handling functions as the gantry bridge, and it is unquestionably the work horse of the stockpile in the steel industry. The greater part of the prodigious quantity of iron ore which each year is moved by the Great Lakes ore-carrying fleet, which in recent years has amounted to more than 95 million tons annually, is being handled by gantry bridges on the ore docks, first from the ore boat to the stockpile and then from the stockpile to the blast furnace.

Gantry bridges are large movable structures and are of either the man-trolley or rope-trolley type. In the **man-trolley type** the operator's cab is part of the self-propelled, electric-motored trolley, which also carries the bucket and its 2-drum hoist engines. A man travels with the trolley and bucket and is always over the point where the work is being done. In the **rope-trolley version** the operator and cab are in a fixed location at one end of the bridge. From this fixed point, all movements of the rope-propelled trolley itself and the bucket-operating functions are remotely controlled electrically and operated, through an ingenious rope-reeving system, from the trolleying hoist and the opening- and holding-drum hoist, which are located in a fixed machinery house (Fig. 5).

The span of gantry bridges varies greatly. Some have cantilever ends and/or hinged aprons. Capacities are based on a number of factors and cannot be expressed in the form of simple statements. Both the man-trolley and the rope-trolley types operate at high speed and are extremely maneuverable, although for large-capacity operations the man-trolley design is favored.

The numerous gantry bridges in use on the iron-ore and limestone-storage docks at the large steel plants and on the large ore- or coal-transfer docks are frequently of the direct-unloading type. Cantilever and/or hinged aprons reach far beyond the water's-edge of the dock and directly unload the ship. The bucket digs the material out of the ship's hold and deposits it on the dock.

When the dock, the storage pile, and blast furnace are appropriately arranged, the bridge will also handle the ore and stone from the storage pile and deliver it directly to the blast-furnace stockhouse bins. More often, the bridge bucket will deliver into an ore transfer car, which can quickly travel the length of the stockhouse and thus serve all bins, regardless of the location of the bridge or bridges.

Mead-Morrison Div., McKiernan-Terry Corp.

Fig. 5. Direct-unloading rope-trolley bridge in 300,000-ton storage area.

Steel plants which depend on the Great Lakes supply of water-borne iron ore and flux stone must provide a materials stockpile to carry them over the four winter months when the ships cannot operate. Stockpiles may be several hundred feet in width, many thousand feet in length, and built to 70 ft. or so in height, holding several million tons. Docks of such proportion and importance are served by several of these movable bridge structures.

Frequently the gantry bridge will perform only the stockpiling and reclaiming function. Separate ship-unloading towers, either of the **man-trolley** or the **Hulett unloader type,** are then provided for the ship-unloading operation.

MAN-TROLLEY UNLOADERS. The man-trolley-type unloaders have an electric trolley with a bucket like that used on the gantry bridge. The unloaders are movable tower structures which travel along the dock front and have a cantilever truss or hinged apron that reaches out over the ship in which the trolley and bucket operate. The bucket removes the material from the ship's hold and carries it back only a short distance to form an initial or cushion pile, usually in a concrete trough built for this purpose. The gantry bridge is used only to transfer the material from the cushion pile in the trough to the main storage pile and later for reclaiming the material.

HULETT UNLOADERS. The Hulett unloader is a movable structure operating along the dock front, on which a counterbalanced pantograph-like superstructure on a carriage moves back and forth, perpendicular to the ship itself. A clamshell bucket is located and functions at the lower end of the vertical leg of the pantograph at ship's side, the inner space of which leg also becomes a part of the operator's cubicle. The bucket opening and closing operations, the raising and lowering of the bucket and the leg, and the movement of the

Wellman Engineering Co.

Fig. 6. Wellman-Hulett type 17-ton ore unloaders.

entire pantograph carriage are all controlled by the operator in the vertical leg cubicle. The bucket is made to open as soon as it has moved within the tower structure, where the load discharged by the bucket is received by a shuttle car. The shuttle car is synchronized to move and dump its load into the cushion pile of the trough during the time the pantograph carriage with the bucket obtains another load (Fig. 6).

Many docks have railroad tracks along the waterfront for rail transfer of bulk commodities unloaded from vessels, either as part of direct transfer operations or after the material has been recovered from storage. The newest and perhaps the most versatile steel plant dock has the combination of two man-trolley unloading towers and a man-trolley gantry bridge, and as an added feature has a long trunk-line belt conveyor equipped with a luffing boom stacker which runs the length of the storage yard. The trunk-line belt conveyor makes it unnecessary to have a costly boat slip and concrete dock for the full length of the storage yard, because the unloading towers operating in the short slip can, by means of the belt conveyor and stacker, deliver material anywhere into the cushion pile trough. The gantry bridge, in the conventional manner, transfers material from the trough to the storage yard. A rotary car dumper is linked to the belt-conveyor system to provide an auxiliary and emergency means for receiving raw materials from railroad cars.

The specific needs of storage plants differ greatly. Some stockpiles handle the same commodity over and over, year after year, while others may store different materials or different grades of these materials from time to time. In the one case, the cleanup of a pile, even occasionally, is quite unnecessary, while in the other case, a thorough cleanup of the storage pile may frequently be necessary. The clamshell bucket and the gantry bridge are especially well adapted to the complete recovery of the material from every square foot of the storage area. Where changes in commodities and changes in grade or size must be considered, as well as periodic cleanups, the bridge is unchallenged as the most versatile means of handling, stockpiling, and reclaiming raw materials in the storage yards at the large steel and industrial plants.

The foregoing description briefly relates how vast quantities of water-borne materials, transported by bulk freighters, are unloaded and stockpiled by gantry bridges. Not all bulk freighters, however, need the assistance of bridges and unloaders, because many are of the self-unloading type and can discharge themselves. During this self-discharging operation they are able to build large storage piles with their boom conveyors without the aid of any shore equipment.

For the greater part, these self-unloading vessels have a capacity of 10,000 or 12,000 tons, although a few will carry up to 20,000 tons. They have unloading rates of about 2,000 tons per hr.; however, one of the newest of such ships will unload itself at the phenomenal rate of 5,500 tons per hr.

In modern vessels of this kind, the cargo hold is hoppered and has many closely spaced openings which have special mechanically operated conveyor gates. Two parallel hold conveyors withdraw the material in a continuous stream and deliver it to a large inclined bucket conveyor which elevates the material above deck and discharges to a boom conveyor. The boom conveyor is able to swing either to port or starboard of the ship, and it can be raised to form a pile on the dock some 70 ft. in height.

Large-capacity storage piles of coal, limestone, and other materials are in this manner formed directly and quickly by the boom of these self-unloading ships. Some piles are placed over tunnel conveyors on the dock, some under gantry bridges, and others are expanded to greater proportions with powered scrapers or mobile equipment. The self-unloading vessel has become another useful means of stockpiling bulk solids in many plants along the waterfront of the Great Lakes.

SPECIAL STOCKPILING SYSTEMS. The following systems are unique in their effectiveness in stockpiling and in their ability to recover all the material from storage by fully mechanical means. They start with a long, centrally placed **stocking-out conveyor,** usually several hundred feet in length, which obtains a regulated load at the initial receiving hopper. A **revolving stacker** with a 150-ft. luffing boom conveyor is associated with the stocking-out conveyor, which will stockpile material on each side. When the boom is at right angles and at full reach to the trunk-line stocking-out belt, a tent-shaped pile is put down, with its crest nearly 150 ft. distant. The space between this remotely placed pile and the trunk-line conveyor is then filled in, to the full height, by the radial boom. Piles of the same or of different materials can be put down on both sides of the central stocking-out conveyor.

Recovery is by means of a reclaiming machine comprised of a low traveling bridge which spans the width of the pile and on which a belt conveyor and a digging-type elevator are carried. The digging elevator, mounted on a motor-driven carriage, operates on top of the bridge span over the width of the pile. In reclaiming, the elevator picks up or digs the material at the toe of the pile and places it on the bridge conveyor, which in turn delivers it to the trunk conveyor—then operating in a reverse direction—for delivery to the processing plant.

The bridge can move in either direction, and since the digging elevator thereon can be revolved 180°, the material can be reclaimed from either side of the low conveyor bridge and in either direction. The system is sequence interlocked and protected electrically for fully mechanized in-and-out handling and provides an efficient method for the full and complete recovery of all stockpiled material from the storage area.

The second of the two special storage methods to be described here is another, but quite different, **fully mechanized in-and-out storage system.** It will not only completely recover all material from storage but will also reclaim the material and deliver it to the process plant in an uninterrupted flow and at a remarkably uniform rate per hour.

Several variations of the system have been built. In the earlier plants an overhead tripper conveyor placed the material in the lengthwise piles, one conveyor operating over each pile. In later plants the overhead truss has given way to a conveyor at ground level, with automatically operated double-boom stacker. This arrangement can build two piles, either individually or simultaneously. Some piles have been built to about 1,000 ft. in length.

Recovery of the material is accomplished by means of a special **reclaiming** machine consisting of a bridge traveling on rails which span the width of the storage pile. A frame, adjustable for slope and given an oscillating motion, is carried at the front of the bridge. This frame rakes the sloping face of the pile cross section to dislodge the material but at the same time prevents its avalanching. A drag conveyor at ground level and at the front of the bridge gathers the dislodged material and moves it to one side, where it is delivered to a belt conveyor in an open trench for transport to the processing plant. The reclaimer itself moves at an extremely slow pace but recovers material at a highly uniform hourly rate, the speed and rate per hour being adjustable. This system has been used just for bulk storage, although storage of material is but one step and is combined with blending as the other step of the stocking and reclaiming function.

Segregation in the material put down by the distributing conveyors is usually objectionable and often a real problem, but the disturbance in particle-size gradation is actually used to special advantage in this system. It constitutes one phase—reclaiming by means of the special reclaimer being the other—in reassembling the particles and reconstituting the mass into a uniformly graded material. A variable material or a combination of several variable materials can be blended into a product of remarkable physical or chemical uniformity through the special operating technique to which this system lends itself.

When blending is made a function or, in fact, a feature of the stockpiling operation, the stacker is made to travel the length of the pile, back and forth. It automatically reverses its direction at the end of each trip, placing one layer of material upon another until, by hundreds of such layers, the tent-shaped pile is built to its full height. However, the layering operation is but one part of the entire blending operation. The several hundred thin layers may differ greatly from one another. Yet the reclaiming machine, because of the raking and conveying action, removes only a small amount—although the same amount—from each contributing layer at any one moment. Then, in combining what may well be referred to as hundreds of small samples, a blend of almost perfect chemical and physical uniformity is created.

When this storage method is used for blending, the stockpiles are often referred to as "beds," and the system is often called a "bed-blending system." Remarkable results have been obtained, and, where fairly large hourly quantities are handled, the stocking and reclaiming costs are surprisingly low. Most "bed" storage systems have been built with open piles, but covered multiple-bed plants are used for protecting more valuable material from the weather and for guarding against wind losses.

BROAD SCOPE OF BULK SOLIDS HANDLING. In the handling and storage of bulk solids there are many opportunities for large and continuing savings when modern equipment and methods are employed to reduce handling time and cost. The engineer confronted with any problem in this field will have ample opportunity to exercise his ingenuity and imagination in finding a solution.

It may seem that, in covering such an important subject, there have been many omissions of methods for handling certain kinds of bulk materials. For example, no discussion was presented on handling sulfur, which is one of the most important industrial chemicals. At the source of production a technique has long been established for handling sulfur in liquid form from the wells to the stockpiles, where it is allowed to solidify in immense wood-fenced vats. The processing method is unique to the commodity, and its adaptation elsewhere is most unlikely; but the unusual procedures serve to explain why it was not discussed along with other either special or well-known methods.

With many commodities it is surprising how readily a choice of method is determined simply by studying the characteristics, behavior, and the quantity of the material to be stored. The following paragraphs discuss the handling characteristics of the more common bulk solids.

FREE-FLOWING SOLIDS. Solid materials with relatively free-flowing characteristics, such as grain and sand, are loaded and unloaded in a number of ways, depending upon the kind of storage employed and the kind of transportation equipment used. In the case of sand, gravel, and other low-cost, non-perishable bulk commodities, the material is usually stored in piles and transported in open cars or trucks. **Gravity unloading** of cars and trucks into a sub-grade hopper is the usual procedure. The material is then elevated by a suitable conveyor to a height for gravity discharge to a storage pile. When received in barges or other water-transportation carriers, the material must be elevated for unloading. This kind of unloading is usually done by use of a crane equipped with a **clam bucket** which discharges directly to a storage pile or a hopper for gravity discharge into cars or trucks.

Other free-flowing solids of a more perishable nature or greater value require more specialized unloading equipment. Grain is easily handled by **vacuum lines,** and perhaps the bulk of grain is unloaded from barges and ships in this manner. Unloading of grain from elevators is, of course, by means of gravity, then chutes. Rail cars of grain and other free-flowing solids are also frequently unloaded by the use of massive **rotary unloading machines.** A loaded car is run into the dumping machine on rails, and while it is held in place by massive clamps, the dumper is rotated and the material is spilled out into hoppers under the machine.

For smaller unloading operations, bucket **conveyors** or screw conveyors are employed. Care must be taken to prevent contamination of the material being handled as well as excessive tumbling and churning, which will cause some materials to be broken up and degraded, particularly in the case of coke and coal.

FLOW-RESISTANT SOLIDS. Certain solids may have a tendency to "cake" or compact while in storage or during transportion. This caking, in turn, will cause the material to "hang up" in chutes and hoppers or to break apart in chunks that are too large for the equipment used to unload or load free-flowing materials. In the case of ores, unrefined clays, etc., where the material is of relatively low value, the open-yard storage method by use of a **clamshell bucket and crane** is used. For refined clays and similar material, **hoist unloading** into a special hopper with a mechanical breaker is recommended. Storage in weather-protected silos is required for clays.

Solids such as coal, ore, limestone, and coke are usually received in large sizes and are stored and used in such sizes. They should not be repeatedly handled, so as to avoid breakage, and **special hoppers and chutes** should be used for the handling.

SPECIAL SOLIDS. Certain solids, such as grains, flour, sugars, and salt, are for human consumption and should be handled with only clean equipment. Most of these food solids are free-flowing and can be handled by gravity flow through **enclosed chutes and tubes.** When these solids must be elevated in handling, **screw-type conveyors** or **movement by air flow** is usually employed.

Other solids in the special category are the corrosive salts and solid chemicals. As in the case of corrosive liquids, the storage and transporting equipment must be of corrosion-resistant construction. So also must be the chutes, tubes, and conveyors used in loading and unloading.

Many specialized devices have been developed for bulk material loading and unloading. Of special interest is the **powered scoop,** basically a large scoop mounted ahead of a tractor. A control mechanism manipulates the scoop, lowers it to pick up the material, elevates it to a height convenient for transportation, then raises and tilts the scoop and empties its contents into a hopper, dump truck, or gondola car.

Storage and Handling of Industrial Liquids

DESIGNING STORAGE AND HANDLING FACILITIES. The design of storage and handling facilities for industrial liquids must result in the development of an adequate installation to serve for a desired period of time at a reasonable expenditure of money. For the **design of an installation to be adequate,** it must be compatible with the physical and chemical characteristics of the liquid to be stored; it must provide for the volumes to be handled, with consideration to possible requirements for flexibility in the optimum volumes; it must meet the requirements of applicable codes and regulations covering the proposed installation; and it must be approved by the authorities having jurisdiction over such equipment.

The **desired period of time** is often thought of as being without limit. Experience has shown, however, that in some installations, tanks have remained in service for longer periods than originally anticipated—usually because of adequate maintenance and timely repairs. For example, oil-industry service experience with the common upright cylindrical cone-roof tank with a capacity of 55,000 bbl. and over has indicated that the useful life of such an installation is about 30 yr., being limited by such factors as general depreciation of the tank steel or the foundations or by the applicability of the tank type, size, or location.

At some point in the life of a tank, depending upon the influence of the limiting factors of physical condition, type, size, or location, it is reasonable to expect that the **cost of repairs** will exceed the value of the tank for continued service. When the estimated repair costs exceed the remaining value of the tank, replacement should be made.

Economical Expenditure for Facilities. The definition of an economical expenditure of money is dependent upon accepted definitions of adequate facilities and desired life of a proposed installation. It is natural to estimate the amount of money involved by the process of elimination, from the less expensive to the more expensive. However, the **decisions regarding investment** to be made must include consideration of these facts: (1) in most cases the value of the liquid plus the more intangible value of having the facilities available and in serviceable condition will be many times the cost of the storage system; and (2) foundations leave little room for compromise in cost. The known or proved load-bearing capacity of the earth, supplemented as required by piling or concrete, must definitely assure support of maximum loading without settlement sufficient to cause abnormal stresses. In those locations where corrosion of tank steel may be anticipated because of soil or drainage conditions, it is advisable to consider the cost of suitable grade preparation or protective coatings for bottom-plate protection along with the foundation.

In the consideration of **storage containers** proper, the concept of economical expenditure has more meaning. In the field of above-ground tanks the tank-builders offer a wide variety of containers and of materials for their fabrication. Knowing the physical and chemical characteristics of the liquid, the volumes and the turnover rates, the location, the vapor conservation to be sought (if applicable), and the desired period of time for acceptable repair costs, a tank or system can be chosen with assurance of an economical investment.

VARIETIES OF STEEL CONTAINERS. Among the varieties of above-ground steel containers for nonpressure service, the **cone-roof steel tank** is the least expensive. Factors leading to consideration of more costly types would include consideration of the possibility of overpressure, either internally or externally; corrosion of roof plates; deterioration of upper shell plates and roof supports if water vapor is present within the tank; evaporation losses; and the possible consequences of fire.

A number of different types of **nonpressure floating roofs** are available, such as the pan roof, the pontoon high deck, the pontoon low deck, and the double deck. Costs vary with increases in tank diameter. Choice will depend upon the particular circumstances; for example, a pontoon high-deck roof would not be suitable for a tank containing a corrosion-causing volatile liquid, such as hydrogen-sulfide-bearing crude oil, because of the entrapped vapor space under the roof plates. If corrosion were not a problem, then the high deck would have an advantage in cost over the double-deck roof. In volatile storage in a warm climate, the greater insulating quality of the double-deck roof may offer an advantage over the pan roof or the single-deck pontoon roof. Roof stability under snow and ice loads may influence the choice. The floating roof has value as a safeguard in the event of fire, a fact recognized by the National Board of Fire Underwriters. Drainage of water from a floating roof should be provided for in cases where water must not be allowed in the stored liquid. If a floating roof is to be used in such a service, a leak-free drain line from roof to outlet nozzle on the shell must be provided.

Storage tanks for **liquid storage** at pressures greater than the 2½ oz., approximately, afforded by the cone-roof tank are generally classed as "low pressure" and "high pressure." There are some differences in these terms as defined by tank-builders and the unfired-pressure-vessel codes. The unfired-pressure-vessel codes cover pressures over 15-lb.-per-sq.-in. gage. The nonpressure containers in the petroleum industry (and in other industries) have been covered for a number of years by the American Petroleum Institute Specifications for Oil Storage Tanks. Therefore, the pressure field between nonpressure and 15-lb.-per-sq.-in. gage has been covered by the tank-builders' designs, which have proved satisfactory for these and higher pressures throughout years of successful operation. The tank-builders' designs according to their definition of low-pressure storage were not, of course, limited to the 15-lb.-per-sq.-in. pressure which appears in the unfired-pressure-vessel codes, but have served for working pressures to about 30-lb.-per-sq.-in. gage. It is obvious that for pressure storage the owner must give consideration to his policy regarding code stamping and to local or state rules regarding the intended service and location.

The types of **low-pressure storage tanks** most commonly used above ground are the **spheroid steel tank** and the **cylindrical-shell steel tank,** with heads made adequate for the design pressure either by stays or by their shape. Included in the latter category is the **hemispheroid tank,** mounted upright and supported on a grade shaped to the contour of the bottom head. In the larger sizes the hemispheroid tank may have noded heads with internal stays. The spheroid tank is characterized by a change in the curvature of the shell from bottom to top and with noded and stayed top and bottom in the larger capacities—upward from about 40,000 bbl.

High-pressure storage depends for definition upon the tank-builders' designs, the owner's policy regarding code-stamping, and the requirements of local or state rules. It is assumed that the owner's policy will be in keeping with local or state regulations wherever they exist.

High-pressure tanks are commonly constructed in two shapes, namely, **spheres** and **elongated cylindrical shells** with hemispherical, ellipsoidal, or torispherical (dished) heads, mounted either horizontally or upright. The latter type is referred to as a "bullet" tank. In cases where **unfired-pressure-vessel code rules** must be applied, the vessels are designed, inspected, tested, and stamped in accordance with the state unfired-pressure-vessel code or, if there is no specific state code, in accordance with the unfired-pressure-vessel code of the American Society of Mechanical Engineers.

Tanks for Bulk Storage. The kinds of above-ground steel tanks which have been mentioned are those most commonly considered for bulk storage. The National Board of Fire Underwriters specifies that storage tanks for flammable liquids lighter than 40° API gravity shall be all-steel, of substantially vapor-tight construction, and suitably vented. The development of industry in general and developments in processes have proved that the **above-ground steel tank,** in some special cases, is more limited in ability to provide economical storage than other methods which have been used. For example, pressure storage of liquefied petroleum gases in large quantities has been accomplished successfully by the use of **underground caverns** prepared by specialists in the work. The storage of large quantities of fuel oil has turned attention to the possibilities offered by **old stone quarries.** Successful utilization of such facilities depends, of course, upon the problems presented by each case and upon approval by the authorities having jurisdiction. Another example of successful large-volume storage to meet unusual situations is the use of **underground rectangular steel tanks** specially designed for low-pressure storage of flammable liquid to meet local rules. A more common problem imposed by local rules is the underground storage of smaller volumes in which steel tanks built to more conventional designs are used. An example would be airport fueling tanks in which water has been used as a displacing medium to keep out air and avoid the formation of explosive vapors.

REFERENCES ON DESIGN DATA. The following references contain information on the design, construction, and operation of storage systems and related equipment. It is not implied that this list is complete.

1. Local and state regulations covering design, installation, safety, fire control, zoning, pollution, etc.
2. The National Electrical Code.
3. National Fire Protection Association publications. A pamphlet listing all publications of the National Fire Protection Association is available. The standards may be obtained in six volumes called National Fire Codes or they may be obtained singly. Titles of the volumes are: No. I. Flammable Liquids and Gases; No. II. Combustible Solids, Dusts, Chemicals, and Explosives; No. III. Building Construction and Equipment; No. IV. Extinguishing Equipment; No. V. Electrical; and No. VI. Transportation. Particular attention should be given to NFPA No. 11: Standards for Foam Extinguishing Systems. A few of the many other standards are: NFPA No. 30-L. Flammable Liquids Ordinance; NFPA No. 30-A. Protection of Tanks in Flooded Regions; NFPA No. 30-C. Rooms, Cabinets, and Houses for Storage of Flammable Liquids; NFPA No. 30-D. Concrete Fuel Oil Tanks; NFPA No. 30-F. Abandonment or Removal of Underground Tanks; NFPA No. 58. Storage and Handling of Liquified Petroleum Gases; NFPA No. 325. Fire Hazard Properties of Flammable Liquids, Gases, and Volatile Solids.
4. National Board of Fire Underwriters Standards for the Storage, Handling, and Use of Flammable Liquids, NBFU No. 30.
5. American Petroleum Institute Specifications for:
   a. Tanks with Riveted Shells, API 12A.
   b. Bolted Tanks, API 12B.
   c. Welded Oil Storage Tanks, API 12C.
   d. Welded Production Tanks (Tentative), API 12D.
   e. Wood Tanks (Tentative), API 12E.
6. American Society of Mechanical Engineers Power Boiler Code, Sec. VIII, for unfired-pressure vessels.
7. State unfired-pressure-vessel codes that have been adopted separately from Reference 6, above.
8. American Petroleum Institute Recommended Rules for the Design and Construction of Large Welded Low-Pressure Storage Tanks (Tentative), API Standard 620.
9. American Water Works Association–American Welding Society Standard Specifications for Steel Tanks, Standpipes, Reservoirs, and Elevated Tanks, for Water Storage, AWWA D100, AWS D5.2; including American Water Works Association Tentative Recommended Practice for Painting and Repainting Steel Tanks, Standpipes, Reservoirs, and Elevated Tanks, for Water Storage, AWWA D102.
10. American Water Works Association Recommended Practice for Inspection and Repairing Elevated Steel Water Storage Tanks, Standpipes, and Reservoirs, AWWA D101.
11. Associated Factory Mutual Fire Insurance Companies Specifications for Gravity Water Tanks and Steel Towers.

12. American Water Works Association–American Welding Society Standard Specifications for Field Welding of Steel Water Pipe Joints, AWS D7.0.
13. American Welding Society Standard Rules for Field Welding of Steel Storage Tanks, AWS D5.1.
14. American Railway Engineering Association Specifications for All-Welded Steel Tanks for Railway Water Service.
15. Evaporation Loss of Petroleum from Storage Tanks, a symposium on petroleum-evaporation losses published in the American Petroleum Institute Proceedings of the 32d Annual Meeting in 1952, Vol. 32, Sec. I. Also available in reprint form.
16. American Petroleum Institute Guide for Tank Venting and Recommended Procedure for Testing Venting Devices for Low-Pressure Above-Ground Storage Tanks for Petroleum and Petroleum Products, API No. RP 2000.
17. American Petroleum Institute Code for Measuring, Sampling, and Testing Natural Gasoline and Other Light Liquid Petroleum Hydrocarbons, API Code 50B.
18. American Petroleum Institute Standard for Measuring, Sampling, and Testing Crude Oil, API Standard 2500.
19. American Petroleum Institute Standard for Calibration and Strapping of Vertical Tanks, API Standard 2501.
20. American Society for Testing Materials Manual on Calibrating Upright Tanks, ASTM Designation D–1220–52T.
21. American Society for Testing Materials Manual on Measurement and Sampling of Petroleum and Petroleum Products, containing the following ASTM Designations: D 1085. Gaging; D 1086. Temperature Measurement; D 1087. Volume Calculations and Corrections; D 96. Water and Sediment; D 287. Gravity; D 270. Sampling; and D 1145. Sampling Natural Gas.
22. American Petroleum Institute Code for Calibrating Tank Car Tanks and for Measuring, Sampling, and Calculating Tank Car Quantities (Nonpressure Type) (Tentative), API Code No. 1201; same except for Pressure-Type Tank Cars (Tentative), API Code No. 1202.
23. American Society of Mechanical Engineers–American Petroleum Institute Code for Installation, Proving, and Operation of Positive Displacement Meters in Liquid Hydrocarbon Service (Tentative), API Code No. 1101.
24. American Petroleum Institute Accident-Prevention Manuals, including: No. 1. Cleaning Petroleum Storage Tanks, consisting of Section A: Crude Oil and Unfinished Products Tanks, and Section B: Gasoline Tanks; No. 11. Safe Transportation of Petroleum Products by Tank Truck; No. 12. Loading Tank Cars (Gasoline).
25. American Standards Association Code for Pressure Piping, ASA B31.1.
26. Interstate Commerce Commission Tariff No. 9, and supplements thereto, or revisions thereof: Interstate Commerce Commission Regulations for Transportation of Explosives and Other Dangerous Articles by Land and Water, Including Specifications for Shipping Containers.
27. Manufacturing Chemists Association, Inc., Chemical Safety Data Sheets for storing and handling chemicals for which special precautions are recommended.
28. American Society for Testing Materials–Institute of Petroleum Joint Petroleum Measurement Tables, ASTM Designation D 1250 and IP Designation 200; also American Standards Association No. Z11.83. Conversion tables are available in the American edition, which uses United States units of measurement; in the British edition, which uses the British (Imperial) units of measurement; and in the Metric edition, which uses metric units of measurement, and in which the explanatory textual matter is printed in English, French, and Spanish. The conversion tables in the American edition are also available in pamphlet form for convenience in those cases where the entire set of tables is not required.
29. American Society for Testing Materials Standards on Petroleum Products and Lubricants (with Related Information), containing methods of testing, specifications, definitions, charts and tables. The publication is issued annually.

In regard to Reference 9, the tank builders' own standards for low pressure tanks, the American Petroleum Institute is in the process of developing a standard for the design and construction of large field-welded tanks for the pressure range from substantially 0 to 15 lb. per sq. in. gage. The work is in draft stage at present.

REDUCTION OF VAPOR LOSSES. The reduction of vapor losses from volatile liquids is receiving increased attention. The use of **pressure-storage** offers one approach to conservation. In the case of substantially nonpressure storage, vapor conservation may considerably influence the choice of tank types. For example, the factor of **conservation of vapors** should direct attention to the floating roof, lifter roof, and balloon roof; the flexible membrane type of vapor retainer within a conventional type steel tank; and a separate vapor-breather tank, which may be connected to the vapor spaces in a number of adjacent cone-roof tanks. Information contained in Reference 15 in the foregoing, Evaporation Loss of Petroleum from Storage Tanks, will be helpful in evaluating potential vapor losses from hydrocarbon storage; tank builders will assist in the design of a satisfactory system. The pressure-vacuum vent valve commonly used on cone-roof tanks is a workable conservation device over a range of a few ounces of pressure differential.

Fig. 7 shows the **approximate cost per barrel of tank capacity** for various sizes of above-ground steel tanks with cone roof, double-deck floating roof, and lifter roof in two dimensions for lift. The table is intended to illustrate relative differences only. The actual unit-cost levels in other circumstances may be different.

Diam. × Ht., Ft.	Approximate Capacity, Bbl.	Approximate Costs, Dollars per Barrel			
		Cone Roof	Double-Deck Floating Roof	Lifter Roof 5-Ft. Lift	10-Ft. Lift
30 × 40	5,000	1.95	3.25	3.14	3.57
42.5 × 40	10,000	1.33	2.11	2.03	2.33
52 × 40	15,000	1.25	1.84	1.79	2.05
67 × 40	25,000	1.04	1.50	1.45	1.72
100 × 40	55,000	0.83	1.08	1.10	1.26
120 × 40	80,000	0.77	0.95	1.01	1.16

Fig. 7. Approximate costs of some roof types per barrel of tank capacity.

In the **selection of tank sizes and capacities,** it is important to consider the fact that in some services not all of the geometric capacity will be usable. Basic sediment and water or solids deposition may make it necessary to draw down only as far as 2, 3, or 4 ft. from the bottom; encrustations on side walls and framing members, such as that caused by wax in crude oil or by a frozen heavy product such as asphalt, may reduce the tank capacity. Also, in filling, it is often the practice to valve-off well before the height to which the tank capacity has been calculated.

Fig. 8 shows capacities, weights, surface areas, and swing-pipe cable lengths for **upright cylindrical steel tanks.** Fig. 9 may serve as a guide for estimating the approximate sizes and capacities of **spheres and spheroids.** Foundation design must be based on data applicable to the specific tanks to be installed.

Tank Size, Diam. × Ht., Ft.	Capacity Bbl.[3]	Cone Roof Total	Cone Roof Per Bbl.	Floating Roof[2] Total	Floating Roof[2] Per Bbl.	Surface, Sq. Ft. Shell	Surface, Sq. Ft. Cone Roof	Length of Swing Pipe Cable, Ft.
10 × 12	170	4,600	27.1			377	79	30
× 18	250	6,050	24.5			566		35
× 24	335	7,500	22.4			754		50
× 30	420	8,950	21.3			943		60
× 36	505	10,400	20.6			1,131		70
15 × 12	380	8,500	22.4			566	177	30
× 18	565	10,750	19.1			848		40
× 24	755	13,000	17.2			1,131		55
× 30	945	15,250	16.2			1,414		65
× 36	1,130	17,500	15.5			1,696		75
20 × 12	670	13,200	19.7	15,900	18.7	754	315	30
× 18	1,010	16,200	16.0	18,800	18.5	1,131		40
× 24	1,340	19,200	14.3	21,700	16.2	1,508		55
× 30	1,680	22,200	13.2	24,600	14.7	1,885		70
× 36	2,010	25,300	12.6	27,500	13.7	2,262		80
25 × 12	1,050	18,300	17.4	22,800	21.7	943	492	35
× 18	1,570	22,050	14.1	26,400	16.8	1,414		40
× 24	2,100	25,800	12.3	30,000	14.3	1,885		50
× 30	2,620	29,550	11.3	33,600	12.8	2,356		60
× 36	3,150	33,350	10.6	37,300	11.9	2,828		70
× 42	3,670	37,200	10.2	41,000	11.2	3,299		80
30 × 12	1,510	24,700	16.4	31,200	20.5	1,131	709	40
× 18	2,270	29,150	12.9	35,550	15.7	1,697		50
× 24	3,020	34,600	11.5	39,900	13.2	2,262		60
× 30	3,780	39,050	10.4	44,250	11.7	2,828		70
× 36	4,530	43,500	9.6	48,600	10.7	3,393		80
× 42	5,290	48,000	9.1	53,000	10.0	3,959		90
× 48	6,040	53,000	8.8	57,900	9.6	4,524		100
35 × 12	2,060	31,600	15.4	40,800	19.8	1,320	965	40
× 18	3,080	36,750	12.0	45,900	14.9	1,980		50
× 24	4,110	41,900	10.2	51,000	12.4	2,640		65
× 30	5,140	47,100	9.2	56,100	10.9	3,300		75
× 36	6,170	52,400	8.5	61,300	9.9	3,960		80
× 42	7,200	58,250	8.1	67,000	9.3	4,620		90
× 48	8,230	64,900	7.9	73,500	8.9	5,280		105
40 × 12	2,690	39,900	14.9	51,500	19.2	1,508	1,260	40
× 18	4,030	45,800	11.4	57,300	14.2	2,262		50
× 24	5,370	51,700	9.6	63,100	11.4	3,016		65
× 30	6,710	57,700	8.6	68,900	10.3	3,770		75
× 36	8,060	64,300	8.0	75,300	9.3	4,524		80
× 42	9,400	71,850	7.7	82,700	8.8	5,278		90
× 48	10,740	80,650	7.5	91,300	8.5	6,032		105

Fig. 8. Capacities, weights, surface areas, and cable lengths for upright cylindrical steel tanks (continued on next page).

Tank		Approximate Weight, Lb.[1]				Surface, Sq. Ft.		Length of Swing Pipe Cable, Ft.
Size, Diam. × Ht., Ft.	Capacity Bbl.[3]	Cone Roof		Floating Roof[2]				
		Total	Per Bbl.	Total	Per Bbl.	Shell	Cone Roof	
45 × 12	3,400	48,900	14.7	63,500	18.7	1,697	1,595	40
× 18	5,100	55,550	10.9	70,000	13.7	2,545		50
× 24	6,800	62,200	9.2	76,500	11.3	3,393		65
× 30	8,500	68,900	8.1	83,100	9.8	4,242		75
× 36	10,200	77,050	7.6	91,100	8.9	5,090		80
× 42	11,900	86,600	7.3	100,600	8.5	5,938		90
× 48	13,600	97,600	7.2	111,500	8.2	6,786		105
50 × 16	5,600	71,600	12.8	89,000	15.9	2,514	1,970	50
× 24	8,390	84,600	10.1	101,900	12.2	3,770		65
× 32	11,190	97,600	8.7	114,800	10.3	5,027		75
× 40	13,990	113,000	8.1	129,800	9.3	6,283		85
× 48	16,790	131,500	7.8	147,900	8.8	7,540		105
× 56	19,580	152,600	7.8	168,600	8.6	8,797		115
× 64	22,380	176,900	7.9	192,400	8.6	10,054		120
60 × 16	8,060	95,800	12.0	121,200	15.0	3,016	2,835	50
× 24	12,090	112,000	9.3	136,600	11.3	4,524		65
× 32	16,120	129,500	8.0	153,300	9.5	6,032		75
× 40	20,140	151,300	7.5	174,400	8.7	7,540		85
× 48	24,170	177,500	7.4	199,900	8.3	9,048		100
× 56	28,200	208,000	7.4	229,700	8.2	10,556		115
× 64	32,230	243,000	7.5	263,800	8.2	12,064		130
70 × 16	10,960	128,200	11.7	158,800	14.5	3,519	3,860	55
× 24	16,450	147,100	9.0	177,000	10.8	5,278		65
× 32	21,930	171,100	7.8	200,000	9.1	7,037		75
× 40	27,420	201,000	7.3	229,000	8.4	8,797		90
× 48	32,900	237,000	7.2	263,800	8.0	10,556		105
× 56	38,380	280,000	7.3	304,200	7.9	12,315		115
× 64	43,870	330,000	7.5	344,000	7.8	14,074		130
80 × 16	14,320	159,300	11.1	201,000	14.0	4,021	5,040	55
× 24	21,490	182,100	8.5	223,200	10.4	6,032		65
× 32	28,650	213,000	7.4	253,600	8.9	8,043		75
× 40	35,810	249,000	6.9	291,400	8.1	10,053		90
× 48	42,970	296,000	6.9	336,700	7.8	12,064		105
× 56	50,130	350,000	7.0	389,400	7.8	14,075		115
× 64	57,300	423,000	7.4	450,400	7.9	16,085		130
90 × 16	18,130	204,200	11.3	250,000	13.8	4,524	6,380	55
× 24	27,190	234,500	8.6	278,700	10.3	6,786		65
× 32	36,260	274,000	7.6	316,800	8.7	9,048		75
× 40	45,320	324,000	7.1	365,000	8.1	11,310		90
× 48	54,390	383,200	7.1	422,500	7.8	13,572		105
× 56	63,450	452,000	7.1	490,200	7.7	15,834		115
× 64	72,520	531,000	7.3	567,300	7.8	18,096		130

Fig. 8. (Continued on next page.)

| Tank | | Approximate Weight, Lb.[1] | | | | Surface, Sq. Ft. | | Length of Swing Pipe Cable, Ft. |
| | | Cone Roof | | Floating Roof [2] | | | | |
Size, Diam. × Ht., Ft.	Capacity Bbl.[3]	Total	Per Bbl.	Total	Per Bbl.	Shell	Cone Roof	
100 × 16	22,380	241,100	10.8	302,700	13.6	5,027	7,870	55
× 24	33,570	278,600	8.3	337,500	10.1	7,540		65
× 32	44,760	328,000	7.3	384,900	8.6	10,053		75
× 40	55,950	390,000	7.0	443,500	7.9	12,567		90
× 48	67,140	465,000	6.9	514,500	7.7	15,080		105
× 56	78,340	551,000	7.0	596,700	7.6	17,593		115
× 64	89,530	650,000	7.3	691,300	7.7	20,106		130
120 × 24	48,340	373,400	7.8	479,800	9.9	9,048	11,340	65
× 32	64,460	444,400	6.9	547,800	8.5	12,064		75
× 40	80,580	532,800	6.6	633,500	7.9	15,080		90
× 48	96,690	631,000	6.5	746,000	7.7	18,096		105
× 56	112,800	754,000	6.7	866,000	7.7	21,112		115
× 64	128,900	893,000	6.9	997,000	7.7	24,128		130
140 × 24	65,800	530,000	8.1	647,300	9.8	10,556	15,430	65
× 32	87,740	623,000	7.1	740,000	8.4	14,074		75
× 40	109,700	741,600	6.8	856,000	7.8	17,593		90
× 48	131,600	881,000	6.7	991,000	7.5	21,112		105
× 56	153,500	1,047,000	6.8	1,156,000	7.5	24,630		115
160 × 32	114,600	830,000	7.2	955,000	8.3	16,085	20,150	75
× 40	143,200	965,300	6.7	1,110,000	7.7	20,106		90
× 48	171,900	1,138,000	6.6	1,308,000	7.6	24,127		105

[1] Stair weight not included.
[2] Floating roof is double-deck type.
[3] Capacities shown are for cone-roof tank.
Total weights are based on theoretical calculations and may vary up to 10% because of plate thickness tolerances and variations in manufacturer's estimated weights.

Fig. 8. (Concluded.)

Diam. Ft.	Capacity, Bbl.	Approx. Shell Weight, Lb. per 0.1 In. Thick	Diam. Ft.	Capacity, Bbl.	Approx. Shell Weight, Lb. per 0.1 In. Thick
10	93	1,285	45	8,498	26,000
15	315	2,890	50	11,657	32,100
20	746	5,140	55	15,515	38,900
25	1,457	8,030	60	20,142	46,200
30	2,518	11,570	65	25,608	54,200
35	3,998	15,750	70	31,984	63,000
40	5,969	20,600			

Fig. 9a. Approximate sizes and capacities of spheres.

Capacity, Bbl.	Approx. Size, Diam. × Ht., Ft.	Capacity, Bbl.	Approx. Size Diam. × Ht., Ft.
5,000	41'6" × 32'6"	40,000	92 × 40
10,000	52'0" × 38'0"	50,000	104 × 40
15,000	60'0" × 40'0"	60,000	112 × 40
20,000	67'0" × 40'0"	70,000	122 × 40
30,000	79'0" × 40'0"	80,000	128 × 40

Fig. 9b. Approximate sizes and capacities of spheroids.

TANK FOUNDATIONS. Tank foundation designs must start with an evaluation of the load-bearing capacity of the soil by a competent engineer. In many cases the soil capacity will be known to the engineer from past experience with other tanks or structures in the area or from experience with subgrade of similar characteristics. In any event the final decisions regarding a foundation to be built must assure uniform support under maximum load, so that there will be no abnormal structural stresses during the life span of the tank. The maximum soil-bearing capacity normally used is about 4,000 lb. per sq. ft. The **load-bearing power of soil** in pounds per square foot may be determined by a qualified civil engineer.

SINGLE TANKS:

Low flash oils [1] ....⎤
High flash oils [2]..⎬100% capacity
Crude oils ....⎦

MULTIPLE TANKS, maximum number in one enclosure:

Unfinished products, low flash:
    1,000 bbl. and under .... 12 tanks
    1,001 bbl. to 2,500 bbl. .... 8 tanks
    2,501 bbl. to 5,000 bbl. .... 6 tanks
    5,001 bbl. and larger .... 4 tanks

Unfinished products, high flash:
    1,000 bbl. and under .... 20 tanks
    1,001 bbl. to 2,500 bbl. .... 12 tanks
    2,501 bbl. to 5,000 bbl. .... 10 tanks
    5,001 bbl. to 25,000 bbl. .... 8 tanks
    25,001 bbl. and larger.. 4 tanks

Enclosure capacity for low and high flash unfinished products must be at least equal to that of the largest tank plus 10 percent of all other tanks.

Crude Oil Tanks: Enclosure capacity must be at least equal to the capacity of all tanks.

Finished Products: In refinery tank fields limited to finished product storage, the number of tanks in any one enclosure listed above may be increased by 50 percent.

This table may be used only if the enclosure capacities are within the requirements of applicable codes or regulations.

[1] National Board of Fire Underwriters Class I and Class II flammable liquids.
[2] National Board of Fire Underwriters Class III flammable liquids.

Fig. 10. Tank enclosure capacities (net).

Surface Preparation. Surface preparation around above-ground tanks is related to the type of the tanks to be installed and their service, to the location of the area in relation to boundaries and other facilities, and to the nature of the terrain. Prior to final layout of the installation it must be determined that **local regulations** will be satisfied. It is recommended that reference be made to the Standards of the National Board of Fire Underwriters for the Storage, Handling, and Use of Flammable Liquids for approved practices regarding design, construction, venting, and piping for various types of installations and liquids; also to the National Fire Protection Association's Standard for Foam Extinguishing Systems. Consideration must also be given to the problem of safe and acceptable **drainage** in order to insure that contaminated water or stored liquid suddenly released because of tank or piping failure will not contaminate streams or endanger sewers, public drains, or other property.

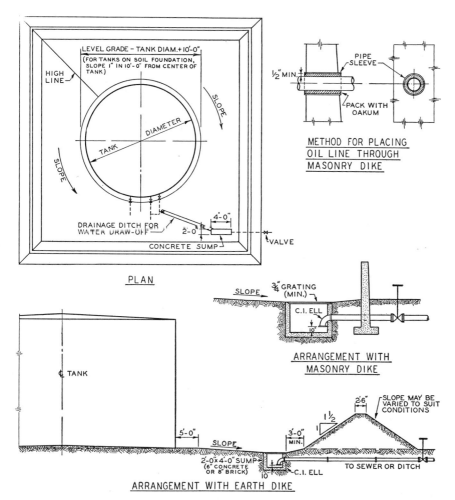

Fig. 11. Typical dike sections and drainage for storage tanks.

The **arrangement and size of dikes and diked areas** is generally related to the capacities of tanks involved; their location in regard to structures, facilities, or areas to which tank failure might constitute a hazard; and to the topography of the area. It is impossible to set a hard and fast rule applicable to all cases; the authority having jurisdiction must establish the minimum requirements permissible. Here, again, reference may be made to the section on dikes and walls in the Standards of the National Board of Fire Underwriters mentioned earlier in this section.

Fig. 10 illustrates **a pattern for tank enclosure capacities** which has been used in oil-refinery tankage remote from other public property. It is emphasized that the table is illustrative only and that proposed tankage arrangements must have the approval of the authority having jurisdiction.

Fig. 11 shows grading, drainage draw-off, and dike construction for one upright tank; this illustration is applicable for several tanks within one enclosure. The **grading and drainage** are important and should not be sacrificed for the purpose of obtaining earth for an earth dike. It is apparent that a hillside location is desirable because the hillside will serve as part of the enclosing wall and drainage will be improved.

PROTECTION AGAINST FIRE. It is important to call attention to a connection between the dike and a fire-protection system. A common requirement and one which is recommended by the National Board of Fire Underwriters is that in those installations with no means for extinguishing a fire in a cone-roof crude-oil tank, dikes or walls enclosing such tanks shall be provided along the top of the enclosure with continuous metal flareback plates designed to turn back a boilover wave. A **boilover wave** may result from the vaporization of water in a crude-oil tank subjected to intense heat. The same provision is required for other liquids which may have boilover characteristics similar to those of crude oil. The drain line should normally be kept closed.

The fire protection system to be used must be selected during the early stages of tankage layout. It is essential that reference be made to the latest edition of the National Fire Protection Association Standards for Foam Extinguishing Systems (NFPA No. 11) and to other applicable publications listed therein. Unfortunately, characteristics of the great variety of industrial liquids preclude a simple answer to the question of fire protection; therefore, the design of a dependable fire protection system will be a specialized undertaking in many cases. In all cases of flammable storage it must be considered as being an essential part of the facilities. The most important feature of any fire protection system consists of well-organized and well-trained **fire-fighting personnel.** All proposed installations and intended changes of any nature must have the approval of the fire marshal.

The oil industry depends largely on **foam application** for fire protection, particularly for large storage tanks. Foam is formed by mixing certain agents, usually aluminum sulfate (Agent A) and bicarbonate of soda (Agent B) with an optimum proportion of water. The foam produced is an aggregate of tiny gas- or air-filled bubbles which will float on the lightest of products generally stored in a refinery; this foam has the ability to extinguish fire progressively as it flows across a burning surface in the form of a blanket. It also has a cooling effect because of the water content dispersed in thin films. It does not dissipate readily, and when applied at a proper rate, it has proved to have a satisfactory retention time over large surfaces. Foam, of course, must be immediately available when and where needed; the type of distribution system will depend upon individual circumstances. The reference to Standards for Foam Extinguishing Systems, given earlier, describes in detail the several kinds of mixing and distributing systems, along with related operating information.

The **wet-storage chemical-foam system** is the most commonly used in the oil industry for protection of tank farms. Solutions of the A and B agents are stored in separate metal containers at strategic locations. The containers may be about 8 ft. diam. × 16 ft. high, built in accordance with the applicable Unfired Pressure Vessel Code. The aluminum-sulfate solution is severely corrosive; therefore, its container is usually provided with an 8 lb. lead internal lining. Thickness of sheet lead is designated by weight. A sheet approximately 1 ft. square by 1/64 in. thick weighs 1 lb. and is designated as 1-lb. lead. Therefore, 8-lb. lead has a thickness of ⅛ in.

The **pumps,** either twin-duplex or separate twin pumps, should be located at the solution tanks. Separate solution lines run from the pumps through con-

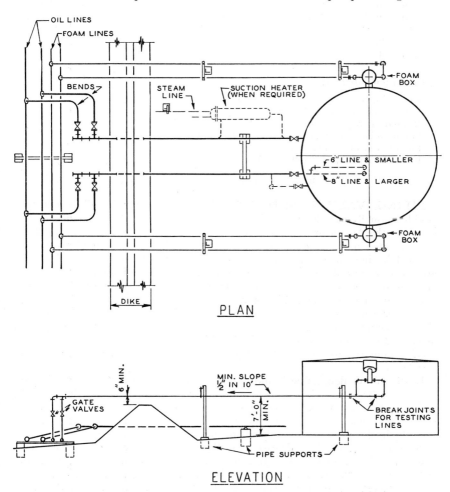

Fig. 12. Typical arrangement of oil and foam lines.

veniently located manifolds to the mixing boxes on the individual tanks, as illustrated in Fig. 12. Fig. 13 shows foam-line sizes, number of foam boxes per tank, and related information applicable to foam protection of oil refinery storage.

Tank Size, Ft. Diam. × Ht.	Area, Sq. Ft.	Solution Req'd, Gal. per Min.	No. of Boxes	Line Size, In.	Max. Length of Line, Ft.	Head Loss, Ft. per 100 Ft.
20 × 24	314	23.6	1	2	1,000	0.8
40 × 30	1,256	94.1	1	2	830	8.4
50 × 40	1,963	147.2	1	2½	800	7.4
60 × 40	2,827	212.2	1	3	1,000	5.6
70 × 40	3,848	288.5	2	2½	800	7.4
80 × 40	5,026	375.0	2	3	1,000	4.5
90 × 40	6,361	477.0	2	3	860	7.0
100 × 40	7,854	590.0	2	3	560	10.5
102 × 40	8,171	613.0	2	3	560	10.6
120 × 40	11,310	848.0	3	3	600	9.5
140 × 40	15,394	1,152.0	4	3	600	9.8

Tabulation based on:

8 in. foam boxes.
1 ft. of foam depth over tank area in 10 minutes.
Ratio of foam expansion per gallon of solution = 10 to 1.
Potential head of wet system at branch = 150 ft.
Potential head of generator at branch = 100 ft.
Inlet water pressure = 100 lb. per sq. in.

Fig. 13. Foamite lines, main to tank.

PIPING, VALVES, AND FITTINGS. Piping for handling industrial liquids is usually installed to specifications which will meet the minimum requirements of the American Standards Association Code for Pressure Piping, B31.1, supplemented in many cases by specifications which have been prepared and adopted by individual companies or plants. Such supplementary specifications are necessary in order to assure safe and economical operation under "corrosive" or "severely corrosive" conditions which go beyond the normal pressure-temperature requirements. **Piping materials** and types of valves, fittings, and flanges for a given service are usually chosen on the basis of past experience or, if that is lacking, on the recommendations of suppliers, coupled with consideration of cost. Eventually, service experience will mold the great numbers of piping specifications required in oil refinery or chemical plant operations into satisfactory form.

In the case of **flammable liquids,** the specifications for piping inside the firewalls are usually more rigid than is normally acceptable outside the firewalls. Inside the firewalls, valves or cocks should be cast steel. Pipe straights and bends should be seamless steel. Expansion and contraction in lines between tank and firewall should be absorbed by bends or other suitable means. Outside the firewalls, valves or cocks may be cast iron. Pipe straights may be lap-welded; pipe bends should be seamless steel. In general oil-tank field service, valves 8 in. and smaller may be cocks; those 10 in. and larger should be gate valves. Where required, valves should be protected against freezing. Flanges should be forged steel of the butt-welding type or forged steel screwed-companion flanges.

It is important that relief valves be provided to avoid the danger of over-pressure due to temperature increase in liquid-filled lines between closed block valves. This protection is usually accomplished by locating the relief valve in main-valve bypass piping. Piping must be adequately supported by hangers or supports to avoid excessive vibration and must be anchored to avoid undue stresses. Hangers and supports must not interfere with the free expansion and contraction of piping between anchors.

Vents. In order to protect against internal or external overpressure, tank vents are required on tanks which are essentially closed. They also serve as vapor-conservation devices for volatile liquid storage. In the case of nonpressure storage, such as in a cone-roof tank, the pressure- and vacuum-conservation-type vents are commonly combined in one piece of equipment, thus requiring just one roof connection per unit. Low-pressure tanks such as the spheroid and the hemispheroid tanks are commonly equipped with separate pressure- and vacuum-relief units. The pressure unit may incorporate a spring-loaded feature in its design. High-pressure tanks such as spheres and bullets are commonly equipped with spring-loaded safety valves; a vacuum relief valve may or may not be required, depending on the design strength of the shell under external pressure.

The use of a **flame-arrester device** between the tank connection and the conservation vent unit will depend upon the tank owner's opinion, with consideration to such factors as local ordinance, flash point of the product, tank location, inspection and maintenance factors, and past experience. The oil industry is divided as to **opinions regarding the use of flame arresters.**

Experience has shown the importance of **scheduled inspection of conservation vents,** with special attention during severe winter weather when pallet movement has been hampered by ice. Safety valves on high-pressure tanks are usually provided in dual units mounted on multiport valves which permit the removal of a unit for inspection and testing.

In the determination of venting requirements, reference should be made to the American Petroleum Institute Guide for Tank Venting, API No. RP 2000, and to the National Board of Fire Underwriters Standards for the Storage, Handling, and Use of Flammable Liquids, Pamphlet No. 30. Fig. 14 illustrates an arrangement of **accessories** commonly used on upright cylindrical steel tanks above ground. Fig. 15 shows a number of details common to such tanks.

Tanks which are to contain **flammable liquids** must be positively grounded. The type of grounding must satisfy the requirements of the authority having jurisdiction, wherein the circumstances of tank location, foundation, and the stored liquid will be considered. Fig. 16 illustrates **grounding connections** which have been used for petroleum products tankage.

CALIBRATION AND MEASUREMENT. The calibration of a storage tank includes the determination of the contained volume of liquid at depths of liquid differing by uniform increments, and the preparation of a gage table which shows the volume of liquid at the differing depths. The volumes shown on the gage table are those at a standard temperature, usually 60° F.

The method to be used in calibrating a tank is usually determined by the circumstances involved. **Liquid calibration,** accomplished by the addition or removal of known increments of liquid at known temperatures is the most nearly accurate method—particularly for nongeometrical shapes such as uneven or unstable so-called flat bottoms; for noded bottoms in spheroids or hemispheroids; for the complete spheroid tank that has a relatively thin shell which changes shape appreciably under varying liquid loads; for barge and ship tanks; and for

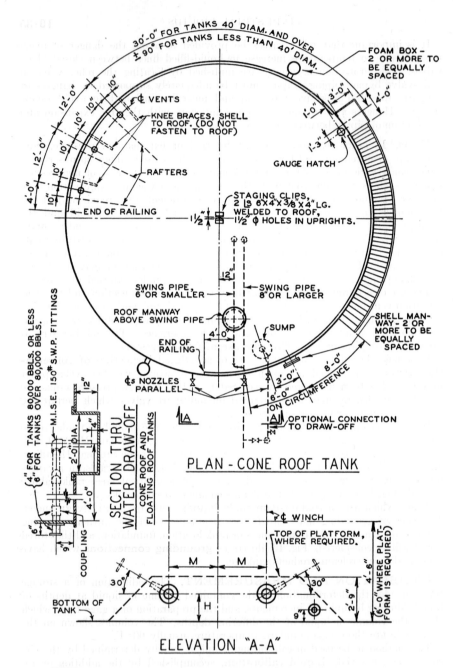

PLAN - CONE ROOF TANK

ELEVATION "A-A"

NOTE:
    FOR CODED DIMENSIONS SEE "TABULATION OF DIMENSIONS FOR TANK ACCESSORIES." DIMENSIONS FOR SHELL CONNECTIONS, WINCH LOCATION, STAIRWAY LOCATION, AND PLATFORM SIZE ALSO APPLICABLE TO FLOATING ROOF TANK.

Fig. 14. Arrangement of accessories for an upright cylindrical tank.

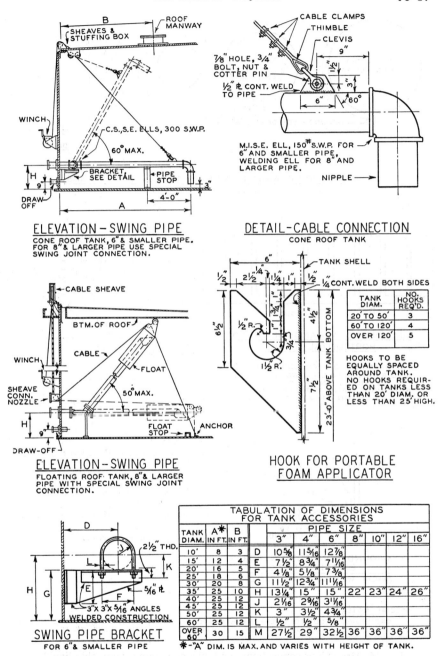

ELEVATION — SWING PIPE
CONE ROOF TANK, 6"& SMALLER PIPE.
FOR 8"& LARGER PIPE USE SPECIAL
SWING JOINT CONNECTION.

DETAIL — CABLE CONNECTION
CONE ROOF TANK

ELEVATION — SWING PIPE
FLOATING ROOF· TANK, 8"& LARGER
PIPE WITH SPECIAL SWING JOINT
CONNECTION.

HOOK FOR PORTABLE
FOAM APPLICATOR

TANK DIAM.	NO. HOOKS REQ'D.
20′ TO 50′	3
60′ TO 120′	4
OVER 120′	5

HOOKS TO BE
EQUALLY SPACED
AROUND TANK.
NO HOOKS REQUIR-
ED ON TANKS LESS
THAN 20′ DIAM. OR
LESS THAN 25′ HIGH.

SWING PIPE BRACKET
FOR 6"& SMALLER PIPE

TABULATION OF DIMENSIONS FOR TANK ACCESSORIES				PIPE SIZE						
TANK DIAM. IN FT.	A* IN FT.	B IN FT.		3"	4"	6"	8"	10"	12"	16"
10′	8	3	D	10 5/8"	11 5/16"	12 7/8"				
15′	12	4	E	7 1/2"	8 3/4"	7 11/16"				
20′	16	5	F	4 1/8"	5 1/8"	7 3/8"				
25′	18	6	G	11 1/2"	12 3/4"	11 11/16"				
30′	20	8	H	13 1/4"	15"	15"	22"	23"	24"	26"
35′	25	10	J	2 1/16"	2 9/16"	3 1/16"				
40′	25	12	K	3"	3 1/2"	4 3/4"				
45′	25	12	L	1/2"	1/2"	5/8"				
50′	25	12	M	27 1/2"	29"	32 1/2"	36"	36"	36"	36"
60′	25	12								
OVER 60′	30	15								

*—"A" DIM. IS MAX. AND VARIES WITH HEIGHT OF TANK.

Fig. 15. Details for upright tanks.

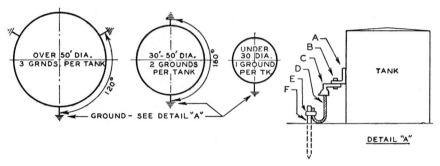

GROUNDING ARRANGEMENT FOR VERTICAL TANKS
SEE SPECIAL NOTE BELOW

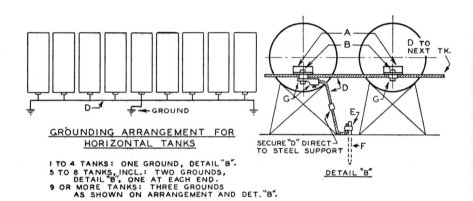

GROUNDING ARRANGEMENT FOR HORIZONTAL TANKS

1 TO 4 TANKS: ONE GROUND, DETAIL "B".
5 TO 8 TANKS, INCL.: TWO GROUNDS, DETAIL "B", ONE AT EACH END.
9 OR MORE TANKS: THREE GROUNDS AS SHOWN ON ARRANGEMENT AND DET. "B".

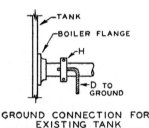

GROUND CONNECTION FOR EXISTING TANK
(WHERE WELDING IS PROHIBITED)

LEGEND:
A- 2" x 2" x ¼" ANGLE 2" LG. WITH $\frac{7}{16}$" HOLE TO SUIT ITEM "B". WELD TO TANK.
B- RUST-PROOF BOLT & NUT.
C- CABLE LUG.
D- #4 BARE STRANDED COPPER CABLE.
E- GROUND ROD CLAMP.
F- ¾" X 10'-0" COPPERWELD GROUND ROD.
G- CABLE LUG.
H- GROUND PIPE FITTING.

SPECIAL NOTE:
GROUNDING REQUIRED WHERE TANK RESTS ON SANDY SOIL, HIGH DRY GROUND OR CONCRETE BASE. GROUNDING NOT REQUIRED WHERE TANK RESTS ON PERMANENTLY MOIST SOIL.

Fig. 16. Grounding connections for tanks containing flammable liquids.

truck tanks and underground tanks. Its principal disadvantages in regard to large tanks include the great amount of time required and the large volume of water or nonvolatile oil required for use as a calibrating medium.

For the calibration of tanks by **linear measurements,** reference should be made to the American Society for Testing Materials Manual on Calibrating Liquid Containers—Upright Tanks, ASTM Designation D–1220, which describes measurement methods for upright cylindrical tank shells above ground, tank bottoms, tank roofs other than fixed roofs, wood tanks, underground tanks, and outside insulated tanks; and to the American Petroleum Institute Standard for Calibration and Strapping of Vertical Tanks, API Standard 2501, which is applicable to the tanks used in the petroleum industry. The American Society for Testing Materials has been preparing calibration methods for spheres and spheroids, stationary and mobile horizontal tanks, and barge and ship tanks.

In intercompany exchanges of liquid volumes it is customary to use **tank gage tables** which have been prepared and certified by a third-party agency specializing in calibration, measurement, and inspection of industrial liquid transactions. In intracompany operations, in which title to the liquid volumes does not necessarily change, accurate tank measurements and gage tables are important for all tanks because taxes are paid on inventory volumes.

The **shape of curved heads** such as the hemispherical, ellipsoidal, dished and bumped shapes, and the shape of the horizontal cylinder will influence the incremental changes in volumes to be shown on gage tables for tanks which include these features of construction. The nature of both the ellipsoidal shape, including the sphere, and of the horizontal cylinder has made possible the development of convenient formulas and tables of coefficients for the calculation of the contained liquid volume at any surface height in the tank. (The following formulas and tables were developed by the Chicago Bridge and Iron Company.)

TABLES OF DATA. Fig. 17 is a table of coefficients for partial volumes of ellipsoids, including the sphere. Fig. 18 is a table of coefficients for partial volumes of horizontal cylinders. Fig. 19 illustrates the ellipsoidal shapes applicable to Fig. 17.

Example. Horizontal tank with ellipsoidal heads, where tank diameter $= 20$ ft., $D = 20$ ft., length $L = 30$ ft. tangent to tangent, liquid depth $= 6.5$ ft., $K_1 = 0.5$, total volume $= \frac{\pi}{6} K_1 D^3$

$$\text{Total volume} = \frac{3.1416}{6} \times 0.5 \times 20^3 = 2{,}094.4 \text{ cu. ft.}$$

$$\frac{H}{D} = \frac{6.5}{20} = 0.325$$

Refer to Fig. 17; at 0.32 in the column headed H/D, proceed to the right to column headed "5" (the third figure in the H/D ratio of 0.325). The coefficient for 0.325 is found to be 0.248219. (Interpolate if there are more than three digits in the ratio being used.) The liquid volume in the tank heads at 6.5 ft. $= 2{,}094.4$ cu. ft. $\times$ 0.248219 $= 519.87$ cu. ft.

For the partially filled horizontal cylinder, illustrated by Fig. 20, the capacity $= \frac{3.1416 \times 20^2 \times 30}{4} = 9{,}424.8$ cu. ft.

$H/D = 0.325$; the coefficient from Fig. 18, following the same procedure as before, is 0.281820. The liquid volume in the cylinder at depth of 6.5 ft. $= 9{,}424.8 \times 0.281820 = 2{,}656.10$ cu. ft. The total liquid volume in the tank at 6.5 ft. depth $= 2{,}656.10$ cu. ft. plus 519.87 cu. ft., or 3,175.97 cu. ft.

HANDLING BULK MATERIALS

H/D	0	1	2	3	4	5	6	7	8	9
.00	.000000	.000003	.000012	.000027	.000048	.000075	.000108	.000146	.000191	.000242
.01	.000298	.000360	.000429	.000503	.000583	.000668	.000760	.000857	.000960	.001069
.02	.001184	.001304	.001431	.001563	.001700	.001844	.001993	.002148	.002308	.002474
.03	.002646	.002823	.003006	.003195	.003389	.003589	.003795	.004006	.004222	.004444
.04	.004672	.004905	.005144	.005388	.005638	.005893	.006153	.006419	.006691	.006968
.05	.007250	.007538	.007831	.008129	.008433	.008742	.009057	.009377	.009702	.010032
.06	.010368	.010709	.011055	.011407	.011764	.012126	.012493	.012865	.013243	.013626
.07	.014014	.014407	.014806	.015209	.015618	.016031	.016450	.016874	.017303	.017737
.08	.018176	.018620	.019069	.019523	.019983	.020447	.020916	.021390	.021869	.022353
.09	.022842	.023336	.023835	.024338	.024847	.025360	.025879	.026402	.026930	.027462
.10	.028000	.028542	.029090	.029642	.030198	.030760	.031326	.031897	.032473	.033053
.11	.033638	.034228	.034822	.035421	.036025	.036633	.037246	.037864	.038486	.039113
.12	.039744	.040380	.041020	.041665	.042315	.042969	.043627	.044290	.044958	.045630
.13	.046306	.046987	.047672	.048362	.049056	.049754	.050457	.051164	.051876	.052592
.14	.053312	.054037	.054765	.055499	.056236	.056978	.057724	.058474	.059228	.059987
.15	.060750	.061517	.062288	.063064	.063843	.064627	.065415	.066207	.067003	.067804
.16	.068608	.069416	.070229	.071046	.071866	.072691	.073519	.074352	.075189	.076029
.17	.076874	.077723	.078575	.079432	.080292	.081156	.082024	.082897	.083772	.084652
.18	.085536	.086424	.087315	.088210	.089109	.090012	.090918	.091829	.092743	.093660
.19	.094582	.095507	.096436	.097369	.098305	.099245	.100189	.101136	.102087	.103042
.20	.104000	.104962	.105927	.106896	.107869	.108845	.109824	.110808	.111794	.112784
.21	.113778	.114775	.115776	.116780	.117787	.118798	.119813	.120830	.121852	.122876
.22	.123904	.124935	.125970	.127008	.128049	.129094	.130142	.131193	.132247	.133305
.23	.134366	.135430	.136498	.137568	.138642	.139719	.140799	.141883	.142969	.144059
.24	.145152	.146248	.147347	.148449	.149554	.150663	.151774	.152889	.154006	.155127
.25	.156250	.157376	.158506	.159638	.160774	.161912	.163054	.164198	.165345	.166495
.26	.167648	.168804	.169963	.171124	.172289	.173456	.174626	.175799	.176974	.178153
.27	.179334	.180518	.181705	.182894	.184086	.185281	.186479	.187679	.188882	.190088
.28	.191296	.192507	.193720	.194937	.196155	.197377	.198601	.199827	.201056	.202288
.29	.203522	.204759	.205998	.207239	.208484	.209730	.210979	.212231	.213485	.214741
.30	.216000	.217261	.218526	.219792	.221060	.222331	.223604	.224879	.226157	.227437
.31	.228718	.230003	.231289	.232578	.233870	.235163	.236459	.237757	.239057	.240359
.32	.241664	.242971	.244280	.245590	.246904	.248219	.249536	.250855	.252177	.253500
.33	.254826	.256154	.257483	.258815	.260149	.261484	.262822	.264161	.265503	.266847
.34	.268192	.269539	.270889	.272240	.273593	.274948	.276305	.277663	.279024	.280386
.35	.281750	.283116	.284484	.285853	.287224	.288597	.289972	.291348	.292727	.294106
.36	.295488	.296871	.298256	.299643	.301031	.302421	.303812	.305205	.306600	.307996
.37	.309394	.310793	.312194	.313597	.315001	.316406	.317813	.319222	.320632	.322043
.38	.323456	.324870	.326286	.327703	.329122	.330542	.331963	.333386	.334810	.336235
.39	.337662	.339090	.340519	.341950	.343382	.344815	.346250	.347685	.349122	.350561
.40	.352000	.353441	.354882	.356325	.357769	.359215	.360661	.362109	.363557	.365007
.41	.366458	.367910	.369363	.370817	.372272	.373728	.375185	.376644	.378103	.379563
.42	.381024	.382486	.383949	.395413	.386878	.388344	.389810	.391278	.392746	.394216
.43	.395686	.397157	.398629	.400102	.401575	.403049	.404524	.406000	.407477	.408954
.44	.410432	.411911	.413390	.414870	.416351	.417833	.419315	.420798	.422281	.423765
.45	.425250	.426735	.428221	.429708	.431195	.432682	.434170	.435659	.437148	.438638
.46	.440128	.441619	.443110	.444601	.446093	.447586	.449079	.450572	.452066	.453560
.47	.455054	.456549	.458044	.459539	.461035	.462531	.464028	.465524	.467021	.468519
.48	.470016	.471514	.473012	.474510	.476008	.477507	.479005	.480504	.482003	.483503
.49	.485002	.486501	.488001	.489501	.491000	.492500	.494000	.495500	.497000	.498500

Fig. 17. Coefficients for partial volumes of ellipsoids (spheres) (continued on next page).

H/D	0	1	2	3	4	5	6	7	8	9
.50	.500000	.501500	.503000	.504500	.506000	.507500	.509000	.510499	.511999	.513499
.51	.514998	.516497	.517997	.519496	.520995	.522493	.523992	.525490	.526988	.528486
.52	.529984	.531481	.532979	.534476	.535972	.537469	.538965	.540461	.541956	.543451
.53	.544946	.546440	.547934	.549428	.550921	.552414	.553907	.555399	.556890	.558381
.54	.559872	.561362	.562852	.564341	.565830	.567318	.568805	.570292	.571779	.573265
.55	.574750	.576235	.577719	.579202	.580685	.582167	.583649	.585130	.586610	.588089
.56	.589568	.591046	.592523	.594000	.595476	.596951	.598425	.599898	.601371	.602843
.57	.604314	.605784	.607254	.608722	.610190	.611656	.613122	.614587	.616051	.617514
.58	.618976	.620437	.621897	.623356	.624815	.626272	.627728	.629183	.630637	.632090
.59	.633542	.634993	.636443	.637891	.639339	.640785	.642231	.643675	.645118	.646559
.60	.648000	.649439	.650878	.652315	.653750	.655185	.656618	.658050	.659481	.660910
.61	.662338	.663765	.665190	.666614	.668037	.669458	.670878	.672297	.673714	.675130
.62	.676544	.677957	.679368	.680778	.682187	.683594	.684999	.686403	.687806	.689207
.63	.690606	.692004	.693400	.694795	.696188	.697579	.698969	.700357	.701744	.703129
.64	.704512	.705894	.707273	.708652	.710028	.711403	.712776	.714147	.715516	.716884
.65	.718250	.719614	.720976	.722337	.723695	.725052	.726407	.727760	.729111	.730461
.66	.731808	.733153	.734497	.735839	.737178	.738516	.739851	.741185	.742517	.743846
.67	.745174	.746500	.747823	.749145	.750464	.751781	.753096	.754410	.755720	.757029
.68	.758336	.759641	.760943	.762243	.763541	.764837	.766130	.767422	.768711	.769997
.69	.771282	.772563	.773843	.775121	.776396	.777669	.778940	.780208	.781474	.782739
.70	.784000	.785259	.786515	.787769	.789021	.790270	.791516	.792761	.794002	.795241
.71	.796478	.797712	.798944	.800173	.801399	.802623	.803845	.805063	.806280	.807493
.72	.808704	.809912	.811118	.812321	.813521	.814719	.815914	.817106	.818295	.819482
.73	.820666	.821847	.823026	.824201	.825374	.826544	.827711	.828876	.830037	.831196
.74	.832352	.833505	.834655	.835802	.836946	.838088	.839226	.840362	.841494	.842624
.75	.843750	.844873	.845994	.847111	.848226	.849337	.850446	.851551	.852653	.853752
.76	.854848	.855941	.857031	.858117	.859201	.860281	.861358	.862432	.863502	.864570
.77	.865634	.866695	.867753	.868807	.869858	.870906	.871951	.872992	.874030	.875065
.78	.876096	.877124	.878148	.879170	.880187	.881202	.882213	.883220	.884224	.885225
.79	.886222	.887216	.888206	.889192	.890176	.891155	.892131	.893104	.894073	.895038
.80	.896000	.896958	.897913	.898864	.899811	.900755	.901695	.902631	.903564	.904493
.81	.905418	.906340	.907257	.908171	.909082	.909988	.910891	.911790	.912685	.913576
.82	.914464	.915348	.916228	.917103	.917976	.918844	.919708	.920569	.921425	.922277
.83	.923126	.923971	.924811	.925648	.926481	.927309	.928134	.928954	.929771	.930584
.84	.931392	.932196	.932997	.933793	.934585	.935373	.936157	.936936	.937712	.938483
.85	.939250	.940013	.940772	.941526	.942276	.943022	.943764	.944501	.945235	.945963
.86	.946688	.947408	.948124	.948836	.949543	.950246	.950944	.951638	.952328	.953013
.87	.953694	.954370	.955042	.955710	.956373	.957031	.957685	.958335	.958980	.959620
.88	.960256	.960887	.961514	.962136	.962754	.963367	.963975	.964579	.965178	.965772
.89	.966362	.966947	.967527	.968103	.968674	.969240	.969802	.970358	.970910	.971458
.90	.972000	.972538	.973070	.973598	.974121	.974640	.975153	.975662	.976165	.976664
.91	.977158	.977647	.978131	.978610	.979084	.979553	.980017	.980477	.980931	.981380
.92	.981824	.982263	.982697	.983126	.983550	.983969	.984382	.984791	.985194	.985593
.93	.985986	.986374	.986757	.987135	.987507	.987874	.988236	.988593	.988945	.989291
.94	.989632	.989968	.990298	.990623	.990943	.991258	.991567	.991871	.992169	.992462
.95	.992750	.993032	.993309	.993581	.993847	.994107	.994362	.994612	.994856	.995095
.96	.995328	.995556	.995778	.995994	.996205	.996411	.996611	.996805	.996994	.997177
.97	.997354	.997526	.997692	.997852	.998007	.998156	.998300	.998437	.998569	.998696
.98	.998816	.998931	.999040	.999143	.999240	.999332	.999417	.999497	.999571	.999640
.99	.999702	.999758	.999809	.999854	.999892	.999925	.999952	.999973	.999988	.999997
1.00	1.000000									

Fig. 17. (Concluded.)

H/D	0	1	2	3	4	5	6	7	8	9
.00	.000000	.000053	.000151	.000279	.000429	.000600	.000788	.000992	.001212	.001445
.01	.001692	.001952	.002223	.002507	.002800	.003104	.003419	.003743	.004077	.004421
.02	.004773	.005134	.005503	.005881	.006267	.006660	.007061	.007470	.007886	.008310
.03	.008742	.009179	.009625	.010076	.010534	.010999	.011470	.011947	.012432	.012920
.04	.013417	.013919	.014427	.014940	.015459	.015985	.016515	.017052	.017593	.018141
.05	.018692	.019250	.019813	.020382	.020955	.021533	.022115	.022703	.023296	.023894
.06	.024496	.025103	.025715	.026331	.026952	.027578	.028208	.028842	.029481	.030124
.07	.030772	.031424	.032081	.032740	.033405	.034073	.034747	.035423	.036104	.036789
.08	.037478	.038171	.038867	.039569	.040273	.040981	.041694	.042410	.043129	.043852
.09	.044579	.045310	.046043	.046782	.047523	.048268	.049017	.049768	.050524	.051283
.10	.052044	.052810	.053579	.054351	.055126	.055905	.056688	.057474	.058262	.059054
.11	.059850	.060648	.061449	.062253	.063062	.063872	.064687	.065503	.066323	.067147
.12	.067972	.068802	.069633	.070469	.071307	.072147	.072991	.073836	.074686	.075539
.13	.076393	.077251	.078112	.078975	.079841	.080709	.081581	.082456	.083332	.084212
.14	.085094	.085979	.086866	.087756	.088650	.089545	.090443	.091343	.092246	.093153
.15	.094061	.094971	.095884	.096799	.097717	.098638	.099560	.100486	.101414	.102343
.16	.103275	.104211	.105147	.106087	.107029	.107973	.108920	.109869	.110820	.111773
.17	.112728	.113686	.114646	.115607	.116572	.117538	.118506	.119477	.120450	.121425
.18	.122403	.123382	.124364	.125347	.126333	.127321	.128310	.129302	.130296	.131292
.19	.132290	.133291	.134292	.135296	.136302	.137310	.138320	.139332	.140345	.141361
.20	.142378	.143398	.144419	.145443	.146468	.147494	.148524	.149554	.150587	.151622
.21	.152659	.153697	.154737	.155779	.156822	.157867	.158915	.159963	.161013	.162066
.22	.163120	.164176	.165233	.166292	.167353	.168416	.169480	.170546	.171613	.172682
.23	.173753	.174825	.175900	.176976	.178053	.179131	.180212	.181294	.182378	.183463
.24	.184550	.185639	.186729	.187820	.188912	.190007	.191102	.192200	.193299	.194400
.25	.195501	.196604	.197709	.198814	.199922	.201031	.202141	.203253	.204368	.205483
.26	.206600	.207718	.208837	.209957	.211079	.212202	.213326	.214453	.215580	.216708
.27	.217839	.218970	.220102	.221235	.222371	.223507	.224645	.225783	.226924	.228065
.28	.229209	.230352	.231498	.232644	.233791	.234941	.236091	.237242	.238395	.239548
.29	.240703	.241859	.243016	.244173	.245333	.246494	.247655	.248819	.249983	.251148
.30	.252315	.253483	.254652	.255822	.256992	.258165	.259338	.260512	.261687	.262863
.31	.264039	.265218	.266397	.267578	.268760	.269942	.271126	.272310	.273495	.274682
.32	.275869	.277058	.278247	.279437	.280627	.281820	.283013	.284207	.285401	.286598
.33	.287795	.288992	.290191	.291390	.292591	.293793	.294995	.296198	.297403	.298605
.34	.299814	.301021	.302228	.303438	.304646	.305857	.307068	.308280	.309492	.310705
.35	.311918	.313134	.314350	.315566	.316783	.318001	.319219	.320439	.321660	.322881
.36	.324104	.325326	.326550	.327774	.328999	.330225	.331451	.332678	.333905	.335134
.37	.336363	.337593	.338823	.340054	.341286	.342519	.343751	.344985	.346220	.347455
.38	.348690	.349926	.351164	.352402	.353640	.354879	.356119	.357359	.358599	.359840
.39	.361082	.362325	.363568	.364811	.366056	.367300	.368545	.369790	.371036	.372282
.40	.373530	.374778	.376026	.377275	.378524	.379774	.381024	.382274	.383526	.384778
.41	.386030	.387283	.388537	.389790	.391044	.392298	.393553	.394808	.396063	.397320
.42	.398577	.399834	.401092	.402350	.403608	.404866	.406125	.407384	.408645	.409904
.43	.411165	.412426	.413687	.414949	.416211	.417473	.418736	.419998	.421261	.422525
.44	.423788	.425052	.426316	.427582	.428846	.430112	.431378	.432645	.433911	.435178
.45	.436445	.437712	.438979	.440246	.441514	.442782	.444050	.445318	.446587	.447857
.46	.449125	.450394	.451663	.452932	.454201	.455472	.456741	.458012	.459283	.460554
.47	.461825	.463096	.464367	.465638	.466910	.468182	.469453	.470725	.471997	.473269
.48	.474541	.475814	.477086	.478358	.479631	.480903	.482176	.483449	.484722	.485995
.49	.487269	.488542	.489814	.491087	.492360	.493633	.494906	.496179	.497452	.498726

Fig. 18. Coefficients for partial volumes of horizontal cylinders (continued on next page).

H/D	0	1	2	3	4	5	6	7	8	9
.50	.500000	.501274	.502548	.503821	.505094	.506367	.507640	.508913	.510186	.511458
.51	.512731	.514005	.515278	.516551	.517824	.519097	.520369	.521642	.522914	.524186
.52	.525459	.526731	.528003	.529275	.530547	.531818	.533090	.534362	.535633	.536904
.53	.538175	.539446	.540717	.541988	.543259	.544528	.545799	.547068	.548337	.549606
.54	.550875	.552143	.553413	.554682	.555950	.557218	.558486	.559754	.561021	.562288
.55	.563555	.564822	.566089	.567355	.568622	.569888	.571154	.572418	.573684	.574948
.56	.576212	.577475	.578739	.580002	.581264	.582527	.583789	.585051	.586313	.587574
.57	.588835	.590096	.591355	.592616	.593875	.595134	.596392	.597650	.598908	.600166
.58	.601423	.602680	.603937	.605192	.606447	.607702	.608956	.610210	.611463	.612717
.59	.613970	.615222	.616474	.617726	.618976	.620226	.621476	.622725	.623974	.625222
.60	.626470	.627718	.628964	.630210	.631455	.632700	.633944	.635189	.636432	.637675
.61	.638918	.640160	.641401	.642641	.643881	.645121	.646360	.647598	.648836	.650074
.62	.651310	.652545	.653780	.655015	.656249	.657481	.658714	.659946	.661177	.662407
.63	.663637	.664866	.666095	.667322	.668549	.669775	.671001	.672226	.673450	.674674
.64	.675896	.677119	.678340	.679561	.680781	.681999	.683217	.684434	.685650	.686866
.65	.688082	.689295	.690508	.691720	.692932	.694143	.695354	.696562	.697772	.698979
.66	.700186	.701392	.702597	.703802	.705005	.706207	.707409	.708610	.709809	.711008
.67	.712205	.713402	.714599	.715793	.716987	.718180	.719373	.720563	.721753	.722942
.68	.724131	.725318	.726505	.727690	.728874	.730058	.731240	.732422	.733603	.734782
.69	.735961	.737137	.738313	.739488	.740662	.741835	.743008	.744178	.745348	.746517
.70	.747685	.748852	.750017	.751181	.752345	.753506	.754667	.755827	.756984	.758141
.71	.759297	.760452	.761605	.762758	.763909	.765059	.766209	.767356	.768502	.769648
.72	.770791	.771935	.773076	.774217	.775355	.776493	.777629	.778765	.779898	.781030
.73	.782161	.783292	.784420	.785547	.786674	.787798	.788921	.790043	.791163	.792282
.74	.793400	.794517	.795632	.796747	.797859	.798969	.800078	.801186	.802291	.803396
.75	.804499	.805600	.806701	.807800	.808898	.809993	.811088	.812180	.813271	.814361
.76	.815450	.816537	.817622	.818706	.819788	.820869	.821947	.823024	.824100	.825175
.77	.826247	.827318	.828387	.829454	.830520	.831584	.832647	.833708	.834767	.835824
.78	.836880	.837934	.838987	.840037	.841085	.842133	.843178	.844221	.845263	.846303
.79	.847341	.848378	.849413	.850446	.851476	.852506	.853532	.854557	.855581	.856602
.80	.857622	.858639	.859655	.860668	.861680	.862690	.863698	.864704	.865708	.866709
.81	.867710	.868708	.869704	.870698	.871690	.872679	.873667	.874653	.875636	.876618
.82	.877597	.878575	.879550	.880523	.881494	.882462	.883428	.884393	.885354	.886314
.83	.887272	.888227	.889180	.890131	.891080	.892027	.892971	.893913	.894853	.895789
.84	.896725	.897657	.898586	.899514	.900440	.901362	.902283	.903201	.904116	.905029
.85	.905939	.906847	.907754	.908657	.909557	.910455	.911350	.912244	.913134	.914021
.86	.914906	.915788	.916668	.917544	.918419	.919291	.920159	.921025	.921888	.922749
.87	.923607	.924461	.925314	.926164	.927009	.927853	.928693	.929531	.930367	.931198
.88	.932028	.932853	.933677	.934497	.935313	.936128	.936938	.937747	.938551	.939352
.89	.940150	.940946	.941738	.942526	.943312	.944095	.944874	.945649	.946421	.947190
.90	.947956	.948717	.949476	.950232	.950983	.951732	.952477	.953218	.953957	.954690
.91	.955421	.956148	.956871	.957590	.958306	.959019	.959727	.960431	.961133	.961829
.92	.962522	.963211	.963896	.964577	.965253	.965927	.966595	.967260	.967919	.968576
.93	.969228	.969876	.970519	.971158	.971792	.972422	.973048	.973669	.974285	.974897
.94	.975504	.976106	.976704	.977297	.977885	.978467	.979045	.979618	.980187	.980750
.95	.981308	.981859	.982407	.982948	.983485	.984015	.984541	.985060	.985573	.986081
.96	.986583	.987080	.987568	.988053	.988530	.989001	.989466	.989924	.990375	.990821
.97	.991258	.991690	.992114	.992530	.992939	.993340	.993733	.994119	.994497	.994866
.98	.995227	.995579	.995923	.996257	.996581	.996896	.997200	.997493	.997777	.998048
.99	.998308	.998555	.998788	.999008	.999212	.999400	.999571	.999721	.999849	.999947
1.00	1.000000									

Fig. 18. (Concluded.)

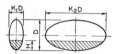

$$\text{Total volume} = \frac{\pi}{6} K_1 K_2 D^3$$

a. General ellipsoid.

$$\text{Total volume} = \frac{\pi}{6} D^3$$

b. Sphere.

$$\text{Total volume} = \frac{\pi}{6} K_1 D^3$$

$$(K_1 = 0.5)$$

c. Two ellipsoidal heads for horizontal tank.

$$\text{Total volume} = \frac{\pi}{6} K_2^2 D^3$$

$$(K_2 = 2.0)$$

d. Two ellipsoidal heads for upright tank.

Fig. 19. Ellipsoidal shapes applicable to Fig. 17.

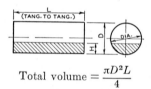

$$\text{Total volume} = \frac{\pi D^2 L}{4}$$

Fig. 20. Partially filled horizontal cylinder.

The use of the coefficients in Fig. 17 for partial volumes of dished heads will give results within practical limits of accuracy; however, a more nearly correct value for the total volume of a dished head may be calculated from the following, using the formula for hemiellipsoidal head volume as a base:

$$\text{Hemiellipsoidal head volume, } V = \tfrac{2}{3} \pi K R^3$$

where V = total volume of one head in cubic feet
R = radius of cylinder in feet
K = ratio of the depth of the head (not including the straight flange) to the radius of the cylinder (for the hemiellipsoidal head, $K = 0.5$ by definition of the ellipse)

For a dished head, $K = M - \sqrt{(M-1)(M+1-2m)}$

where M = ratio of radius of dish, in feet, to the radius of the cylinder, in feet
m = ratio of the radius of the knuckle, in feet, to the radius of the cylinder, in feet

The volume of a bumped head, $V = \dfrac{\pi}{2} K R^3 \left(1 + \dfrac{K^2}{3}\right)$

where V = total volume of one head, in cubic feet
R = radius of cylinder, in feet
$K = M - \sqrt{M^2 - 1}$, where M is defined as above

The **total volume or the straight length** to be required in a horizontal cylindrical tank, Fig. 21, with ellipsoidal or hemispherical heads may be determined by the following formulas:

$$V = \frac{\pi D^2}{4}\left(L + \frac{4B}{3}\right)$$

$$L = \frac{4V}{\pi D^2} - \frac{4B}{3}$$

where V = total volume in cubic feet
L = length of cylindrical shell, in feet
B = depth of heads, in feet
D = diameter of cylinder, in feet

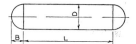

Fig. 21. Horizontal cylindrical tank with ellipsoidal or hemispherical heads.

Surface areas of tank heads and roofs can be computed as follows:

Ellipsoidal and dished heads: $S = \pi R^2 [1 + K^2(2 - K)]$

Bumped head: $S = \pi R^2(1 + K^2)$

where S = approximate surface area, in square feet
R and K are as defined earlier

Conical roof: $S = 0.787\ D^2$ when pitch is ¾ in 12
$S = 0.792\ D^2$ when pitch is 1½ in 12
Umbrella roof: $S = 0.842\ D^2$ when radius equals diameter
$S = 0.882\ D^2$ when radius equals 0.8 diameter

where S = approximate surface area, square feet
D = tank diameter, feet

Measurement of Liquid Volumes. The measurement of liquid volumes is described in the American Society for Testing Materials Manual on Measurement and Sampling of Petroleum and Petroleum Products, which includes procedures, equipment, and calculations for different types of tanks and gaging facilities in nonpressure, low-pressure, and high-pressure storage. Reference should also be made to the American Petroleum Institute Standard No. 2500—Measuring, Sampling, and Testing Crude Oil, and to the ASME-API Code No. 1101 for Installation, Proving, and Operation of Positive Displacement Meters. Many companies have prepared similar detailed instructions for the measurement of liquids in their own operations.

The use of so-called **automatic gaging and temperature measuring devices is** increasing. The two devices are not necessarily installed in all cases. The greater number of installations at the present time make use of a liquid-level indicator only, to be read on the ground at the tank site or, through transmission of electrical impulses to a receiving instrument at a central location, such as a pump house. The receiving instrument may be connected to a number of tanks. The instruments offer considerable savings in time, in lessened exposure to possible hazards in manual gaging, and in the safe utilization of a greater percentage of actual tank capacity.

TANK MAINTENANCE AND SERVICE. The internal cleaning of storage tanks may present a number of potential hazards, such as the possibility of fire or explosion; poisoning from toxic liquids, vapors, or dust; asphyxiation; and physical injury caused by poor lighting, insecure footing, falling objects, etc. It is imperative that prior to the start of the work a **proper procedure** be adopted with regard to the volatility and toxicity of the stored liquid; the availability of water, steam, air, electricity, and necessary equipment; and disposal facilities for oil and sludge. With proper precautions, procedures, and equipment the **potential hazards** need not cause trouble. Proposed procedures and time schedules must be approved by the authorities having jurisdiction, including the fire and safety departments.

For a detailed description of preparations, equipment, and cleaning methods applicable to hydrocarbon storage, reference should be made to the American Petroleum Institute Accident Prevention Manual No. 1—Cleaning Petroleum Storage Tanks, which consists of two parts available separately: Section A—Crude Oil and Unfinished Products Tanks, and Section B—Gasoline Tanks. The **manuals** may serve as guides in preparing procedures for liquids other than crude oil, unfinished petroleum products, and gasoline.

It is important that everyone engaged in a cleaning operation be made aware of the circumstances to be encountered, such as the **presence of combustible or poisonous gases,** such as hydrogen sulfide and the aromatic hydrocarbons, and of the ability of dry iron sulfide to ignite combustible material. In addition, all workmen must be thoroughly trained in the operation and care of safety equipment; they must know the limitations of this safety equipment as well as all practical safety rules and the reasons for them.

In the study of the literature on the subject of tank cleaning, it will be noted that tanks in some services may be entered without masks after the gas concentration has been reduced to a safe percentage. The limits of safe concentrations may be generally satisfactory, but exceptions may arise in the case of certain individuals whose skin, eyes, or respiratory tracts are unusually sensitive to certain irritants. Susceptibility to irritants would not be limited to tank-cleaning work alone, of course, but would be troublesome in all phases of the storage and handling operations.

Freeing tanks of gas by steam or air ventilation has not proved entirely satisfactory because safe performance of this operation takes a considerable amount of time. If steaming is required owing to the presence of combustible gases, the tank interior should be heated to at least 170° F.; this factor has limited its effectiveness to the smaller sizes. A fairly recent development in gas-freeing which is receiving attention (Petroleum Processing, vol. 10) makes use of water-fog nozzles in roof openings through which air enters the tank—a method which assures a thorough wetting of interior atmosphere and metal surfaces. Gases are displaced by the entering moisture-burdened air through a flexible tube which extends from a roof opening to a point near the tank bottom but above the sludge. Several roof openings must be available before this method can be used.

HIGH-VISCOSITY LIQUIDS. The loading and unloading of high-viscosity liquids involves the problem of rate of flow. Oils, tars, and similar material shipped in tank cars or in ships are normally loaded by **gravity flow** through relatively large-diameter pipes and hoses. The viscosity being variable in relation to the heat of the material, it is usually necessary to **apply heat** to the material in its storage tank and heat to the delivery pipes and flexible hoses. Steam or hot-water coils in the storage tanks, and jacketed pipes and hoses are basic requirements in both the loading and unloading of carriers. If gravity flow is not adequate, additional flow speed may be had by the **use of pressure** within the storage container or by **special pumps** in the delivery lines. Pressure is usually obtained by compressed air, but with certain products hydraulic pressure is used. Unloading of tank ships and tank cars of viscous materials likewise requires the use of heat and pumping equipment.

LOW-VISCOSITY LIQUIDS. Gasolines and similar liquids are loaded and unloaded by **gravity flow** or are pumped by **special pumps.** Heated lines are not required, although with some highly volatile liquids, **cooling jackets** may be required in hot weather. Special attention must be given to the particular hazards inherent in the liquid being handled. Low-flash-point liquids require careful installation and operation of handling pumps and hoses. Standard fire and insurance regulations specify in detail the protection required for the hazards involved (see Fire Protection Systems).

Another consideration in handling liquids, particularly those of low viscosity, is the chemical reactions to the handling equipment. Highly corrosive liquids—sulfuric and nitric acids, alkali solutions, etc.—require special **corrosion-resistant equipment** and special care in the connecting and operation of handling equipment.

SPECIAL LIQUIDS. Under the heading of special liquids can be placed liquids for human consumption. These include milk, beverages, and special items in the baking and confectionery fields. Obviously, these liquids require absolutely clean containers and connecting pipelines, including the loading and unloading lines and pumps. Other special requirements for the storage of particular liquids will apply to the loading and unloading equipment.

IN-PROCESS HANDLING OF BULK MATERIALS

CONTENTS

CONTENTS *(Continued)*

IN-PROCESS HANDLING OF BULK MATERIALS

Bulk Solids Blending and Allied Processes

SCOPE OF BLENDING. The term "blending," as applied to chemical and metallurgical processes, is sometimes used rather loosely to designate a number of inherently different specific operations. Applying the designation to those processes concerning bulk solids only, the term is often used in reference to processes that might more accurately be described as proportioning or mixing.

PROPORTIONING OPERATIONS. Some operations involve adding one or more ingredients to a base element or combining several major components, all in predetermined proportions. Merely bringing raw materials together in definite amounts often satisfies the requirements of this operation. Since no steps other than measuring by weight or volume are necessary, a term more accurately describing this process would be "proportioning."

Proportioning is the operation of **accurately combining proper components** in specified quantities to produce a final product of predetermined analysis. The proportioning may be **by weight** or **by volume**. It can be done **batch by batch** or **continuously,** by drawing predetermined proportionate amounts of materials from bins, silos, or piles by means of feeders discharging to a common collecting conveyor. The volume delivered by each feeder may be predetermined by controlling the feeder speed, or the feeders may be self-controlled according to the weight per unit being discharged.

Among the representative examples of proportioning by batches are those connected with the charging of a blast furnace, in filling the mixer in an asphalt plant, or in loading ready-mix trucks at a concrete plant. In all such cases, predetermined quantities of the various elements used are drawn from storage and charged, individually, into the processing receptacle.

The problems associated with proportioning are essentially those of accuracy of measurement, and the relationship between the cost of increasing such accuracy, as well as the physical requirements of the process and the economic results brought about from such increased costs.

FUNDAMENTALS OF MIXING. In many operations a homogeneous product is required when the components have been proportioned. For this purpose an entirely different process most accurately termed "mixing," must be applied. Mixing may be defined as the process of intimately combining two or more constituents, each of which is assumed to be continuously uniform in the properties required in the end product. Among the kinds of equipment used for this process are paddle mixers, pug mills, and mullers. Mixing can be carried on in **batches,** as is the case with concrete or molding sand, or **continuously,** as when streams of high-volatile and low-volatile coal for the production of coke are combined.

Mixing to **regroup material that has been segregated during storage** is often carried on without a preliminary proportioning step. When material is piled in a cone, whether on the ground or in a bin, coarse particles roll to the edge. As the pile increases in height, fines are concentrated at the center and coarse material around the perimeter. When material is drawn from below such a pile or bin, a narrow shear cone is formed, and only fines are drawn out until coarse pieces from the edges start to roll into the top crater. From then on the draw-off contains progressively greater percentages of coarse material. Fig. 2 illustrates the segregation of fine and coarse particles in storage.

One method of **remixing** such segregated material is to draw it off continuously, from a series of bins which are filled in rotation, onto a single conveyor. The result is that full or nearly full bins will be discharging preponderantly fine material, while nearly empty bins will be discharging mostly coarse material. When material is being reclaimed from open storage piles by grab bucket or dragline, mixing can be carried on by digging—in rotation—from the top and center of the pile, where fines are concentrated, to the bottom and sides, where the coarse material is located.

In any case and for whatever reason the process of mixing is carried out, the problems involved are primarily those of equating the costs of the process selected with the requirement for high degrees of homogeneity in the end product.

BLENDING. When a high degree of uniformity in the end product is essential, or economically justified, merely proportioning the raw materials with maximum accuracy and mixing them with the greatest thoroughness will not produce the desired results if all or any of the raw materials are variable within themselves in any of the important elements. To avoid having such a condition occur, still another process is applied: minimizing the variation in the chemical and/or physical characteristics of the basic constituents that make up the final end product. This process is called "blending," and it may be defined as the **combining of any number of constituents** which may be individually, or relatively, variable—physically or chemically. The resultant product, when drawn from the blending process, will be uniform and homogeneous and will have the same physical and chemical properties as the average of the entire input of raw material.

Advantages of Blending. Among the important factors determining the capacity of any bulk-material processing plant are the physical and chemical uniformity of the raw material used. If physical characteristics—for example, size distribution, percentage of moisture, or specific gravity—vary widely, handling and processing equipment must be provided which can cope with the most unfavorable combinations of such conditions. During periods of normal operation this equipment will not be operating at full capacity.

If chemical analysis shows that the mix varies, the make-up of the charges to the process must sometimes be changed. The **number of such changes** usually is kept as low as possible by overcompensation, which may result in an increase of waste products or slag, and lowered plant production. Proper blending of the raw materials, however, will result in making the individual components of the charge both physically and chemically uniform. Under such conditions all processing and handling equipment can run at peak capacity, and the chemical reactions can take place under the most favorable conditions.

When it is important that a **uniform end product** be produced, it is essential that uniform ingredients be used. If the blending system used is suitable and properly operated, the raw materials supplied to the process will be of uniform analysis, and operating problems inherent in attempting to compensate for fluctuating characteristics in the feed will be eliminated. Furthermore, the risk of quality variation in the final product will be reduced to a minimum.

If reserves of high-grade raw materials can be blended with fractional proportions of lower-grade materials, then the reserve stocks may last for many years beyond their normally expected life. If the elements are thoroughly blended, a uniformly homogeneous product having a predetermined physical and chemical analysis of acceptable quality will result. For example, it might be impractical to recover low-cost coal, containing 50 percent ash, for use in power plants, but the blending of 1 ton of such coal with every 2 tons of an 8-percent-ash coal would give a usable 22-percent-ash fuel of uniform quality.

In considering the **economics** of such an operation, the extra costs must be balanced against the savings. The extra costs will include items such as first cost and operating expense of the blending system, and possible increase in plant operating cost due to the use of a lower-grade raw material. These costs would be offset by the lower over-all first cost of raw material because of its lower grade, reduction in operating costs brought about by consistent uniformity of raw material, postponement of the exhaustion date of high-grade reserves (which might then necessitate operating on a still lower grade of material), or even relocation of the plant to a point closer to the source of its supply of raw material.

Another phase of this problem is the need for **upgrading raw material reserves,** which by analysis may be found to be deteriorating. This upgrading may be done by blending the inferior materials with fractions of higher-grade materials in proper proportions to produce a commercially acceptable product.

The advantages of product uniformity obtained by blending can be gained by any industry that uses, or processes, bulk materials in which variations in either physical or chemical properties would reduce production, cut down efficiency, and sacrifice quality.

PRINCIPLES OF BLENDING. Fluctuation in analysis of any one of the component materials used in a process can often be compensated for by suitable variations in other components—thus obtaining a commercially acceptable uniformity in the final product. Such practices, however, are costly. Irregularities in production, increase in man power, and greater consumption of the compensating elements are some of the measurable cost-raising factors. An evaluation of such costs will lead to a determination of the savings that can be made by the installation of a **blending system.** The type of blending system selected must be determined by checking the values of greater degrees of product uniformity obtainable against the cost of systems that will give such uniformity.

In Fig. 1 it is assumed that one of the raw materials used in a process is received from five sources. It contains a component X that varies, as shown, in the material received from each source.

Source	Percent of Total	Percent of X		Percent of X in Total		
		Minimum	Maximum	Minimum	Average	Maximum
A	10	5	10	0.5	0.75	1.0
B	15	5	15	0.75	1.50	2.25
C	20	0	5	0 —	0.50	1.0
D	20	10	15	2.0	2.50	3.0
E	35	0	10	0 —	1.75	3.5
	100	0	15	3.25	7.00	10.75

Fig. 1. Typical variation of component X in materials received from each source.

Consider the effect on the **analysis of the combined raw input** by handling it in three different ways:

1. It can all be put into a stockpile as received and withdrawn for processing as needed.
2. Material from each source can be put into its own individual bin as received and drawn out of the five bins (in the same proportion as needed) onto a single conveyor.
3. Raw material as received from all sources can be deposited in many thin layers in one long bed and recovered by taking thin vertical slices from the pile (each slice would then contain a sample of every layer, like the slices of a seven-layer cake).

In any case, the over-all average amount of X will be 7 percent, but when using a single stockpile, samples may vary between 0 and 15 percent, or as high as 114 percent over average. With the bin system, if the five superimposed layers on the collecting conveyor could be thoroughly mixed, samples would vary between 3.2 percent and 10.75 percent, or up to 53 percent above the average. With a bed-blending system, the more layers that are in the pile, the greater is the reduction in the range of variation. With 400 layers, 99.7 percent of all samples in the foregoing hypothetical blend would vary between 6.62 percent and 7.38 percent, or up to 5.4 percent over the average.

Blending reduces analysis variation not only in the desirable component of a raw material but also in all the other components. The result is that **less fluxing or correcting additives are used,** and greater net tonnage production per gross ton is charged. In the hypothetical case analyzed above, ideal operating conditions are assumed. In actual practice, however, circumstances of sufficient importance may exist that in themselves will determine the type of blending installation that can be used. Four such governing factors are segregation, stickiness, weather, and dust.

Segregation. If the material put into piles or bins is not all of one size, segregation of fine and coarse particles will result. The bed-blending diagrams in Fig. 2 show this effect. When building up a pile, the large pieces will roll to

Fig. 2. Segregation of fine and coarse particles in storage.

the bottom edges (A); opening the gate underneath draws off fines through the central shear cone (B); when the crater is refilled, coarse material rolls down into the cavity (C); and subsequent draw-offs bring down first a wedge of fines and then the accumulated coarse layer (D). The fine material drawn off in B does not compare with the coarse material drawn off in D, and a uniform blend cannot be expected under these conditions.

Stickiness. When blending the products from several bins or piles, a uniform controlled rate of feed from each bin or pile is necessary. If the material contains an appreciable percentage of fines, and moisture is present in sufficient quantity, the material will pack and arch in bins, and a uniform continuous flow will not be obtained. This condition is common, for example, in the case of washed fine coal, copper concentrates, and certain iron ores.

Weather Conditions. The effect of rain, snow, or freezing temperatures on the material being blended should be considered in determining the kind of system that would be workable. In some climates, for example, blending might have to be done under cover or even in heated buildings.

Dust. If a material contains values which are finely divided and dry, as in the case of copper-ore concentrates, blending should not be done in open piles or beds, because high winds will cause loss of the valuable product and might also cause objectionable working and living conditions in built-up areas.

BLENDING PROCEDURES. In many industries the raw materials used are so variable that blending has become recognized as an essential procedure. Casual attempts to obtain a blended product are often carried on without special facilities. The results obtained through such methods are far from consistent or uniform. Practically all methods of large-scale blending of bulk materials, no matter how crude or how elaborate they may be, operate on the "seven layer cake" principle. That is, from three or four layers to many hundreds of layers are piled one on top of another, and "slices" are removed which contain increments from a few or from all of these layers. The highest degree of uniformity in the blended product will obviously result when a maximum number of layers has been piled, and when recovery is made simultaneously from all these layers.

One such form of blending is practiced in the ore yards of many blast furnaces by spreading bucket-loads of ore in such a manner as to approximate an **overlapping series of layers or piles** until the entire storage area is covered. The ore is reclaimed by a bucket digging approximately cross-sectionally from one end of the area toward the other end. The amount of blending done is spotty at best and completely unpredictable. Furthermore, the results depend entirely on the human element. The possibilities obtainable cannot always be realized because of space limitations or lack of the extra time required.

Coal used to manufacture coke for metallurgical purposes and to produce power in steam-generating plants may vary widely in ash and sulfur content, in coking properties, and in Btu. value. These variations may be reduced to some extent by **systematic stocking and reclaiming methods.** One large coke plant, for example, builds up its coal storage pile by making a windrow alongside a conveyor line with a traveling stacker and spreading the coal over a considerable area with a bulldozer. Many layers are built up in this manner. Reclaiming is started at one end by working across the entire pile with a second bulldozer that pushes the coal within reach of a crane which loads the reclaiming conveyor. Actual results showed a slight reduction in daily fluctuation, but the weekly averages of ash content in the reclaimed coal varied just as widely as in the coal put into storage.

Another method of blending coal is by **building up a large pile in layers** under a high-line tripper conveyor. The coal is reclaimed through a series of gates by a tunnel conveyor running under the center line of the pile. The gates are opened progressively from one end, with the result that a "cross section" of the pile is represented in any reclaimed increment. The "cross section" is irregular and nonuniform, and the segregation problem is not overcome. Whatever reduction in deviation of ash and sulfur content is obtained by this method will not be consistent because of the difficulties of securing reliable average samples.

BLENDING BINS. The simplest form of bin used for blending consists of a **series of cells or silos** laid out either in one row or in two or more **parallel** rows. Each element of the required blend is put in its own compartment by chute, tripper, or shuttle conveyor from above and is drawn off through a gate below onto a common collecting conveyor by a conventional feeder of suitable kind. The material is laid on this conveyor in a series of layers corresponding to the various bin components and must pass through units that will thoroughly mix it, such as a crusher, paddle, mixer, or other piece of equipment, before it can approach a blended state.

An arrangement of this kind can serve as a **proportioning as well as blending unit,** but over a basic period of time the input to the individual silos must be at the same rate as the required drawoff. The material must be free-flowing, and the content of any one bin compartment must be, within itself, both chemically and physically uniform and must remain uniform if there are to be acceptable results. Since these ideal conditions are seldom found in practice, only very rarely can a closely blended product with a high degree of uniformity be pro-

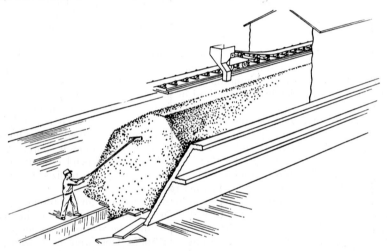

Fig. 3. Storage bin in the shape of a long rectangle with unobstructed interior.

duced by this method. If the material put into any one section should vary in composition, a blend will not result, since with this system it is not possible to blend material on one section of the gathering conveyor with the material following it a hundred feet or so behind. If the particles vary in size, pouring the material into a bin will segregate them, so the coarsest will roll to the edges while the finest will remain in the center. Furthermore, if moist fines are present, plugging and bridging may take place; the flow through one or more sections of the bin would thereby be restricted or possibly cut off altogether, thus defeating the objective.

Many bins are in operation that have been designed specifically for blending and that overcome some of the objectionable features of the conventional silo-type blender. Such bins are usually in the shape of a **long rectangle** with an unobstructed interior (see Fig. 3). Material is put in by overhead tripper line or shuttle conveyor in a series of layers extending the full length of the bin. Sometimes the contents of several cars are dumped at one time followed by additional successive series of dumpings until the bin is full. This procedure produces the effect of "layering" material of variable analysis. The bottom of the bin has a continuous slot along the center line which is closed by transverse planks or railroad ties. A gathering conveyor served by a traveling feeder runs under the slot. When a bin is to be emptied, planks are removed at one end of the bin, and additional planks are successively removed as material is drawn out, so that the bin is emptied from one end to the other. It is frequently necessary to have men inside the bin to remove the planks and to rake material down the slope of the pile.

Since material is drawn out approximately cross-sectionally, elements representing **several different layers** are present in any sample from the gathering conveyor; some degree of blending is therefore accomplished. A bin of this kind is more suitable than the conventional silo, because material of varying characteristics and damp or sticky material can be handled. This method reduces the range of variability in the components of the raw material, but the results will be neither predictable nor consistent. Since the human element is involved in emptying the bin, the chance of obtaining uniform results is remote, and the need for having men inside the bin to clean out the material presents an occupational hazard because of the possibility of injury to the workers employed there.

BED-BLENDING SYSTEM. The most highly developed method of blending large volumes of bulk materials with the greatest degree of uniformity is the bed-blending system. This method of blending is actually a large-scale sampling system. Any unit of material drawn out is representative of all the material which has been put in. Since any unit is representative of the whole, all units are alike, and a perfect blending of the input has taken place.

The sampling principle applied under this system is that of intermittently taking a uniform section from a moving stream under the following conditions:

1. Constant intervals must be maintained between cuts, so that all sections along the length of the stream will be equally represented.
2. Cuts must be taken at intervals sufficiently frequent to make sure that abrupt changes in the character of the stream will be represented.
3. A constant rate of flow must be maintained, so that all samples will equal the others in size.

The application of this principle requires taking two steps:

1. Spreading the material at a uniform rate, back and forth over a long area, thus gradually building up a pile generally triangular in cross section and composed of hundreds of layers.
2. Reclaiming the layered pile or bed after it has been completed, by consecutively removing small cross-sectional increments.

This system is shown diagrammatically in Fig. 4.

Any individual slice cut from the bed will contain elements from each of the horizontal layers. For example, if a bed contains 8,000 tons of ore and is made up of 400 layers, it will take 20 tons to make one layer. If the pile is 200 ft. long, it will contain 40 tons per lineal ft., or 6,667 lb. per lineal in. If material is brought from the bedding system at the rate of 250 tons per hr., reclaiming will be at the rate of 1½ in. per min. A conveyor traveling 250 ft. per min. carries 400 lb. of ore on a 12-ft. length of belt. This load is made up of 1-lb. increments from each layer, or 1 lb. from every 20 tons originally laid down.

When a **new bed is started,** the first pass spread along its length will form a windrow roughly triangular in cross section. Assuming that the material handled weighs 100 lb. per cu. ft. and has a 45° angle of repose, the windrow will be about

34 in. across the base and 17 in. high. The second pass will add a layer about 5 in. thick on top of the windrow, and each additional pass will add another layer. These layers will get thinner and thinner because of the increasing surface area of the pile, until, at the 400th pass, the last layer will be about 0.3 in. thick. Even though the layers get progressively thinner, the cross-sectional area remains constant because the tonnage deposited per ft. is uniform. Thus, by laying down the same amount of material on the pile in each layer, the principle of sampling requiring that increments of equal size be taken has been satisfied.

Actual methods of building up the layered bed are described later in this section, but a typical method is to **run a tripper back and forth** along the belt conveyor over the longitudinal center of the pile. If the tripper travels at the same speed in both the forward and return direction less material will be deposited per foot of pile when it is going in the same direction as the belt than when it is traveling against the belt. Therefore, to accomplish the uniform result necessary,

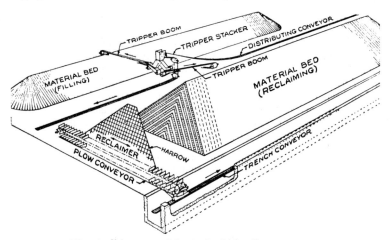

Fig. 4. Diagram of basic bed-blending system.

suitable speeds must be selected (with the faster travel against the belt), so that uniform layers will be formed, regardless of the direction in which the tripper is moving. With the bedding system, a blend of predetermined accuracy and high degree of uniformity can be obtained that will be unaffected by segregation and does not require that the material be free-flowing. The necessary physical components of this system are a storage area, equipment for building a layered pile, and equipment for reclaiming the material from the bed.

Storage Area. The storage area ideally should be of sufficient size so that each individually laid bed or pair of twin beds is large enough to contain a complete cycle of proportionate receipts of incoming material from each source. Under this condition, the material reclaimed will always be of the same uniform analysis. In practice, however, receipts of raw material from various sources of supply may not follow a definite pattern, and in this case, the analysis of material reclaimed from different beds may vary slightly. The minimum requirements when only one general kind of material is to be blended would be **two beds**, so that while blended material is being reclaimed from one bed, the second bed is in the process of being built up. It is usually preferable to provide for a minimum of three beds, so that one will be available as a surge pile to take care of possible irregularities in the receipts or in consumption.

Bedding Equipment. Many different methods may be employed to build up a layered bed. The choice of the most economical method is determined by factors such as the space available, the number of beds to be used, and whether the beds are to be covered or open. With covered beds a minimum roof span and amount of structure will be required when a single belt conveyor is used with a tripper running in a monitor over the top of each bed for its full length. When a large number of relatively **short beds** are to be formed one at a time, an installation can be made consisting of a **high-line conveyor** running across the foot of all the beds, with a tripper to feed onto a traveling bridge conveyor that is spotted over the bed being formed. This bridge conveyor also carries a tripper to build up the layers.

When the system includes only a small number of beds, or when because of capacity requirements, several beds are to be formed simultaneously, a double-wing stacker traveling between two adjacent beds provides a very satisfactory arrangement. This stacker may be restricted to movement along its own conveyor, or it may be detachable from the tripper and moved from one pair of beds to another by means of a transfer car. The **boom conveyors** on this stacker may be lowered when the bed is first started and to minimize dust, gradually raised as layering progresses. Also, in case only one bed is to be made, the second boom can be raised to permit passage of the reclaimer on the adjacent bed.

EQUIPMENT USED IN RECLAIMING MATERIALS. Thin cross sections of the pile are continuously reclaimed by means of specially designed reclaiming machines. One such kind of machine consists of a **low-level traveling bridge** which carries a harrow of the same general shape as the face of the pile. This harrow oscillates slowly, and as it progresses into the pile, the many projecting spikes mounted on its forward face disturb the material sufficiently so that particles from the entire cross section slowly work their way to the foot. This continuous downward travel of particles throughout the face of the pile is further induced by the fact that the angle of the harrow is slightly steeper than the angle of repose of the material in the pile.

Also mounted on the bridge of the reclaimer is a **scraper conveyor** traveling along a bottom plate, which collects the accumulated material from the foot of the pile and carries it to one side. This scraper-conveyor may operate in one direction only, or the flights may be so designed that it can be reversed and discharged to either side. The scraper-conveyor discharges the blended material directly onto a gathering conveyor located in a trench running alongside the full length of the pile.

TYPE AND EXTENT OF BLENDING. The decision as to the type and extent of the blending method to be used depends primarily on the economics of the problem. Blending is done for two main reasons:

1. To **reduce the cost of subsequent processes** by producing a raw material of uniform analysis that will give smooth plant operation without the need for making frequent adjustments and compensations to accommodate variations.
2. To **conserve high-grade raw material** by blending it with lower-grade fractions to obtain a homogeneous, acceptable product, or to upgrade raw materials which may be depreciating in analysis, by blending them with higher-grade fractions.

In any case, the **degree of variance of the raw material** and the economics of its utility as received must be balanced against the anticipated economies that will result from the use of a product blended to a high degree of uniformity. The cost of normal storing and reclaiming that would be required in any case, even without blending, should also be taken into account. With this information available it will be possible to determine which kind of blending system should be selected and the expenditure that would be justified in making the proposed installation.

EVALUATION OF RESULTS OF BLENDING. Intelligent evaluation of the result of any system of mixing, proportioning, or blending requires a determination of the chemical and physical properties of each of the components being combined and also of the resultant product. **Representative samplings** of each constituent as well as of the end product, and **correct analyses** of the results require that careful selection be made of the proper kind and scope of the sampling procedure to be followed. Detailed standard methods are presented in the publications of recognized authorities on the subject. Oversampling increases the cost of sampling, while undersampling or improper sampling produces misleading data.

To evaluate the results of the analysis of properly obtained samples as applied to a blending operation, it is necessary to have a suitable yardstick for measuring the **degree of uniformity** of the characteristics of the product. The most common and useful scale is **Standard Deviation,** which is the square root of the average of the squares of the individual deviation of all samples from their mean. A discussion of the advantages of this index as a suitable measurement of uniformity can be found in standard statistical references.

Screens and Screening

ROLE OF SCREENING IN MATERIALS HANDLING. Screening or sizing is the grouping of materials according to their particle sizes by passing them through and/or over apertures (the screen-deck openings). As such, screening might more correctly be considered under materials processing. It is so basic an operation, however, and so frequently involved in the handling of bulk materials, that special consideration of it here is expedient.

Because screens are used for widely divergent purposes—for example, for removing lint from waste water and for separating animal hair from meat scraps and gristle in a rendering plant—no attempt at presenting a comprehensive discussion will be made. Rather, concern will be with the application of screens for the **sizing of granular materials.** Screen types discussed, however, will have application in more divergent applications, such as suggested in the foregoing. In addition, although many of the elements of theory and application under discussion will hold for screening in its broadest sense, that is, screening on shakers, vibrating screens, rotary trommels, and stationary grizzlies or screens, the primary concern will be screening on **vibrating screens,** which are the most widely used.

A few additional definitions are necessary:

1. Screening medium—the surface containing the openings or apertures (examples are screen cloth, punched plate, parallel-rod deck).
2. Screen—the **machine** which supports the screening medium and imparts a motion to it, often still referred to as a shaker.
3. Undersize—the material or particles in the feed that are smaller in size than the deck apertures.

4. Nearsize—that part of the undersize which is between approximately 75 and 100 percent of the size of the deck apertures; also referred to as marginal particles.

5. Oversize—the particles in the feed that are larger in size than the deck apertures.

THEORY OF SCREENING. The statement has been made that screening, and the application of screens, is an "art." There is involved such a multiplicity of interrelated variables in screening, that no single workable formula can be developed which will allow selection of screen or screening medium simply by the substitution of numerical values in an equation. For example, familiarity and **experience** with the peculiarities of magnetite concentrate pellets from taconite are mandatory for the proper selection of a screen and screening medium.

In any case, a completely theoretical approach to screening has never been successful, and such methods, formulas, and factors as are used to **guide** in the selection of screens were developed empirically. There are treatises on the theories involved in determining for a given set of conditions the amplitude and frequency combination which would effect a desired trajectory of a particle on a vibrating screen deck. Under these combinations a particle would be thrown forward from a solid portion of the screening medium in such a path that it would land in the center of an opening, thus greatly increasing the "probability" that the undersize particle will fall through the deck. All this is determined, only to have to admit that the conditions were oversimplified; the indeterminable effect of other particles of various sizes on a screening medium, bounding and rubbing against each other, cannot be neglected. This makes the original stated problem only a theoretical exercise, with little practical application.

Sound understanding of the fundamentals of screening is necessary to make proper selections. In **commercial sizing** or screening two basic processes take place:

1. Stratification—the process, or the phenomenon, whereby larger-size particles rise to the top of a bed of material being shaken or vibrated, while the smaller-size particles sift through the voids and find their way to the bottom of the bed.
2. Separation—the process of particles presenting themselves to apertures and being **rejected** if larger than the opening or **passed** through if smaller.

Proper **stratification** is an obvious necessity; without it, separation could not take place. In selecting a screen, **depths of beds** at both feed and discharge ends (for a continuous feed, as opposed to a batch, condition) must be reasonable for the size of the material and the size of the separation to be made. Thus for a given rate of feed, the **width** of screen selected is the predominant factor affecting stratification. Other interrelated factors on vibrating screens which affect stratification are:

1. Rate of travel—in turn a function of the material specifications, screening medium specifications, depth of bed, stroke or motion characteristics, and primarily **slope** of screen.
2. Stroke characteristics such as frequency, direction of rotation, type of motion, and, primarily, **amplitude.**

Peculiar as it may seem, there is such a thing as not having enough bed on a vibrating screen. Fig. 5 is a typical plot of the efficiency of a separation against various feed rates for a given screen size and feed breakdown analysis. With very small tons-per-hour feeds up to point *a*, efficiency actually increases with increased tonnage. This occurrence is explained by the fact that a certain bed of oversize material on top of the marginal particles prevents them from bouncing excessively, increases their number of tries to get through, and also helps to push them through. Beyond the optimum, point *a*, efficiency rapidly decreases with increased tonnage, simply because the screen is not large enough to handle the larger loads.

Stratification is continually upset, or nonexistent, in a **rotary-type screen** or trommel. This fact offers some insight into the recognized lesser efficiency of rotary screens as compared to that of vibrating screens. **Shaker screens,** because of the relative "gentleness" of their motion, effect little stratification and are consequently fed beds of material only a few lumps thick, which accounts in part for their relative inefficiency.

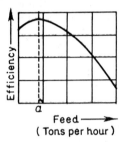

Fig. 5. Efficiency of separation vs. various feed rates.

Efficiency, as used in the preceding comparisons of screen types, refers to the ability of equal screening areas, in the various types, to remove undersize material from a given feed.

In the **separation** process it is important to recognize that, since particles are infinitely varied in shape, nearsize particles must have the opportunity to present themselves to an opening in many different positions. Conversely, particles with all dimensions considerably smaller than the deck openings will fall through readily.

The resulting situation is pictorially illustrated in Fig. 6. The graph at the bottom of Fig. 6 indicates the relative rates of flow through the screen deck, plotted along the deck length. This graph may also be considered as a cross section of the height of the material that has passed through the screen deck and has been allowed to pile up underneath it, after a batch feed, containing an even distribution of material smaller than the deck opening, has been screened. A corollary to this situation is that all the particles of the next smaller size (for example, ½ in. to ¾ in.) pass through the screening medium before all of the particles of the succeeding larger size (for example, ¾ in. to 1 in.). The position of the peak rise between *a* and *b* (Fig. 6), instead of being at the feed end, *a*, shows the effect of **stratification.** The area *a* to *c* is often referred to as the area of **saturation screening;** it is where particles of about 75 percent of aperture size are crowding through the screen deck. From *c* to *d*, the process of fit and pass, or reject, takes place.

It should also be recognized that a perfect screen separation (100 percent efficiency) is not commercially practicable, because from point *d* on, the "return" or capacity through the deck is extremely low. Theoretically, it can be argued that for an absolutely perfect separation, the screen would have to be infinitely long, thus making perfect screening an impossibility; that is, the curve of Fig. 6 would become asymptotic to the *X* (screen length) axis.

More practically, however, a **perfect separation** is defined by the standard of a sieve analysis, where a sample is retained on a sieve and the nearsize particles

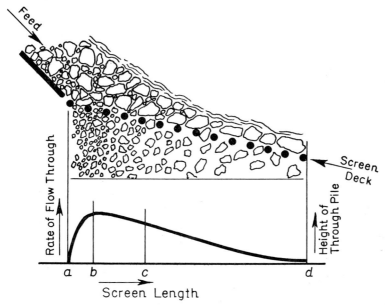

Fig. 6. Rates of flow through screen deck, plotted along deck length.

are given an opportunity to fit and try themselves for periods normally up to three minutes. A typical test-sieve run of crushed stone may take about 1½ min. Commercially, this time period is roughly equivalent to the travel time of material down the length of a 90-ft.-long screen. A 16-ft.-long screen, however, is about the biggest single unit manufactured. From these considerations, therefore, it is seen that on the basis of a simple screen separation, perfect screening is not commercially practicable. Screening is normally regarded "commercially perfect" if it is 95 percent efficient.

EFFICIENCY. Screening efficiency, or the efficiency of a separation, is generally and acceptably defined as follows:

(1) Efficiency =

$$\frac{\text{Percentage of feed (or amount) which actually passes through}}{\text{Percentage of feed (or amount) which is undersize (should pass through)}}$$

Since the job in every case is **to get undersize in the feed to pass through the screen deck,** the above definition is basic, following the universal concept that efficiency equals work or results achieved, divided by work put in or the potential.

A convenient way to determine the efficiency of a screen operation in the field is to obtain simultaneous samples of the feed and screen deck "overs" products, run a size breakdown or sieve analysis on them, and apply the following formula:

$$(2)\ \text{Efficiency} = \frac{100\ (a{-}b)}{a\ (100{-}b)}$$

Where a = percentage undersize in feed
b = percentage undersize in overs product

Efficiency, as defined in the foregoing, does leave something to be desired in so far as a complete indication of the performance of a screen is concerned. It does not reflect, say on a 1-in. separation, that the undersize in the feed in one instance may be made up largely of —¾-in. particles, which pass through the apertures readily, while in a second case this same amount of undersize may contain considerably more —1-in. +¾-in. or **nearsize** particles, which pass with greater difficulty and require many more opportunities to fit themselves into apertures before passing through. Formulas modifying the one above, and said to be more truly reflective of the efficiency of a screen, have been suggested. They involve the determination, with various definitions, of "difficult or critical sizes." These formulas, however, are not in general use.

On the basis of the argument that it is most applicable in those operations where oversize (waste or for recrush) is to be eliminated from the desired undersize product, efficiency as defined in the foregoing is also referred to as the **efficiency of recovery.** A second definition, called **efficiency of removal**, is then suggested, primarily to cover those applications where undesired fines are to be removed from the oversize product. Efficiency of removal is defined as the percentage of oversize in the feed divided by the percentage of feed actually going into the oversize product. Because efficiency of removal also fails to reflect the effect of nearsize particles, however, the same criticism made against efficiency of recovery applies.

Quite frequently, the practice is to state efficiency as the percentage of the overs product that is actually oversize material, or **100 minus the percentage of undersize in the overs product.** This latter item—the percentage of undersize in the overs—is the percent contamination of the overs (b in Formula 2). This third commonly used method of defining or expressing efficiency can be most misleading, because it does not account for the fact that there may be relatively little oversize in the feed, and even such a small amount of carry-over of marginal undersize particles that may occur still appears unfavorable in comparison with the small amount of true oversize.

Example. 1 in. separation, 100 tons-per-hr. feed, 90% efficiency (per Equations 1 and 2).

Case 1. Feed 90% minus 1 in., only 81 tons per hr. get through the screen, 9 tons per hr. of —1 in. material carries over, or $\left(\dfrac{9}{10+9}=0.47\right)$ 47% —1 in. in +1 in. product.

Case 2. Feed only 50% —1 in., 45 tons per hr. get through, 5 tons per hr. —1 in. carry-over, or $\left(\dfrac{5}{50+5}=0.09\right)$ 9% —1 in. in +1 in. product.

It should be noted that in both cases the efficiency of the screening performance is the same, yet in Case 1, with only 10 percent of +1-in. in the feed, the overs product was contaminated with undersize to the extent of 47 percent. This amount compares with only 9 percent in Case 2, where the only difference is that the feed contains 50 percent + 1 in. Thus it is seen that the apparent performance of a screen based on the simple analysis of its "overs" product may be deceiving. The relationship thus demonstrated is illustrated in Fig. 7. Again it is to be noted that for higher values of a (less oversize material in feed), considerable contamination of oversize product, b, occurs even at high efficiencies, as defined by Equation 1. This situation is strictly a result of the mathematics and definitions, not of empirics. Consequently, it is sound practice to be particularly conservative in screen-size selection where, for a given separation, the undersize material in the feed is in excess of 70 percent, and contamination of oversize product with undersize material is desired to be maintained below, say, 15 to 20 percent.

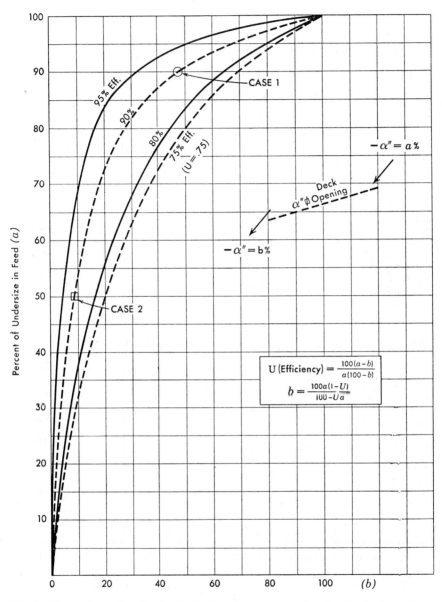

Fig. 7. Percentage of undersize in feed vs. percentage of undersize in "overs" at given efficiencies.

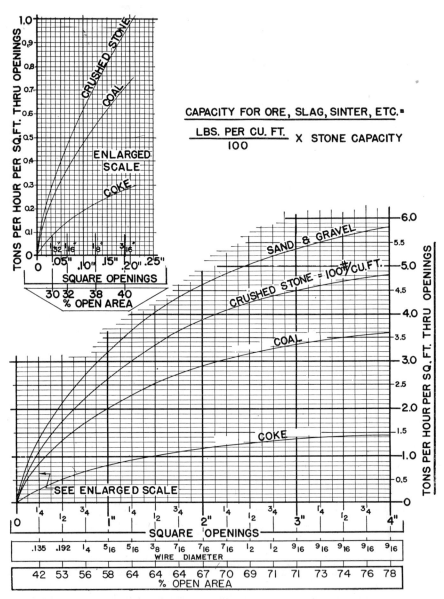

CAPACITY FOR ORE, SLAG, SINTER, ETC. =

$$\frac{\text{LBS. PER CU. FT.}}{100} \times \text{STONE CAPACITY}$$

Fig. 8. Screen capacity per square foot.

CAPACITY CALCULATIONS. There are three basic methods used for calculating capacity, and each has its proponents. These methods are:

1. Overflow method.   2. Through-flow method.   3. Total feed method.

Because of confidence gained through experience in the use of the through-flow method, only this one is explained here. Even for this one method, however, there are some differences of opinion as to values to be used for the various factors.

The basic formula for a given size separation is:

$$(3) \quad \text{Area} = \frac{\text{Capacity through}}{\text{Capacity through sq. ft.} \times \text{modifying factors } (f_F \times f_O \times \ldots)}$$

The unit capacity or capacity through per sq. ft. is obtained from Fig. 8 for the various **size openings** and **materials** indicated.

The **factors**, which are multiplied together in the **denominator** of Equation 3, are:

1. f_F—**fines factor** (see Fig. 9) selected against the percentage of feed **to the deck**, that is, one-half the size of the opening in the deck. It is a measure of the difficulty of the operation as compared with 40 percent "fines" ($f_F = 1$) for which the unit capacity is applicable.

Per-cent	Factor		
	Fines f_F	Overs f_O	Efficiency f_E
0	.44		
10	.55	1.05	
20	.70	1.01	
30	.80	.98	
40	1.00	.95	
50	1.20	.90	
60	1.40	.86	
70	1.80	.80	
80	2.20	.70	1.75
85	2.50	.64	1.50
90	3.00	.55	1.25
95	3.75	.40	1.00

Fig. 9. Fines, oversize, efficiency, and deck factors.

2. f_O—**oversize factor** (see Fig. 9) selected against the percentage of feed **to the deck** that is oversize. It is a measure of the effect of looking for the "needle in a haystack"; that is, although there may be little undersize, it will take screening area to allow stratification to occur. **This factor may be used as 0.80 in the range of 70-95 percent oversize if the screen selected is wide enough to effect a reasonable** (see Selecting Screen Size) **depth of bed at the discharge.**

3. f_E—**efficiency factor** (see Fig. 9) selected against the percentage of efficiency desired. Scalping (rough removal of fines from feed) efficiency is usually considered at **85 percent.**

Size Opening (Square)	f_w
$\frac{1}{32}$" or less	1.25
$\frac{1}{16}$"	3.00
$\frac{1}{8}$" and $\frac{3}{16}$"	3.50
$\frac{5}{16}$"	3.00
$\frac{3}{8}$"	2.50
$\frac{1}{2}$"	1.75
$\frac{3}{4}$"	1.35
1" or more	1.25

Fig. 10. Wet-screening factor vs. opening.

Fig. 11. Feed-chute sprays.

Pressure in Pounds per Square Inch	Diameter of Orifice in Inches											
	$\frac{5}{32}$	$\frac{3}{16}$	$\frac{7}{32}$	$\frac{1}{4}$	$\frac{9}{32}$	$\frac{5}{16}$	$\frac{11}{32}$	$\frac{3}{8}$	$\frac{13}{32}$	$\frac{7}{16}$	$\frac{15}{32}$	$\frac{1}{2}$
	Capacity in Gallons per Minute											
20	2.1	3.0	4.0	5.2	6.6	8.1	9.8	11.7	13.7	15.8	18.2	20.1
30	2.5	3.6	4.8	6.4	8.1	10.0	12.0	14.4	16.8	19.5	22.4	25.4
40	2.9	4.1	5.7	7.4	9.3	11.5	13.9	16.5	19.4	22.4	25.8	29.4
50	3.2	4.6	6.3	8.2	10.4	12.8	15.5	18.5	21.6	25.0	28.8	32.9
60	3.5	5.1	6.9	9.0	11.8	14.0	17.0	20.2	23.8	27.5	31.6	36.0
70	3.8	5.6	7.5	9.7	12.3	15.1	18.3	21.8	25.6	29.6	34.0	38.8
80	4.1	5.9	8.0	10.3	13.1	16.2	19.5	23.3	27.3	31.6	36.3	41.4
90	4.3	6.2	8.5	11.0	14.0	17.2	20.8	24.8	29.0	33.6	38.7	44.0
100	4.6	6.6	8.9	11.6	14.7	18.1	21.9	26.1	30.6	35.4	40.7	46.4

Link-Belt Co.

The width of the sheet spray is approximately equal to the distance from the hole in the pipe (usually 6 to 9 in.). Holes in the water pipe should be staggered slightly, longitudinally, to prevent adjacent sprays from striking each other when deflectors are closely spaced.

Fig. 12. Spray-pipe capacities (using drilled holes in pipe with duck-bill deflectors or nozzles).

4. f_D—**deck factor** (top deck = 1.00; 2d deck = 0.90; 3d deck = 0.75). This factor is used to make allowance for the fact that the screening decks other than the top deck do not receive their entire feed immediately at the feed end and consequently have less effective area than the apparent total area; that is, the second deck has its feed presented to it as indicated by the through product distribution in Fig. 6.

5. f_W—**wet-screening factor** (see Fig. 10) selected against the opening upon which the screening is being done. When water is sprayed on the material being screened, with a shower effect over the screening area, this water is particularly helpful in removing or screening the finer sizes. Water must be in sufficient quantity and well distributed over the screen deck, or it may actually be a deterrent to the removal of the finer (say $-\frac{3}{16}$ in.) particles. **To apply the wet-screening factor,** 3 to 5 gal. per min. of spray water per cu. yd. per hr. of feed must be added.

   In practice, part (one or two spray pipes) of the spray water should be added in the feed chute immediately before the screen. In this manner a thoroughly soaked feed is presented to the screen for maximum utilization of the screening area, and the advantage of a scrubbing action is utilized in the feed chute. To obtain the optimum scrubbing action, wash or feed boxes, such as shown in Fig. 11, are often used in conjunction with feed-chute spray.

   The chart in Fig. 12 is a helpful guide for interpreting gal. per min. of spray water into number of spray pipes (or conversely, in determining if the number of spray pipes in use measures up to a normal recommendation). Typical line pressures run between 30 and 60 lb. per sq. in., usually 40 lb. per sq. in., and $\frac{5}{16}$-in. to $\frac{1}{2}$-in. orifices are normally encountered.

6. f_{OA}—**open-area factor.**

$$f_{OA} = \frac{\text{Percent open area of the screening medium to be used}}{\text{Percent open area corresponding to the unit capacity (Fig. 8)}}$$

   The general practice is to accept the capacity (for a given aperture) as directly proportioned to the open area available in the screen deck. Where the deck preparation varies considerably in specification from that corresponding to the unit capacity, the open-area factor should be applied. Open area is appreciably altered when instead of the typical woven wire cloth, heavy-webbed perforated plates, slotted or rectangular opening cloth or plates, and parallel rod deck constructions are used. Open areas for the myriad combinations are generally tabulated in the various manufacturers' deck preparation catalogues. Fig. 13 lists formulas which may be used in calculating percentage of open areas.

7. f_S—**slotted-opening factor** (see Fig. 14), **used in addition** to f_{OA}, the open area factor, makes allowance for the fact that elongated or oblong openings will pass material with greater dispatch simply by virtue of the removal or minimizing of the cross-bar or cross-wire obstructions in the screening medium. To take full advantage of this fact, the long dimension of the slots should be parallel with the flow of material and in line with the motion of the screen. For slotted-opening screen cloth on the wider 5- and 6-ft. screens, and when employing very long slots (length/width>6), it may be advisable to consider better cloth life by having slots crosswise to the flow, which allows side tensioning of a much greater number of cloth wires. Where screened materials specifications are based on square or round openings, oblong openings normally can not be considered as a screening medium.

Up to this point nothing has been said about **moisture.** Dry or wet (with spray water) screening has been assumed. As often as not, however, bulk materials which have been quarried, milled, or mined contain varying amounts of moisture, making them at times difficult to screen. In such situations some increase in screen size should be considered. This is an area in which few or no formulas or

Percent open area:

P = percent open area
d = diameter of wire or horizontal width of bar (for rate)
a = clear opening dimension

By definition:

$$P = \frac{\text{Area of one opening}}{\text{Shaded area (see sketch)}} \times 100$$

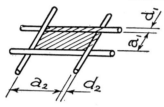

$$P = \frac{100\, a_1 a_2}{(a_1 + d_1)(a_2 + d_2)}$$

For square openings:

$$P = \frac{100\, a^2}{(a + d)^2} = 100\left(\frac{a}{a+d}\right)^2 \quad \begin{aligned}a_1 &= a_2 = a\\ d_1 &= d_2 = d\end{aligned}$$

For square openings
Specified in mesh (m):

$$P = 100\, a^2 m^2 \qquad m = \frac{1}{a + d}$$

For parallel rod decks:

$$P = 100\, \frac{a}{(a + d)}$$

For special weaves
(Ty-rod, non-blind, etc.):

Assuming $a_3 = a_1$

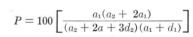

$$P = 100\left[\frac{a_1(a_2 + 2a_1)}{(a_2 + 2a + 3d_2)(a_1 + d_1)}\right]$$

Fig. 13. Formulas for the more common apertures.

Typical Deck Preparations	Length/Width Ratio (a_2/a_1, Fig. 14)	f_S
Square and slight rectangular openings	<2	1.0
Rectangular openings Ton-Cap	>2 but <4	1.1
Slotted openings Ty-Rod, Non-Blind	>4 but <25	1.2
Parallel rod decks	>25	1.4

Fig. 14. Slotted-opening factor.

tabulated guides exist. As a rule of thumb, where a slotted deck preparation (Non-Blind, Ton-Cap, or Parallel Rods) is figured on because of experience with square-opening cloth "blinding" due to moisture, then the f_S factor listed above should be neglected (equals 1.0); and the open-area factor (f_{OA}) strongly modified or neglected.

As a rough guide—applicable to a fair cross section of ores, coal, and aggregates—of when to turn to special opening shapes to offset blinding due to moisture, the following tabulation is offered. If **moistures** by weight exceed those indicated for the **size separation**, consider special aperture constructions. Moist materials are discussed below under the heading, The Moisture Problem.

Size	*Moisture*	*Size*	*Moisture*
Less than 1/16 in.	0 percent	5/16 in. to 3/8 in.	4 percent
1/16 in. to 1/3 in.	1 percent	7/16 in. to 1½ in.	6 percent
3/16 in. to 1/4 in.	2 percent	Over 1½ in.	No limit

In addition, consideration must be given to the theoretical **depth of beds** on a screen, which, as discussed under "stratification," serves as a guide in selecting the width of screen. Fig. 15 is a useful tool to this end, indicating the tons per hour

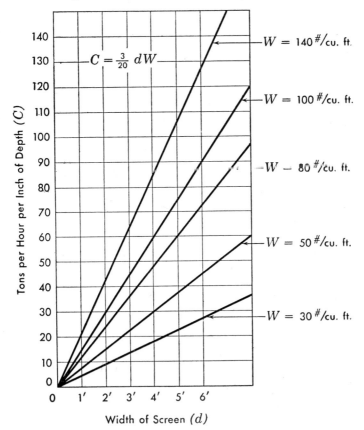

Fig. 15. Tons per hour per inch of depth of material traveling over screen at 1 ft. per sec.

VIBRATING SCREEN QUESTIONNAIRE

1. Material to be screened _____

2. Characteristics of material:
   Bulk density (pounds per cubic foot) _____
   - ☐ Bone dry.
   - ☐ Hot, _____ degrees F.
   - ☐ Flaky.
   - ☐ Damp.
   - ☐ Angular.
   - ☐ Clayey.
   - ☐ Sticky.
   - ☐ Granular.
   - ☐ Washed.
   - ☐ Wet.

   Moisture Content:
   % Surface (free) moisture.
   % Total moisture.
      ☐ By weight.

3. Feed analysis:
   Maximum size of piece in feed _____
   Minimum size of piece in feed _____
   Feed Breakdown Size Analysis:

Opening Size	Percent Passing Through Opening		
☐ Square or ☐ Round	Finest Analysis	Coarsest Analysis	Average Analysis

4. Rate of feed:
   Maximum (peak)_____ Tons per hr.   Average_____ Tons per hr.

5. Will water be added in screening? If yes, how many _____ gal. per min.?

6. How many separations (decks) are required? _____.

7. What **size** (or mesh) and **shape** (square, round, rectangular, non-blind) screening openings required for each separation:
   1st (top deck) _____   3d (bottom deck) _____
   2nd (middle deck) _____   4th _____

8. State requirement or preference in deck preparation for each separation:
   a. Screen cloth or perforated plate (skid bars).
   b. Wire diameter or web thickness.
   c. Direction of long dimension for slotted openings.
   d. Type of steel: plain, spring, oil tempered, stainless, manganese, other.
   1st _____
   2d _____
   3d _____
   4th _____

9. Maximum rate of material through each deck (or separation) (may be omitted if a comprehensive breakdown is given in Item 3, above).
   1st _____Tons per hr.   3d _____Tons per hr.
   2d _____Tons per hr.   4th _____Tons per hr.

Fig. 16. Vibrating screen questionnaire.

10. a. Efficiency (% of minus material to deck which passes through) required: _____% or
    b. Permissible percent of undersize in products:
       Product (size): _____   _____ %
                       _____   _____ %
                       _____   _____ %
11. Duty: Check (indicate if different for decks).
    ☐ Scalping.   ☐ Sizing wet.   ☐ Dewatering.   ☐ Rescreening.
    ☐ Sizing dry.   ☐ Washing.   ☐ Other _____
12. Condition of Feed:
                                    ☐ Conveyor.
    ☐ Continuous. How fed? by ☐ Feeder, kind _____
                                    ☐ Other _____
    ☐ Uniform or constant.   ☐ Varying.
    Spread uniformly across screen? _____.
    ☐ Batch fed, How?:
       ☐ Shovel _____   Batch size? _____   How often? _____
       ☐ Skip hoist _____ Batch size? _____   How often? _____
       ☐ Other _____   Batch size? _____   How often? _____
13. Screen will be operated:
    ☐ Continuously, _____ hr. per 24 hr.
    ☐ Intermittently, _____ (length of time) _____ times per 24 hr.
    Ambient temperature _____ ° F.
14. Is quotation on motor desired? _____ If yes, state characteristics of
    available electric circuit.
    ☐ AC_____ volts. _____ phase. _____ cycle.
    ☐ DC_____ volts.
15. Please indicate as completely as possible what screen you have in mind
    for this application.
    ☐ Single.
    ☐ Double deck, size _____ x _____, _____ in. stroke at _____ r.p.m.
    ☐ Triple.
    Other _____
    _____

       Type screen:
       ☐ Horizontally operating.
       ☐ Positive-stroke.   ☐ Right- hand drive, facing in direction
       ☐ Unbalanced-pulley.   ☐ Left-   of flow.
       ☐ Suspended, ☐ Base- or floor-mounted.
       Inclination _____ degrees, ☐ Forward
                                    ☐ Counterflow rotation.
16. Special features? (Examples: hoods, enclosures, hoppers, etc.). _____
    _____

17. Any physical layout restrictions? Additional remarks _____
    _____

    (Attach sketch of proposed installation.)
              By: _____ Title: _____
Proposal to be sent to:
    Firm _____ Your Inq. Ref.: _____
    Individual _____ Title: _____
    Street _____
    City and State _____

Fig. 16 (Continued.)

per inch of depth for various screen widths and material bulk densities. The chart is based on 1-ft.-per-sec. rate of material travel down the screen deck, which is typical or average for the great majority of applications on either inclined or horizontally operating vibrating screens.

There is no hard and fast rule for deciding what is an acceptable depth of bed. For a moist (say, 4 percent), cementitious —⅜-in. limestone, it would be best, even at the feed end, to have the bed no more than 1½ to 2 × average particle size of the feed, or a relatively thin bed. Generally with dry, free-screening materials, the bed at the feed end is of secondary importance to the bed at the discharge end. At the feed end it need be only within reason as far as the vibrating screen structure is concerned. The bed at the discharge is the controlling consideration and should be within 1½ × average particle size of the product over the deck for short screens (6, 8, and 10 ft.), and within 2 to 2½ × average particle size for the longer screens (12, 14, 16, 20, 24, and 28 ft.). For scalping operations considerable liberties may be taken with the above rules of thumb.

SELECTING SCREEN SIZE. A very homely and general way of stipulating a guide for the selection of the proper screen width is to say that it should be possible to see the screen deck through the bed within 1 to 2 ft. of the discharge end. In figuring a screen or approaching a screen manufacturer for a recommendation, it is fundamental that the more specific the data as to the application, the sounder can be the recommendation. Fig. 16 is a comprehensive **vibrating screen questionnaire.** In estimating the screen size, at least the following items must be known or practical assumptions of them made.

1. Material: (a) type, (b) bulk density, (c) percentage of moisture.
2. Tons-per-hr. feed.
3. Number of separations to be made (deck openings).
4. Analysis of size breakdown of feed; or percentages of the feed that are smaller and larger than openings, plus maximum size lump.
5. Wet screening.
6. Efficiency desired.

Example. Wet-screening separations of 100 lb. per cu. ft. of crushed stone are to be made at 1-in. and ⅜-in. square opennigs. Feed is 160 tons per hr. of —1½ in., with 90 percent —1 in. and 60 percent —⅜ in. Commercially perfect, or 95-percent-efficient, screening is desired. From the information given, and a knowledge of typical breakdown analysis for bank-run gravel, it is possible to plot (points 1 to 4) an assumed size breakdown analysis, as shown in Fig. 17. Fig. 18 is a tonnage analysis for a double-deck screen that might be selected for this application. Next comes the evaluation of the different factors; the result of this evaluation is tabulated in Fig. 19.

Note: Figs. 9 and 10 are interpolated for values other than those listed.
Each deck is considered as a separate problem; see especially f_F and f_O for the second deck.

Formula 3 can now be applied:

$$\text{Top Deck Area} = \frac{144}{2.65 \times 1.72 \times 1.05 \times 1 \times 1 \times 1.25 \times 1 \times 1} \doteq 24 \text{ sq. ft.}$$

$$\text{Bottom Deck Area} = \frac{96}{1.45 \times 1.11 \times .97 \times 1 \times 0.9 \times 2.5 \times 1 \times 1} = 27 \text{ sq. ft.}$$

The area requirement indicates a 3 × 10-ft. or 4 × 8-ft. screen. The longer screen would generally offer the higher efficiency. To help decide, however, the theoretical depth of beds needs to be checked. Using the figure of 45 tons per hr. per in. of

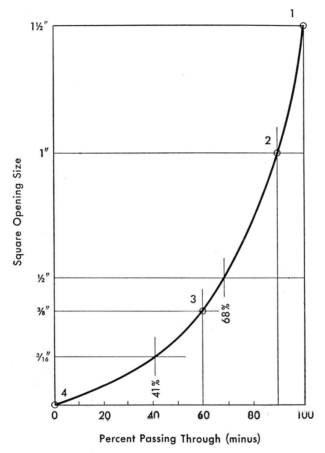

Fig. 17. Size breakdown analysis.

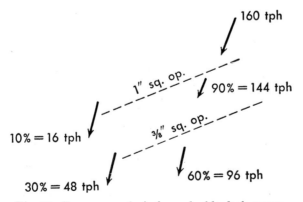

Fig. 18. Tonnage analysis for a double-deck screen.

	Top Deck	Bottom Deck
Unit capacity (Tons per hr. per sq. ft.)	1 in. opening stone 2.65	⅛-in. opening stone 1.45
f_F	68% fines 1.72	$\frac{41}{90}$ or 45.5% fines 1.11
f_O	10% overs 1.05	$\frac{48}{144}$ or $\frac{30}{90}$ or 33.3% overs..... 0.97
f_E	95% 1.00	95% 1.00
f_D	1st deck 1.00	2d deck 0.90
f_W	1 in. sq. opening......... 1.25	⅜-in. sq. opening.............. 2.50
f_{OA}	1 in. sq. opening 1.00	⅜-in. sq. opening.............. 1.00
f_S	1 in. sq. opening... ..... 1.00	⅜-in. sq. opening.............. 1.00

Fig. 19. Evaluation of factors for given example.

depth from Fig. 15 for a 3-ft. wide unit, the theoretical depths of the beds are as indicated in Fig. 20. The beds appear sensible, and, applying the rules of thumb:

Top Deck: 1½ × 1¼ in. (estimated average particle size) = 2-in. vs. ⅜-in. bed
Bottom Deck: 1½ × ⅝ in. (estimated average particle size) = 1-in. vs. 1-in. bed

Thus, the 3-ft. width is ample, and the selection is a double-deck 3 ft. × 10 ft. screen. It would not be inconsistent with good practice if a 4-ft. × 10-ft. or 12-ft. unit were finally selected and used so as to (1) be conservative at relatively little additional investment, (2) allow for surge loading, and (3) allow for overloading the plant.

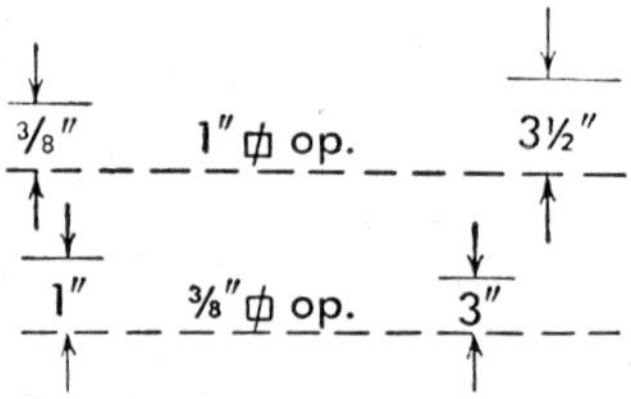

Fig. 20. Theoretical depth of beds.

In the foregoing example, which involves a multiple-deck screen, the **size** of the unit is based on the "critical deck" or the separation requiring the greatest area, in this case the bottom deck with 27 sq. ft. The **width** selection is often a compromise of the depth of bed considerations on the separate decks, since the rule of thumb affords some leeway. Screen **slope** is based on the deck with the greatest tonnage passing over the end.

When an inclined screen is selected, the matter of **slope** arises. Stroke and speed characteristics of horizontal screens usually effect a rate of travel in the order of 1 ft. per sec. For the inclined unit, this is also a good average rate of travel to expect and is the rate on which the empirical unit-capacity (see Fig. 9) is based. Factors affecting the rate of travel were indicated under the discussion on stratification. With so many variables it is most difficult to indicate in a simple, useful chart the precise angle for every application. The optimum slope for a given set of operating conditions is something to be determined by field adjustment. However, the table in Fig. 21 is useful in indicating an angle from which to start. The angles indicated in the inclination table (Fig. 21) are on the steep side, on the premise that inclined screens may be flattened without too much consequence as far as interference with chutes, etc., is concerned, while with the reverse (going from flat to steep) this would generally not be true. For the example worked out previously, a slope of 22° would be recommended, with counterflow rotation of the vibrator.

Width of Screen	Tons per Hour Passing Over									
	15	25	40	50	60	75	100	125	150	175 up
24″	18°	20°	23°	25°	27°					
36″	17°	19°	21°	22°	23°	25°				
48″	16°	18°	19°	20°	21°	23°	25°	28°		
60″	16°	17°	18°	19°	20°	21°	23°	25°	27°	
72″			17°	18°	19°	20°	21°	23°	25°	27°

For multiple-deck screens, base selection on deck passing greatest tonnage over its end.

Angles from horizontal listed are for counterflow rotation of vibrator which is generally recommended.

Slopes may be reduced by 5°–8° for with-flow vibrator rotation.

Fig. 21. Inclination table for circle-throw or modified circle-throw screens.

With the selection of an inclined screen, there is also the matter of stroke, speed, and direction of rotation. Some types and models of screens, usually intended for limited and/or specific applications, are available with only one stroke, usually with some speed variations. Still others have a straight-line motion which, in these instances, obviates any concern over direction of rotation. The following discussion applies to the predominant circle-throw (or modified circle-throw) screen specifically, but some of the considerations apply generally.

First, as indicated in Fig. 21, counterflow direction of rotation with a steeper angle produces higher efficiencies than with-flow rotation at a correspondingly flatter angle, in both cases the angle being such as to produce equal rates of travel. A matter of particular interest is the fact that tests have shown that the direction of rotation on circle-throw screens is a factor more critically affecting efficiency than variations in stroke and speeds within commercially accepted limits, again for equal rates of travel and with slopes varied to suit.

Reflection on the first observation removes credence from the arguments that by operating a screen flat, efficiency is increased because the openings present themselves more fully to the particles. Although, as in Fig. 22, the horizontal projection of the opening $b = a \cos a$ is smaller as the deck angle increases, its effect in preventing marginal-size pieces from fitting and passing themselves through the opening is negligible and certainly far outweighed and overcome by the beneficial effect of counterflow rotation, as one factor alone. There is evidence that at angles of 22° or greater, the effect of the small horizontal projection of the opening does become an appreciable factor.

Stroke (double amplitude or 2 × eccentricity) is the factor that predominantly affects the ejection of marginal oversize pieces from the openings they may be hanging in or plugging. (Speed, direction of rotation, and slope are also direct factors.) Thus the stroke should always be of sufficient amplitude to prevent plugging. This idea is illustrated in Fig. 22. Yet the stroke may be so large in

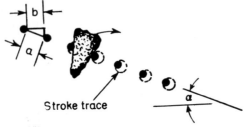

Fig. 22. Lump ejection vs. stroke.

relation to the deck-opening as to make it difficult for marginal size pieces to go through. This latter condition, illustrated in Fig. 23, primarily applies to the finer-mesh openings. Fortunately, because it simplifies the manufacturer's screen-design problem, it is also true that the higher amplitudes require considerably less frequency or vibrator speed, while with the smaller amplitudes higher frequencies are required in order to provide enough whip (centrifugal acceleration = a constant × stroke × speed^2) to agitate the material and effect stratification.

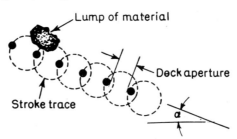

Fig. 23. Deck aperture vs. stroke.

Fig. 24 is a helpful **guide** in selecting strokes and approximate corresponding speeds. The effect indicated by Fig. 23 is relatively slight in its resultant effect on efficiency. When in doubt, or in borderline situations, it is better to choose the larger stroke, if available. In certain fine-mesh separations where moist, sticky fines are encountered, increasing the strokes beyond those recommended by the chart, has actually increased efficiency, because the increased agitation effects the loosening of the fines from the larger-size particles to which they stick.

Generally, however, for screening fine **moist** materials where the apertures tend to "blind" over, the smaller, high-speed strokes (high accelerations or whip) will best prevent blinding; but unless the bed depth is at a minimum, even at the feed end, there will be a tendency for the material to "pack." In one instance where —1/16-in. flotation coal was to pass through 1-in. × 4-in. openings on a cleaning screen, blanketing or matting took place with a 1/4-in. stroke at 1,000 r.p.m., with no blinding of opening, and with the result that every bit of the feed passed over the screen. Changing to 1/2-in. stroke at 625 r.p.m. completely relieved the situation. This sort of thing cannot be expressed in generalized charts.

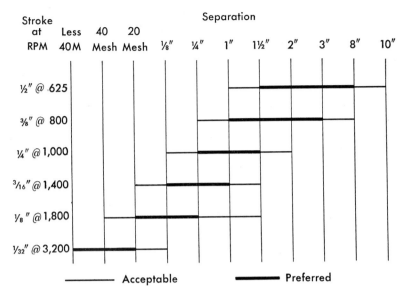

For multiple-deck screens, base selection on separation with *largest* opening.

Fig. 24. Circle-throw screen-stroke selection chart.

THE MOISTURE PROBLEM. Up to this point, the moisture problem has been covered only in its relation to the following:

1. Allowance of additional screening area.
2. Use of elongated deck openings.
3. Screen stroke and frequency.

In regard to the second item, it has been found that recourse to the smaller-diameter wires in slotted-opening screen cloths (Ty-Rod, Non-Blind, etc.) has a more pronounced effect on the prevention of blinding caused by moisture. The explanation is that a secondary or sympathetic vibration exists in the wires parallel to the long dimension of the slotted openings, or at least a deflection caused by the oversize lumps contacting them takes place. This beneficial effect is eliminated or not sufficiently pronounced if the diameter of the wire is too large in relation to the span and other variables (stroke, etc.). Placing the slotted cloth so that the tensioning or holding down is done through the groups of three "cluster wires" also enhances the opportunity for a secondary vibration or movement in the "long" wires. The factors which help eliminate blinding adversely affect cloth life through wear or fatigue or both; thus again arises a matter calling for a practical compromise.

A relatively recent development to offset the deck-blinding effects of moisture is **electrically heated screen cloth.** Fundamentally, the heating in this screen cloth is resistance heating, using one direction of the screen-cloth wires as the resistance to the 5–15 v. secondary voltages used across them. With voltages in this order, danger to personnel is not a factor, even though currents in the feeder buses to a section or sections of screen deck may run as high as 4,000 amp., although normally ranging down to about 1,000 amp. Typical cloth temperature while screening moist materials is 105–120° F. The temperature rises to about 200° when the feed is interrupted. Where square mesh openings are not demanded by the breakdown-size specification on the material, slotted-opening (nonblind) cloths are generally used with heated wires parallel to the long dimension of the slots.

The means by which blinding is prevented through electric heating consists of evaporation of the moisture between a facet of a particle and the surface of the cloth wire to which it is adhering. It thus follows that the **moisture content of the feed is not appreciably reduced.** Electric cloth-heating only keeps the apertures open. Therefore it further follows that moisture contents can still be sufficiently high for the fines to cling somewhat permanently to the coarser oversize particles or to one another, obviating the possibility of a separation, especially if the depth of bed is so appreciable that the great bulk of the particles is not directly subjected to the scrubbing action of the vibrating deck.

Experience has indicated that separations with electrically heated cloth can usually be made at openings about 25 percent smaller than is possible without it. It is used for openings up to about ½ in. or ⅝ in. Cloth construction is generally of stainless steel because of its higher electrical-resistance properties. Costwise, heating equipment adds roughly 80 to 90 percent to the initial investment for a vibrating screen alone. Operating costs (electrical consumption) are in the order of 35 to 60 cents per hr. per screen.

Gas-flame heating from the underside of a screen has also been used in some instances to eliminate blinding caused by moisture. Burners are usually so placed or arranged that the flames are thrown parallel to the underside of the screen deck, and thus material falling through the deck is prevented from excessively fouling the burners. The application of gas flames has predominantly been to iron ore screening at openings in the order of ¾ in. and coke screening at ¼ in. When it is used, auxiliary cooling methods are usually required for the vibrator mechanism.

Another method, with limited application in preventing blinding caused by moisture, is the use of **ball-tray decks.** Here resilient rubber balls are confined in roughly 1-sq.-ft. compartments immediately under the screen-cloth deck, with the consequence that they rap or impinge on the screening medium, creating a definite secondary vibration and wiping effect on the wires. The application of ball trays is limited on one end to about ³⁄₁₆-in. openings, because wire diameters encountered become so stout as to be unaffected by the bouncing rubber balls. At the other end, or at about 20-mesh openings, wire diameters become so fragile that reasonable cloth lives are not attained. Further, ball-tray decks are not so effective as electrically heated cloth in eliminating blinding, nor are they applicable to higher moisture contents. They are best suited for the borderline situations where moisture contents just begin to effect a progressive blinding condition.

PLUGGING. The mechanical method of cleaning utilized by ball-tray decks is applicable to alleviating plugging conditions where sharp-cornered **marginal-size pieces** wedge themselves into the apertures. In openings ⅛ in. and up, however, proper stroke, speed, and inclination of the equipment will generally relieve this wedging. In the case of finer openings the application of ball trays is limited by the fragility of the deck structure.

In some instances the material being screened contains an appreciable number of **marginals** which are extremely elongated in shape (longest/smallest dimension greater than 3). In such instances, commercially available amplitudes are usually insufficient to eject the materials. The same situation can exist on openings in the order of 6 in. square and with marginal material which is only slightly elongated in shape (long/short dimension >1½<3). Rod-deck construction (if material specifications allow) offers about the only positive solution. Here the crosswise obstructions are completely eliminated, and the bars of special tapered construction are of further advantage. The taper is such that the smallest constriction (maximum width of bar) in the opening is immediately at the top of the deck surface, thus making a self-clearing opening. Further, the bars can be fanned out from the feed end of the screen with an ever increasing opening.

The use of a perforated plate as opposed to screen cloth is also to be considered in plugging situations. The former will rigidly hold the shape of the opening, whereas the latter will often allow a wire to shift or spring open and more firmly wedge a marginal-size particle in the aperture.

The situations that arise from plugging are often self-curing; the piece that gets plugged may, for example, (1) wear itself through the opening, (2) fracture because of the vibration or the oversize material contacting it, and fall through, or (3) be rolled out because oversize material gets behind it. These effects, either individually or collectively as the case may be, must be sufficient to keep a required number of openings clear for the passage of fines.

Automatic Weighing

WEIGHING AND PROPORTIONING. The science of automatic weighing and proportioning progresses with the development of electronics, instrumentation, and punch-card data systems. The data here presented indicate what is available for solving a weighing problem in materials handling and what can be expected in regard to further developments. The problem in each case is usually handled by a process engineer working out a solution **in cooperation with a weighing expert,** rather than attempting to arrive at a final solution by himself.

Automatic weighing in bulk materials handling almost invariably involves a materials handling system of hoppers, feeders, discharge mechanisms, and conveyors. This system must be designed to handle the particular materials to be weighed, otherwise no scaling device developed can function properly. The vast majority of failures in automatic weighing result from incompetent materials handling rather than from a fault of the weighing mechanism itself. Handling systems vary with the materials to be weighed, which in turn may vary, for example, from fine sand to large rock, from dry powders to sticky pastes, and from dense ore concentrates to bulky mineral wool. An **automatic scale** suitable for one material may well be a failure if even moderate changes in material characteristics are encountered. The weighing solution must therefore be developed specifically around the materials to be handled. Fig. 25 illustrates a typical diagrammatic arrangement of automatic weighing, with scales and airslides.

PREWEIGHING AND POSTWEIGHING. Every industrial weighing application must fall into either the preweighing or the postweighing category. Preweighing involves the delivery of a prescribed quantity of material according to processing requirements. Postweighing is the simpler determination of the weight of an unknown mass of material. Preweighing is the more difficult and more commonly a problem; emphasis, therefore, will be given to it here, but many questions concerning postweighing will also be answered.

BATCH WEIGHING VS. CONTINUOUS WEIGHING. Bulk materials handling may involve the weighing of prescribed batches according to weight, or it may call for continuous weighing, that is, weighing material "on the fly"—usually as it goes past a weighing section on a conveyor belt. Both systems will be considered here, but more emphasis will be given to **batch** weighing because (1) it is used in the vast majority of industrial applications, (2) it is the

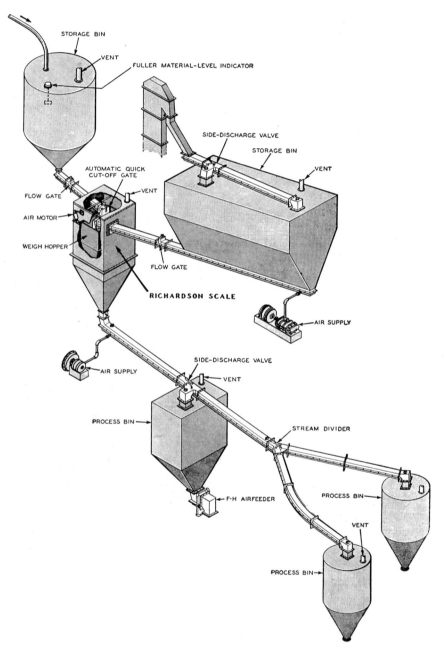

Fig. 25. Automatic weighing with Richardson scale and F-H Airslides.

more accurate, and (3) it alone is recognized as legal weighing by official authorities in weights and measures.

Continuous weighing has its important place where low first cost, low headroom, and high tonnages are involved. Batch weighing, however, with its inherent superior accuracy can produce a continuous weighed delivery where the process requires it. For example, weighing 300 lb. per min. on a **continuous scale** may mean only 3 lb. will be on the scale mechanism at one time; ½ percent of 3 lb. means ¼-oz. sensitivity, which is difficult to obtain in practice. On the other hand, 300 lb. per min. on a **batch scale** discharged each 60 sec. by a timer means an easy 1.5-lb. sensitivity for the same ½ percent of tolerance. The batch scale for the same tonnage could approach continuous delivery by discharging 75 lb. each 15 sec. or even 30 lb. each 6 sec. For like quantities, the stability of a **batch system** is more conducive to accuracy than **motion weighing** at its best. However, as tonnage requirements increase to hundreds of tons per hour, continuous weighing or **integrating** is the only practical method in the great majority of applications.

PREWEIGHING (BATCH). The factors considered in the foregoing discussion basically explain the significance of a material supply, feeding mechanism, weighing receptacle, load-sensing device, discharge mechanism, electrical or mechanical control, and instrumentation as it may be required.

Materials Handling Factors. Material supply hoppers and feeding mechanisms might appear to be subjects for discussion elsewhere, but in preweighing, a controlled feed to the scale is essential for accuracy. Material must not arch, rat-hole, or flush from a bin to a scale. Proper bin design will reduce the problem, and proper feeder design will eliminate it entirely, producing a more nearly constant feed rate in pounds per second to the batch scale.

Compensation is necessary in automatic weighing to correct for, or anticipate, the extra material that inevitably falls to a weigh hopper after the scale indicates a correct weighing and stops the feed. The **lag** in the closing of a gate, or the coast of a feeder, will otherwise cause overweight with every draft. With a feed rate of 10 lb. per sec. and a lag in stopping the feed of 0.5 sec., the compensation becomes 5 lb. If, because of an erratic feeding stream, the rate is momentarily reduced to 9 lb. per sec., the compensation will be wrong and an error of 0.5 lb. will result. Similarly, if the lag varies by 1/20 sec., there will again be an error of 0.5 lb. This explanation illustrates the need for constant feed and a constant lag in stopping that feed upon the completion of a weighing. These are functions of the materials handling part of an automatic scale, and they are of utmost importance to accuracy.

Dribble flow. Where the feed to an automatic scale is erratic or the lag in stopping the feed cannot be consistent, the error can be minimized by reducing the full flow to a reduced or "dribble" rate just before cutoff. This step adds to a scale's complication, both mechanically and electrically, besides reducing its capacity in weighings per minute. The dribble flow, therefore, should not be considered as essential to automatic weighing, and in most cases it can be omitted to advantage.

A scale should always draw from a **full head** of material to assure a uniform feed rate and accurate compensation. Bin-level controls are available which can be interlocked with the control circuit of the scale so that an alarm is sounded or the machine will not operate if the head recedes below an established minimum.

PREWEIGHING SCALES (CONTINUOUS). A continuous gravimetric delivery of material at a prescribed rate of ounces or pounds per second can be obtained with **continuous scale feeders,** usually of the belt-feeder type. As the rate of delivery becomes more or less than is prescribed, a scale beam will react to adjust the flow, either mechanically or electrically, according to design. These machines have the outstanding advantages of continuous-stream delivery, low headroom, and relatively low cost when the tonnage rate is high (50 tons per hr.). Unfortunately, they lack the accuracy of batch weighing and are not self-proving as is a dial scale. For these reasons they do not meet the tolerance specifications of weighing authorities, but they still have wide application in process measurement of materials. Provision should be made for sample checking against a dormant scale to keep continuous weighers in calibration.

POSTWEIGHING SCALES (CONTINUOUS). To determine and record the weight of a continuous flow of solid material, usually on a belt conveyor, it is common industrial practice to pass the belt over a section of idlers suspended from a scale lever system. By means of a mechanical integrator, which automatically multiplies the weight per linear foot by the linear feet of belt travel, a total weight is achieved. Recently, electronic and hydraulic load-cells have been used with considerable success in replacing the mechanical scale system at lower cost.

Continuous weight totalizers of this kind are most practical and are used almost exclusively where high tonnages are handled in motion, especially where headroom is not available for batch weighing. As with the continuous preweighing feeders described above, provision should be made for calibration against a known weight of material weighed on a truck, track, or other dormant scale. Care should be taken to maintain a uniform belt loading and belt tension, and uniform linear tare weight of the empty belt itself. Most continuous weighers record the total weight of material at the point of weighing by direct connected mechanical counters, but remote indication and recording are available.

CONTINUOUS-BATCH WEIGHING. When a stream of material can be momentarily interrupted or punctuated in increments, the recognized accuracy of dormant weighing then becomes possible. The conveyor must be started and stopped with each cycle or a falling stream at the head pulley must be interrupted by a catch gate so that the parcels or increments can be check-weighed automatically on a dormant scale (or section of conveyor on a dormant scale). These interruptions permit a determination of accuracy by established standards and so meet with the approval of weighing authorities. Unfortunately such interruption of a continuous stream will reduce capacity and increase cost, but this may be justified where accuracy to a fraction of 1 percent is mandatory.

MATERIAL CUTOFF CONTROL. When the prescribed quantity of material has been weighed, the scale must actuate electrical or mechanical devices which will stop the feed as quickly as possible. Typical devices are:

1. The **mechanical trigger,** tripped by the beam movement, to release a spring-loaded or power-operated cutoff gate. This device requires a low-ratio beam with ample inertia and movement to do the job with consistent accuracy.
2. **Mercury switches or mechanical limit switches,** used on higher-multiplication lever systems where there is less power available for the work. The switch is wired into the control circuit of a power-operated gate or feeder.
3. **Mercury magnetic switches or photoelectric cells,** used on the face of dial scales and actuated by the scale pointer itself to control the material feed.
4. The **potentiometer,** a resistive rotary device driven by direct connection to a

dial-scale spindle. This spindle produces a signal resulting in an electrical impulse to stop a feeder when the position of the scale pointer matches the setting of a remote weight-selecting vernier (a second potentiometer). Because of its accuracy (0.1 percent) and its applicability to **remote-control** systems, this device is finding wide acceptance.

5. The **synchro,** a rotating inductive transducer driven by direct connection to the dial scale spindle. This device produces an electrical signal proportional to its angular position and when electrically coupled with a mating synchro and an amplifier can be used to control the start/stop action of feeders, gates, etc.

6. **Differential transformer,** an axial inductive device driven by a linkage from the dial-scale spindle, which produces a signal resulting in an electrical impulse to stop a feeder when the position of the scale pointer matches a remote weight-selecting means.

7. **Pressure switches** in hydraulic and pneumatic load-cell control systems can stop a scale feeder when a prescribed quantity has been delivered.

WEIGH-HOPPER OR RECEPTACLE. The weigh-hopper is suspended from or mounted on scale levers or load cells to accumulate the material being weighed. Its capacity is designed for the maximum unit weighing at the lightest possible weight per cubic foot. While it should be no larger than necessary, a 10 percent margin is recommended.

Weigh-hoppers are discharged (a) **instantly,** by drop doors or radial gates, either gravity- or air-operated, or (b) **gradually,** by feeders directly mounted on the weigh-hopper itself. Feeders are usually of a vibrating, screw, or belt type. To obtain rapid weighing cycles and a continuous discharge it is common practice to employ instantaneous discharge to a lower hopper equipped with a feeder. Thus, while the scale is weighing one batch, the previous weighment is being fed gradually to the process.

The weighing receptacle can also be a length of conveyor, entirely suspended from scale levers. The conveyor runs continuously but is fed at one end, so the weighing is streamed out along the conveyor length. The feed stops only momentarily to punctuate the stream into weighed increments. Any scale-discharge mechanism must be interlocked mechanically or electrically with the feeding device to prevent both from operating simultaneously, which, of course, would pass material through unweighed.

WEIGHT-SENSING DEVICES. There are many weight-sensing devices, of which the following are typical:

1. **Simple scale lever.** This device has been used since the time of the Pharoahs and is still the most accurate load-sensing device known, as evidenced by its use today for weighing gold at the mint. It is unlikely that anything will ever surpass it for accuracy, at least not in the present era. A lever or train of levers terminating in a counterweight, or a steelyard and poise, can actuate a trigger or switch to control automatically the flow of material according to weight. This system is the one most extensively used, but unfortunately it does not lend itself to automatic indication, printing, totalizing, remote-weight setting, and other requirements of modern materials handling. Accordingly, it has been supplemented, and in some cases replaced, by the other weight-sensing devices listed here.

2. **Spring dial.** Because of its simplicity and accuracy, this device deserves much more credit than it usually receives.

3. **Pendulum dial.** This is well known throughout industry.

4. **Traveling poise.** This motor-driven device positions itself where required along a steelyard, according to the presetting of a geared stop counter.

5. **Cantilever beam** equipped with a strain gage, this device measures deflection under load.
6. **Load cells** (electronic, hydraulic, and pneumatic). These cells react to pressure applied to them.

INSTRUMENTATION IN AUTOMATIC WEIGHING. Because the field of instrumentation is almost unlimited, a review here of what has already been accomplished in the field must serve to inform the materials handling engineer as to what he may reasonably expect from the manufacturer of automatic scales.

Weight Indication. The **scale beam** indicates a degree of balance at the scale, and a mechanical indicator shows the deviation from true balance. The scale beam does not usually show an empty balance or tare weight except by the manual removal of the counterweight or the return of the poise to zero.

The **dial scale** indicates accumulating weight ranging from zero to full load. **Remote analog indication** from a dial can easily be determined by use of servo units, one actuated by the dial spindle which electronically drives the remote indicator through a corresponding angular motion. The former must have no measurable drag on the dial-scale spindle, but the latter, being motor driven, can have unlimited torque. **Remote digital indication** is obtained by having the servo drive a high-speed counter at a distant point. The counter can be geared to count once for each graduation or at any other required ratio. Automatic clutching will permit a counter to operate only as the scale accumulates a weighing or only as it discharges, as requirements may dictate. Obviously such digital indication (counting) can be fed into computer systems, where weight is a function.

The **traveling poise** will indicate the weight setting by its visible position along a steelyard. Since the equipment is motor-driven, the same motor can also be used to drive a direct-connected or remote electrical counter, geared to establish a count in pounds, corresponding to the travel of the moving poise. This mechanism is particularly applicable to postweighing for determining the weight of an unknown mass. The poise travels as far as is necessary to find a balance, totalizing as it goes, by automatic clutch or ratchet. The counter can be disengaged when the poise returns to the zero position. Constant tare is not important, because the poise returns only to a correct empty-balance position and begins its next cycle from there rather than from a theoretical zero.

Load-cell indication, when electrical, is provided through millivolt meters or an electrical bridge plus a null-balance instrument. With pneumatic or hydraulic load cells a pressure gage provides a direct reading or indication of the load applied.

Weight Recording. Chart recorders (circular and strip) provide an analog recording of weight applied to dial or load-cell scales. The resolution of chart recording is usually coarser than that of a pendulum dial scale.

Weight printers directly connected to a dial-scale head provide the most nearly accurate record of weight applied. Some accuracy may be sacrificed when these printers are remotely located, but the variation is only a small fraction of 1 percent. Printers will record in pounds the amount of each weighing, tare weights as each is discharged, and even a negative tare when a scale is out of adjustment. They will also record time and date, consecutive numbering, and other identifications called for. Such printers are equally adaptable to load-cell weighing.

Weight totalizing is simple when digital counting is involved. As explained previously, under "Remote digital indication," accumulating weight can be recorded on a digital counter. If the counter is clutch-controlled to operate with each scale weighing and is disengaged while the scale discharges (or vice versa), a totalizer will meet most requirements. The **tape printer** for listing individual scale weighings is used most commonly in materials handling, but until recently it has been necessary to add these figures clerically to obtain a total. Now it is possible to feed these individual digital weights in the form of electrical impulses directly to an **automatic adding machine**, which will provide a total that can be taken off at will.

Punch-card monitoring. It is sufficient here to say only that automatic scales can be used:

1. For automatically recording the weight of an unknown mass (postweighing) by punching coded holes in a standard card.
2. In combination with a computer, for giving an adjusted net weight and correcting for such factors as moisture, tare, yield, etc.
3. For providing complete programming of a multiple-scale and multiple-ingredient proportioning system by using a single punch card and automatic punch-card reader.

PROPORTIONING BY WEIGHT. Where multiple ingredients, solid or liquid, are to be proportioned by weight, this work can be done by using (1) individual scales—one for each ingredient, (2) a single scale weighing multiple ingredients cumulatively, or (3) a single scale weighing multiple ingredients consecutively.

Individual scales—one for each ingredient. Two or more scales, one for each material, can be interlocked to discharge their respective weighings simultaneously or at prescribed time intervals to proportion multiple ingredients. Where formula changes are infrequent, the amount to be weighed can be established at the scale itself. For frequent changing, remote formulation can be accomplished from a central control panel by the methods already described.

Where headroom is limited and for **inexpensive remote control**, it is frequently possible to employ scales of small unit-weighing capacity and, by means of remote stop counters, make multiple weighings. Thus the unit weighing becomes a common denominator of the total batch, e.g., 6 weighings of 50 lb. for a 300-lb. batch, the number being adjustable.

Four **advantages** of individual scale proportioning systems are:

1. Each scale can be specifically designed for its material.
2. All scales can operate together for high-speed proportioning.
3. Timed discharge to a take-away conveyor system will provide an intimate, continuous blend of ingredients.
4. Low headroom.

Single-scale cumulative weighing. A single-batch hopper scale can be fed by multiple feeders, one for each ingredient, operating in a selected sequence to accumulate a batch. The load-sensing devices will actuate the feeder controls to start and stop the ingredient flow as the prescribed weight of each is delivered. Typical weight-control methods are as follows:

1. A **lever scale** terminating in multiple steelyards, each with a poise manually set for the corresponding ingredient. The steelyards are mechanically picked up in sequence by the lever system, a balance being indicated at each stop. Remote control, whereby any of the steelyards can be remotely selected in or out according to formula requirements, is also possible with this system.

2. A **dial scale with multiple photoelectric cells** or magnetic mercury switches manually set around the periphery of the dial for automatic feeder cutoff as the scale pointer reaches the established settings.
3. A **dial scale with potentiometric control** (see previous discussions of potentiometer under "Material Cutoff Control") whereby cutoff points can be established remotely by the setting of weight-selecting potentiometers on a control panel. This system lends itself to the control of an unlimited number of feeders per scale.

Two **advantages** of cumulative weighing are: (1) it is a less expensive system than using several multiple scales, and (2) it provides a centralized weighing location. The chief **disadvantage** is in the **limitation of weighing range.** Where a dial scale is used, the dial must have a capacity equal to the maximum batch. While this scale may be accurate to one graduation (0.1 percent of full capacity), the accuracy diminishes in terms of percent when smaller quantities are weighed.

Single-scale consecutive weighing. A single-batch hopper can be fed and controlled as above with the following difference. After each feeder has delivered its selected amount of material, the scale hopper discharges immediately instead of accumulating the entire formula. The **advantage** of such consecutive weighing of ingredients is in better dial-scale accuracy. The dial capacity need be equal only to the maximum single ingredient rather than the entire batch. Thus accuracy in terms of one graduation will be proportionately better percentage-wise. With such a system a lower collecting hopper for the individually weighed ingredients is usually required.

BAGGING. Materials like feed, flour, sugar, salt, fertilizer, and chemicals are usually sacked in 50-lb., 80-lb., and 100-lb. bags. The process of handling such packagings constitutes high-speed industrial automatic weighing rather than the use of conventional package machinery. The National Bureau of Standards Handbook 44 now includes industrial packaging scales in its category of equipment. Wherever such scales are used for a product sold to the public, care should be taken to be sure that the design of the scale conforms to standard requirements.

Bagging-scale operations are basically the same as for batch-weighing scales, but the speed is usually much faster, and the accuracy is relatively more important. Loading speeds of ten to twenty 100-lb. bags per min. are common, and accuracy on many materials can be held within a range of from 2 to 4 oz. per bag. Of paramount importance in obtaining such accuracy is proper bin design and feeder control to obtain a consistent feed of material to the scale.

ACCURACY MEASUREMENT. Statistical analysis (statistical quality control) is the modern method used for measuring the consistency of any repetitive operation, including repetitive weighing of packages and bags. Accuracy can be predicted with mathematical certainty from a sample of test weighings. Based on a distribution curve, if 68 percent of the weighings are within plus or minus a certain **tolerance** (sigma), then 95 percent will be within twice that tolerance (2 sigma), and 99.7 percent will be within three times that tolerance (3 sigma). Thus a scale's accuracy on repeated weighings should be stated in terms of "sigma"; for example, if sigma equals 1 oz., in normal operation 68 percent of the weighings will be within plus or minus 1 oz., 95 percent within plus or minus 2 oz., and 99.7 percent within 3 oz. Not more than three in a thousand will exceed a 3-oz. error. This method of accuracy-measurement is widely used today, and because it is **mathematically correct,** it will be universally used in the future.

GOVERNMENTAL REGULATION IN INDUSTRIAL WEIGHING.

Scales used in commercial transactions (such as buying and selling or paying for services rendered) have been treated as "clothed with a public interest" throughout history, and they have been subjected to regulation by various codes and by the federal government. Summarized below are the requirements with regard to maintaining scales according to these regulations, as stated by Arthur Sanders, Executive Secretary, Scale Manufacturers Association.

The federal government has **almost no jurisdiction** over the regulation and inspection of commercial scales, but through the National Bureau of Standards it encourages good **uniform control of weighing equipment.** The bureau does this through its sponsorship of the National Conference on Weights and Measures, a voluntary body of state and local officials which prepares and recommends for state adoption model laws, specifications, and tolerances for supervising commercial scales. (The specifications and tolerances are contained in the **H44 Scale Code** and are published by the Bureau in NBS Handbook H44.)

Generally, scales meeting the H44 Scale Code are **acceptable in every state.** In fact, for approval in most states, commercial types must meet the H44 requirements. Some states even require approval of the type before sale. This is known as "type approval" and is required in about ten states. Understanding scale performance as they do, weights-and-measures officials have a practical approach to the establishment of tolerances. Tolerances are so fixed that the permissible errors are kept so small that neither buyer nor seller will be injured, but they are not so small as to make manufacturing or maintenance costs disproportionately high.

The H44 Scale Code furnishes an excellent guide for **purchasing and manufacturing** all types of good modern weighing equipment, even though the particular scale may not be for commercial use. Scale manufacturers generally follow the H44 Scale Code, unless purchaser requirements stipulate otherwise.

The **plus or minus error tolerances** allowed by weights-and-measures authorities are usually about 0.1 percent of the applied test load for scales inside the plant, and 0.2 percent for "outside" scales which are subjected to the interferences of the elements. In general, the 0.1 percent is a reasonable rule-of-thumb tolerance for good scales, except those installed on the outside and those of quite small capacities, where it would be most difficult to read the indications correctly in order to determine a value as low as 0.1 percent.

Material-Level Control

EQUIPMENT FOR MATERIAL-LEVEL CONTROL. Material-level-control equipment of the mechanical, pneumatic, and electronic types is responsible to a great extent for continuity of flow and the consequent reliability of process operations in many industries today. Automatic control of modern bulk-materials handling systems requires detecting devices which can be used for a variety of applications wherever materials are stored or handled and positive action is required to control their flow. Through the use of this equipment, constant attention to insure continuous flow can be almost eliminated, which reduces human failures, provides closer control, and increases the speed of operations. Although material-level-control devices have most commonly been referred to as indicators, an even more important use is as sensing or detecting devices to detect the presence of material and to actuate allied equipment in a positive manner, thereby providing a preplanned function. Fig. 26 lists certain material-level-control devices and gives data concerning them.

Type	Manufacturer	Design	Application Information	Operation
Mechanical Diaphragm	Richardson Scale Company	6", 12", 18"dia. sizes. Plunger, spring, switch.	Adjustable to suit material. Recommended for general duty. Bin should be vented to relieve air pressure. Prefer use on vertical side of bin having two adjacent straight sides. Explosion-proof.	Diaphragm connected to the plunger which operates the switch. Make point of switch occurs when diaphragm is depressed 1/8" at the center. Break point of switch occurs 1/16" before diaphragm returns to extended position.
	The Bin-Dicator Company	10 1/4"O.D., 5 3/4"O.D. sizes. Counterweighted lever system, switch, no springs.	Adjustable to suit material. Available for general and special duty. Available for use under pressure or vacuum. Can be mounted on curved surface, and inside of bin as well as outside. Explosion-proof.	Diaphragm is forced against the counterweighted lever system, tipping the lever plate and actuating the switch.
	The Jeffrey Manufacturing Company	4 1/2", 7" dia. sizes. Counterweighted lever system, switch, no springs.	Adjustable to suit material. Recommended for general duty. Can be mounted horizontally, vertically, or on curved or sloping surface. Weather and sparkproof.	Counterweight operates the lever system and actuates the switch.
	Tate & Roe Incorporated	8"O.D. Diaphragm is free from switch. Unit does not contain counterweight. Diaphragm is backed up by pressure plate.	Adjustable to suit material. Available for general and special duty. Can be used under high temperature. Can be mounted horizontally, vertically, or on a curved or sloping surface. Explosion-proof.	1/32" diaphragm movement operates the switch.
	The Fairfield Engineering Company	10" O.D. Diaphragm is free from switch. Unit does not contain counterweight.	Adjustable to suit material. Available for use on coal and other lumpy, heavy bulk materials. Can be mounted in any position.	Diaphragm movement operates the switch.

Type	Company	Components	Application	Operation
Mechanical / Pendant	Stephens Adamson Manufacturing Company	Pendant, universal pivot, switch.	Can be mounted vertically, horizontally, or on a sloping surface. Available for normal and heavy duty. Explosion-proof.	20° movement of the pendant through the universal pivot collar operates the switch.
Electromechanical / Paddle	Fuller Company	Shaded pole induction motor, tension spring, spur gear train, cam, two switches. 6" long to 12'-0" long paddle shafts.	Can be mounted vertically or horizontally. Available for general duty, also liquids. Protective guard recommended when used for low-level operation. Available for use under high temperatures. Requires alternating current.	Paddle is constantly rotated by the motor. When paddle is restrained from turning, the motor and its mounting revolve about the drive shaft, actuating two switches. One switch operates the desired control. The other cuts out the level-control motor. A tension spring returns motor to its initial position.
Electromechanical / Paddle	Convair Incorporated	1/200 h.p. motor, torsion spring.	Available for use under pressure or vacuum. Recommended for general duty, also wet materials and slurries. Available in standard, heavy-duty, high-temperature, and explosion-proof models.	Motor is connected to a shaft by a torsion spring. When the paddle stops, the motor keeps turning until the spring by torsion actuates the switch which cuts out the motor and actuates the desired control. The paddle turns the spring away from the switch and again starts up the motor.
Electronic	Robertshaw Fulton Controls Company	Relay circuit, two switches, cable, probe electrode.	Can be used for operation under medium-high pressure and temperature. Available with special disc or plate electrodes to suit material characteristics. Recommend probe be installed horizontally, also liquids. Weatherproof.	A simple, highly stable-capacity relay circuit operates the two switches as a result of any slight change in electrical capacity at the probe electrode. One switch operates the signal control on front of the case, the other the desired external control.
Electronic	Hewitt-Robins Incorporated	Relay circuit, cable, probe electrode.	Recommended for general duty. Recommend probe be installed vertically. Can be used under temperatures up to 140°F. Available for general duty, also liquids. Weather-resistant.	A single-pole, double throw relay is acted upon by a high frequency field established by the tip of the probe. Disturbance to the high frequency field unbalances the relay circuit.

Fig. 26. Available material-level-control devices.

SELECTION AND APPLICATION OF EQUIPMENT. Equipment for material-level control can generally be made to suit individual material characteristics and conditions of flow or storage wherever pulverized, granular, lumpy, hot, sticky, dry, or free-flowing bulk ingredients are handled. Certain kinds of equipment are applicable for use with liquids, viscous materials, and wet or damp ingredients. Each device or kind of equipment should be used only in the specific applications for which it is recommended by the manufacturer.

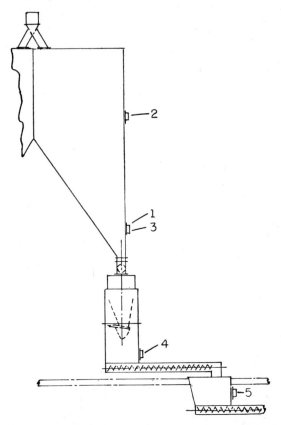

Fig. 27. Vertical storage bin with screw-conveyor feeder.

Flow-control devices are available for operation under pressure or vacuum. They are also available in explosion-proof models, as designated by underwriters' laboratories, which can be used in hazardous atmospheres containing explosive dusts or vapors. Since these devices are only detectors, additional equipment in the form of indicators or other equipment to be controlled is involved. Most types can be arranged for remote electrical control for the following general applications, as shown in Fig. 27.

  1. As a **low-level-control device**, to maintain a constant supply of material in a supply bin by actuating a warning signal when the material has reached low level. In the case of a non-automatic system, the signal can be either a visual indication by a pilot light, or the audible alarm of a horn or bell. This warning

would direct the operator's attention to the refilling of the supply bin. In the case of an automatic system, the low-level-control signal can start the feeding cycle to reload the supply bin, and if necessary stop or start the discharging equipment delivering the material from the bin to the process (Fig. 27).

2. As a **high-level-control device,** (a) to actuate a warning signal when the material has reached high level in the supply bin, (b) to automatically stop the feeding stream loading the bin, or (c) where several adjacent bins are being filled, to divert the feeding stream to the next bin. This control device may also be used to impulse the bin-discharging equipment.

3. To establish a **low-level control** and so insure a supply large enough to provide a consistent rate of flow of material to weighing or packaging machines. This is necessary for proper performance.

4. As a **pace-setter** for impulsing the discharge of automatic batch-weighing equipment, to keep an adequate supply of material above a device metering a stream of material, and so insure an uninterrupted flow to a continuous process.

5. As a **control medium,** to increase or decrease the flow of material to or from a surge supply, thereby eliminating a material shortage or material choke-up in the system.

Level-control devices can be made to accomplish even more **specialized functions.**

The diagram shown in Fig. 28 illustrates **multiple storage bins** used for handling lumpy materials in predetermined quantities. Each bin compartment is equipped with a slide gate which opens or closes to permit the fall of material

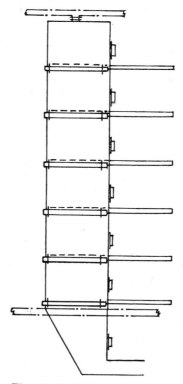

Fig. 28. Multiple storage bins.

from bin to bin, or from the bottom bin to processing. The action is entirely automatic, by virtue of the signals from the level-control devices and the limit switches. Loading is accomplished with all the slide gates closed. When material reaches the level control device in the top bin, the top bin slide gate is opened and closed, dropping the load to the next lower bin in stepped sequence down to the bottom compartment. Upon the closing of the top slide gate, the material is again accumulated and then lowered, following the first load. The slide gate below the loaded bin must be closed before the bin's upper slide gate will open and drop the load.

The **level control** in the bottom hopper beneath the lower storage compartment is used as a low-level control over the automatic scale (see item 3 above). It controls the supply of material by opening the bottom slide gate on the lower storage compartment. The slide full-open-position limit switch mounted on the slide-gate guide and the level control in the bottom storage compartment combine to actuate the closing of the bottom slide gate. A full-closed-position limit switch on the bottom slide-gate guide is used to signal opening of the next upper bin gate, provided a material supply is in that compartment.

In a similar application, a material-level-control unit and motor-driven slide gate may be mounted on a hopper below an automatic batch-weighing machine. Here the requirements call for a certain hourly tonnage and a continuous flow of material to process. The batch-weigher provides the required hourly tonnage with close accuracy and can easily be tested to verify its performance. The motor-driven slide gate is used to stream out the material. Automatic regulation of the slide gate is accomplished by the level-control device working in conjunction with high- and low-position stop switches. When the gate is at its low position (small opening), the material slowly backs up until the level-control device operates. This action signals the gate slide to adjust to its high position (large opening). As the level of the material recedes within the hopper, the level-control device operates again, causing the motor to return the gate to its low position, where it remains until the material level rises again and the cycle is repeated.

INSTALLATION OF CONTROL DEVICES. Mechanical, pneumatic, and electronic types of level-control devices are manufactured in various forms, each suited to certain materials and operational conditions.

Level-control devices should never be installed directly in the path of the incoming stream. When used as a high-level control device, and to protect against overflow of material, the unit should be located to allow for the angle of repose of the material, with a safety margin to insure operation of the unit. When desired for low-level control in a large-capacity bin, the unit should be protected by a baffle from the impact of the falling material.

Some materials will at times "hang up" on the sides of the bin while flowing freely through the center of the bin thus causing a "rat hole." This condition is likely to arise with materials which compact and where the storage bin has a center discharge opening. Under such conditions, a wall-mounted level-control, or one suspended in the center of the bin, might not indicate the actual conditions of storage. Care should therefore be exercised in storage-bin design so that it is possible to get **proper storage indication.**

MECHANICAL DIAPHRAGM-TYPE EQUIPMENT. Mechanical detector diaphragm-model control devices, such as that shown in Fig. 29, are mounted on the side of the hopper, bin, or chute to permit direct contact of the material with the diaphragm. Some diaphragm models are counterweighted or spring-loaded and operate, through the lateral pressure of the material, a simple lever system connected to a suitable switch. Most of these devices are adjustable for sensitivity to suit material characteristics. They are generally available with electrical contact arrangements which are either normally open or normally closed.

The diaphragm is of a construction suitable for the material with which it is to be used. Composition-coated fabric, rubber, and neoprene are in general use because they are sensitive and have good wearing and corrosion-resistant qual-

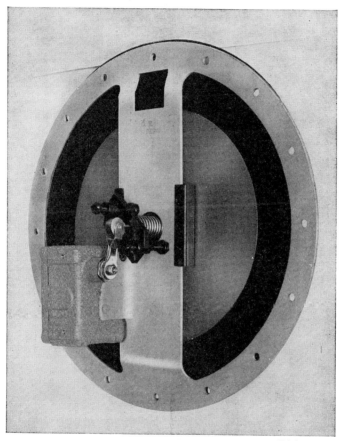

Richardson Scale Co.

Fig. 29. Mechanical diaphragm-type control device.

ities. Special applications for use with hot and highly abrasive materials require stainless steel diaphragm construction. Diaphragm construction is also available which resists the build-up of sticky material on the diaphragm surface.

The diaphragm unit should, whenever possible, be mounted on the vertical side of, and flush with, the inner surface of the bin. This arrangement minimizes the possibility of build-up of the material on the diaphragm surface.

The unit must be located at a point where the material, through its normal flow, will reach and operate the diaphragm, and upon receding will fall freely away from the diaphragm.

ELECTROMECHANICAL PADDLE-TYPE CONTROL DEVICES.

The motor-driven paddle- or impeller-type control devices shown in Fig. 30 are usually mounted on top of the hopper or bin, but may also be mounted horizontally when given proper protection. The paddle shaft is extended to locate the paddle in the path of the angle of repose of the material at the desired predetermined point of operation. The main mechanism of the apparatus is totally

Convair, Inc.

Fig. 30. Electromechanical four-blade impeller-type control.

enclosed in a dust-tight housing. The paddle shaft, driven by a small motor, is free to turn when not in contact with the material. The **torque reaction** created by resistance of the material on the paddle is detected through a spring-controlled motion of the mechanism which actuates the controlling limit switch. Specially designed units are available with heat-dissipating provisions for operations requiring temperatures up to 1,200° F.

A variation of the paddle-type is available in a **pendulum-type** level-control device for installation where a long extension of the paddle shaft is required. These devices are used to reach the point of low-level control in large bunkers. Movement of the paddle is permitted with the shifting of the material inside the bunker, and therefore no special support is required.

MECHANICAL PENDANT-TYPE DEVICES. Pendant float-type control switches, as shown in Fig. 31, are used to achieve the same general results as

Fig. 31. Heavy-duty, normal-duty, and explosion-proof Tellevels.

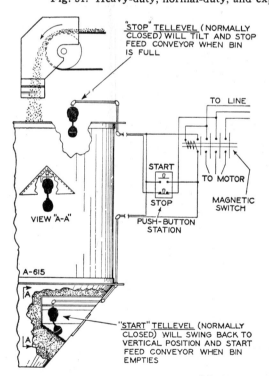

"STOP" TELLEVEL (NORMALLY CLOSED) WILL TILT AND STOP FEED CONVEYOR WHEN BIN IS FULL

TO LINE

START

TO MOTOR

STOP

MAGNETIC SWITCH

VIEW "A-A"

PUSH-BUTTON STATION

A-615

"START" TELLEVEL (NORMALLY CLOSED) WILL SWING BACK TO VERTICAL POSITION AND START FEED CONVEYOR WHEN BIN EMPTIES

Fig. 32. Wiring diagram for two Tellevels to start and stop conveyors automatically.

are obtained with the diaphragm- or paddle-type units, and can be mounted inside a tank or bin to effect the desired control.

The **float ball,** or float cone, connected through a universal pivot, operates a sensitive switch when the material level changes. As a high-level control, the float mechanism should be placed near the top of the bin where the angle of repose of the material at the desired level will tilt the float ball. Care should be taken to allow clearance for movement of the float ball. Its location should allow for surges of the material resulting from the action of the loading equipment. When used as a low-level control, the float ball should be located under a protective guard so that it will not become completely embedded in the material. The protective guard should not interfere with the action caused by the normal angle of repose of the material on the float ball (see Fig. 37). Vertical mounting adjustment is recommended to locate the device at the desired level of operation. Fig. 32 shows wiring of Tellevels used to control conveyor action.

PNEUMATIC LEVEL-CONTROL DEVICES. The principle of the pneumatic level-control device is a neutral balancing system. In operation the unit establishes an air pressure in the transmitting section proportional to the external pressure of the material.

Referring to Fig. 33, for example, assume that the pressure in the medium increases. The increased pressure causes the diaphragm C to move toward nozzle B, which throttles the flow of air through the nozzle. This throttling action increases the pressure in the transmitting section. The increased pressure in the transmitting section opens the differential valve E a little more until the increased flow of air from the supply balances the pressure on the two sides of the differ-

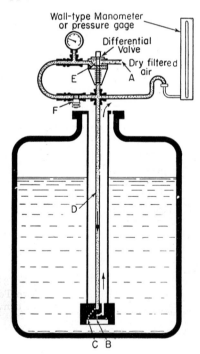

Instruments, Inc.

Fig. 33. Pneumatic level-control device.

ential valve diaphragm. With these pressures balanced, the valve E is in a slightly open position and the flow of air through the system continues in sufficient volume to maintain the air pressure in the transmitting section at the same pressure as that of the medium being measured, and so to maintain the diaphragm C in a neutral position. On the other hand, if the pressure in the medium decreases, the diaphragm C moves away from the nozzle. The resulting drop in pressure in the transmitting section closes the differential valve a little until the air bleeding through the restriction orifice F has brought the differential valve to neutral and the diaphragm C to a balanced condition. A pressure gage or similar instrument, graduated to indicate a variance in material capacity, is actuated by the change in air pressure to provide a **continuous level-change indication.**

The pneumatic type of level control is particularly effective for use with liquids and viscous materials. Variations of the design are available for use when vapor pressures or vacuums are present.

Hewitt-Robins, Inc.

Fig. 34. Electronic-type level-control device.

ELECTRONIC LEVEL-CONTROL DEVICES. Electronic level-control devices are so versatile that they can be applied to almost all solid ingredients and liquids. A **probe-type electrode,** mounted properly to sense the presence of material, is used in conjunction with a relay remotely located in a cabinet. The probe is part of a high-frequency circuit which is affected by the presence of material and which signals the relay to operate the desired controls for the material in process. Since the probe does not have to be in direct contact with the material, it can be mounted outside the bin wall. In this application, however, the bin wall cannot be thick, and it should be made of a nonconductive material. Different types of electrodes are available to suit individual material characteristics and applications, for example, enclosure of the steel probe in glass for use with corrosive materials. Other special electrode designs have been developed such as one providing an insulated steel plate to withstand abrasion and shock, for use in coal and ore bunker installations.

The cabinet containing the relay should be easily accessible for servicing, and should not be subject to excessive vibration, shaking, moisture, dirt, or shock. Electron tubes should be changed periodically as they deteriorate. All electrical

Richardson Scale Co.

Fig. 35. Paddle-type unit used to detect lack of material in hoppers or spouts.

connections should be kept clean of grease and dirt, and material accumulating on the probe should be removed at regular intervals. The sensitivity adjustment control should always be kept at the minimum necessary for operation of the unit. The sensitivity required to operate the unit depends largely on the nature of the material, its density, dielectric constant, and the presence of voids and moisture.

Fig. 34 shows an electronic level-control device used in a coal pile. The probe on the tip of the telescopic chute automatically causes the chute to rise as the height of the coal pile increases. Each time the coal pile approaches the chute, the probe device impulses a motor which lifts the chute an additional 12 in. Accordingly, both constant manual attention and costly mechanical trouble which might otherwise result are eliminated.

A salient feature of the electronic-type level control is that it will operate within accurate limits. It is, however, generally more expensive to obtain and install than either the mechanical or the pneumatic types.

OTHER DETECTING AND INDICATING DEVICES. Other types of controls, in addition to the three major categories already discussed, are available

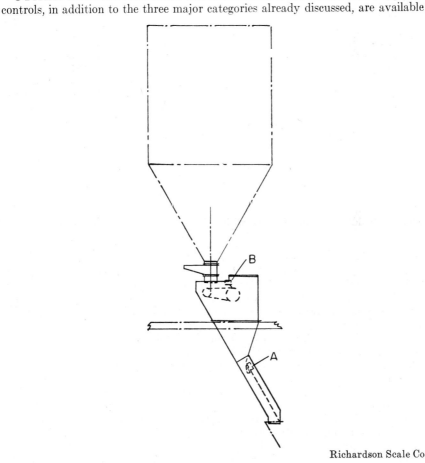

Richardson Scale Co.

Fig. 36. Paddle-type mechanism to detect materials-shortage conditions at belt feeders and in hoppers or spouts.

for use both as detecting devices and as indicators. These controls include photo-electric cells, strain gages, and atomic-type controls. Atomic level-control units are now used in many applications. However, they require special technical maintenance and therefore have not yet reached major prominence in bulk-materials handling.

Other kinds of material-control devices are shown in Figs. 35, 36, and 37. These units, however, are not material-level devices but instead **flow-control** devices. The simple mechanical unit shown in Fig. 35, and in Fig. 36 at location *a* is used to detect materials-shortage conditions in hoppers or spouts. It has been designed for use in coal-handling installations to maintain a constant supply of material as in weighing coal to be fed to a stoker. Here the blade-type unit is used to sound

Richardson Scale Co.

Fig. 37. Paddle-type unit for use with belt feeders or conveyors to indicate lack of materials.

an alarm when a materials shortage exists, indicating failure of the conveying or weighing equipment to supply the demand for more material. The unit is designed to be automatically reset by contact with the material when the conveying or weighing conditions have been corrected and the flow of coal is resumed. The equipment should always be mounted on the straight side or top slope of the hopper or spout.

Similarly, in Fig. 36, at location *b*, and in Fig. 37 are shown the paddle-type unit, which is suitable for use with belt-feeders or conveyors, to detect the lack of material. The faulty condition may exist because of unreliable flow of material in cases where storage bunker slopes are not sufficiently steep or occasional large lumps of material clog the flow, or where the storage bunker is empty. The design of this unit is such that movement of the paddle when material is lacking closes a circuit, which sounds an alarm. When the condition has been corrected, flow of material on the belt feeder or conveyor will re-position the paddle and automatically open the alarm circuit.

Wherever material-level control equipment is to be installed the equipment selected must fit the needs of the particular kind of material it is to handle and the particular conditions under which the handling is to be done.

UNIT HANDLING FOR VARIOUS SHAPES

CONTENTS

CONTENTS (*Continued*)

SECTION 12

UNIT HANDLING FOR VARIOUS SHAPES

Handling Box Shapes

IMPORTANCE OF PROPER HANDLING METHODS. The principles and fundamentals concerning different kinds of materials handling equipment and systems are the bases upon which all materials handling operations are carried on. The experiences of various users of materials handling devices in solving economically their problems of handling box shapes are useful. In adopting the practices shown in the case studies below, due consideration must be given to the nature of the specific situation to which they are to be applied. Before applying these practices, one should analyze and weigh all facts in the light of his specific needs, subject to any limitations and advantages existing in his own plant.

A large part of the movement of boxes, cartons, and the like is by pallet. Palletized loads, however, require separate treatment.

HANDLING EQUIPMENT AND SYSTEMS FOR BOX SHAPES. The following kinds of equipment have been found well suited for handling box shapes:

1. **Trucks:** industrial. Hand: 2-wheel and 4-wheel; hand lift. Riding and walking power types: platform; high- and low-lift platform; tractor with trailers; fork; crane; side-loading; straddle.
   Highway types: 4-wheel; 6-wheel; tandem and semitrailer units.
2. **Conveyors:** fixed and portable; horizontal and inclined; overhead and ground level; flat belt; roller, live and gravity wheel; slat; pallet; pusher bar; trolley; drag chain, rolling and sliding chain; arm and suspended tray; vertical. Transfer units: round tables; switches.
3. **Chutes and slides:** metal, wood.
4. **Overhead systems:** mobile equipment. Traveling bridge cranes; gantry cranes; jib cranes; monorail cranes.
5. **Elevators and lifts:** industrial. Standard types; stackers and lifters; tiering machines; elevating tables.
6. **Hoists:** traveling and local. Chain; cable; electric; pneumatic; block and tackle.
7. **Slings, tongs, grips, grabs:** hand, mechanical, truck-operated, electrically operated.

USE OF INDUSTRIAL POWER TRUCKS. Many kinds of industrial power trucks, with or without accessories, can be used for handling box shapes. There are, however, some special forms and applications that have particular advantages.

Probably the most common type of industrial power truck is a line of **light-capacity fork trucks.** Capable of handling loads of up to 2,000 lb. in weight, these trucks have simplified automotive-type controls—steering wheel, foot accelerator, pedal brakes, and gearshift-type lifting and tilting controls—all within easy reach of the operator. Another feature of these fork trucks is a magnetic contactor control that prevents drivers from subjecting the motor to unnecessarily heavy loads.

Heavy-duty load carriers are valuable in handling large, bulky loads. One such type of truck, made in capacities up to 36,000 lb., is used for carrying heavy machinery in crates from the assembly and boxing areas to the shipping docks and railroad sidings. Loads are placed on and removed from the load carriers by fork trucks or cranes. To allow the driver better visibility in handling extra-large loads, the trucks can be driven backward. Four-wheel steering helps to make operation easy and provides greater maneuverability.

Loader and Transporter Trucks. One form of a combined loader and transporter truck handles loads hydraulically by means of a **fork lift** located in the center of the truck. It operates on a side-loading arrangement whereby long boxed goods, unitized loads of boxed materials, and large flat boxes can be placed on the truck's carrying platform, which is arranged to distribute the load as evenly as possible over the truck's two axles and four wheels. This type of truck lifts, loads, transports, unloads, and stacks. Double crane attachments make it additionally useful for handling large items of awkward size and shape.

Straddle trucks also pick up, transport, and deposit long boxes, crates, and other heavy and bulky loads. Their versatility makes them useful in mills, docks, warehouses, and industrial plants for picking up and transporting any loads they can straddle.

CONVEYOR SYSTEMS. Conveyor facilities for handling box-shape goods are practically limitless. The various types of conveyors may be used singly or in combinations, thus giving this form of materials handling extreme versatility and wide-range application.

In one plant a very complete and extensive system of **roller conveyors** is used to lower food products from ovens on the upper floor to the lower floor, and to handle the cartons of food products on through weighing and labeling and thence to storage. This system operates under continuous streamlined production.

Other roller-conveyor equipment which has been introduced into production lines includes such devices as switches to transfer boxes from one conveyor line to one or more other lines. **Transfer cars** are also used to shift boxed goods from one line to another, or to and from work stations. **Tilting devices,** for example, are installed along a line where it is necessary to up-end boxes so as to conserve space on the conveyor line for storage purposes.

Ball transfers are also used to move containers and packages from main lines to side lines without having to lift or drag them manually. **Wheel conveyors** have many similar applications for lightweight and medium-duty jobs, such as the handling of cases of empty bottles and filled bottles of various kinds, and also empty and filled cartons from packing operations to storage. **Slides, special chutes, and roller spirals** are employed extensively for lowering box shapes from one level or floor to another in a limited space. Devices of this sort are often used in combination with other systems. A large wholesale warehouse, for example, has a special chute for bringing packages down from the second floor. On the main floor roller-conveyor lines are employed. Boxed goods from the basement come upstairs by means of a pusher-bar conveyor. All these lines converge into a roller-conveyor line for delivery of the packages to the shipping platform.

Vertical lifts are also integrated into conveyor lines to elevate cases, cartons and boxes from one floor to another, also for lifting box shapes from a low-level line to an overhead line on the same floor so as to avoid obstacles and interferences at work-station levels. **Reciprocating lifts** may be designed for the automatic loading and unloading of box shapes at the two ends of travel on a conveyor line. These lifts operate in either direction, up or down, according to the direction in which the boxes are to be moved. They conserve considerable space. Loading and unloading can be automatic or manual, and may be arranged to be done either from the same side or from opposite sides of the lift. The lift may be equipped with a roller, sheet metal, or wooden bed.

Slat conveyors are applied to many jobs of handling cases, cartons, boxes, etc. They can be installed at various heights but are usually positioned at the height most convenient for the particular working needs. In one particular case, for example, the conveyor was placed at floor level for the greatest convenience in use, and there is no interruption to conveyor traffic even when the line is walked on while it is in motion. Slat conveyors on **inclines** are also employed in moving goods from one level to another.

Packaged goods are also handled on trays attached to a **trolley conveyor.** In one large assembly plant, congestion in aisles and around machines caused confusion and made it difficult to supply work stations with production parts, which were handled in boxes. A trolley-conveyor system with tray carriers was therefore installed for carrying boxed and individual items high above the work level. At convenient discharge and loading points along the line, the overhead track was brought down to a level at which the trays were at a convenient handling height for taking off and putting on units or packages of parts and assemblies.

PORTABLE CONVEYORS AND ELEVATORS. Portable conveyors of many kinds—belt, roller, wheel, slat, etc.—find many applications in the handling of boxes, crates, cases, cartons, and related shapes. Most of these portable units can be used both for horizontal movements and for carrying goods up or down inclines. They can be moved at will around a plant, warehouse, or other establishment for tiering and for loading and unloading trucks and freight cars.

A typical **portable belt conveyor,** for example, can be used to stack boxed goods in a warehouse, to carry cartons up or down from one level to another, to perform booster service in a gravity conveyor line, and in other helpful services. On inclined transports and belt conveyors, angles up to 30° or so are common. Belts used for steep climbs are made of rough or nonslide surface materials, or they may have cleats.

Portable elevators commonly go under such names as **stackers, lifters, tiering machines, elevating tables,** etc. They perform those specifically named purposes in handling boxes, cartons, and crated products.

ROLLER-CONVEYOR APPLICATIONS. Installations for handling box shapes by conveyor are almost unlimited. The typical handling solutions presented here illustrate economical systems and arrangements which can be readily varied to meet different conditions and needs.

Fig. 1 shows how heavy boxes and kegs of hardware coming from the manufacturing departments are sorted over an ingenious system of alligator switches, curved sections, and curved, hinged sections. Kegs move on roller conveyors to storage lines and shipping. Boxes converge from three lines, by means of a switch, to a slat-conveyor booster and pass on to the nailing machines. To conserve space the boxes are then up-ended by an automatic tilter, and pass over a switch to three storage lines for shipment.

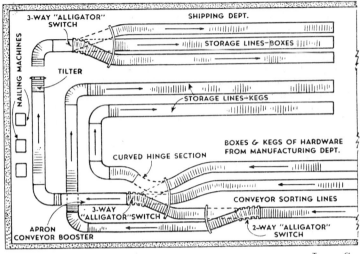

Logan Co.

Fig. 1. Conveyor layout for handling boxes and kegs.

Fig. 2 illustrates a method whereby incoming material from cars moves over portable gravity-conveyor sections to vertical lifts carrying it to the second floor, where various spur lines of roller conveyors serve the storage area. Coming out of storage or processing, material is lowered to the first floor by means of a spiral chute discharging to a gravity packing line. A gravity roller conveyor with a 2-way switch forwards outgoing material to trucks or railroad cars.

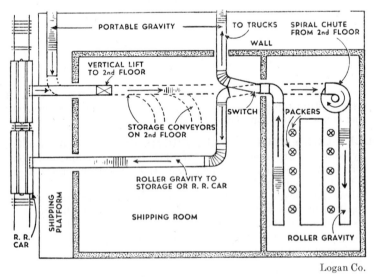

Logan Co.

Fig. 2. Combination of conveyors, lifts, and chutes.

Fig. 3. shows a layout whereby tote boxes of parts pass through machining areas by means of a roller gravity conveyor and belt booster and are then raised by an inclined slat conveyor to an assembly line on the second floor. A second inclined apron conveyor lifts the finished products to third-floor packing and storage. A roller spiral lowers the finished product in shipping cases to cars and trucks on the first floor. Both live-roll and gravity-roller conveyors are used in the assembly on the second floor.

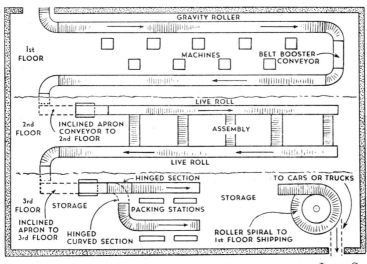

Logan Co.

Fig. 3. Handling through machining, assembly, packing, storage, and shipping.

FLOOR TRUCK TOW-CONVEYOR SYSTEM. Considerable savings in materials handling in industrial plants, commercial enterprises, warehouses, and railroad, motor-carrier, and aircraft terminals have been effected by the use of **caster-equipped trucks** of various kinds. Trucks of this sort, suitable for moving boxes, crates, cartons, etc., may be pushed or pulled manually, or they may be connected to a powered towline which operates in a conduit below the floor level or by means of an overhead tow-conveyor system. Disconnected easily by disengaging them from the towline, the trucks can be readily positioned manually along a loading dock for convenient access to, and for handling of, goods into and from trucks, freight cars, or airplanes.

The main considerations in terminal and warehouse applications are the **prevention of weaving** of the truck and the **avoidance of shock** when attaching the trucks to the conveyor chain. Caster alignment and proper mounting of main wheels assure a steady course.

VERSATILE CONVEYOR SYSTEM. A versatile conveyor system (Fig. 4) for handling boxed goods was installed in the Philadelphia branch of an abrasive manufacturer (Mill and Factory, vol. 50). Formerly, crated abrasive wheels were carried to and from basement storage by elevator. Three operations were involved in this procedure: the elevator had to be loaded, moved up or down, and then unloaded. When the elevator was required for other purposes, cases accumulated on the shipping platform, causing congestion and delay.

A reversible, 25-ft.-long, inclined belt-conveyor system was installed, operating in both directions—from the ground floor to the basement, and from the basement to the ground floor. A continuous flow to and from storage was thus made possible. Incoming crates or packages weighing from 100 to 400 lb. are taken off trucks, placed on the roller-conveyor section, and moved onto the belt conveyor for transfer to the basement for storage. A motor-truck load can be handled in 1½ hr. Outgoing boxes are placed on the roller loading section and transported in reverse direction upward to the shipping platform. The elevator is now freed for other work.

Lamson Corp.

Fig. 4. Reversible belt conveyor for two-floor movement of boxed goods.

A safety feature of this installation is a trap fire door which is suspended at the conveyor opening on the ground floor. In case of fire, the abnormally high temperature will melt a fuse in the suspension chain and drop the trap door.

RETRACTABLE LIVE-ROLLER BOOM CONVEYOR. A printing plant wished to move heavy unit packages from the packing room to the warehouse. The two buildings were separated by a railroad siding on which freight cars were occasionally switched. A boom conveyor which could be withdrawn to permit freight cars to pass was installed. The drive mechanism of this retractable live-roller boom conveyor is fully enclosed and self-contained. To protect the packages as they pass from one building to the other, an enclosure with hinged doors was constructed as an integral part of the structure. The hinged doors open as a package passes along the conveyor.

FACTORY-TO-WAREHOUSE HANDLING. Efficiency in the movement of carton-packed goods is typified by the methods of mechanical handling at an eastern lamp works. Industrial lift trucks, belt-conveyor systems, and a gravity spiral chute are employed (Mill and Factory, vol. 44). Relatively lightweight lamps in cartons are being handled. The cartons, however, are of many sizes, depending upon the type and size of the lamps packed in them.

Since the warehouse is next door to the lamp works, finished goods are moved mechanically to the warehouse by belt conveyors through an all-weather covered bridgeway. Lamps from other nearby factories come by short-haul, door-to-door carload freight transportation. These carload shipments are received on a special railroad siding, the tracks for which enter the building for direct unloading from car floor to main floor.

Packaged lamps are unloaded from the cars by lift trucks, many of which are electric units, and are economically loaded on pallets for pickup and movement to the proper storage sites by high-lift industrial power trucks, which also position and tier the pallet loads.

Belt-Conveyor System. An ingenious triple-decker conveyor system 500 ft. long was installed between the warehouse and the factory. After the cartons of lamps are sealed, they go to the beginning end of the conveyor in the factory.

The three-level belt-conveyor lines travel through an enclosed passageway from building to building at a speed of 80 ft. per min. The two top belts move goods from the factory to the warehouse in 6¼ min. The third, and lowest-level, belt is arranged for the carriage of cartons in the reverse direction, for the return of any cartons to the plant. The two top belts are 20-in. wide, and the return conveyor is 24 in. wide.

The two top lines carry the goods to the roof of the warehouse, where they drop into a two-lane gravity spiral conveyor which chutes the packages down to the main floor of the warehouse. There they are discharged onto a double-decker belt-conveyor system. As the cartons travel along these conveyors, they are removed by hand and sorted onto pallets according to the kind, type, and size of lamp.

Pallet loads of lamps are then removed by industrial fork trucks to the appropriate storage areas on the main floor to await their outward shipment. Any packages for basement storage are placed on the lower of these two belt lines. Items that are relatively slow in movement out of stock are kept in the basement. The return belt-conveyor system starts in the basement, rises to the main floor, travels horizontally to a point near the spiral chute, then upward to the overhead passageway, and back to the factory.

Control of Conveyors. To control the operation of the belt conveyors in case of a jam or backup of goods along the system are two electric-eye stations. One is located at the middle of the bridgeway to control the passage of cartons between the buildings. The other is at the top of the chute for signaling the jam if cartons get stuck in the chute and back up. The electric eyes also count the packages.

At the bottom of the chute is a signal and control board for the electric eyes. There are three indicators for each eye location, one for each belt line. A white light flashes on when an electric eye beam is interrupted by a passing package. If the white light stays on for more than 30 sec., denoting an interruption of that length at that point, a red light goes on and an alarm horn starts to blow. The belt is stopped automatically. The red light shows the attendant where the congestion is, and he takes the steps necessary to clear the jam.

Pallet Loads. Economical pallet loads, depending upon the size and type of lamps, are moved by power trucks from the storage area to the two loading areas for outgoing shipments—one for railroad cars and one for trucks. The lamp cartons are placed in the freight cars and trucks with hand-operated fork trucks.

The outgoing freight-car siding runs along one side, on the inside of the building. The main floor is at car-floor level for the easy moving of goods into freight cars. The truck court has accommodations for loading 16 trucks. A complete load for a truck is set out along the warehouse floor in line with the truck.

STORING BOXES AND CARTONS. The proper storing of boxes and cartons is another important concern of materials handling, since boxes have to be handled with ease and economy in placing them in and removing them from storage racks. A case in point is that of a company which dyes and finishes cotton and rayon fabrics. The problem, a common one in textile and other fields, is that of sorting and carefully handling boxes and cartons of cloth in such a way as to make them easily available for quick shipment. Formerly the company piled these boxes one on top of another. Then, when it was necessary to get at a bottom box, all those on top of it had to be removed.

A cantilever rack, composed of an H-frame section 14½ ft. high with 30-in. arms which are readily adjustable up or down, was developed and installed. There are seven pairs of arms on each side and each pair can take a 1,000-lb. load, the load on a section being 14,000 lb. The rack is so arranged that a fork lift truck can place the boxes directly on the arms. No pallets are needed and any particular box can be selected and removed without disturbing any others. The user can stack more goods in considerably less space than before.

HANDLING BOXES AND CARTONS WITHOUT PALLETS. Several methods have recently been developed for handling unit loads of rectangular, uniform packages without pallets. They are especially suitable for handling commodities in rigid or semi-rigid packages such as corrugated, wood, metal, or plastic boxes, or bottle cases. These methods involve the use of fork truck attachments such as the package-clamp, chisel plate with load stabilizer clamp, and grip-tine (see section on Industrial Trucks). Palletless handling systems promise great savings when large volumes of cartons are handled. They may be used with automatic pallet loaders, conveyors, trailers, and other types of equipment. Economies are realized in vehicle loading and unloading, elimination of investment in pallets, and increased storage capacity.

Handling Long Stock

USE OF MECHANICAL EQUIPMENT. The handling of long stock— bars, rods, tubes, pipes, structural shapes, rolled goods, etc.—with modern mechanical handling equipment is not so difficult as it might seem when considering the bulky lengths of such items. However, limiting conditions may sometimes be encountered.

Manual handling of long stock can be eliminated—or at least greatly reduced —by the judicious use of hand and power lift, fork, platform, and other trucks; levelers, lifters, side loaders; tractor trailers, auto trucks, crane trucks; traveling cranes, overhead rail and track arrangements, hoists; belt, roller, and other conveyors; bar racks; slings, grabs, and tongs; and other mechanical handling equipment.

HANDLING BY CRANE TRUCK. An interesting job done by a crane-type industrial truck is the removal of **bundled units** of 20-ft. lengths of steel tube stock from box cars having a 6-ft. door opening. Previously the tubes were hauled out one at a time. It took four men to do this manual work. One company now does this job with a crane truck and two men. One man operates the crane and the other works in the car. The man in the freight car attaches the sling load of tubes to the crane hook and steers the bundle suspended from the crane through the car door at an angle out onto the shipping dock. This new method has reduced the man-hour requirements by 60 percent.

USE OF CRANE TRUCKS AND PORTABLE RACKS. At a large steel company warehouse the use of a crane truck and specially designed **portable sectional racks** has cut former handling costs more than half. Storage capacity was also increased. The previous method of handling steel bars entailed laborious manual effort. Bars were stored in upright position by hand, and six to ten men were required to pile the steel and fill the orders. Now the work is done by three men, and unloading and racking of stock are performed in one handling operation. The sectional racks are placed in bays 15 × 15 ft. and the 6,000-lb. crane easily handles the work. The crane is used to unload incoming shipments of bar and rod stock, store the stock on the special racks, remove the stock from the racks to fill orders, and load carriers for outgoing shipments.

APPLICATION OF LOW-LIFT PLATFORM TRUCK. Another industrial power-truck application has been made at an asbestos pipe plant in Latin America, where pipe sections are placed on **steel cradles** for movement to and from autoclaves. These heavily loaded cradles are carried by a low-lift platform truck (Fig. 5) which has a load capacity of 20,000 lb. and a platform 12 ft. long. The load, the dimensions of which are 180 × 60 × 60 in., varies in weight from 16,000 to 21,000 lb. The truck has been in service 24 hr. a day for 6 days a week. Another low-lift platform truck of 10,000 lb. capacity is also in use for the manufacturing operations at this plant.

USE OF TRACTOR-TRAILERS. In Fig. 6, a load too long for one trailer is shown being carried by two trailers. Swivel bolsters, which can be attached quickly, are used with these caster-steer trailers. The tractor pulls the two trailers, and a man guiding the rear one can snake the load around corners and through narrow aisles.

UNLOADING CARS BY MEANS OF OVERHEAD CRANES. Overhead materials handling equipment has many advantages for the economical movement of bar stock. An interesting case is presented by an installation in a modern plant in Texas where a **monorail cab-operated transfer bridge** (Fig. 7) unloads open railroad cars in one-twentieth of the time formerly needed when manual methods were used. It now takes only 3 man-hours to unload a car; formerly from 64 to 96 man-hours were required for the job.

The 5-ton bridge, which is completely motorized, travels on a 3-track runway. The two electric hoists, which have a lift of 24 ft., are located on the bridge, one on each side of the cab. Rods up to 65 ft. long are handled with a lifting beam. The overhead monorail system interlocks with four spur tracks in the area where cutoff machines are located. These machines are served by roller conveyors onto which bundles of rods are lowered. This mechanical handling installation saves time not only in the unloading of incoming rods but also in making deliveries from storage to the cutoff machines and in loading shipments of rods into outgoing trucks.

Elwell-Parker Electric Co.

Fig. 5. Heavily loaded cradles of pipe carried by a low-lift platform truck.

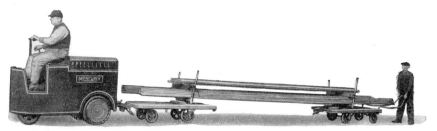

Fig. 6. A load too long for one trailer can be carried on two trailers pulled by a tractor.

Fig. 8 shows an overhead system, consisting of a 3-ton double-girder, under-runnning, **single-leg gantry crane** with cantilevered girder extension. The operator has magnetic controls for the three motions of the crane which enable him to spot long loads accurately. This type of crane is also used in many plants as an auxiliary crane operating under high-capacity, top-running, mill-type cranes.

HANDLING BY V CONVEYORS. Roller conveyors of the V design are applied to the handling of pipe, bars, structural shapes, boards, and the like, as is shown in the accompanying diagrams in Fig. 9. The slight tilting of each roller, with **adjacent rollers tilted in opposite directions,** forms a trough along which long items can roll, automatically centered without side rails or guards. Various

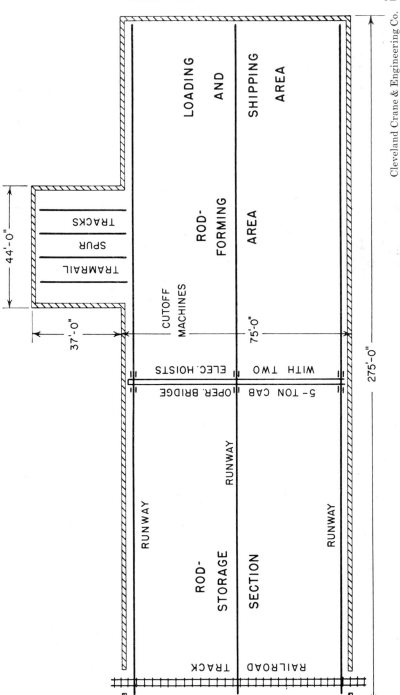

Cleveland Crane & Engineering Co.

Fig. 7. Layout of bar stock unloading area.

Fig. 8. Long-steel-fabricated structures are accurately moved with this single-leg gantry crane with a cantilevered extension.

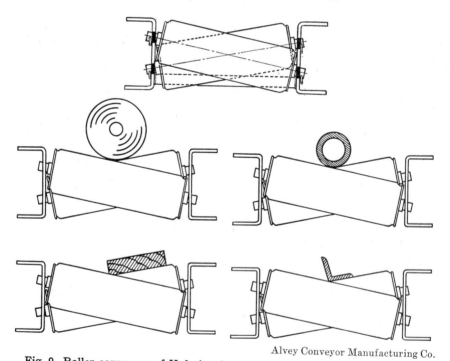

Alvey Conveyor Manufacturing Co.

Fig. 9. Roller conveyors of V design for handling many kinds of long goods.

widths and roller load capacities are, of course, provided for different require-ments. Concave roller conveyors serve the same purpose and are particularly adapted to handling heavy loads.

HANDLING FOR SHORT-TERM STORAGE. A method of handling tubing for short-term storage was sought by one manufacturing company. Ease in handling relatively small quantities of a wide range of lengths, diameters, and alloys of special tubing was essential. The separate units involved averaged about 100 lb. Valuable mill floor space also had to be conserved for production work.

The problem was solved by an arrangement of storage racks facing one another, with an open space of about 20 × 25 ft. between them. A mobile electric platform lifter operates in this open area. The vertical members of each rack are 3-in. channels, and the horizontal members are 1½-in. hollow stock. The lattice frame-work of the rack is about 25 ft. wide, 12 ft. high, and 21 ft. deep. Three hundred openings, 12 in. square, are provided in each rack. Intermediate horizontal mem-bers run the width of the latticed structure to provide support for various lengths of tubing up to 21 ft., the maximum depth of the racks. Each opening is marked with two numbers, which designate its horizontal and vertical position and serve as the stock-card means of easy identification.

Bundled and tagged units of tubes are placed on the platform of the lifter, which is then positioned in vertical alignment with the opening in which the tubes are to be stored. The lifter rises to the height of the opening, and the tubes are easily set into the correct rack space. The lifter is operated from the floor or from the platform. The whole job can be done by one man, except that long, heavy tubes require two men.

AUTOMATIC TONGS FOR STEEL ROUNDS. By means of specially developed automatic tongs, the crane operator in the storage yard of a manufac-turer of steel pipe and tubing can handle by himself loads of rolled steel rounds that weigh up to 30,000 lb. No hookup man is needed since an automatic locking device built into the tongs permits the craneman to pick up, move about the yard, and deposit unit-load quantities of rounds which are anywhere from 4 to 13 in. in diameter. Narrow-gage stake cars carry the rounds from the produc-tion runout tables to the finishing operations. The automatic tongs attached to the traveling crane can pick up from, and deposit in, these stake cars unit quanti-ties of the steel rounds. Fig. 10 shows the construction of the tongs and the methods of their use.

HANDLING BAR STOCK IN RACKS. An unusual case which shows the large extent to which bar stock racks are used is an installation at one of the large aircraft plants. At the time it was installed it was said to be the largest ever fabricated of Unistrut metal framing. It has 2,376 individual compartments 9½ in. high and 12 in. wide. Designed to support a load capacity of 4,700 tons, it is a 2-section rack 132 ft. wide and over 25 ft. deep. The lower part is 9 tiers high. Just above the ninth tier is a catwalk for easy access to the upper 9 tiers of compartments. Steel bars, rods, and structural shapes are stored in the lower group of tiers. The upper section holds aluminum and magnesium extrusions and various types of tubing.

INTEGRATED SYSTEMS FOR WAREHOUSE ECONOMY. A sys-tem of materials handling that integrates overhead cranes, racks, and tongs has cut warehouse costs in an Indianapolis, Indiana, plant. Raw materials are handled faster, housekeeping has been improved, floor space is utilized more advantage-ously, stock selection is easier, and men have been made available for other duties.

Heppenstall Co.

Fig. 10. Handling steel bars by overhead traveling crane.

Among the items handled economically are steel bars, rounds, shapes, and pipe. Three types of fabricated racks were obtained for handling materials: one for bars and pipe, another for coils of wire, and a third for finished chains. Tongs for each kind of rack were designed for the installation.

The **portable racks** for bar stock are open at the top and ends, as shown in Fig. 11, so that various lengths of stock can be placed in and removed from them. The construction of the top and bottom ends of the side framework of the racks allows them to be tiered and locked together to prevent shifting. Side clearance

Palmer-Shile Co.

Fig. 11. Cranes, racks, Heppenstall tongs, and a portable control board vastly facilitate rapid, safe handling.

between racks is not necessary when tiering them. The **special tongs,** which provide easy pickup and safe carriage of the racks, operate in a minimum headroom of 23 in. so that high tiering is possible. The tongs will not lift the rack unless they grip it securely. Two tongs, each of which can handle loads of 3 tons, serve some 519 bar racks.

Bars, tubing, rounds, etc., are delivered to the plant by truck. At the unloading platform, the steel is graded and the sizes gaged; then the stock is placed in racks. The loaded racks are picked up by the tongs, which are attached to an overhead crane hoist, and moved to platform scales. After being weighed, the load is carried by crane to the warehouse. In the warehouse the loaded bar racks are stacked six tiers high. The tong design makes it possible to place the top tier close under the runway of the overhead crane system. The craneman works from the floor, operating the crane hoist and rack loads from the suspended control panel.

When bar stock is wanted in the production area, the operator positions the crane and tongs over the rack containing the needed material. The tongs grip the rack, which is then moved out into the main aisle and lowered onto a 6-wheel warehouse truck. Power equipment moves the truck to the proper work area. If less than a full rack of stock is wanted, the desired number of bars is removed from the loaded rack and placed on the warehouse truck for delivery to the production area.

This advantageous installation has **reduced the hazards of accidents** in handling this bulky material. It has cut down the time of unloading steel from cars and trucks to one-tenth of the former task period of some 20 hr. with a crew of men. Now an incoming shipment of 120,000 lb. of steel bars, in 3-ton bundles, can be unloaded, graded, sized, and moved to storage in $1\frac{3}{4}$ hr.

HANDLING LONG, ROLLED GOODS. Mechanized equipment is being used widely by companies that handle and ship long rolls of heavy goods such as carpets. These organizations include both the manufacturers of the products and the commercial establishments that distribute and sell the goods. A case application of this sort makes use of an overhead traveling crane system, slings and grabhooks, movable cradle units, cutting tables, and storage racks.

Rolls of carpet are received by a company that distributes and sells a wide assortment of products which come to it either wrapped in burlap covers or packed in wooden shipping cases. In the first instance, the roll is picked up in the receiving department by **slings** attached to the hook of an overhead rail crane and transported to the cutting-table floor. Here the rolled goods are lowered onto a movable **cradle** unit set inside the steel-framed cutting table.

The cradle, which is independent of the cutting table, has steel angle sides to which wheels are attached. Spanning from side to side are strips of heavy duck webbing which support the roll in a cradlelike effect. The rolls of carpet stay on the cradle all the time they are handled and stored and until they are sold.

The cutting table, which is also of steel construction, serves several functions. One is as a carrying device for a roll-loaded cradle so the roll can be stored in one of the steel compartments of the rack structures that are located along both sides of the cutting floor. To handle the table, the overhead crane is equipped with two lifting bars which are lowered to straddle the table. Push-button controls anchor it to the crane. The table, with its load, is then lifted by the crane and carried to a point opposite the compartment into which the carpet roll is to be deposited.

The track on the table along which the wheels of the cradle run is lined up with the steel channel track in the rack compartment. The cradle with its roll of carpet is thus easily pushed into the storage compartment. For the removal of a roll of carpet, the procedure is reversed. A cutting table is moved by crane to line up with the right compartment and the cradle is then rolled out onto the cutting table.

If a piece is to be cut off the roll, the table and cradle are deposited on the floor wherever the cutter wants them. A system of rollers, which are a part of the cutting table and which move upward between the spacings between cradle webbing, lifts the roll of carpet out of the cradle so that the cutter can pull out as much carpet from the roll as necessary. When the table is again lifted by the crane, the roll slips back into the cradle.

Sometimes the carpet comes to the receiving room packed in a wooden case. The long, crated package is moved to the cutting floor by grabhooks attached to the overhead crane hoist. At the cutting table the crate is laid alongside the table on two arm supports. Two straps, which are attached to the arms, are hooked to the crane lift. As the hoist is elevated, the shipping box is tilted on its side enough to spill out the carpet roll onto the cradle in the cutting table. From there on the handling procedure is the same as that already described.

Another commonly used system, the "Trak-Rak," is illustrated in Fig. 12.

Bigelow-Sanford

Fig. 12. Carpet-roll handling equipment.

HIGH-PRODUCTION BUNDLING. The bundling of steel pipe in one factory is handled in a way that saves much walking and lifting. Bundles of pipe range from 12 pieces of ½-in. pipe to 3 pieces of the 1½-in. size; pipe sections average 21 to 22 ft. in length. Three men tie each bundle—one in the middle and one at each end.

Formerly, after making his tie, the middle bundler had to walk half the length of the pipe to get out of the way so that the bundle could be lifted and dropped into cradles behind him. Now, with the use of a specially designed elevated steel platform, bundles pass under the middle bundler and are lowered by gravity into cradles which are attached to a scale platform at floor level. No longer is it necessary to lift the bundles, or have the bundler walk away from his tying station.

Pipes are loaded onto the specially made bundling table, which is made up of four skid rails, each skid having at its end a bundling wheel, which is a 20-in. steel disk with three equally spaced nests cut into it. Sufficient pieces of pipe to make up a bundle are moved from the table into the nests and tied together. After a bundle has been tied up, one of the operators works a foot pedal which rotates the bundling wheels one-third of a revolution. This action not only discharges the tied bundle but also positions the next grooved nest to receive another bundle of pipe. A modification in the bundling of conduit makes use of automatic bundlers and pressure-sensitive tape. In this application a single operator controls the flow of conduit into the taping mechanism.

Handling Flat Stock

ADVANTAGES OF HANDLING IN UNIT LOADS. The handling of any material in unit loads is desirable because it allows movement and storage of compact, neat, orderly, and standardized loads. It aids in utilizing space by making high tiering possible, helps cut down handling labor, time, and cost, and makes for safer handling and less damage in handling. Unit handling is especially important for flat materials. Large, flat material is cumbersome and difficult to handle in individual pieces. It may pose safety hazards and is often easily damaged.

The materials falling in the category of flat stock vary widely in their physical characteristics. Flat stock may be tough, fragile, brittle, hard, soft, etc. The handling methods best suited for **flat stock** must take these properties into consideration. Yet, there are many handling solutions that are common to flat stock even where the physical characteristics vary widely.

Some common materials found in the category of flat stock and long stock are:

Sheet metal.	Sheet paper.
Lumber.	Paper board.
Plate glass.	Roofing materials.
Wallboard.	Ferrous and nonferrous slabs.

Handling methods for flat stock depend to some extent on the **purpose of the handling.** There is a difference in handling requirements for moving the same material through the receiving operation, the storage operation, the interplant and intraplant operations, in fabrication, loading, shipping, etc. Thus, the equipment and the method used should be chosen with the purpose of the handling in mind.

Equipment for Handling Flat Stock. The kinds of equipment which have been found well suited for handling flat stock are:

1. **Industrial trucks:** Hand lift, platform, fork, straddle, side loader, crane truck, tractor-trailer.
2. **Overhead systems:** Traveling cranes; trolley track and rail; chain, gantry, and cantilever cranes; hoists, grabs, slings, and tongs.
3. **Conveyors:** Fixed and portable, horizontal and inclined belt; roller, live, and gravity; skate-wheel; pusher; drag chain, overhead and underfloor level; transfer units.
4. **Portable lifters:** Lifts, stackers, tiering machines, elevating tables.

PREPARING FLAT LOADS FOR INTRAPLANT HANDLING. Flat stock is packaged in unit loads usually for intraplant handling or for shipment to some purchaser. Intraplant unit loads are made up according to manufacturing requirements. The load specifications depend on the size, shape, and weight of the material, the type and capacity of the handling equipment, and the rate of use at the production and assembly stations being supplied. After **standard unit-load specifications** have been determined for flat stock, the loads may be placed on pallets, skids, special racks or supports, or directly on conveyors to go into storage or be transported to point of use. Special racks are available which prevent the enameled surface of long metal braces from being scratched. Large sheets of rough plate glass are often moved on special A frames.

Flat unit loads are often packaged with **integral skids,** usually by placing the load on commercial-size timbers, such as 2×4 in. or 4×4 in. cut to suitable length and secured by bands or wires. Unit lifts may be arranged with sheets on crosswise skids or on lengthwise skids. Such patterns can be designed for handling by fork truck, platform truck, or by slings or special grabs. Ordinary bound loads are often tiered in storage with **wooden runners between the loads** to permit entry of forks. Runners are also used on trailers for stacking bound loads.

Flat stock is often left **unpalletized on a sheet of heavy paper** where a push-pull pack loader is used. The attachment on the truck grips the load and pulls it, with the paper, onto the forks. In many cases the load is then deposited on a conventional pallet for further handling. When flat unit loads are handled with an **electromagnet,** the load is either unbound, in the case of single slabs, or it must be securely bound.

PREPARING LOADS FOR SHIPPING AND RECEIVING. The user has the responsibility for specifying the packaging, shipping methods, and unit load sizes for purchased flat stock. In the case of sheet steel, for example, the user should specify whether the steel is to be oiled or dry; the type of protection, if any; the desired or maximum weight of lifts; the method of loading for shipment, and other factors.

The common **protective packaging methods** for sheet steel are:

1. Paper wrapped, each lift being completely wrapped in water repellent paper and secured by steel strapping or wire. Fig. 13 shows this kind of packaged lift being handled by fork truck and grabs.
2. Shrouded, waterproof paper being secured over the top, ends, and sides of previously bound lifts of sheets.
3. Both paper wrapped and shrouded.
4. Shipped bare, with no protection.

The type of protection depends upon the method of shipment, the distance from supplier to user, condition of storage at user's plant, and handling method used at user's plant. Long, flat stock shipped a short distance by truck is often completely unprotected, while the same stock shipped a long distance in an open gondola will require maximum protection.

Long, flat stock is often mounted and strapped to **common skids or on pallets,** especially if the shipment is to be unloaded with an industrial truck. In this case, the user should specify the amount or maximum weight on each skid or pallet.

USE OF INDUSTRIAL TRUCKS. Industrial trucks of many kinds are useful for handling long, flat stock. They can be used for loading and unloading in shipping and receiving operations, for storage operations, for movement of long, flat loads throughout a plant, and for spotting loads at work stations. Hand- and power-driven lift or platform trucks find wide application for transporting long, flat loads stored on pallets or skids, or on properly spaced runners. Often special oversize pallets and skids are used with conventional fork trucks.

Fig. 13. Handling lifts of paper-wrapped steel.

The **powered driver-ride or driver-walk type of platform-lift truck** may be used, as is, for many moderately long pallet or skid loads of flat stock. Two gas-powered fork trucks can be operated simultaneously for transporting long stock. In one application, two trucks as a team take a 10,000-lb. load of sheet metal from a trailer to place it in storage. This cooperative handling method prevents sagging and bending which otherwise would ruin the sheets.

Numerous **fork truck attachments** are available, many of which find application with the flat unit load. Among these useful attachments are the push-pull pack loaders, the general purpose clamp, the slope piler or tilt apron, the veneer handler, the bin loader, the side loader, crane attachments, load stabilizers, and extra fork attachments and extensions.

The **veneer handler attachment** can handle loads up to 17 ft. in length and up to ½ ton in weight. The lift mechanism has two sets of lever arms fitted with pads. The arms close against the sides of the load by hydraulic pressure. The supporting frame is hinged to the truck's lift frame and is fitted with a hydraulic cylinder piston. The application of pressure in this cylinder rotates the supporting frame, thus enabling a load to be picked up horizontally and turned up on end to be stored vertically.

With a **bin-loader** attachment long, flat unit loads can be transported and stacked into bins. The attachment is built in two sizes for packages 40 and 48 in. wide and up to 20 ft. in length. The fork truck is positioned as closely as possible to the bin opening with the bottom of the load slightly higher than the floor of the bin. When the load is in position, the operator flips a lever, and hydraulically powered rollers move the load endwise into the bin, leaving a small portion of the load sticking out. Only orders for less than a packaged unit are filled from the loads in the bins. An extra set of detachable forks, wide-spaced, pictured in Fig. 13, gives additional support to a long, flexible, 10,000-lb. unit load of sheet steel.

Fig. 14. Crane truck fitted with a vacuum pump and vacuum clamps for handling sheets of rough plate glass.

An ingenious arrangement that enables a standard fork truck to pick up firmly packaged long, flat loads is a wire rope attached to the carriage, with a hook at the other end to grab and support the far end of the load. Other industrial trucks which find application for handling long, flat loads are crane trucks, straddle-type powered stacking trucks, straddle trucks, and side-loading trucks. The **crane truck** can handle long, flat loads by using special grabs, slings, or electromagnets. An illustration of the use of a special grab is shown in Fig. 14. This grab is comprised of ten rubber suction cups fitted to a vacuum system which can be controlled by an operator. The crane operator positions the vacuum frame on a large sheet of plate glass, turns on the vacuum, and can pick up, transport, and set down this fragile material easily and safely.

Long flat loads can be moved into and out of racks by means of a **roller platform with an integral catwalk,** used together with a straddle-type powered stacking truck. With this combined handling unit, a 6,000-lb. load 24 ft. long can

Fig. 15. Wallboard handled with special V-rack and straddle carrier.

be elevated up to 120 in. The hydraulic lift can be controlled either from the floor or from the catwalk. The truck can be used to handle miscellaneous skid loads when the roller platform is detached, and the platform unit can be moved by hand on its own casters.

Where long distances are involved, industrial trucks or overhead handling systems are often used in conjunction with **tractor-trailers.** The tractor pulls one or more trailers to the unloading point, usually a storage area. The loaded trailers are detached, and emptied trailers are then picked up and brought back to the loading point. The industrial truck or an overhead handling system may then be employed to unload the trailers and position the load as desired in the storage area. Fig. 6 shows a tractor-trailer which can be used to haul flat stock.

The **straddle carrier,** developed originally for lumber handling, has been used considerably in many industrial applications for handling long, awkward loads. These carriers come in standard models for loads ranging from 10,000 lb. to 45,000 lb. They can travel at speeds up to 50 mi. per hr. and are operated on highways or rough ground as readily as in industrial plants. They can be loaded or unloaded by one operator in about three seconds and are highly maneuverable because of 4-wheel steering. Straddle carriers of this type can easily handle a unit load as much as 80 ft. long. Fig. 15 shows long, flat sheets of wallboard on a special V-shaped rack about to be lifted by a straddle carrier—rack and all.

Fig. 16. Steel plate handled by side-loading fork truck.

A **side-loading fork truck** is well suited to load, transport, unload, or stack long, flat materials. Because of its side-loading design, such a truck can carry loads through narrow aisles or narrow roadways, thereby gaining the advantage of all available space. Trucks of this kind are available in 10,000-lb. and 30,000-lb. capacities, travel at 30 mi. per hr., and have a 12-ft. lifting range. Fig. 16 shows such a truck, equipped with adjustable-width forks, handling steel plate. These trucks can also be equipped with a twin crane attachment for unloading long material from a gondola car.

USE OF OVERHEAD TRACK EQUIPMENT. Overhead systems consisting of an overhead track or rail network employing cranes and hoists are found most useful for picking up, transporting, and placing flat unit loads. These systems vary considerably in their complexity and in their range of utility, and are of many different types, ranging from a simple fixed-path rail employing a hand-operated hoist to an interlocking network of tracks employing traveling bridges with cab-controlled cranes for completely traversing a large area. Fig. 8 shows the application of a single-leg gantry crane.

Cranes, hoists, grabs, and slings are usually associated with one another in such overhead handling systems. The **grabs** used for long, flat stock vary from the simple hand-operated type through an extensive range of powered types. A **mechanically coupled automatic grab** is available for such operations as moving individual slabs from a conveyor to the feeding table of a slab miller. The grab is adjustable for various widths and thicknesses of slabs.

An ingenious grab for **handling extra-long loads** of brass slabs is illustrated in Fig. 17. This grab has a number of legs which can move not only in and out horizontally but also can turn 90° to get under a load. To engage a load, the

Fig. 17. A grab handling long, flat brass slabs. (The supporting legs on the grab rotate 90° to bring them under the load.)

grab is adjusted to the approximate width of the sheet and lowered into the pickup position. The legs are then rotated to extend under the bundle and engage the load. Rotation of the legs is accomplished by turning the small chain wheel.

Fig. 18 shows another type of sheet grab. This 30,000-lb.-capacity grab has adjustable motor-driven end legs as well as side legs and handles sheets varying from 72 in. to 74 in. in width and from 72 in. to 168 in. in length. Thus this grab may be used effectively for loads of flat stock varying considerably in both length and width.

Vacuum-type devices are used as grabs for handling nonferrous slabs in rolling mills. Floor space is conserved and handling time is reduced to a minimum by stacking the slabs by means of overhead cranes with suction grabs on a comprehensive system of roller conveyors which connect practically all the equipment used in processing the nonferrous stock.

Since slabs are fed into and discharged from the processing equipment one at a time, it is necessary to provide for individual handling of the slabs by means of a vacuum-cup device as well as providing for their handling in multiples on the roller conveyors. The unit consists of a load-carrying beam with a series of rubber vacuum cups. Each cup is connected by hose to a pipe header, which, in turn, is connected to an exhauster which removes the air and creates the necessary vacuum in the cups. A pressure differential of some 7 lb. per sq. in. was used in the design. Thus, a vacuum cup having an area of 50 sq. in. within the rubber seal around the circumference of the cup would possess a theoretical lifting capacity of 350 lb. Under ordinary room pressure a 2,000-lb. flat slab could then be lifted by using a sufficient number of cups along the load-carrying beam.

Fig. 18. **A 30,000-lb.-capacity motor-driven sheet grab. (It has motor-driven end-hooks which permit the handling of sheets which vary considerably in both width and length.)**

The load-carrying beams are supported in two ways. One consists of a traveling bridge structure which has trucks at each end, like a bridge crane. The other consists of runway rails above the slabs to be handled; the rails carry the trucks. **Longitudinal and lateral movement** is obtained by using hydraulic cylinders, although electric motors or pneumatic cylinders could be employed. The vertical raising and lowering of the slabs and beam is accomplished by means of pneumatic or hydraulic cylinders, preferably the former to avoid oil drip.

In the other method of support, the load-carrying beam is attached to **stands and pivoted arms.** The stands have vertical cylinders to elevate the slab and horizontal cylinders to swing the arms after a slab has been picked up. Both movements are obtained with hydraulically operated cylinders. The vacuum equipment has sufficient capacity to handle flat slabs weighing up to 2,000 lb. in lengths of from 9 to 64 ft., widths of 16 to 29 in., and thicknesses from 0.40 to 2½ in. This special handling equipment is installed, for example, at both entry and delivery sides of the 2-Hi cold rolling breakdown mill, at the two ends of the slab annealing furnace, at the entry of the slab milling apparatus, and at the up-cut shear line and entry side of the first 4-Hi mill.

CONVEYOR HANDLING. There are several kinds of conveyors which can handle flat unit loads with equal efficiency and correspondingly low cost. Loading, unloading, transporting, and storage of such materials raise no particularly difficult problems. Conveyors alone may be used, or they may be employed in conjunction with other kinds of handling equipment for flat unit-load handling.

Live- and gravity-feed-roller conveyors are perhaps most frequently used for handling flat stock in metal-rolling mills for both hot and cold rolling operations. Roller conveyors are used to great advantage for moving and storing flat slabs between processing operations. Conveyorized handling has largely eliminated the former laborious manual handling associated with such mill work and has aided considerably in eliminating the dents, pits, gouges, and other defects which formerly constituted major difficulties in the fabrication of high-quality end products. Stacking the slabs on roller conveyor systems conserves floor space and greatly reduces handling time. The load capacity of roller conveyors depends upon the capacity of the bearings, the length of the load, and the spacing of the rollers or other supports. By changing these factors it is possible to accommodate a wide range of loads.

Roller, skate, or belt conveyors are usually used for loading or unloading comparatively lightweight flat stock. The conveyor runs into the freight car or truck, and the flat stock is placed on the conveyor. Loading or unloading the conveyor within the car or truck is usually done manually. If the distance is short, these conveyors can extend directly to the storage point; if not, they can deposit the load on the dock, where it is picked up and moved to storage by other means. The conveyor setup may be a temporary arrangement, or it may be a type of setup for extended service. Regular powered belt conveyors may be used in conjunction with roller or skate-wheel conveyors for elevating or lowering loads at either or both the point of storage and the loading dock. Often portable belt conveyors are used, instead of the more permanent setup, if the receiving schedule does not require continuous conveyor service. The portable conveyors can then be utilized at various places as required.

Handling Bags and Sacks

HANDLING BAGS BY HAND TRUCK. There are many kinds of hand trucks for carrying boxes, bags, sacks, and other containers from one point to another, into and out of freight cars, and into and out of storage areas. Many varieties of hand trucks of the so-called cargo type are used for these purposes. They are made of wood and metal, or all metal, and are designed for flexibility. One common type of such a hand truck is designed with a hinged plate mounted over the nose. The plate is flipped down for handling bags and locked up, exposing the nose, for boxes.

BAG FLATTENING. When paper bags in large quantities are to be emptied, placed in temporary storage, and later reclaimed for filling purposes, it is customary in large plants to have bag-flattening equipment for compressing the empty paper bags so as to save space in handling and storing them. In Figs. 19

and 20, bags are being compressed and palletized. The successive steps are as follows:

1. Empty multiwall bags are loaded manually, flat, onto a pallet.
2. The pallet load of empty bags is then ready to be hydraulically pressed. Before this operation is performed, a kraft wrapper and steel straps are placed around the load.
3. After pressure has been applied, the steel straps are tensioned.
4. The fork truck removes the loaded pallet to the freight car transporting them to the bag-filling plant.

Fig. 19. Press in position for compressing bags.

CHARACTERISTICS OF BAGS AND SACKS. Bags or sacks are containers made up usually in standard sizes of one or more layers of paper, plastic, or fabric and intended to contain standard weights or volumes of loose materials. Essentially, the empty bag consists of three closed sides, the fourth one being left open to receive the designated contents. As a **package**, it has certain features which sometimes make it difficult to handle. But because it is inexpensive and easy to fill on automatic machinery, it is not likely to be superseded as a container. Because of this fact, techniques have been evolved that help to simplify bag-handling problems.

Fig. 20. Bags after flattening.

Bags are flexible and as a rule cannot be used on skate or wheel conveyors unless a stiff support is provided for the bags to ride on. Many warehouse men use scrap corrugated board as small "pallets" on which the bags may ride. For large-scale continuous operations, bag-handling machinery units often costing $10,000 and over are sometimes installed.

Paper Bags and Sacks. Paper bags, prior to filling, are usually stored flat in moderately high stacks, and, if possible, in a room which is neither dry nor hot. The relative humidity should be about 50 percent or slightly higher, especially in the wintertime when, because of the operation of the heating system, the humidity will drop considerably. The paper bags may then become brittle and may crack, tear, or burst when being filled. This damage occurs generally along the seams. To overcome this trouble some companies install commercial humidifying equipment to keep the warehouse humidity at around 50 percent. Ordinarily, the **wire-tied kind of closure** tends to cause the greatest problem. Dry, brittle paper is often cut by the wires, particularly if the wire is improperly applied, thus rendering the bags useless.

Multiwall Bags. Most of the bags and sacks in use today are multiwall, the advantages being numerous. The claim of the Hudson Pulp and Paper Corporation is that "Multiwall sacks and bags are the most versatile, economical, strong, flexible packaging, shipping, and storing containers for a wide range of industrial and consumer products on the market today."

The trade term "multiwall" is descriptive since such sacks are built of two or more walls or plies of special, heavy-duty kraft paper. The weight of the paper and the number of plies used for the individual sack depend entirely upon the product which is to be packaged and shipped. Multiwall sacks are being used successfully for innumerable products, ranging from foods to corrosive chemicals. Their construction, therefore, is necessarily "custom tailored" to the job, since each product has its individual physical properties, weight, and density. The endless variety in sizes, closings, weights, types of coatings and finishings, numbers and combinations of plies, and printed surfaces—possible only with paper—make multiwall sacks ideal, low-cost, package-type containers with ample opportunity for product identification.

The **reasons for using multiwall bags** are many. Offhand, it might be concluded that a single sheet of 140-lb. paper, when made into a bag, would be strong enough to use as a shipping carrier. Actually, a single sheet of 140-lb. paper would be stiff and hard to handle. However, a multiwall sack consisting of four plies of paper in combinations of two 30-lb. and two 40-lb. sheets, with a total base weight of 140 lb., has greater flexibility and durability, allowing for greater facility in methods of packing, shipping, and storing.

The most efficient procedure for filling multiwall bags is as follows:

1. The operator takes an empty multiwall bag and holds it on the bag chute.
2. The preweighed material drops through the bag chute and the filled weight drops the bag onto a moving conveyor.
3. As the filled bag moves down the conveyor, the operator reaches for another empty bag.
4. As the filled bag goes through the sewing head, the operator takes a "contents tag" from the tag bin and sews it to the bag. Filled, sewn bags then travel by conveyor either to the warehouse or to a waiting truck.

Problems in Handling Bags and Sacks. A major problem in connection with sacks and bags arises in shipping or receiving them. There are several methods of loading and unloading trucks and railroad cars with bags and sacks, but in the main three kinds of handling equipment are usually employed:

1. Hand trucks.
2. Fork trucks, for handling palletized materials.
3. Conveyors, either gravity or powered.

Lift trucks or conveyors can carry the loaded bags directly from the filling machines to, and even right into, trucks or cars. Loading rates are determined by one of two factors, either the rate of the operation of the **filling machines** or the rate of operation of the **loading crews.** One handler is at one end of the conveyor, the other handler at the other end. If the filling machine works at a rate of 6 bags per min., and a conveyor carries the bags directly into the box car where they may be picked up at shoulder height, then a two-man crew can handle the job without any difficulty (Fig. 21). Under the same conditions, but at a rate of 14 bags per min., two men can also keep up with the machine, but a relief man will be required to "spell" the loaders.

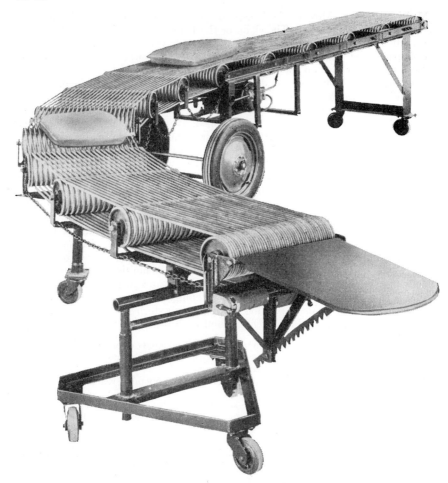

Fig. 21. Flexible cable conveyor for moving bagged materials to storage or shipping.

Unit loads are made up in various **patterns** (Fig. 22), **a row arrangement** (Fig. 23), or in a variation of these arrangements. The cloth bags are all interlocked, with the weight of the upper tier locking the lower tiers together. In stacking paper bags, a plywood sheet is used to distribute the weight of the upper pallet over the lower one. The paper bags are usually protected from possible tears or punctures caused by projections on the pallets, such as protruding nails.

The Association of American Railroads lists various rules regulating the safe loading of commodities into bags and the bags into closed cars. These rules, of course, can also be applied in toto, or with minor modifications, to other transportation equipment. The bags in question contain flour and other grain products, sugar and related commodities such as rice, salt, coffee, beans, and peanuts. Details are set forth in a publication of The Association of American Railroads, Freight Loading and Container Section (Pamphlet No. 3).

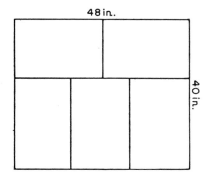

Fig. 22. Arrangement of pallet layer, plan view.

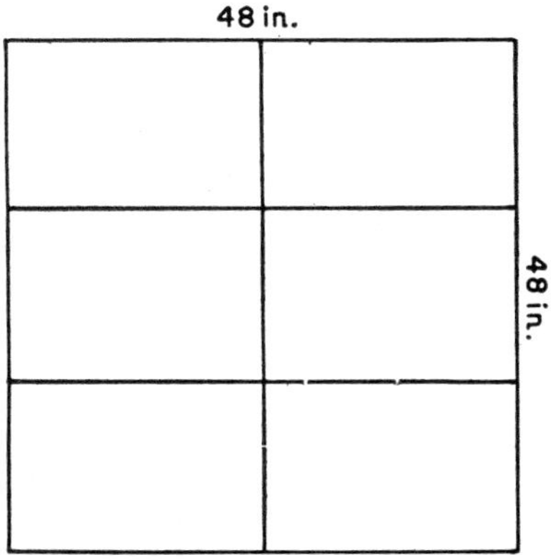

Fig. 23. Representative row arrangement of a pallet layer, plan view.

Granular or powdered bulk products are usually packaged in bags and sacks to simplify batching, handling, and selling. Because there is no inherent stiffness in either the product or the package, certain handling techniques and precautions must be followed which are not usually needed when working with other kinds of packages. Moreover, since bags have a certain amount of flexibility, they lend themselves to handling methods that would not be feasible with other kinds of containers.

Protection of the Container. Bags, whether of cloth, paper, or plastic, are likely to tear if brought into contact with sharp objects, or if roughly handled. When an accident of this kind happens, not only is some of the product lost but also the remainder is subject to contamination. The working area may become messy and in some cases the atmosphere may even become hazardous. To prevent such occurrences, overslips and pressure-sensitive tapes should be kept handy at all times in connection with bag-handling operations.

Floors, pallets, skids, trucks, and railroad cars must be inspected for **projecting nails, sharp splinters,** and other projections which may cause ruptures in the bags. Before loading highway trucks or box cars, the interiors should be cleaned out, dried, and lined with paper where necessary. Bags should be picked up only by placing the hands under them at both ends. They should never be dragged. When they are picked from a pile, the bottom bags should be inspected for punctures and tears. Should they be ripped or torn, they must be carried, torn side up, to a repair station where they can be patched or placed in an overslip. If bags have to be dropped as they are unloaded, care should be exercised to have them land on their ends or edges.

Since **granular materials** in bags tend to settle while the bags are in storage or transit, it is best to use a bag-flattener when making up unit loads. The bag-flattener is a device built into a short length of conveyor which carries the bag through a rolling and kneading action under controlled pressure, leveling the material uniformly, displacing air, and forming a neat, solid package, uniform in thickness throughout, as shown in Fig. 24. Thus the bags not only make a firmer and more solid load, but they are also reduced in thickness. Three flattened bags will usually make a pile no higher than two unflattened bags. Thus the number of bags that will fit into a fixed stacking height is increased (see Fig. 25).

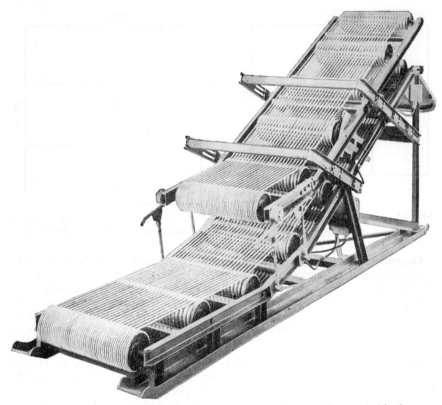

Fig. 24. Bag-flattener press for stabilizing loads for handling and shipping.

Fig. 25. Flattened bags showing added stability obtained by the flattening operation.

In using overhead equipment for the handling of bags, care must be exercised not to have slings, grabs, or prongs bite into the bags. The handling should usually be done by use of platform slings (Fig. 26) or in unit loads on wing-type pallets.

HANDLING UNIT LOADS. When bagged or sacked materials are made into unit loads, bags are often placed on pallets or skids in either a **pinwheel** or a **criss-cross pattern.** The pinwheel seems to be preferred because of the load-locking arrangement, but often the bag size or pallet size makes this arrangement impossible. If the load is not sufficiently firm to undergo transportation, there are several ways to keep it from falling apart. The first method to try consists of inserting large sheets of paper between the last three layers of sacks. The smooth

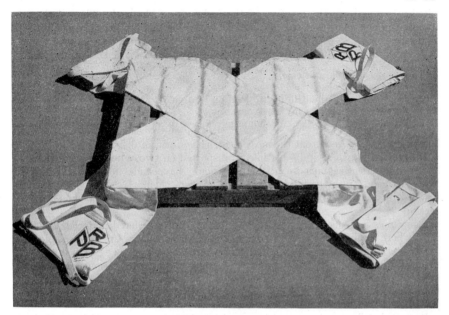

Fig. 26. Canvas carrier for packing up bags and sacks and loading them into freight cars.

surface of the multiwall paper bags often becomes slippery and causes the load to spread. To prevent this spreading, some bags are now available which have crepe outer surfaces.

When a **firmer load** is required, the bags can be glued together as they are placed on the pallet. Adhesives are available that will hold the bags against lateral stress (shearing), but have no strength when the bags are lifted apart. This adhesive can be applied by hand or it can be applied automatically as the bags go through a bag-flattener. When it is known that glue will be used on **multiwall bags,** it is important to specify that any label that appears on the outside wrapper also appear on the second wrapper. These glues are not foolproof and sometimes even the fronts of the bags get torn off.

A good **unitizing adhesive** should have the following characteristics:

1. Ease of application.
2. High shear to resist sway.
3. A lower tensile strength than the surface to which it is applied.
4. No objectionable color or odor.
5. Resistance to humidity and moisture.
6. No residual stickiness.

If unit loads are being made up for truck or rail transportation, **steel strappings,** or the new **filament tapes,** can be used to bind them together. Some sort of **protective cushioning** must be used under the straps to prevent them from biting into the sacks. A reusable canvas binder, previously shown in Fig. 26, has been developed that can be used with or without pallets. It buckles onto the pallet load and is sent back to the supplier after the sacks are delivered.

Bagged materials are often moved without pallets. A **paperboard insert** is placed between the pallet and the first layer of bags. One of the ends can be tilted up so as to facilitate entry of the forks of a fork truck. These forks are usually thinner than standard, and are highly polished and sometimes even waxed. The paperboard inserts will handle any load the lift truck can carry, require little space, and can be used with glued and locked loads. Their advantages are:

1. Lowest possible unit cost.
2. Very expandable.
3. Double stack without injury to load on bottom.
4. Four-way pickup by lift truck.
5. Freight charges on tare and dunnage reduced to an absolute minimum.

These boards thus represent the most inexpensive form of disposable pallet.

Individual bags are still sometimes transported on **two-wheeled hand trucks,** and if used for this purpose, the latter should have wide lips. Narrow-lipped blades may bite into the bottom bags and rupture them. If trucks with narrow blades are used, as for crates, they should be extended with wooden or metal racks.

Sometimes it is necessary to handle granulated or powdered materials in loose form where applications of belt, trough, or zipper conveyors are not feasible. In such cases a truck with an **attached scoop** must be employed. Scoop loaders of this kind have great flexibility for use in loading and transportation because they are able to handle bags and sacks either in the scoop or by quickly substituting forks for the scoop. These scoop loaders are also used to position sacks on stock piles.

Bags and sacks can be moved in a variety of ways, most of which are limited only by the ingenuity of the materials handling engineer. For example, a **clamp** in one case is used to hold bags by squeezing them. Bags are also readily used as the recipients of weighed quantities of mixes. There are on the market many varieties of weighing and bagging machinery, all of which can be conveniently installed in an assembly line processing such material.

Automatic scales are available that weigh, fill, and bag at high speeds. Many companies, including manufacturers of bags, offer other kinds of machinery, some of which are integrated to the point of having a scale-feeder, automatic scale, bag-holder, bag-shaker, and sewing machine to complete the enclosure. These high-speed machines can handle 50- to 150-lb. bags made of paper or textiles at the rate of from 600 to 750 bags per hr.

There are many companies on the market making **bag-closing, weighing,** and **filling equipment,** each manufacturer producing equipment applicable to some special need. Among such kinds of equipment are the following:

1. Portable bag closers.
2. Wrapping material which is applied directly to the merchandise (not granu-lates), in the form of a cover which has the following advantages over conven-tional bags:
   a. Quick application.
   b. Elimination of waste.
   c. Reduction of inventories.
   d. Lightness in weight.
   e. Easy stenciling easily applied.
3. Drawstring bags.
4. Many types of equipment for gluing and sewing seams.

The Richardson Scale Company has developed a kind of weighing equipment known as the Y-Veyor. This installation consists of a V-belt sewing conveyor fed by two spiral conveyors set in the shape of a Y. The two packers are located next to the spiral conveyors and are paced by one man, who loads the first packer during the interval when the second machine is packing, and vice versa. This system, therefore, makes maximum use of sewing load, sewing conveyor, and sewing operator.

Other machines for filling, bagging, and related operations are plentiful and varied. Some are gravity fed, some are vacuum fed, and some consist of a combination of the two. They can be manually operated, semiautomatic, or fully automatic, as part of a conveyorized process. Devices used for control are mostly electronic, such as electrical strain gages, improved beam scales, and inspection devices. Conveyors that service these machines are equally varied and consist of vibrating feeders, collectors, and punched card programed conveyors that move bags automatically and discharge them automatically at their correct locations.

Open-top, multi-ply bags have had the advantage of low initial cost, but they took longer to fill than the **valve-type bags.** The latest open-top machines can fill the valve-type bags faster than open-top bags. Even the subsequent sewing operation has been done away with. New materials, such as nylon conveyor belts, plastic construction members, and plastic films and coatings are now available, which aid vastly in packing and conveying sacks and bags.

The following rules should be observed in handling and storing bags:

1. **Burlap bags.**
    a. Resale value can be greatly increased by careful handling of the empty bag.
    b. Burlap bags should not be opened with a knife; slashing reduces resale value and ruins bags for re-use.
    c. Instead, pick the rip cord at the top with an icepick, nail, or other pointed instrument; bags will then open easily.
    d. In packing grain or other feeds, reverse the bag and shake it out well, so that rodents will not be attracted by remaining bits of feed.
    e. Store bags in one or a few convenient places, thus making collection and counting easy.
    f. When burlap bags are full, they can be stacked tightly, because air will filter through the porous weave and keep the contents fresh. Burlap withstands rough handling, even with bulky contents, and burlap bags can be stacked solid and high. Burlap bags can also be shifted by slings without fear of damage or bursting.
    g. Whether full or empty, burlap bags should be stacked on boards or pallets raised 3 to 6 in. above the floor, thus protecting bags and contents from moisture. Empty bags should be piled on pallets or folded over rafters or partitions to keep them dry.
    h. Empty burlap bags should be bundled in batches of 50 to 100, thus making storing, counting, and shipping easy. Ship empties several times a season to clear space and reduce loss from damage. Graded bags will bring higher prices than those sold at a flat rate.
    i. When bags no longer have a good resale value, they can be used for many purposes around a farm. They can be employed to screen poultry houses, wrap shrubbery, carry seed or fruit, and serve in many kinds of work.
    j. Sell bags to reliable used bag dealers who pay more than occasional bag collectors.
    (The Burlap Council of The Indian Jute Mills Association, Inc.)
2. **Paper bags.** Most of the above-listed rules apply to paper bags as well as to burlap bags, in addition to which the following points should be observed:
    a. Supply sufficient moisture in storage locations.
    b. Do not use heated or unventilated rooms as storage locations.

Bags and sacks are carried to and from many locations by means of conveyors which include many well-known and standard pieces of equipment. One common application is the transfer of bags and sacks to and from points of loading, such as trailers and railroad cars. On other occasions, **fork trucks** which run pallet loads of sacks and bags into trailers and railroad cars are used. Trucks carrying unit loads into carriers usually have **movable steel ramps** to bridge the differences in level between the loading dock and the car. These ramps are available in a number of materials, such as lightweight magnesium. Another valuable aid, commonly used for piling sacks and bags, is a movable, **inclined conveyor,** which can be used automatically to transfer bags from warehouse conveyors to storage areas.

BAG HANDLING CONVEYORS. There are many kinds of conveyors which are particularly suited to the handling of bags. Such conveyors are used wherever large quantities of bags have to be moved quickly in warehouses, for

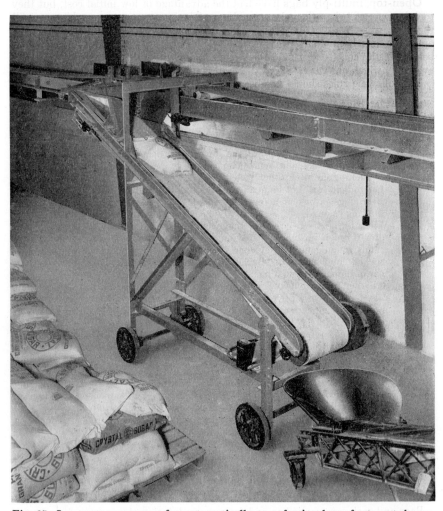

Fig. 27. Lowerator conveyor for automatically transferring bags from warehouse conveyor to portable conveyor and a bag-piling system used in a sugar warehouse.

example, and in the loading and unloading of ships, box cars, or trucks. Often these conveyors are flexible, or come in jointed sections, as in the accordion type, and are small enough to curve in and out of box cars and trucks, and up and down at storage piles. They are highly efficient, in addition to being readily portable, and are available in a wide variety of types, such as belt (Fig. 27), screw, rope, slat, roller or gravity, skate, chain, and other forms.

Conveyors are also used on **production lines** where the material is first bagged and then sent to storage or the reverse, as in Fig. 28. Usually a short belt conveyor carries the filled bags from the filling machines and transfers them to the

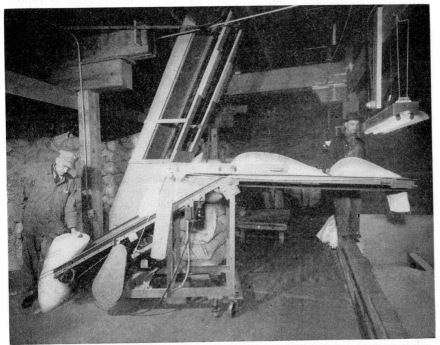

Fig. 28. Conveying and elevating sacks of seed from pile to bin.

main line that goes to the storage or shipping area. At the storage area, the main conveyor line may feed various portable conveyors that will carry the sacks to the point where they are to be stacked. These portable carriers can be adjusted to the height of the pile and to the speed of handling.

Filling and sewing machines are generally set up on short lengths of conveyors that will carry the filled and sewed bags out of the way. They are then delivered either to a gravity conveyor or to a belt conveyor which will take them to a storage or shipping area. In a typical case seven sacks per min. are dropped onto the main conveyor that leads to a chute for further disposition. Sacks are carried from the stitching machines and dropped horizontally onto a pickup station. An overhead conveyor with special arms drops down to pick them up. They are then carried up above floor traffic and can be unloaded by trippers at any point along the route.

When a large number of sacks have to be **emptied,** it is often advantageous to do the work mechanically. Two systems may be used. The first system has an overhead conveyor that travels at the same speed as the belt conveyor. Tongs are spaced on the overhead chain and are attached to the bottoms of the bags while the tops are being slit. As the open and hooked bags move along, the chain conveyor rises, lifting the closed ends of the bags. This action spills the material onto the belt and draws the bag clear.

Fig. 28 shows the bag moving on a short portable conveyor. As the opened end of the bag runs off the conveyor, the material falls out into the bin. A man stationed there picks up the empty bags, shakes them out, and puts them aside for salvage. Other conveyors which are also used to handle in-process work are of the various **overhead types.** They can pick up and deliver items at various locations while moving bags between processes and stations.

Granular material, such as sugar or sand, is often dumped and processed in bulk. As such it is then conveyed between process stations and even stored prior to shipping. A variety of conveyors, such as zipper, bucket, belt, and trough types, are usually used in moving the material in question over long distances, and shovels or buckets are used to dump the material onto a belt.

Roller Conveyors. Roller conveyors are basically of two kinds—**gravity** and **power-driven.** Gravity units operate by conveying the loads by means of gravity flow. Any object that has a relatively smooth riding surface can be transported by means of a roller conveyor. There are certain general rules which should be followed in selecting the kind of roller conveyor for a particular installation:

1. Rollers should be spaced so as to have at least three rollers under the shortest commodity to be transported.
2. If there is danger of the load not following the rollers because of curves or excessive overhang of the objects or packages being transported, the rollers can be mounted lower so that the frame which thus projects above the roller will act as a guide or guardrail.

Roller conveyor sizes and capacities vary widely, the general sizes ranging from 1 to $3\frac{1}{2}$ in. in diameter, with load capacities of from 35 to 55 lb. per roller. Loads up to several tons can be easily handled if the particular installation is suitably designed.

A wide selection of **curves,** powered and free rolling, is available for installation with standard-length conveyors. The curves are of 30°, 45°, 60°, and 90°. Radii will vary in accordance with the length and kind of item to be conveyed, $3\frac{1}{2}$ ft. being used for units up to 18 in. in length and $4\frac{1}{2}$ ft. for commodities up to 30 in. in length. Other curves should be designed for specific purposes.

True-tapered rollers should be used on curves for transporting cartons and cases as well as bags. Roller conveyors are often constructed of lightweight metal, notably aluminum, and can be readily moved from place to place. Usually one man alone can move one straight or one curved section at a time. Sections can easily be moved simultaneously by truck or trailer.

There are many suitable **switches** available for this kind of conveyor so that the material moved can be readily routed to various sections. These switches vary from the usual 2-way and 3-way switches to ball table transfer units which permit rerouting into any avenue and any angle.

Many kinds of stands are also manufactured which enable the user to place conveyor sections at any desired height. These stands are often adjustable. They come in the form of horse-type supports, fixed supports, castered supports (these are usually fixed supports mounted on casters), and pony-type supports. Even curves can be placed on casters. Sections can also be hinged to be set at various elevations, and, if desired, whole systems as well as sections can be hung from the ceiling by means of standard hangers, which are also supplied by the manufacturers.

Wheel Conveyors. Wheel conveyors, also known as skate or skate-wheel conveyors, can be used for bags. A smooth support, such as a piece of fiberboard or cardboard, should be placed under each bag so as to prevent puncturing of the bag. Wheel spacing should be at distances of 6, 8, 10, or 12 wheels per ft. for 12- or 18-in. frames. If this distance does not suffice, it is usually better to change to a roller conveyor. Similar specifications are usually set for spacing of curved sections.

Belt Conveyors. Belt-conveyor equipment can be used to move bags and sacks from storage locations to loading areas. A system of this nature dealt with the handling of mail bags at a printing plant. Previous to the installation of the new equipment, these mail sacks were handled by platform trucks, through elevators, by motor-trucks, and by railroad cars. The bags are still handled by railroad cars at their final destination, but up to that point the operation is virtually automatic. The new equipment installed consisted of a regular power-belt conveyor, a ceiling-mounted power-belt conveyor, and an enclosed floor conveyor, another power conveyor, and a portable power-belt conveyor at the end for easy positioning of bags in railroad cars. The advantages brought about by this system consist, first of all, in economies, i.e., saving in time and man-power over the previous methods, as well as increased hourly output. In addition, the operation was made considerably safer and maintenance costs were reduced.

Short sections of power-driven belt conveyors are often used for elevating boxes, sacks, etc., to storing heights and for loading or unloading sacks and box-type units. These conveyors can also be used for loading and unloading cars, trucks, and trailers. These conveyors are available in various sizes and horse-power ratings, depending on the specific applications for which they are to be used. They are mounted on casters to increase their flexibility and have adjustable boom heights, usually from horizontal to 65°, which makes them serviceable wherever flexibility of operations is required.

These units, which can also be equipped with a belt feed, come in many kinds and sizes and have flexible adjustments. All, however, have the same general advantages. As **horizontal conveyors,** they can be used as connecting links from one fixed position to another, or between other conveyors, or as feeder conveyors, and can usually be moved and operated by one man.

Another portable belt conveyor is one which is both **extendable and retractable.** It can be expanded to reach varying lengths and can be extended into trailers, trucks, warehouse areas, railroad cars, and across platforms. The greatest advantage of this kind of conveyor is that it can be retracted quickly without being moved. It can also be adjusted so as to deliver sacks at shoulder height to facilitate storing and stacking.

These conveyors are also available in "fixed units," that is, in units or sections for permanent installations instead of as portable or movable conveyors. These conveyor sections usually extend between floors and are furnished either with or without guard rails. The recommended maximum angle of lift for burlap bags filled with granular materials is about 30° and for paper bags and flour bags about 20°; by comparison, cartons and cases can be lifted over 28°. Many of these units come equipped with a leveling-off construction at the top end of the belt, which is important in the handling of bags and sacks and, in general, for any commodity of over 2 ft. which is transported up a steep incline. It eliminates the slight impact that occurs when a long object tips from an inclined position to a horizontal position at the top.

General Considerations. There are certain general considerations to be kept in mind in transporting units over these conveyors with maximum effectiveness:

1. All items transported must have a smooth surface on which to travel on gravity with roller or live-roller conveyors.
2. To obtain the proper rollers for gravity-roller or live-roller conveyor spacing, divide the length of the shortest item by three. For belt conveyors the roller spacing should be the same as the length of the shortest item conveyed, unless the weight exceeds 20 lb.
3. The conveyor should be about 2 in. wider than the widest units conveyed on it.
4. If sacks or bags are conveyed on the conveyor, and they ride on a platform, not less than ¾ in. per ft. slope should be used. This slope will vary with the size, shape, and weight of the unit moved.
5. If the system is an overhead system, guardrails should be provided—at the very minimum—on all curves.
6. Level belt conveyors, up to a slope of about 12°, should be constructed of canvas belting. Rough-top belt is recommended for belt conveyor slopes above 12°.

Sacks and bags are not ordinarily adaptable for roller conveyor transportation. Roller conveyor systems have nonetheless been described because they are often used to move bags resting on a smooth, hard surface. The main advantages of the systems discussed are their flexibility, ready installation, convenient movement to other areas, ease of assembly into whole systems, versatility of purpose, flexibility in speed of movement, wide selection of equipment, and suitable auxiliary adapters such as feeders, lift tables, turn-over devices, and other facilities.

Applications of Package Conveyors

ORIGIN AND WIDE APPLICATION OF PACKAGE CONVEYORS.

Archimedes, about 400 B.C., invented the first continuous conveyor, which bears a surprising resemblance to present-day screw conveyors. About 1790, Oliver Evans advertised that he could save at least half the labor cost of "attending" a flour mill by use of conveyors. In 1868, Lyster, an English engineer, described to the British Engineers' Society his work on conveying bulk materials on belt conveyors. W. S. Lamson, in 1880, built the first unit to convey cash between sales personnel and a cashier. This unit was among the first of the great number of present-day pneumatic tube conveyor systems herein discussed, carrying papers, cash, small tools, etc., between different stations in commercial and industrial establishments. In the developing era of the "automatic factory," conveyors, including pneumatic tubes, play important roles in making such factories possible.

Filling Multiple Roles. Conveyors, especially package or unit-load conveyors, are not only a means of transportation but can in man instances be made to play multiple roles. Fig. 29 tabulates many of the uses for conveyors, including pneumatic tubes.

KINDS OF PACKAGE CONVEYORS.

The kind of conveyor to be used in a particular installation is dictated by several factors. The nature of the package, object, or load to be conveyed, the operation to be performed on the conveyor,

1. Packages, objects, loads.	Weighed while being conveyed.
2. Loads.	Counted automatically while being conveyed.
3. Complete units.	Assembled on conveyors.
4. Products under manufacture.	Automatically deflected to various areas.
5. Work in process.	Fed directly into machines.
6. Work banks.	Use of conveyors for live-moving storage.
7. Accumulating work.	Into pallet load units, shipping slugs, groups ahead of sealer operations.
8. Use of scales.	Weighing incoming and outgoing loads in transit.
9. Counting in transit.	At receiving or shipping docks, while in transit.
10. Assembling in transit.	Use live rollers, wheels, belt conveyors, etc., as assembly lines.
11. Conveying to fixed stations.	For assembly of main unit.
12. Directing loads automatically.	Use of deflectors operated by timers.
13. Use of accessory mechanisms.	Automatic loading of machines.
14. Use of trolley, etc., conveyors.	Putting parts into live storage for subsequent operations.
15. Accumulating loads on conveyors.	To release groups of loads in desired sequence.
16. Grouping loads.	For assembling shipments, or unsealed cartons, ahead of sealing operations.
17. Use of pneumatic tubes.	To dispatch tools, fixtures, etc., to work stations, then back to tool cribs.
18. Steel mill operations.	Dispatching sample pouring to laboratory for analysis and report.
19. Dispatching blueprints, time tickets, etc.	To keep paper work in pace with performance of work.
20. Department store uses.	Collecting parcels in delivery room.
21. Mail order houses.	To dispatch orders to stockrooms, packing departments, and mailing room.
22. Post offices.	Receiving, handling, sorting, dispatching parcel post and mail bags.
23. Post office substations.	Forwarding important mail between main post office and branches.
24. Railway and express terminals.	Transfer of parcel post and mail bags.
25. Railroad yards.	Car identification, breaking or assembling trains.
26. Insurance companies, large offices.	Distribute and assemble mail, policies, records.
27. Libraries.	Handle books, pamphlets, etc., between central desk and stack levels.
28. Hospitals.	Transport food, records, and supplies.
29. Hotels and restaurants.	Conveying trays, dishes, food, luggage, mail, messages, etc.
30. Pharmaceutical plants.	Transporting drugs through processing, packaging, etc., on sanitary and sterilized conveyors.
31. Publishing houses, book binderies, newspaper plants.	Moving paper, proofs, mats, plates, bundles, mailing bags, etc.
32. Banks and security houses.	Connecting tellers' cages with bank records for authorization of payment on checks, and connection of vault with offices for transporting securities.

Fig. 29. Uses of conveyors and pneumatic tubes.

12·41

if any, and the physical conditions surrounding the installation—all play a part in determining the kind of conveyor to be used. It is, of course, impossible to formulate a standard that would permit proper choice of the kind of conveyor best suited to a **particular problem,** but the following generalities will help in the selection:

1. **Gravity conveyors** should be used wherever possible, for economic reasons. Since there is no practical way of controlling speed on loads of variable weights, the use of gravity conveyors is confined to nonfragile loads. **Roller and wheel gravity conveyors,** in addition, must be confined to use with loads which have reasonably solid, rigid, and flat riding surfaces. **Chutes,** both straight and spiral, can be used successfully with loads having soft bottoms, such as bags, sacks, bundles, etc.

Gravity conveyors are seldom used where operations other than transportation are to be performed. On the other hand, such conveyors (roller and wheel) when installed level are sometimes used as assembly lines and provide a convenient means for advancing objects, manually, along assembly areas. Gravity conveyors naturally require a vertical drop of from $\frac{1}{4}$ in. per linear ft., for wheel conveyors and $\frac{1}{2}$ in. per linear ft. for roller conveyors to as much as $4\frac{1}{2}$ in. to 6 in. per ft. for chutes. The use of gravity conveyors is therefore confined to those installations where **vertical drop** is available in the physical arrangement.

2. **Live-roll conveyors** can be used with any load having a reasonably solid, rigid, and flat riding surface. They can be used readily, in place of belt conveyors, for heavy loads whose riding surface is such that the belting on a belt conveyor would be damaged. Live-roll conveyors can be used successfully as assembly lines, and loads may be blocked momentarily for accumulation of parts or for operational purposes. In most cases such conveyors are installed for level, horizontal operations.

3. **Belt conveyors** should be used for any loads whose shapes or construction would not result in damage to the belting. Small 1 cc. bottles, Christmas tree ornaments, pieces of paper, light bulbs, fuses, sticks of chewing gum, individual packages of food products, cartons of soap products, paper products, canned goods, bottled goods, radio and television cabinets, tote boxes and baskets up to heavy boxes and cases weighing hundreds of pounds can all be transported on belt conveyors. Belt conveyors, in addition to conveying fragile loads, will handle any load that will travel on a gravity conveyor when vertical drops or grades are not present in the particular installation.

Belt conveyors are ideally suited to assembly-line operations because they can be operated at almost any speed with equal success. They can be used where speed of travel and spacing of loads must be controlled, and where automatic distribution of loads (deflecting and insertion of loads in line) is necessary. When steep descents are designed for **fragile loads,** the belt conveyor is usually the best solution because it can negotiate steep declines with complete control over the speed of the descending load.

4. **Chain conveyors**—including horizontal, incline, or decline installations such as slat, roller-slat, pusher-bar, drag, and rolling or sliding chain conveyors—can be used for almost any kind or shape of load. The chain conveyor is frequently used where loading or operating conditions prevent the use of belt conveyors. The slat conveyor, equipped with flat steel or wood slats, is frequently **installed at floor level** and in effect provides a moving section of floor that will transport a great variety of loads. At the same time it will permit trucking across the conveyor itself and use of the surrounding floor area, even when the conveyor is in operation.

The **roller slat conveyor** is the ideal conveyor to be used when loads must be blocked or accumulated on the conveyor. The **pusher bar conveyor** is ideal for application where loads must be elevated or lowered at steep angles and is generally confined to nonfragile loads. Any type of the chain conveyor group equipment may be used for assembly lines or conveyor lines where productive operations are to be performed while loads are in transit.

5. **Vertical conveyors** are used for all types of loads—ranging from the very light in weight to those weighing several thousands of pounds. **Automatic transfers** to and from the vertical path can be obtained, and such transfers can be from or to any other type of conveyor. The vertical conveyor, generally, does not have very high capacity in number of loads handled per minute as the speed is usually slow. About 100 ft. per min. is the maximum speed, with speeds of 30 to 50 ft. per min. being most common. The vertical conveyor **must not be confused with the freight elevator.** The chief difference between the two is that the vertical **conveyor** is usually an automatically loaded and unloaded unit while the **car** usually handles a single load-unit and not a multiple number of units, as does a freight elevator. Operating personnel are not required or allowed to ride on the vertical conveyor.

6. The **pallet loader** will handle almost any carton, box, case, bag, or sack that is normally stacked on a pallet for unit handling of small loads. It is the first conveyor accessory of sufficient magnitude and flexibility to warrant a separate classification. The loader is the connecting link in any materials handling system between conveyor operations and lift-truck or stacker operations.

7. **Pneumatic tube conveyors,** as previously mentioned and as discussed in the present classification, cover only those units conveying carriers in which the material being conveyed is confined while in transit. Almost any article small enough to fit into the carrier can be conveyed. Special carriers are available for transporting fragile articles. In addition to the more common articles—such as paper, complete files, blueprints, X-ray films, and coins—carriers can convey liquids in vials and bottles, explosives, metal samples, pharmaceuticals, etc. Pneumatic tubes present no problem in installation. They can be made to negotiate bends at will, avoiding all structural obstructions, can be buried underground, or in floors and in walls and ceilings. They can also be operated in vertical or incline travel as readily as in horizontal travel.

PACKAGE-CONVEYOR DRIVES. Since most package conveyor installations are made near sources of electric power, **electric motors** are used almost exclusively to operate power conveyors. Most conveyor drive shafts are operated at speeds of 50 r.p.m. or less, and as the motors are usually run at 1,800 r.p.m., the method of obtaining the proper reduction in speed is of concern. The average package conveyor uses small-size motors (5 hp. or less in most cases), and for this reason the type of gear reduction used in the drive is not so important an economic factor as would be the case if large motors were used.

Many conveyor drive reductions employ **worm-gear drives,** and in recent years most of these drives have been equipped with the worm-gear type of geared-head motor. The final reduction from the slow speed shaft of the worm-gear or geared-head motor is made with roller chain drives. This arrangement results in a very compact but still flexible drive and is one of the most economical drives available. Another kind of drive consists of a **gear-reducing unit** that can be attached directly to the headshaft. This unit consists of spur, herringbone or planetary gearing, and the high-speed shaft of the gear reduction is connected directly to the motor by means of a V-belt drive.

Some drives are equipped with **overload protection.** This protection may take the form of a **fluid coupling,** a **torque-controlled coupling** that will slip when overloaded, a torque-controlled coupling that will **shut off the electric power** when the conveyor is overloaded, or it may consist of one of several **mechanical devices that shut off the motor** when the drive is overloaded. It is advisable to **standardize motor and drive sizes** whenever possible. On an installation using many power conveyors of varying lengths, the horsepower calculations may call for almost as many different motor sizes as there are conveyors. If different sizes are used, complications arise concerning maintenance and spare parts. Because the motors are usually small in size, it is best to group the conveyors and use only a few different sizes of motors. It is not unusual to see installations with as many as 70 power conveyors, using only three or four different sizes of motors and drives.

The drive for conveyors may be one of constant speed, or the installation may require the use of variable-speed drives. **Constant-speed drives** are used most often because they are economical, and in most installations variable speeds are not necessary. If it is assumed that the exact speed of the conveyor cannot be determined at the time the conveyor is engineered, it does not necessarily follow that a **variable-speed drive** should be provided. An approximate speed can usually be agreed upon, and if a worm-gear reduction or geared-head motor is used with roller chain drive to the headshaft, it is a simple matter to change one or both sprockets of this drive to change the speed of the conveyor, if required. Such a procedure is much more economical than specifying a variable-speed drive.

On an **assembly conveyor,** or one on which work operations are to be performed while loads are in transit, the number of units being worked on or assembled may vary from time to time. In such a case a variable-speed drive is indicated, and its cost is justified. Generally speaking, the use of variable-speed drives should be confined to this kind of installation.

UNIT HANDLING IN MANUFACTURING

CONTENTS

CONTENTS (*Continued*)

UNIT HANDLING IN MANUFACTURING

Materials Handling in Mass Production Industries

FUNCTION OF MATERIALS HANDLING IN PRODUCTION. According to the Production Handbook the over-all objective of materials handling is to transport materials from point to point, without retrogression and with a minimum number of transfers, and to deliver the materials to their appropriate workplaces or production centers in a manner to avoid congestion, delays, and unnecessary handling. Mass production industries are those in which a product or a number of products are manufactured in volume through a fixed process. The schedule of the end product governs the entire process, from the purchasing of materials to the subassembly and assembly of parts and the simultaneous end processing.

Nature of Mass Production Industries. Mass-production operations are classified as either continuous or repetitive, according to the nature of the process involved. Examples of both kinds are:

1. **Continuous process:**

   a. Blast-furnace industry.
   b. Brick industry.
   c. Cement industry.
   d. Chemical industry.
   e. Coke industry.
   f. Glass industry.
   g. Lime industry.
   h. Pottery industry.
   i. Sugar industry.

2. **Repetitive process:**

   a. Automobile industry.
   b. Electrical-appliance industry.
   c. Garment industry.
   d. Jewelry industry.
   e. Machine-tool industry.
   f. Millinery industry.
   g. Screw, bolt, etc., industries.
   h. Shoe industry.
   i. Textile industry.

The chief distinction between these two classes is that a **repetitive-process industry** does not of necessity operate continuously, although it may do so for schedule requirements, economy of equipment, or departmental bottlenecks. The **continuous-type production unit,** because of its nature, runs to specific time units—days, weeks or longer—and in many cases the distinction between continuous and repetitive manufacture may disappear. For a specific industry of either type, however, coordination of materials handling is necessary for whatever methods of production and production control may be in use. **Production planning** indicates the necessity for proper routines and dispatching of work, in order to maintain the predetermined schedules; and materials handling is the medium through which the prompt and correct dispatching of material and work in process over the established routes is carried through to meet these schedules, thus becoming the service which ties processing operations into a system of straight-line production.

In industries which are **both continuous and repetitive in process,** such as the chemical, cement, flour, sugar, oil, and paper industries, materials handling directly ties together the processes necessary to manufacture the product. This is done through pipe lines, gravity flow systems, and conveyors—all of which are ways of connecting the various operations in an industry. In **repetitive manufacturing,** which constitutes all varieties of mass production, attended by mechanized parts production and assembly procedures, the planning and installation of materials handling equipment is an obvious requisite. The amount of planning and installation work will depend on the requirements of the individual plant or process, ranging from comparatively simple warehousing to the extreme of "automation" a word, coined by D. S. Harder of the Ford Motor Company, that expresses the philosophy of using a mechanized integration of basic machine tools in mass manufacturing (Production, vol. 33). D. T. Davis, also of the Ford Motor Company, says:

> The determination of the right method of manufacture or assembly for each component of your product is the most important phase of planning for production. To ascertain maximum efficiency in manufacturing operations, well-planned materials handling techniques and equipment must be applied, together with the establishment of proper organizational controls for policing performance. Technological progress exemplified by transfer machines and automation has made this approach mandatory.

Principles of Automation. R. E. Cross of the Cross Company quotes a definition of automation as "the automatic handling of parts between progressive production processes." Charles A. Hautau (Production, vol. 33) gives **ten principles of automation:**

1. Start automation lines as close as possible to the raw material state. Good automation takes raw material and carries it through to the finished package product.
2. Until it is finished, never let go of a part.
3. Avoid intermachine storage of machine parts; mechanically translate parts immediately from operation to operation.
4. Automatically gage each machining operation immediately upon completion.
5. Correct the previous operation setup based on gaging tolerance drift.
6. Gage trends in gaging measurements, in microinches, to correct each previous operation. Do not gage only upper and lower limits.
7. Regulate individual machine cycles to achieve a straight line flow of parts. If necessary, slow down fast machines and thus obtain maximum automation simplicity.
8. Specify specially integrated production machinery designed to meet specific product requirements, thus achieving maximum production line compactness and economy.
9. Electrically control all production line cycle functions from one master control panel.
10. Integrate all assembly and packaging operations into the automated line.

The nature of mass production, therefore, calls for **control of necessary materials handling,** and this handling must move the materials continuously and at a uniform rate through a series of balanced operations which permit simultaneous performance throughout, the work progressing toward completion along a reasonably direct line. The refinements of completely integrated mass production are seldom attained, because of design, material changes, and other factors, but in all cases the basic procedures and ultimate aims are all the same. Various designations have been assigned to this method of manufacturing, the following being those most frequently applied:

1. Line production.
2. Layout by product.
3. Straight-line production.
4. Direct-line production.
5. Progressive manufacture.
6. Serialized production.
7. Flow production.
8. Unit manufacture.

As Muther (Production-Line Technique) points out, the German term is *fleissarben* (flow work) while the French use *travail à la chaîne* (chain work).

INTERRELATIONSHIP BETWEEN HANDLING AND PLANT LAYOUT. The interrelationship that exists between materials handling and plant layout has a parallel in the field of economics. For years economists have been debating whether cost determines price or price determines cost in marketing a product. The question of whether plant layout determines materials handling or materials handling determines plant layout is likewise debatable. Engineers, however, are generally obliged to forego the moot aspects of a problem and to consider rather the practical operating factors involved.

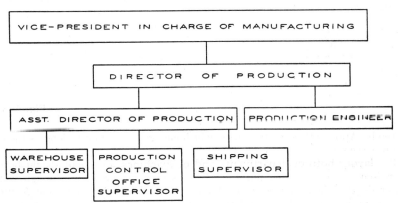

Fig. 1. Breakdown of the manufacturing process into the three functions served by materials handling—warehousing, production, and shipping.

Fig. 1 shows diagrammatically the breakdown of manufacturing into the three functions which are served by materials handling in the industrial plant—**warehousing,** to receive and store incoming materials; **production control** to call for delivery of materials at points of use; and **shipping,** to control the delivery of finished products from the stockroom to outgoing carriers. A check list of data required for analyzing a materials handling project is given in Section 4. Its purpose is to develop an organized listing of the factors which must be taken into account when planning an installation.

As Mallick and Gaudreau (Plant Layout, Planning and Practice) point out, an improvement made in materials handling methods usually affects the plant layout, and changes made in the layout invariably influence materials handling

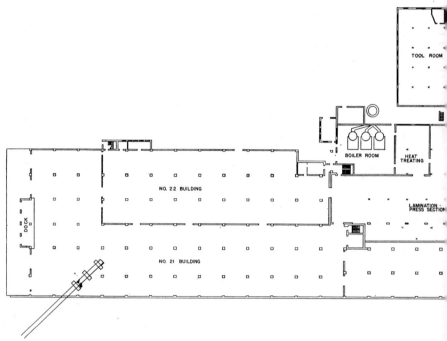

Fig. 2. Convey

methods. Apparently it matters little which change comes first as long as the end result is the same.

The **layout both of departments and of machines** in a plant should be the expression of an operating purpose. To this end, the processes through which materials pass, their sequence of work flow, the machines and equipment required for the anticipated volume, and the location of many auxiliary departments—receiving, shipping, toolroom, and lavatories, for example—are vital. Fig. 2 shows the first-floor layout, and Fig. 3 shows the second-floor layout in the vacuum cleaner manufacturing plant of the Electrolux Corporation. In planning such layouts, the practical and psychological aspects of other factors—the building structure, heating, ventilation, lighting, noise control, and the like—must likewise receive thorough consideration. Although essentials of plant layout are substantially the same for all industries, in application results will vary widely, depending upon type of product, size of plant, variety of output, and building limitations.

It is pointed out in the Production Handbook that ideal circumstances may exist when an entirely new plant is to be designed and erected, but seldom is this the case. More commonly, the **layout must be fitted into existing buildings** despite their inherent limitations. The problem facing the production engineer is usually one of **relayout** to improve the operating efficiency of the manufacturing processes or to provide for making new products. These new products or methods in mass-production industries, according to the Production Handbook, fall into

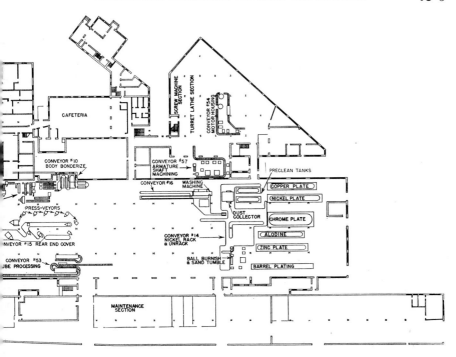

...youts on first floor.

product or straight-line layout, in which the equipment necessary for the performance of all the operations on a given product are grouped in a section or department in the sequence in which the operations are performed, as opposed to process or functional layout, in which manufacturing is departmentalized according to the processes employed in production. In a **product layout,** obviously, well-standardized products manufactured in large quantities are prerequisites, these being the basic characteristics of a mass-production industry. The classic example of this type of manufacturing is the automobile industry, which the Production Handbook cites as fulfilling these conditions:

1. Flow of work over direct mechanical routes, which cuts down delays in manufacturing.
2. Less materials handling because of shorter travel of work over a succession of adjacent machines or work stations.
3. Close coordination of manufacturing because of the definite sequence of operations over adjacent machines. Less likelihood of loss of materials or delays in operations.
4. Less total time of production. Delays between machines avoided.
5. Smaller quantities of work in process, little banking of materials at individual operations and in transit between operations.
6. Smaller floor area occupied per unit of product because of concentration of manufacturing.
7. Limited amount of inspection.

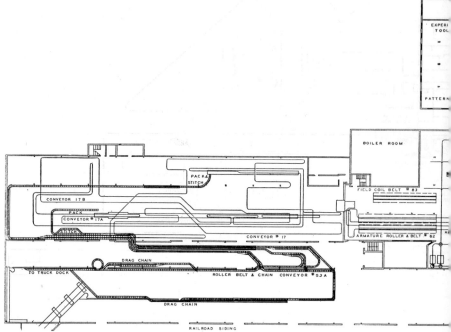

Fig. 3. Second-floo

8. Simplification of production control. Visual control replaces much of the paper work. Fewer forms and records used. Work checked on and off production line. Few work orders, inspection tickets, time tickets, move orders, etc.; less accounting and lower clerical costs.
9. Less complicated job breakdown.

When these objectives are even partially realized, it is because of sound engineering, which may embrace a wide range of methods for accomplishing its purpose, depending on the physical structure of the particular plant, the processes developed or adapted for the manufacture, and the caliber of management in charge of operations. In mass production, where of necessity there is much **layout work** to be done in conjunction with materials handling, a staff assigned to layout alone spends full time working on the many problems. Each person is skilled in certain areas of layout work; tasks are subdivided so that the individual parts will be performed by trained experts; and a coordinated layout and materials handling system is built up from their combined contributions.

PREREQUISITES FOR MATERIALS HANDLING ADMINISTRATION FOR MASS PRODUCTION. There are certain large plants which require little in the way of continual layout revisions or changes in materials handling systems, because of the nature of the processes in these plants. These plants are in the process-industries field—in steel, rubber, petroleum, glass, etc.— where the plant, once satisfactorily laid out, remains relatively unchanged for long periods of time.

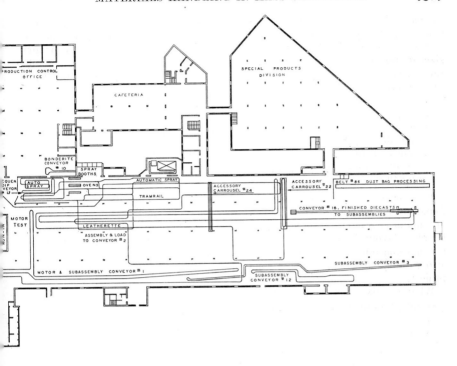

nveyor layouts.

In other kinds of industries there are continual changes, which are brought about by changes in product, in product design, in materials and methods, and, because of expansion, in administration, and other factors. Where such fluctuations occur, it is necessary to have organized plant groups whose specific activities may vary considerably from one plant to another, depending on the size of the plant, the importance of the layout in the particular plant, and the organizational plan of the enterprise. Layouts such as those shown in Figs. 8 and 9 may be the most efficient arrangements for a long time. On the other hand they may be changed from time to time as more efficient arrangements or changes in equipment are worked out.

Organization for Uninterrupted Work Flow. In large plants where mass production is carried on, it is particularly important to organize operations for uninterrupted flow of work. The personnel will need, in addition, operational information as to how the many and varied activities are set up and carried on.

Plants manufacturing the same kind of product or line of products will differ considerably in their organization, so no general rule is applicable throughout the mass production industries. Materials handling is a part of plant layout which may be handled by consulting engineers, industrial architects, building contractors, engineers, draftsmen, department superintendents, supervisors, etc.; and the size of the plant layout and materials handling department will depend on the nature of the specific processes, the degree of development in the past, and the changes which may be expected in the present and for the future. Mallick and Gaudreau (Plant Layout, Planning and Practice) cite a large metal-trades manufacturing company that operates widely scattered plants of varying sizes, ranging from a plant of 200 employees to a concentrated establishment of over 25,000 workers. This company has developed the following yardstick for determining the **proper size of the plant layout staff.** The calculation is based on the number of full-time employees in order to insure adequate handling of the normal layout work at the various plants.

1. For the first 500 employees on the payroll: One engineer capable of supervising temporary assistants.
2. For each additional 1,000 employees: One additional plant layout engineer and one draftsman.
3. For each 10,000 employees: One plant layout consulting engineer on the company payroll. These consultants are usually staff members of the headquarters organization.

For normal, everyday activities this size of plant layout organization has been found, over a number of years, to be satisfactory. During periods when projects of a major character are undertaken, temporary personnel are added to the regular plant layout force as they are needed. On single projects of significant scope it is not uncommon to find as many as 20 plant engineers and draftsmen working at one time, particularly when a time schedule has to be set up and met for the project.

Whatever the number of engineers required, whatever designation is used, the necessary **qualifications** will be the same:

1. An analytical mind.
2. A working knowledge of time and motion study, manufacturing processes. operation analysis, and production control; and operative experience in the plant.
3. The ability to visualize theoretical applications of all types of materials handling equipment to a wide range of manufacturing processes.
4. A working knowledge of various types of industrial buildings, plant services, and building codes.
5. The ability to develop alternative plans and select the one most preferable, whether they are for individual work stations or for entire plants.
6. Patience and fortitude. There should be a reasonable amount of ability to get along with people in all levels of the organization, especially on the production floor, not only for preliminary investigations but particularly because successful operation of the installation will depend largely upon the cooperation of those who are to use the equipment and their understanding of its purpose, capacity, and operation.

Operational Information. Whatever the size of a plant layout department and wherever its location on the organization chart, the personnel concerned with the application of materials handling methods will require a diversified and detailed amount of information for operating purposes. This information will include:

1. Building-construction drawings showing the characteristics of the building which houses the operations being performed.
2. A plant layout drawing showing the relative positions of the various production operations and the flow of the product or products from operation to operation (as shown in Figs. 3 and 4).
3. Data on the building: elevation structure, ceiling heights, column spacing, structural strength, door openings and clearances, aisles, ramps, floor-load capacities, elevator capacities; and locations of service facilities, such as communications systems, water lines, electric-power and lighting conduits, ducts for conveying liquid materials, and process characteristics that may influence recommendations as to layout.

4. Size and layout of aisles:
   a. If possible, for one-way traffic of vehicles aisles should be 2 ft. wider than the pallet.
   b. If possible, aisles should be 3 ft. wider than the pallet for two-way traffic. If the plant operates especially large trucks (as shown in Fig. 7), main aisles at least will have to be wider than the normal width.
   c. If possible, there should be separate aisles for pedestrian traffic.
   d. If possible, cross traffic should be eliminated. ("If possibles" are prevalent because most aisle widths tend to diminish as floor space becomes more valuable.)
5. A detailed description of the materials to be handled: their kind, condition, shape, size, weight; the nature and size of any containers; and the means by which they are handled.

With this information in hand, and after it has been carefully checked, the department will have the necessary **physical data** for developing the layout. Deviations from architect's drawings, irregularities, omissions, alterations and additions in construction prints are not uncommon; all measurements should be verified in the field. Air lines, temporary lights and wiring, additional machines, benches, tables, desks, storage racks, and clothing racks may spring seemingly from nowhere; elevations and sections may be on so small a scale as to be useless in actually planning the layout. No **field notes** are ever so voluminous as to preclude additional visits to each particular location under layout. It is best to be thorough in originally planning the layout, because improvisation during the later installation is usually costly and embarrassing.

In addition to the physical data available the plant layout department requires information on all phases of internal handling of materials, whether specific or general, between receiving and shipping. Whether the problem confronted is plant-wide or an individual case, the amount of available information will vary, but not the range, which should cover:

1. Unloading at receiving dock.
2. Transferring to materials handling equipment.
3. Moving to storage.
4. Type of storage: palletized, live, dead, etc.
5. Moving to point of use.
6. Moving in process.
7. Moving to subassembly.
8. Moving to assembly.
9. Moving to shipping or storage.
10. Loading on an outgoing carrier.

This information may be recorded in a number of ways, such as on **flow charts, operation charts, process charts,** and **flow process charts**—all intended to show both a continuous sequence in the manufacturing operations and assembly steps of converting raw stock to finished products, as well as the materials handling operations necessary to move the materials between operations. Details and size of layout drawings are governed by the time available, size of the project, requirements of the management, intricacy of the product, and other variables; but the main purpose of collecting the data is to provide information, from workstation to entire department setups, so that the procedures followed under the existing methods can be shown in relation to the physical structure of the building. With this information assembled, the department, whether designated as a plant layout or a materials handling department, may be authorized to:

1. Design workplace layouts.
2. Plan workplace interrelationships.

3. Plan materials handling methods.
4. Draw layout plans.
5. Prepare construction drawings.
6. Design auxiliary equipment.
7. Supervise construction for new layouts or changes in layouts.
8. Study completed layouts for further improvements.
9. Keep files of layouts.
10. Determine costs of setting up layouts, and savings from the improvement of layouts.
11. Determine processing procedures with the aid of methods engineers.
12. Establish time standards with the aid of the time and motion study department.
13. Determine numbers of machines required for the respective processes.
14. Determine work methods with the aid of time and motion study engineers.
15. Design buildings to house manufacturing and other layouts.
16. Plan nonproductive operations associated with the manufacturing processes.

PLANT LAYOUT DEPARTMENT. The position of the plant layout department in the organization varies as do its duties, with the size of the plant, the nature of the product or products, the relative importance of the plant layout function, and the company's over-all organizational plan. In a survey (Apple, Plant Layout and Materials Handling) of 70 plants in the United States it has been found that 35 or more titles have been given to the persons in charge of plant layout. The plants surveyed ranged in number of employees from 600 to 102,000. The average plant of the 70 had 2,500 employees, with slight alterations in the specific titles as reported. The following list indicates **typical titles** assigned, from the most common to the least common.

1. Plant engineer.
2. Plant layout engineer.
3. Supervisor of plant layout.
4. Methods and equipment engineer.
5. Master mechanic.
6. Industrial engineer.
7. General superintendent.
8. Foreman.
9. Superintendent of maintenance.
10. Manager of production engineering.
11. Engineer.
12. Technical assistant.
13. Manufacturing-analysis engineer.
14. Manager of engineering design and construction.
15. Superintendent of planning.
16. Chief engineer.
17. Process engineer.

Likewise, the title of the person to whom the plant-layout group reported varied widely. Again with slight changes in **titles reported,** and listing them from the most common to the least common, that person is:

1. Works, plant, factory, or general manager.
2. Vice-president.
3. Works or plant engineer.
4. Plant or general superintendent.
5. Chief engineer.
6. Master mechanic.
7. Methods engineer.
8. Manager of industrial engineering.
9. Production engineer.
10. President.
11. Manufacturing engineer.
12. Tool engineer.
13. Supervisor.
14. Standards head.
15. Planning engineer.
16. Department manager.

FUNCTIONS OF THE MATERIALS HANDLING DEPARTMENT. As Apple (Plant Layout and Materials Handling) points out, the functions of the materials handling department will, of course, vary from plant to plant, as will its degree of activity. Industrial organization charts are rarely parallel, even in the case of competitive companies, each about the same size and each engaged in purchasing, processing, shipping, and selling. When it comes to the question of materials handling, a comparatively new industrial specialty, there is considerable variance in responsibility, authority, and range of work. In some cases, a division can be made into (1) operational materials handling and (2) analytical materials handling. The **operational phase** refers to running an existing activity, the day-by-day job of supervising materials handling. The **analytical phase** refers to methods analysis, or the developing of new systems and procedures, and installation of new equipment. The materials handling administration may devolve upon a staff man working under the chief industrial engineer. He may be a methods man who concentrates on materials handling reports to the chief methods engineer. Sometimes this materials handling engineer is a recognized staff man operating a separate department under the manager of the plant. He may embrace in this position the two aspects of the job, engineering better systems and operating all materials handling activities such as shipping, receiving, packaging, and inter-building transportation.

Sometimes the **materials handling engineer's assignment** is divided among three men:

1. One in charge of the materials handling between plant buildings and between the common carriers and the shipping docks.
2. One in charge of the shipping and receiving activities themselves, including the loading and unloading of common carriers and the storage of raw materials and finished goods in warehouses on the premises.
3. One in charge of the materials handling activities in a given product division.

Some of the larger plants are, in effect, three, four, or even more separate businesses occupying the same premises. Here there may be a **materials handling man for each division.** This person should have charge of the materials handling activities throughout that entire division.

The materials handling manager may operate the materials handling activities rather than engineer new studies. When the materials handling man is the manager of materials handling activities, he is usually responsible to the production manager. Sometimes he is in the office of the works manager, as a cross between a line and staff assistant. In some plants the plant engineer assumes the materials handling duties or has a man on his staff to do so. Such a procedure is good or weak to the extent that the plant engineer either is given a free hand to define operations in the production departments or is excluded from them. In many organizations the plant engineer is regarded as a service manager, and his materials handling scope is limited to providing for interbuilding transportation.

Large corporations usually go a step further. On the staff of the vice-president in charge of manufacture is placed a **corporation materials handling specialist,** who acts as a consultant, coordinator, supervisor, and perhaps as head of materials handling research activities for all plants. (Modern Materials Handling, vol. 9.)

Organizing a Materials Handling Department. In planning to organize a materials handling department in a mass production industry, it is difficult to set up rules which would cover the needs of every factory organization. In many industries such departments have not been definitely segregated, but, regardless of the organization chart, the duties of a materials handling department should be:

1. To study the characteristics of raw materials and products that have to be handled.

2. To classify them into analogous groups with the knowledge of quantity to be handled.
3. To know what materials or groups of materials are to be moved from what point to what point.
4. To establish the most effective routing and dispatching.

Where there are numerous departments and overlapping operations, it is essential that materials handling be considered as a **definite part of general factory planning.** In many plants, the functions of receiving, storing, transportation, and shipping are part of the materials handling program.

The importance of arranging equipment for the most direct flow of materials through the plant is evident. Plant layout charts indicate how to study the flow of materials to determine any crisscrossing paths, with their resultant losses. These charts may also show how rearrangement of machines will save floor space, provide more direct lines of travel, avoid congestion, and bring about better operational procedures.

Plant-wide Development of Materials Handling. When the plan of conveyorization is expanded to include all sequences of operations which can be associated together under product layouts, the advantages extend to all such **conveyor lines.** In many cases gravity roller conveyors, such as shown in Fig. 4, are very useful as interconnections between different kinds of operations. Further improvements and savings result from the use of modern **industrial truck equipment** under an organized system of operation. The trucking system interconnects the processes carried out on different conveyor systems and forms a flexible,

Fig. 4. Gravity roller conveyors carrying parts to and away from welders.

rapid means for such work and for other work which is not conveyorized (as are most of the operations shown in Figs. 2, 3, 8, and 9). In some cases, of course, the trucking system may be the main if not the only feasible method to use, because of the way in which the plant is laid out and the manner in which operations must be carried on.

It is of considerable importance, as held by the Production Handbook, that the materials handling department establish complete cooperation with the stores department, because the proper methods of piling, separation of lots, and handling of goods in storage, as well as the storage equipment used, play an important part in handling materials. So that this cooperation may exist between materials handling departments and other sections of the particular industry, there must be a very definite knowledge of how and where the manufacturing processes are carried on. Here again the **functions of materials handling and plant layout** are so similar as to be practically identical, and here again plant engineering must supply considerable data or be an integral part of the department. Among such data are the following:

1. Information on buildings, grounds, services, and utilities.
2. Layouts of existing production facilities, services, and utilities.
3. Flow charts of existing and proposed manufacturing methods.
4. Layouts, both template and three-dimensional.
5. Cost information, standard hours on jobs, etc.

With reference to contemplated product changes, production rates, output required, duration of production runs, etc., past experience shows the necessity for collecting and coordinating information from managers, designers, all classes of supervision (including superintendents and foremen), production-engineering and manufacturing-engineering departments, time-study, methods, and other departments.

For **plant layout**, such as that shown in Fig. 5, there are a number of methods used, depending on the individual preference of the engineer in charge. With the plant layout available, flow charts can be made and keyed to the existing or proposed system, and the use of and reference to route sheets, operation cards, process charts, time-study analyses and specifications can be as detailed as required or as time permits. From information and data obtained from the **cost department,** the current cost of materials handling can be approximated, and a change in layout or handling methods usually follows. In this cost should be included not only transportation of materials from one location or operation to another but also handling done by each operator at a work station. This latter information is obtained from observation or by actual time study. When the current cost is determined, the **cost reduction** with new or improved materials handling equipment is set against it, and against the reduction must go the cost of the equipment and its installation and maintenance. Whether the change can be justified economically is usually the decision of management, which weighs such factors as increased fixed charges, obsolescence, and accounting practice or budgetary requirements.

When the studies or analyses of current costs are being made, a number of possibilities suggest themselves, and these possibilities must be thoroughly analyzed and considered before elimination. The first step to take is to **review the processing operations** to find out whether it is possible to reduce them in number or to combine certain operations, such as multiple die setups on larger presses. The second possible step is to **change the sequence of operations,** with a possible resultant reduction in the number of handlings. The materials handling

120, inspect and load to bonderite conveyor; 110, weld switch bracket; 100, weld two sleigh brackets; 90, weld switch pocket; 80, weld end bulkhead; 75, locate end bulkhead; 70, weld end bulkhead; 65, locate end bulkhead; 69,* locate and weld end bulkheads; 60, rotary-weld motor bulkheads; 50, locate and spotweld motor bulkhead; 40, rotary-weld center bulkhead; 30, locate and spotweld center bulkhead; 20, seam weld; 10 spotweld bottom pieces to top half.

Electrolux Corp.

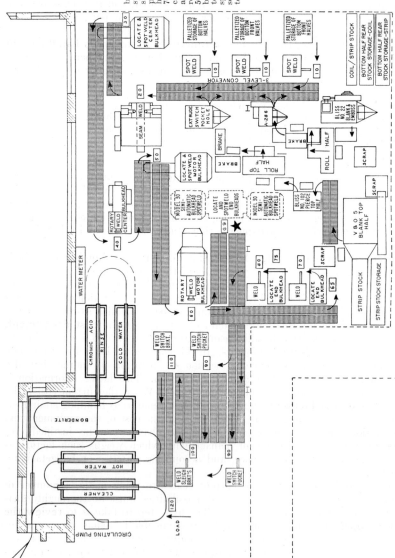

* Operations 65, 70, 75, and 80 will be replaced by operation 69 after conversion of Model 30 semiautomatic bulkhead welders.

personnel should by this time have at their disposal enough information to analyze the problem on a plant-wide, departmental, or section scale.

The solution of a problem depends on the ability of the analyst; to this task the analyst brings his individual background of past solutions, knowledge of a particular industry and its manufacturing setup, an imaginative mind, and the ability to attack new kinds of problems and work them out to a successful solution. An industry rarely reaches the mass-production stage without passing through various layout stages, from test or pilot runs for the development of tool tryout lots with existing handling methods to approximately straight-line production, with its many changes in handling methods. During these stages the materials handling personnel builds up a large background of experience peculiar to the particular industry. As methods of manufacturing are adapted to an individual organization, this experience, with the existing physical manufacturing structure, will affect the problem of materials handling to the point where only the most generalized principles can be listed as applicable to mass production in the general sense.

MATERIALS HANDLING PRINCIPLES. The following are the fundamental principles which have evolved from experience in materials handling; it is important that these principles be checked when a materials handling installation is being developed.

1. Eliminate unnecessary handling where possible by a combination of operations performed mechanically, as in cases, where dies can be set up in a sequence on large bed presses, in special-purpose drilling, with tapping and reaming machines, such as Kingsburys, Bodines, transfer machines, multislides, etc.
2. Use gravity wherever possible for economy and dependability.
3. Specify definite routes for process operations, feeds of necessary parts to subassemblies, feeds of subassemblies and assemblies to packaging or shipping.
4. Determine the most desirable distance between operation points as dependent on the necessary "bank," "float," or storage of finished and unfinished stock, which may be stored by materials handling equipment and accessible to the operator.
5. Select materials handling equipment for installation on the basis of how much it will facilitate manufacturing. Standard data on capacity, adaptability, flexibility, and proved operation; initial cost, installation cost, repair cost, replacement cost, and obsolescence should be carefully weighed in alternative methods.
6. Provide for instruction in use, adequate maintenance, and periodic inspection while operating.

EVOLVING OF MATERIALS HANDLING PATTERNS. An intensive study of any particular materials handling problem will usually suggest to the analyst a pattern which will gradually appear, so that some **general method of handling** will begin to seem most desirable, such as by industrial trucks, belt systems, roller conveyor systems, overhead conveyors (such as that shown in Fig. 6), or a combination of all these kinds of equipment, depending, as previously stated, on the physical structure of the plant, the product or products made, the methods and processes employed in the plant, and the general attitude of management. When a general method has been developed for solving a particular problem, planning is simplified from initial basic flow to final individual work stations. Thus, if a considerable investment has previously been made in industrial trucks, materials handling may assume a trend toward containers with drop-type bottoms, positioning racks, and the like. In this case, previous study may have indicated industrial trucks where manufacture of the product involved cross-routing flow, long distance travel, mixed size or weight of components, or unit loads.

Fig. 6. Chain conveyor systems on three levels.

Another pattern might evolve from the **physical structure of the plant** where overhead space is ample, roof structure is strong, and the manufacturing processes demand large quantities of comparatively small parts. Such a case would be that of a manufacturer of air gages, in volume production, occupying a building originally designed for assembly of helicopters. Here overhead conveyors could travel over fixed routes to standard operations, with continuous flow from stockrooms or receiving divisions, through production lines to inspection, packaging, and shipping areas, by-passing cross traffic, and be designed for any range of future requirements.

If there seems to be no definite reason for a specific kind of installation, **cost may become the criterion,** and here intangibles are so numerous that decision should be made on individual cases, as in the instance where individual trucks are already in use and a department exists for their maintenance and repair. A small expansion, or none at all, might service additional trucks, whereas a belt and roller system might necessitate another maintenance section.

On the other hand, **space might be at a premium,** and an overhead system might save building cost; quotations from several manufacturers of equipment may enable the engineer to compare unit costs per piece handled by using formulas developed by the Materials Handling Division of the American Society of Mechanical Engineers.

MATERIALS HANDLING EQUIPMENT FORMULAS. The materials handling equipment formulas were developed by James A. Shepard and George E. Hagemann under the direction of a committee appointed by the American Society of Mechanical Engineers. The following factors were decided upon as those of importance in any calculation of the economy of introducing new or better equipment to supersede existing equipment considered to be inadequate or approaching obsolescence.

A = Percentage allowance on investment (interest)
B = Percentage allowance for insurance, taxes, etc.
C = Percentage allowance for maintenance
D = Percentage allowance for depreciation
E = Yearly cost of power, supplies, and other items
S = Yearly saving in direct labor cost
T = Yearly saving in fixed charges, operating charge, or burden
U = Yearly saving in earnings through increased production
X = Percentage of working year during which equipment is used
I = Initial cost of equipment
Z = Maximum investment justified by the above consideration
Y = Yearly cost to maintain mechanical equipment
V = Yearly profit from operation of mechanical equipment

$$\text{Then } Z = \frac{(S + I + U - E)X}{A + B + C + D}$$

$$Y = I(A + B + C + D)$$

$$V = [(S + T + U - E)X] - Y$$

Application of Formulas. Assume an installation for bonderizing of cylinders preparatory to lacquer dip and spray. The original installation consists of a 6-tank setup—chemical clean, hot water, two bonderite tanks, cold water, chromic acid solution, followed by oven bake. This system uses two air hoists and multiple rack setup, an overhead monorail, with a direct labor cost of 13 hr. per 1,000. Material supply of cylinders is to and from wooden rack trucks (Fig. 7). Trucking from welding and to second floor (by elevator) is indirect labor; cost and maintenance of trucks is disregarded. Assume a revision of welding methods to permit consolidation of press, welding, and bonderizing, and the selection of an overhead chain to carry cylinders from last welding inspection to lacquer dip on second floor (Fig. 8).

The various factors are estimated as follows:

A = 6 percent interest on investment
B = 4 percent insurance and taxes
C = 20 percent upkeep

Fig. 7. Large pallet-type 4-wheel truck for moving cleaner bodies between work stations.

D = 33 percent depreciation
E = \$100 power, grease, maintenance
S = Saving in direct labor cost, \$17,810
T = Saving in fixed charges, etc., not considered
U = Earnings through increased production, not considered
X = Percentage of working year during which equipment is used, 63 percent
I = Initial cost of equipment, installation, new tanks, racks, oven-building alteration, fire doors, etc., \$8,678.87

$$Z = \frac{(S + I + U - E)X}{A + B + C + D} \qquad = \$17,810$$

$$Y = I(A + B + C + D) \qquad = \$\ 5,406.69$$

$$V = [(S + T + U - E)X] - Y = \$\ 5,750.21$$

APPLICATION OF ANALYSES. The correct application of physical and variable data to the assigned project is usually a matter of individual ability. The engineer's training, experience, and background will largely influence his approach to the problem, and some allowance must be made for these same factors in the ranks of supervision and management. Previous successful installations of equipment, made by the engineer or by the management in charge, may often lead to the selection, within certain limits, of same particular type of installation (and, incidentally, the same make of equipment). Lip service is always paid to impartial consideration of types of equipment; in actual practice there exists a

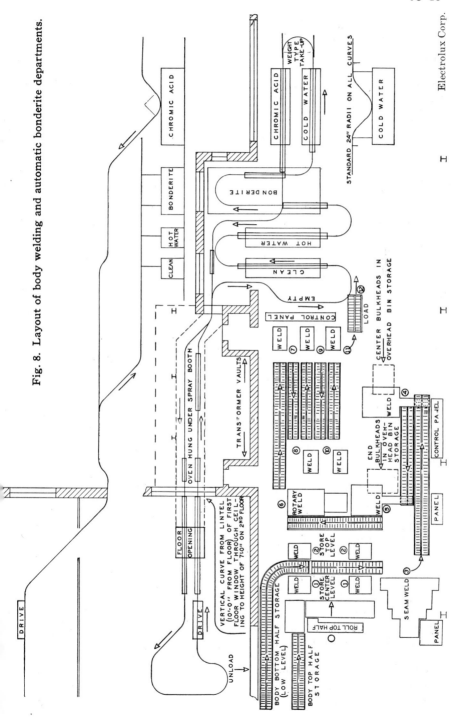

Fig. 8. Layout of body welding and automatic bonderite departments.

Electrolux Corp.

conservatism favoring previous successful experience. Usually the analysis will lead to some alternatives, where the materials handling supervisor will indicate the pattern to be followed. The final decision may also be referred to management, depending again on the organizational setup.

To have the plan approved, through prints, templates, 3-dimensional layouts, or whatever method is in vogue at the particular plant, a **cost estimate** must parallel the layout study and recommendations and may be the basis for an appropriation to cover the cost of the installation. This cost estimate may be made by materials handling equipment manufacturers, or the equipment may be purchased and installed by the plant's own maintenance department, as decided by management, because of the time required to handle the project, the nightwork sometimes necessary, the dislocation of production, etc.

The materials handling section, having planned the installation, may also provide a **schedule of moves** and will usually try to use the organization's own maintenance personnel, the reasons being that:

1. The cost is usually less, particularly for nightwork or overtime.
2. Installation by the firm's own men gives them a familiarity with the equipment and therefore makes maintenance and repair work easier.
3. Paperwork, contracts, detailed blueprints, security clearances, insurance coverage, etc., are eliminated.
4. Outside contractors are not always available because of other work for which they may have been engaged; moreover, they will usually be less efficient in working with the company's maintenance organization, which may be doing supplementary work or installing other operating facilities. There may also be some jurisdictional or trade friction.

If the equipment to be installed is purchased from a reputable manufacturer, and the installation or operation of the equipment is unfamiliar to the user, a competent man may be obtained from the vendor to **supervise installation and train operators,** as in cases with pneumatic conveyors, cranes, plating units, foundry equipment, and all other materials handling equipment.

Training programs are often set up for industrial truck drivers, and specific maintenance check lists are usually prepared for battery charging and lubrication of equipment. The number of **hazards** in using mobile equipment may be reduced and better operation may be attained by:

1. Clearly marking aisle lines with paint or by discs.
2. Keeping aisles unobstructed.
3. Providing adequate lighting.
4. Keeping floors in repair.
5. Installing glass panels on aisle doors.
6. Avoiding too-high loading.
7. Adhering strictly to a no-riders rule.
8. Equipping trucks with overhead guards.
9. Using automatic door openers when possible.
10. Providing a signal system to call fork trucks to serve machine operators.
11. Providing a system for direct communication from dispatcher to fork trucks on fixed routes.

MAINTENANCE OF EQUIPMENT. Including in the term "conveyor" all belt conveyors; truck tow conveyors; apron, bucket, flight-chain, gravity-roller, live-roller, overhead trolley, screw-type, and slat conveyors, good general maintenance practice is as follows:

1. Guard drive machinery.
2. Lubricate through piping where possible.

3. Check clearances periodically.
4. Emphasize visibility in loading and unloading sections and in control locations.
5. Confine the operation of conveyors to authorized employees.
6. Confine repair functions to trained maintenance employees.
7. Provide a smooth cover under slat conveyors to avoid shearing.
8. Do not permit riding or stepping on conveyors.
9. Instruct employees using conveyors in the methods of loading and unloading them and the clearances required for safe operation.
10. Screen all overhead chain installations, on the side as well as on the bottom.
11. In general, do not load mechanical equipment beyond its rated capacity.
12. Locate take-ups in accessible places, and enclose the counterweight type.
13. Interlock conveyors to prevent jamming in a multiple belt setup.
14. Lubricate conveyors on a regular schedule, with definite responsibility assigned to particular individuals for doing the work and making signed reports.
15. Use lockouts in fuse boxes during maintenance operations, and have push buttons or cord lines for emergency stops.
16. Insist on high-quality heavy electrical equipment and strict adherence to electrical codes.

When the equipment has been selected that will best fulfill processing requirements, the materials handling engineer proceeds with the **physical layout and installation** of the system. As auxiliary information he will need parts lists, operation sheets, flow process charts, work station layouts, building drawings, and sketches of service lines and facilities. He may run across major difficulties. For example, it may not be possible to relocate certain departments, such as plating, receiving, and shipping, because of the building layout. During the planning period frequent consultation with the operating personnel is extremely helpful in visualizing the materials flow, in eliminating difficulties that have occurred with the existing system, and in providing all the facilities necessary for serving the materials handling needs.

It is seldom that any layout, or the use of any particular kinds of equipment, will become permanent. **Materials handling is a progressive function** in plants, in warehouses, on chipping docks, and in yard operations, and the individual plant should keep in touch with equipment developments and methods improvements which will still further simplify operations and cut materials handling costs.

EQUIPMENT FOR HANDLING A PART THROUGH PRODUCTION. To explain the typical methods employed in materials handling, an example is presented here. The part going through the series of operations, which includes a considerable amount of materials handling, is a shell approximately 8 in. in diam. and 3 in. deep, drawn from a cold-rolled-steel disc 12 in. in diam. and 0.020 in. thick. The disc falls through the die to a container positioned on a roller conveyor, terminating at the right hand of the following sequence (Fig. 9):

1. First draw.
2. Redraw center.
3. Draw down center, form small pocket, form down flange.
4. Pierce for switch and two rivet holes, iron pocket.
5. Trim edge.
6. Pierce face, extrude, and flatten.

These operations are roughly similar in that all presses used are equipped with Possons guards and the parts are disposed of by hand because the following polishing and plating operations require reasonably careful handling to avoid denting and scratching. The **previous method of storage and handling** was by the use of wooden crates, 36 in. long, 20 in. wide, and 26 in. high, positioned on

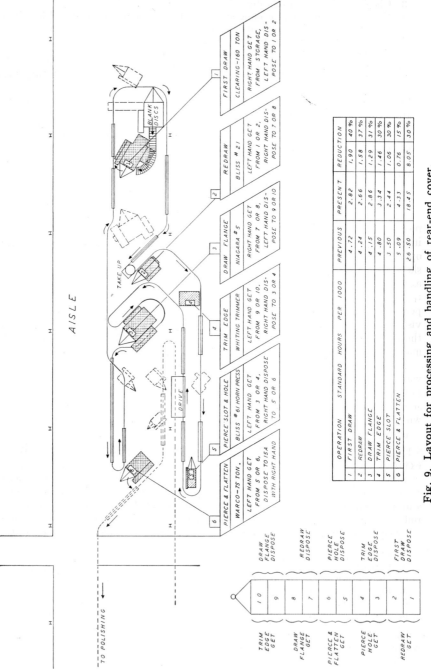

Fig. 9. Layout for processing and handling of rear-end cover.

tilted stands for the press operations and stacked flat for intermediate storage, 64 pieces to a crate, 8 pieces to a layer, with a cardboard separator for each layer. Press runs were in lots of 40,000, so that several hundred crates were necessary, and intermediate and final storage, though ceiling high, involved considerable indirect cost in stock handling and took up a rather large amount of badly needed floor space. The cost of the crates was $4.87 each on a yearly basis, this amount including original cost of labor and material, and repair and replacement as charged against a yearly shop order.

Of this group of presses three had pit foundations, which would have made relocation costly; the alternative of moving them was therefore dismissed as an impractical possibility, both for that reason and, mainly, because handling was to be improved with absolutely no interruption to current production.

Included in the piecework standards were **time elements** for removing the finished work in crates from the tilted stands, for placing empty crates at the finished-work tilted stand, and for placing unfinished work in crates at the tilted stand. These operations recurred with every 64 pieces for the six operations, and except when the Whiting trimmer was being used, time was also allowed for the removal and replacement of the Possons guards, a device which keeps the operator's hands away from the die during the punch-press ram travel.

Some assistance was required to position the filled crates. This assistance was not always immediately available, and the size of the crates in position on the tilted stands made getting and disposing of the stock in the crates vary the worker's arm motions to points outside the effective working area. The range was from knee to shoulder in height, and from close to extreme in depth. Theoretically, the operator was supposed to take unfinished pieces from the top of the layer, in order to prevent the nicking, denting, and scratching which would occur when the closer pieces were removed from the bottom of the layer and the top pieces slid down the inclined separator.

Analysis of the time-study standards indicated a probable **decrease of 16 percent in direct-labor costs** if hand handling could be eliminated. Indirect costs, and overhead or burden were not considered in the existing costs but were to be charged against the new installation—a special accounting decision.

Planning the New Installation. A conveyor system was then planned as shown in Fig. 10, using No. 348 chain, 5-ft. vertical curves, with 325 carriers on 1-ft. centers. A female attachment is used on alternate carriers since the load is comparatively light; this factor halved the cost of the trolleys. A caterpillar-drive, 24-in. sprocket-type take-up, No. 348 rivetless chain, trolleys, and horizontal roller turns were available from the material pool established by management for materials handling; installation of a purchased 3-in. I-beam was estimated; a 10-compartment carrier was made as a sample; and bids were requested from outside sheet-metal fabricators.

For 325 racks the low bid was $2,600. This quotation was considered unreasonable and the maintenance department personnel were assigned to estimate the cost of fabrication.

Manufacturing Operations. The conveyor was laid out to move the 10-shelved carrier past each operation, receiving the finished piece from Operation 1 in either of the two bottom spaces (Spaces 1 and 2); raising to ceiling height, then dropping to ideal operating level to present Spaces 1 and 2 to Operation 2; traveling 140 ft. to receive the finished work from Operation 2 in Spaces 7 and 8. In the course of the 140 ft., Spaces 3 and 4 receive the trimmed pieces from the Whiting trimmer operator, who gets the pieces from Spaces 9 and 10, where they

Fig. 10. Multiple carrier conveyor supplying rear-end covers to a forming operation.

have been placed after the third operation. Once the conveyor is loaded, **continuity of operation is unimportant** so far as availability of stock is concerned, and machines need not be located adjacent to one another. The primary requirements are:

1. Full spaces to bring the work and empty spaces to take it away.
2. A reasonable balance of time allowed for the respective operations, so that the "float" or "bank" storage between operations can be maintained for a reasonable time cycle.
3. Understanding on the part of the machine operators about the use of the equipment.

After the trimming operation, Operation 4, has been performed, the conveyor:

1. Rises to ceiling height.
2. Drops to Operation 5 for piercing.
3. Rises again, to vacate floor area and give access to machines.
4. Again drops.
5. Loops, as indicated on the illustration, passing under the flywheel guard of the "draw flange" operation.
6. Again rises to ceiling height.
7. Drops to the final operation.
8. Finally returns to the starting point.

In a loop-type installation such as this, with processing equipment on both sides of the loop, a carrier which faces only one way complicates the layout to some extent.

Cost Estimate of the Conveyor Installation. A cost estimate of the installation, with an "Application for Appropriation," was prepared, comprising these items:

Material (drive, turns, I-beam)..................	$1,810
Take-up, vertical curves, etc.	620
Angle iron	140
	$2,570
Erection (400 hr.)	1,200
	$3,770
Miscellaneous electrical work, controls, etc........	100
	$3,870
Racks: 3,500 ft. of 14-gage 0.078 × 1½ ⎫	
125 ft. of 5/16-in. round stock ⎬	$ 250
300-0.031-in.-sheets, 24 in. × 48 in. ⎭	
Fabrication of racks.............................	500
Total cost................................	$4,620

A cost reduction of 4.75 hr. per thousand pieces was projected against the estimated total production for a year; this meant a reduction of 3,800 standard hr. minimum in direct labor, and the installation was therefore authorized.

The installation was completed in a 5-wk. period, with a total labor charge of 380 hr., including week ends at time and a half and double time, and a night-work differential charge of 10 percent.

Materials and operations for construction of the conveyor itself were estimated to cost the following amounts:

Fabrication of racks, setup men doing the shearing, brake work, and welding setups...........	$ 286.00
Material for racks............................	250.00
	$ 536.00
Material for conveyor........................	2,670.00
Erection	1,140.00
	$4,346.00

Results in Operation. The speed of the conveyor was set at 10 ft. per min. to take care of 600 pieces per hr. with a 100 percent float, bank, or storage. Operations were started on the first day of the workweek and 325 pieces were produced on the first draw, at which time the second operator began his work. This schedule was continued until all operations were in process. The sequence of operations covered a 32.5-min. time cycle and was obviously too short. As familiarity with the "get" and "dispose" developed, the discrepancy between theory and practice began to widen. Conveyor speed was progressively advanced until, at 14 ft. per min., the float stabilized. At the end of the day's run, production was 46 percent above normal. The increased output led to some interesting piecework earnings and an increased raw-stock and final-storage problem. The second operational day, on a 23.5-min. cycle, brought a decision to reduce the number of operators from six to four. The four men were organized into a bonus group and instructed in "leap frogging," or moving from operation to operation. This arrangement naturally cost a slight loss in efficiency because of travel time and lack of operating skill on operations new to the individual, but at the end of the workweek the members of the group had thoroughly grasped the operation of

Fig. 11. Spiral conveyor leading to shipping department.

the installation and had adjusted themselves to production requirements. The six operations were retimed the following week, and a standard was established for the group (reductions in standard hours are shown in Fig. 9).

It became obvious from "cold" time-study figures that previous interruptions for stock handling at every 64 pieces had **prevented the development of rhythm and smoothness.** At all events, some decreases verged on the unbelievable. For example, the first operation specified: "Pick up disc, apply drawing compound, locate to die, operate press, remove finish, and dispose to Space 1 or 2." This operation has been timed for a 60-min. period, and with consecutive operations working out to provide space (this happened when a raw-stock shipment was late), it has shown an actual production of 1,500 pieces per hr. The third operation, "Get piece, apply compound, place to horn of die, operate press, remove and dispose of piece," has been checked at 1,680 pieces per hr. for short intervals. The operator who was checked, incidentally, was at one time exclusively left-handed but has become ambidextrous on punch-press operations (Fig. 10). Because of these facts, considerable latitude was taken in the establishment of a group bonus standard. Base pay rates were raised (1) to compensate for ability to perform more operations than before, (2) to make ready and clean up on as many as three setups per hour, and (3) for use of the conveyor without supervision.

Under this plan, and disregarding (1) the cost of containers, (2) indirect labor for storage between operations, and (3) floor space for installation of other equipment, the following results have been secured:

1. A direct labor saving of 30 percent, or the elimination of two operators, who were shifted elsewhere in the department. The installation was considered paid for in 5 months.
2. Increased group earnings, considerably above the departmental average (friction in the plant because of this situation has been minor).
3. Quality maintained at a higher degree than before. Deviations in quality are detected almost immediately because of the rapid flow of work through operations. Die maintenance may be higher; no previous figures existed for comparison.

The conveyor is operated under a **preventive maintenance schedule.** Cost of drive grease, oil, necessary adjustments of take-up, etc., is small; there has been no down time since the operation was established. Racks or carriers are removed when necessary to allow other setups to be made in the press group. This plan is sometimes followed when production quotas permit. No additional machine guards were installed, and to date there have been no accidents.

Spiral conveyor installations leading to storage and shipping areas are shown in Fig. 11. The flexibility of gravity roller conveyors, ball conveyors, and slides in plant handling operations are also indicated in this figure.

HANDLING METHODS IN APPLIANCE MANUFACTURE. Efficient materials handling and flexibility of layout were preplanned for the 1,000,000-sq.-ft. appliance plant of the Frigidaire Division of General Motors Corporation. The layout is based on the use of conveyors, with provision made for flexibility through the available height provided for possible relocation of overhead systems. Separate **"layers" of space** were assigned to plant engineering and production departments after a production layout was made. Fig. 12 shows the layout.

Planning the Facilities. A very considerable amount of care was used in planning the construction and layout of the Frigidaire building to provide facilities for highly efficient materials handling, as the following data indicate:

1. Width of building was determined by:
   a. Floor conveyors for assembly.
   b. Adequate floor area for these conveyors with space between them.
   c. Service aisles and 100-ft. bands of floor area on each side of the assembly layout for plant services and small departments.
2. Plant size was determined according to the production goal, with adequate provision for expansion, by converting machine and manpower requirements into floor area needs, giving gross areas. The shape of the layout determined the width; the gross area divided by the width determined the length.

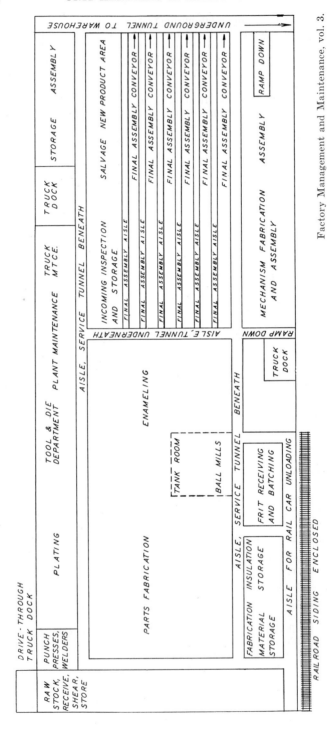

Fig. 12. Layout of the Frigidaire Division plant of General Motors Corporation (continued on next page).

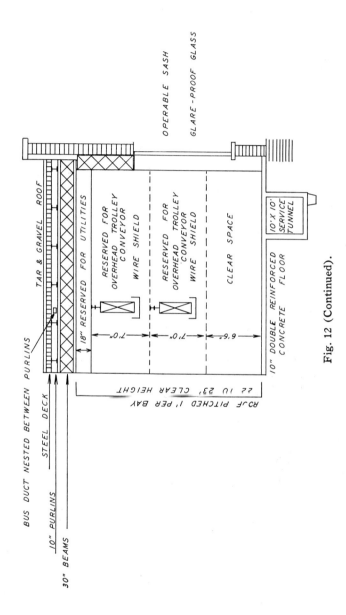

Fig. 12 (Continued).

3. Perimeter space was allocated to miscellaneous departments to keep production areas clear of special-purpose and service departments. This plan was adopted to eliminate secondary moves if changes should occur in production layouts.
4. Stock conveyors were placed overhead for a floating inventory. Unit-loading and floor-banking with industrial trucks comprised about 30 percent of the storage area.
5. Adequate dock space for unloading incoming material by two 10-ton overhead cranes is provided. Specialized docks are provided, where incoming stock can be received near its use location.
6. Ramps and a tunnel provide for delivery of finished goods to the warehouse, located ¼ mi. away. Ramps have a 12 percent grade.
7. Production offices and restrooms are located above the production floor.

Results Obtained. Many important results have been attained by the construction, layout, and provisions for materials handling in the Frigidaire plant:

1. Conveyor handling has been improved because of a 22-ft. clear space between floor and beams. Utilities are in the first 18 in. under the beams, with the next 14 ft. down allowed for double-decked conveyors and their guards. The 6½-ft. headroom exists only where conveyors are double decked—a small fraction of total floor area.
2. Truck handling is facilitated by having the main aisles 12 ft. wide and 1,600 ft. long. Departmental aisles, 8 ft. wide, adjoin production areas. The standard container size is 60 × 37 × 40 in. The high ceiling permits loaded pallets to be stacked to the desired height without the limitation often imposed to provide the necessary sprinkler clearance.
3. Production areas are concentrated in the 1,600 × 400 ft. center section of the plant, flanked on each side by one of the main aisles. Straight-line flow is a reality, from receiving to shipping. The number of overhead conveyors is kept to a minimum. Subassembly areas can be spotted across the aisle from the main assembly sections they feed. There is no basic interference which would limit layout changes.
4. Service areas are out of the way, the locations being governed by the production areas they serve. Repair shops, toilets, storage tanks, etc., are in these perimeter sections.
5. Service lines are underground in 10 × 10 ft. tunnels, for the most part. Steam, condensate, water, and de-ionized water lines, when located in tunnels, do not hamper layout changes. The mains are in two large tunnels that run directly under the two long production aisles. The service mains are tapped as required, and risers come up through the floor at the columns. Laterals are taken off the risers as needed, leaving the ceiling relatively free of piping and wiring. Oxygen and acetyline lines are not in the tunnels, but overhead, because of the explosion hazard. The steam main comes up out of the tunnel at the north end, goes to the ceiling, across the plant, and down into the other tunnel. This layout was adopted so that the many presses could be rearranged, and new presses could be added, without interference from plant service facilities whenever changes in layout were desirable.
6. Raw steel stock comes into a drive-through truck dock at the northeast corner of the building, adjacent to which is an area for the preparation of steel. Insulation for ranges comes in by carload on the opposite side of the building, reasonably close to its use point. Palletized loads can be moved from carriers to production parts banks.
7. Crating and shipping are centralized in a warehouse building a quarter of a mile away. The large appliances are transported in an underground tunnel under a highway, below another plant and a railroad main line, and up into the warehouse. An interlocked switching system on the powered roller conveyor permits it to handle the output of six (eventually eight) final-assembly con-

veyors. Electric eyes control the switching operation and assemble groups of appliances into short trains before releasing them to the tunnel conveyor.

8. Allowance in the original layout has been made for production increases.
9. Physical expansion is possible should it be desirable to extend the plant. Underground sewage and utility lines are laid out to come within the tunnels if the plant is enlarged.

FEATURES OF THE MANUFACTURING PLANT. Side walls are 12 in. thick, one course of red brick used outside with a back-up wall of 8 × 8 × 4 in. concrete block, tied to the brick mechanically at every fourth row. The roof is a steel deck, with 1 in. of insulating board, topped with a built-up tar and gravel finish. Floors are of wood block.

Heating and Ventilating. Two types of steam-operated heaters are used: recirculating heaters and fresh air heaters. The amount of fresh air brought in is regulated by a thermostat reacting to outside air temperature. Most heating units are in the perimeter areas and force heat toward the center. Forced ventilation is provided during the summer months. Eventually, the heating and ventilating units will be balanced to keep the plant under slight pressure to avoid drafts. Large process-air equipment users, such as the porcelain furnace, have their own air intake and exhaust systems.

Water Supply. Drains for water-cooled welders are overhead and in the floor. About 90 percent of the plant has sprinklers. The standpipe is located out of the way of future expansion.

Power. Power is supplied from roof vaults, five on each side of the plant. These penthouses have floor hatches that can be opened for installation or removal of heavy equipment, and the vaults are interconnected for emergency switching.

Waste Disposal. Underground tanks, of 40,000-gal. capacity, will hold industrial wastes, both acid and alkaline. Equipment will be installed to meter these effluents to a 66-in. storm sewer leading to the river. The metering device includes an automatic sampler that pulls six samples per hour from the big sewer, and there is a continuous dilution of the effluent so that it will have little effect on aquatic life in the river. Raw sewage goes to the county treatment plant.

Dust and Fume Control. Fumes from the plating area are drawn down through gratings surrounding the tanks and into tunnels. These feeder tunnels lead to a master tunnel, which in turn leads to an underground room where fumes are washed out of the air, which is then exhausted through the roof. The capacity of the system is 273,000 cu. ft. per min. All ducts and tunnels are of concrete. The collecting basins are of rubber and are tile-lined. Metal-finishing dust is drawn down alongside the finishing conveyors to a 48-in. concrete pipe, which leads to a dust-removal system on the roof. After the air is cleaned, it is returned by a duct to the plant, above the finishing area, and distributed through grills; its capacity is 140,000 cu. ft. per min.

Materials Handling in Special-Order Plants

DEFINITIONS. The term "special-order plants" as used in this section covers a wide scope of industrial activity. Special-order plants comprise, first of all, all those manufacturing establishments which are neither mass-production nor processing-industry plants. The special-order plant manufactures products upon special orders from its customers. The customers may be other companies, individual users, or both. The orders may be for single special products or for limited production runs of one or more products. The individual orders may be repeated later, or they may never be run again. A later order may be for a different quantity of an identical part or unit, or it may call for products of the same kind as furnished before but with major or minor changes in design.

The term "special-order plants," however, covers more than those plants which manufacture only to order, because some essentially mass-production or processing-industry plants also manufacture to special order. Likewise, some essentially special-order plants sometimes also mass produce a product or products. However, even though considerable overlapping exists, it is usually possible to recognize a plant as being **essentially special-order** rather than a mass-production or processing-industry plant.

The variety of special-order manufacturing concerns is too great to be listed here. A few typical examples, however, are die and tool shops, special machinery fabricators making machines of various types to special order, jobbing foundries, and shops that manufacture stamping, spinning, welding, grinding, plating, plastic-moulding, and automatic screw machines. Sometimes standard machinery manufacturers produce many models or adaptations of the same type of machine, where some of the subassemblies are standard, yet each completed machine is different and made to special order. An example of this kind of manufacturing plant may be found in the field of industrial sewing machines. Also, numerous examples of combinations of the above and other types of special-order plants, with each other or with mass-production or processing-industry plants, may be found throughout practically the entire range of industry.

BASIC PRINCIPLES. The basic principles for materials handling in special-order plants are included in the general principles for good handling in other types of plants. Although it is difficult to formulate hard and fast principles in the field of materials handling, there are a number of fundamentals which apply specifically to special-order plants. These fundamentals are given in the following paragraphs:

1. **General-purpose rather than specialized materials handling equipment** should be used for maximum flexibility.

Specialized materials handling equipment naturally tends to afford greater economy where a particular type of handling is done frequently and repetitively over a long period of time or where the nature of the handling is such that it cannot be done at all with standard materials handling equipment. Although this situation often does occur in special-order plants, it is usual to expect "normal" handling problems on short-duration jobs. An exception would occur in the jobbing-foundry industry where the same sequence of operations involving the same materials handling equipment is used, despite the fact that different types of jobs are being processed. For most handling operations in most special-order plants, however, general-purpose materials handling equipment, with its wide range of capacity and high adaptability, provides the greatest utility.

2. Materials handling equipment should be selected to meet the capacity required for the **heaviest or most difficult handling job anticipated,** rather than with capacity to handle the most frequent job.

This principle does not apply, of course, to extreme cases where the heaviest or most difficult job occurs very infrequently. For example, it would not pay to purchase and install a 10-ton crane where the usual loads are in the range of 1 to 5 tons simply because it is probable that a 10-ton load will be moved, say, once every 2 yr. It would be best to buy a 5-ton crane and engage the services of outside movers for the special 10-ton job. In all cases an economy study should be made before selecting equipment, especially in borderline cases. In general, however, in the special-order plant it is advisable to weight the selection in favor of the equipment with greater capacity or greater flexibility because of the changing handling problems inherent in this type of plant.

3. In addition to being highly adaptable, special-order materials handling **equipment should be as mobile as possible.**

Because of changing job requirements and the need for frequent relayout, it is advisable to choose mobile handling equipment wherever possible and to preplan for the possible repositioning of handling equipment.

4. **Production equipment** as well as materials handling equipment should be **as adaptable as possible.**

The slower speeds and greater adaptability of general-purpose production equipment should be balanced against the higher initial cost and greater inflexibility of specialized machines, taking into account the anticipated variety of jobs and length of runs over a considerable period of time. Job variety will differ from plant to plant, and an economy study should be made in each case to determine the degree of adaptability of equipment which seems necessary. It should be remembered that even standard machinery and equipment can frequently be made more flexible by using special tools and attachments. Portability may be enhanced by installing self-contained machines and by preplanning the installation of service systems at the time a manufacturing building is constructed. Features such as electrical ducts and cutting-compound lines can then be installed overhead, down the center of bays, or through special channels in steel beams located in the floor at the time the building is erected. Apple (Plant Layout and Materials Handling) presents a description and typical photographs of such installations.

5. In special-order plants **materials handling costs** should be minimized over a long period of time.

Because of the relatively large expansions and contractions in business volume that often accompany special-order manufacturing, the most economical handling equipment for present needs may not be the most economical in the long run. It is not enough to select the best equipment for the present setup, with allowance for future expansion. It must be remembered that in the special-order plant the future may not only require a different volume of business but also may involve handling problems of a different nature.

6. **An integrated materials handling system** should be used throughout the plant, even at the expense of certain individual handling operations, to provide an over-all maximum plant handling efficiency.

By an integrated materials handling system it is meant that a decision should be made to lay out the plant around a basic materials handling system. The basic system may involve primarily overhead conveyors, industrial trucks, or some other method or combination of methods. Even though the particular system chosen may not be the best for any individual handling operation, it may provide greater over-all economy. The decision as to the particular plant handling system to be chosen, of course, should be based on a thorough economic analysis.

7. In general, in special-order manufacture, the longer **the fabrication or operation time** at each work station becomes, the less important the materials handling between operations becomes, and the less critical is the distance between these work stations.

In many special-order plants the fabrication time at one or more work stations is longer than is usual in most mass-production plants. Thus, the time spent in handling materials between such work stations tends to be a small percentage of the manufacturing time and usually represents a correspondingly small percentage of the cost of manufacturing. Such a condition does not mean that proper materials handling is not important between these operations; it means only that it is not as important there as it may be between other work stations. It is advisable, therefore, to concentrate attention on the handling of materials between short cycles first and then go on to progressively longer operations, especially in cases where funds are very limited.

This principle may also serve as a guide for relayout of plants to accommodate changing jobs. Relayout is often a costly and time-consuming job. No move should be made unless the improvements and savings to be derived exceed the cost involved. Since the distance between long-cycle operations is less critical than between short-cycle operations, long-cycle stations should be repositioned last. Planning for plant layout and planning for materials handling should occur simultaneously, since the two factors are inextricably interrelated.

8. **An economy study** should precede the selection of materials handling equipment.

A careful study of the operating and financial benefits which may be obtained should be made in selecting equipment of any kind for use in any type of plant. It is of particular importance in selecting materials handling equipment for special-order plants. The term "economy study" as used here is meant to include nonmonetary as well as monetary factors. A study of factors applicable to all alternatives, rather than hunches or opinions, should form the basis for handling equipment selection. Some of the noneconomic factors which are relevant are:

1. **Reduction of handling fatigue** because of the ease of operating mechanized handling equipment.
2. **Availability of excess capacity** at times of peak loads without the necessity for assigning additional men to handle materials sporadically for short periods of time.
3. **Improved worker morale** owing to the safety advantages of mechanized handling.
4. **Ease of administration** and control of handling equipment as compared with handling labor.

MAJOR FACTORS IN MATERIALS HANDLING OPERATIONS.
Materials handling operations constitute a considerable part of the procedures in special-order manufacturing. There are definite **relationships** between materials handling and many factors related to the efficiency, economy, and morale of an enterprise.

The basic factors which are of most concern in materials handling are:
1. Time required for handling.
2. Quantity and/or weight to be handled.
3. Distance over which materials must be moved.

These three factors are of prime importance in calculating the costs of alternative handling methods.

Time required for handling should be directly proportioned to time required for production. Where production is capable of proceeding more rapidly than materials are being moved into production machinery, a tremendous incentive for improving materials handling facilities exists. Where handling methods can provide materials more rapidly than production equipment can process them, an incentive for improving production equipment exists.

The **quantity** to be handled involves two questions. First, what is the over-all quantity to be handled per minute, per day, or per job? Second, what is the desired unit quantity at each handling operation? The whole quantity required can be subdivided into a variety of unit loads. By varying the time per unit load, a number of alternative unit-load sizes may be chosen which are compatible with the use of alternative handling methods. For example, one unit every 30 sec. may be supplied with a conveyor, or the equivalent amount of 120 units every hour may be supplied as a single pallet load with the aid of a fork lift truck (assuming a convenient weight and volume per unit).

The **distance** involved in handling is a factor which should be reduced whenever possible. Usually, reduction of distance means the reduction of handling time, with a corresponding reduction of handling cost. However, it is again possible to visualize the use of alternate materials handling methods and equipment for the movement of materials over a fixed distance.

For any materials handling job it is the amalgam of the three factors of time, quantity, and distance which must be considered in choosing alternative handling methods and equipment. It is the kind and quantity of materials to be moved over a given distance in a given time which comprise the **major variables** in the materials handling equation.

Other factors, of course, must be considered; in individual instances any of these other factors may be the decisive ones. Some of these factors are:

1. The fragility of the materials to be handled and the required condition in which they must be received.
2. The tendency of the rate to vary at the point of origin or the point of destination of the materials in question.
3. The probability that the route will vary.
4. The nature and characteristics of the material—whether the material is bulky, heavy, slippery, corrosive, etc., and whether it is in powder, solid, or liquid form.
5. The possible expansion or contraction of production plans.
6. The percentage of time during which the equipment will be in use.

STAFF VS. INDIVIDUAL MANAGEMENT. Materials handling methods and the services to which they are to be applied require **specialized knowledge** and ability on the part of the individual in charge of materials handling operations. In addition a broad and **comprehensive approach** is necessary, because materials handling affects and is directly related to many other important plant functions, such as plant layout, production control, safety engineering, quality control, personnel relations, and plant maintenance. Materials handling, together with plant layout, is organizationally best suited either as a staff function of the industrial engineering department or as the responsibility of one or more individuals who may constitute a separate materials handling department. In any case there is a great need for **coordination and cooperation** between the materials handling function and other industrial engineering functions. Materials handling engineers deal with various department heads and key personnel and should report to a line executive well up in the organizational ranks.

The **nature of the organizational setup** varies to a great extent with the size and kind of company. Since special-order plants range in size from very small to very large, the organizational setup of the materials handling function will vary considerably. The great majority of special-order plants, of course, are small or medium-sized companies.

In practice, only in large firms is it usual to find a **staff organization** of the materials handling department. The medium-sized and small firms often delegate responsibility for materials handling to plant managers or plant superintendents, who, although qualified for this work, are usually overburdened with other plant problems and cannot consistently devote much time to materials handling. Many small firms do not even have a full-time industrial engineer. It is possible, however, for the small or medium-sized firm to set up a materials handling committee in cases where it is impractical to have a separate materials handling department or engineer. Such a committee could be composed of one member from each of the groups concerned with materials handling and should report to some high executive of the company.

Where members of existing plant personnel are either not qualified or are too busy with other duties, the services of a qualified materials handling **consultant** may be engaged. When a consultant is employed, it is advisable to make a full-time employee, who follows the work of the consultant, responsible for carrying out the handling program set up.

Richman (Unpublished survey) found that in a large number of special-order plants the person or department responsible for dealing with materials handling varied considerably and included materials handling departments, production control departments, plant superintendents, plant managers, department supervisors, and foremen.

Typical Organizational Setups. Some typical organizational setups in existing special-order plants are as follows:

Plant A. This plant is engaged in contract manufacturing and job-lot fabrication in all ferrous and nonferrous metals. It is a medium-sized plant producing under special orders which sometimes include medium to large runs. The organization chart showing the relative position of the materials handling foreman in the organization is given in Fig. 13.

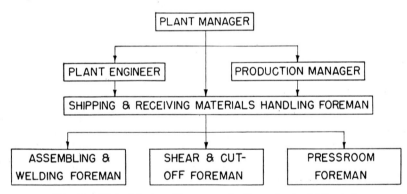

Fig. 13. Materials handling organization chart of Plant A.

In this plant, materials handling is generally carried on by the shipping and receiving department and falls under the direction of one foreman, who reports to the plant engineer and production manager as well as to the plant manager. The materials handling equipment under the supervision of the shipping and receiving foreman consists of 1 elevator, 7 traveling cranes and hoists, 3 hand lift trucks, 40 hand platform trucks, and a considerable number of skids. No pallets are used, but if space were available, power fork trucks would be used.

The management of this plant is well aware of the importance of materials handling; it estimates that from 25 to 40 percent of the cost of manufacturing its products, depending upon the nature of the product being fabricated, consists of materials handling costs. To meet its complicated and varied materials handling problems a day-to-day survey is conducted, and the necessary corrections are made by holding meetings between foremen. Recognizing its handling limitations, the management recently made major changes in the plant layout and in the materials handling equipment employed. It reports:

We had a low-ceiling condition, with columns on 12-ft. centers. We eliminated one row of columns, reinforced the ceiling, and engineered and built cranes with 25 × 80 ft. runs. We also constructed an addition to our building to increase our headroom, giving us 2 crane runways 30 × 60 ft. span. In each instance where we have made the above installation, the materials handling situation was greatly improved.

Plant B. This plant is strictly a special-order plant making dies, tools, jigs, fixtures, and special machinery. The plant is considerably smaller than Plant A. Materials handling is under the direction of the assistant plant superintendent, who receives instructions directly from the plant superintendent. The materials handling equipment under the supervision of the assistant superintendent consists of 7 hand-operated fixed cranes, 2 traveling cranes, 2 power fork lift trucks, and 7 hand platform trucks, together with skids and pallets. The management has not attempted to analyze materials handling cost apart from other costs of manufacturing and is under the impression that materials handling comprises "a very minor part of our cost." Fig. 14 shows this company's organization chart relative to materials handling.

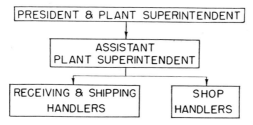

Fig 14. Materials handling organization chart of Plant B.

Plant C. This is a fairly large plant which manufactures to special order only. The company makes heavy machinery, rolling mills, iron and steel castings, and hot-metal and cinder cars. The company's materials handling organization chart is shown in Fig. 15. The materials handling department, consisting of the trans-

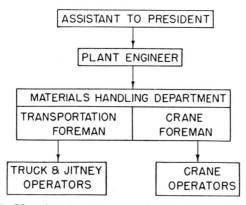

Fig. 15. Materials handling organization chart of Plant C.

portation foreman and crane foreman, is directly under the supervision of the plant engineer. The materials handling equipment supervised by the transportation foreman consists of approximately 6 hand platform and lift trucks, 3 power fork lift trucks, and 1 power platform lift truck, together with about 150 skids and 500 pallets. Under the transportation foreman's supervision there are also two 5-ton dump body trucks, 2 automobile trucks, and 2 scoop loaders. Under the crane foreman's supervision there are about 20 fixed cranes or hoists, 13 traveling cranes, and 8 portable and fixed conveyors. The management of this plant estimates that approximately 12 percent of the company's cost of manufacturing is for materials handling.

Plant D. This is a very small plant which does hot forming and quenching of special equipment on a special-order basis only. The materials handling organization chart is given in Fig. 16. The shop superintendent is in charge of materials

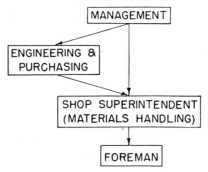

Fig. 16. Materials handling organization chart of Plant D.

handling. His instructions come either directly from the management or through the engineering and purchasing department. The materials handling equipment supervised by the shop superintendent consists of 10 fixed cranes, 2 traveling cranes, 4 hand lift trucks, and 12 hand platform trucks. There are skids at each machine and shipments are palletized. The management estimates that about 10 percent of the cost of manufacturing is incurred in materials handling.

Plant E. This is a medium-small plant which makes heavy-duty forging equipment and other special machinery to special order only. The engineering department is in charge of materials handling and reports directly to the plant manager. The company's organization chart relative to materials handling is given in Fig. 17. The plant has 10 fixed cranes, 3 traveling cranes, 4 hand lift

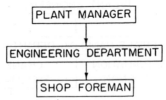

Fig. 17. Materials handling organization chart of Plant E.

trucks, and a number of pallets. The company plans to rearrange the shop layout to provide for use of a fork lift truck. It is estimated that 5 percent of the cost of manufacturing is that for materials handling.

Plant F. This is a combination special-order and mass-production plant manufacturing office appliances and doing aircraft subassembly work. It is a medium-size plant which just recently modified its plant layout to provide wider aisles and dock areas to facilitate materials handling. A production control department engineer is directly responsible for materials handling. The organization chart relative to materials handling in this plant is given in Fig. 18. The present mate-

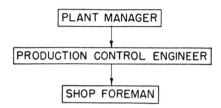

Fig. 18. Materials handling organization chart of Plant F.

rials handling equipment consists of 2 traveling cranes, 1 electric power fork lift truck, 3 hand lift trucks, 8 hand platform trucks, and about 300 skids and 300 pallets. The management estimates that since the new plant layout was adopted, materials handling represents only 3.6 percent of the cost of manufacturing the company's products.

Plant G. This is a small plant manufacturing machinery for the cold processing of strip steel and wire-mill machinery to special order only. The organization chart covering the company's materials handling operations is shown in Fig. 19.

Fig. 19. Materials handling organization chart of Plant G.

The company recently moved into a new plant, for materials handling reasons, and now has 5 traveling cranes (four 2-ton cranes and one 10-ton crane) and 3 hand lift trucks. Although the company executives feel that the materials handling cost is considerably less since moving, they hesitate to estimate the actual percentage of materials handling costs compared with their costs of manufacturing.

ANALYSIS OF MATERIALS HANDLING PROBLEMS. The analytical methods for selection of the best materials handling procedures and equipment for special-order manufacturing vary only in extent and scope, depending on whether a new plant is to be built and equipped or an existing plant is to be modified. The main steps in the analysis of special-order materials handling problems are:

1. Finding out what is needed.
2. Gathering the necessary data.

3. Evaluating the data.
4. Selecting suitable alternative materials handling equipment.
5. Making an economic analysis to determine the best alternatives.
6. Reporting findings to plant executives.
7. Following up to secure approval for making the proposed changes.

FINDING OUT WHAT IS NEEDED. Before proceeding with any materials handling problem it is first necessary to get a clear and complete understanding of what the **problem** is. What exactly is the materials handling need? What handling functions are involved? Why is a change necessary? The proper insight into the nature of the **objective** will provide a firm foundation for the approach and solution of the materials handling problem.

GATHERING THE NECESSARY DATA. The materials handling engineer at this point should evidence his ability to deal with others in the organization to gain their cooperation. He should question all who are affected by any changes, from the plant manager to the handling equipment operator. It will be necessary to gather a great deal of factual information about the following:

1. Policy factors.
2. Layout factors.
3. Process factors.
4. Materials factors.
5. Materials handling equipment factors.
6. Cost factors.

Policy Factors. Top management is the source of data concerning policy factors. It is especially important for the materials handling engineer in the special-order plant to have a knowledge of many **management policies,** since plant expansions and contractions are common to this type of manufacture. It is necessary for the materials handling engineer to know something about the **future direction** planned for plant activities. Is the plant to remain a special-order plant, or is it the intention that it shall become partly or completely a mass-production or process-industry plant at some future date? Does the management plan for and expect to develop an ever-increasing volume of business, or is the intention to stabilize activities at about the present level? If the plan is that the plant shall remain a special-order manufacturing company, is it possible that **cost analysis** has revealed certain types of special-order products more profitable than others? If so, is it the intention to specialize in the more profitable items? What is management policy concerning **rate of return** on materials handling equipment? What is the **depreciation** policy regarding materials handling equipment? These are the types of policy matters on which the materials handling engineer must be informed in order to make effective analyses of handling problems.

Layout Factors. Data should be gathered concerning the existing or proposed building and layout in order to evaluate their **relationships and limiting effects** on alternative materials handling methods and equipment. Information should be gathered about such matters as the size, shape, and condition of the building and the shipping, receiving, and storage facilities; about column spacing, beam and truss capacities, floor-load capacity, stairway and elevator locations, aisle widths, ceiling heights, and the location of power and water lines and other service facilities.

Process Factors. Data should be gathered about the nature of the process or processes involved in the manufacture of the type of special-order products for which the company contracts. What are the advisable **sequences of operations?** How do they vary for different types of products manufactured by the company? Are the sequence patterns fixed and definite ones, or is it possible to change them to suit the present and anticipated plant layout? Is the **nature of the work** such that primarily heavy fixed equipment, which is not readily movable, must be used? Is a complete functionalism or departmentalization desirable because of the nature of the process? How many and what type of machines and machine departments are in existence or are being planned? The **type of manufacturing equipment** and the nature of the processes through which materials must be handled must be known in detail before the materials handling system which will be best suited for the purposes can be chosen.

Materials Factors. Data should be gathered about all the materials normally going into the products manufactured. It is necessary to know how many different materials are used; what sizes, shapes, and weights they come in; where they are kept; their **characteristics** as to flow, stability, corrosiveness, flammability, explosiveness, fragility, and other fundamental factors. What unit-size loads can the materials be divided into as raw materials and as partly or completely fabricated or assembled units? This information must be assembled when a selection is to be made of the handling equipment best suited for the materials used in manufacturing.

Materials Handling Equipment Factors. Before making a materials handling change, all the facts about existing or available materials handling equipment should be assembled and analyzed. It is necessary to know the size, capacity, speed, mobility, portability, weight, range, power, service, and **maintenance requirements** of the materials handling equipment which may be installed in the plant. It is also important to investigate the availability of spare parts, and the engineering and **service facilities** which can be provided by the equipment manufacturers. Equipment cost data must be obtained for comparison in deciding on which type of equipment will entail the least investment commensurate with the services it gives.

Some of the factors which require special emphasis for the special-order plant are the general need for a **wide range of capacity** and a high degree of portability and mobility. Many of the necessary data are available from experience and the past records of the company. A great deal of information can be supplied by materials handling equipment manufacturers through their catalogs and the data and aid given by their representatives. It is very important to assemble all the data concerning the materials handling equipment which might be used in any installation before making a handling change.

Cost Factors. In addition to the need for knowing the cost of **alternative handling equipment,** it is advisable to know how much materials handling operations cost and what portion of the manufacturing expense they comprise. Present and past records should be studied for determining handling costs and costs of delays, damage, spoilage, and other losses incurred through improper handling. It is important to know what unnecessary costs are incurred by wasted time and what delays are caused by **inadequate handling equipment.** The anticipated equipment depreciation or obsolescence rate should be calculated as well as the fuel, maintenance, interest, taxes, and insurance costs. Although certain of these costs are difficult to obtain, they will be found most useful in the proper solution of materials handling problems in special-order plants.

EVALUATING THE DATA. The evaluation of the data is the most difficult and the most important part of the materials handling problem analysis. It requires the examination and sifting of all the information collected, the elimination of unnecessary and nonpertinent information, the use of handling study aids, such as operation and flow process charts, the ability to coordinate and integrate the diverse factors involved, and the exercise of a high degree of engineering judgment.

First of all, the **over-all plan** must be kept in mind. The attainment of higher productivity, better working conditions, lower costs and prices, and higher profits is the goal toward which the materials handling project must be aimed. The needs of a given work area or given department must be kept in line with the goal of the plant as a whole. An integration of handling facilities throughout the plant is of greater importance than supplying each area with suitable equipment which may, or may not, tie in with the rest of the plant. To achieve this purpose it is necessary to formulate **management policies** regarding future plans for improvements in materials handling equipment and operations, and to design the plant layout and materials handling facilities simultaneously.

Certain **charts** have proved useful to the plant layout and materials handling engineer to help provide a perspective of the over-all manufacturing and materials handling plans and programs. These charts are (1) the assembly chart, (2) the operation process chart, and (3) the flow process chart. In addition the plant layout drawing or model helps to visualize the physical arrangement of both production and materials handling equipment.

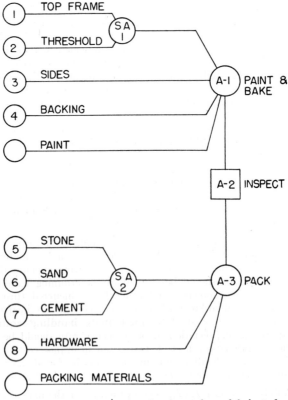

Fig. 20. Typical assembly chart (production of prefabricated shower unit).

The Assembly Chart. An assembly chart shows how the parts of a manufactured product combine or go together to make up subassemblies and completed assemblies. It shows what parts make up each subassembly and gives the order in which the parts go together. Despite its lack of many details, it gives a **rough over-all picture** of the manufacturing process. Apple (Plant Layout and Materials Handling) gives the details of the construction of the assembly chart. A typical assembly chart is shown in Fig. 20.

The Operation Process Chart. An operation process chart is an extension of the assembly chart in that it shows in **greater detail** how parts are assembled. In addition it indicates in a graphic way the operations to be performed on each part and the sequence to be followed. For very simple products the assembly chart and operation process chart may be effectively combined. The operation process chart generally does not give an indication of the relative timing of operations, nor does it indicate distances to be traveled or materials handling equipment to be used. Fig. 21 shows a typical operation process chart.

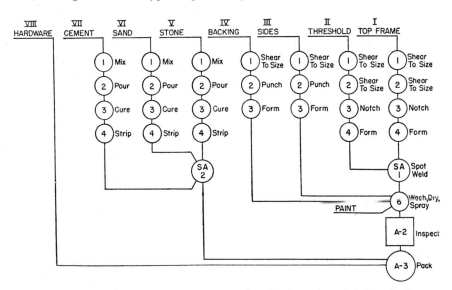

Fig. 21. Typical operation process chart (production of prefabricated shower unit).

There are **several types** of flow process charts used. A detailed description of the flow process chart is given by an ASME pamphlet (Operation and Flow Process Charts). A particular adaptation which is well suited for materials handling problems is given in Fig. 22. This chart differentiates between production operations and materials handling operations and also indicates moves, inspections, and storages. Each material or part may be traced from its receipt into the plant and through all storages, operations, and assemblies until its eventual shipment as a part of a group of finished products. This chart emphasizes materials handling equipment used and distances moved. Time can also be noted. The flow process chart enables the user to present certain information about materials handling that can be seen in no other way. It serves as a basis for comparing the handling and the manufacturing operations and leads to a knowledge of

Oper. No.	Operation Description	Manufacturing Operation	Handling Operation	Move	Inspection	Storage	Dis-tance in Feet	Handling Equipment	Remarks Time in Minutes
1	Steel for top frame and threshold received at rear door of Bldg. no. 3	○	◎	∘	□	△			
2	Unloaded onto tow motor	○	◎	∘	□	△	10	Jib crane	6.00
3	Move to storage area	○	◎	∘	□	△	40	Power lift truck	2.75
4	Temporary storage on skids	○	◎	∘	□	△			
5	Move to shears (no. 1)	○	◎	∘	□	△	30	Power lift truck	3.20
6	Fed to shears where cut to size and restacked	○	◎	∘	□	△			
7	Move to shears (no. 2)	○	◎	∘	□	△	50	Power lift truck	4.00
8	Cut to size and restacked	○	◎	∘	□	△			
9	Move to punch press	○	◎	∘	□	△	70	Power lift truck	3.50
10	Notched and restacked	○	◎	∘	□	△			
11	Move to brake (no. 3)	○	◎	∘	□	△	50	Power lift truck	3.00
12	Formed	○	◎	∘	□	△			
13	Move to spot welder	○	◎	∘	□	△	90	Power lift truck	4.20
14	Spot welded and restacked	○	◎	∘	□	△			
15	Move to finished material storage area	○	◎	∘	□	△	20	Power lift truck	1.80
16	Same operations as sides and backing—Steps 15 through 24	○	◎	∘	□	△			

Fig. 22. Portion of typical flow process chart (production of prefabricated shower unit).

materials handling operations which can be translated into costs. Such cost knowledge can be most valuable in leading to the accounting for, control of, and eventual reduction of the cost of manufacturing.

The use of the various charts and the data gathered can serve as a basis for preparing the **plant layout diagrams** showing the actual positioning of the machinery and handling equipment selected. Different layouts will be required for depicting the use of suitable alternative materials handling equipment for the purpose of choosing the plan which will best serve the needs and reduce the costs of materials handling operations.

In the special-order plant the procedure for determining proper plant layout and the integration of the right kinds of materials handling equipment into manufacturing procedures is considerably more complicated than in other kinds of plants, typically those engaged in mass production. The procedures involved are not simple matters of planning flow patterns for a single product or group of products which will be manufactured over a long period of time; rather, they are usually **major problems of planning** to produce several different products for a short period of time and still different products in the future. One common solution to this problem is to lay out the plant on a departmental basis. While it is true that this plan will result in somewhat different flow patterns for different products, with much backtracking between operations and a greater amount of materials handling, there is less need for relayout. At the same time there is much greater freedom in scheduling and balancing operations. The decision to departmentalize, however, still leaves the problem of how and where to position the departments to the best advantage in relation to one another.

The **preparation of charts** and layout diagrams for several of the most important products to be made now, and those anticipated for the future, can serve as a guide for departmental location. The simultaneous analysis of all these important products, and the superimposition of the various flow patterns, often leads to revealing similarities in the operation sequences and handling needs. This result is not surprising, since many special-order plants usually have the knowledge and equipment necessary for the manufacture of a range of products of the same general types, even though there may be considerable difference in the individual products.

The **analysis of the combined flow patterns** desired for many important products may even lead to the conclusion that certain departments should be split into two or more subgroupings and placed in a sequential arrangement which best fits the needs of most of the products, thus making possible a more efficient layout with less backtracking of work and better materials handling coordination.

A complete **work-flow analysis** should be made for a proposed special-order plant for which a new building is to be constructed or for a plant which is looking for a suitable existing building. A **modified analysis,** depending upon the extent of the problem, should be made for an already existing special-order plant faced with major or minor materials handling problems.

To make a most effective analysis of the materials handling problem, the importance of preliminary meetings and **conferences** between management, supervisors, foreman, and workers connected with the project cannot be overemphasized. The preliminary layouts and flow diagrams should be shown, and suggestions and criticisms invited. The entire problem should be restudied, and revised if necessary, in terms of these suggestions and criticisms.

SELECTING SUITABLE ALTERNATIVE MATERIALS HANDLING EQUIPMENT.
Since it frequently happens that materials handling equipment of a type different from that originally considered will prove suitable

for performing many of the necessary handling operations, it is advisable to consider the possible **advantages** of all alternative methods and select that equipment which seems to meet best the needs of the particular plant. This exploration will often require the preparation of different plant layout diagrams or models for each handling alternative. The equipment chosen should be adequate for the individual job in question, fit in with the over-all plant materials handling pattern, and also prove desirable from the standpoint of suitability, first cost, and ultimate economy.

Certain **types of materials handling equipment** appear to be generally best suited for special-order plants because of the characteristics and limitations involved in special-order manufacture. These types are, according to Wilson (The Tool Engineer, vol. 32), hand or power platform and lift trucks employing skids and pallets, fixed or traveling overhead cranes and hoists, and portable conveyors and elevators. Other materials handling equipment also, of course, can be and is profitably used in special-order plants to meet special needs.

MAKING AN ECONOMIC ANALYSIS TO DETERMINE THE BEST ALTERNATIVES. When the alternative technical solutions to the materials handling problems have been completed, an economic analysis should be made to determine which solution should be recommended to the engineers or executives who are authorized to approve or disapprove the proposals and obtain the necessary appropriations for purchasing the equipment and making the installation. The economic analysis should take into account all **cost factors** and make a comparison of alternatives on some comparable basis, such as materials handling cost per unit, per ton, or per department. This economic analysis should also list nonmonetary advantages of the different alternatives, such as greater **flexibility,** reserve **capacity** to meet possible future needs, **reliability** of the manufacturer, etc. The alternatives should then be listed in order of preference, based on these factors.

REPORTING FINDINGS TO PLANT EXECUTIVES. When all the preliminary studies are finished, the findings of the materials handling engineer or department should be prepared as a **formal report** to management. The report should be clear, concise, and accurate, for it is to serve as a basis for management's decision regarding the project.

The report should contain a **presentation of the problem** and a condensed statement of the **proposals,** together with economy-study **conclusions.** The economy study should list all costs which it is expected will be incurred and all savings which it is believed will be derived from the undertaking, together with an analysis of all related noneconomic factors. An installation schedule should also be included. The main body of the report should be short and to the point, presenting the over-all problem and the proposed solutions. All necessary explanatory data, drawings, blueprints, flow charts, specifications, etc., should be included in the appendix of the report. Layout diagrams or models should accompany the report.

FOLLOWING UP TO SECURE APPROVAL FOR MAKING THE PROPOSED CHANGES. Whether the materials handling function is in the hands of a planning group or a single individual, it is most important that the organization be set up to allow for an effective follow-up of materials handling proposals in order to see to it that, with management's approval, the plan can be installed and put into operation in accordance with an agreed-upon schedule. It is especially important to provide for **continuous planning** in special-order plants where materials handling and plant layout changes are frequently made. The materials handling department or engineer should keep equipment and **operating records** up to date. He should also be fully prepared to proceed in an organized way with the development of new plans or the setting up or installation of any approved new materials handling methods or equipment. Finally, he should make revisions of these plans, change existing layouts of manufacturing equipment and materials handling installations, and carry on **new materials handling studies** wherever the possibility exists of further reducing manufacturing costs through these improvements.

SCRAP CLASSIFICATION AND HANDLING

CONTENTS

CONTENTS (*Continued*)

SCRAP CLASSIFICATION AND HANDLING

IMPORTANCE OF SCRAP MATERIALS. In many industries a considerable amount of scrap material is produced in the course of operations. While these materials, products, and items of equipment are of no further primary value to the owner, they are often potentially usable—in their present state, or as secondary raw materials—by other industries. The value of these assets is changed in the course of manufacturing and also through use and obsolescence, likewise by the prudence, or lack of it, with which they are treated. Any and all of these assets which later on become scrap or waste through use or carelessness lose value. All values are calculated in cash units.

More than fifty years ago a leading British economist defined industrial waste material thus: "Scrap is raw material in the wrong place." That scrap is a **genuine asset** is indicated, for example, in the current use of more than 8,000,000 tons of waste paper annually as a raw material in the paper-making industry at a cost of approximately $160,000,000. Also the steel mills of the country use in excess of 50,000,000 tons of scrap iron and steel annually valued conservatively at $1,250,000,000. In other scrap-consuming fields the pattern is very much the same. The material thus used was an asset to the industries which produced it. It is the purpose here to outline **established and tested practices and procedures** for handling these materials in the most efficient and economical manner.

In both production and procurement of **new basic materials,** analysis should be applied to reduce to a minimum the amount of scrap that will be unavoidably generated. Thereafter, every possible re-use should be made of the scrap collected in the plant where it is produced. It may be possible to secure regular outlets in other industries for scrap re-use. The over-all economy of material use is thereby best served, and the owner recovers the greatest remaining value after primary use of the material. When the possibility for re-use has been thoroughly explored, the assets then automatically become commercially **salable scrap material** or useless **rubbish.** As rubbish they must be disposed of by burning, dumping, or in some other manner, subject necessarily to local ordinance limitations.

Commercially Salable Scrap. As commercially salable scrap the materials may be disposed of to industries that are highly specialized or technically diverse in scrap handling and re-use. The scrap industry itself has learned how to organize and dispose of its materials to the best advantage. As a result, that industry is now made up of groups that specialize in broad breakdowns of the over-all scrap area:

1. Iron and steel scrap.
2. Nonferrous metal scrap.
3. Waste paper.
4. Textile scrap.
5. Rag scrap.

6. Plastics scrap.
7. Rubber scrap.
8. Re-usable barrels and drums.
9. Bags and other re-usable containers.
10. Bakery refuse.

There are numerous areas of **specialization** even in these broad groups. In small operations in the scrap industry, two, three, or four of the broad groups may be interlocking, but in the larger scrap operations, the degree of specialization becomes more and more marked.

DISPOSAL OF SCRAP. The main volume of **iron and steel scrap** moves through a relatively small number of specialist companies in this field who are large processing dealers and brokers. In the **nonferrous metal field** a large percentage of the total tonnage likewise moves through a comparatively limited number of large processors to the smelters, refiners, or the mills, and foundries. Processing waste paper, rag, plastic, and rubber scrap are also large-scale operations. Iron and steel scrap dealers usually handle only iron and steel scrap; waste paper plants generally limit their activities to waste paper, and so on through the basic groupings.

Problems arise when some inexperienced individual is given the responsibility of properly assembling and handling wide varieties of scrap. Industral employees generally must rely on information not gained through first-hand experience, because they have only intermittent contact with scrap users and markets. The responsibility for scrap handling may be assigned to an industrial employee who has little time to devote to it because of his other duties, in disregard of the fact that a considerable degree of specialization is vital.

The best results can be secured if some employee—one of executive status where that is warranted—is definitely assigned the responsibility for controlling the collection of the material and directing it into re-use channels or into scrap channels. The executive chosen must be given adequate **orientation** in the work he will be expected to perform and much analysis will be necessary to provide him with a basic understanding of the materials. **Market information** from disinterested sources will be required. Unfortunately, there is little printed matter on the subject. Therefore it will be necessary basically to define here the common grades of industrial waste material or scrap and to explain the importance of **salvaging** these materials.

Using these waste materials and the information in available trade journals, a start can be made. For particular assistance in **grading** and **marketing** the most important materials, one or more of the scrap service organizations may be consulted for a thorough analysis of the operation. Such services are now being successfully furnished to many of the nation's leading industries. These organizations represent the producers exclusively, and therefore their advice and assistance is devoid of bias and self-interest. Fundamentally, the seller of any service or commodity should know as much about its actual make-up and its proper value as does the prospective purchaser.

Scrap Dealers. Some thousands of scrap dealers carry on operations scattered throughout the country and are very necessary as outlets for the materials discarded from manufacturing operations. These dealers have investments running into millions of dollars in materials handling and scrap-accumulating equipment. It is the scrap dealers' function to process and prepare scrap for the ultimate consumer where it is neither economical nor practical to do so in the particular industrial plant itself. It is not suggested here that all industries should sort the various kinds and grades of material that become commingled, nor is it recommended that any but very large industries should endeavor to prepare or process their scrap materials as incident to their production procedures.

Segregation and Disposal of Waste Materials

WASTE MATERIALS SEGREGATION. Segregation of waste materials or scrap **at the source,** however, should not be confused with the sorting or processing of mixed materials. Segregation, instead, should be properly understood as keeping the different kinds of scrap **unmixed,** because, if unnecessary mixing takes place, revenue from the scrap will be materially reduced and additional labor costs will be incurred by the purchaser before the materials can be used or sold. Mixing can be so final that no unmixing can be fully accomplished economically. For example, the mixing of bushy or tangled steel turnings and brass turnings, to a degree that they become physically intermeshed, prohibits mechanical separation by magnetic processes and also renders physical separation manually impractical and uneconomical. Likewise, the unnecessary mixing of various paper grades, particularly in shaving form, renders their later separation impractical and altogether too costly for commercial use.

In conducting a well-organized scrap disposal program, proper **supervision** is as necessary as in any other industrial function. Such supervision will necessarily include the provision of adequate equipment for the collection, sorting, and storage of the scrap prior to its sale and removal, so that its identity can be recognized and its sales value therefore increased. This supervision also presupposes the position and authority necessary to work with the plant superintendents and foreman in accomplishing maximum results without encroaching upon the primary manufacturing procedure.

Necessarily, this supervision will also include the keeping of adequate **records of scrap produced** in relation to material used, and a complete accountability for its sale after market surveys have been made, because the scrap is an asset and should be treated accordingly, with strict control. These records of progress, improvement, and revenue increases should be adequate so that the salvage department may gain the understanding and cooperation of management. Thus it can be sure that its recommendations will be carefully considered and that its budget will be adequate.

SALVAGE DEPARTMENT ORGANIZATION. The operation of the salvage department should be subject to the same regulations as are the manufacturing and service departments in the plant. Proper handling, proper supervision, and a ready understanding by the personnel involved in the activities will increase the returns from scrap. Any deficiencies therein will affect the revenues adversely.

So that the **supervisory functions** may be put into operation with the best results and a minimum of friction, they should at least initially be treated as a staff or management matter. All personnel, including those in the plant, should be acquainted with the objectives so that maximum cooperation will be forthcoming at the earliest possible date after the program is put into effect.

The scrap handling and disposal operations should be based upon a careful and thorough study of present procedures, adequate accumulation and storage space, and the equipment available for their accumulation. The types of scrap being produced should be studied carefully with special reference to the recommendations to be made in relation to the equipment for their accumulation and the space available for their storage. Ways and means for improvements in final salvage results should then be sought. **Analysis** and **research** throughout related industries usually will result in assembling valuable data gathered from the experience of other manufacturers.

Data from the **over-all study** should be detailed and made available in writing to all personnel who will be in a position to implement it and improve upon it. It should cover exhaustively all the grades and classifications of scrap resulting from manufacturing operations as well as from obsolescent equipment and tools. It should also include a study of re-usable containers of all kinds, reclaimable oils, chemicals, tools which may be unusable in their present condition but subject to repair, and other salvable items. The salvage department will then be in a position to inaugurate an objective program, one so clear-cut and profitable in its prospects that the cooperation of management at all levels may be readily obtained. Finally, the participation of all department heads, superintendents, and foreman should be invited in laying out the program.

In making this preliminary study, information regarding **new values of waste material** will be secured so that, entirely aside and beyond the benefits of good housekeeping and accident reduction, the self-sufficiency of the program and the prospect of definite profit will be shown clearly from increased income. This increase in revenue is very important as a means for demonstrating the wisdom of the investment in labor and equipment so necessary to successful salvage operations. Usually the outlay will not be large, especially in relation to the practically assured return in revenue.

The proposed program may require the **purchase of certain equipment,** such as cut-off tools for stamping operations, baling presses for waste paper, and special containers for accumulation of the various grades of materials or alloys or combinations of basic scrap materials that are produced in manufacturing processes. The benefits and added revenue that are being secured must be clearly demonstrated, otherwise the program may be shunted aside and fall short of its goal. **Service organizations** in the plant can be of great assistance in collecting, sorting, and disposing of scrap. **Trained specialists** in the various scrap fields acquire competence in plant scrap handling and equipment, and experience from actual operation in nearly all types of industry.

When the program has been set up and put in operation, the manager must be alert to keep the initial study up to the minute and applicable to any new conditions and changes in product, in in-plant handling of the waste material, need for new or additional equipment, and the possible adoption of added scrap grades or classifications.

In large manufacturing plants the initial study of scrap materials, their codification, and the methods used for their collection, sorting, and disposal, can form the basis for a good **scrap manual.** Changes in procedure will occur from time to time. All personnel concerned with scrap should be notified in writing of these changes so that they understand precisely why the changes have been made and will readily understand and follow them. If this feature of the program is not attended to promptly, the resultant failure of the personnel to adapt operations to these changes may result in errors of grading or lapses in the accumulation procedure, both of which will be reflected in reduced revenues from scrap.

One of the most important steps in the scrap reclamation program is the recovery of a considerable volume of materials and products, as well as tools, that are often needlessly scrapped. As the program develops, the **salvage manager** should take steps to reduce this kind of scrap to a minimum.

PROTECTION AGAINST CONTAMINATION. Another revenue-producing function is that of protecting segregated materials from contamination as they pass from the machine or other source to the supply dock or accumulation area. It is here that reasonably adequate and properly adapted containers and procedures will be necessary. During World War II, the War Production Board, through its industrial salvage section, carried on huge operations in the collection and reclamation of scrap materials of all kinds. The basic principles for the proper segregation and protection of usable materials against contamination may be summarized in one sentence: Provide **separate, plainly-marked containers** for each kind of scrap material right at the machine—or other source—where the scrap is generated, and remove, empty, and replace the containers as they again become full, or when the material in process is to be changed.

The manufacturing supervisors—superintendents and foreman—should be fully informed of the kinds of materials being used in manufacturing. From the salvage program they are aware of the grading, the classification, and the alloys or combination of materials being processed. The degree of their understanding, and the stated objectives of the salvage program, will contribute greatly to their familiarity with the types of materials handled and the **cleanliness** of the scrap as it leaves the plant. By thus enlisting and securing their cooperation in maintaining the segregations and keeping the scrap clean right to the salvage department, the maximum financial returns may be secured.

All **scrap materials should be segregated** up to the maximum point of practicality. This undertaking will require knowledge of the raw materials being used and will require a study to determine the volume of scrap being generated hourly, daily, weekly, or monthly, so that an economical determinaton can be made as to the degree of segregation or the number of grades that are finally to be accumulated and sold by the salvage department.

In the interest of product production, it is of utmost importance to **move the scrap out** of the manufacturing department as often as is feasible. Unless the importance of uninterrupted production is fully realized, not only in the salvage department but also by the production personnel, bad housekeeping and intermixing of scrap materials will result. The degree of cooperation received by the salvage department from manufacturing and maintenance personnel will be considerably lessened. Under the salvage program, therefore, steps should be taken to see that at no time is there any jamming or backlog in the movement of salvage material out of production departments to the area where it is accumulated and stored for final disposal.

Entirely aside from the materials which may be present in the waste from a basic point of view, the **size and type of the waste** has a definite bearing upon its salvage value. Later in this section there is provided a basic grading and classification of such waste; this listing cannot be all-inclusive, however, because of the complexity of the materials.

MOVING SCRAP INTO THE SALVAGE AREA. The moving of scrap materials out of production into the salvage area should be carefully studied because there are many ways by which this transfer can be made. The plan adopted should be one that will best adapt itself to the particular operations or manufacturing processes involved. Proper equipment, well designed containers, and adequate moving facilities should be provided, just as it is necessary to provide for the flow of raw materials into and through the manufacturing processes.

Depending upon the size of the operation and the amount of scrap generated, as well as its weight density, it may be necessary to use **lift trucks** or **motor trucks** for the removal. For certain materials **heavy handling equipment** may be necessary; **blower systems** may be used for lighter scrap materials. The provision of a well-adapted system to handle the salvaged material is important in that it will not only reduce the cost of handling but will also facilitate the movement of the materials away from manufacturing operations.

BASIC GRADE DEFINITIONS. The material covered in this presentation includes major scrap groupings with basic grade definitions in each. There are other grades of a specialty nature in each grouping. Many of these are borderline to one or more of the basic grades. These are infrequent, however, and represent only a small percentage of total scrap production.

Re-usable Equipment

BARRELS AND DRUMS. There are three main classes of barrels and drums: steel drums, wooden barrels, and fiber drums.

Steel Drums. Steel drums should be accumulated separately according to size, type, and former contents. Sizes may be grouped by trade custom into 30 to 39 gal. and 40 to 58 gal.

By far the most common drum used by industry is the 55-gal. size. The most important kinds of drums are bung-type drums, open-head drums (leverlock), and agitator drums. The importance of knowing the former content of the drums is explained below under "Reclaimable Containers." Among the general industry classifications of drums are the following types: food drums; alcohol, oil, and grease drums; chemical drums; and paint, glue, and ink drums. Besides the factors of size, type, and original content of the drums, their value is also affected by their condition. Depending on their state of repair, they are classified as No. 1 or No. 2.

Wooden Barrels. Wooden barrels in general fall into two classifications: tight cooperage hardwood barrels and slack barrels. Original content is also a factor affecting the value of wooden barrels. As in the case of steel drums, wooden barrels are likewise classified according to size and as No. 1 or No. 2, depending upon their condition.

Fiber Drums. Fiber drums must be classified into the following sizes and types:

Sizes: under 38 gal.; over 38 gal.
Types: Drums with steel top and bottom; drums with wooden top and bottom.

RECLAIMABLE CONTAINERS. Certain incidental kinds of waste materials or scrap do not come directly from the manufacturing line. Barrels and drums, both steel and fiber, and wooden barrels of both tight and slack types, are of this kind and in many cases are returnable to the supplier. Open-head drums should be returned with covers and locks undamaged. Bungs should be replaced in the bung-type containers. Such containers should be stored inside because they deteriorate rapidly if exposed to the weather. Nonreturnable containers can be sold in the re-usable container market. The usual methods of disposal are the following:

1. Return to the original supplier.
2. Adaptation for use within the owner's plant.

3. Sale to second-hand barrel and drum dealers, if the containers are not damaged beyond re-use.
4. Sale to scrap-iron dealers if damaged to a point where they can be recovered only as scrap steel.

Returnable containers sold to second-hand dealers command a higher value if the salvage department is aware of the material which they originally contained. Drums which have contained edible materials should be disposed of, through second-hand dealers, to the producers of edible products. Drums that originally contained inedible oils or chemicals should be sold to those industries where their re-use is possible.

In the various areas the salvage values vary appreciably. Certain areas are known as "feeder" areas for these kinds of waste materials, whereas the end users or the refillers are in other areas. The difference in value is the cost of transportation from the feeder area to the end-use area.

Maximum recovery of **corrugated boxes** can best be obtained by carefully opening the boxes in the receiving room so that they will not be damaged in the handling. The boxes may then be collapsed, tied in bundles, and sold as re-usable boxes at a higher level of income than can be obtained if they are damaged or sold merely as waste paper under the grading of old corrugated containers.

BAGS AND OTHER RE-USABLE CONTAINERS. Another kind of container of great importance in certain industries is that of the bag variety—**textile** or **paper**. Maximum return from the sale of these containers can be obtained only if they are properly handled. They should be opened without destroying their value as a container so that they can be sold for second and third, or more re-uses. Hooks should not be used because they destroy the bags or necessitate costly repair. Textile bags and paper bags are stitched, after they are filled by the original user, in such a manner that they can readily be opened without destroying the container as such. Manufacturing personnel should be instructed in the proper way to open these bags.

A very substantial revenue can be derived by selling containers for **re-use.** If bags are damaged by use of hooks or by slitting so as to remove the contents, they must be sold as scrap-textile or paper. The value or the revenue so derived will be materially less than if the proper value of the container had been originally understood and protected. Certain kinds of textile bags—more particularly paper bags of the multiwall variety—have one or more walls of a plastic or latex material. If properly opened, they can readily be used again as containers; if they are damaged beyond re-use, they must be destroyed. The salvage department should also be familiar with the kind of materials which the bags originally contained. If they have contained certain chemicals, they may have to be destroyed.

Re-usable Materials

OILS AND GREASES. Cutting oils and lubricating oils may be re-used several times before losing their effectiveness. Their degree of salvage value may depend upon the amount of the particular material in use at the plant. Where the volume does not warrant the purchase of handling equipment, its possible outside sale or reclamation should be explored. Cutting oils, lubricating oils, and greases should not be mixed because, if mixed, reclamation is either more expensive or altogether impossible. In plants lacking centrifuging equipment, oils and greases may be reclaimed through the use of settling tanks, filtering operations, and disinfection. Some oils, even after they have lost their usefulness in manufacturing processes, can—if properly settled and filtered—be added to the fuel tanks for re-use.

PAINTS, LACQUERS, AND SOLVENTS. Where large quantities of paints, lacquers, and solvents are used in industry, salvage possibilities are extensive and profitable. Paints and lacquers **must be recovered promptly,** because if they are allowed to harden or oxidize, their reclamation is practically impossible. The materials must be kept **free of contaminants.** To prevent their hardening or oxidization, water or some appropriate colloid should be used so that the material to be recovered can be conveyed to a collection tank where the paint or lacquer sludge will settle and be in condition for recovery procedures. Where no recovery, other than the accumulation procedure, is warranted in a plant, the material should be sold to recovery plants or dealers.

Solvents used as thinners for paints and lacquers may be salvaged in several ways, of which perhaps the most common is by distillation. Where a salvage program is warranted by the volume of the material that can be recovered, the salvage department should **keep the different types of solvents separate,** since in distillation they have different boiling points. If they are mixed together the reclamation is made difficult and in many cases impossible.

PLASTICS SCRAP. Plastics in general are divided into two basic categories —**thermoplastic** and **thermosetting.** Both are salvable for subsequent re-use, although in the case of thermosetting materials the salvage possibilities are limited. Thermoplastic material, however, is readily re-usable, and most operations engaged in molding or extrusion re-use the material that collects as waste in flashing and trims. Even after the waste from this kind of plastic is no longer usable by the possessor, it may be sold for secondary uses and should, therefore, be salvaged in uncontaminated form.

Where an industry is using already fabricated plastics material in sheets or in other forms, practically as a converter, the waste resulting therefrom should be kept separate by **grades,** to facilitate ready re-use either by the producing plant or by other secondary users. The secondary uses to which such material can be put depend upon accurate knowledge of the type of plastic involved and also upon the size and shape of the waste generated. Relatively all of the thermoplastic material thus produced can be sold and brings in considerable returns, particularly in the case of scrap that is grouped under the remnant class generated from sheets. It can be used by secondary users without regrinding or regenerating, and as a consequence a high percentage of the original cost can be reclaimed.

RUBBER SCRAP. The basic segregations of rubber scrap are **natural** rubber and **synthetic** rubber. Some of the most common synthetic rubber grades are neoprene, G. R. S. (buna), and G. R. I. (butyl). There are also **mixtures** of natural and synthetic rubber, such as natural rubber and G. R. S. (buna). Black stock should be kept segregated from colored stock. Cured rubber has a considerably lower value than uncured rubber and, therefore, these two grades should be accumulated separately.

The present stage of development in the manufacture of synthetic rubber makes rubber scrap a most complex subject. Reclamation and re-use here depends, even more than in other materials, upon clear-cut **segregations** of various grades or kinds of materials. Re-use within the producing industrial plant is limited but should be carefully explored. Thereafter, the salvage program should be concentrated upon proper segregation so that the material may be sold to reclamation dealers and other secondary users on a known chemical or consistency basis.

This material is very frequently combined with other raw materials—sometimes to a degree that subsequent separation is impractical or impossible. Nevertheless, even in this form it may be subjected to secondary re-uses if it is kept clean and uncontaminated. **Conveyor belting,** for example, can be used in making washers, gaskets, door mats, etc.

WASTE PAPER. Paper may be subdivided into two major categories— groundwood papers and groundwood free papers. The second subdivision, for all practical purposes, may be divided again into sulphite papers and sulphate or kraft papers. Waste or scrap from these materials, prior to any processing or printing, should be kept segregated because it can be resold as **direct pulp substitutes** in remaking the grade of paper involved. In this manner the maximum possible revenue will be derived.

As the material is subjected to further use or manufacture, it is combined with other materials. Its subsequent reclamation or regeneration requires processing, which naturally reduces its value and, therefore, the revenue to be derived from it. The materials most commonly added to paper are inks and adhesives. Groundwood and groundwood free papers are combined by publishers and other users of paper in large quantities. These combinations limit the re-use possibilities and consequently reduced values, for where the paper has been subjected to treatment with, or in combinations with latex, rubber, asphalt adhesive, or other plastic resins that are insoluble in water, the regeneration uses are limited or completely eliminated, and such papers must be disposed of by **burning or dumping.** In this category are wet-strength items, which can be sold only if segregated and clearly identifiable.

All other treatments result in waste paper that can be re-used or regenerated into new sheets of paper. The degree of treatment or combination of different types has resulted in well-established waste paper grades that are listed and defined later in this section. In a well-run salvage department, waste paper will be segregated to the maximum degree, thus insuring the recovery of the higher grades and a greater revenue. Where there are mixtures of different grades of waste paper, the financial loss is considerable because such mixtures must usually be sold at the value of the lowest grade of which they consist. Obviously, where manufacturing requirements demand the use of different grades or kinds of paper, mixture cannot be avoided. A further discussion of the segregation of waste paper is also presented at the end of this section.

RAGS AND TEXTILE SCRAP. The basic complexity of rags and textile scrap is gradually heightened as synthetic fiber production broadens and expands. It is therefore imperative for the salvage department and the manufacturing or production department to work in close cooperation with one another so that segregations may be made to the maximum possible degree consistent with production schedules and procedures. Much of this waste material is diverted into a multitude of **re-use fields** entirely aside from the one of regeneration into basic fiber. Among these fields are those of rug making, novelty manufacturing, wiping rags, textile paddings, wadding manufacturers, and furniture manufacturers.

It has become common practice in large industries to launder and sanitize purchased **wiping rags.** Where the quantity makes such an operation efficient and economical, the salvage department concentrates its attention on that possibility. Where the volume does not represent sufficient incentive for the plant to conduct this operation, the salvage department should analyze the economies to be effected by having soiled wiping rags sent to a laundry for washing and return for subsequent use. Industrial plant materials such as used **canvas belting, cloth gloves,** and **aprons** are also salable for financial return when they have served their usefulness in the plant and the material is in a quantity sufficient to warrant salvage.

Where the material used falls into a single category, such as cotton, wool, rayon, nylon, or other chemical or synthetic fibers, the problem is relatively simple. Where the fabric used is a combination of one or more of these basic materials, however, the necessity for segregation will be readily apparent if the material is subsequently to be sold for re-use, or regeneration, at its proper value.

Grades of Textile Cuttings. There are hundreds of grades of textile cuttings produced in textile manufacturing plants. Some of the largest-volume grades of cotton cuttings are white shirt cuttings, unbleached muslin, overall cuttings, bleached cotton cuttings, No. 1 light prints, and percales.

Some of the most frequently encountered grades of woolen clips are: Men's wear—worsteds, topcoating, overcoating, tweeds, coverts, gabardines. Women's wear—shetlands and gabardines.

Rayon, nylon, orlon, dacron, and other synthetic material cuttings should be kept strictly segregated for maximum returns on their sale.

BAKERY WASTE. Bakery operations are sources of many common kinds of scrap, such as waste paper, reclaimed oils and greases, discarded containers, iron and steel scrap, and metal scrap. There is, however, a more important item of waste in this industry; it consists of product and raw material breakage, spoilage and spillage—broadly termed bakery refuse. The fact that this material is to be of **animal edibility status** highlights the necessity for keeping it free from rubbish and all inedible materials.

The following materials are reclaimed from **bakery refuse**:

1. Dry-ground cookie meal and cracker meal.
2. Flour—unusable.
3. Sweet and iced scrap.
4. Sponge and salted crackers.
5. Raw and partially cooked scrap (cone and wafer trimming, spoiled dough).
6. Floor sweepings (flour, crumbs, etc., from clean floor free of paper, etc.).
7. Bread slicing crumbs.

The grading of bakery refuse is indicated by the grade names, as listed above.

Heavy concentrations of **salt** from conveyor belts or accumulation traps are worthless and should be disposed of with other unsalable or contaminated materials.

Iron and Steel Scrap

BASIC GRADES. Basic open-hearth and blast furnace grades are covered in the listing of the various grades of steel given below:

No. 1 Heavy Melting Steel. This grade consists of clean wrought iron or carbon steel scrap ¼-in. and over in thickness, not over 18 in. wide nor over 5 ft. long. Individual pieces must be free from attachments and cut to lie flat in the charging box. It may include new mashed pipe ends, 4 in. and over.

No. 2 Heavy Melting Steel. This is wrought iron or carbon steel scrap, black or galvanized, ⅛-in. and over in thickness, not over 18 in. wide nor over 3 ft. long. Individual pieces must be free from attachments, cut to lie flat in the charging box. It may include pipe cut 3 ft. and under but not automobile body or fender stock.

No. 1 Busheling. This is clean new wrought iron or steel scrap $\frac{1}{16}$-in. and over in thickness, not exceeding 12 in. in any dimension, including new factory busheling 20 gage or heavier (for example, sheet clippings, stampings, etc.) and steel cartridge cases 40 mm. or less. It may not contain burned material or auto body and fender stock and must be free of metal-coated, limed, or porcelain-enameled stock.

No. 1 Bundles. This grade comprises new black steel sheet scrap, clippings, or skeleton scrap, hydraulically compressed or hand-bundled to charging-box size and weighing not less than 75 lb. per cu. ft. (Hand bundles must also be tightly secured and must stand handling with a magnet.) It must be free of paint or protective coatings of any kind and may include Stanley balls, mandrel-wound bundles, or skeleton reels, tightly secured. It may include chemically detinned material, but no tin can will be deemed to be detinned unless it has undergone fully the chemical process for the removal and recovery of tin. It may not include electrical sheets or any material containing over 0.5 percent of silicon.

No. 2 Bundles. These consist of body and fender carbon steel scrap or old black and/or galvanized carbon steel scrap, hydraulically compressed to charging-box size and weighing not less than 75 lb. per cu. ft. They may not include turnings, beadwire, vitreous enameled stock, tin cans, tinplate, terneplate, or other metal-coated material. Painted or lacquered material shall not be considered as metal-coated material. It may include hydraulically compressed black or galvanized fence wire and light coil springs.

No. 3 Bundles. These are composed of off-grade material compressed to charging-box size and weighing not less than 75 lb. per cu. ft. They may include tin cans; tinned, galvanized, or vitreous enameled and other coated ferrous scrap not suitable for inclusion in No. 2 bundles. They must be free of dirt, nonferrous metals, and nonmetallics.

Incinerator Bundles. These are made up of tin-can scrap, compressed to charging-box size and weighing not less than 75 lb. per cubic ft. The scrap must have been processed through a standard-type garbage incinerator and must be free of dirt, nonferrous metals, and nonmetallics.

Machine Shop Turnings. This grade consists of clean steel or wrought iron turnings, free of cast- or malleable-iron borings, nonferrous metals in a free state, scale, or excessive oil. It may not contain badly rusted or corroded stock.

Mixed Borings and Turnings. Shoveling turnings mixed with cast- or malleable-iron borings and drillings, free of scale or excessive oil or nonferrous metals in a free state, make up this grade. It may not contain badly rusted or corroded stock.

Shoveling Turnings. This grade consists of clean short steel or wrought iron turnings, drillings, or screw cuttings, and may include any such material whether resulting from crushing, raking, or other processes. It must be free of springy, bushy, tangled or matted material, lumps, nonferrous metals in a free state, scale, grindings, or excessive oil.

No. 2 Busheling. This is made up of cut hoops, netting, cut unbaled fence wire, light sheets, rusted car sides, cotton sides, and galvanized light material. No dimension may be over 12 in. It may be black or galvanized and may include oil-field or similar cable cut to lengths of 2 ft. or less and machine gun clips. No hard steel, porcelain-enameled, or metal-coated material may be included.

Cast-Iron Borings. These are clean cast-iron or malleable-iron borings and drillings, free of steel turnings, scale, lumps, and excessive oil.

STAINLESS STEEL SCRAP. The most commonly used stainless steel alloys fall under the nickel-chrome type of the 300 Series and the straight-chrome type of the 400 Series. There is a considerable difference in value between scrap generated from the fabrication of the 300 and the 400 Series stainless steel. These materials should be kept segregated and, wherever possible, identified by the exact specification numbers. As in all nonferrous scrap grades, clippings and punchings, rod ends, castings, borings, and turnings should be accumulated separately.

ELECTRIC FURNACE AND FOUNDRY GRADES. The grades of steel scrap specified as follows are suitable for electric furnace and foundry melts:

Billet, Bloom, and Forge Crops. This grade consists of billet, bloom, axle, slab, heavy plate, and heavy forge crops, not over 0.05 percent phosphorus or sulfur and not over 0.5 percent silicon, free from alloys. It must not be less than 2 in. in thickness, not over 18 in. in width, and not over 36 in. in length; it must be new material delivered to the consumer directly from the industrial producer.

Bar Crops and Plate Scrap. This consists of bar crops, plate scrap, forgings, bits, jars, and tool joints containing not over 0.05 percent phosphorus or sulfur, not over 0.5 percent silicon, and free from alloys. It must not be less than ½ in. in thickness, not over 18 in. in width, and not over 36 in. in length.

Cast Steel. Steel castings not over 48 in. long, 18 in. wide, and ¼ in. in thickness, containing not over 0.05 percent phosphorus or sulfur and free from alloys and attachments, make up this grade, which may include heads, gates, and risers.

Punchings and Plate Scrap. This consists of punchings or stampings, plate scraps, and bar crops containing not over 0.05 percent phosphorus or sulfur, not over 0.5 percent silicon, and free from alloys. All material must be cut 12 in. and under and, with the exception of punchings or stampings, must be at least ⅛ in. in thickness. Punchings and stampings may be of any gage but must not be more than 6 in. in diam.

Electric Furnace Bundles. These are composed of new black steel sheet scrap hydraulically compressed into bundles 14 by 14 by 20 in. or smaller.

Cut Structural and Plate Scrap, 3 Ft. Maximum Length. Clean open-hearth steel plates, structural shapes, crop ends, shearings, or broken steel tires make up this grade, which must be not less than ¼ in. in thickness nor over 3 ft. in length and 18 in. in width. It must not contain over 0.05 percent phosphorus or sulfur.

Cut Structural and Plate Scrap, 2 Ft. Maximum Length. This is made up of clean open-hearth steel plates, structural shapes, crop ends, shearings, or broken steel tires. It must be not less than ¼ in. in thickness nor over 2 ft. in length and 18 in. in width and must not contain over 0.05 percent phosphorus or sulfur.

Cut Structural and Plate Scrap, 1 Ft. Maximum Length. This is composed of clean open-hearth steel plates, structural shapes, crop ends, shearings, or broken steel tires. It must be not less than ¼ in. in thickness nor over 1 ft. in length or width and must not contain over 0.05 percent phosphorus or sulfur.

Foundry Steel, 2 Ft. Maximum Length. This is steel scrap ⅛ in. and over in thickness, not over 2 ft. in length or 18 in. in width. Individual pieces must be free from attachments and may not include nonferrous metals, metal-coated material, cast or malleable iron, body and fender stock, cable, enameled or galvanized material.

Foundry Steel, 1 Ft. Maximum Length. This is steel scrap ⅛ in. and over in thickness, not over 1 ft. in length or width. Individual pieces must be free from attachments and may not include nonferrous metals, metal-coated material, cast or malleable iron, body and fender stock, cable, enameled or galvanized material.

Nonferrous Scrap

COPPER SMELTER AND REFINER SCRAP. The following listings define and present the essential features of the kinds of metals covered in this tabulation:

No. 1 Heavy Copper and No. 1 Copper Wire. These consist of unalloyed clean, unsweated copper wire, copper cables, and pieces having a copper content of not less than 98.5 percent. Such scrap must be free of wire and cable smaller than 16 B & S wire gage, ashy wire and cable, burned wire and cable which is brittle, and brazed, soldered, tinned, plated, and painted material.

No. 2 Copper Wire and Mixed Heavy Copper. This scrap consists of copper wire, cable, and pieces having a copper content of not less than 95 percent and must be free of silicon bronze, aluminum, bronze, and copper-nickel alloys.

Light Copper. This consists of miscellaneous copper having a copper content of not less than 90 percent; it must be free of radiators, gaskets, bronze and brass screens, and electrotype shells.

Copper Borings. This type of scrap consists only of unalloyed copper borings and turnings, and must be free of all other material and contamination other than free iron, oil, moisture, and nonmetallics.

Lead-covered Copper Wire and Cable. This consists of tinned and untinned copper wire and cable covered with a sheathing of lead; it may contain rubber, plastic, fabric, and paper insulation but must be free of steel-armored and other metallically armored material.

Insulated Copper Wire and Cable. This consists of tinned and untinned copper wire, cable, and pieces covered with rubber, plastic, paint, enamel, fabric, and other insulation. It must be free of steel-armored and other metallically armored material, asbestos covering, and porcelain.

Refinery Brass. This consists of any copper scrap which has a dry copper content of 50 percent or more but which fails to meet the specifications for any other grade of copper scrap set forth in this classification.

High-Grade Bronze. This must have a copper content of not less than 87 percent, a tin content of not less than 9 percent, and a lead content of not more than 1.0 percent.

Red Brass Castings. This grade consists of clean red brass castings having a copper content of not less than 82 percent and a tin content of not less than 4 percent.

Heavy Yellow Brass Castings. This grade consists of clean yellow brass solids free of silicon bronze, aluminum bronze, manganese bronze, and iron.

Red Brass Borings. This grade must have a copper content of not less than 77 percent, a tin content of not less than 3 percent, and a lead content of not more than 6 percent. It may not contain more than 0.35 percent antimony, 0.35 percent alloyed iron, or 0.35 percent aluminum, manganese, and silicon combined.

Yellow Brass Borings. This grade consists of yellow brass borings; it may not contain more than 0.25 percent antimony, 0.50 percent alloyed iron, and 0.35 percent aluminum, manganese, and silicon combined.

Mixed Brass Borings. These must have a copper content of not less than 70 percent and a tin content of not less than 2 percent. They may not contain more than 0.35 percent antimony, 0.35 percent alloyed iron, or 0.35 percent aluminum, manganese, and silicon combined.

Plated Rolled Brass Sheet, Pipe, and Reflectors. This grade consists of clean plated brass sheet, pipe, tubing, and reflectors. It must be free of Muntz metal, Admiralty tubing, soldered, tinned, corroded, and aluminum-painted material, and material with cast brass connections.

Nickel Silver Castings and Turnings. These consist of nickel silver having a minimum copper content of 55 percent and minimum nickel content of 8 percent, free of stainless steel and all foreign material.

BRASS-MILL SCRAP. Brass-mill scrap includes all grades of nonferrous scrap materials which are the waste or by-product of any fabrication of new brass-mill products. Since brass-mill scrap is new scrap generated directly from brass-mill products, the scrap grades conform to the various grades of brass-mill products. Each kind of scrap must be segregated into "punchings and clippings," "rod ends," and "turnings."

For example, yellow brass scrap should be sold as one of these three grades:

1. Yellow brass punchings and clippings.
2. Yellow brass rod ends.
3. Yellow brass rod turnings.

Some of the brass-mill grades are:

Copper	Cupro-nickel 20%
Gilding 95%	Cupro-nickel 10%
Commercial bronze 90%	Herculoy
Red brass 85%	Nickel silver:
Low brass 80%	5%
Best quality brass	8%
Yellow brass	10%
Muntz metal	12%
Naval brass	15%
Manganese bronze	18%
Hardware bronze	Phosphor bronze:
Bridgeport bronze	5%
Roman bronze	5% Gr. B.
Everdur	8%
Tobin bronze	10%
Duronze III	4%
Cupro-nickel 30%	Free cutting

ALUMINUM SCRAP. Aluminum scrap is generated in industrial plants as a result of fabrication of aluminum mill products and castings. All such scrap should be identified with the same grade designation as that under which the raw material was purchased. Scrap of each alloy must be segregated into "punchings and clippings," "castings," "rod ends," and "borings and turnings." The most frequently encountered aluminum grades are:

1100	(2S)	5052	(52S)
3003	(3S)	6053	(53S)
2011	(11S)	6061	(61S)
2017	(17S)	7072	(72S)
2024	(24S)	7075	(75S)
6151	(51S)		

ZINC SCRAP. The galvanizers generate most of the industrially produced zinc scrap in the form of "unsweated zinc dross." Fabrication of zinc sheets will result in "zinc clippings." Engravers and lithographers should sell their zinc scrap as "engravers zinc," and "lithographers zinc," since these designations are accepted zinc scrap grades. Zinc die cast scrap consists of an alloy of zinc and a small percentage of aluminum. Scrap solids and borings must be kept segregated.

LEAD SCRAP. Lead scrap materials generated in industrial operations comprise primarily the following grades:

1. Whole batteries.
2. Battery lead plates.
3. Soft lead scrap.
4. Hard lead scrap (antimonial lead).

NICKEL AND NICKEL ALLOY SCRAP. Pure nickel scrap is produced as a result of fabrication and plating operations. Nickel solids must be kept segregated from borings and turnings. There are a number of nickel alloy materials, among the most common being monel metal. There are several alloys of monel metal, and, to obtain a maximum scrap return from the sale of these high-priced materials, all grades of monel metal and other nickel alloys should be accumulated separately and sold under the same alloy designation as that under which they were purchased.

Waste Paper

NATURE OF WASTE PAPER. Large volumes of waste paper are accumulated in many industries and businesses. This type of waste includes cuttings, shavings, kraft cuttings and waste, tabulating cards, white ledger, colored ledger, kraft bags, book and magazine packings, corrugated containers, mixed papers, and many other classes. Prohibitive materials may not exceed 2 percent tare. **Prohibitive materials** include ink wads, laminated, waxed, black-brown or blueprint, cellophane, wet strength, parchment, carbon paper, dirt, trash, rubber, rags, strings, sweepings, rotted or burned stocks, or any other types or grades of stock such as may be designated by the buyer from time to time. Types or grades of paper not specifically designated in a grade definition are termed **outthrows.** Waste paper scrap is classified and described as follows:

Superhard White Envelope Cuttings. These consist of baled cuttings or sheets of untreated white envelope papers of reasonably uniform brightness free of printing, groundwood, and soft stock. Outthrows may not exceed 0.5 percent; no prohibitive materials permitted.

Hard White Envelope Cuttings. These consist of baled envelope cuttings or sheets of untreated hard white papers free of printing, groundwood, and soft stocks. Outthrows may not exceed 0.5 percent; no prohibitive materials permitted.

Hard White Shavings. These consist of baled shavings or sheets of all untreated white bond ledger or writing papers and must be free from printing and groundwood. Outthrows may not exceed 0.5 percent; no prohibitive materials permitted.

Supersoft White Shavings. These consist of baled shavings and sheets of all-white sulfite printing papers of reasonably uniform brightness free of printing and may contain not more than 5 percent of coated and filled papers. This grade may also include sulfite papers containing a small percentage of groundwood. Outthrows may not exceed 0.5 percent; no prohibitive materials permitted.

No. 1 Soft White Shavings. These consist of baled shavings and sheets of all-white sulfite printing papers, free from printing and may include sulfite papers containing a small percentage of groundwood. Outthrows may not exceed 1.0 percent; no prohibitive materials permitted.

Tinted Shavings. This grade consists of baled shavings and sheets of all-white sulfite papers. It may contain not over 10 percent light colored tint printing but may include sulfite papers containing a small percentage of groundwood. Outthrows may not exceed 1.0 percent; no prohibitive materials permitted.

Superresorted Brown Kraft. This consists of baled, clean, repacked brown kraft papers entirely free of tar, twisted or woven stock, sewed edges, heavy printing, gum, sealing wax, asphalt, latex, colors, bleached or semibleached stocks, oils, waxes, and original contents. Bales must be 60 in. or more in length. Outthrows may not exceed 2 percent; no prohibitive materials permitted.

New Brown Kraft Cuttings. These consist of baled new unprinted brown kraft cuttings or sheets entirely free of tar, twisted or woven stock, gum, sealing wax, asphalt, latex, colors, bleached or semibleached stocks, oils, and waxes. Outthrows may not exceed 1.0 percent; no prohibitive materials permitted.

New Brown Kraft Bag Waste. This consists of new brown kraft cuttings and sheets, including misprint bags. Stitched or sewed papers are not acceptable in this grade. Outthrows may not exceed 1.0 percent; no prohibitive materials permitted.

New Brown Kraft Envelope Cuttings. These consist of baled, new unprinted brown kraft envelope cuttings or sheets entirely free of tar, twisted or woven stock, gum, sealing wax, asphalt, latex, colors, bleached or semibleached stocks, oils, and waxes. Outthrows may not exceed 1.0 percent; no prohibitive materials permitted.

Supermanila Cuttings. These consist of baled cuttings and sheets of untreated manila-colored sulfite or sulfate papers, free of printing. Outthrows may not exceed 0.5 percent; no prohibitive materials permitted.

Manila Tabulating Cards. These consist of printed manila-colored cards, predominantly sulfite or sulfate, which have been manufactured for use in tabulating machines. This grade may contain manila-colored tabulating cards with tinted margins but may not contain beater or calendar-dyed cards in excess of 0.05 percent. This grade may be shipped in securely wrapped bales, in bags, or in cardboard boxes. Outthrows may not exceed 1.0 percent; no prohibitive materials permitted.

White Ledger. This grade consists of all-white sheets and shavings of untreated ledger, bond, writing papers, and other hard papers which have similar fiber content which are free of solid color printing. It may contain sulfite papers containing a trace of groundwood and must be packed in machine-compressed bales, securely wired, weighing not less than 800 lb. Outthrows may not exceed 2 percent; no prohibitive materials permitted.

New Colored Envelope Cuttings. These consist of baled, untreated colored envelope cuttings, shavings, or sheets of colored papers, predominantly sulfite or sulfate, free of all printing. Outthrows may not exceed 2 percent; no prohibitive materials permitted.

No. 1 Colored Ledger. This consists of white and colored sheets and shavings of untreated ledger, bond, writing papers, and other hard papers which have a similar fiber content. This grade may include bleached sulfite or sulfate papers containing a trace of groundwood and must be packed in machine-compressed bales, securely wired, weighing not less than 800 lb. Outthrows may not exceed 2 percent; no prohibitive materials permitted.

Colored Tabulating Cards. These consist of printed colored or manila cards, predominantly sulfite or sulfate, which have been manufactured for use in tabulating machines. This grade may be shipped in securely wrapped bales, in bags, or cardboard boxes. Outthrows may not exceed 1.0 percent; no prohibitive materials permitted.

New 100 Percent Brown Kraft Corrugated Cuttings. These consist of baled corrugated cuttings having all liners and corrugated medium of 100 percent brown kraft fiber, free from solid color printing. Butt rolls are not acceptable in this grade. Outthrows may not exceed 1.0 percent; no prohibitive materials permitted.

New Double Kraft-lined Corrugated Cuttings. These consist of baled corrugated cuttings having all liners of brown kraft, free of solid colored printing. Single-faced cuttings and butt rolls are not acceptable in this grade. Outthrows may not exceed 2 percent; no prohibitive materials permitted.

Used Brown Kraft Sugar and Flour Bags. These consist of baled, untreated brown kraft sugar and flour bags. Outthrows may not exceed 0.5 percent; no prohibitive materials permitted.

Used Kraft Bags. These consist of baled, used kraft bags free of twisted or woven stock and other similar objectionable materials. Outthrows, including a maximum of 2 percent of prohibitive materials, may not exceed 5 percent.

No. 1 Brown Kraft Paper. This consists of baled, used brown kraft papers, excluding twisted or woven stock. Outthrows, including a maximum of 2 percent of prohibitive materials, may not exceed 5 percent.

No. 1 Flyleaf Shavings. These consist of baled trim of magazines, catalogs, and similar printed matter. This grade may contain the bleed of cover and insert stock to a maximum of 10 percent of dark colors and must be made from predominantly bleached chemical fiber. Beater-dyed papers may not exceed 2 percent; shavings of novel news or newsprint grades may not be included in this packing. Outthrows may not exceed 1.0 percent; no prohibitive materials permitted.

New Manila Envelope Cuttings. These consist of baled envelope cuttings, shavings, or sheets of manila-colored papers, predominantly sulfite or sulfate, free of all printing. Outthrows may not exceed 2 percent; no prohibitive materials permitted.

No. 1 Manila Papers. These consist of baled manila-colored papers, predominantly sulfite or sulfate, which may contain only light print. Outthrows may not exceed 5 percent; no prohibitive materials permitted.

No. 2 Manila Papers. These consist of manila-colored papers which may contain printing other than solid colors. Outthrows, including a maximum of 1 percent of prohibitive materials, may not exceed 5 percent.

No. 1 Repacked Heavy Books and Magazines. These consist of dry, clean, used, and overissue books and magazines, stitchless stock, quire waste, and similar printed matter, and may contain such bleached sulfite and sulfate books and magazines adulterated with fine groundwood as are acceptable to the consumer. This grade should be packed in machine-compressed bales, securely wired, weighing not less than 1,000 lb., or in air-compressed bales weighing about 150 lb. Outthrows—including coarse groundwood papers, newsprint magazines, so-called pulpwood magazines, novel news, all other papers containing coarse or shivey groundwood, hard backs, unbleached kraft covers, gilt, aluminum, varnished or heavily inked poster paper, lithograph rotogravure, labels, deep-colored printing, wet and dirty paper—may not exceed 2 percent.

Mixed Books and Magazines. These consist of clean dry books and/or magazines and similar printed matter in bales, bags, boxes, or bundles. Books and magazines not acceptable in the No. 1 grade may be included.

Repacked Heavy Books and Magazines. These may not exceed 20 percent of the total weight of the shipment. Outthrows, including maximum of 2 percent of prohibitive materials, may not exceed 5 percent.

One-Run White Newsblanks. This grade consists of baled, unprinted cuttings or sheets of white newsprint of uniform brightness and quality. Outthrows may not exceed 0.5 percent; no prohibitive materials permitted.

White Newsblanks. This grade consists of baled, unprinted cuttings and sheets of white newsprint paper or other papers of white newsprint quality. Outthrows may not exceed 1.0 percent; no prohibitive materials permitted.

Publication Blanks. These consist of baled, unprinted cuttings or sheets of white coated or filled white groundwood content paper. Outthrows may not exceed 1.0 percent; no prohibitive materials permitted.

No. 1 Groundwood Shavings. These consist of baled trim of magazines, catalogs, and similar printed matter free of beater-dyed papers and may contain not over 5 percent of solid colored printing. Outthrows may not exceed 1.0 percent; no prohibitive materials permitted.

Mixed Shavings. These consist of baled trim of magazines, catalogs, and similar printed matter, not limited with respect to groundwood or coated stock, and may contain the bleed of cover and insert stock as well as beater-dyed papers and solid colored printing. Outthrows may not exceed 2 percent; no prohibitive materials permitted.

New Corrugated Cuttings. These consist of baled corrugated cuttings having two or more liners of either jute or kraft. Butt rolls are not acceptable in this grade. Outthrows, including a maximum of 1.0 percent of prohibitive materials, may not exceed 5 percent.

Corrugated Containers. This grade consists of corrugated containers having liners of either jute or kraft, packed in bales of not less than 54 in. in length.

Outthrows, including a maximum of 1.0 percent of prohibitive materials, may not exceed 5 percent.

Solid Fiber Containers. This grade consists of solid fiber containers having liners of either jute or kraft, packed in bales. Outthrows, including a maximum of 2 percent of prohibitive materials, may not exceed 5 percent.

Overissue News. This grade consists of unused overrun regular newspapers printed on newsprint, baled or securely tied in bundles, and should contain not more than the normal percentage of rotogravure and colored sections. No outthrows permitted; no prohibitive materials permitted.

Supernews. This grade consists of repacked fresh newspapers, not sunburned, packed in bales of not less than 60 in. in length, free of papers other than news, and containing not more than the normal percentage of rotogravure and colored sections. Outthrows may not exceed 2 percent; no prohibitive materials permitted.

No. 1 News. This consists of newspapers packed in bales of not less than 54 in. in length, containing less than 5 percent of other papers. Outthrows, including a maximum of 0.5 percent of prohibitive materials, may not exceed 2 percent.

Boxboard Cuttings. These consist of baled new cuttings of paperboard such as are used in the manufacture of folding paper cartons, setup boxes, and similar boxboard products. Outthrows, including a maximum of 0.5 percent of prohibitive materials, may not exceed 2 percent.

Mill Wrappers. These consist of baled wrappers manufactured from sulfite screenings, kraft screenings, groundwood fiber or chemical woodpulp fiber and used as outside wrappers for rolls, bundles, or skids of finished paper. Outthrows, including a maximum of 0.5 percent of prohibitive materials, may not exceed 3 percent.

Supermixed Paper. This consists of a cleaned repacked mixture of various qualities of papers, packed in machine-compressed bales not less than 60 in. in length and containing less than 10 percent of soft stocks such as newspapers. Outthrows, including a maximum of 0.5 percent of prohibitive materials, may not exceed 3 percent.

No. 1 Mixed Paper. This consists of a mixture of various qualities of paper, packed in bales weighing not less than 500 lb., and containing less than 25 percent of soft stocks such as news. Outthrows, including a maximum of 1.0 percent of prohibitive materials, may not exceed 5 percent.

No. 2 Mixed Papers. This grade consists of a mixture of various qualities of paper not limited as to type of packing or soft-stock content. Outthrows, including a maximum of 2 percent of prohibitive materials, may not exceed 10 percent.

WASTE PAPER SEGREGATION AND BALING. Where the bale size is included in the grade definition, the reference is to the finished packaging for waste-paper mill delivery. Paper which otherwise meets the remainder of the definition should be so classified and sold.

Materials Handling Equipment

Barrels. A number of drums can be moved at one time by placing them on pallets for movement by lift trucks.

Bags. Transportable bins can be used to advantage in the stacking of bags. Vacuum cleaners should be utilized where volume and other factors make it economical.

Cutting Oils, Paints, Lacquers, and Solvents. These materials should be stored in 55-gal. steel drums.

Plastics Scrap. Plastics scrap is usually accumulated in drums. Sheet scrap may be compressed in bales for more economical handling and shipping. The size of the baler will depend on scrap production and plant layout.

Rubber Scrap. Drums or burlap bags may be used as containers.

Waste Paper, Rags, and Textile Scrap. In-plant collection is usually handled best by wooden crates with or without casters or by burlap bags suspended from a stand or rack. Where quantities warrant it, the material should be baled. There are a number of sizes and types of balers. This equipment involves considerable investment and industrial plants should be careful to choose the proper baler, with the assistance of a specialist in that field.

Ferrous and Nonferrous Metal Scrap. In-plant handling can be facilitated and mechanized by many types of materials handling equipment, including chain and belt conveyors, transportable tote boxes, Roura hoppers, Dempster-Dumpsters, etc. Preparation equipment such as balers or shears should be installed only if large tonnages are generated. There are many types and sizes of this equipment and a considerable investment is usually involved. Specialists should be consulted. If ferrous scrap is shipped in carload quantities, cranes with magnet attachments should be used in most instances.

Scrap Handling Systems

INTEGRATED SYSTEM. The following description of a chip handling system illustrates an integrated system making principal use of pneumatic pipeline conveyors and also employing many other types of materials handling equipment. To achieve the full utilization of a complete chip handling installation, it may be necessary to crush the turnings to provide a product of a size that can be conveniently handled. It may also be necessary to remove the oil from the turnings and chips, and for this purpose centrifugal oil-extraction equipment of the batch or continuous type may be used. Because of their long, stringy nature, raw turnings cannot be conveyed pneumatically, and may require handling in mechanical conveyors to carry them to crushing equipment. To dispose of chips after they have been completely processed, it may be necessary to store them in bins and accumulate railroad-car lots prior to shipment.

STEPS IN CHIP HANDLING. In general, there are five steps or stages in most chip handling installations:

1. Removal of turnings from the machine tools.
2. Transportation of the turnings collected from the tools to a central area.
3. Processing the turnings.
4. Ultimate disposal of the turnings.
5. Oil reclamation.

These stages may be explained as follows:

Removal of Turnings from Machine Tools. In general, machine tools are equipped with a storage bed in the base of the machine, where the chips drop as they are cut from the work, and the cutting fluids are usually held in the same area. In most machine tools the removal from this area is manual, and the chips are raked up a trough from the machine base into some form of container. In many automatic machine tools, self-contained mechanical chip-removal conveyors are built into the tool for the continuous discharge of chips into containers. Certain special-purpose machine tools produce sufficient chips to warrant special handling from single machines. In one such case an installation was applied to a wire-shaving tool in which a mechanical apron-type conveyor collected the turnings at the chip discharge of the machine tool, delivered them to a crusher, and after size reduction, dropped them by gravity into a pneumatic system for transportation to a storage bin. While this method is not a standard procedure, it does indicate that as the special-purpose requirements for machines of this type expand, chip handling becomes a major consideration, and mechanized handling is mandatory for the efficient functioning of the machine tool.

In grinding operations low-pressure exhaust systems are often used to collect the grinding dust, and while these units are in widespread use, they fall more into the category of dust-control and ventilating systems and as such are not usually considered with pneumatic handling of metal chips. In recent years there has been a trend toward eliminating manual raking of turnings from the machine-tool bases, and now lines of automatic screw machines have been set up over a common trench, holes cut in the bases of the machines, and chips and cutting fluids dropped directly from the machine tools for either mechanical-conveyor removal or sluice removal to a central area. It is expected that this kind of handling will be expanded in the future. When this system is specified the cutting fluids are handled in a central system and returned to the machines through a common piping network.

Transportation to a Central Area. The usual method of handling turnings from machine tools is by means of **power-operated trucks** which transport **tote boxes** or **hopper trucks** loaded with turnings to the central chip-processing area. **Overhead trolley conveyors** have been installed from time to time for this purpose but are not in wide use. **Apron conveyors** are being applied more and more to this service. The lines of machine tools are set up with their chip discharges on a common line for delivery to a single apron conveyor which can conveniently service a large number of machine tools. Drag scraper conveyors are used to some extent in handling turnings from machine tools, and while bushy turnings will occasionally cause problems, there is an advantage in carrying turnings and cutting fluids in a single oil-tight casing.

The above methods, of course, do not employ pneumatic conveying, since the turnings are usually too long and stringy to be handled pneumatically. However, cast-iron borings are being handled pneumatically from machine tools to central processing areas. Vacuum-type **pneumatic conveyor systems** are used for this purpose, with a common duct constructed through the plant area. Branch lines from individual feed stations, strategically located in areas of high borings production, convey the chips and borings to the central processing area.

Operators deliver chips to these feed stations by **wheeled trucks** or other convenient means, which include a floor hopper of sufficient capacity to store at least an hour's run of the borings production in the particular area. Each of these feed stations is cycled, with one at a time delivering its load to the vacuum-type conveyor duct controlled by a master timer. Automatically operated valves and electrical interlocks, along with the timer system, conduct the operations in sequence.

The borings are delivered to the intercepting equipment described above, and they are usually discharged from there by gravity to storage bins for collection of railroad-car lots. In some cases these storage bins are mounted over briquetting presses, and the cast-iron borings are fed directly to machines for briquetting for foundry use.

Processing the Turnings. There are eight procedures in the processing of chips and turnings. They are:

1. **Crushing the turnings.** The standard metal-turnings crusher is of the rolling-ring type with toothed rings which size the chips by passing them through slotted grate bars of cast-manganese steel. The sizes of these slots and the tooth form of the rolling ring, control the size of the chip product. For efficient conveying and bin storage, all the resultant product should pass through a screen with openings 1-in. square or less. These crushers are usually manually fed, but for efficient feed, apron conveyors of the piano-hinged type, which discharge into specially designed crusher inlet hoppers, may be used.

Crushers should be equipped with some means for separating or trapping work, tramp metal, bar ends, etc. The rejects from the crushing operation should be kept separate and should be handled in individual containers. After the chips are crushed, they are dropped by gravity into a collecting hopper, from which they are fed to the pneumatic conveying system.

Chips fed to the crusher are usually covered with oil, since the oil-extraction operation invariably occurs after crushing. The pneumatic conveyor moving material from a crusher is therefore usually designed to handle a considerable amount of oil which finds its way through the crusher with the chips. While a well-designed system will handle this oil with ease, all joints and flanged connections in the pneumatic system should be adequately gasketed to prevent leakage of the oil.

2. **Drying the chips—oil extraction.** After they are crushed, the chips are normally blown to what is termed an "oily-chip hopper" for storage prior to oil extraction. This hopper should be designed with sufficient capacity to suit the needs of the extracting system, whether it is of the batch or the continuous type, as described below. The oily-chip hopper should be vented, and the vent area should reduce the velocity of the exhaust to a point where chips cannot be carried out with the exhaust air. Where the conveying air must be exhausted inside the building, oil-mist collectors of the mechanical or electrical type should be installed to eliminate the emission of oil vapor from the hopper.

3. **Batch-type extraction.** In handling to batch-type extractors it is standard practice to elevate the oily-chip hopper and provide a swivel-type spout at the discharge end to load the extractor basket in place in the machine. The basket is removed by means of a monorail hoist. After the extractor basket is filled from the oily-chip hopper, the swivel spout is swung clear of the unit, and the cover is then locked. The extractor is started and whirls the oil from the chips at high spinning speeds. Most extractors have wringing periods from 4 to 6 min. to remove the oil effectively from the chips. After the extraction operation is completed, the cover is opened, and the basket is removed and dumped into a separate hopper. This hopper is connected to the pneumatic chip-conveyor system, and the chips are blown to ultimate disposal.

4. **Continuous-extracting equipment.** In the system using continuous-extracting equipment, manual removal of the basket is not required, since the

basket is of the bottom-discharge type. Although the operation is carried on in batches, it is still essentially continuous. Material stored in the oily-chip hopper is withdrawn by means of a screw feeder and delivered to the continuous-extractor basket, which is rotated at low speed for loading. The chips fall onto distributor plates and are thrown off by centrifugal force to the sides of the rotating basket, where they are held by centrifugal force. By the centrifugal action the oil is removed through special perforations and slots in the basket.

After the extraction period is completed, the basket again slows down and is braked to a stop; during this period, the chips—no longer held by centrifugal force—fall by gravity into a collecting hopper below. This collecting hopper is connected to the feed equipment of the pneumatic system for delivery to ultimate disposal.

5. Dryers. In remelting aluminum, brass, and other metals, it is necessary to remove all the cutting fluids which adhere to the chips before they are fed to the electric furnace. The oils have a detrimental effect on the metallurgical consistency of the melt and also cause a bad fume condition, because of gases emitted from the furnace stack. Therefore, in this type of plant, rotary drying equipment is widely used. In some cases where a plant has its own foundry, rotary drying equipment is used to prevent the fume condition described above in the melting operation.

Some means of elevating the material must be used to feed the dryer. Pneumatic conveying is widely used for this purpose, and in many cases chips are blown directly from the crusher discharge to a cyclone-type storage hopper over the dryer inlet for feed by gravity to the dryer.

After drying, the chips have a temperature ranging from 300° to 600° F. At this point, the most practical method for handling is pneumatic conveying, since the heat has no detrimental effect on the conveyor duct. Ejector-type feed nozzles are effectively applied in these systems and eliminate the need for flexible-tipped rotary air locks, which may be damaged by the high temperatures.

In most smelters numerous alloys are handled through a common system. Diverting selector valves are widely used, and chips are delivered from the dryer discharge to multiple storage bins, segregated by alloy, for future remelting in electric furnaces.

6. Washing the chips. When chips are to be briquetted or remelted or both, it is feasible to wash the chips in a solvent in order to flush off the oils or coolants used in cutting the chips. After the washing operation, dewatering-type conveyors are used to direct the chips to pneumatic conveying equipment for blowing to storage bins or ultimate disposal.

7. Briquetting. Briquetting is employed primarily by smelters or by plants with their own foundries. Chips and borings are hydraulically compressed into cylinders of 2-in. to 5-in. diameters and approximately 2- to 6-in. lengths. These cylinders are very dense. In the case of cast iron the density is 87 percent of a solid cast-iron piece of the same size. This density provides an excellent product for remelting, since the dense material will not oxidize rapidly and does not require so long a charging time as do the low-density bulk chips or borings. Briquetting installations are in use mainly in plants with their own foundries or in smelters where the resultant economies can justify the cost of the equipment. Plants that sell their chips to scrap dealers can seldom achieve savings enough in the advanced price of briquettes over that of the chips to warrant the installation of such equipment.

8. **Miscellaneous processing.** Chips of aluminum and brass, having a greater pound value than iron, must be separated from the iron to insure that the price paid is solely for the product desired. Magnetic separators of the drum type, or a magnetic head pulley on a belt feeder, are used for this purpose.

Chips are also screened, particularly in aluminum smelters, where considerable dirt and dust is present in the chips. The screening operation is justified in that the waste material that has been screened out is not paid for and represents in some cases a reasonable percentage of the total load. In some cases, dewatering-type screening has been utilized to effect the removal of water-soluble oils from crushed chips. This system has been found to be fairly efficient in small-quantity operations where it is desired to remove only the most objectionable part of the cutting fluid.

Ultimate Disposal of Turnings. Plants with large chip production find it most feasible to load chips directly into **gondola cars** instead of putting them into bin storage. If a railroad gondola car can be filled in two days, it is usually stated that a storage bin is not required, since demurrage is not charged on the car. The **pneumatic conveying system** lends itself most suitably to loading gondola cars. A common conveyor duct with selector valved branches can be run along a railroad spur to load one or more cars laid up on the track. The conveyor branches are swiveled and supported by means of **overhead jib cranes** independently mounted and can swivel over a large radius, filling one-third of the area of a normal gondola car from each jib crane. Thus, three jib cranes will completely fill a car without spotting, and by locating successive cranes along the tracks, additional cars may be so loaded without the necessity of respotting them.

For smaller tonnages, for emergency use, or for holding chips while cars are being spotted, **overhead storage bins** are in wide use. Fig. 1 shows such a bin. The design of a bin for holding metal chips is of great importance. Sufficient slope must be allowed for the discharge of the chips, and discharge-gate areas must be kept large to insure that the material will discharge and not bridge or hang up in the bin. Gates must be designed to close quickly against the flow of chips and should be controlled from a platform so that the inside of the railroad car or truck is visible to the operator. Even with well-designed oil-reclamation equipment, some oil still adheres to the chips and is drained to the discharge gate. Therefore, all joints should be continuously field welded, and all connections should be provided with gaskets. Oil troughs should be supplied to collect the drippage and deliver it to the oil reclamation system or to sewers for disposal. Soluble oils will freeze, and steam jackets must be provided for efficient operation in cold weather.

In designing a bin it is important that the total material carried in a single compartment should not be allowed to exceed 60 to 70 tons, since the resultant pressure on the lower portion of the bin from the burden above can cause packing and serious difficulties in unloading.

In delivering materials to storage bins pneumatically, a target plate and brackets should be applied to the discharge of the pneumatic-conveyor duct discharge to preclude high-velocity discharge against the storage-bin wall. Good practice provides for bin design with a trussed main support having bin plates welded inside the truss, the truss strength being calculated to carry the entire load of the bin.

Storage bins for use with pneumatic conveyors should be adequately vented, and to prevent the ejection of chips with the exhaust air, the discharge velocity through the vent should not be greater than 200 to 300 ft. per min. The jib-crane

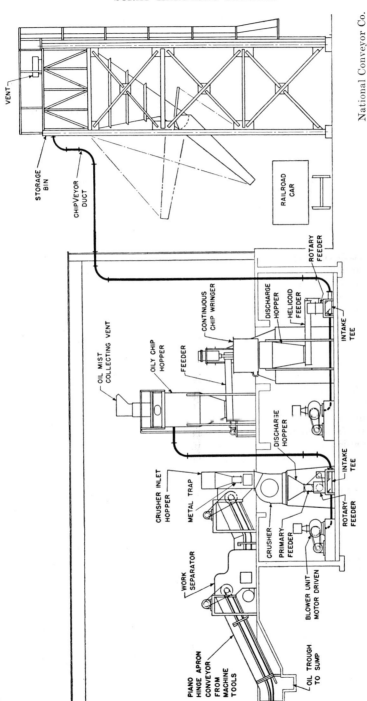

National Conveyor Co.

Fig. 1. Pressure pneumatic pipeline system with overhead storage bins.

discharge and the storage bin described above can, of course, also be applied to loading motor trucks or any other kinds of vehicles.

It is standard practice to handle aluminum, copper, and copper-alloy chips in closed, locked boxcars. Aluminum in the form of fine chips oxidizes and its value is thereby reduced. Copper and brass chips have high resale values and should be shipped in locked boxcars to afford protection against pilferage. These kinds of materials are usually stored in bins and are shipped out in carload lots. Some kind of mechanical feeding equipment is provided at the discharge end of the storage bin to deliver the material to a pneumatic conveyor system. The pneumatic conveyor system lends itself ideally to loading boxcars with such materials. In the case of aluminum, it has heretofore been very difficult to load a car completely and thus obtain minimum carload rates. Now, however, pneumatic loading can accomplish the task readily, since the chips can be blown practically to the roof of the car.

Oil Reclamation. Chip handling systems usually include oil-recovery equipment. This equipment will sterilize oil, clean it, and separate it from water and water-soluble cutting compounds, and return the oil to storage tanks for re-use.

CAPACITIES OF SYSTEMS. In general, the capacities of a normal pneumatic chip handling system range from less than 1 ton per hr. to approximately 15 tons per hr. Plants seldom require a capacity greater than this, and in cases where greater tonnage is handled, the handling should be separated into two systems—particularly the crushing equipment—to be sure that maintenance work can be done on one system while some operations are maintained through the second unit. Pneumatic chip conveyor ducts range from 4 to 10 in. in diameter, determined by the tonnage handled, the product, and the weight per cubic foot of the product.

Materials to be handled vary greatly in density. Crushed aluminum chips may weigh as little as 15 lb. per cu. ft., averaging between 20 and 40 lb. per cu. ft. Crushed steel chips may weigh from 70 to 135 lb. per cu. ft., based on the degree of crushing, the machining operations, and the alloy from which the chip was produced. Cast-iron borings seldom weigh less than 110 to 120 lb. per cu. ft. and may weigh as much as 175 lb. per cu. ft.

The normal velocity of air through conveying ducts ranges from 4,000 ft. to 10,000 ft. per min., depending on the material handled and its density.

SELECTING THE EQUIPMENT. The wide variations in the characteristics of materials which are handled by pneumatic means make it mandatory that the designer of equipment for conveying and handling this material have a thorough knowledge of chip handling. For example, a bin designed for steel chips weighing 80 lb. per cu. ft. would be structurally inadequate for handling cast-iron borings which weigh 175 lb. per cu. ft. The bin designed to contain cast iron of a high unit weight would be uneconomical if loaded with steel chips with a much lower unit weight.

Many machining operations produce turnings that are rather fine and to the untrained eye would seem completely suitable for conveying and storage in bins. However, a turning exceeding 1 in. in length should be looked on with suspicion when considering pneumatic handling and, in particular, bin storage.

In planning a chip handling installation all factors of the operation should be considered, based on the five important steps in chip handling previously outlined; and it is advisable to put the entire job into the hands of a reputable manufacturer who will be responsible for choosing the proper equipment for each individual job. It would be extremely imprudent, of course, to consider the use of a pneumatic conveyor installation for delivering long, stringy steel turnings from machine tools. It would be just as unwise to consider mechanical conveying equipment where chips are to be delivered from one point to another several hundred feet away.

One general rule that it is well to follow is to use mechanical conveying means exclusively for uncrushed, bulky turnings and use pneumatic chip handling systems for handling the product once it is crushed or is in a state fine enough for handling in the pneumatic type of conveyor.

The pneumatic conveyor, with its inherent flexibility, lends itself to installation in existing plants that were constructed without thought to future conveying problems.

In the construction of new plants, certain aesthetic features should be considered. Storage bins for metal chips can be designed to conform to the general plant construction. Their over-all height can be kept low, because the pneumatic conveyor can fill a bin level, and there is not the waste area at the top of the bin which occurs in loading by bucket elevators or other conventional means. A simple pipeline delivers material to the storage bin.

The wearing parts of a pneumatic conveying system are confined to the duct itself and to the feed equipment. When wear occurs, the replacement of an individual part is a minor operation, can be accomplished in a short time, and is low in cost. Where mechanical conveyors and bucket elevators are used, fine chips find a way of working into all of the pins in the chain links and into all wearing parts of the system. The numerous moving parts in this type of equipment are attacked by these fine particles, which ultimately break them down. Maintenance and replacement are extremely difficult, and often the entire length of chain must be replaced. The chain represents a considerable portion of the initial investment in the unit. In the pneumatic system the costliest item is usually the air-production unit, and since it is completely out of the dust-laden area of the air stream, service from this type of equipment is practically unlimited, with minor repairs required only at infrequent intervals.

ADVANTAGES FROM CHIP HANDLING EQUIPMENT. The benefits of the over-all chip handling installation must necessarily include those from all of the processing and allied equipment usually installed with pneumatic chip handling systems, and these may be listed as follows:

1. **Good housekeeping.** The installation of chip handling, crushing, and oil collecting facilities greatly promote good housekeeping in industrial plants. Spilled and dripped oil is eliminated. Chips can be stored in bins or delivered direct to railroad cars without the necessity of trucking oily, uncrushed turnings throughout the plant. Where street or highway trucking of unprocessed turnings occurs, the dripping of oil from the truck bodies through city streets is a source of constant friction between the plant management and the municipal authorities. By concentrating chip handling and processing equipment in a central area within the plant, all the oil dripping from turnings being handled from tote boxes to chip decks can be caught in specially designed pans which collect the oil and drain it away to sumps for ultimate collection and purification.

2. **Increased scrap value.** Crushed, de-oiled chips bring a premium price from scrap buyers and often can increase by approximately $4 the per ton price obtained from the sale of the chips.

3. **Oil reclamation.** The oil which is a source of annoyance to the scrap buyer has great re-use value, and from 40 to 60 gal. of oil per ton of chips can be reclaimed. In many plants the cost of this oil ranges from 30 to 50 cents per gal., and approximately 95 percent of the oil contained in the chips can be reclaimed by conventional chip wringing methods.

4. **Full-car loading.** Crushed chips can be loaded in railroad cars to the full load limit of the car, which is practically impossible with uncrushed turnings. Thus, in shipping these chips to the scrap buyer by railroad, the shipper gains the minimum carload rate and the maximum carload tonnage. Bin storage of chips for railroad-car disposal allows the manufacturer to ship the chips in large quantities to the best market. When the oil is removed from the turnings, the shipper, of course, does not pay for the transportation of this oil, which has no value to the scrap buyer and can often result in a penalty to the shipper.

5. **Labor savings.** The use of automatic, mechanized conveyor installations greatly reduces the manual labor required for handling chips and in some cases can bring premiums to the plant operation amounting to approximately $5 per ton of chips handled. The use of mechanical equipment such as the continuous oil extractor increases this figure still further, because once the chips are delivered to the crusher, they are automatically handled from this point to ultimate disposal without further manual operation.

6. **Segregation of alloys.** The use of pneumatic conveyor equipment permits the installation of multiple-compartment storage bins, which can be loaded most efficiently with materials consisting of various alloys. Selector-type segregating valves insure the delivery of the proper material to the proper compartment and eliminate the chance of mixing one alloy with another. The pneumatic duct can be blown clean to prevent contamination when changing from the handling of one alloy to the handling of another.

7. **Briquetting.** Plants with their own foundries find it highly economical to briquette cast iron and steel for remelting in their own furnaces. This briquetting can provide up to 25 percent of the bar-stock charge required to melt down pig iron, and because only interplant handling is required from the briquette press discharge to the foundry, the cost for this make-up charge is greatly reduced. Central-station vacuum-type pneumatic conveyors permit delivery of borings from machine tools directly to the briquetting press.

8. **Facility location.** The use of pneumatic conveying equipment permits chip processing areas to be set up close to the machine tools producing chips, thus doing away with the trucking of raw turnings into a processing area. In mechanical systems, processing areas must be located adjacent to the ultimate disposal point. In pneumatic systems, extremely long pneumatic lines—from 1,000 to 1,500 ft. in length—have been used to deliver chips from the processing area to railroad sidings. Thus the pneumatic conveyor makes possible installations which would not be feasible with other kinds of equipment.

USES OF CONTAINERS IN INDUSTRY

CONTENTS

USES OF CONTAINERS IN INDUSTRY

DEFINITION OF CONTAINER. As applicable to industrial use, containers are best defined as **carriers formed to retain a quantity of an item** for movement between processes, into or out of storage, or in transit from a point of manufacture through to a point of ultimate disposal. Any activity which facilitates any of the above procedures individually, or unitized, in bulk liquid or gas form is considered as meeting the conditions of containing.

Uses of Containers and Supports. The importance of containers is often overlooked when equipment to perform a specific function as an integral part of a materials handling system is being selected. A wide variety of containers—standard and made to order—are available, designed to carry a wide variety of in-process and finished parts, assemblies, or products through all phases of the manufacturing cycle, including shipment of the end product.

Materials of Construction. There are several **basic kinds of materials** from which industrial containers are made, each serving a particular need. Combinations of materials are common for containers and supports, with each kind of material being used for particular characteristics, such as those listed in the following:

1. Wood, which has long life, stands moderate abuse, is of lowest cost, is non-abrasive, and possesses sufficient strength for normal purposes.
2. Metal, which has the highest strength and durability.
3. Plastic, which is readily fabricated in molds, but is somewhat fragile.
4. Fiber, which is light, economical, and available in a wide variety of styles.
5. Glass and ceramics, which handle corrosive liquids but are fragile.

DEVELOPING UNIT LOADS. The unit-load principle has been accepted in industry as a means for accomplishing difficult handlings and storage by mechanical methods—and at considerable cost savings. Bins are designed for holding quantities of like parts or to contain different kinds of bulk materials. Portable racks and easily handled small in-process containers provide flexible transportation. Frequently, product demand does not warrant the development of expensive containers or the installation of racks.

In certain cases plate patterns supported on a predetermined pallet or skid base and equipped with durable or re-usable layer-dividers and covers have been devised and installed. The unit is then reinforced by use of steel strapping, and the container can be stacked. All items in the unit load are subject to return to the point of origin for re-use, with the exception of the steel banding, which is scrapped once the unit load is broken down. In most instances unitized containers are being used in in-plant or interplant handling to replace the heavy types of containers. The product itself may constitute the means to handle such unit loads, especially in the handling and storage of such items as brick, ceramic products, and corrugated board (see sections on Palletization and Pallets).

Conditions Which Containers Must Meet

REQUIREMENTS FOR A SUITABLE CONTAINER. There is no ideal all-purpose container, but a container which meets seven basic conditions approaches the ideal. It is important to emphasize that this approach to the ideal obtains only for the particular product involved; no one container, material, or method will be best for all kinds of production: each requires **individual analysis and treatment.**

The container which will **perform best** in a given situation will fill the following qualifications:

1. Protect the contained item.
2. Provide all-around economy.
3. Be adaptable to good warehousing practices.
4. Simplify the loading and unloading operation.
5. Conform to good handling practices.
6. Be convenient to use.
7. If a shipping container, identify the contained item.

In most instances the first two conditions, **protection and economy,** will govern the selection and use of the individual containers, although the extra conveniences that can now be built into containers are receiving and will continue to receive increased attention.

Proper protection becomes the major requirement of any in-process or shipping container, but again it is stressed that this protection means many different things for different productions. Adequate protection requires detailed analysis and extensive testing before the best and most economical of engineered containers is achieved. In this, time and money is well spent by reducing damage, maintaining lower costs, and increasing user satisfaction either at the machine or on the part of the customer. The accompanying chart (Modern Materials Handling, vol. 8) in Fig. 1 highlights common hazards and can be used as an initial guide for building into the container the proper preventive measures.

Container economy is not limited to only one feature but is comprised of the following factors summing up the over-all lowest cost:

1. **Production volume.** The duration of the current product design and quantity becomes the outstanding consideration in choosing the container, as volume and design frequently dictate the amount of planning and effort required to supply the best container. The most economical design and material for long production runs may be entirely impractical for relatively low volume or short production runs.

2. **Availability of materials.** Materials specifications must always follow a consideration of the obtainability of a material from a variety of local sources and a knowledge of the limitations of the facilities to supply the material. A single-source container material, one of highly specialized material and design or one obtainable only from great distances, will cost considerably more in the long run than a more common type locally obtainable, even at a higher initial cost.

3. **Container types.** Conventional containers are preferable to highly specialized designs from the standpoint of both cost and availability. Also, with the use of conventional containers the possibility of realizing the benefits of competitive bidding is increased.

4. **Standardization of in-plant operations.** Flexibility in the loading and/or packaging function will be realized from a standardization program whereby a

Hazard	Where it usually occurs	What causes it	What may happen to product	Some methods of preventing it
Vertical compression	Warehouses Ships	High stacking Power stowing for export	Possibility of top and bottom damage Damage to vertical structural members	Build in vertical strength— Vertical corrugations Interior braces and partitions Interior or exterior cleats Floating or suspended load
Horizontal compression	Railroad Highway carriers	Voids develop in transit Sudden stops, starts, and reversals (impact)	Damage to sides Damage to horizontal structural members Shock or impact damage to components	Build in horizontal strength— Horizontal corrugations Special flap construction Internal braces, partitions, and pads Interior or exterior cleats Cushioning and resilience devices Floating or suspended load
Puncture Scuffing Tearing	Warehouse aisle corners Loading of carriers Handling operations	Careless vehicles operation Conveyor pileups Contact with sharp objects	Damage to finish Product contamination Damage from vermin	Extra thicknesses of material Liners and sleeves Stronger panels Secure loads internally near center of gravity Clearances between product and containers Absorbent cushioning for liquids Treated boards
Abrasion within container Chafing	In transit	Vibration Loose packing	Damage to finish Structural fatigue	Paraffined pads Cellulose padding Other protective padding or coatings "Hold down" or anchoring devices
Torque	Storage on uneven floors or crowded decks Handling improperly	Lifting unevenly or with too small a support area under the package Dropping on one corner	Damage to structural members or protuberances	Build in diagonal bracing Provide for mechanical handling (skids and lifting lugs)
Atmosphere	In ships' holds On open docks and carriers In yard storage In damp buildings	Rain Warehouse with drastic day and night temperature changes Hull sweat	Corrosion Deterioration by chemical decomposition or water absorption	Waterproof barriers VCI coatings or lining Coat product with compounds Desiccants Treated board
Pilferage	At transfer points	Item can be concealed in workers' clothing Container can be opened and reclosed without detection	Incomplete shipments Higher insurance rates Customer dissatisfaction	Don't flagrantly advertise contents on container Disassemble product to useless components—example, all "left" shoes in one container Simplify detection—use printed sealing tape— cover nails with tension-strapping stitched closures

Fig. 1. Hazards which may cause damage to or loss of containers.

variety of finished products or in-process handlings are adaptable to interchangeability of both materials and labor.

5. **Material costs.** Generally speaking, materials and shipping costs will be reduced in direct proportion to the reduction of the container cube. The container shape and possibly the product design can be changed to permit nesting of easily assembled components. Overpacking is as poor container-engineering as is underpacking.

6. **Labor charges.** Simplicity of design is usually taken into account in direct proportion to the cost of setting up a container. It is all important that a designer take into account the time in man-minutes required for setting up a container, relating it to the cost of materials and the special features included in the container proper.

7. **Reduced transportation charges.** A greater volume of production can be shipped for the same charge when tare weight is reduced, as freight charges are based on gross weight. Volume, in turn, is important when overseas shipment is being considered, and it should be given the same consideration as domestic shipment by weight only.

When considering good storage and warehousing practices, the **cost of space utilization and handling** becomes all important. A container in turn must be factored to fit in with the plan for storage and disposition. For instance, the container that lends itself to high-stacking will in the long run be less costly than one that requires special and expensive racking in order to save space. A container also should lend itself to long-range handling practices, with the need for highly specialized attachments minimized, or it should be capable of being handled in one fashion alone. When not of a re-useable nature, a container is unacceptable if it cannot easily be knocked down and disposed of through normal **scrap** channels. Containers that offer extras, such as an incoming unit load to the first in-plant operation, or those that act as bins for small-load disposal of container parts are highly acceptable.

Container Analysis

BASIS FOR ANALYSIS. Container systems and the economics of their use are subject to detailed analysis when one or more of the **following conditions** are to be met:

1. Change in the manufacturing process.
   a. Introduction of new or modified types of equipment—machine or manual.
   b. Improvements in the methods allied to the process.
   c. Conversion to production line techniques or automation.
2. Change in the product.
   a. Redesign of item or introduction of diversified product.
   b. Change or substitution of product material.
   c. Revisions in inventory and scheduling position.
   d. More stringent quality requirements.
3. Change in physical plant.
   a. Rearrangement of facilities—layout.
   b. Relocation of facilities—new plant.
   c. Extension of container system in use.
   d. Introduction of revised materials handling system.
4. Static or rising handling costs.
   a. Unit cost standards not met.
   b. Cost reduction program goals not brought about.

ANALYZING THE OBJECTIVES. The major objective in any study of container systems or any other handling problem is to achieve **low cost in operations.** This lower cost may be achieved through **reduced initial investment** or through **low-cost use and movement.** Present container problems and proposed systems must be studied to determine every job the containers will do and to discover every condition under which they will be used. When applications have been considered and a container system tentatively selected, that system must be studied in the light of the following objectives:

1. **Universal use.** The entire system must be analyzed to arrive at as few types of basic structures as possible to contain all varieties of parts and materials.
2. **Availability** of contained materials. So that parts may be placed in and removed from containers easily, dunnage must be studied carefully. This study must be carried out to arrive at as few adaptations of dunnage-spacers as possible.
3. **Mobility.** Every container must be selected for ease of positioning and movement, considering all physical dimensions of the container and its environment and the complete cost of making the container mobile.
4. **Power units.** The basic objective is to keep every power-unit in constant use (limited, of course, by such practical considerations as maintenance). These units must be able to handle all or most of the container structures.

DEFINING THE REQUIREMENTS. Every container analysis requires development of data pertinent to the **physical aspects of the item,** in-transit protection, and the effect of subsequent manufacturing processes as regards common container use. The principal data are given (with examples) in the following list and described in the ensuing paragraphs:

1. Description of material: Tufting yarn.
2. Physical condition: Precision wound.
3. Shape of material: Tapered cone.
4. Unit size: 9⅛-in. diameter tapered to 7⅛-in. diameter × 9 in. high.
5. Unit weight. 10 lb., 3 oz.
6. Container description: Bin-type pallet.
7. Container construction: Wirebound, resawn hardwood, drive-screw cement-coated nails and hinged drop panel. 38 × 46 × 36½-in. I.D., 107 lb.
8. Container loading: 80 cones, 20 per layer, 4 layers high; nested alternate inverted pattern.
9. Container disposal: Return via dolly and tractor-trailer train to filling mill winding room.

Description of Material. The description of the kind of material need be only general: canned goods, bottled goods, castings, wire, eggs, hay, flour, cloth, paper, tar, acid, tobacco, ingots, bar stock, sheet stock, frames, motors, hatch covers, tires, etc.

Physical Condition of Material. The physical condition of the material can be described by such terms as the following: liquid, molten, frozen, perishable, granular, wet, flammable, powdered, explosive, fragile, and hot.

Shape of Material. Such descriptions as bar, sheet, round, cubical, bundle, bunch, roll, reel, and bulk sufficiently indicate the shape of material.

Size of a Material Unit. The size of a material unit is expressed in such terms as pipe lengths, roll sizes, reel sizes, box dimensions, board lengths, bulk granules, bulk liquid, and continuous length.

Weight Range of Individual Material Units. The weight range is given for individual units, whether the material is handled singly or in containers. Weight is expressed in tons, pounds, or ounces, depending upon the relative size of the material.

Description of Container. The container is described in brief terms, such as bale, bag, bolt, ream, roll, crate, box, pallet, skid, carton, reel, keg, and barrel.

Construction, Size, and Weight of Container. The construction, size, and weight of a container are self-explanatory.

Container Packing. Container packing is simply the number of material units or pieces held or carried in one container, such as a pallet of 7 tanks, a carton of 24 cans, a keg of 100 lb., a reel of 500 ft.

Disposal of Empty Containers. The means of disposing of the empty container is indicated in order that proper provision be made in the plant layout for the handling of empty containers at the termination of each materials handling or manufacturing cycle.

The first basic decision with regard to the handling of individual items concerns the container in which the material is moved. If new containers are needed, consideration must be given to the facilities for storing these containers between production operations. The containers must therefore lend themselves to tiering or collapsing and inexpensive return transportation to the starting point. Other considerations given the containers are as follows:

1. Are the containers too large or too heavy?
2. Do the containers necessitate manual removal of material in order to empty them into hoppers?
3. Could the vendor's containers be changed in size or design to facilitate materials handling?

ANALYZING THE MATERIALS. Dimensions and weight of materials to be contained are the key factors in container design. The characteristic of all materials that contain these factors is **density.** Density, then, is the basis of container design or selection. But density may vary widely between different materials. The following are the density variations to be considered in container selections:

1. Small, dense, heavy. Parts falling into this class (e.g., small castings) must be contained in a vessel which has a bottom, sides, and ends. Density and allowable weight of the loaded container must be considered. Means of loading and unloading materials into and out of the container must be considered.
2. Medium bulk, medium density, light weight. Packaged parts and small metal stampings fall into this category. The container must be designed with the bulk, allowable weight, and quantity of parts to be contained kept in mind. Means of placing and removing the parts easily must be provided. The container must have a bottom, sides, and ends.
3. Very bulky, little density, varied weight. Large metal stampings are typical of this class of materials. The container must have bottom, sides, and ends, must be designed to accommodate unlimited bulk, and must provide easy placement and removal of the materials.

In the analysis of the classes of materials, one feature stands out. It is the basic identity of **container requirements.** Each class requires a container that has a bottom, sides, and ends and has been engineered for easy placement and removal of the materials. One additional factor must be considered in all three cases—that of suitable lifting, transporting, and positioning equipment to handle the containers.

Principles of Container Standardization and Selection

From the standpoint of investment and in the light of the analysis of the materials handled, the following **principles of container standardization** should be applied:

1. Employ a minimum number of basic structures to accommodate the variations of density. Use removable dunnage to accommodate contour variations in the contained materials.
2. Employ durable, compact container structures for intraplant and local-area commercial carrier transportation.
3. Employ light-weight, durable, collapsible structures for long-distance commercial carrier transportation.
4. Employ durable, wheeled dolly structures for intraplant transportation only. These dollies must not be tied up under loads in storage.
5. Consider the design of standard lifting, transporting, and positioning power equipment when designing containers and dunnage.
6. Design power units and/or attachments for flexibility of application to basic container structures.
7. Design dunnage to require a minimum of time for assembly and disassembly.

APPLYING THE PRINCIPLES TO THE PROBLEMS. Analysis of the container requirements of materials to be handled has indicated that materials fall into three categories distinguished by degrees of density. Study of the principles of materials handling and containerization has revealed the foregoing **seven principles** to be applied to the solution of the problem. The appropriate principles must be applied to each category and to the problem of standard moving and positioning units.

Case 1: Small, Dense, Heavy Materials.

a. **Principles.**
Use a minimum number of basic structures.
Use durable structures intraplant.
Consider prime movers.

b. **Required container characteristics.**
Kinds of bottoms, sides, ends.
Ease of loading and unloading.
Pallet or skid base.

c. **Solution.**
Use a corrugated steel bin box and durable, self-leveling dunnage insert. This kind of box has a solid bottom and sides and ends to prevent small parts from slipping out. The spring-loaded dunnage insert maintains parts at working height regardless of weight of load. The skid bottom makes fork truck handling easy. Hooks are provided for crane handling. Boxes may be stacked for storage.

Case 2: Medium-Bulk, Medium-Density, Light-Weight Materials.

a. **Principles.**
Use a minimum number of basic structures.
Use durable structures intraplant.
Use light, durable, collapsible structures for long hauls.
Use durable dollies intraplant.
Consider prime movers.

b. **Required container characteristics.**
Bottom, sides, ends.
Ease of loading and unloading.
Pallet or skid base.
Flexibility of dunnage.

c. **Solutions.**
(1) Intraplant handling:
Use a tubular-steel rack 80 × 39 × 31 in. (capacity 45 cu. ft.) and durable dunnage. For flexibility, the following dunnage is prescribed:
 (a) Welded-steel wire-basket panels and tubular-steel rack enclosures for side and end adaptations. Three or four of the basket sides may be used.
 (b) Tubular side bars, which will, in effect, build a "fence" around the load.
 (c) To hold in materials in 3-sided basket adaptations, slant floors sloping toward the closed side.
(2) Interplant handling:
Use a collapsible, durable welded-steel wire container with four sides and 4-way pallet bottom.

Case 3: Very Bulky Materials of Variable Density and Weight.

a. **Principles.**
Use a minimum number of basic structures.
Use removable dunnage to accommodate contour variations.
Use durable structures intraplant.
Use durable, wheeled dolly structures intraplant.
Consider prime movers.

b. **Required container characteristics.**
Bottom, sides, ends.
Must accommodate unlimited bulk.
Must provide easy placement and removal of load.

c. **Solutions.**
(1) Intraplant handling:
Use a tubular steel rack 108 × 48 × 31 in. high.
(2) Interplant shipping:
Ship loose in boxcar with appropriate dunnage.
Ship loose in special boxcar with built-in dunnage.

The next step is the preparation of a detailed analysis, as described under the heading "Defining the Requirements."

In-Process Containers

HANDLING WORK IN PROCESS. An important application for containers is in the handling of in-process parts, such as those passing through machine operations. No matter what the conditions are within a work area, containers can practically always be designed for specific jobs. Some containers are designed for handling by hand lift trucks, others by walkies, fork trucks, etc., with permanent pallet or skid bases. Such containers are usually of large capacity. Some of these larger containers are mounted on casters so that they may be readily moved by hand. The most versatile container is probably the one that is designed with a pallet or skid base, often with lugs for overhead handling as well. Some units are designed for handling by overhead equipment only.

SELECTION AND USE. This conception envisions the product in unit load form, surrounded in whole or in part by a container which not only retains the unit but also affords proper protection, permits ease of feed to succeeding operations, facilitates inspections, and utilizes minimum storage cube at required hold or delay points.

Employment of **specially designed containers,** excepting the development of pallet and rack systems used in conjunction with lift truck and overhead handling, has until quite recently been generally overlooked as a means to facilitate the processing activity and reduce manufacturing costs. Now, however, the role of both **conventional and rack-type containers** is undergoing extensive re-examination in the light of being an integral part of a **modern engineered materials handling program.** Anticipated improvements from this planned approach, no matter what the particular manufacturing endeavor may be, can be broadly stated as:

1. **Improved warehousing.** Both raw- and finished-goods warehousing operations improve with planned space utilization and ready accessibility to stored material. **Adjustable racking** provides flexibility to fluctuating storage patterns while holding a variety of small unit containers. Larger unit containers usually are designed so as to tier and, further, can be nested or knocked down when not in use, for additional saving of space.

2. **Improved in-process storage and handling.** Increased mechanization emphasizes the need not only for efficient unit handling between processing centers but also for unit storage as close to the point of use as possible without unnecessary waste of valuable floor space. Consequently, there is under development and in use a variety of special containers applicable to **cube storage** and **mechanized handling.** Not only must the container serve between, and feed, manufacturing steps; it also should be multipurpose as an **interplant shipping unit.** This facility permits bulking stores in outlying areas, yet moving quickly and in quantity to point of use.

3. **Better production scheduling.** Containers holding predetermined quantities speed up and simplify the taking of a physical **inventory.** Closer control and scheduled turnover will shorten lead time and give, in addition, improved handling equipment utilization.

The economics which is concerned with container selection cannot be stressed overstrongly, nor can its importance be overemphasized. Changes are often undertaken without the necessary economic justification warranting the change. In other instances, all possible contingencies are built into the container without appreciation of the fact that the simplest and least costly well-designed unit states its own case in the best light for adoption by top management.

TYPICAL EXAMPLE OF IN-PROCESS CONTAINER USE. As an example of container use, assume that certain purchased subassemblies arrive loose, or in cartons, at the receiving dock in a manufacturing plant. At the same time, sheet steel arrives at the plant in gondolas. The former are transferred into **wooden, wire, or steel skid bins** (Fig. 2) and trucked to temporary storage. Sheet steel is moved by **overhead equipment** to the start of the production area.

The raw material is fed into the press, emerges in the form of small parts, and is processed through a further succession of operations. Between the work stations it may be transported in **tote boxes** if the parts are small and/or it is desirable to move them in smaller lots, or in skid bins or other heavy-duty, larger-capacity containers.

Meanwhile, the purchased subassemblies, after an additional operation, have been transferred to **perforated wire baskets, trays, or tote boxes** and dipped by overhead equipment into degreasing baths. Next, they are stored in **wire-mesh**

containers awaiting transportation to the final assembly line. During the various phases of production, some parts are moved in tote pans equipped with handles and are carried along in overhead conveyors. Where short moves are indicated, **castered floor containers,** which are easily pushed by an operator, are used.

Some of the production of a particular plant may be shipped to other plants in the form of subassemblies to be worked into final products. After all the manufacturing operations have been completed the finished products are loaded in **collapsible wire or wooden containers** and sent by highway carrier to the customer. The empty containers are knocked down and delivered back to their original owner.

Ironbound Box & Lumber Co.

Fig. 2. Transfer skid box.

Warehouses use many different kinds of containers for order-packing purposes. Processing companies, mail-order houses, bottling plants, service firms (large laundries, distributors, etc.,) and other kinds of nonmanufacturing companies make extensive use of such containers.

STANDARD AND SPECIALIZED CONTAINERS. One military tank plant set up a highly effective rack-container program which adopted many standardized units and included many other features which are specially designed for specific kinds of loads. Among the **standard items** are the following:

1. **Corrugated skid bins** measuring 40 in. × 48 in., which are used only for in-plant handling.
2. **Collapsible wire-mesh pallet boxes** measuring 40 in. × 48 in. These collapsible boxes are used for shipping castings, rough parts, etc., to other plants. They may be either returned to their destination or kept for use in receivers' plants.
3. **Wire pallets,** usually measuring 40 in. × 48 in. These are used for shipping items which are received either loose (armor plate, assemblies, etc.) or in cartons and not palletized. The pallets are then used for interdepartmental flow of these items.

4. **Wire baskets** measuring 12 in. × 20 in. × 7 in. which are stackable and are used for transporting miscellaneous small parts, for degreasing, etc.
5. **Racks** measuring 40 in. × 80 in. with retaining members at 36-in. intervals in a vertical plane. These racks are used for interdepartmental flow of materials and for flexible storage for cartons, special parts, castings, etc. The units are often placed on racks, which are transported to the assembly line and stored there until needed for assemblies or for shipment. The units are often modified slightly in the case of special items.

Containers such as those included in the above listing should be of standard size and design so that any one of them can be handled by any standard kind of lifting and transporting equipment. They are all stackable and are of sufficient variety to enable the plant transportation system to handle the carriers with whatever equipment there may be in the plant. Racks are so designed that loads can be picked up in the same position as that which they will take on the assembly and/or completed-product line. Since parts are not turned or repositioned several times during assembly, valuable assembly time is conserved.

Specialized Containers, Racks. Because of the vast number and wide variety of parts handled, standard kinds of containers have been found unsuitable in certain plants. One of the motorcar companies has designed many different kinds of **specialized carriers** for its own assembly lines. These units were made as standard as possible by applying certain common basic materials handling features. Racks and carriers can now be handled by overhead equipment, fork trucks, or walkies, and they fit in with the company's shop trailers. Racks stack on one another and fit into either highway trucks or railway cars. In designing the special racks the objective was to obtain **maximum utilization** of the equipment through all phases of handling, and the **pre-positioning** of the parts in the best possible location for subsequent machine or assembly operations.

Three major considerations prompted an aircraft company to design a series of specialized **container racks,** namely, (1) protection of parts from damage or marring, (2) conservation of factory space, and (3) ease of handling the parts.

Minimum Space—Maximum Number of Parts. The container racks custom-tailored by this aircraft company are designed in various shapes, but all are so compactly arranged that only a minimum of space is needed to accommodate a maximum number of parts. The container racks were constructed by the company's mechanical maintenance department according to the specifications of the plant engineering department.

Some racks, such as those for the engine struts, have a **bird-cage** appearance. On others, rubber-encased supporting hooks have been mounted in a way that gives them a similarity to **clothes trees.**

Protection of Parts. The general principle in the protection of parts is that each piece has its own allotted compartment so that surfaces are prevented from rubbing against one another. The **separation** also conserves space. Thus, one of the "bird cages" can hold 204 struts, several times more than the former carrier which occupied almost as much actual floor space. The newly designed container racks can be pulled, several at a time, by a small truck, which moves them to inspection, shipping, and final packing.

USE OF VENDOR CONTAINERS. When a survey of in-process containers is being conducted, the study should be extended even farther back than the first raw material or parts receiving and storage. It is entirely possible that the container program within a plant can be adjusted and even incorporated with the container or package in which the vendor ships to the user plant. There is a twofold basis for this: the economy of using the **incoming container** at least through the first several processes, thereby effecting economies of rehandling; and secondly, mutual development of the largest unit pack which the user plant can process, not into storage but instead to his initial operation. **Mechanized handling equipment** has been designed to handle one- and two-ton loads, which in most instances are composed of a multitude of small containers. A bulk container in this capacity would to a great degree eliminate the loading and unloading of individual packs. If it is advisable to issue fork truck load lots, it is logical to purchase in the fork truck-side container.

The **steps to follow** in the subject analysis are:

1. Determination of the economical unit of issue to the initial plant operation.
2. Determination of the largest container which it is feasible to receive.
3. Work in conjunction with the vendor to establish that container size as the standard unit of receipt.

Upon completion of the initial steps and establishment of the **economical procurement** unit which is the design of the quantity container, it will be necessary to develop:

1. The part number and description identifying the material.
2. Pounds per cubic foot, which to a great extent will determine container material.
3. Duration of stores life from point of receipt to point of use.
4. Quantity in storage or that amount of the material to be found under the average stores condition.

The foregoing basic data will, in turn, determine the **economical unit of issue** to the quantity per unit load, which frequently will be factored by the lift capacity of the handling equipment, coupled with contamination, deterioration, etc.

A pattern of parts contained for high volume items will be required with the analysis. Many unforeseen contingencies will be successfully overcome before introduction of the pack load.

The economics of **container selection** will follow that established for in-process containers and the features of material design. Handling and use will to a great extent be identically factored only to the extent that the vendor, user, and carrier must agree on the materials, size, and return of re-useable types to point of origin.

A far-reaching program such as that outlined involves not only the operating personnel but many of the service and staff departments within an organization and liaison throughout the development and approval prior to use. The advantages will be numerous and outstanding. They will include the standardization of receipt, storage, and issue operations; simplicity of inventory position; reduced terminal time for the over-the-road carriers, and savings in the handling activities at both the shipping and receiving docks.

The **third panel-type of rack** is usually of permanent construction and designed to **accept a specific product** such as carpet rolls, reels, bar stock, and large dies; that is, one article is retained in one predetermined-type cubicle. The cubicles, if necessary, can be vertically adjusted to accommodate changes in the size and/or design. Refinements of the structure determine whether the rack should be of roll-bed type, Christmas-tree type, etc. Where necessary, the cubicles will be equipped with flooring, again either permanent or removable.

THE INTEGRATED SYSTEM. Study of all the kinds of equipment operating together in a container-standardization program shows how well the basic units fill the requirements for carrying the parts. Six kinds of container and dunnage structures and three kinds of mobile units usually completely cover the containing-handling requirements for inter- and intraplant movement of a wide variety of materials.

Right Container—Right Job

WIDE VARIETY OF CONTAINERS. In manufacturing and assembly plants wide varieties of industrial containers are used to carry the vast flow of **in-process and finished parts** going through all the particular phases of production, packaging, and shipping. Whatever his particular field, the packaging engineer should be thoroughly familiar with metal, wood, fiber, and glass shipping containers—their present and future possibilities, their limitations, and all regulations which pertain to their use. They are, at least, part of his professional "stock in trade."

Container Construction. There are six basic kinds of material from which industrial containers are made: (1) wood, (2) sheet metal, (3) wire, (4) plastic, (5) glass, (6) fiberboard, and (7) canvas. Metal containers are designed for heavy loads and long life and will withstand considerable abuse. Wooden containers have a long life but are not designed to undergo excessive abuse. **All-metal containers** are of two basic types—solid and open construction. The former are used for heavy parts and for certain small parts. The **wire-mesh** and perforated, or expanded-metal containers are lighter and are used for parts which will not drop through the container. These containers have the strength afforded by metal, but they are not as heavy as solid-metal containers because of their open construction.

Fiberboard containers, usually in the form of tote boxes, are rugged yet sufficiently light-weight in construction to be easily hand-handled at work stations. **Canvas shop baskets** are light in weight, may be put on skids by hand, and are frequently used where cleanliness is an important factor. **Plastic containers** have the advantage of light weight and can be constructed in the form of solid or woven containers.

Features of Design. The very nature of the different designs of containers gives them over-all versatility. For example, many kinds of containers, made of different materials, are collapsible so that they will take up only a minimum of space when not in use. **Collapsible** containers are often used for shipping purposes as well as for in-plant use. When empty and collapsed, they may be handled more conveniently on the return run. (See section on Containers and Pallets.)

Other Important Features of Containers. An important feature of many containers is that they may be **fitted with casters** and handled by hand. Almost all of the larger types of containers can be so adapted. Other containers are made with **pallet or skid bases** so that they may be picked up by powered or free-rolling equipment without first being spotted on some kind of carrying platform.

The crowded conditions of many industrial plants have made necessary the wide use of **stackable containers** to take advantage of the vertical storage space in main storage areas and in and around machines. The stacking feature of these containers makes it possible to load them into cars or trucks for return to the original shippers, at a considerable saving to the owner companies. When not in use, many of the smaller containers, such as tote boxes, may be **nested** to conserve space. Some units can be both nested and stacked for this purpose.

Many kinds of containers are of perforated or open construction for special reasons, such as **drainage of the loads carried.** Likewise, **perforated tote boxes** are widely used for degreasing purposes because the degreasing solution can be circulated throughout a load while the load is still in the container. **Wire-mesh containers** are made so that their contents may be readily seen. This factor is especially valuable for spot inventory purposes. Moreover, the open mesh construction reduces the total over-all weight of the container.

Inspecting and Testing Containers

FUNDAMENTALS OF CONTAINER TESTING. Proof testing of a container design is an all-important function which must be undertaken if one is to have a measure of assurance that the container will withstand the rigors of numerous handlings and the rough usage it will encounter during its useful life. Prior to the testing, a thorough **inspection** should be made, inside and outside dimensions taken, and respective cubes calculated and checked against design values. Structural members, welds, rivets, doors, hinges, and locking mechanisms should also be inspected to detect any weaknesses or malfunctionings. Deflections of all faces and edges should be measured, with the unit empty, and the data recorded. These data are necessary in determining the extent of deflections resulting from tests under load.

To determine the ability of the unit to afford protection to its contents against heavy rain conditions, the unit should be subjected to a uniform water spray on all its surfaces—top, sides, and ends—from various angles and different directions for a total time of 1 hr. At the completion of the test the doors should be opened and the interior examined for evidences of free water.

TESTING PROCEDURES. The ability of the container to carry its rated load and to be efficiently and safely tiered is determined by the following testing procedures:

1. Load the container uniformly with rated load, secured against shifting.
2. With a straightedge held longitudinally against lower surfaces, check the four floor edges for deflection.
3. Superimpose two loaded containers onto the test unit; allow to set for 48 hr.
4. Check for difficulties in nesting arrangements.
5. Check the doors and locking mechanisms for satisfactory operation under load.
6. Measure the center deflection of edges and vertical faces.
7. Remove the superimposed load.
8. Repeat Operation 2 (above).
9. Inspect the roof for deformations at points of bearing.
10. Criteria: The container is acceptable if there are no permanent distortions or deformations, no weld or rivet failures, and if the operation of doors and locking mechanisms under load is satisfactory.

Testing Lift Operations of the Loaded Unit. While it is not intended that the container will normally be lifted by only two of its four lifting eyes, lift test operations of the loaded unit by several combinations of two lift eyes will indicate their ability to support the unit under emergency loadings and give an indication as to the overload capacity of the lift eyes. The test is conducted as follows:

1. Hoist the loaded unit by diagonal pairs of lift eyes, one pair at a time.
2. Hoist the loaded unit by two rear lift eyes, throwing the entire weight of the container against the closed doors.
3. With the unit suspended, check the doors for deflections.
4. Return the unit to a level position on ground.
5. Criteria: After the test the doors and locking mechanism must operate satisfactorily, with no evidence of yield or deformation of lift eyes.

Superimposing Cargo on the Container. Stowing the container in the hold of a vessel and superimposing cargo on it, both with and without dunnage, will cause stresses as previously indicated. This condition can be simulated by the following test:

1. Position a load equal to 100 lb. per sq. ft. of roof area directly on the roof of the unit, distributing the load evenly within the periphery of the container.
2. Measure the deflections of the edges and vertical faces.
3. Remove the load, then repeat Step 2.
4. Measure the center deflection of the roof..
5. Position a load equal to 400 lb. per sq. ft. of roof area on the roof of the container. Support the load by the use of dunnage (4 in. × 4 in.) extending from side to side.
6. Allow the load to set for approximately 48 hr.
7. Repeat Step 2.
8. Repeat Steps 3 and 4.
9. Criteria: No permanent distortion or deflection, no weld or rivet failure.

Drop Tests. In the course of normal shipping operations, containers will be subjected to damaging stress as a result of falls or drops on corners or edges, which will tend to distort them from a rectangular to an oblique parallelogram shape. If the container is not constructed with sufficient strength, maintenance costs will be considerable and eventual replacement will be necessary. Tests to indicate reaction to this type of stress are made as follows:

1. Place the loaded container on a level concrete floor. Position a 6 × 8 in. timber flat under one end, and allow the opposite end to rest on the floor.
2. Starting from floor level, raise the unsupported end to heights of 6 to 24 in. by 6-in. increments, and allow it to drop after each 6-in. rise.
3. Check for a center deflection of vertical faces, maximum deflection of edges, inclination of each corner post from vertical axis, deformation of skids, and a vertical displacement of each door at upper edges.
4. Replace the loaded container on the level concrete floor; add 6 in. × 8 in. timber under one corner of the unit.
5. Repeat Step 2.
6. Repeat Step 3.
7. Criteria: No permanent distortion or deformation, no weld or rivet failures, satisfactory operation of doors and locking mechanisms.

Tension Loads. During the stevedoring operations, when the unit is hoisted aboard vessels, tension loads are imposed up to and including 3 to 3½ G's, that is, the impact caused by an acceleration of the mass of three to 3½ times that of gravity. This condition is occasioned when the lift is brought to a relatively abrupt stop just above the deck before lowering to its final place of rest. The following test procedure is applied:

1. The uniformly loaded container is hoisted by four lift eyes, approximately 25 ft. above ground level. The brakes of the hoisting equipment are released,

allowing the unit to descend freely at full speed. The unit is brought to a full stop 5 ft. above ground by application of full brake. (G values can be determined by use of an accelerometer.)

2. Repeat the above procedure three or four times. Check the doors and locking mechanism for satisfactory operation, doors for vertical displacement, deflection of floor edges and vertical faces, lift eyes for evidence of yield.

3. Criteria: No permanent distortion of deflection, no weld or rivet failure, or lift eye yield.

Resistance to Shear. When it is expected that the container will be transported by rail, the suitability of the container to withstand **normal railroad freight operations** is a necessary determination. Resistance to shear when opposing forces have been applied to the top and bottom faces must be determined, and the following test procedure is used:

1. A uniformly loaded test unit is placed on a railroad flatcar, its long axis at right angles to the track.

2. The container is blocked in place by use of timbers laid flat against skids and/or side panels. Additional blocking is provided through use of timbers in the stake pockets of the car. All timbers are checked.

3. The container is tied down to the car by use of wire or steel strapping.

4. The car carrying the test unit is humped at a speed of 9 to 12 mi. per hr. Speeds can be determined by use of impact recorders and timing devices.

5. Check all faces and edges for deflections and distortions.

6. Criteria: No permanent distortions or failures; satisfactory operation of doors and locking mechanism.

INDUSTRIAL PACKAGING

CONTENTS

INDUSTRIAL PACKAGING

PACKAGING. The packaging field may be divided into two major functional categories, namely, consumer packaging and industrial packaging. **Consumer packaging** is concerned with the unit package—its appearance, utility, adequacy for ultimate utilization, and the protection it affords against moisture, foreign contaminants, injurious temperatures, and the hazards of transportation. **Industrial packaging** is concerned fundamentally with the safe and economical transportation of packages to their destination and the protection of their contents during transportation, handling, and warehousing.

It may appear that consumer and industrial packaging are independent of one another, but this is far from true. The packaging engineer aims to establish an ideal relationship between the **inner consumer unit** and the **outer shipping container** for practical utility. Package designs and component materials must be equally acceptable to the production, sales, advertising, traffic, purchasing, and technical departments.

Package Design and Development

DESIGN OF PACKAGES. Certain basic steps must be taken in designing a package, whether it is a folding box, paper sack, crate, corrugated shipping container, or any other form. These steps include:

1. A careful check on present packaging. This is necessary when developing packing methods for a new product or when redesigning a container.
2. Investigations to determine compliance of the packaging with pertinent regulations covering shipments by truck, express, parcel post, air express, and freight as set forth by the common carriers.
3. Determination of the durability of shipping containers, adequacy of interior packaging, and protection afforded contents by the packaging.
4. Determination of the availability of the material or combinations of materials needed for the proposed packaging.
5. Determination of the specific protective qualities required by the nature of the contents—for example, resistance to moisture, water, puncturing, scuffing, or abrasion; protection against vibration, insect infestation, odor, grease, acid, temperature changes, tarnish, pilferage, and other hazards.
6. Selection of packaging style in consideration of "end use" or consumer aspect, including multiple packaging, display, and vending characteristics.
7. Testing for adequacy in comparison with existing competitive packages. Testing should not only determine the quality of the component materials used for the package but also evaluate the completely packaged unit as prepared for transportation.
8. Consideration of sales volume, consumer buying habits, and methods of distribution—all of which contribute largely to the ultimate design.
9. Determine the value of the packaged item, the profit margin, and the economic allocations provided for the packaging.

16·1

In the **application of the general fundamentals** listed above, consideration must also be given to the following factors:

1. Shape of the packaged item.
2. Compatibility of materials.
3. Retention of contents.
4. Stability of contents.
5. Separation of contents.
6. Cushioning.
7. Clearances.
8. Support of contents.
9. Positioning of contents.
10. Surface protection.
11. Suspension of the item.
12. Exposure.
13. Closure.
14. Printing.

Some of the specific factors listed above may seem to overlap, but careful examination will disclose that each factor must be separately considered. All the items are related, and all have a bearing on the fully assembled, packed, sealed, and reinforced shipping container.

Finally, it is the function of the engineer to reduce and assemble all these data in the form of completely detailed **written specifications** covering the design of both old and new packages. The ultimate objective is to obtain a proper relationship between the inner packaged unit and the outer shipping container at minimum cost.

General Packaging Specifications

NEED FOR SPECIFICATIONS. The advantages of developing and adopting adequate purchasing specifications are manifold. Proper **economy** and reliable **protection** can be obtained only through such means. Once established and followed, the specifications **protect against variations in the quality** of the packaging materials which are purchased.

Manufacturers of packaging containers may sometimes **substitute materials** other than those usually used in manufacturing the containers, particularly when there is a shortage of the regular materials. These substitutions are not necessarily of inferior grade. From the supplier's standpoint it is sometimes more economical to furnish for a particular order a grade of material that is better than usual rather than to make extensive machine changes and time-consuming setups. Materials substitutions of this kind, however, are potentially as troublesome as substitutions involving the use of inferior kinds or grades of component materials.

DEVELOPMENT OF GENERAL SPECIFICATIONS. The nature of the general specifications varies considerably among the different packaging materials. Each individual specification is based upon some minimum rule established by a carrier. A study of tests and methods of testing packaging materials and containers is practically a necessity as a guide to the development of general specifications. Common-carrier regulations constitute a basis for proper specifications for shipments, but federal and military specifications furnish additional information. In addition, many **industry trade associations** publish information which may prove helpful for this purpose. Organizations such as the American Management Association, the Packaging Institute, the Society of Industrial Packaging and Materials Handling Engineers, and the Porcelain Enamel Institute, among others, have made many valuable contributions to the development of adequate and effective specifications. The American Society for Testing Materials and the Technical Association of the Pulp and Paper Industry, among other organizations, have published and made available many and varied testing methods for evaluating the adequacy and acceptability of the wide range of containers shipped over the vast network of modern transportation lines.

The establishment of reasonable and realistic performance levels for packaging materials is of great importance. The next step is to secure the acceptance by vendors of the terms of the specifications. It is worthwhile in this connection to investigate commercial practices in regard to quality and workmanship for the given material. Certain producers of packaging materials have become more familiar than others with the general specifications. This situation has arisen in part from the fact that the **contents of specifications** may vary widely for different packaging materials.

The advantages of individual sets of specifications are as follows:

1. All basic data and requirements are contained in one particular set of specifications.
2. The need for repeating these requirements in individual or detailed specifications is avoided.
3. A sound basis for inspection and control of incoming shipments of materials is provided.
4. When changes are made in methods of specifying fundamental requirements, only an individual specification need be changed, not a number of separate specifications.
5. Specifications set forth realistic standards which are necessary for good performance.

Content of General Specifications. The specifications for corrugated fiberboard shipping containers provide a representative example of the content of general specifications, since a large percentage of all containers are made from this material. The **general specifications** for material of this nature should touch on the following major points:

1. Compliance with common-carrier regulations.
2. Styles of containers.
3. Materials specifications and requirements.
4. Fabrication, workmanship, flutes, printing, scoring, etc.
5. Manufacturer's joints on containers.
6. Dimensions and tolerances.
7. Packing and marking.
8. Methods of inspection and tests:
   a. Conditioning materials for tests.
   b. Bursting strength.
   c. Flat crush resistance.
   d. Evaluation of printed areas.
   e. Compressive resistance.
   f. Puncture resistance.
9. Rejection.
10. Combination of facings and corrugating media.
11. Standards and expectancies for various grades of materials and types of flutes as well as for all sizes and shapes of containers.

Specifications for Materials

TYPICAL GENERAL SPECIFICATIONS. For illustrative purposes typical general specifications for domestic corrugated fiberboard are presented in Fig. 1. In most instances performance specifications have been purposely omitted

---

1. **General**

    1.1 All corrugated fiberboard furnished to the XYZ Manufacturing Company shall be in accordance with these specifications and supplementary specifications and/or drawings for each individual container. Furthermore, the containers shall comply in all respects with the requirements of Rule 41 of the Uniform Freight Classification for the particular grade of material specified.

2. **Styles**

    2.1 These specifications cover the styles of corrugated containers illustrated in appended sheets. In addition they cover all other generally accepted styles of corrugated containers as well as specially designed containers which may be specified in detail in supplementary specifications and/or drawings.

3. **Materials**

    3.1 These specifications cover the grades of facings and corrugating medium listed in appended sheets.

    3.2 The facings or liners used in the manufacture of the corrugated fiberboard shall be in strict accordance with the materials specified in supplementary specifications.

4. **Fabrication**

    4.1 Workmanship shall be of the highest quality and all parts shall be furnished with true, clean-cut edges.

    4.2 There shall be no separation between facings and corrugated medium.

    4.3 Score lines shall be clearly visible and deep enough to be easily formed and yet shall not cause surface breaks in the facings.

    4.4 Unless otherwise specified, containers constructed of board having facings of unlike weight and test shall be scored and assembled with the heavier, higher-strength facing on the outside.

    4.5 Printing shall be applied in a way that will cause no significant crushing of the combined board. The criterion for good printing shall be the difference in caliper between unprinted and printed areas. These tolerances are furnished in appended sheets.

    4.6 Corrugations shall be rigid at all times and shall be firm and hard when pressed between the fingers. In case of dispute, tests shall be made to measure rigidity in accordance with the method described in Paragraph 9.5 below.

    4.7 Corrugations shall be A-, C-, or B-flute as specified and shall have the following measurements:

Type of Flute	Approximate Number per Foot	Approximate Height * (In.)
A	36	0.167
C	42	0.130
B	50	0.090

* With minus tolerance of 0.008 in. and unlimited plus tolerance.

Fig. 1. **General specifications for corrugated fiberboard (continued on next page).**

5. Dimensions and Tolerances

5.1 Container dimensions will be specified as to length, width, and depth in the order named and will be actual inside dimensions. The length is the longer dimension at the opening; the width the shorter dimension at the opening; and the depth is the dimension between the top and bottom flaps.

5.2 When actual distances are shown between scores on supplementary drawings for scored sheets, etc., such distances will be from center to center of score lines and will include scoring allowances.

5.3 Inside dimensions of containers shall be within plus or minus $\frac{1}{16}$ in. of those specified up to 12 in. and an additional $\frac{1}{32}$ in. for every additional 12 in.

5.4 Suppliers shall furnish A-flute, C-flute, or B-flute as specified on purchase orders or in supplementary specifications and/or drawings. Written authorization shall first be obtained to substitute an alternate flute for the specified flute. When so authorized, suppliers shall assume responsibility for making any necessary scoring allowance adjustments required to provide the specified inside dimensions of containers or size of finished details. In addition suppliers shall assume responsibility for the proper fit where inner containers are overpacked in master shipping containers. These adjustments apply to both single-wall and double-wall combinations.

6. Manufacturer's Joint on Containers

6.1 The manufacturer's joint on all containers shall be either glued or stitched. A taped manufacturer's joint may be used only on small reshipper cartons or for special cartons where a specific exception has been given. A glued manufacturer's joint is preferable where a carton is used in a high-speed packaging operation. Where glued joints are used, care must be exercised in the application of the adhesive so that the joint is properly formed with no "runoff" of excessive adhesive. This condition may cause the boxes to stick together.

6.2 Stitches shall be evenly spaced not more than 2½ in. apart in single or double rows as specified.

    6.21 The stitching tab shall overlap not less than 1¼ in. for single-row and not less than 2½ in. for double-row stitching.

6.3 Stitches shall be formed from commercial-grade steel wire, treated to resist rust.

6.4 Tape, only when specified, shall comply in all respects with the requirements of Rule 41 of both the Uniform and Consolidated Freight Classifications.

6.5 Tape, only when specified, shall be centrally located plus or minus $\frac{3}{16}$ in. over abutting edges of the joint and minus $\frac{3}{16}$ in. plus nothing from center to center of the top and bottom score lines.

7. Printing

7.1 Unless otherwise specified, containers shall be printed in accordance with instructions contained in the purchase order.

7.2 Containers designed for the shipment of flammable products shall be marked in accordance with ICC Specification 12B.

7.3 Additional information, such as caution legends, etc., shall be printed as specified.

Fig. 1. (Continued on next page.)

8. **Packing and Marking**

8.1 Unless otherwise specified, containers and interior parts shall be securely bundled or packaged in order to prevent damage during shipment and storage.

8.11 No single bundle or package of containers shall contain more than 25 units or exceed 50 lb. gross weight.

8.12 No single bundle or package of interior parts shall contain more than 100 units or exceed 50 lb. gross weight. The quantity per package may be increased when details are very small, and are boxed or are securely wrapped and tied.

8.2 When indicated by special instructions, palletized shipments shall be required.

8.3 Each bundle or package shall be marked to show the quantity and code number of the items contained therein.

9. **Methods of Inspection and Tests**

9.1 Conditioning Materials for Tests

9.11 All tests on materials shall be made after the latter have been exposed to a controlled atmosphere of 50 percent plus or minus 2 percent relative humidity at 73° F. plus or minus 3.5° F. for a period of 6 hr. This conditioning shall be preceded by exposure for a minimum of 3 hr. to a lower relative humidity so that moisture content equilibrium in the controlled atmosphere will be attained on an absorption basis.

9.12 In case of dispute or referee tests, materials shall be conditioned as above except that the periods of exposure to the preconditioning atmosphere and to the conditioning atmosphere shall each be 24 hr.

9.2 Bursting Strength

9.21 The bursting strength of combined board shall be determined as outlined in Rule 41 of the Uniform Freight Classification. Likewise, failure to comply with the requirements of Rule 41 shall be considered as failure to comply with the conditions of this specification.

9.3 Tests on Score Lines

9.31 Materials testing 175 lb. per sq. in. or more shall permit that all flaps be bent back on the score lines at 180° for a specified number of times without fracturing the facings.

9.4 Compression Tests on Empty Containers

9.41 This test provides a measure of the ability of the container to resist external compressive loads applied to its faces and is one of the best measures of fabrication efficiency.

9.42 This method of test shall be in accordance with ASTM Standard Method of Compression Test for Shipping Containers D642–47.

9.43 Results shall be based on not less than three representative specimens of a given size and type of container in each direction of compression. No specimen shall be used for more than one type of test.

9.44 The containers fail to meet this specification when the average of three tests falls more than 10 percent below the requirements listed in the compression curves furnished with this specification.

Fig. 1. (Continued on next page.)

9.5 Flat Crush Tests on Corrugated Fiberboard

    9.51 This test provides a scientific measure of the rigidity of the corrugations and shall be employed in case of dispute regarding the fabrication quality specified in Paragraph 4.6 above.

    9.52 Circular or square specimens of corrugated fiberboard with an area of either 9 or 10 sq. in. shall be carefully cut from the panels of the boxes. The area selected for the specimens shall be at least 1 in. removed from the score lines and the manufacturer's joint and, as far as possible, shall be free from printing.

    9.53 The specimens shall be individually compressed with pressure applied to the flat surfaces until the corrugations are completely crushed. The load required to cause complete collapse of the corrugations shall be noted.

    9.54 Results shall be based on not less than four specimens selected from a minimum of two containers of a given size and type.

    9.55 The containers fail to meet this specification when the average resistance for A-, B-, or C-flute is less than that listed in appended pages.

9.6 Tests on Manufacturer's Joint

    9.61 Stitched joints shall be tested by pulling the joined pieces in opposite directions until failure occurs. Failure shall occur by rupture of the board itself and not in the stitches. When failure occurs in the stitches, a further visual examination shall determine whether the quality of stitching is faulty.

    9.62 Glued joints shall be tested by separating the glued joints by tearing the edges of the blank away from one another. Failure of the joint shall show evidence of fiber tear and not fracture of the glue line. An additional test shall be made by immersing the glued joint in water at room temperature to show its waterproof qualities. Failure shall be considered to occur if the glued joint separates in less than 1 hr. of immersion.

    9.63 The adequacy of adhesion of a taped joint shall be determined by grasping the tape at one end-flap score line and pulling it away from the joint. The tape itself shall not delaminate and shall show evidence of fiber tear rather than fracture of the glue line.

9.7 General Electric—Beach Puncture Test

    9.71 This test provides a means of measuring the puncture resistance of the combined corrugated fiberboard and provides a fair indication of the efficiency with which the board has been manufactured.

    9.72 This method of test shall be in accordance with ASTM Tentative Method of Test for Puncture and Stiffness of Paperboard, Corrugated, and Solid Fiberboard, ASTM D781–44T, with the following revisions:
A minimum of four determinations shall be made, two with the outer facing uppermost and two with the inner facing uppermost. In each pair, one test shall be made with the corrugations parallel to the plane of the puncture arm, and the other with the corrugations perpendicular.

    9.73 The corrugated fiberboard fails to meet this specification when the average of the four tests is less than the criteria supplied.

Fig. 1. (Continued on next page.)

10. **Rejection**

  10.1 Failure to meet any of the above requirements, or those specified on supplementary specifications and/or drawings, shall be sufficient cause for rejection. The XYZ Manufacturing Company reserves the right to reject any portion or all of such material under the terms of the order or contract covering purchase of the material.

Appendix A

Grades of Materials Referred to under Fig. 1, Paragraph 3.

Corrugating Materials

	Minimum Weight Per 1,000 Sq. ft. (Lb.)	Minimum Caliper (In.)
*Semichemical hardwood corrugating material.........	26	0.009
*Fourdrinier Kraft corrugating material............	26	0.009
*Chestnut corrugating material......................	26	0.009

  *Other corrugating materials which meet the flat crush requirements of paragraph 9.55 may be substituted for those specified when supporting test data are furnished.

Combinations of Above Materials to Produce Specified Bursting Strengths

Test of Combined Board Specified (Lb. per sq. in.)	Minimum Combined Weight of Facings (Lb. per 1,000 sq. ft.)	Minimum Weight of Facings (Lb. per 1,000 sq. ft.)		
		Inner	Center	Outer
Single-Wall				
125	56	28		28
175	75	38†		38†
200	84	42		42
275	138	69		69
350	180	90		90
Double-Wall				
200	92	33	26	33
275	110	42	26	42
350	126	42	42	42
500	222	90	42	90
600	270	90	90	90

  † A combination of a 33-lb. inner and a 42-lb. outer facing may be used for 175-lb.-test combined board.

Fig. 1. (Concluded.)

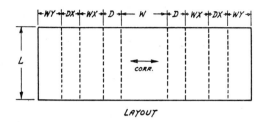
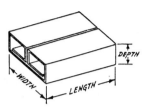

LAYOUT

FORMULAS FOR SHEET SIZES

DESCRIPTION OF BOARD	L	W	D	WX	WY	DX
DOUBLE FACE – "A" FLUTE	L-0"	$W-\frac{1}{8}$	$D-\frac{1}{8}$	$\frac{W}{2}-\frac{1}{8}$	$\frac{W}{2}-\frac{1}{4}$	$D-\frac{5}{16}$
DOUBLE FACE – "B" FLUTE	L-0"	$W-\frac{1}{8}$	$D-\frac{1}{8}$	$\frac{W}{2}-\frac{1}{8}$	$\frac{W}{2}-\frac{3}{16}$	$D-\frac{1}{4}$
DOUBLE WALL – "A" & "B" FLUTE	L-0"	$W-\frac{1}{4}$	$D-\frac{1}{4}$	$\frac{W}{2}-\frac{1}{4}$	$\frac{W}{2}-\frac{7}{16}$	$D-\frac{3}{16}$
DOUBLE FACE-"C" FLUTE	L-0"	$W-\frac{1}{8}$	$D-\frac{1}{8}$	$\frac{W}{2}-\frac{1}{8}$	$\frac{W}{2}-\frac{3}{16}$	$D-\frac{1}{4}$

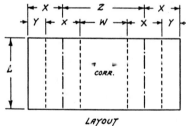
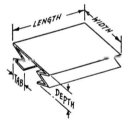

LAYOUT

─ · ─ INDICATE SCORES ON OPPOSITE SIDE

FORMULAS FOR SHEET SIZES

DESCRIPTION OF BOARD	L	W	X	Y	Z	DEPTH-FOR ITEMS UNDER 15 LBS.	OVER 15 LBS.
DOUBLE FACE – "A" FLUTE	L+0"	W+0"	2 x TAB	TAB	W+(2 x TAB)	1	$\frac{7}{8}$
DOUBLE FACE – "B" FLUTE	L+0"	W+0"	2 x TAB	TAB	W+(2 x TAB)	$\frac{3}{4}$	$\frac{5}{8}$
DOUBLE WALL – "A" & "B" FLUTE	L+0"	W+0"	2 x TAB	TAB	W+(2 x TAB)	$1\frac{1}{4}$	$1\frac{1}{8}$
DOUBLE FACE-"C" FLUTE	L+0"	W+0"	2 x TAB	TAB	W+(2 x TAB)	$\frac{7}{8}$	$\frac{3}{4}$

L, W, and D represent outside length, width, and depth of the space to be filled.

Fig. 2. (Top) air-cushion filler (scored sheet) and (bottom) spring-pad filler.

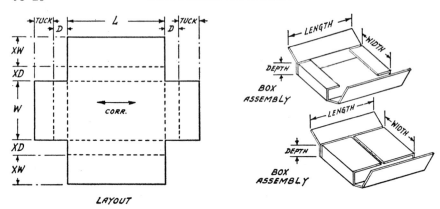

LAYOUT

BOX ASSEMBLY

BOX ASSEMBLY

FORMULAS FOR SHEET SIZES

DESCRIPTION OF BOARD	L	W	D	XW	XD	TUCK	
						FOR ONE-PIECE	FOR SPECIAL
DOUBLE FACE – "A" FLUTE	$L+\frac{1}{4}$	$W+\frac{1}{4}$	$D+\frac{1}{4}$	$\frac{W}{2}+\frac{3}{16}$	$D+\frac{3}{8}$	AS SPECIFIED	$\frac{L}{2}+\frac{1}{8}$
DOUBLE FACE – "B" FLUTE	$L+\frac{1}{8}$	$W+\frac{1}{8}$	$D+\frac{1}{8}$	$\frac{W}{2}+\frac{1}{8}$	$D+\frac{3}{16}$		$\frac{L}{2}+\frac{1}{16}$
DOUBLE WALL – "A" & "B" FLUTE	$L+\frac{3}{8}$	$W+\frac{3}{8}$	$D+\frac{3}{8}$	$\frac{W}{2}+\frac{1}{4}$	$D+\frac{5}{8}$		$\frac{L}{2}+\frac{3}{16}$
DOUBLE FACE–"C" FLUTE	$L+\frac{3}{16}$	$W+\frac{3}{16}$	$D+\frac{3}{16}$	$\frac{W}{2}+\frac{1}{8}$	$D+\frac{5}{16}$		$\frac{L}{2}+\frac{1}{16}$

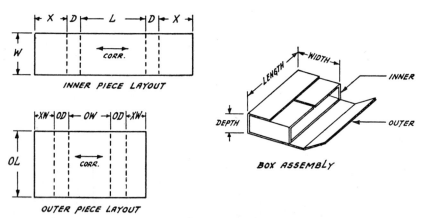

INNER PIECE LAYOUT

OUTER PIECE LAYOUT

BOX ASSEMBLY

FORMULAS FOR SHEET SIZES

DESCRIPTION OF BOARD	L	W	D	X	OL	OW	OD	XW
DOUBLE FACE – "A" FLUTE	$L+\frac{1}{4}$	$W+0''$	$D+\frac{1}{4}$	$\frac{L}{2}+\frac{1}{8}$	$L+\frac{3}{8}$	$W+\frac{1}{4}$	$D+\frac{9}{16}$	$\frac{W}{2}+\frac{1}{8}$
DOUBLE FACE – "B" FLUTE	$L+\frac{1}{8}$	$W+0''$	$D+\frac{1}{8}$	$\frac{L}{2}+\frac{1}{16}$	$L+\frac{1}{4}$	$W+\frac{1}{8}$	$D+\frac{5}{16}$	$\frac{W}{2}+\frac{1}{16}$
DOUBLE WALL –"A" & "B" FLUTE	$L+\frac{3}{8}$	$W+0''$	$D+\frac{3}{8}$	$\frac{L}{2}+\frac{3}{16}$	$L+\frac{5}{8}$	$W+\frac{3}{8}$	$D+\frac{11}{16}$	$\frac{W}{2}+\frac{3}{16}$
DOUBLE FACE–"C" FLUTE	$L+\frac{3}{16}$	$W+0''$	$D+\frac{3}{16}$	$\frac{L}{2}+\frac{1}{16}$	$L+\frac{5}{16}$	$W+\frac{3}{16}$	$D+\frac{1}{2}$	$\frac{W}{2}+\frac{1}{16}$

L, W, and D represent inside length, width, and depth of the containers.

Fig. 3. (Top) one-piece folder and (bottom) special one-piece folder.

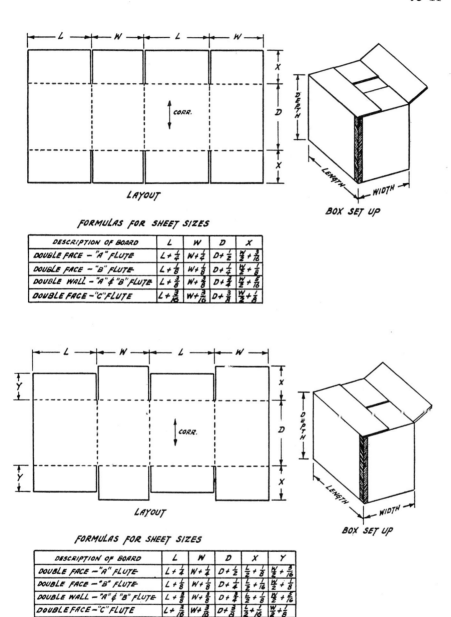

FORMULAS FOR SHEET SIZES

DESCRIPTION OF BOARD	L	W	D	X
DOUBLE FACE – "A" FLUTE	$L+\frac{1}{4}$	$W+\frac{1}{4}$	$D+\frac{1}{2}$	$\frac{W}{2}+\frac{3}{16}$
DOUBLE FACE – "B" FLUTE	$L+\frac{1}{8}$	$W+\frac{1}{8}$	$D+\frac{1}{4}$	$\frac{W}{2}+\frac{1}{8}$
DOUBLE WALL – "A" & "B" FLUTE	$L+\frac{3}{8}$	$W+\frac{3}{8}$	$D+\frac{3}{4}$	$\frac{W}{2}+\frac{5}{16}$
DOUBLE FACE – "C" FLUTE	$L+\frac{3}{16}$	$W+\frac{3}{16}$	$D+\frac{3}{8}$	$\frac{W}{2}+\frac{1}{8}$

FORMULAS FOR SHEET SIZES

DESCRIPTION OF BOARD	L	W	D	X	Y
DOUBLE FACE – "A" FLUTE	$L+\frac{1}{4}$	$W+\frac{1}{4}$	$D+\frac{1}{2}$	$\frac{L}{2}+\frac{1}{8}$	$\frac{W}{2}+\frac{3}{16}$
DOUBLE FACE – "B" FLUTE	$L+\frac{1}{8}$	$W+\frac{1}{8}$	$D+\frac{1}{4}$	$\frac{L}{2}+\frac{1}{16}$	$\frac{W}{2}+\frac{1}{8}$
DOUBLE WALL – "A" & "B" FLUTE	$L+\frac{3}{8}$	$W+\frac{3}{8}$	$D+\frac{3}{4}$	$\frac{L}{2}+\frac{1}{8}$	$\frac{W}{2}+\frac{5}{16}$
DOUBLE FACE – "C" FLUTE	$L+\frac{3}{16}$	$W+\frac{3}{16}$	$D+\frac{3}{8}$	$\frac{L}{2}+\frac{1}{16}$	$\frac{W}{2}+\frac{1}{8}$

L, W, and D represent inside length, width, and depth of the containers.

Fig. 4. (Top) regular slotted container and (bottom) special slotted container.

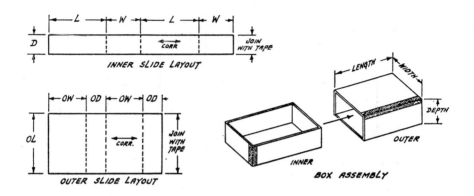

FORMULAS FOR SHEET SIZES

DESCRIPTION OF BOARD	L	W	D	OL	OW	OD
DOUBLE FACE – "A" FLUTE	$L+\frac{1}{4}$	$W+\frac{1}{4}$	$D+0''$	$L+\frac{3}{8}$	$W+\frac{5}{8}$	$D+\frac{3}{16}$
DOUBLE FACE – "B" FLUTE	$L+\frac{1}{8}$	$W+\frac{1}{8}$	$D+0''$	$L+\frac{1}{4}$	$W+\frac{3}{8}$	$D+\frac{1}{16}$
DOUBLE WALL – "A" & "B" FLUTE	$L+\frac{3}{8}$	$W+\frac{3}{8}$	$D+0''$	$L+\frac{1}{8}$	$W+1$	$D+\frac{1}{16}$
DOUBLE FACE – "C" FLUTE	$L+\frac{3}{16}$	$W+\frac{3}{16}$	$D+0''$	$L+\frac{5}{8}$	$W+\frac{1}{2}$	$D+\frac{3}{16}$

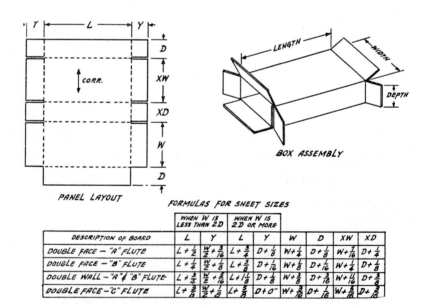

FORMULAS FOR SHEET SIZES

DESCRIPTION OF BOARD	WHEN W IS LESS THAN 2D		WHEN W IS 2D OR MORE		W	D	XW	XD
	L	Y	L	Y				
DOUBLE FACE – "A" FLUTE	$L+\frac{1}{2}$	$\frac{W}{2}+\frac{3}{16}$	$L+\frac{3}{4}$	$D+\frac{1}{8}$	$W+\frac{1}{4}$	$D+\frac{1}{8}$	$W+\frac{7}{16}$	$D+\frac{1}{4}$
DOUBLE FACE – "B" FLUTE	$L+\frac{1}{4}$	$\frac{W}{2}+\frac{1}{8}$	$L+\frac{3}{8}$	$D+\frac{1}{8}$	$W+\frac{1}{8}$	$D+\frac{1}{16}$	$W+\frac{1}{4}$	$D+\frac{1}{8}$
DOUBLE WALL – "A" & "B" FLUTE	$L+\frac{3}{4}$	$\frac{W}{2}+\frac{5}{16}$	$L+1\frac{1}{8}$	$D+\frac{1}{8}$	$W+\frac{3}{8}$	$D+\frac{3}{16}$	$W+\frac{11}{16}$	$D+\frac{3}{8}$
DOUBLE FACE – "C" FLUTE	$L+\frac{3}{8}$	$\frac{W}{2}+\frac{1}{8}$	$L+\frac{5}{8}$	$D+0''$	$W+\frac{3}{16}$	$D+\frac{1}{16}$	$W+\frac{5}{16}$	$D+\frac{3}{8}$

L, W, and D represent inside length, width, and depth of the containers.

Fig. 5. (Top) double-slide box and (bottom) five-panel folder.

from the tabulation since such specifications are subject to modification whenever changes occur in preferences of the public, merchandising techniques, shipping practices, and regulatory restrictions. Where the specifications are listed, they apply to existing federal requirements or common-carrier regulations.

CHECKING MATERIALS AGAINST GENERAL SPECIFICATIONS. To evaluate the quality of incoming materials, periodic checks are made at regularly scheduled intervals on random samplings of **materials submitted** or on materials suspected to be substandard in quality. Many of these checks may be made by the purchaser without the aid of specialized testing equipment. For corrugated fiberboard receipts the purchaser can fairly readily check such items as style, flutes, printing, joint construction, and dimensions. To some extent the purchaser can also evaluate workmanship as it relates to the alignment of the box blank, alignment and positioning of the manufacturer's joint, and the appearance of cut edges and slotting.

Two simple instruments can also provide a great deal of data directly on the purchaser's premises. These instruments are an **accurate scale or balance,** for weight determination, and a **caliper or micrometer,** for thickness determination. For more specialized properties **complex testing apparatus** is required. For these tests, and in case of dispute, the use of an independent testing laboratory is invaluable. The laboratory checks the compliance of a material against the provisions of specifications. The purchaser can then notify the supplier of any variations in quality.

Detailed Packaging Specifications. In many instances it is necessary to translate packaging requirements into **drawings** or sketches. This requirement is particularly true when the packaging and interior details are complex or have special characteristics, such as die cutting, multiple scoring, etc. The drawing provides a working blueprint for the supplier and guards against misunderstandings and misinterpretations of terms. In addition the detailed drawing assists the manufacturer in the preparation of his bid. The typical specifications, shown in Fig. 1 would therefore include charts and diagrams, as indicated by Paragraph 2.1. Figs. 2, 3, 4, and 5 are examples of such supplementary drawings.

Interior Packaging

INTERIOR PACKAGING DETAILS. To satisfy such design requirements as cushioning, separation, suspension, surface protection, clearance, etc., it is often necessary to include interior packaging details. These interior pieces may take many forms and can be made of any of a number of materials or combinations of materials, including corrugated or solid fiberboard, wood, excelsior, shredded paper, foam rubber, rubberized hair, etc. All these media may take various shapes or forms and are available in varying grades and constructions. The nature of the interior packaging to be used is contingent upon the requirements of the contents. For many items the type, quantity, and arrangement of the interior packaging are specified in the regulations of the common carrier. Quite often, the carriers will specify **minimum requirements** for any given commodity, and it may be necessary to add more material in some instances. For new packages it is important to provide enough interior packaging to protect against the hazards which may be encountered by the shipping container in handling and transit. The type of carrier, the length of travel, the number of handlings, the nature of the warehousing, etc., are all contributing factors.

The shipment of articles too **fragile** to withstand the shocks and vibrations of handling and transportation requires special packaging consideration. Less fragile articles may survive the hazards of shipment because of the cushioning that is provided by ordinary rigid containers. Since fragile articles require additional cushioning, there is a considerable increase in the **cost** of the packaged article. Not only is the cost of the cushioning material to be considered but also the **volume and weight** that the cushioning adds to the package. To attain a high degree of economy, the amount of cushioning material must be kept to the minimum consistent with adequate protection. Obviously, the determination of this minimum safe amount of cushioning material presents problems. Inasmuch as it is impossible to estimate the correct amount, and since it has generally not been feasible to determine it empirically, mathematical methods have been developed.

Cushioning. The **mathematical problem** of determining the amount of cushioning required to protect a fragile article during shipment depends upon the following factors:

1. The shock and the vibration that are encountered.
2. The capacity of the article to withstand shock and vibration.
3. The mechanical properties of the cushioning material.

There are several kinds of **shock** and **vibration.** In handling, a package may drop onto one of its corners and roll onto one of its faces, or it may be dropped flat onto a face. In transportation it may be subjected to vibration over wide ranges of frequencies and may undergo jolts of varying force and duration. Many of these shocks may be reduced in passing through the outer container. The capacity of an item to withstand shock and vibration may depend on the way in which the article is mounted in its container. Its shock resistance may also depend on the direction of the shock and on its duration.

With respect to the mechanical properties of a **cushioning material,** consideration must be given to its shock-absorbing properties. The shock-absorbing properties depend on the material's load-deflection characteristics, which, in turn, are affected by the material's inertia and damping. The load-deflection characteristics may also depend upon the shape of the cushion. The relationship of these factors to the amount of cushioning material required to protect a fragile article is therefore quite complex. There is no mathematical determination of cushioning requirements to take all these factors into account. A system has been developed, however, to provide for a solution of the cushioning problem based upon the information presently available.

Considerable simplification has been achieved by considering that the shocks that have to be met can be represented by those which occur when the package is **dropped from a height.** This procedure is justified by experience with the proof-testing of packaged articles for safe transit. Experience has shown that there is generally a certain height of drop which may be used to proof-test packaged articles for a given transporting and handling system. In other words, the relatively simple shock pattern that is produced by dropping a packaged article is generally adequate to indicate its performance under the more complex shocks of transportation and handling. The simplified shock pattern of the **drop test** is the basis of the existing theoretical studies of cushioning. To achieve further simplification of the shock pattern, the drop test has been limited to a drop squarely onto a face of a package. There are excellent theoretical treatments of this case (R. D. Mindlin, "Dynamics of Package Cushioning," Bell System Technical Journal, Monograph B-1369. R. R. Janssen, "A Method for the Proper Selection of Package Cushioning Materials to Provide Minimum Container Cubage," North

American Aviation, Inc., 1952). The application of these studies, however, requires a stress-strain curve for each cushioning material under consideration. Moreover, the concepts and mathematics involved are highly complex.

An **alternate solution** to the problem of the drop test has been developed by the Forest Products Laboratory ("Manual of Cushioning Material, Design Criteria, and their Application," Supply Engineering Division, U. S. Naval Supply Research and Development Facility, Bayonne, New Jersey). A set of tables has been prepared which shows the required thicknesses of various cushioning materials for a drop height of 30 in. These tables, however, are rather voluminous, to accommodate a wide range of package weights and sizes; and new sets of tables would have to be issued periodically for new cushioning materials. Nor does this technique readily indicate the best cushioning material for the problem at hand.

To overcome all these difficulties and to make cushioning calculations feasible for those who are faced with a cushioning problem, a **single chart of cushioning calculations** was developed recently by Container Laboratories, Inc., Washington Division, in consultation with R. D. Mindlin. This cushioning nomogram (Fig. 6) was prepared for the Bureau of Ordnance, Naval Ordnance Laboratory, and serves as a valuable tool in the application of package cushioning materials. In using this chart, only the simplest arithmetic is required. To facilitate calculations, the compressive performance of each cushioning material, which is usually represented by a stress-strain curve, is expressed numerically. These compression performance numbers were determined for many cushioning materials and have been set up in the form of tables. To calculate the **thickness required** to cushion an article with a particular material, the chart is entered with the compressive performance numbers for this material. Only the chart and the table of compressive performance numbers are required to make cushioning calculations for a wide range of materials. For simplicity the chart has been prepared in alignment form. The chart itself does not require modification for new materials, but the compressive performance numbers of a new material would have to be determined.

General

This nomogram is an alignment chart which is read by connecting known points on adjacent vertical scales with a straight line and extending this line until it intersects the adjacent vertical line (see line *A-B* on example). Another straight line is then drawn from this intersection through a known point on the next vertical scale and extended to the next vertical line. This procedure is continued across the chart in either or both directions until a line is drawn to intersect the vertical scale whose value is to be found (see example on nomogram).

To use this nomogram it is necessary to know the stiffness factor and deflection factor of the cushioning materials being considered. These factors are derived from the load-deflection curve for the material in accordance with a prescribed procedure and must be furnished by the manufacturer or a testing laboratory.

Instructions

This nomogram can be used to solve quickly several types of cushioning problems, such as the following:

1. At the outset of a package design problem, it is often desirable **to estimate the minimum possible thickness** of a cushioning material if the proper combination of bearing area and stiffness of materials could be attained. This preliminary operation will show whether a pad-type cushion will provide a practical solution and will set a minimum thickness at which to aim.

PART 1

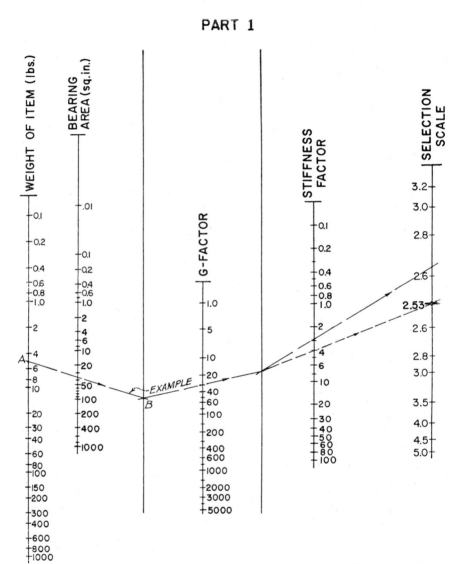

Fig. 6. Cushion-

PART 2

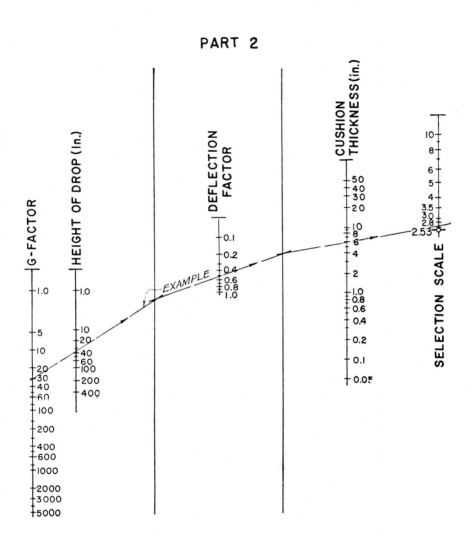

ing nomogram.

Procedure. Enter Part 2 with the G-factor and height of drop. Use the largest deflection factor of the available materials. Use the number 2.53 on the Selection Scale. Read the cushion thickness. (This is a preliminary operation, and neither the material selected nor the thickness read should be considered final. Read the remaining instructions.)

2. One of the most common cushioning problems is **to determine the required thickness** of a given cushioning material, when the bearing area is fixed.

Procedure. Enter Part 1 with the weight of the item, its bearing area, its G-factor, and the stiffness factor of the material. Read the number on the Selection Scale, and transfer this number to the Selection Scale in Part 2. Enter Part 2 with the G-factor, height of drop, and the deflection factor of the material. Read the cushion thickness.

3. Another common cushioning problem is **to select a material which will provide a cushion of minimum thickness** when the bearing area is fixed.

Procedure. Enter Part 1 with the weight of the item, its bearing area, its G-factor, and the number 2.53 on the Selection Scale. Read the stiffness factor, and select a material whose stiffness factor is close to this value. (Then determine the required thickness by the procedure described in Instruction 2.)

4. It is sometimes desirable, where practicable, to modify the package design **to provide the bearing area that results in a cushion of minimum thickness** of a given material.

Procedure. Enter Part 1 with the weight of the item, its G-factor, the number 2.53 on the Stiffness Scale, and the stiffness factor of the material. Read the bearing area. (Then determine the required thickness by the procedure described in Instruction 2.)

Protective Packaging

PURPOSES OF PROTECTIVE PACKAGING. Protective packaging can be analyzed from various standpoints and has been defined in several different ways. It is generally agreed, however, that protection is a function of all elements of the package, including the shipping container, interior-packing details, reinforcing materials, and closure media. The discussion here is limited to the subsidiary aspects of protective packaging, such as prevention of abrasion; defenses against water, moisture, and grease; safeguards against thermal and barometric changes; protection against light; control of the moisture content of the product; protection against insect infestation, odor, mold, pilferage, etc.

Prevention of Abrasion. It is important to position the product in its container so that finished surfaces do not come directly into contact with the shipping container itself or with any of its other contents. Preventive methods include inserting extra protective materials between the surface of the product and the packing materials. Typical inserts include cellulose wadding; unbacked, paper-backed, and/or embossed macerated newsprint or excelsior within retaining paper linings; papers coated or impregnated with wax or oils; felts or blankets; and other protective separations.

Protection Against Water, Moisture, and Grease. Coatings, hot- and cold-dip strippable compounds, and petroleum preservatives are among the protective materials commonly used. Excellent descriptions of cleaning and preservative methods and materials are readily obtainable. With most of these special coatings, supplementary greaseproof wraps are required. Joint Army-Navy specifications list and describe the use of many of these protective coatings.

Waterproof liners in the form of bays and overlapping-seam sheets are another means for protection against moisture and grease. These bags are vented or remain unsealed. They are usually made of laminated, coated, or impregnated papers, which may be flat, creped in one or two directions, or, occasionally, reinforced with fibers in one or both directions. The coatings or impregnants may be waxes, resins, etc., and the barriers may be asphalt, film, or foil. They are classed under Specification JAN-P-125, covering flexible waterproof barrier materials; JAN-P-117 for waterproof, greaseproof, and/or water-vaporproof interior-packaging bags; MIL-B-131A for water-vaporproof barrier materials and MIL-L-10547A covering waterproof case liners.

To prevent condensation of moisture on ferrous metal parts when changes in temperature occur, a **low relative humidity must be maintained** within a package. Water-vaporproof barriers in the form of bags, liners, or pouches are used to enclose packaged items. Closure is usually accomplished by heat-sealing after the entrapped air is exhausted by suction. The materials used for **water-vaporproof** barriers include paper- or scrim-backed lead and aluminum foils, laminated polyethylene and vinyl sheets, and similar protective media.

When the volume of air enclosed in a barrier is relatively large, it is common practice to use a desiccant to maintain low relative humidity. The amount of **desiccant** needed is computed by taking into consideration the moisture-vapor transmission rate of the barrier material, the area of the barriers, and the amount of dunnage enclosed. Silica gel and montmorillonite are the products used most commonly in dehydrated packs. Reference material covering desiccants is contained in military specification MIL-D-3436.

Volatile-corrosion inhibitors are becoming more widely used for protective packaging. VCI papers should be placed as close to all surfaces of the item as possible. VCI packaging is designed primarily for the protection of iron and steel parts, and care should be exercised when it is used for protecting nonferrous metals and nonmetallic surfaces.

Whichever method is chosen to inhibit corrosion, it is essential to follow **established cleaning methods** before packing the article to be protected. None of the methods will remove rust, and all are less effective when corrosion has developed in the article before packaging. Grease-resistant materials, such as laminated films and foils, wax-impregnated or wax-coated papers, glassine or other paper products, are generally used to retain light oils on protected parts. These same materials retain essential oils in packaged food products and prevent dissipation of such staples as butter, lard, etc.

Protection Against Temperature and Barometric Change. The principles followed for guarding against temperature change are simple and effective. Frequently materials of an insulating nature are used for surrounding the packaged items, thus forming dead air cells. The **insulation** usually consists of built-up corrugated fiberboard forms, macerated newsprint between two paper facings furnished in liner or bag form, glass-fiber products, mineral-wool mats, or plain and quilted pads. Lead or aluminum foil is sometimes incorporated in the packaging to serve as a reflector to reduce temperature changes. Methods for **precooling or preheating** the entire package immediately before packaging for shipment have also been utilized. Ice or Dry Ice are used as refrigerants in some packages to minimize spoilage from temperature changes.

Packages moving by airplane are subject to certain **special hazards,** such as sudden changes in air pressure. Cargo compartments of airplanes, although pressurized to some extent, are such that in many instances the pressure on the packages will be reduced in less than an hour from atmospheric to that existing at about 10,000-ft. altitude. Most cargo is not affected by this hazard, but some items, especially liquids, are. In most instances packages transported by airplane should be so designed that they will be able to withstand internal pressures up to

10 lb. per sq. in. without damage. Most cargo-airplane compartments are rather poorly heated, and sometimes rapid changes in temperature also occur.

Protection Against Light. Many products require complete or partial protection against light. Foils, opaque papers, metal cans, and colored glass are some of the materials utilized for this purpose. One of the most light-sensitive products packaged is photographic film.

The degree of exposure to light obviously must be kept under control during both packaging and distribution operations. **Colored packaging materials** for filtering light have been used successfully with some products; for example, they are used to help prevent rancidity in potato chips. Opaque packages have likewise been used for other food products, such as bacon.

Controlling the Moisture Content of a Product. The control of moisture and water vapor is an extremely important consideration in packaging. Products which require moisture protection can be classified into two general categories: **dry** products and **wet** products. Examples of dry products are cereals, cake mixes, dried milk powders, crackers, etc. Wet products include dried fruits, meats, bread, frozen foods, etc. For dry products the moisture-protective barrier must prevent absorption of an excessive amount of moisture. For wet products the barrier must prevent drying out of the product or absorption of more moisture where there are moist storage conditions. Factors to take into account in packaging both kinds of products include:

1. Ratio of area of packaging materials to weight of product.
2. Hygroscopicity of the product.
3. Moisture level of product.
4. Shelf life.
5. Handling of packaged product.
6. Moisture protection during product use.

Insect Infestation. Certain items, such as cereals, powdered products, and cellulose products, are highly susceptible to insect infestation. Control of this condition initiates in the manufacturing departments and extends throughout all distribution channels. Insect infestation can be minimized by careful rotation of stock.

Most manufacturers have succeeded in **eliminating infestation** during manufacture by use of modern insect-control methods. Thereafter it is primarily a function of packaging to keep out insects. The tightly closed package is the best defense against insects. Packaging materials which retain product odors within the package have also materially assisted in this problem. **Insecticide-treated packaging materials** have been used with some success, particularly on bags for flour. Chemically treated packaging materials have been used more widely for repelling rodents.

Guarding Against Odor and Mold. The presence of odors may present a number of packaging problems, depending upon the nature of the product. With some products the packaging must protect against undesirable loss of odor. In other instances the packaging must not impart odor to the contents. Some products tend to absorb odors and must not be stored near odoriferous merchandise. It is frequently the practice to print recommended storage conditions on shipping containers to guide the recipient of merchandise.

Packaging materials with low gas-transmission rates are necessary for the packaging of products which lose their odors. Glass and metal are excellent **gas barriers** and are commonly used for such products. Some foods are high in chemical activity and will react with unlined metal cans to give the foods a metallic flavor. Care must be taken to select a can lining which will prevent this chemical interaction. Some packaged products may absorb **packaging-material odors.** Fiberboard, ink, solvent, and chemical odors may develop in packaging materials.

Products subject to bacterial or mold action must be handled and processed with utmost care before and during packaging. The package itself must be of such construction as to arrest bacterial action after packaging. **Glass and metal containers** are generally used for products susceptible to bacteria. It is necessary for the package to be of such construction that it will withstand processing operations at high temperatures and high humidity. This factor presents another reason for the use of glass and metal containers.

Cold temperatures help to cut down the development of mold in food products. The exclusion of air or oxygen is also important in preventing mold growth. The removal of air or oxygen from within packages can also extend the shelf life of a product.

Reducing Pilferage. Preventing pilferage has always been a perplexing problem. Packages cannot readily be made completely pilferproof, but many safeguards can be taken which will minimize losses. Materials and packages cannot be constantly guarded, but one of the best rules to follow is to make potential pilferage very time-consuming.

Prevention of **tampering with merchandise** is also a serious problem. Many kinds of protective devices are employed to reduce tampering, including printed tape or wrappings, special inserts for bottles and jars, and similar measures.

Packaging and Materials Handling

MECHANIZED MATERIALS HANDLING. Mechanized materials handling facilities are employed in production. However, the coordination between materials handling and packaging is often imperfect. Production-line techniques can be utilized in packaging merchandise for warehousing and ultimate shipping.

Rarely can mechanized materials handling be successfully introduced into the packaging operation without some **modification in the packaging.** Therefore it is necessary to balance the advantages and disadvantages of such a transition. Materials handling devices are advantageous where their use lessens the over-all cost of storage, shipment, materials, or space and when it prevents damage to merchandise. Materials handling devices are worthwhile when they provide greater utilization of facilities or shorten distribution time. The disadvantages include initial investment for such devices, storage and maintenance, increased shipping weights, and the necessity for adequate terminal equipment. The degree of efficiency of those packaging operations and general plant facilities, which naturally precede the introduction of materials handling methods, will have a large bearing upon the extent to which these methods can be economically justified.

TESTING THE PHYSICAL CHARACTERISTICS OF PACKAGING. Container and materials testing is a technique for predetermining the probable performance of containers and materials when they are put into actual use. Scientific instruments have been developed that simulate almost every conceivable stress and condition to which packages and their component materials are known to be subjected during their useful life. This life extends from the factory processes of forming, filling, and closing through the sometimes tortuous path of conveyors; over the shocks of movement in trucks, freight cars, ships, and airplanes; under the pressure of loads piled upon them; in conditions of heat, cold, sun, and moisture; and under the handling by warehousemen, stevedores, and mechanical devices.

Test cycles can be devised to simulate any of the conditions which may likely be encountered by the package under consideration. A representative number of tests through this cycle will give an accurate indication of the actual performance to be anticipated from the tested package. **Performance tests** on complete packages or on properly predetermined segments of packages are the key to the selection of the best functional designs and to the maintenance of acceptable quality once the proper designs have been selected. Pretesting can prevent wasteful initial expenditures and damages to improperly protected packaged products. Some of the more commonly used testing devices are described herein. Although designed for specific purposes, each may be adapted to fit specialized needs.

Container Testing

TESTS FOR CONTAINERS. Before containers developed for shipping purposes are put into service, it is necessary to apply exhaustive tests to them in order to determine whether or not they will stand up under the considerable abuse they will be subjected to in actual use. The kinds of tests described here are typical of a considerable range of containers in general service. If the majority of the containers put through these tests stand up satisfactorily, hold their shapes to a reasonable degree, and in the main protect the contents from breakage, spillage, crushing, and other hazards, it is likely that these particular containers can be trusted to carry the contemplated loads with maximum safety and satisfaction.

Bursting Test. The bursting strength of fiberboard sheets is perhaps the most universally accepted basis for evaluating their quality. This measure represents a convenient means of identifying various grades of corrugated and solid fiberboard and, in addition, is one of the properties frequently specified in the Uniform and Consolidated Freight Classifications and other carrier regulations.

The **Mullen tester** is the instrument most frequently used to measure this property. Operation of the machine, usually electrically driven, exerts hydraulic pressure on a rubber diaphragm through a circular area of approximately 1 sq. in. The resultant upward bulge of the diaphragm causes it to puncture the specimen. The force required for the burst is recorded on a calibrated dial. This basic test is applied wherever papers and paperboards are made or used in fabrication.

Revolving-Drum Test. The revolving drum subjects containers to treatment closely simulating handling during transportation. The machine used in this test is a 7-ft. **hexagonal drum** resembling a large barrel placed on its bilge. On the inside faces of the drum is arranged a series of baffles which cause the container to fall on its various parts in succession as the drum revolves at a constant rate of nearly 2 r.p.m. The number of falls which the loaded container can withstand in the revolving drum before failure is a measure of its serviceability. The failures occur gradually, so weaknesses of design and construction can be readily detected. **Check tests** on new or redesigned packages can be made in this manner.

The revolving drum does not simulate all of the hazards of handling and shipment—nor does any one testing device—but it does cause buffeting similar to that encountered in transportation. Furthermore it represents a convenient means of simulating such shocks, of comparing resistance to tearing and bursting open, and of observing protection provided to the contents.

Tape tests can also be carried out with this instrument. A tape which is to be tested is affixed to the manufacturer's joint of a specially designed box whose unusual dimensions provide an exceptionally long joint, although the volume of the container is not too large. The tape at the manufacturer's joint is subjected to severe stresses which are likely to result, eventually, in its failure.

Puncture Test. The puncture test is performed on a General Electric puncture-tester and is a measure of the energy required to force a **puncture head** of designated size and shape completely through a sample of the material to be tested. The specimen is held between two clamping plates, and a pendulum that has an arm in the form of a 90° arc is released by trigger action from a horizontal position. A puncture point affixed to the end of the rod and having the shape of a right-angle triangular pyramid 1 in. in height punctures the specimen. A reading, in inch-ounces per inch of tear, is made on a scale after the pendulum has completed its swing. By a suitable variation in technique the stiffness of the tested materials can also be measured.

The puncture test, although similar in some respects to the bursting test, differs in that it reflects the structural nature of the material being evaluated and, in the case of corrugated fiberboard, also reflects to a certain extent the quality of the adhesion of the facing materials to the fluted medium. Thus it provides a better measure of effectiveness of fiberboard, plywood, etc., as a component of a container.

Compression Test. The compression test subjects containers to compressive forces similar to those to which they may be subjected while en route in freight cars and when stored in warehouses. Each container is tested individually in a large compression machine which consists of a platform scale over which a power-driven crossbeam is mounted. The container to be tested is placed between two parallel surfaces (one, the scale platform; the other, a platen under the crossbeam), and the applied pressure is read upon an attached calibrated dial at each increase of 0.1 in. in the compression or distance that the opposite surfaces of the container are forced together.

One of the most common uses of compression tests is to measure the **quality of fabrication of containers,** since the test specimens tend to fail at points of structural weakness. However, results of compression tests can also be used within broad limits for determining safe stacking loads and warehousing periods of loaded containers. For most purposes the boxes are tested empty, but filled boxes may be tested, for example, to determine distortion of contents under piling loads or end compression, as in freight cars.

Incline-Impact Test. The incline-impact test simulates the stresses applied to merchandise in carriers such as freight cars or trucks when they make sudden starts or stops. It consists essentially of releasing a loaded container, mounted on a movable-platform dolly which rides on a plane inclined 10° from the horizontal, from a known distance up the incline and permitting it to strike against a fixed backstop at the bottom of the plane and perpendicular to it. The magnitude of the impact shock is varied by using different release points.

A variation of this test, frequently employed when the gross weight of the loaded container is small or when the distribution cycle includes gravity chutes at the end of conveyor lines, consists of placing a weight equivalent to that of the loaded container on the dolly behind the sample being evaluated, thus allowing it to compress the tested package upon impact. This test applies stresses to the loaded container similar to those encountered when it is part of a full carload or truckload.

Cushioning Test. The cushioning test is based upon the principle that for most packaged products subjected to arrested motion, such as in an incline-impact test, the maximum value of the **rate of change of velocity** (that is, the maximum rate of deceleration) is a good measure of the shock to which the object is subjected. One instrument used to measure the deceleration is a General Electric cushioning meter, or "G-meter," consisting of an electric indicator and a detector head connected to the indicator by a flexible cable.

A typical application is to attach the detector head to the object or to a dummy of equivalent dimensions, weight, and center of gravity, the object or dummy then being packaged in the normal manner. The package is next subjected to shocks, such as in incline-impact tests. At each shock the detector head responds to the maximum value of deceleration reached by the object or dummy and actuates an electronic circuit which causes appropriate lamps to glow on the indicator. The lamps are calibrated directly in G's, one G being the acceleration of a falling body due to gravity, or 32.2 ft. per sec. per sec.

Fragile items, such as bottles for liquids, lend themselves to this kind of testing. An interesting use of the cushion meter is in determining the relative cushioning qualities of materials such as excelsior, cellulosic wadding, etc. Blocks of various weights and shapes are permitted to fall upon the materials, to which the cushion-meter head, which will measure the amount of shock absorbed by the materials, has been attached.

Vibration Test. Vibration tests are designed to simulate the **forces, motions, accelerations, bumps, jars, and weaving** that are typical of railroad freight cars, motor trucks, conveyors, etc. The vibration machine consists of a sturdy wooden table supported on two cross-shafts, one near each end of the table. Each of the shafts carries two eccentrics which have a total amplitude of 1 in. resulting in a movement by the table of the vibration machine similar to that of the floor of a boxcar or of a truck. The speed or number of cycles per minute and the type of motion or combinations of motions may be varied by suitable adjustments.

Although vibration tests rarely cause failure in shipping containers, they frequently produce deterioriation or partial crushing of the unit or interior packing. In addition, the vibration tester can disclose weaknesses in the assembly of the packed item and susceptibility to smearing or blurring of printed surfaces in contact with one another. The vibration is generally used in cycle with one or more other tests.

Basis-Weight Determination. "Basis weight" expresses the weight of a known quantity of a specimen of a given area. Thus for the components used in the manufacture of corrugated fiberboard boxes, basis weight is expressed in terms of **pounds per 1,000 sq. ft.,** while for most papers it is determined for pounds per 500 sheets, 24 × 36 in. in size. Determinations can be carried out upon special basis-weight scales or by weighing a known area of a sample on a precise scale and making the necessary calculations. Thus the amount of material in a given area of board is measured.

Tensile Test. Tensile tests determine the **tenacity of fibers** comprising a sample and are performed by clamping the ends of a specimen of known length and width between two jaws of an electrically driven machine. The operation of the machine separates the jaws, and the force required to rupture the sample is read from a calibrated dial. Rope and twine, as well as other materials, may be evaluated in this manner. The tensile test can be adapted to indicate the strength of the manufacturer's joint of corrugated fiberboard containers, and another variation permits measurement of the nailhead pulling and shearing resistance of plywood and fiberboard used for the paneling of cleated boxes.

Greaseproof Tests. Greaseproof tests measure the resistance of a sample to the transmission of grease. One method of carrying out the test consists of placing a medium, such as turpentine or a specific type of oil, on one surface of the sample and determining the time required for the medium to penetrate the sample and spot book paper previously placed beneath the test piece. The medium is usually dyed to facilitate identification of the time when complete penetration occurs.

Tearing Test. Tearing tests are made on a standard Elmendorf tearing tester; they determine the **internal tearing resistance** of a material. Test specimens cut to a specified length are torn by a pendulum action. An indicator records the amount that the free swing of the pendulum is retarded by the tearing of the specimen. Tearing tests are usually performed upon papers, plies of multiwall shipping sacks, folding boxboard, wrapping materials, and tapes, although these tests need not be restricted to these materials.

Drop Test. The drop test consists of releasing a loaded container from a known height onto a concrete floor or flat metal base. The height can be varied, and the test can be controlled so that just the part of the box to be tested will strike the base. The exact treatment given each tested container is therefore known. Any suitable device which permits reproducibility can be employed for this most basic performance test. An electric hoist with a releasing mechanism and the Acme drop tester are the instruments most frequently used. A modification of this test, frequently employed in the evaluation of loaded containers to be transmitted by parcel post, consists of placing the sample upon the floor and dropping an object of known gross weight upon it from a given initial height.

Ring Stiffness Test. Tests which measure the stiffness or rigidity of paper or paperboard are particularly valuable in establishing the **rigidity** of uncombined liners and corrugating material before they are fabricated into single- or double-wall sacks or boxes. A $6 \times \frac{1}{2}$ in. specimen is cut and inserted into a grooved holder to form a ring or collar 6 in. in circumference. Specimen and holder are then placed between two small parallel platens of the stiffness tester. The latter is in effect a small compression machine in which compressed air is used to raise the lower platen against the fixed upper platen. The force required to crush the specimen is transmitted directly to a platform scale which records this measure of rigidity on a calibrated dial.

Scuffing Test. The scuffing test measures the resistance of a material to scuffing and surface peeling that result from **continual rubbing** against a similar material. Such abrasion frequently is encountered in transit when boxes with surfaces in contact are kept in continual motion by the jouncing or vibration of the transport vehicle. The test is made by mechanically rubbing together, under a pressure of 0.2 lb. per sq. in. at maximum contact area, the outer or finished surface of two identical specimens. The number of double strokes required to produce peeling of the surface of one of the two specimens is noted as the point of failure. This test should not be confused with an abrasion test, in which the test sample is rubbed against a known abrasive. The scuffing test is useful primarily for comparative analysis of two or more materials, because the end point representing failure differs markedly for various wrappers, papers, and kindred materials.

Flat Crush Test. Flat crush tests measure the force required to crush the corrugations in a sheet of combined corrugated fiberboard. A circular specimen with an area usually of 9 sq. in. is tested in a small compression machine. Electrically driven pressure is applied to the flat surfaces of the specimen, and the **load required to cause the corrugations to collapse** is read on a calibrated dial. This test accurately simulates the "thumb-and-forefinger" test, which many purchasers of corrugated fiberboard containers perform as a crude measure of quality. Flat crush resistance is related to cushioning properties and, in general, is influenced by the flute of the corrugations, the type of corrugated medium employed, and the efficiency with which the board has been fabricated.

Visualator. The Visualator is a device for measuring the visual characteristics of packages, car cards, advertisements, and billboards. The device, which projects color photographs of the subject upon a screen, has calibrated mechanical controls to change the three variables influencing visibility. The three variables are **focal quality** ranging from distortion to perfect reproduction, thus giving effect to deviations from normal or 20–20 vision; **illumination quality,** ranging from invisibility to full visibility to measure legibility under varied light conditions; and **time quality,** ranging from 1/200 sec. to stationary view, thus evaluating the time interval at the threshold of legibility.

Values determined at the point of legibility under each of these test procedures may be used for comparing several printing designs for the same product or for several competing products. Tests can be made to evaluate isolated segments of designs, such as trade-mark, color, typography, product description, or illustration. Photographs may be made under controlled conditions or at point of sale or display, singly or in groups.

Caliper Determination. Caliper determinations measure the **thickness** of the sample of material being investigated. Although thickness is not a direct strength property, it is often correlated with such properties. In any event measurement of thickness constitutes a frequently employed means of identification of various grades of material. Furthermore, it is a specific requirement for such diverse items as the cleats on wood-cleated containers, the corrugating medium in corrugated fiberboard boxes and weatherproof solid-fiberboard boxes. Vernier and standard automatic dial micrometers are employed for more precise determinations of this kind. These instruments are sufficiently precise to measure the difference in thickness of various human hairs.

Weatherproofness Test. Weatherproof corrugated and solid fiberboard containers are made from special materials and are combined with a special adhesive so that the bursting strength will remain relatively high and the separation of the components will be extremely slight, even after prolonged submersion in water. There are several grades of weatherproof materials, and the requirements for them are contained in joint Army–Navy Specification JAN-P-108. This specification includes dry bursting-strength minimums, caliper minimums, wet bursting-strength minimums, and ply-separation maximums. A prerequisite for measurement of wet bursting strength and ply separation is submersion for 24 hr. of 6 × 10 in. specimens in a prescribed fashion in a tank of water maintained at a temperature between 70° and 80° F.

PALLETIZATION

CONTENTS

PALLETIZATION

DEFINITION AND IMPORTANCE OF PALLETIZATION. A pallet is a platform made to hold one or more boxes, bags, cartons, etc., in a group, thus permitting the load to be transported and stored as a unit. The pallet is one of the simplest and most important single devices in the whole range of modern materials handling equipment. It is the basis of the new philosophy of handling materials in lots of 3, 5, 10, 100 or more instead of handling one at a time, and its use is thus the most obvious way to save time, money, and human effort in handling. Generally speaking, it is advantageous to use as few pallet sizes as possible in any plant or warehouse, so that the handling procedure can be standardized.

Pallets are almost mandatory today in any industry that handles commercial quantities of **material that lends itself to stacking.** It is claimed that the greatest single gain in industrial handling efficiency has come through the introduction of pallets and the special-purpose machinery, such as the fork truck, for handling pallets. Reports of efficiency gains of 200 to 300 percent through a system of palletization are commonplace.

The next most important gain in industrial efficiency through pallets is brought about by increasing their area of use. Ideally, palletized loads should be made up at the point of manufacture, with all storage, shipping, distribution, and other handling operations, up to the actual point of use, retaining the original unit load. While this practice is being followed to some extent, there is vast room for further expansion.

Pallets are constructed in several types, according to their various uses. They are usually made in standard sizes and arrangements. The typical **standard wooden pallet** is 4 ft. × 4 ft. in area and 6 in. high; it consists of two layers of 1-in. boards held apart by 2 × 4 in. stringers—one down each of two opposite parallel sides and one down the middle, thus allowing the forks of a lift truck to enter the gap between the upper and lower layer of boards. The boards may be close together sideways, or they may be spaced to lighten the pallets. For lighter service, pallets may be constructed as single-face pallets with boards on one side only. Where durability, lightness, repetitive use, or stacking of one load on another are essential, there are in use several kinds of pallets made from different materials, such as steel, aluminum, wire mesh, and paperboard, each of which serves particular needs.

Classification of Pallets

EXPENDABLE VS. PERMANENT PALLETS. Pallets are divided basically into two classes: **expendable** and **permanent.** Any pallet that is light enough to ship economically and that is inexpensive enough to scrap, usually after one use, is said to be expendable. Expendable pallets may be made of wood or paper. They offer the following **advantages** (Modern Materials Handling, vol. 6):

1. To the **shipper** where materials are palletized but heretofore have not been shipped on pallets:
   a. Reduced loading time of carriers.
   b. Reduction in cost of space for empty pallet storage.
   c. Reduction in cost of handling empty pallets.
   d. Reduction in demurrage and peak load expense.
   e. Reduction in damage losses to shipper.
   f. Reduction in strength, quantity, and cost of individual packaging.
   g. Tax savings.
   h. Less stenciling and marking costs.
   i. Less pilferage.
   j. Reduction in accidents from handling empty wood pallets.
   k. Fewer shortage and inventory losses.
   l. Savings in intermediate handling for shipper and/or receiver.
   m. Improved service to customer.
2. To the **shipper** where materials are already shipped on permanent pallets:
   a. Reduced freight charges on weight of pallets.
   b. No freight on return of pallets.
   c. No investment in permanent pallets.
   d. No pallet maintenance.
   e. Less space required for empty pallet storage.
   f. Less cost to handle empty pallets.
   g. Fewer accidents.
   h. Tax saving.
3. To the **receiver** when materials are received on pallets:
   a. Less unloading time.
   b. Less annual cost of pallets.
   c. Less empty pallet storage space needed.
   d. Less cost to handle empty pallets.
   e. Reduction in demurrage and peak load costs.
   f. Fewer damage losses, less time sorting damaged goods.
   g. Less cost for sorting incoming material.
   h. Elimination of pilferage.
   i. Less congestion at receiving platform.
4. To the **carrier** when he can ship materials on pallets:
   a. Reduction in terminal time.
   b. Reduction in shipping damage.
   c. Reduction in loading and unloading costs.

METAL VS. WOODEN PALLETS. There are some special applications (foundries, metal shops, etc.) where metal pallets are almost a necessity because of extreme loads, high temperatures, and rough usage. For general-purpose applications, however, there are two separate factors which determine the selection of wooden vs. metal pallets. They are (1) **original cost** and (2) **replacement cost.**

McClelland (Modern Materials Handling, vol. 6) presents a chart (Fig. 1) which shows these factors applied to both metal and wooden pallets. The chart is based on an assumed lot of 1,000 pallets to be used over a 5-yr. period. The original cost of the metal pallets was assumed to be $15 each, and of the wooden pallets, $4 each. McClelland further assumes that **metal pallets** can be loaded 500 times without replacement and that **wooden pallets** would require replacement after 10 loadings. The estimated repair cost for wood pallets was 4 cents per handling and for metal pallets, ¼ cent per handling. If the above assumptions are accepted, the chart shown in Fig. 1 is correct in showing a break-even point of about 40 loadings per yr. for the wooden pallets.

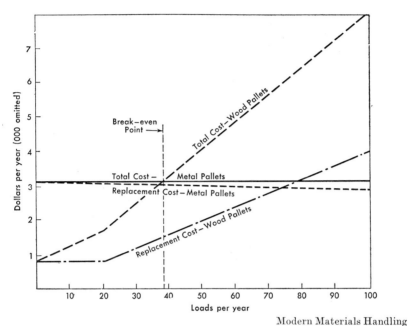

Modern Materials Handling

Fig. 1. Factors involved when selecting pallets.

From this calculation it can be concluded that **low maintenance costs** make metal pallets economical when they are to be frequently loaded or unloaded, while **low initial cost** makes wooden pallets economical for long storage or less frequent handling.

1. **Advantages of wooden pallets:**
   a. Low first cost.
   b. Easier to repair than metal (although metal may need less repair).
   c. Load security. Metal pallets sometimes become slick with wear and cause loads to slip, unless the pallet has a raised edge.
   d. Noncorrosive. Metal pallets rust or corrode; although they can be painted, paint will wear off. Galvanized metal pallets give the best service.
2. **Advantages of metal pallets:**
   a. Less repair needed.
   b. Cleanliness. Metal pallets can easily be cleaned if necessary.
   c. Weight-saving (in some types).
   d. Not a fire hazard. (In some cases flammable pallets affect insurance rates.)
   e. Have a salvage value.

Wooden pallets are still by far the most commonly used, and this use will almost certainly continue to predominate. There are many situations, however, in which metal or wire-mesh pallets are the most economical in the long run because of their ruggedness and durability.

ESTIMATING PALLET REQUIREMENTS. There are three methods for approximating the number of pallets which an operation will require:

1. **Floor-area method.** Take 60 to 80 percent of the total square footage of storage area, and divide by the area of the selected pallet; then multiply by the number of tiers that the ceiling height will permit.
2. **Weight method.** Estimate the total tonnage of material to be moved or stored, and divide by the known net weight of a unit load. Then add 10 to 20 percent for empty pallet storage, partially loaded pallets, and pallets in transit.
3. **Unit method.** In the storage of bulk commodities, peak inventory figures can be divided by the number of units loaded per pallet.

If possible, pallet requirements should be worked out by all of these methods for comparison and check.

Important Factors in Palletization. The following factors are important in palletization:

1. Weight of pallet.
2. Strength of pallet.
3. Size of pallet.
4. Maintenance necessary.
5. Moisture content of pallet (wooden).
6. Stackability of pallet (tiering).
7. Entry possibilities.
8. Material of which made.
9. Cost.
10. Construction features.
11. Load capacity.
12. Suitability for bagged goods.
13. Nesting and dunnage capacity.
14. Reassembly characteristics.
15. Suitability for conveyor handling.
16. Suitability for use with steel strapping.
17. Suitability for use with special processing operations (live steam, acid, etc.).
18. Suitability for use with gluing.
19. Suitability for use with stevedoring operations.
20. Suitability for use with freight humping.

Pallet Loading Patterns

ESTABLISHING STANDARD PALLET LOADING. For most unit loads it is essential that some standard pallet pattern be established. Workmen must be given suitable training to follow the patterns that should be used for the company's standard packages. Supervisors, at least, should be familiarized with patterns for making up unit loads of any unusual package sizes which they are likely to be called upon to palletize. Use of the wrong pallet pattern can be dangerously wasteful of storage space and hazardous from the safety standpoint. While **efficient patterns** can be discovered by trial and error, simply by taking products and placing them in various arrangements on pallets, this method is laborious and time-consuming and, considering all of the possible combinations, usually impractical.

Factors in Developing Pallet Loading Patterns. Important factors which must be taken into consideration when choosing the most efficient pallet loading pattern for any one group of materials on any one pallet are:

1. **Size of material.** For a given pallet there may be several, one, or no ways to palletize a given size material.

2. **Weight of material.** In the case of very heavy material, fewer layers will be stacked on a pallet. To a certain extent the number of layers will depend on the strength of the containers, if any are used.
3. **Size of the unit load.** Taken as a whole, the length, width, and especially the height of the load must be considered.
4. **Loss of space within unit load.** Some patterns have too many large gaps between units. This kind of piling is particularly bad when paper pallets are used, because the weight should be distributed evenly and the units should brace one another.
5. **Compactness.** Some patterns do not tie together well; they will not interlock.
6. **Methods of binding products in patterns.** If the units of a load are **glued** together, one kind of pattern may be ideal; with **strapping**, another type may be the best; and if no fastening at all is used, some combination type of **stacking** may be the most suitable method to interlock and hold the load together.

Common types of pallet loading patterns are:

1. Block.
2. Row.
3. Pinwheel.
4. Honeycomb.
5. Split row.
6. Split pinwheel.
7. Split pinwheel—for narrow boxes.
8. Brick.

Illustrations of these types are given in Figs. 2 to 9, inclusive.

HOW TO CHOOSE A PALLET LOADING PATTERN. Assume that a 48 × 48 in. pallet is available and that it is necessary to know whether cartons of a certain size, say 14 × 10 × 6 in., can be palletized on it. The following method is a quick way to check the possibilities. List the carton dimensions; then list **several multiples of each dimension** in the manner shown in the following diagram :

$$14 \times 10 \times 6$$

```
           14 × 10 × 6
   (1) │ 28    20 │  12
         42 │ 30    18 │ (2)
         56    40    24
```

It can immediately be seen that there is one good way to combine these dimensions to get a 48-in. total, and possibly one other way. If the first (1) combination above is used, the pattern shown in Fig. 10 will be obtained. The numbers blocked in the tabulation show that there must be two rows in the 14-in. dimension and two in the 10-in dimension. Using the second set (2) of figures would involve laying some cartons on their sides—which may or may not be possible or desirable, depending upon the product and the container used.

To develop a complete **group of pallet patterns** for any one pallet size, it is possible to set up some basic formulas to represent the pattern type and then work out all possible patterns with a simple limit equation. For example, a simple row pattern of the type shown in Fig. 11 would have a basic formula of

$$4y = L$$
$$3x = W$$

where L is the total length of the pallet and W the total width. From this formula it is possible to set up a series of limits for the x and y dimensions which can

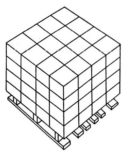

Fig. 2. Block pattern.

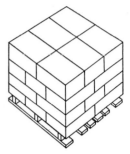

Fig. 3. Row pattern.

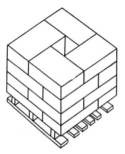

Fig. 4. Pinwheel pattern.

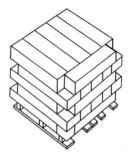

Fig. 5. Honeycomb pattern.

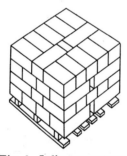

Fig. 6. Split-row pattern.

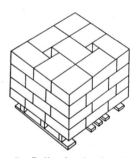

Fig. 7. Split-pinwheel pattern.

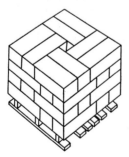

Fig. 8. Split-pinwheel pattern for
narrow boxes.

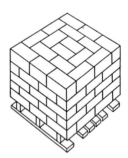

Fig. 9. Brick pattern.

be effectively palletized on this pattern. For the 48 × 48 in. size (allowing for overhang and underhang) these limits would be:

1. $x = 15$ 2. $x = 17$ 3. $x = 15$ 4. $x = 17$
   $y = 11$ $y = 11$ $y = 13$ $y = 13$

These limits are given to the nearest inch, for simplicity. It may be necessary to work to the nearest ½ or ¼ in., depending on the pallet, product, or shipping method. The limits assume an **allowable overhang and underhang** of 2 in. on a side, or a total of 4 in. in any one dimension. This overhang may or may not be permissible in individual cases.

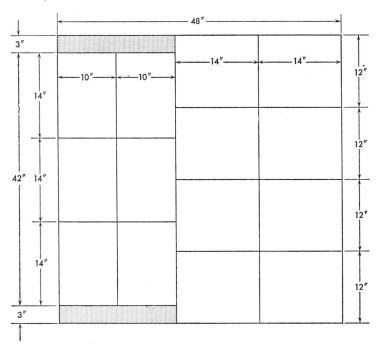

Fig. 10. Trial pallet-loading pattern.

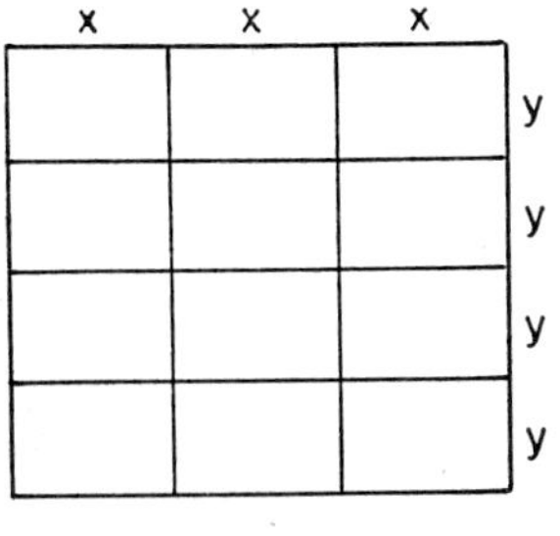

Fig. 11. Basic development of pallet pattern.

After a company works out limits for all common pallet patterns for each pallet size used, the x and y limits can be charted to show possible combinations. For a large organization handling a great variety of materials on a number of pallet sizes and using a variety of patterns, this process of calculation can involve literally thousands of man-hours; but even so, it has proved worth while in ultimate time saved.

Chart for 48″ x 48″ Pallet

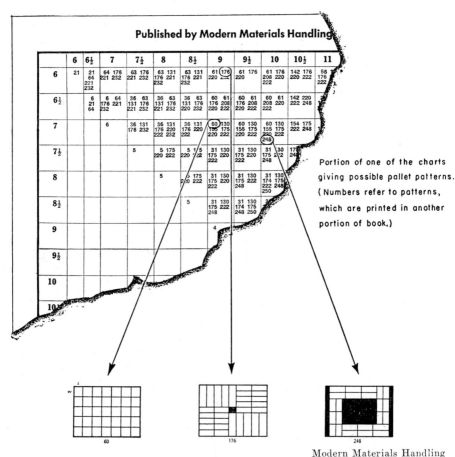

Portion of one of the charts giving possible pallet patterns. (Numbers refer to patterns, which are printed in another portion of book.)

Modern Materials Handling

Fig. 12. Palletizer procedure for selecting pallet size.

PALLETIZER METHOD OF DEVELOPING A PALLET LOADING PATTERN.

Fortunately, another system, which eliminates all calculations in most cases, is in existence. A manual prepared by Materials Handling Laboratories, Inc., (The Palletizer) covers all **possible patterns for the most common pallet sizes:** the 32 × 40 in., the 40 × 48 in., and the 48 × 48 in. pallets. It can be used in any case where these pallet sizes are used and where the underhang of containers is no more than 2 in. to a side (or a total of 4 in. for any dimension) and the overhang is no more than a total of 4 in. for any dimension, except in the case of the 40-in. dimension, where the overhang is limited to a total of 3 in. Since these figures reflect common handling practice and are the ones recommended by the Department of Commerce and the armed services, this guidebook method works in the great majority of cases.

An explanation of the Palletizer method is given in Fig. 12, which shows part of a chart for the 48 × 48 in. pallet. In many cases several pallet patterns will be usable for any one package and pallet size. Often two different patterns will be used alternately in one unit load to provide interlock of successive layers.

When there is **more than one feasible pattern** for a particular carton size, the following factors will help determine which pattern to use:

1. If the pallet is to be shipped, some **overhang** may be desirable, unless the load comes out flush with the edge of the pallet.
2. **Underhang** should be eliminated wherever possible; on expendable pallets, underhang is definitely undesirable.
3. **Large voids** in the load should be eliminated wherever possible.
4. A pattern which will provide **interlock** when alternate layers are reversed is desirable.
5. If one pattern does not provide this interlock of the load when alternate layers are reversed, a **second pattern** may be necessary.

How Package Size Affects Palletization

CONFORMING PACKAGES TO PALLET SIZES. After a company has standardized its pallet sizes and pallet patterns, it is often found that **a few packages will not fit** into these standards. In this case it is advisable to redesign these packages, if at all possible, to conform to the pallet size and fit some usable pattern, rather than to invest in large numbers of different-sized pallets. The tables given in The Palletizer were worked out to show immediately whether or not a particular package will fit a particular pallet for three standard sizes treated, and if not, to show the nearest package size that will fit the pallet.

Designing Packages That Are To Be Palletized. The Committee for Redesign of Packages, National Bureau of Standards, Department of Commerce, lists the following points which should be considered when designing packages to be palletized. The recommendations are for handling food products, but they apply in most other applications where sizes and weights are comparable.

1. **Strength.** Cartons should be strong enough to permit stacking to 4-unit loads in height, or about 16 ft. Fiberboard cases should be made with the corrugations vertical to give the maximum supporting strength.
2. **Weight.** A single case weight of about 35 lb. is good. A weight of more than 50 lb. is not recommended since it is hard to handle individually when stacking on the pallet.
3. **Cubage.** Both unduly large and unduly small cases increase handling cost. Approximately 1 cu. ft. is the ideal size for palletizing.
4. **Height.** For maximum stability, container height should be less than either the width or the length. As a rule of thumb, the height should not exceed 14 in. Over-all unit load height should be not more than 72 in. but may be less, depending upon the commodity, transportation, and warehouse problems.

TYPES OF PACKAGES UNSUITED FOR MECHANICAL HANDLING. The following types of packages are not suitable for mechanical handling and should be redesigned, according to Hupp (A.M.A. Bull., Packaging Ser. No. 21), who calls them a "veritable chamber of horrors" for the materials handling engineer:

1. The container that is a **perfect cube.** It is difficult to palletize or even stack successfully a container whose three dimensions are the same.

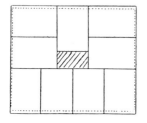

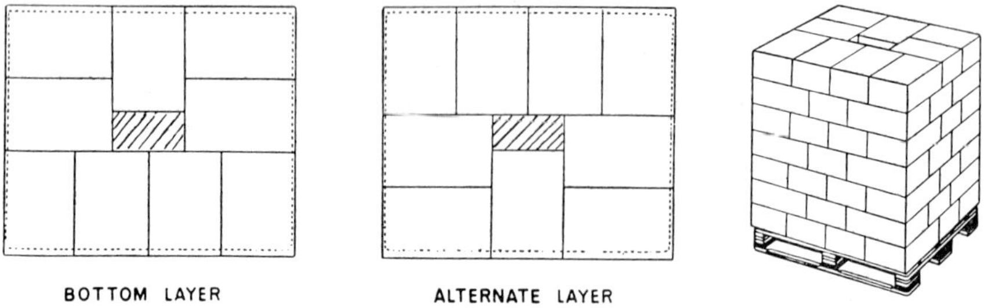

BOTTOM LAYER   ALTERNATE LAYER

Item: Tomatoes
Size: 10 Tin   Pack: 6/10 Tin
Type of Container: Fiber
Dimensions: L. 18⅞   W. 12⅝   H. 7½
Shipping Weight per Case: 48
Shipping Weight per Unit Load: 3,024

Load Dim'ns: L. 50½   W. 44⅛   H. 58½
Container Cube: 1.01   Load Cube: 75.33
Cases per Layer: 9   Per Load: 63
Cases per 50'6" Car: 1,688   Wt. 78,624
Cases per 40'6" Car: 1,396   Wt. 66,529

(a) Pallet pattern of No. 10 tin tomatoes.

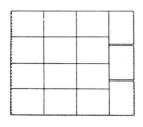
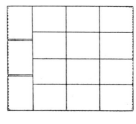

BOTTOM LAYER   ALTERNATE LAYER

Item: Tomatoes
Size: 2 Tall   Pack:24/2 Tall
Type of Container: Fiber
Dimensions: L. 13⅞   W. 10½   H. 9⅝
Shipping Weight per Case: 36
Shipping Weight per Unit Load: 3,240

Load Dim'ns: L. 51   W. 42   H. 63⅜
Container Cube: .806   Load Cube: 78.56
Cases per Layer: 15   Per Load: 90
Cases per 50'6" Car: 2,520   Wt. 90,720
Cases per 40'6" Car: 1,980   Wt. 71,280

(b) Pallet pattern of 2-tall tomatoes.

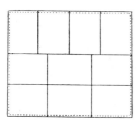
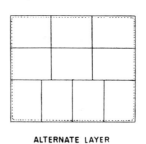

BOTTOM LAYER   ALTERNATE LAYER

Item: Tomatoes
Size: 2½ Tin   Pack: 24/2½ Tin
Type of Container: Fiber
Dimensions: L. 16⅜   W. 12⅜   H. 10
Shipping Weight per Case: 55
Shipping Weight per Unit Load: 3,300

Load Dim'ns: L. 50   W. 41½   H. 65
Container Cube: 1.165   Load Cube: 78.05
Cases per Layer: 10   Per Load: 60
Cases per 50'6" Car: 1,680   Wt. 92,400
Cases per 40'6" Car: 1,320   Wt. 72,600

(c) Pallet pattern of No. 2½ tin tomatoes.

Fig. 13. Pallet patterns, 40 × 48 in. size.

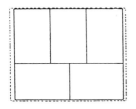 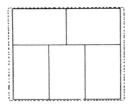 

BOTTOM LAYER   ALTERNATE LAYER

Item: Tomatoes
Size: 10 Tin   Pack: 6/10 Tin
Type of Container: Fiber
Dimensions: L. 18⅞   W. 12⅝   H. 7½
Shipping Weight per Case: 48

Shipping Weight per Unit Load: 1,440
Load Dim'ns: L. 37⅝   W. 31½   H. 58½
Container Cube: 1.01   Load Cube: 30.30
Cases per Layer: 5   Per Load: 30

(a) Pallet pattern of No. 10 tin tomatoes.

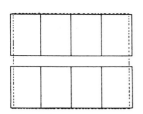 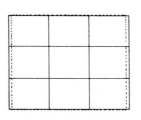 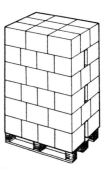

BOTTOM LAYER   ALTERNATE LAYER

Item: Tomatoes
Size: 2 Tall Pack:24/2 Tall
Type of Container: Fiber
Dimensions: L. 13⅞   W, 10¼   H. 9⅞
Shipping Weight per Case: 36

Shipping Weight per Unit Load: 1,836
Load Dim'ns: L. 42   W. 31½   H. 63¾
Container Cube: .806   Load Cube: 41.11
Cases per Layer: 8/9   Per Load: 51

(b) Pallet pattern of 2-tall tomatoes.

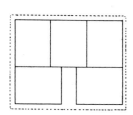 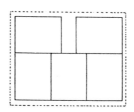 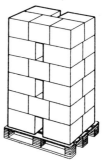

BOTTOM LAYER   ALTERNATE LAYER

Item: Tomatoes
Size: 2½ Tin   Pack: 24/2½ Tin
Type of Container: Fiber
Dimensions: L. 16⅜   W. 12⅝   H. 10
Shipping Weight per Case: 55

Shipping Weight per Unit Load: 1,650
Load Dim'ns: L. 37⅛   W. 28¾   H. 65
Container Cube: 1.165   Load Cube: 34.95
Cases per Layer: 5   Per Load: 30

(c) Pallet pattern of No. 2½ tin tomatoes.

Fig. 14. Pallet patterns, 32 × 40 in. size.

2. The container that is **too weak** to be palletized and stacked to ceiling height.
3. The container that **will not fit** on a pallet of common size. Among the common sizes are the 32 × 40 in., the 40 × 48 in., and the 48 × 48 in.
4. The container that is **too heavy.** Even in the most mechanized system, packages will probably be handled by hand somewhere along the chain of distribution.
5. The container that is **too full.** The top and sides will often bulge, making stacking difficult; moreover, the weight of the stack will rest on the product rather than on the container.
6. The container that is **not full.** This condition results in a waste of storage space as well as packaging materials.
7. The **inadequate** container. It often breaks open in transit, causing a product spoilage and pilferage problem as well as a handling problem.
8. The container in which **too much packaging material** is used. With a pallet system individual packages are infrequently handled, and a package need not be as strong as one that will be moved repeatedly. To ignore this advantage is a sheer waste of packaging material and time.
9. The container that is **too hard to open.** Overtaping or overgluing or overstrapping are the causes.
10. The container of **odd shape.** Conical, hexagonal, and other nonstandard shapes not only are difficult to palletize and stack but also waste storage space.
11. The container that **does not fit "a family of containers."** Any group of containers used by one company should fit one or two standard pallets.
12. The **improperly marked** or identified container. Often a container can be palletized in only one or two ways. In this case, it is important to mark the container with labels, addresses, etc., in such a manner that they are not obscured when the package is palletized. Safe practice is to duplicate markings on several sides of the package.
13. The container that could just as well **be its own pallet.** Household appliances, such as washing machines or refrigerators, are good examples. Units of this size and shape can constitute a unit load if strips of dunnage are nailed across the bottom of the packing crate.

TYPICAL PACKAGING PATTERNS USED IN THE GROCERY INDUSTRY. The kinds of pallet patterns shown in the 40 × 48 in. size (Fig. 13) and in the 32 × 40 in. size (Fig. 14) are commonly used in the grocery industry. This will apply, however, to practically any industry.

Securing Unit Loads

METHODS OF APPLYING STEEL STRAPPING. To move, transport, or ship a unit load, it is usually necessary to secure the load and pallet in some fashion. The object is to make a solid unit of the many individual parts of the load and the pallet. Common methods include steel strapping, gluing, using pressure-sensitive tape, or tying with twine. The choice of method depends upon the distance moved, the type of pallet pattern, the material to be palletized, the method for loading the shipment, the method of shipping, the type of pallet, the size and weight of the load, etc.

Steel Strapping. Steel strapping of either the **flat or the round wire type** provides one of the strongest unit loads. The common methods of strapping are:

1. **Vertical strapping parallel to stringers.** Vertical strapping parallel to the stringers (Fig. 15a) is particularly well adapted to rail shipment because it braces the load against the fore and aft shock imposed by the dynamic conditions of freight-car movement. This type of strapping, when used in conjunction with straps running in other directions, should be applied last, over the others. In this

way the possibility of snagging a strap is greatly reduced, since all other strapping is bound in close to the load by the final strapping. In most instances, vertical strapping parallel to the stringers permits economical utilization of strap because it enables the articles to be bound together and bound to the pallet at the same time.

2. **Vertical strapping at right angles to stringers.** Vertical strapping at right angles to the stringers (Fig. 15b) is used only to bind the load together when applied to 2-way pallets. It cannot be employed in binding the load to the pallet because the strapping would interfere with pallet slings as well as hand pallet

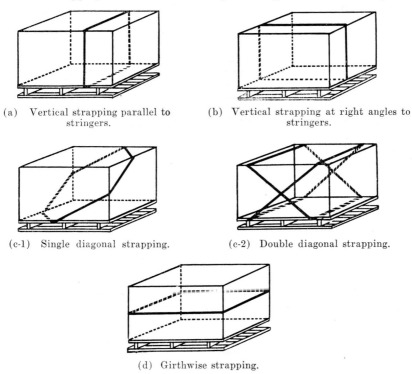

(a) Vertical strapping parallel to stringers.

(b) Vertical strapping at right angles to stringers.

(c-1) Single diagonal strapping.

(c-2) Double diagonal strapping.

(d) Girthwise strapping.

Fig. 15. Various methods of applying steel strapping.

trucks. This condition does not exist when 4-way pallets are used, since the stringers in this case are open in both direction. For this reason, both types of vertical strapping can be considered as identical patterns. When used in conjunction with 2-way pallets, the straps must be laid on the pallet before the load is set down, unless the pallet stringers are specially slotted.

3. **Diagonal strapping.** Diagonal strapping (Fig. 15c-1 and 15c-2) offers the principal advantage of more effectively preventing shearing of the load. Consequently, this pattern is most applicable to tall loads which are to be subjected to rough handling. The diagonal method, like vertical strapping parallel to the stringers, can be used in securing the load to the pallet as well as in binding single articles into a load. However, the application of diagonal strapping is limited in most instances, since the method requires stapling the strap to two or more faces to insure that the strap stays in place.

4. Girthwise strapping. Girthwise strapping (Fig. 15d) is the easiest of the four patterns to employ since it is applicable only to binding articles into a load. A strap around tall cases in many instances offsets the tendency of vertical strapping to fall out of place. Similarly, a strap around the top layer often keeps packages together in instances where multidecked loads are likely to fall apart. Articles bound by girthwise strapping are not fastened to the pallet.

Although girthwise strapping and vertical strapping at right angles to the stringers, when used in conjunction with 2-way pallets, do not permit binding articles to the pallet, **improvisations** may be made which accomplish the same result of securing the load to the pallet. A wooden block may be nailed to the middle of the pallet and the load built around it so that shifting is prevented. Another method of securing the load is the use of blocks nailed on opposite sides of the pallet after the articles have been strapped.

EFFECTIVE USE OF STRAPPING OR GLUING. The most effective use of strapping calls for consideration of the **type of package** or article being strapped. Packages of paper fiberboard and similar light materials should be stacked on the pallet in a way which provides the strongest possible support against the pressure of the strap. Such stacking offsets the crushing effect caused by the tendency of the strap to draw into a circle when tensioned. Metal corners may effect the same result. Pieces of vertical dunnage may be employed to relieve corner crushing, while horizontal dunnage placed on top of the load keeps the strap from biting into the top edges of the load. It is important that green lumber be dried out as much as possible before being strapped, since shrinkage of lumber in the boxes causes loosening of the strapping.

Only when strapping is **tightened nearly to the breaking point** is maximum holding power maintained. Strapping, once selected and properly applied, must not be abused. It is not intended to be used for picking up or pulling pallets but for forming solid, efficient units out of what would otherwise be loose piles of material.

Heavy steel wire or banding may be used to hold certain materials together during shipment. For example, metal pigs may be stacked on two sets of pigs forming a base, on top of which, crosswise, other pigs may be piled. The pigs have a notched crevice on the bottom side into which heavy wire fits; the wire is then passed tightly around the load above, in both directions, and firmly fastened. A fork truck can pick up such a load and place it into a railroad car or heavy truck. If the single bundle is not too heavy, such loads may even be stacked one on the other.

Fiber strapping is handled and sealed in the same manner as steel strapping. While it has a lower tensile strength, it is sufficient in many instances. It should be applied in the same patterns as steel strapping.

Pressure-sensitive tape is comparable in strength and application to steel strapping. It should be applied in the same pattern. A new glass filament-lined tape has maximum strength and little stretchability (stretching being a problem with some tapes).

Gluing a unit load is an inexpensive and effective means of securing the component parts of the load to each other and of securing the load to the pallet. The glue selected should have a **high shearing strength** at the adhesive bond and a relatively **low tensile strength**. Special glues have been developed that break at the bond, not inside the surface of glued cartons. The adhesive penetration should be slight, to prevent excessive tearing of the carton when breaking up the load. One method for preventing such tearing is the use of small **chipboard strips** dipped into glue; these act as a sandwich between the cases and break apart easily instead of tearing the cases when the load is broken up. Only the bottom of the carton should be glued—not any other part—since it would be difficult to break up a unit load if the sides were glued. When multiwall paper bags are used, the glue often tears the outside ply of the bag and sometimes destroys printed instructions or labels printed on this layer. This damage can be remedied by printing duplicate instructions on the second ply of the bag as well as on the outside ply.

A number of **gluing machines** have been developed to apply the right amount of glue in the right place automatically as a package comes off the packing line and is ready to be palletized. Some of these machines print glue in predetermined patterns or dots on the bottom of the containers. This method is advantageous when there are labels, lot numbers, printed instructions, or other printed data on the bottom of the case which should not be obscured by the glue.

Often, for **short hauls**, it will not be necessary to glue or strap loads. A tight pattern may suffice, or twine tied around the top layer of cartons may be sufficient. Tying the top layer gives the effect of laying a large solid block on top of the load. Inexpensive, low-strength tapes can be used in the same way.

Palletizing Unusual Shapes and Sizes

DEVELOPMENT OF SPECIAL METHODS AND EQUIPMENT.
There is almost no theoretical limit to the kinds and shapes of materials that can be palletized. The practical limit depends not so much upon the difficulty of palletizing an odd-shaped material as on a balance between the cost of palletizing and the advantage of palletizing the particular object. Thus, complete tractor assemblies are packed on a special pallet in one industry, while groups of small castings are not palletized in another because the method of shipping, receiving, storing, etc., does not lend itself to palletized loads.

Odd-shaped materials are palletized by one or a combination of any, or all, of the following methods:

1. Special size or type pallets.
2. The use of palletizing aids.
3. By nesting two or more of the palletized objects.
4. By adding dunnage.
5. Disassembly of component parts.

Small parts usually lend themselves to crate- or bin-type pallet storage, while long, bulky, or unwieldy parts or materials are usually palletized by disassembly or through the use of special-size pallets or palletizing aids. **Standard palletizing aids** are available from a wide range of manufacturers. Corner posts and other aids can be purchased to fit standard wooden pallets as well as special pallets.

Many palletizing aids are also **shop-made devices** developed to suit a specific material. They range from a simple strip of wood to a fairly complex and expensive spacer construction. Many of them are offered as standard accessories by leading pallet and accessory manufacturers. The following palletizing aids are fairly common:

1. **Center posts,** which are straight wooden strips measuring about 1×2 in. and 3 or 4 ft. long. These strips are about ¼ in. shorter than the palletized load and are placed upright in the center of the load so as to help support the next tiered load. They bear against the bottom of the pallet immediately above.
2. **Cleats,** which are simple wood strips nailed on the pallet to hold or support the load on the pallet.

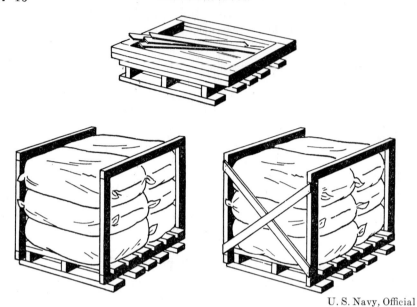

U. S. Navy, Official

Fig. 16. Picture-frame pallet.

Materials for One Dunnage Collar

Quan.	Description
4	2″ × 8″ lumber, 41″ long
2	2″ × 8″ lumber to form (approx. 44″)
8	⅝″ × .020 steel strap, 20″ long fastened with 8d nails
24	30d nails (3 per joint)

No collar on top tier

48″x48″ pallet

Collar

5/8″ x 0.020 steel strap

16½″ 8″ 16½″ 41″

To prevent splitting drill holes (same gage as nails) in outside 2 x 8's before nailing at corners

U. S. Navy, Official

Fig. 17. Unit loading of acetylene cylinders using dunnage collar (for storage purposes only).

3. **Blocks,** which serve much the same purpose as cleats, except that they are usually taller and are for support alone.
4. **Picture frames,** which are rectangular frames that support a tiered load. Two frames (see Fig. 16) are fitted between the top and bottom deck of the pallet, and cross braces are nailed on to make the frames rigid.
5. **Cradles,** which are made to fit one particular type of material and are cut to the contour of the material.
6. **Collars,** which are made of wooden strips in the form of oblong frames with inside dimensions the same as the palletized load. They tie the load together.
7. **Notched spacers,** which are cut to fit the contour of the material and are a variation of the cradle.
8. **Trays,** which serve to separate layers of materials or parts in a unit load. They can be made of plywood or fiberboard.
9. **Separators** of many standard and special kinds, which are used to divide and to brace loads.

Illustrations of various palletizing aids are shown in Figs. 16 to 21, inclusive.

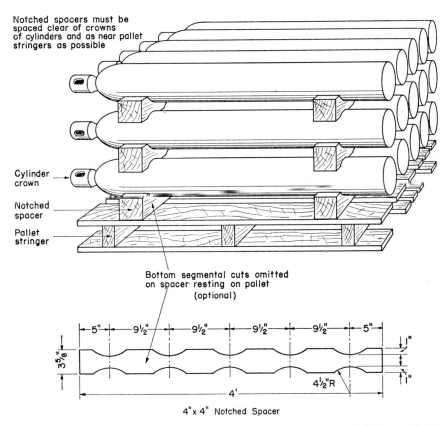

Notched spacers must be spaced clear of crowns of cylinders and as near pallet stringers as possible

Cylinder crown

Notched spacer

Pallet stringer

Bottom segmental cuts omitted on spacer resting on pallet (optional)

4" x 4" Notched Spacer

U. S. Navy, Official

Fig. 18. **Palletized oxygen cylinders on 48 × 48 in. pallet. (For additional security, this type of load may be wired or strapped.)**

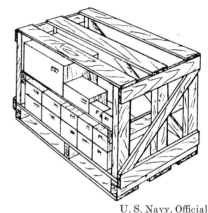

Fig. 20. Box pallet for items not suitable for flat pallets.

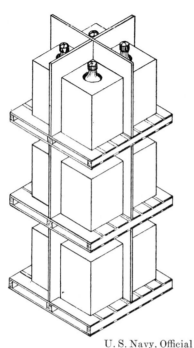

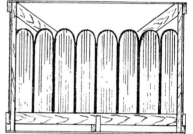

Fig. 19. Dividers for acid storage.

Fig. 21. Special box pallets for storing aircraft tires.

Economics of Palletized Shipping

COSTS OF SHIPPING PALLETIZED LOADS. In many industries the practice of shipping palletized unit loads by rail and truck has become standard procedure for cutting costs in loading and unloading, reducing damage, saving packaging, bracing, etc. Friedman (Modern Materials Handling, vol. 4) cites the following **methods of cost calculation** that can be used to decide whether or not palletized shipments are economically feasible for any particular operation. In **interplant shipments** the particular company is both shipper and receiver and therefore benefits from savings on both ends. In **producer-to-consumer shipments,** two companies divide any savings. Since the shipper pays loading costs, this second type of shipment may or may not be to his advantage.

Two case examples of loading shipments from a warehouse are given below, the first being the traditional **piece-by-piece loading,** and the second, the **unit-load method of loading.** In the latter case warehouse operations are palletized, loaded pallets being carried in unit loads by fork truck or conveyor to the shipping dock. Under the hand method the unit load is broken and each piece loaded by hand on a piece-by-piece basis.

Figures are based on an assumed shipment of 1,320 cases of 24 No. 2½ cans of asparagus, each case weighing 52 lb. The boxcar will hold 22 palletized unit loads.

A single steel strap is placed girthwise around the top layer of cartons on each pallet.

Elements of **fixed costs** are:

1. Direct labor.
2. Machine costs.
3. Securing costs.
4. Capital charges.

Only the first two of these fixed charges apply to the piece-by-piece method. All four elements of cost apply to the unit-load method.

Elements of **fixed costs** are:

1. Freight charges, at the commodity rate, of any accessory equipment, such as pallets, since the pallets must be shipped with the load.
2. Freight charges for the return of the accessory equipment, such as pallets.

Neither of these charges applies to the piece-by-piece method. The cost of returning pallets can be computed at the carload or LCL rate that applies, or the pallets can be returned by truck, at truck rates.

GENERAL GRAPHICAL SOLUTION. The graph in Fig. 22, in general form, compares the cost of the **palletized shipment** method with the cost of the **piece-by-piece method.** The horizontal axis is scaled in miles (distance shipped), the vertical axis in dollars of cost. The horizontal axis may be scaled in terms of distances to common shipping points noted on the chart. The vertical axis to

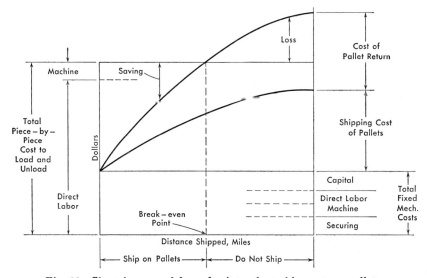

Fig. 22. **Chart in general form for interplant shipment on pallets.**

the left (Fig. 22) shows the cost of piece-by-piece loading and unloading, and the vertical axis to the right shows the cost of palletized shipping. The **break-even point** occurs at the intersection of the lines representing the two types of shipment. Shipments made to points short of the break-even point are more economical if they are in palletized loads. Shipments to points to the right of the break-even point are more economical under piece-by-piece loading.

APPLICATIONS OF THE ANALYSIS. The following calculations show the economics of specific examples of shipment on standard wooden pallets, lightweight metal pallets, and expendable pallets, as well as the difference between interplant shipment and producer-to-consumer shipment.

1. **Standard wooden pallets—interplant shipment.**

Fixed charges: The comparative fixed charges for loading costs alone, whether the shipment is to be interplant or producer to consumer, are shown in the tabulation in Fig. 23. This table is based on the shipment of 22 wooden pallets per railroad car, with a turn-around time of 30 days for the pallets, and on the average labor and equipment costs which prevailed at the time the figures were compiled. When other types of returnable pallets are used, and variable turn-around times are anticipated, the charges shown in Fig. 24 may be applied. Unloading is assumed to cost the same amount as loading. For interplant shipments the fixed costs are twice the amounts shown. In the example under discussion, **fixed charges,** as computed from Fig. 22 and plotted in Fig. 25 are:

     a. Piece-by-piece method, loading and unloading: (2 × \$18.27) = \$36.54.
     b. Mechanical (unit-load) method, loading and unloading: (\$9.02 + \$1.75 + \$1.00) = \$11.77.

ELEMENTS OF FIXED COSTS FOR LOADING A BOXCAR

Elements	Piece-by-Piece Method			Mechanical Method		
	Rate/hr.	Time-hr.	Cost	Rate/hr.	Time-hr.	Cost
1—Checker	\$1.50	1¾	\$ 2.62	–	–	–
1—Fork truck operator..	1.75	1¾	3.06	\$1.75	1	\$1.75
4—Laborers	1.55	1¾	10.84	–	–	–
1—Fork truck	1.00	1¾	1.75	1.00	1	1.00
22—Straps and labor	–	–	–	–	–	4.62
Capital charge on pallets —30-day turn-around..	–	–	–	–	–	1.65
Total charges			18.27			9.02

Fig. 23. **Loading costs: piece-by-piece method vs. mechanical method.**

CAPITAL CHARGES FOR PALLETIZED SHIPMENTS

Type	First Cost	% Depr. and Maint.	Capital Cost per Pallet for Turn-around Time of:			
			1 week	2 weeks	1 month	2 months
Wood	\$ 3.00	30	\$0.0173	\$0.0346	\$0.075	\$0.15
Steel	15.00	15	0.0433	0.0866	0.188	0.375
Aluminum	26.00	15	0.075	0.150	0.325	0.650

Fig. 24. **Capital costs per pallet for different turn-around periods.**

Variable charges: Assuming that the shipment originates in New York, distances to three points will be used to calculate freight rates, for purposes of comparison. Assuming also 22 returnable wooden pallets per car, weighing about 100 lb. each, the carload-lot freight rates for outward shipment would be:

New York to Chicago
$0.841 × 22 = $18.50

New York to Buffalo
$0.565 × 22 = $12.43

New York to Utica
$0.427 × 22 = $ 9.39

(These figures, and all cost figures to follow, are based on freight rates which are probably subject to some changes. The method of calculation nevertheless remains valid.)

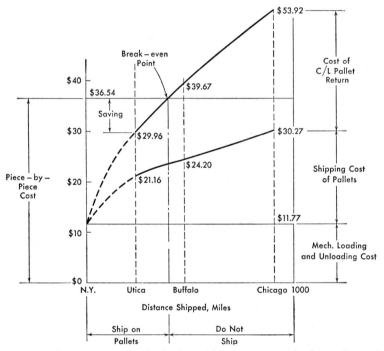

Fig. 25 . Break-even chart for interplant shipment on standard wooden pallets.

The cost of freight carload return of these pallets would be:

Chicago to New York
$1.075 × 22 = $23.65

Buffalo to New York
$0.703 × 22 = $15.47

Utica to New York
$0.400 × 22 = $ 8.80

When all the above figures are plotted on a chart, as in Fig. 25, it is seen that the break-even point is just short of Buffalo and that all palletized shipments short of this point are economically justifiable.

2. **Lightweight metal pallets—interplant shipment** (see Fig. 26). It is assumed that the same load previously shipped will be shipped on metal pallets rather than on wooden ones. The metal would probably be aluminum. The same loading and unloading costs would apply. The method of binding the load, etc., would be exactly the same. The turn-around time would also be the same— 30 days.

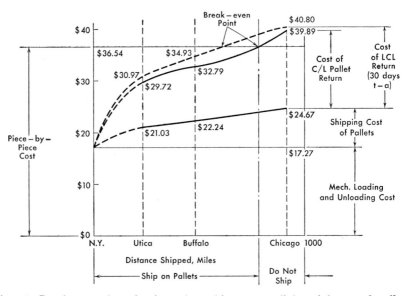

Fig. 26. **Break-even chart for interplant shipment on lightweight metal pallets.**

However, several new factors will be introduced because of the metal pallets. The first (see Fig. 24) is the capital charge against metal pallets, which is considerably higher than that for wooden pallets. Second, because the metal pallets are lighter (about 40 lb. as against 100 lb. for the wood), the shipping cost at the commodity rate is lower. The charges that make up Fig. 26 are derived as follows:

Fixed charges:

    a. Loading and unloading, piece-by-piece method: $2 \times \$18.27 = \$36.54$.
    b. Loading and unloading cost (including capital charge and securing costs), unit-load (mechanical) method: $17.27.

Variable charges: The carload freight costs of shipping pallets at the commodity rate existing when the study was made were:

$$\text{New York to Chicago}$$
$$\$0.841 \left(\frac{40 \times 22}{100} \right) = \$0.841 \times 8.8 = \$7.40$$

$$\text{New York to Buffalo}$$
$$\$0.565 \times 8.8 = \$4.97$$

$$\text{New York to Utica}$$
$$\$0.427 \times 8.8 = \$3.70$$

The carload cost of returning pallets (30,000 lb. minimum carload) was:

Chicago to New York
$$\$1.075 \left(\frac{30.000 \times 22}{440 \times 100} \right) = \$1.075 \times 15 = \$16.13$$

Buffalo to New York
$0.703 \times 15 = \$10.55$

Utica to New York
$0.579 \times 15 = \$ 8.69$

The cost of LCL return of 22 pallets was:

Chicago to New York
$1.723 \times 8.8 = \$15.16$

Buffalo to New York
$1.419 \times 8.8 = \$12.49$

Utica to New York
$1.130 \times 8.8 = \$ 9.94$

When carload return of the pallets is practical, the break-even point in Fig. 26 occurs just short of Chicago. In the case of LCL return, the point occurs about halfway between Buffalo and Chicago. However, since the lightweight pallet may not reach the minimum carload weights, LCL return will usually be more economical. Also, since the capital charges are $0.325 per pallet per mo., it is important that these pallets be speedily returned and reused.

3. **Wooden pallets—producer-to-consumer shipments** (see Fig. 27). **Fixed charges** can be taken from Fig. 21. The elements of **variable charges** are:

New York to Chicago
$0.841 \times 22 = \$18.50$

New York to Buffalo
$0.565 \times 22 = \$12.43$

New York to Utica
$0.422 \times 22 = \$ 9.39$

The cost of carload return of the pallets is:

Chicago to New York
$1.075 \times 22 = \$23.65$

Buffalo to New York
$0.703 \times 22 = \$15.47$

Utica to New York
$0.400 \times 22 = \$ 8.80$

When the return of the pallets is required, the break-even point, as shown in Fig. 27, occurs only a short distance from the point of origin. If the pallets are to be returned LCL, the cost will be even higher, and the shipment will be uneconomical even if the receiver shares the variable cost.

4. **Expendable pallets** (see Figs. 28 and 29). By far the most economical method of shipping by unit loads is through the use of expendable pallets. The

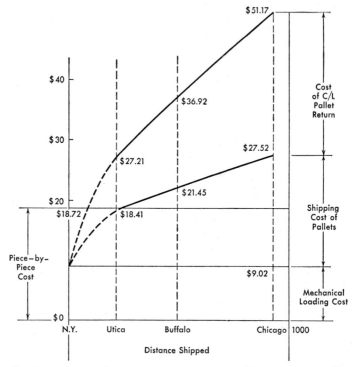

Fig. 27. Break-even chart for producer-to-consumer shipment on wooden pallets.

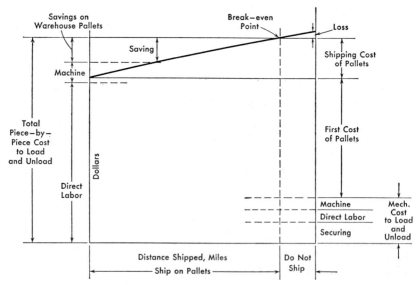

Fig. 28. Break-even chart for interplant shipment on expendable pallets—general form.

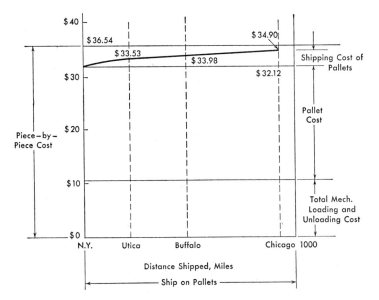

Fig. 29. Break-even chart for a specific case of interplant shipment on expendable pallets.

general chart for this type of shipment is shown in Fig. 28, and a specific example is given in Fig. 29. The calculations for expendable pallets vary for three reasons:

    a. The **capital charges** that accumulate on returnable pallets do not apply to expendable pallets. These charges are replaced in the formula by the first cost of the pallets.

    b. The **lightness** of the expendable pallet (from 10 to 15 lb., assumed weight 15 lb.) reduces the shipping charges proportionately.

    c. **No return shipment** need be considered.

The data used to construct Fig. 29 are derived from the following calculations:
Fixed costs:

    a. Total mechanical loading, unloading, and securing costs: $10.12.

    b. First cost of pallets (at **$1.00** per pallet, for 22 pallets): $22.00.

Variable costs: The shipping cost of the pallet at the class rate of the commodity at the time of the study was:

New York to Chicago

$\$0.841 \left(\dfrac{22 \times 15}{100} \right) = \$0.841 \times 3.3 = \$2.78$

New York to Buffalo
$\$0.565 \times 3.3 = \$1.86$

New York to Utica
$\$0.427 \times 3.3 = \$1.41$

These data, plotted on Fig. 29, show savings all the way to Chicago, and beyond to an uncharted distance. Under the heading "Expendable vs. Permanent Pallets," in the fore part of this section, a more detailed discussion on shipping with expendable pallets has been given and may be reviewed in connection with the above cost analysis.

TYPES OF UNIT LOADS HANDLED WITHOUT PALLETS. It is often possible to handle unit loads directly without the use of pallets. The kinds of handling equipment which can be employed to move various kinds of containers or materials are listed in the tabulation given in Fig. 30 (Modern Materials Handling, vol. 7).

Handling Equipment	Material or Object Handled
Side clamps	Crates Bales Large boxes and cartons Drums
Drum handlers	1 to 2 drums 4 drums
Sheet pallet clamps	Cartons (glued or unglued)
Chisel forks	Large boxes Crates Bales Glued small boxes
Pushers, multiforks	"Take it or leave it" pallets Bags
Special forks	Bricks, building blocks
Standard forks	Special sheet pallets molded to unitized loads Runners with large boxes Unitized loads
Finger lifts	Crates
Rams	Rolls, pipes, coils

Fig. 30. **Examples of materials handled without pallets.**

Pallet Maintenance

REPAIRS TO PALLETS. All the comprehensive studies made to date on pallet maintenance practice and maintenance cost have apparently dealt only with the common wooden pallet. Cost figures on metal pallet maintenance have not been assembled and analyzed to any great extent. Although it can be presupposed that metal pallets need maintenance less frequently, they entail a **greater repair cost** once they do need repair.

The results of an extensive survey made throughout industry on wooden pallet maintenance are shown in Fig. 31 (Modern Materials Handling, vols. 7 and 8). The most significant data to come out of this study are the **average number of trips to the repair shop** in the life of each pallet, and the **average cost of repair per pallet** per trip to the repair shop. Fig. 31 shows the average to be 3 overhauls in the life of each pallet, at the rate of $2.06 per pallet per trip, giving a total repair cost of $6.18 per pallet during its life. That figure is, of course, over and above the original cost.

INDUSTRY	NUMBER OF COMPANIES	AVERAGE NUMBER PALLETS PER COMPANY	AVERAGE AGE OF PALLETS					AVERAGE TRIPS TO REPAIR SHOP DURING LIFE OF PALLET	PALLET REPAIR COST				PERCENTAGE FAILURE DUE TO FASTENINGS	PERCENTAGE THAT KEEP RECORDS
			% UNDER 1 YEAR	% 2-3 YEARS	% 3-4 YEARS	% 4-5 YEARS	% OVER 5 YEARS		LABOR	MATERIAL	TRANSPORTATION AND OVERHEAD	TOTAL REPAIR COST		
Chemicals and Petroleum	42	3,880	29	18	13	13	27	3	$ .93	$ .69	$ .88	$2.50	79	21
Fabricated Metal Products	85	3,445	63	18	8	6	5	3	.43	.58	.88	1.89	81	12
Food and Kindred Products	32	4,335	33	15	15	10	20	4	.62	.50	.59	1.71	89	15
Papers, Printing, and Allied Products	16	4,500	33	19	24	17	6	3	.97	.94	.57	2.48	90	25
Textiles, Leather, Rubber, and Related Products	17	2,980	25	8	18	21	28	3	.80	.42	.55	1.77	81	33
Distribution (Dept. Stores, Transportation and Wholesale)	12	1,850	22	22	27	15	14	2	1.00	.38	.51	1.89	78	12
Warehouses	27	12,733	21	18	21	18	21	4	.87	.58	1.01	2.46	80	35
Miscellaneous Manufacturing Industries	52	1,877	33	31	11	13	12	4	.66	.52	.60	1.78	84	8

Fig. 31. Results of an extensive survey on pallet repair costs.

Another chart developed from this study (Fig. 32) gives an example of the **buying, replacement, and repair costs** of one company for pallets over a 13-yr. period (Modern Materials Handling, vols. 7 and 8). This company invested $45,000 in pallets. Within 6 yr. the pallets began to fall apart, and several thousand dollars were appropriated for repairs. Nevertheless, some pallets were discarded, of necessity, and the pallet inventory was allowed to drop. During the following year it was necessary to spend some $10,000 in pallet repairs and to scrap a considerable number of the remaining pallets. Within the next 2-yr. period the total pallet repair bill was almost $20,000, and during the following year it was necessary to buy additional pallets. After 13 yr. of experience the company's records showed that the total pallet investment had been $140,000, and the total number of usable pallets remaining was less than the number with which the company started.

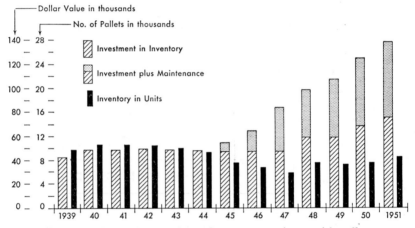

Fig. 32. Results of one company's 13-yr. experience with pallets.

All evidence indicates that the following steps should be taken by a pallet user to **keep maintenance costs to a minimum:**

1. Select pallets on the basis of a **rigid specification** rather than on a straight-price basis.
2. Establish a definite **throw-away criterion** for pallets. Some companies automatically throw away a pallet when estimated repairs reach $1.50 or some comparable figure. Others impose a physical criterion, such as a broken stringer or two broken deckboards, or automatically scrap a pallet when it reaches a certain age.
3. Assign some one man to **decide when to repair or replace** pallets and a man or one group of men to do the repairing.
4. **Provide a definite place** in which to make these repairs; equip this repair shop with the necessary machines and tools; and keep on hand a reasonable quantity of **replacement parts,** at least those which are most likely to wear or become broken in service.
5. Establish a **record-keeping and cost-control system** which takes into account labor, overhead, materials, transportation to and from the repair shop, and the cost of merchandise damaged by faulty pallets. Many companies stencil lot numbers on all new shipments of pallets and use these numbers in keeping a record of pallet maintenance.

Use of Automatic Pallet Loaders

FEATURES OF AUTOMATIC LOADERS. When a palletizing operation involves as many as 15 to 18 cartons per minute during one shift, it is feasible to install an automatic pallet loader according to Barker (Modern Materials Handling, vol. 5). These loaders take cartons into the machine on live sections of roller conveyors and load them onto pallets in any predetermined pattern. The whole operation is automatic, with the machine controlling the feeding of cartons, the feeding of pallets when required, the reversing of alternate layers, etc. One machine will handle only one size pallet but may use up to six pallet patterns. There is also a limit to the size of the cartons.

There are several **different types** of automatic palletizing machines on the market, but they are basically similar in operation. One type, for example, can feed from two conveyor lines; another a semiautomatic type, provides mobility and flexibility as to pallet patterns and operates at low cost.

Analysis of Automatic vs. Hand Pallet Loading. The economic factors of one type of automatic pallet loader, as measured against hand pallet loading, are shown in Fig. 33, as developed by Landon (Modern Materials Handling, vol. 6). In actual fact the manual operating cost curves are "stepped" lines, the plotted line of which joins the minimum points. The steps occur at even multiples of

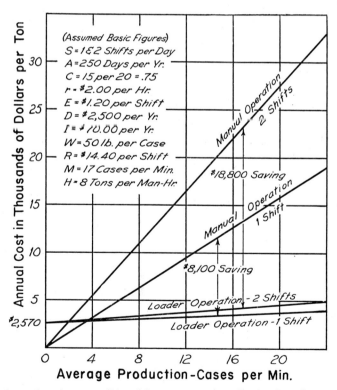

Fig. 33. Annual savings possible with an automatic pallet loader. Curves for one-
and two-shift operations are shown.

the average number of filled cartons one man will pile per minute, or 5⅓ cartons, as figured back from an assumed 8 tons of 50-lb. cartons per man-hr.; and the "treads" of the steps are horizontal. A production of 10 cartons per min. would require two men to do the piling, while any number from 11 to 16 cartons per min. would require three men to do the work. Since the loader operation cost is a straight sloping line, this stepped curve indicates a greater saving for about 12 cartons per min. than for 16. This condition is logical, because it is more efficient for three men to handle 16 units in a given time than for three men to handle 12 units.

The chart in Fig. 33 was developed from a hypothetical group of figures typical of motor lubricant packing. For the lower line, Annual Cost of Pallet Loader Operation, the formula used in developing the chart is:

$$S \times A \times C \,(1.5r + E) + D + I$$

For the upper line, Annual Cost of Manual Operation, the formula is:

$$\frac{60S \times W \times A \times R \times M}{2{,}000H}$$

where S = number of shifts worked per day, in units
A = number of days operation per year, in units
C = average number of cartons per minute divided by 20 units
(This is an empirical factor which allows for the variable number of cartons handled per minute. The number 20 is the average speed of the pallet loader.)
r = hourly wage of mechanic, including overhead, in dollars
E = cost of 10 hp. (electrical) for one shift, in dollars
D = annual depreciation of installation, in dollars
I = annual insurance on the machine, in dollars
W = weight of a single carton, in pounds
R = laborer's daily rate (including overhead), in dollars
M = maximum cartons per minute produced, in units
H = average tons handled per man-hour, in units

From this chart it is possible to figure the potential savings from the use of an automatic pallet loader. The following figures apply to the automatic pallet loader used by the Sun Oil Company and are representative of other pallet loaders:

Cartons: Minimum size: 8⅛ × 8½ × 3 in. high.
Maximum size: 18 in. wide × 24 ft. long × 31 in. high, if turned slightly. Slightly larger if not turned.

Pallets: One size per pallet loader.
Length: 32 to 48 in.
Width: (open side) 40 to 50 in.
Height: 4 to 6 in.
Number: up to ten standard 5½-in. pallets.
Loads: maximum weight about 3,000 lb. with present design.

Control Cartridges: One required with each stacking pattern.
Same one may be used for cartons of same plan dimensions, but varying height, with the same number of layers per pallet load.

Space Occupied: About 15 × 40 ft., or 600 sq. ft.

Weight: 16,000 lb.

Power Required: Approximately 10 hp., using five motors.

SECTION 18

WAREHOUSING AND YARD HANDLING

CONTENTS

WAREHOUSING AND YARD HANDLING

Factory Warehousing

STORAGE SPACE ANALYSIS. Warehousing is a necessary part of factory operation. The major problem is deciding how much storage space should be provided. This problem resolves itself into (1) determination of **inventory requirements,** and (2) converting inventory requirements into **space requirements.**

DETERMINING INVENTORY REQUIREMENTS. The basic study of how much storage area will be needed may be divided according to five factors: finished goods, in-process goods, raw materials, packing materials, and plant supplies.

FINISHED GOODS. Finished goods inventories result from differences between production rates and shipping rates. The following is the procedure for determining inventory requirements for finished goods:

1. List each finished goods item.

   a. If more than one size, color, style, or flavor of the same item is manufactured, list each.

   b. Include any finished goods items received from outside sources and merely carried in stock.

   c. Include promotional packs, if they are regularly handled.

2. If historical records are available, list **production, shipments, and inventories** for 1 yr. for each item.

   a. List them by months or, better still, by weeks.

   b. Pick a recent year.

   c. If possible, pick a yearly period representative of anticipated future fluctuations in production, shipments, and inventories due to seasonal variations, shutdowns, etc.

   d. If production, shipments, and inventories remain level throughout the year, a shorter period may be used.

3. Chart **historical production, shipments, and inventories.**

   a. Chart individual items.

   b. If possible, chart a summary which combines all items. For example, in cases where products of wide varieties are manufactured, the summary chart might be based on total tonnages or the total number of cases of product or dollars.

   c. Chart by months or, better still, by weeks. A weekly charting of inventories is especially desirable.

4. List **future estimated production, shipments, and inventories** for each item.

   a. Use sales forecasts as a guide, if they are obtainable.

   b. Use the historical data already recorded and charted as a guide.

    c. Add to the list any new finished goods items to be added to the line.

    d. Do not estimate items that are to be dropped from the line.

    e. The future estimated production, shipments, and inventories may be listed for an entire year, if desired, or for a representative level of operation. For example, they may be listed based on the plant operating at a normal average volume or a normal peak volume.

5. Select a **recommended future inventory** for storage purposes for each item.

    a. Use the historical data, charts, and future estimated inventories already recorded as guides.

    b. Check possible daily inventory fluctuations. For example, the production department may plan on operating three shifts per day, the shipping department only one. This time difference will build up an inventory peak at the end of the third shift each day.

    c. Check possible weekly inventory fluctuations. For example, the production department may plan on operating 6 days per wk., the shipping department only 5. This time difference will build up an inventory peak at the end of the sixth day each week.

    d. Examine slow-moving items. For example, a minimum production run may result in a 3-wk. inventory.

    e. Observe whether inventories on all items reach a peak at the same time or at staggered times. (1) If they peak at the same time, the recommended inventories for storage purposes must be the peak inventories. (2) If inventory peaks are staggered, storage space may be used interchangeably. The recommended inventories for storage purposes will be somewhere between the average and peak inventories. Set them as close to the average as possible.

    f. Consider the storage location and storage facilities to be used for each item. For example, if an item must be stored in one specific area good for only that one item, storage space for peak inventories of that item must be provided.

    g. On promotional pack items, determine the number of promotional packs to be handled at any one time; also the method of handling and storing them. For example, if a large inventory is to be accumulated for release at one time, the recommended inventory requirement must be for the total stock to be run.

    h. Examine the size of the orders received. For example, an item on which all of a month's production is shipped at one time will require a month's inventory.

    i. Examine the back-order situation. Some items may require larger inventories because of constant back-order on insufficient inventories.

    j. Examine possibilities for reducing the recommended inventory figure selected for storage purposes by improving production and shipping schedules, for example, by shorter production runs on slow-moving items, shipping on two shifts instead of one, etc.

6. **General factors** must be taken into consideration.

    a. Sometimes inventories recommended for storage purposes must be arbitrarily estimated or merely guessed at, for example, for a new factory, in a new location, on an entirely new product. In cases like this, guess how many days of inventory will be required, and calculate the production output for that many days.

    b. Selecting inventories to be recommended is not and cannot be an exact or scientific procedure. Judgment enters into the selection. It is not always possible to collect all the background data suggested herein, but the more background data collected the more intelligent the selection of recommended inventories will be.

    c. Inventory levels selected for storage purposes are not always the same as those selected for inventory control purposes. For example, the recommended inventory for storage purposes for an item which can be stored in only one specific area must be based on the peak inventory requirement for that item. For inventory control purposes, it would be lower.

d. In selecting recommended inventories for storage purposes, it is necessary to confer with experienced manufacturing, shipping, and scheduling personnel. In all cases it is necessary to keep in mind Item c above.

e. It is not the primary function of a materials handling engineer to determine recommended inventories, even for storage purposes. If possible, the recommendations should be obtained from other sources. However, the methods explained in this section show how to develop the recommendations, if necessary, and will guide the estimator along proper channels no matter from which branch of the company he may come.

IN-PROCESS GOODS. In-process storage results where processing machines are operated independently of one another at different production rates. Goods must be taken from one machine into temporary storage until they can be accommodated at one or more subsequent processing machines. The following is the **procedure for determining in-process goods inventory requirements** for storage purposes:

1. List the hourly **production rate** for those machines whose varying rates of production necessitate temporary storage between them.

2. List the **accumulated production** for one shift, two shifts, three shifts, and 1 wk. for each machine.

3. Calculate the daily and weekly **inventory build-up** which will occur between machines.

a. Examine the daily operating schedules which might be used for the machines. For example, one machine may feed three subsequent machines. To handle the production, two of the subsequent machines may operate three shifts, the third only one shift. This program of operation would build up a peak inventory between machines at the end of the third shift.

b. Examine the weekly operating schedules which might be used for the machines. For example, one machine feeding three subsequent machines might operate three shifts 5 days per wk.; in order to handle the production the three subsequent machines may operate 6 days per wk. This program of operation would create a peak inventory between machines at the end of the third shift on the fifth day of each week.

RAW MATERIALS AND PACKING MATERIALS. Inventories of raw materials and packing materials result from differences between **usage rates** and **receiving rates.** Raw materials and packing materials are purchased, or brought in, from outside sources. Inventory requirements are dependent on usage, purchase quantities, delivery quantities, and delivery time. The following is the procedure for determining inventory requirements for raw materials and packing materials:

1. Determine **usage** for 1 day, 1 week, and 1 month for each item.

a. Base this usage on the anticipated normal peak production level.

b. Calculate it based on production capacity, taking into consideration probable production scheduling for the finished goods which use each item. For example, 1 week's usage may not be 1 day's usage times the number of days in a week. The item under study may be used only 3 days out of the week because of production scheduling of the finished goods items which use it.

c. Use records of past usage as a guide, if they are available.

2. Determine **inventory requirements,** as shown in the example below:

a. Estimate the minimum reserve inventory required . . . . 3 days' supply
b. Determine the delay in transmitting an order to the supplier. . . . 1 day
c. Determine the delay before the supplier ships the order . . . . 4 days
d. Determine the transit time from the supplier's plant . . . . 5 days
e. Determine the quantity per receipt (for example, 60,000-lb. rail
    car = 10   days)   . . . . 10 days' supply

f. Total maximum inventory required for storage purposes . . . . 23 days' supply
g. Average inventory required for storage purposes (3 days + 23
    days) ÷ 2 = ... 13 days' supply
h. Inventory required for storage purposes: 13 days × daily usage = Inventory re-
    quired for stor-
    age purposes

3. Carefully **check the estimate** in the table above.

a. The minimum reserve inventory (Item 2a) is an allowance to compensate for
    unusual delay in receiving an order or for orders received ahead of time or for
    unusual fluctuation in usage. Usually this allowance will range between 1
    and 7 days.
b. Means should be taken to regulate delivery times by a system of careful
    preplanning.
    (1) Advance ordering and scheduling of shipments from suppliers promotes
        a steady flow of materials into the plant with minimum allowance for these
        delays.
    (2) A check of various suppliers may turn up a new one who can deliver more
        promptly.
    Items b, c, and d can often be reduced by such means.
c. Sometimes the amount per receipt (Item e) can be reduced. Check the pur-
    chase price and delivery cost for smaller shipments.
d. In the case of a raw material or packing material which can be stored in only
    one specific area, the inventory required for storage purposes must be the
    maximum inventory needed.
e. Check most closely the possibility of reducing any large inventories or inven-
    tories of bulky items which require great amounts of storage space. It is not
    necessary to check large inventories of small, compact items, because the total
    floor area required for such items is very small.
f. Remember that raw material and packing material inventories cannot be per-
    mitted to run wild, but on the other hand, lack of them can cause an expensive
    plant shutdown.

PLANT SUPPLIES. Plant supplies include expendable items—small tools,
light bulbs, glue, paper towels, and other articles usually purchased and brought
in from outside sources. Many of these supplies are common items purchased
locally, with quick delivery. Usage is fairly uniform. Inventories are mostly
dependent on convenience in purchasing, receiving, and distributing within the
plant for use. Others may be special and require larger inventories because of
variations in usage or delivery time.

The method of determining inventory requirements for plant supplies is essentially the same as for raw materials and packing materials. It is as follows:

1. Determine **usage** for 1 week and 1 month for each item.

a. Base this usage on anticipated normal peak production level.
b. Use records of past usage as a guide, if available.

2. Determine **inventory requirements,** as shown in the example below:

a. Estimate the minimum reserve inventory required............. 2 days' supply
b. Determine the delay in transmitting an order to the supplier.... 2 days
c. Determine the delay before the supplier ships the order......... 3 days
d. Determine the transit time from the supplier's plant........... 1 day
e. Determine the quantity per receipt.......................... 7 days' supply

f. Total maximum inventory required for storage purposes......... 15 days' supply
g. Average inventory required for storage purposes (2 days +
   15 days) ÷ 2 = ... 9 days' supply
h. Inventory required for storage purposes (usually the maximum
   inventory because of noninterchangeability of storage space
   from one item to another): 15 days × average daily usage = Inventory required for stor-
   age purposes

General comments. Many items of plant supplies require very little storage space and do not merit spending a great deal of time determining inventory requirements. Other items require considerable space, or they are important to the production department, or delivery on them is slow. These items require more careful inventory determination. If all plant supplies are stored in a store-room or tool crib, the inventory determination is more important than if the various items are distributed to points of usage immediately upon receipt. When they go to a storeroom or tool crib, most items must have space strictly allocated to them. If supplies are distributed to points of usage immediately upon receipt, many items can be tucked into almost any small, unused area, and they do not require much consideration from a storage space standpoint.

DETERMINING STORAGE SPACE REQUIREMENTS. After inventory requirements are determined, they must be converted into storage space requirements. The amount of storage space required for any item is dependent on the **method of storage** to be used. The materials and products to be stored may be piled by power truck, by hand, or by overhead crane.

If storage is by means of **power truck,** the materials or products may be pal-letized or racked, or handled by any one of a wide variety of power truck attach-ments which do not require pallets or pallet racks. If the items stored are **hand-piled,** they may be piled directly on the floor or on shelving, racks, bins, or cabinets or in special storage rooms. If storage is by means of **overhead crane,** the materials or products may be piled on the floor or put into storage racks.

The following methods are used in determining storage space requirements under the various storage methods:

PALLETIZED GOODS STORED BY POWER TRUCK. This includes also goods in pallet racks which are stored by power truck.

1. Obtain the **length, width, height, and weight** of each item to be palletized.

   a. This information can be tabulated with the name of each item in the first column and the length, width, height, and weight of each item, respectively, in the second, third, fourth, and fifth columns.
   b. Other items below may be listed in subsequent columns.

2. Select one or more **pallet sizes** for consideration.

   a. Start with the 48 × 40 in., 48 × 48 in., and/or 32 × 40 in. pallet sizes. These are the standard sizes.

b. Nonstandard pallet sizes may also be selected as possibilities, such as 46×54 in., 40×60 in., 48×60 in., 48×96 in.

c. In selecting possible pallet sizes, consider the size of the **items to be palletized.** For example, 48×96 in. wallboard sheets would require 48×96 in. pallets.

d. If palletized shipments are planned, select a **pallet size that will fit the carriers to be used.**

   (1) Four-way or 8-way 48×40 in. and 32×40 in. pallets fit both railroad cars and trucks.

   (2) 48×48 in. pallets fit railroad cars.

   (3) Minor variations from these standard sizes will also fit railroad cars and trucks.

     (a) Boxcar widths inside are 8 ft. 6 in., 8 ft. 9 in., and 9 ft. 2 in.

     (b) Boxcar inside lengths are 40 ft. 6 in. and 50 ft. 6 in.

     (c) Truck inside widths usually range between 6 ft. 8 in. and **7 ft. 6 in.**

e. Select a pallet size that will **fit between columns of the storage building** with a minimum of waste space. The generally accepted minimum space between pallet rows is from 2 in. to 4 in.

3. Determine the **number of units of each item** which can be piled onto a pallet for each pallet size selected.

a. Determine the number of units per layer (or tier) on a pallet.

   (1) Draw the pallet sizes to scale on separate sheets of paper. ⅛ in. = 1 in. is a good scale to use.

   (2) Cut templates of the items to be palletized. Use the same scale as for item (1) above.

   (3) Lay the templates on the pallet drawings to determine the **number of units per layer** (or tier) for each item on each pallet size.

   (4) Obtain an **interlocking pallet pattern,** if possible.

   (5) For the three standard pallet sizes and for case goods, a handbook such as The Palletizer may be referred to in **determining pallet patterns.**

   (6) As an alternative the items themselves may be **experimentally palletized** to determine the best pallet pattern. Sheets of corrugated paper cut to the size of the pallets under consideration may be laid on the floor and used in place of actual pallets.

   (7) Pile goods onto the pallet in such a way as to **nearly cover the pallet.** (Utilize as much of the pallet face area as possible, with minimum voids.)

   (8) **Avoid excessive overhang** of goods around the edges of the pallet. A maximum of 1 in. overhang all around is considered allowable.

   (9) Pile goods onto the pallet to obtain **stability.** If possible, stack the items with the shortest dimension vertical.

   (10) Pile goods onto the pallet to best **resist crushing** from other goods piled above (the strongest dimension vertical).

b. Determine the **number of layers** (or tiers) to be piled on each pallet size for each item.

   (1) In general, do not pile higher than the longest dimension of the pallet.

   (2) Measure the allowable stacking height of the storage area. Try to obtain pallet heights for each item a multiple of which will most completely utilize the allowable stacking height.

   (3) Check the weight of each kind of item to be palletized. If the units are heavy the allowable height of piling on the pallets may be reduced because of limited power truck capacity.

   (4) Consider the convenience of loading and unloading items on pallets manually. This limits the piling height.

   (5) Consider the stability of the pallet load. Tall, thin items should not be piled in as many layers as short items which have a large base.

(6) Measure the heights of any doorways, elevator cages, overhead piping, etc., and highway truck-body vertical clearances where the pallet loads must be transported, especially if they are to be transported two-high.

c. Determine the **number of units per pallet load.** Multiply the number of units per layer (Item 3a above) by the number of layers per pallet (Item 3b above).

4. Determine the number of loaded pallets per **pallet stack** for each item and for each pallet size.

    a. Determine the allowable stacking height of the storage area. (The allowable stacking height is 18 in. below the sprinkler heads or 6 in. under any obstructions below this 18-in. point.)

    b. Determine the number of pallet loads which will fit into the allowable stacking height for each item.

    c. Crushability of the product may limit this stacking height on some items. The stability of the individual pallet loads may limit stacking height on others.

    d. The **floor loading capacity** may also limit the stacking height on some items.

5. Determine **total pallet loads** required for each pallet size.

    a. Divide the inventory required for storage purposes for each item by the number of units per pallet load for that item. Do this for each of the pallet sizes previously selected. This calculation converts inventories into pallet loads.

    b. In performing Step a, raise fractions of a pallet load to a full pallet load. For example, 847 units divided by 75 units per pallet = 11.3 pallet loads; call this 12 pallet loads.

    c. Total all pallet loads required for all items for each pallet size.

6. Calculate the **outside dimensions and total weight** for each pallet load.

    a. Do this for each item and each pallet size.

    b. In calculating the height of each pallet load, be sure to include the thickness of the pallet. This is 5½ in. for standard double-faced wooden pallets.

7. Determine the total **net number of pallet stacks** required for each pallet size.

    a. Divide the number of pallet loads required for each item by the number of pallet loads per stack. Do this for each of the pallet sizes previously selected.

    b. In performing Step a, raise fractions of a pallet stack to a full pallet stack.

    c. Total all net pallet stacks required for all items for each pallet size.

8. Determine **total gross pallet stacks** required for each pallet size.

    a. Multiply the number of net pallet stacks for each item and each pallet size by the factor 1.25.

    b. In performing Step a, raise fractions of a pallet stack to a full pallet load.

    c. The factor 1.25 is called a rotation factor. It allows extra storage space of 25 percent to provide for normal inventory fluctuations.

    d. Total the gross pallet stacks required for all items for each pallet size.

9. Determine the **floor area per pallet stack** for each pallet size.

    a. If the items on each pallet are within the standard 1-in. overhang, add 4 in. to the pallet width and 2 in. to the pallet length.

    b. The following is an example for 48 × 40 in. pallets with no more than 1-in. overhang:

$$Length \quad Width$$
$$48 \text{ in.} \times 40 \text{ in.}$$
$$\underline{2 \qquad\quad 4\quad}$$
$$50 \text{ in.} \times 44 \text{ in.} = 2{,}200 \text{ sq. in.}$$

2,200 sq. in. ÷ 144 = 15.3 sq. ft. per pallet stack

    c. If the items palletized overhang the pallets by more than 1 in., add 4 in. to the actual over-all width and 2 in. to the actual over-all length of the pallet loads.

10. Determine the **net floor space** required for each pallet size.

    a. Multiply total gross pallet stacks required (Item 8d) by the floor area per pallet stack (Item 9b or 9c).

    b. This calculation gives the floor space required for storage only.

11. Determine the **gross floor space** requirement, including aisles.

    a. Multiply the net floor space required (Item 10a) by the factor 1.25.

    b. This calculation adds 25 percent additional space for aisles.

12. Determine the **gross floor space requirement, including aisles and services.**

    a. Multiply Item 10a by the factor 1.8.

    b. This calculation allows extra space for aisles and services.

    c. Services include offices, washrooms, locker rooms, fire-fighting equipment, space losses caused by columns, risers, etc.

13. Select the **final pallet size or sizes** to be used.

    a. Compare total pallets required for each size pallet originally selected (Item 5).

    b. Determine the pallet investment required for each pallet size. Multiply Item 5 by the cost per pallet for each pallet size.

    c. Compare the net and gross floor area requirements for each pallet size (Items 10, 11, and 12).

    d. Select the pallet size or sizes which require the lowest investment in pallets and the least building space.

14. Make a **warehouse layout** using the final pallet size or sizes selected in Item 13.

    a. A layout is the only sure way of obtaining actual floor space requirements. It is needed as a check of Items 10, 11, and 12.

    b. General information on layout is contained in the latter part of this section, under the heading of Factory Warehouse Layout.

DEAD-PILED GOODS. Dead-piled goods are those **piled directly onto the floor.** Dead piling may be accomplished by hand, by a power truck with an attachment such as a clamp or grab, or by an overhead crane. The following is the method for determining storage space requirements for dead-piled goods:

1. Obtain the length, width, height, and weight of each item to be stored.

    a. These data can be tabulated with the name of each item in the first column, the length, width, height, and weight in the second, third, fourth, and fifth columns.

    b. Other items below may be listed in subsequent columns.

2. Determine the **square feet of floor space required to store one unit** of each item. Allow a small amount of lost space between units when stored on the floor—¼ in. for case goods, whatever minimum is necessary for irregular-shape items and items which require space between them to permit air circulation.

3. Determine **how many units high** each item will be piled.

    a. Consider the allowable stacking height of the storage area. The allowable stacking height, as previously stated, is 18 in. below the sprinkler heads or 6 in. under any obstructions below this 18-in. point.

b. Consider the height to which it will be possible to pile by the hand or mechanical method which it is expected will be used. The nature and capacity of such equipment may limit the piling height.

c. Consider the crushability of the product. This factor may limit piling height.

d. Consider the shape of each item and its stability when piled. The danger of its falling when piled may limit piling height.

e. Consider the weight of each item and the floor loading capacity in the storage area. The floor loading capacity may limit the piling height.

4. Divide No. 2 by No. 3 for each item to determine the **net square feet of storage space** required per unit of each item.

5. Multiply No. 4 by the inventory requirement for each item. This calculation gives the total base square feet of floor space required for **storing the required inventory** of each item.

6. Total all figures under No. 5 to obtain **total base floor space** required for storage of all items.

7. Multiply No. 6 by the rotation factor 1.25 to obtain **total net floor space** required for storage. This allows 25 percent extra space in the base storage area for normal inventory fluctuations.

8. Multiply No. 7 by the factor 1.25 to determine **total floor space** required, including aisles.

9. Multiply No. 7 by the factor 1.8 to determine total floor space required, including **aisles and services.** Services include offices, washrooms, locker rooms, fire-fighting equipment, space losses due to columns, stairways, etc.

10. Make a **warehouse layout** to determine actual floor space requirements.

a. A layout is the only sure check of floor space requirements.

b. General information on warehouse layout is contained in a later portion of this section.

Goods Piled in Storerooms. Storeroom items are usually **hand piled** into shelving, racks, bins, or cabinets. Some items are **dead piled** directly onto the floor, or they may be palletized. The method for calculating space requirements is to obtain the cubic volume of the inventories to be stored and then the amount of **shelving, rack, bin** or **cabinet space** required, as well as the floor space needed for those inventories which are to be dead piled on the floor or palletized. The following is a detailed description of the method used:

1. Obtain the **length, width, height and weight** of each item to be stored.

a. This information can be tabulated, with the name of each item in the first column, the length, width, height, and weight of each item in the second, third, fourth, and fifth columns.

b. Other items below may be listed in subsequent columns.

2. Select the **type of shelving, racks, bins, or cabinets** required for the various items.

a. This selection can be made from catalogs available from manufacturers.

b. Try to standardize on the least possible number of different types of shelving, racks, bins, or cabinets.

3. Calculate **shelving, racks, bins, and cabinets** of each type needed for storing the required inventory of the various items.

4. **Lay out the storage area** with necessary shelving, racks, bins, cabinets, and dead-piled or palletized storage, as well as with receiving doors, dispensary windows, and office space.

DECLINE IN USE OF CENTRAL STOREROOMS. Central storerooms are losing popularity in present-day plant layout. Preference is for storage of supply items in the immediate vicinity of usage. However, the principles outlined above for determining shelving, rack, bin, cabinet, and floor space requirements are the same regardless of location in the plant.

PLANNING THE WAREHOUSE LAYOUT. In each of the preceding articles it was suggested that a warehouse layout be made as a **check of calculated storage space requirements.** Many volumes are available on plant layout, including layout of factory warehousing. The purpose of this section is mainly to stress the important factors in factory warehouse layout.

Basically, factory warehouses consist of storage areas and aisles. Other elements which require consideration include aisle width, aisle frequency, aisle location, column spacing, and clear stacking height. The following points on the various elements should be kept in mind when planning the layout.

STORAGE AREA. The storage area should include a **2-ft. walkway** between stored goods and any walls. Such aisles give access for fighting fires. Narrow walkway aisles (usually 2½ to 3 ft. wide) must also be provided for access to **fire-fighting facilities.** Fire-fighting facilities include wheeled hose reels, sprinkler and hose valves, wall- or column-mounted hoses, and fire extinguishers.

AISLES. Location and layout of aisles will vary with the amount and nature of the various kinds of products, supplies, etc., to be stored.

Aisle Widths. Aisle widths depend on the method of handling goods and supplies into and out of storage. Power trucks require aisle widths ranging from 6 ft. to 22 ft., depending on the size and type of power truck to be used, the size of the pallet loads to be carried, and the purpose of the aisle.

Shipping and receiving aisles are usually made sufficiently wide to enable two loaded power trucks to pass one another comfortably in opposite directions. Sufficient additional aisle width is usually needed to provide for lining up one row of palletized goods on one side of the aisle. This plan makes it possible to accumulate a reserve of palletized goods immediately ahead of loading or immediately following unloading.

Main aisles are usually made wide enough to enable two loaded power trucks to pass one another comfortably in opposite directions. **Cross aisles** are made wide enough to enable a power truck to comfortably angle-stack into storage. Following is the method for determining the minimum aisle width for right-angle stacking into storage.

Determining Aisle Widths for Power Trucks. The following formulas referring to Fig. 1, from the Material Handling Handbook (U. S. Army Air Corps) give the method for calculating aisle widths which will allow trucks to make right-angle turns to stow pallets along the storage aisles of warehouses:

For loads with widths W less than $2B$

$$A = TR + X + L + C$$

For loads with width W greater than $2B$

$$A = TR + \sqrt{(X + L)^2 + \left(\frac{W}{2} - B\right)^2} + C$$

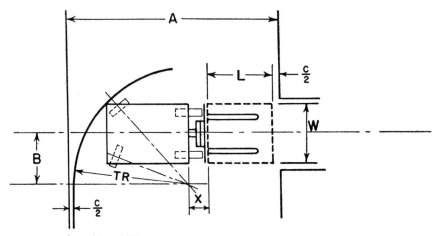

A = aisle width
B = distance from center line of truck to center line of
    point about which truck turns when steering wheels
    are fully turned
TR = turning radius
L = length of load
W = width of load
C = clearance (usually set at 6 in.)
X = distance from center line of drive axle to face of fork

Fig. 1. Method of determining aisle widths for trucks.

The most common method of stacking in factory warehousing is **right-angle stacking into storage from the aisle.** Aisle widths can be reduced by stacking at an angle less than 90°, such as 30°, 45°, 60°.

A careful study should be made before selecting an angle less than 90°. Storage layouts must be made with 90° angle stacking and other lesser angles to determine the effect on the over-all storage capacity of the warehouse. In many cases **stacking at angles less than 90° will reduce the storage capacity** of a warehouse despite the reduction in aisle widths.

Aisle widths can be kept to a minimum by careful selection of the power trucks to be used. Rider-type outrigger pallet trucks, which are available in 2,000- to 4,000-lb. capacities, will right-angle stack 48-in.-long pallets from aisles 6 ft. to 7 ft. wide. Counterweighted power trucks of the same capacity require aisles 11 to 12 ft. wide.

Aisle widths for dead piling manually depend on the size of the items to be stored and the method to be used to get these items to and from storage. Small case goods items brought to and from storage on conventional narrow, 2-, 4-, or 6-wheel hand trucks require minimum cross-aisle widths of only 3 to 4 ft. Main aisles are usually 7 to 8 ft. wide.

Shipping and receiving aisles are usually from 10 to 16 ft. wide, depending on whether it is desired to accumulate one or more rows of hand trucks along one side of the aisle and whether the accumulated hand trucks are to be stored with their lengths parallel to the aisle or perpendicular to it.

Aisle Frequency. The number or frequency of aisles used for stacking into storage depends on the **stock accessibility** desired. For example, palletized items on which large inventories are carried may be stored with 10 pallet stacks between aisles. This arrangement provides accessibility to 5 pallet stacks from each aisle. Items on which smaller inventories are necessary should have more frequent aisles. Items in bins, cabinets, or racks require aisles every other row. Palletized items on a pick line require aisles every 2 to 4 pallet stacks. This layout provides accessibility to 1 or 2 pallet stacks per aisle.

The aisle frequency can be determined only by making a warehouse layout and fitting the inventories of the various items into the layout to provide the best practical accessibility. It is desirable to keep the number of aisles to a practical minimum since they reduce storage capacity. It is also desirable to locate heavy volume commodities so that travel distances are minimized in placing goods in storage and removing them from storage.

Location of Main Aisles and Shipping and Receiving Aisles. The locations of main aisles are determined by access doors, elevators, conveyors, or chutes into the storage area from adjacent manufacturing, shipping, and receiving areas. Shipping and receiving aisles must be located along railroad-car and truck spot locations.

COLUMNS AND COLUMN SPACING. The columns in a warehouse should be as small as possible; for this reason steel columns are preferred. Column spacing should be based on an even multiple of the size or sizes of the pallet to be used between columns. Columns are wasters of storage space. From a storage standpoint the wider the column spacing, the better. But from the standpoint of economy in building cost, **column spacing should not exceed 40 ft.** Bay sizes of 20 × 40 ft., 30 × 40 ft., and 40 × 40 ft. are common. Before column spacing over 40 ft. is used, careful consideration should be given both to the advantages and to the higher building cost.

CLEAR STACKING HEIGHT. The clear stacking height of a warehouse is 18 in. below the sprinkler heads or 6 in. below the bottom chords of trusses or lower surfaces of roof supporting beams. A common clear stacking height today is 18 to 20 ft. This height allows storage of four to five pallets per stack for the common pallet sizes (48 × 48 in. and 48 × 40 in.) and minor variations of these sizes.

The clear stacking height of a warehouse must be determined by its purpose. If the majority of the items to be stored can go only 12 ft. high because of crushability or tipping danger or limitations on floor carrying capacity, the clear stacking height should be reduced accordingly. Extra height would be wasted. Correspondingly, if the product can be stored 25 ft. high, the clear stacking height of the warehouse should be adjusted upward.

From a building cost standpoint, it is usually cheaper to **limit warehouse clear stacking height to a maximum of 20 to 25 ft.** and to spread the storage out over more floor space. Greater heights also create difficulties and inefficiencies in stacking.

DOOR HEIGHTS AND WIDTHS. Doors in factory warehouses are usually 8 ft. wide × 8 ft. high. This size accommodates most power trucks with their pallet loads. Occasionally the masts of high lift power trucks exceed 8 ft., which necessitates higher doors. Before deciding on door heights it is important to determine the **mast heights** of equipment which may possibly be used. Consideration must also be given to the **widths of the loads** to be handled. Wider doors may be needed.

FLOOR ELEVATION. Most modern warehouses are built with the **floors approximately 48 to 50 in. above grade** (ground level). This height is called

"Car-door height." It was selected because it facilitates loading and unloading railroad cars and trailer trucks.

If the floor of an existing warehouse is **at ground level,** platforms 10 to 20 ft. wide may be constructed in front of shipping and receiving doors at car or truck floor height. This provision is especially helpful where power trucks are used to feed the shipping and receiving operations. After the power truck operating on the floor deposits a loaded pallet onto the platform at the shipping door, it is moved into the railroad car or truck for loading by another truck on the platform.

Some warehouses are purposely built with the floor at ground level, to enable flat-bed highway trucks carrying palletized merchandise to enter the warehouse for loading and unloading by power trucks or to enable the power trucks to go outside for loading and unloading the flat-bed highway trucks. This type of operation is especially adaptable to bottling plants and breweries.

Before selecting the floor height of a warehouse it is necessary to consider the shipping and receiving methods which best fit the operations performed.

FLOOR LOAD CAPACITY. The floors of a warehouse must be designed to support the **dead load of items** to be stored and the **movement of loaded power trucks.** The stack weights of various items to be stored must be determined, and reduced to pounds per square foot of floor loading. The floor must be designed accordingly. The **wheel loadings of loaded power trucks** must also be determined and taken into consideration in designing the floor. An important factor in determining wheel loadings of power fork trucks is the fact that approximately 85 percent of the weight of the truck and its load is concentrated on the front wheels.

In cases where the storage area already exists, and the safe floor loading is known, stacking heights of the various items, as well as power truck loadings, must be controlled so as not to exceed these safe floor load capacities.

FLOOR FINISHES. Most warehouse floors are made of concrete. When so, the aisles must have a **hardened surface** if they are to withstand heavy power-truck movement without scaling or spalling. In cases where the nature of ware-housing operations causes wet or slippery floors, various **nonskid aggregates,** such as emery chips, can be incorporated in the floor surface.

HEATING UNITS. Heating units must be so located that they will not interfere with storage and handling operations or adversely affect products being stored.

AIR CONDITIONING, HUMIDITY CONTROL, AND COLD STORAGE. Some products require air conditioning, humidity control, or refrigerated storage. A separate room must be provided for air conditioning or freezer units. Air conditioning ducts, pipes, coils, and humidity control equipment should be so located that they will not interfere with storage and handling operations.

VENTILATING. Factory warehouses are usually equipped with ventilating apparatus, except in refrigerated storage areas. Ventilating equipment is especially important if **gasoline, diesel, or liquefied-petroleum-gas-powered trucks** are to be used in the warehouse.

LIGHTING. It is important to **locate the aisles before laying out a lighting system.** In the storage area, lights are needed only over the aisles. Lights are also needed over the shipping and receiving aisles. If night shipping and receiving operations are customary, supplementary lighting reels or spotlights are also needed at truck and car spots to light the interior of trucks and cars.

All lights should be sufficiently high not to interfere with storing and handling operations. **Switch panels** should be located where they will be accessible with minimum sacrifice of storage space for access walkways.

FIRE-FIGHTING EQUIPMENT. Fire-fighting equipment consists of wheeled hose reels, wall- or column-mounted fire extinguishers, and hoses, riser pipes, valves, and overhead sprinklers. The clear stacking height of a warehouse is 6 in. below the bottom chord of the trusses or beams or 18 in. below the sprinkler heads. The sprinkler heads should preferably be mounted at least 1 ft. above the bottom chords of trusses or lower surface of beams. The location of other items of fire-fighting equipment mentioned above should be planned to minimize storage losses resulting from access walkways.

DRAINAGE. Adequate drainage must be provided, especially where the warehousing operation causes wet floors.

SHIPPING AND RECEIVING FACILITIES. Shipping and receiving facilities include railroad car spots and truck spots. The **number of car spots and truck spots** required can be estimated only by determining the number of cars and trucks to be received and shipped each day and the time requirement for loading and unloading them.

The **time requirements for loading and unloading** the various items to be shipped or received vary considerably, depending on the nature of the items and the methods of handling, shipping, and receiving. For example, a trailer truck load of palletized goods can be loaded or unloaded in 12 to 15 min. by fork truck or electric pallet truck. The same goods dead-piled in the truck require 1½ to 3 hr. to load or unload.

Space for **temporary storage** adjacent to shipping and receiving is often desirable. For example, a truck can be unloaded quickly into this temporary storage area, and the goods transported to permanent storage later. Outgoing items can be accumulated just ahead of loading, which speeds the loading of outgoing cars and trucks. In some cases outgoing stock to be loaded the following day is accumulated during the night shift in storage areas adjacent to shipping.

Truck and car dock heights are important. Most truck-bed heights range between 42 and 58 in. The majority are in the 44- to 52-in range. A careful study should be made of the bed heights of the trucks to be handled. It might be desirable to set some truck docks at 44 in. for city trucks, some at 48 in. for city trailers and some at 52 in. for road trailers.

Railroad-car heights are equally important. Car-floor heights vary to some extent. It is advisable to consider at least those car-floor heights which will be encountered.

The **bridges used between the building and railroad cars or trucks** are also important. A wide variety of bridges are available. If the dock heights are carefully selected to fit the carriers, portable bridge plates made of steel, aluminum, or magnesium will be satisfactory. If a wide range of bed heights is expected at the same dock, permanently installed adjustable bridge plates are desirable. These are more costly than portable bridge ramps.

The **floors of standard railroad cars** cannot be depended on to support more than a 4,000-lb. capacity fork truck with its load. The floors of standard trailer trucks cannot be depended on to support more than a 2,000-lb. capacity free-suspended-type fork truck with its load. In planning for palletized shipments or receipts, it is necessary to be sure the carriers will take the power trucks which shippers and receivers plan on using. It may be found necessary to reduce pallet loads or arrange for special railroad cars or trailer trucks.

Also, it is necessary to be sure that the **mast heights of the power trucks** in use will go into the carriers which are to be loaded. The standard mast height for loading trucks is from 68 to 70 in. The standard mast height for loading railroad cars is 83 in. The **door heights** of the carriers should be checked to see what mast heights can be used. If it is planned to stack the upper pallet in the carrier, it is necessary to check the height of the mast when hoisted to stack the upper pallet load. It may strike the roof of the car or truck.

Railroad sidings and truck spots may be inside or outside the building. **Inside railroad and truck spots** are desirable in cold climates. In spite of this, outside rail and truck spots are often used, because they require a smaller building. A good part of the cold can be blocked off by using **canvas dock covers** to close the opening between the building and the railroad car or truck.

Single-track sidings are preferable to double-track sidings. Double-track sidings necessitate loading railroad cars on the outside track through the railroad cars on the inside track. With this plan there is a longer haul when loading cars on the far track and interference with car-loading on the near track.

Canopies are desirable over outside railroad and truck spots to protect loading and unloading operations from rain or snow. Before setting canopy heights over railroad cars, a careful check of rail regulations is needed. A check of truck heights is required before setting canopy heights over truck spots.

MAINTENANCE FACILITIES. Adequate maintenance facilities must be provided for power trucks and other materials handling equipment used in the warehouse. If such facilities are not available in another section of the plant, they must be provided in the warehouse. A satisfactory room size for such maintenance facilities is approximately 20 × 25 ft. for five to ten power trucks and 20 × 40 ft. for eleven to twenty power trucks. A list of **maintenance equipment** required for power trucks may be obtained from power truck manufacturers.

If **gasoline-operated power trucks** are used, a gasoline pump and an underground tank outside the building are desirable. Details on the installation can be obtained from the oil companies. If **electric trucks** are used, battery-charging facilities must be provided. Details on **battery-charging facilities** may be obtained from battery and charger manufacturers. In some factory warehouses both gasoline- and battery-operated power trucks are used. For example, gasoline-operated fork trucks might be used for storage purposes, and battery-operated pallet trucks for car-loading operations. Small single-circuit chargers are commonplace for electric pallet trucks and are often located along a wall or back in a corner adjacent to their point of use. Battery-operated fork trucks have larger batteries and chargers. A separate room is usually provided adjacent to the power-truck maintenance room for charging these larger batteries.

OFFICES. Factory warehouses are usually adjacent to shipping and receiving facilities. In most cases, the shipping and receiving facilities are incorporated right in the warehouse. For this reason a shipping and receiving office must often be planned into the layout of a factory warehouse. If the warehouse is operated separately from shipping and receiving, proper office space must be provided for warehouse supervision and clerical personnel.

The **office facilities** required in a factory warehouse can vary considerably, depending on the products stored in the warehouse, the type of warehousing operation, and the amount of inventory control and recording carried on within the warehouse proper. Some factories have **decentralized setups** which locate all clerical, accounting, engineering, maintenance, and other operations in each segment of the plant. Under this decentralized arrangement more office space is required in the factory warehouse than with centralized control from a main office located somewhere else in the plant. Personnel requirements within the factory warehouse must be determined, and the warehouse office space must then be tailored to fit these requirements.

TOILETS, LOCKERS, AND LUNCHROOMS. Toilet and locker facilities for warehouse employees must be provided within the warehouse or nearby. **Personnel requirements** in the warehouse must be determined, and the toilet and locker facilities installed to fit these personnel requirements. If both men and women are to be employed, separate toilet and locker facilities must be provided. In many plant warehouses **lunchroom facilities** are also provided.

Installation of Mechanized Handling Operations

MULTISTORY BUILDINGS. The seven-story warehouse of The Pittsburgh and Lake Erie Railroad Company in Pittsburgh, Pennsylvania, offers an illustration of many of the principal materials handling advantages which a multistory building possesses over a one-story structure. In this warehouse each floor forms a rectangular area 322 ft. × 188 ft., equivalent to $1\frac{1}{3}$ acres per floor. Including the combined areas of the six upper floors, the shipping floor, and the basement, the building houses more than 9 acres of floor area over a ground area of only $1\frac{1}{3}$ acres. Merchandise can therefore be moved directly from any spot in the 9 acres of floor area down to a highway truck located at any spot within a 1-acre area. Thus in dropping 13 ft. from floor to floor, the merchandise is moved the equivalent of $1\frac{1}{3}$ acres of ground space.

The structure of the building offers a distinct advantage over a comparable space in a one-story building spread over 9 acres of ground. With the latter kind of building, trucks picking up merchandise are often compelled to move from one truck spot to another. This operation slows down delivery to the customer's truck, increases the customer's trucking cost for waiting time, and lengthens the floor distance traveled by a given shipment from stock area to shipping platform.

PLANNING FACILITIES FOR ECONOMICAL HANDLING. Modernizing buildings which are used for storage purposes may yield most of the advantages which can be provided in a new warehouse, even of the one-story type, thus avoiding the erection of a new structure, and the demolition of the old one.

A case in point is that of a particular warehouse which stocks and distributes to retailers thousands of items of paper stock, floor coverings, carpetings, electric wares, janitor supplies, and a seasonal line of toy goods. These items are received and shipped in virtually as wide a diversity of packages as may be found in a department store warehouse. Representative units include rolls of butcher paper, bundles of grocery bags, cartons of tissue paper, flat sheets of paper on skids, reels of rope, pails of cement, 12-ft. rigid rolls of floor covering in cartons, 12-ft. limp rolls of carpeting in burlap covers, cartons of floor tile, a wide range of cartons and crates containing fragile toys, and an extensive line of juvenile furniture. Individual packages range in weight from about 5 lb. for small cartons up to 400 lb. for long rolls of carpeting and linoleum.

Determining the Proper Kind of Handling Equipment. Mechanizing the handling of such a broad variety of packages, many of them awkward in size, length, and/or weight, and of fragile construction, required the initial consideration of several types of mechanical handling devices. Some merchandise, such as rolls of paper, carton goods, and case stock, could be easily palletized. Rolls of linoleum and other floor coverings in a wide variety of patterns could be readily stored individually in upright position for quick selectivity. Rolls of carpeting could be stored horizontally and kept accessible for unrolling and cutting.

For many commodities, powered fork trucks appeared to be ideal. For other items, conveyors, monorails, and traveling bridge cranes possessed advantages. Powered lifters, hydraulically elevated platforms, tractors and trailers, jib cranes, hoists, and an assortment of prefabricated racks, bins, and benches offered opportunities for the piling or stowing of merchandise. Where the merchandise had to be transferred from one kind of equipment to another, floor trucks and semi-live skids were found to be the most convenient and economical kinds of equipment to employ.

When all these different kinds of equipment were brought together to integrate them into a unified system, it was found that most of the devices considered were of a **one-purpose type.** The overhead equipment, for example, could handle only the merchandise stored directly beneath it and, therefore, could not be utilized in other sections of the warehouse. Furthermore, the activity of merchandise movement in any one section was not of sufficient volume to justify the investment in single-purpose devices.

What was most needed was versatile, mobile, powered handling equipment which could be used throughout the entire warehouse. Such **general equipment** was preferable in most respects to specialized equipment for each different line of merchandise. The choice narrowed down to electric-powered, high-lift fork trucks working in conjunction with liftable floor trucks and pallets carrying loads on semi-live skids. With this arrangement, long and awkward pieces could be laid down on liftable floor trucks which can be raised or lowered by fork trucks as needed.

OVERCOMING STRUCTURAL DEFICIENCIES IN OLD BUILD-INGS. Floor trucks require suitable aisles, fairly level floors, and adequate aisle spacing. Old buildings do not always provide these facilities to an adequate degree. For example, three adjoining buildings in a particular warehouse were notably deficient in these respects, the first floor being at a different level in each of the three buildings. The space between two of the long structural walls in one building was but 19 ft., barely enough width for a truck aisle and a single row of pallet stacks along each wall.

The three buildings, as shown in Fig. 2, had a combined warehouse floor area of 125,000 sq. ft. All three buildings extended back to a railroad siding running along a river bank in the rear. Two more rail sidings, parallel to one another, ran along the right wall of the main building. The truck ports were placed at the front end of two low buildings and down along the right wall of the main building. These facilities permitted 13 freight cars to be unloaded at one time, while 14 trucks were being loaded with shipments from the warehouse stock.

The main building at the corner consisted of a three-story structure with its first floor raised to car-bed level. The building at the extreme left had only one floor, but this floor had two elevations, namely, at street level in the front half and 2 ft. higher in the rear. In the space between these two buildings, and set back 35 ft. from the street, was a low-roofed, one-story structure—once an alley —with its floor at street level.

Overcoming Differences in Floor Levels in Adjoining Buildings. To permit uninterrupted travel of fork lift trucks from one building to another in the foregoing example, the raised first floor level in the main building was used as the

Fig. 2. Warehouse in three adjoining buildings.

basing point for extending a one-level main thoroughfare throughout all three buildings. The disadvantages of the varying floor elevations in the other two buildings were overcome (1) by constructing a **raised receiving platform** across the two one-story buildings at the rear and along the river, thus providing a uniform floor elevation for all three buildings along the rail siding in the rear; and (2) by constructing a similarly raised platform to serve as a **shipping dock** across the front end of the center building and extending clear across the outer low building, which was at the left. This latter arrangement allowed the **truck-spotting area** to function at night as a closed garage at street level at the front end of this building. In daytime this garage served as a shipping port. The extended platform provided a uniform floor level for all three buildings along the street in the front.

These two new platforms formed two legs of the letter "U" extending out from the raised first floor of the main building. The sunken space enclosed within this letter "U" constituted the **sunken floor**, or "pit," described later.

The first of the two raised platforms previously mentioned is the elevated receiving dock serving inbound freight cars. The new receiving dock in Fig. 3 runs across the rear end of the building and shuts off the sunken floor on which the fork truck on the left operates.

The fork truck lifts a pallet load of incoming bundles of grocery bags from the empty semi-live skid in front of it on the receiving dock. The truck turns around to transport this load into storage on the sunken floor. The other semi-live skid on the receiving platform is wheeled into position to permit its pallet load to be picked up by the fork truck on the lower level. These pallets are being loaded by the freight handlers in the rail car seen through the open receiving door in the right background (Fig. 3).

A **ramp** connects the sunken-floor level with the receiving-dock level and is used only for transferring fork trucks into and out of the pit. It is not intended to be used for transporting merchandise loads at any time.

The second raised platform, similar to the one described above, runs across the front of the two low buildings in Fig. 2 and forms a raised shipping platform serving outgoing highway trucks. A fork truck lifts a pallet load of outgoing merchandise from the sunken floor and deposits it on the raised shipping dock. This truck then goes for another load, which is order-selected in the pit.

In the meantime a fork truck traveling at the higher level on the shipping platform picks up a pallet load previously placed there by the truck in the pit. The truck on the raised platform then transports the load to the pallet storage rack located to the left of a specified door. Later, when a highway delivery truck backs up against that door, the pallet loads stored temporarily on the pallet rack next to it will be taken down as needed, one load at a time, by a fork truck on the shipping dock and deposited at the tail gate of the highway truck. The existence of the 43-in. difference in floor levels between the pit floor and the shipping dock is thus completely obviated by the lift trucks. It makes no difference whether the load is deposited on the surface of the sunken floor down in the pit or up on the surface of the shipment dock. Each truck operates on one floor level only; one on the shipping dock and the other in the pit. In this way the break in floor levels is completely overcome by the use of lift trucks stationed on the two levels. This arrangement gives rise to no more handling than would take place if all these operations had been performed on but one level common to all the trucks concerned.

The street-level floor in the center building (Fig. 2) and the corresponding low floor in the outer low building were therefore left unaltered. To raise these two floors up to the 43-in. elevation of the ground floor in the main building would have meant an additional construction cost of $35,000, plus a 43-in. loss in overhead storage space.

The elevated docks at both ends of these two buildings provide the one-level thoroughfare connecting all these buildings. This arrangement thereby saved the cost of filling in the sunken floor, or "pit," enclosed between the receiving and shipping elevated docks. It also provided all the advantages of a one-story warehouse for the entire ground floor of the three buildings.

Bypassing Structural Obstacles in Existing Buildings. In making the planned building alterations, no walls were torn down. Wherever blank structural walls stood in the path of the layout of truck aisles, doors were cut through to make way for these aisles. As a result, the floor layout was arranged as if no walls interfered with the plans.

The narrow, 19-ft. strip of floor area, extending for over 200 ft. between the two structural walls in the outer low building (Fig. 2), posed a unique layout problem. It did not lend itself to the accommodation of a truck aisle in the center, with a single row of pallet stacks of merchandise on both sides, without an undue waste of floor space. This arrangement would have consumed an amount of floor space for the aisle disproportionate to the narrow storage area actually served by it.

It was therefore decided to cut as many traffic doors as would be needed through these two walls to permit the traffic aisles to enter this building at right angles to its length. The storage areas created between the aisles cutting across this narrow strip of floor space could then be serviced by fork trucks operating from the cross aisles.

The net result of this arrangement was to eliminate completely the original obstacle presented by the existence of these walls. The stacking can now be spotted from wall to wall along either side of the cross aisles, just as though no walls existed at all.

The two upper stories in the main building presented no particular problem. The second floor has a load capacity of over 500 lb. per sq. ft. but a ceiling height of only 12 ft. This floor was therefore given over to the storage of merchandise normally kept in bins, such as small items of paper stock, electric wares, janitor supplies, and toys. All package-wrapping operations incidental to the sale of these items were likewise located on this floor. To facilitate delivery of small packages from the second floor to customers' trucks calling at the shipping dock on the first floor, a spiral gravity chute was installed. For the reverse movement of odd packages from the first to the second floor, an inclined powered belt conveyor was installed alongside the gravity chute.

The third floor, on the other hand, has a floor load capacity of only 250 lb. per sq. ft. However, as the ceiling height is 21 ft., palletizable merchandise of a light, bulky, or slow-moving nature was assigned to this top floor.

Fork Trucks Negotiating Three Floor Levels Along a Main Aisle. One of the several 235-ft. truck aisles on the sunken floor makes a direct connection between the two raised shipping platforms in the outer one-story building (Fig. 1). This truck aisle contains two successive ramps, thus permitting lift trucks to travel uninterruptedly from the sunken floor level up to the midway floor level at the center of the building and thence to the raised receiving dock in the rear.

Lift trucks can readily travel up or down these two low-pitched ramps. The stepped-up truck aisle in this case provides a gradual climb from the sunken floor to the raised dock without perceptible effort and without loss of storage space at any point along the aisle or alongside the ramps.

Palletized loads of roll paper are solidly high-stacked on both sides of the aisle. The trucks can mechanically stack a large number of items, as high as 24 ft. There is installed on the shipping dock a scale for weighing outbound rolls of paper.

Receiving Carload Lots into Sunken Storage Pit. Fig. 3 was taken from the sunken floor in the center building, looking toward the raised receiving platform serving inbound freight cars. The fork truck has lifted a pallet load of incoming merchandise from the semi-live skid (No. 122) on the receiving dock and

Fig. 3. Operation with raised receiving dock.

is lowering it to within a few inches above the sunken floor for transportation purposes. This truck can then swing around 180° and transport the load to its storage spot in the pit. It may stack the load at that point and then return to the shipping dock parapet for another. As a rule, however, the truck transports two pallet loads at a time, one above the other.

In the center background of Fig. 3 two men are shown unloading a carload of bundles. These bundles are being stacked on a pallet resting on top of a semi-live skid. In the right background one of these loaded skids is being moved toward the pit edge of the receiving dock so that the pallet load itself will be available to the forks of the lift truck operating in the pit.

Car-unloading is thus confined to the level of the receiving dock and to the use of semi-live skids which can readily be maneuvered into and out of freight cars by the car unloaders without the aid of powered trucks. This is as far as the manual handling can go. The powered lift trucks, on the other hand, can begin only where they are at their best, namely, at the point where manual operations cease to be inevitable. In the present case this point is at the pit edge of the receiving dock.

Balcony Storage over Sunken Floor. The elevated truck aisles enclosing the sunken floor in the center building provided a balcony storage facility not anticipated in the original modernization plans. This facility may be seen in Fig. 4, photographed from the shipping dock at the front end of the center building, looking toward the receiving dock in the background.

This elevated truck aisle is on the same floor level as the dock level at each end. It provides a direct link between the shipping dock and the receiving dock, both of which run to the left in the background. These three elevated platforms make up the U-shaped enclosure surrounding the sunken floor, which is located on the left in the illustration.

Fig. 4. Balcony adds to storage space.

This arrangement permits fork trucks to run freely around the three sides of the sunken floor, just as they would normally travel around three aisles surrounding a storage area on the aisle level. The fact that the storage area in this particular case is located on a sunken floor rather than on the same floor level as the truck aisles does not in any way detract from the efficiency of truck transportation along these passageways.

The unforeseen advantage offered by the elevated runway shown here is that it serves incidentally as a mezzanine floor or balcony along the storage pit on the left. It permits the use of elevated storage bins and racks based fully 9 ft. above the level of the sunken floor on which long rolls of floor coverings are stored in upright position in vertical stalls. The balcony racks are constructed directly above the vertical storage stalls. These racks extend up to the roof of the building. They make readily accessible an elevated storage space which could not otherwise have been utilized. While access to the rolls is from the level of the sunken floor, access to the balcony racks above them is from the raised runway.

This balcony storage extends along the entire 235-ft. length of this building. This superimposed storage space is 9 ft. high, extends back about 15 ft. over the pit, and provides the equivalent of two-story storage along the sunken-floor area. Much of this storage space would have been lost had the level of the sunken floor been raised to that of the receiving and shipping docks at the respective ends of the building.

BENEFITS DERIVED FROM MECHANIZED HANDLING. Through the utilization of pallets, fork lift trucks, and powered "walkies," the contents of a railroad car can now be unloaded and placed in storage within 2 hours by three men. From the moment the merchandise has been unloaded piece by piece from a boxcar and placed on pallets, it is handled on a pallet-load basis. Depending on the kind of merchandise, a pallet load may weigh anywhere from $\frac{1}{4}$ ton to about 2 tons. Thus, instead of handling one package at a time, the warehouse handles on the average about 1 ton at a time.

Once merchandise has been placed on a pallet it is essentially "on wheels," that is, it can be picked up, transported, and deposited bodily by a powered vehicle at any time without any manual handling. Even while in storage this merchandise can be said to possess mobility because palletized merchandise is quickly transferable by motorized equipment.

High-stacking is made possible by palletized loads handled by fork trucks. Pallet loads may be piled five or six tiers high, 2 tons at a time, instead of stacking one roll or one package at a time, as was done before mechanization. Furthermore, one or two such high stacks can be moved out and placed elsewhere in a matter of a few minutes. This facility permits the constant retention of all lots of a given item in one storage spot. It also permits the quick transfer of the entire stock of a given item from one spot to another to fill in open spaces.

Three-Foot Rolls of Sheathing Paper Boxed Upright on "Play-Pen" Pallets. Rolls of building paper, such as rosin-sized and asphalt-saturated sheathing, tend to flatten if piled horizontally like cord wood. When stood up on end, their 6-in. diam. provides a base too narrow for their 46-in. height to permit them to retain a vertical position, even when the load is lashed together at the top of the rolls.

By bolting a vertical post at each corner of the pallet, topping these posts with 2 in. × 4 in. stringers, and bracing the framework on all four sides, a "play-pen" box pallet is readily obtained for handling these rolls. With this simple arrangement, 40 rolls can be placed on a 40 in. × 48 in. pallet. They can be held in unit loads of this size from the time the rolls are received at the warehouse until they are shipped out to customers. Thus, instead of piling and unpiling one roll at a time in unloading cars, then piling in storage and unpiling out of storage, these rolls are now handled in unit loads of 40 or 80 rolls at a time throughout the warehousing cycle.

Order-selecting in Pallet Loads for Warehouse Shipments. In order-selecting, even where cartons, cases, bundles, or rolls of an item are ordered one or two at a time by customers, mechanized equipment offers distinct advantages. A customer's order, which may consist of various items selected from different points in the warehouse and funneled into a pallet load, is stored temporarily on a pallet rack near a truck port to await the arrival of the highway delivery truck which is to take it away. A rider-type truck is used to handle merchandise thus pre-assembled. Merchandise is deposited directly at the tail gate of the truck by the pallet load instead of package by package.

Several pallet loads of merchandise can thus be made ready for immediate delivery on arrival of the highway trucks. This method eliminates the former coolie-gang method of passing one package at a time, from hand to hand, through a chain of handlers extending from an assembly area near the shipping platform over to the tail gate of the highway truck.

The former practice of piece-by-piece handling into and out of the warehouse has now given way to the modern concept of load-by-load handling, even to the tail gate of a delivery truck. Each pallet load consists of from 40 to 50 cu. ft. of merchandise, weighing up to 2 tons per load in the case of floor tile.

Yard Storage

SCOPE AND IMPORTANCE. The expansion of production activity in a plant is normally accompanied by a commensurately increased need for adequate storage facilities. The rapid rise in industrial construction costs in recent years has placed a high premium on **indoor storage facilities.** As an alternative to these mounting costs for indoor floor space, significantly increased attention is now being directed to **outdoor storage** in the plant yard.

The rapid advent of newer techniques for applying protective coatings on materials of a corrosive nature, and the use of better shipping containers and improved yard-storage boxes have made it safe to store outdoors a far wider variety of materials than was possible before. Better facilities for **protective storing** and the increasing use of newer kinds of materials handling equipment for **outdoor transportation** have made it possible to reduce considerably the cost of outdoor storage.

Sound principles for selecting and laying out storage yards have opened the way to new possibilities of savings that heretofore were not available. Existing yard areas have been adapted to yard storage. Palletization of yard stock and special techniques for handling awkward and heavy shapes have been developed. Improved methods have already been applied to coal storage yards, lumber yards, scrap yards, shipyards, and other areas where outdoor storage is permissible. Fig. 5 shows the layout of a railroad yard and waterfront in which a very considerable amount of outdoor storage is done. In this paper mill, newsprint rolls are produced in mills A and B, both situated on a hillside 50 ft. higher than the water level, where wharf sheds 1, 2, 3, and 4 are located. The output of each of the mills is moved on the flatcars of a plant railroad to the four wharf sheds, over an average distance of 3,850 ft. per round trip. There are no highways

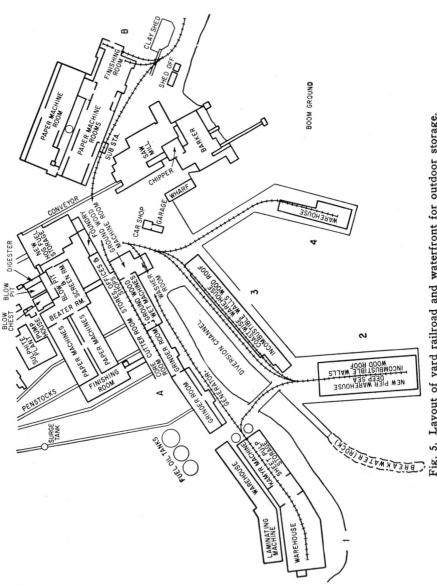

Fig. 5. Layout of yard railroad and waterfront for outdoor storage.

or outside railroads within 75 mi. of this plant in the Canadian northwest, and all shipping is done by water. Pulpwood is transported uphill by straddle carriers, and wood chips are stockpiled by trestle-mounted conveyors.

Kinds of Materials Stored Outdoors. Experiments conducted by the U. S. Navy showed that, when properly protected by coating, container, tarpaulin, or roofing paper, practically anything could be stored economically in outdoor areas. Perhaps the Navy itself stores a wider variety of materials outdoors than is done in any industry. Outdoor ground storage for industry at large is rapidly increasing in importance as a medium for handling large and varied quantities of materials in the following two main classified areas:

1. **Bulk materials:** Coal, coke, sand, pig iron, scrap iron, and other materials and aggregates not readily damaged by the elements.
2. **Piece materials:** Castings and forgings, irregularly shaped forms, long piping and tubing, structural shapes, lumber, metal sheets and plates, drums, barrels and skid boxes, fabricated parts and assemblies, machine dies, bales of cotton, metal scrap, bundles of flat stock, large rolls of paper, and reels of cable.

Among the representative kinds of materials which can be actually stored outdoors are the following:

Ashes	Crushed stone	Pulpwood
Bags (cement)	Cylinders	Punchings
Bales (cotton, paper)	Dies (machine)	Rails
Bar stock	Drums	Reels
Barrels	Fittings	Rims
Baskets	Forgings	Rolls
Beams	Gears	Sand
Blocks	Hogsheads	Scrap
Boards	Ingots	Sheets
Boxes	Joists	Skins
Brick	Kegs	Slabs
Bundles	Limestone	Slag
Cable reels	Logs	Strips
Cans	Lumber	Structural shapes
Cases	Machinery	Tanks
Casks	Millwork	Ties (railroad)
Castings	Ore	Tile
Cement	Pails	Timber
Cinders	Patterns (wood)	Tires
Coal	Pig metal	Tubes
Coils	Pipes	Turnings
Concrete	Planks	Valves
Conduit	Plates	Wheels
Crates	Poles	Wire

PRESERVATION OF MATERIALS STORED OUTDOORS.

Corrosive materials stored outdoors require the application of a protective coating to preserve the surface condition and the appearance of the materials as well as to keep their correct dimensions. This protection against corrosion can be eliminated, however—when costs are not prohibitive—by substituting for the corrosive materials such noncorrosive alloys as stainless steel, Monel metal, or aluminum. The corrosive nature of the surroundings, of course, can be offset, but the cost of this remedy frequently outbalances all savings from this measure.

The only remaining alternative for combating corrosion lies in the application of **external protective coatings** on the surface of the corrosive materials. In the selection of corrosion preventives, the following four fundamental factors should be considered:

1. Cost and method of applying the coating.
2. Amount of protection provided by the coating.
3. Cost and method of removing the coating.
4. Range of temperature in the storage area.

Easily removable coatings include oils, grease, and solvent mixtures, as tabulated in Fig. 6.

Kind of Coating	Methods of Application	Quality of Protection	Removability
Oil application	Dipping Spraying Brushing Slushing	Good. Also adequate in less-exposed storage areas	Does not have to be removed but is easily removable
Grease compound	Dipping Brushing	Excellent for long periods	Requires much labor
Dry film of paint or varnish		Thin but hard. Excellent coat. Good as grease. Withstands abrasion and handling	Somewhat difficult to remove
Plastic strippable film	Spraying (used in "mothballing" U. S. Fleet)	Excellent protection	Easily removed
Plating, chemical treatment, and porcelain enameling	Special types of applications	Excellent. Temporary applications	Fixed protection superior to removable coatings

Fig. 6. Easily removable outdoor coatings used for protection from weather.

Combating Inclement Weather. The ever threatening factor of bad weather presents one of the outstanding problems of outside storage. In northern latitudes snow removal is usually a crucial, costly factor which is successfully overcome to an economical degree by one of the following five methods:

1. Mechanical handling equipment fitted with special attachments designed for snow removal.
2. The use of chemical agents such as salt or calcium chloride for melting the snow. Calcium chloride melts ice and anchors abrasives much faster than ordinary salt but should be used sparingly on concrete surfaces because of its tendency to cause surface breaking and scaling.
3. Hot water and steam sprays may be used effectively provided the snow and ice are completely drained off and the area is scraped to prevent refreezing.
4. Subsurface radiant heating in concrete driveways and platforms eliminates the need for shoveling snow and chopping away ice.
5. To combat rain and soft ground, solutions offered include good water drainage, steel mats, and caterpillar equipment for handling materials.

PLANNING AND CONSTRUCTION OF STORAGE YARDS. Many companies which have spent much money to modernize their indoor handling and plant layouts to conform with the latest performance standards overlook the costliness and inefficiency of outmoded handling methods in the yard. An efficiently laid out outdoor storage area can provide an economical area for the temporary storage of materials not subject to weather damage.

Caterpillar Tractor Co.

Fig. 7. Storage yard.

Through good layout planning, roadways can be properly laid out to provide ready access to all materials. The extensive yard shown in Fig. 7 has well-spaced light posts and clearly marked aisle lines. These roadways should be wide enough and smooth enough to expedite materials handling activities. An experienced observer can make a fairly accurate appraisal of the three component factors of an efficient storage yard, namely:

1. Smoothness and speed of materials handling.
2. Proper planning of aisle layout and area utilization.
3. Degree of operator safety and avoidance of damage to stock.

Yard handling equipment, including mobile cranes and industrial trucks, should be operated at efficient speeds and within standard safety codes. Materials should be stored according to systematic plans. Poor stacking of materials results in the loss of much space through honeycombing.

Another indication of inadequate yard conditions is the existence of practically impassable roadways during rainy or snowy weather. When fork trucks are impeded by deep mud, and the bottom tier of storage stacks sinks into the mud, yard operation becomes a costly, inefficient, and unsafe activity. Surfaced roadways become indispensable modernization improvements for obtaining the maximum benefits from the yard storage area.

Locating the Storage Yard. The location of outside storage areas is usually influenced by two main factors:

1. Distances from receiving areas to storage areas.
2. Distances from storage areas to production areas.

Since the outside storage area is basically a way station between a **carrier unloading point** and a point of **first use of materials** in a plant, the relative distances separating the storage yard from these two main areas of handling activity have a direct influence on the cost and expediency of operating the yard. Furthermore, the location of the storage area directly influences the selection of the **kinds of materials handling equipment** best adapted for negotiating the ground dis-

Norfolk and Western Railroad

Fig. 8. Storage strip between car tracks used for salvaging scrap.

tance from receiving to storage and, in turn, from storage to production or other points of first use. The farther away the storage yard is located fom the plant, the more **mobile** the handling equipment will have to be. In storage areas close to the plant buildings, the equipment used in the yard might consist of overhead cranes, conveyors, and industrial trucks. For distances in excess of 500 or 1,000 ft., it may be economically preferable to operate a plant railroad, a trestle-mounted conveyor, tractor-trailer trains, or straddle carrier trucks. A plant layout in which all of these conveyors are being used is shown in Fig. 5. Fig. 8 shows a very lengthy belt conveyor system used by workers for sorting reclaimable scrap into outside storage bins. Useless scrap is discharged at the end of the conveyor.

Layout of Yard Storage Areas. In planning the layout of a storage yard, the following information should be assembled for use as a guide:

1. **Roadways** and yard approach: Type and condition of ground surface of roadways and cross routes.

2. **Aisle widths** required for fast-moving operations with the kinds of materials handling equipment under consideration, such as for crane trucks, straddle trucks, tractor trains, and conveyors. **Crane runways** are also planned at this stage.
3. **Materials stored:** Approximate tonnage of each kind and whether the materials are to be stored in pallet loads, box loads, or by special handling equipment, such as for long piping or lumber.
4. **Flow of material:** Sizes of lots received and of lots issued. These lot sizes will aid in determining the location of the stacks, ground loads, and stockpiles, for the purpose of holding to a minimum the time required per trip into and out of storage.
5. **Handling costs:** Comparative costs of labor and equipment expense for the various kinds of mechanical equipment under consideration.

The yard storage areas should clearly be marked with **signs** on durable posts at least 8 ft. high to permit visibility from a distance and over snowbanks. If a number of detached storage areas are in use within the same plant site, each such area should be properly numbered to facilitate the traffic on connecting roadways or plant railroad tracks.

Construction of Outdoor Storage Areas. Among the factors involved in the construction of outdoor storage areas are drainage and the surface material. The load-bearing capacity of yard surfacing in a given area may vary considerably at various times, depending upon the amount of rain water absorbed in the sub-surface. For example, whereas wet sand carries but ½ ton per sq. ft., compacted dry sand may carry up to 4 tons per sq. ft. To provide good drainage in level sections of the yard it may be necessary to use drain tile under the surface.

Recent surveys of a country-wide scope indicate that about one-half of all storage yards are **paved** and that the kind of paving laid is about evenly divided between bituminous material and concrete. The plant yards not covered with hard paving are, however, **surfaced** with such hardening material as cinders, crushed stone, slag, sand, or waste materials supplied by the production areas. Between bituminous paving and concrete, however, a number of relative advantages and disadvantages exist in both cases, as may be observed in the tabulation in Fig. 9.

Factors Compared	Bituminous Paving	Concrete
Initial cost	Lower	Higher
Maintenance	Lower	Higher
Frost heave	Lower	Higher
Construction	In stages	In lump job
Removal of pavement	Easier	Harder
Salvage value of surfacing	Some	None
Traffic noise	Quieter	Louder
Traffic movement	Slower	Faster
Surface glare	None	Some
Load-bearing capacity	Surface softens in hot weather	Substantial strength at all times

Fig. 9. Bituminous paving vs. concrete for yard paving.

Construction costs and the effects of **hot and cold weather,** as well as the relative speed of traffic, are the governing factors underlying the various advantages and disadvantages listed in Fig. 9. Only a complete economic evaluation of all relevant factors can provide an impartial basis for gaging the net benefits of one kind of paving over another in a given storage yard.

PROGRESSIVE STEPS IN YARD MODERNIZATION. The modernization of handling in an existing storage yard can usually be attained by degrees of improvement based on an integrated program without disrupting existing storage activities. When the program is followed carefully, the transformation of the yard into a modern facility may be accomplished with little or no rehandling cost during the process of changeover.

As experienced in plant yards covering several acres of ground, progressive steps in the modernizataion of outdoor handling tend to follow a pattern somewhat like the following sequence:

1. **Laying out yard areas:** Storage space is allocated in accordance with production requirements as to quantity of materials and distance of travel into and out of storage areas.
2. **Surfacing yard areas:** It is advisable to provide smooth, rapid, and safe travel for powered mobile equipment, such as trucks, cranes, and tractor trains, and to permit proper drainage.
3. **Marking storage areas:** Aisle lines, high marker posts, and flood lights are indispensable aids for efficiency in operation.
4. **Ground-storage materials:** Bulk materials which must be stockpiled, and irregularly shaped items and long items which cannot be handled economically on pallets or in pallet boxes should be segregated to permit common use of special handling equipment such as gantry cranes, trestle-mounted conveyors, and mobile cranes.

Fig. 10. Outside storage of crated apparatus.

Fig. 11. Outdoor overhead monorail handling system in a yard.

5. **Palletization of stock:** All materials which can be handled more economically in containers or on pallets should be removed from storage on the ground. Unit-load handling by fork trucks (Fig. 10), straddle carrier trucks, or tractor-trailer trains should be developed to reduce ground-storage items to a minimum.

6. **Coating corrosive materials: Protective coatings** of oil, grease, paint, varnish, or enamel should be applied on corrosive materials and on equipment stored outdoors and not protected by closed containers.

7. **Training yard workers:** Instructing and training **equipment operators** and other yard workers is an important factor in the operation of the modernization program.

8. **Visual stock control:** Continual vigilance should be exercised over unusual bulges and depletions in customary **quantity** of individual materials stored in the yard. **Visual watchfulness** over these items is frequently more effective than looking through book balances, is less expensive to maintain, and is conducive to quicker remedial measures.

9. **Use of mechanical equipment,** such as the outdoor overhead monorail system shown in Fig. 11.

STOCKPILING OF BULK MATERIALS. The basic purpose of a stockpile is to provide a surge capacity between the receipt of raw materials and the consumption of these materials into production. Basic industries such as steel, aluminum, and power are continually dependent upon large quantities of bulk materials such as ore, bauxite, and coal, respectively. In addition to the immense quantities of bulk materials stored by the basic industries, there are many different kinds of other materials purchased and stored in practically all manufacturing industries. Storage of this type of material is covered in the section on Handling and Storage of Bulk Materials.

Palletization of Yard Stock. To meet the necessity of increasing storage volume without incurring the often prohibitive rising costs of constructing new buildings, more and more **palletization** has been introduced in yard storage. Experience gained with indoor methods of handling palletized loads has now been extended into plant yards. The former practice of building up heaps of material scattered haphazardly about the plant yard has given way to the orderly layout of checkered storage areas, marked off by traffic aisles in the manner developed for indoor storage.

Bricks, castings, and forgings nowadays are piled neatly in vertical stacks of boxed or palletized loads tiered up to four loads high. Even with large and heavy items, once moved singly by **overhead cranes,** the tendency today is to handling in unit loads of one or more tons each by **powered industrial trucks** capable of traveling in any direction, over long distances, at considerable speed, over rough or inclined ground, and under all kinds of weather conditions.

In yards where the unit loads handled are heavy and where accidental bumping of stacks may cause them to fall over, fork trucks are given 2 ft. of extra aisle width over normal indoor requirements as a safety measure. The condition or firmness of the ground surface and the trueness of the ground level must be considered in determining permissible stacking heights. Generally, boxed and palletized unit loads can be stored up to about 16 ft. in height. Higher stacking may be possible, but 16 ft. from the floor is considered the maximum for economic handling.

Steel storage yards, scrap-metal yards, lumber yards, shipyards, ordnance depots, and a number of other enterprises handling extra-heavy unit loads usually favor the use of **fork trucks** for loads stacked up to about 9 tons, because of the greater flexibility of directional movement offered by these powered units. For loads beyond this 9-ton weight range, straddle carrier trucks, mobile floor cranes, or overhead bridge cranes are usually necessary. The gas-powered truck is generally favored over its electric counterpart for traveling over rough terrain, inclined surfaces, and long distances in transporting and storing material in yard operations. Where travel distances exceed 400 or 500 ft. per round trip, however, tractor-trailer trains and straddle carrier trucks are usually considered to be more economical for use than fork trucks.

To control the movement and utilization of mobile equipment in the operation of a yard fleet which may include a dozen or more such powered units, it is often desirable to install a **two-way radio system** on such key vehicles as fork trucks, tractors, straddle trucks, motor trucks, station wagons, and sometimes mobile cranes. A central dispatching system operated through this communication medium can assist materially in avoiding wasted trips and in reducing unnecessary backtracking movements.

Transition from Cranes to Straddle Carriers. The increased utilization of outside areas for storage purposes has not only provided an escape from rising construction costs but has also led to the adaptation of **mobile handling equipment** to the particular requirements of storage yard handling operations. In some cases rail-car transportation within the yard has been supplanted by overhead conveyors, such as trestle-mounted monorails. In other cases, overhead bridge cranes have been replaced by straddle carrier trucks.

At the yards of a major steel plant in Pennsylvania, **straddle carriers,** which were substituted for cranes, move 170,000 tons of product per month between secondary mills and widely separated conditioning storage yards serving as intermediate points between the mill operations. In this steel mill, an average of 500 crane-serviced rail cars were required each day for handling materials. Plant yards were congested with traffic throughout the day as the 500 cars were switched, spotted, loaded, and unloaded. Traffic problems and congestion arose, and demurrage costs became inevitable. The mill decided to study the possibilities of using **trackless mobile equipment** for its in-plant material transportation between mills and yards. This study clearly indicated that the congestion could well be eliminated from the major bottleneck areas and that the interbuilding and interyard handling could be performed by straddle carriers and fork trucks for one-third less than the existing joint cost of overhead cranes and rail cars. Yard roadways 20 ft. wide were laid out, and to accommodate the material being transported, the storage areas were made 30 ft. wide between the aisles. To move the 170,000 tons of steel produced per month at this mill, six 45,000-lb. carriers and three 18,000-lb. fork trucks, averaging 17,000 trips per month, were required.

VARIETIES OF YARD HANDLING EQUIPMENT. The efficiency of yard handling operations and the extent of their mechanization are determined largely by the **suitability of the kind of handling equipment used.** In addition to considering the kinds of materials stored outside, the condition of the ground surface, the ground slopes, the weather elements, the layout of the storage areas, the distances traveled, the weight of the loads handled, and the number of trips required to handle the necessary tonnage each day, consideration must also be given to the operational features of the various kinds of handling equipment available for yard handling operations. Such features center largely on the mobility of the equipment, its load-handling capacity, its travel speed, and its operating cost including depreciation, repairs, fuel, and operator labor.

Major kinds of yard handling equipment include those listed in Figs. 12 and 13.

Not until a comparison has been made of the **mechanical features** of all the various devices applicable to any particular yard handling problem under consideration can the final selection of the most suitable devices be made on a

Earth-moving Equipment	Conveyors
Bulldozers	Fixed stocking-out conveyors
Carryalls	Trestle-mounted shuttle belt conveyors
Power shovels	Ground-based traveling tripper
Drag scrapers	Pneumatic conveyors
Radial stackers	Truss-mounted trimmer conveyors and reloaders
	Vertical continuous bucket elevators
Cranes	Tunnel conveyors underneath stock piles
Overhead bridge cranes	Portable belt and flight conveyors
Gantry cranes	Cableways
Ore bridges	Skip hoists
Mobile cranes:	
Truck-mounted	**Hoppers**
Crawler-mounted	Fixed reclaiming hoppers
Locomotive-mounted	Draw-off hoppers
Barge-mounted	Movable hoppers on tracks

Fig. 12. Yard equipment for handling bulk materials.

Trucking Equipment	Conveyors
Industrial trucks	Belt conveyors
Powered wheelbarrows	Roller conveyors
Straddle carriers	Wheel conveyors
Tractor-trailer trains	Apron conveyors
Industrial tractors	Tow-chain conveyors
Motor trucks	Monorails (see Fig. 11)
Truck-mounted cranes	Cableways
Skids and pallets	Ropeways
Cranes	**Railroad Equipment**
Overhead bridge cranes	Car spotters and pullers
Gantry cranes	Car-moving devices:
Mobile cranes:	Tractors
Truck-mounted	Tractor shovels
Crawler-mounted	Switch locomotives
Locomotive-mounted	Power winches
Barge-mounted	Capstans
Ships' booms	**Fixed Equipment**
Derricks	Multilayer racks
Jib cranes	

Fig. 13. Yard equipment for handling pieces and unit loads.

sound basis. In addition to all the performance factors surrounding a given application, all **cost factors** and **economic alternatives** must be thoroughly evaluated if a selection is to be made of equipment which will be the best selection from all angles.

TRUCK TERMINAL HANDLING

CONTENTS

TRUCK TERMINAL HANDLING

MOTOR TRUCK TRAFFIC. Motor carriers are of increasing importance to the national economy. In one year, the 9 million registered trucks, tractors, and trailers hauled an estimated 170 billion ton-miles of freight, or 16 percent of all land-moved freight.

Freight transported by motor common carriers can be classified into two groups —**truckload** or volume business which does not cross terminal platforms, and **less-than-truckload** business which is handled through terminals. To take care of increased shipping, $60,000,000 to $70,000,000 were spent in one year for truck terminals.

Definitions. The following definitions explain the nature of the various physical and operating factors characteristic of motor truck terminal activities.

1. **Apron.** Maneuvering space in driveway beyond that required for spotting distance; also known as ramp.
2. **Available cube.** Three-dimensional storage space available, considering height as well as horizontal length and width.
3. **Block loading.** Loading of trucks in sections or units for drop-offs en route. Each section contains one or more shipments.
4. **Charges on equipment.** The costs of owning and operating equipment, including fuel, depreciation, insurance, maintenance, etc.
5. **Checking.** The verification or investigation of correctness of the physical aspects of a shipment as related to the accompanying paper work.
6. **Consolidation of shipments.** Grouping or combining of shipments to facilitate handling and reduce over-all expense.
7. **Cross aisles.** Trucking or movement aisles running the width of the dock.
8. **Delivery sheet.** A listing of the freight to be delivered by each pickup driver showing consignee, weight, and charges.
9. **Digging.** The breaking apart of a stack of freight to find one particular shipment or piece.
10. **Direct loads.** Loads picked up or delivered on the road equipment used to transport them.
11. **Dog.** A mechanical device for gripping or holding something. In this section it means a connection on a towline.
12. **Down time.** Out-of-service time for repairs, maintenance, etc., or time lost for other reasons.
13. **Filler freight.** Relatively light or small freight used to fill in around larger and heavier pieces thus making use of all available cargo space.
14. **Floor freight.** Heavy, long, or bulky freight placed on the floor of a truck because of its physical qualities.
15. **Floored freight.** Freight temporarily stored on a terminal dock.
16. **Inbound freight.** Freight arriving at a terminal from some other locality over its system, for delivery in the local area.
17. **Interline freight.** Freight delivered to, or received from, another carrier.
18. **Intraline freight.** Freight arriving on a carrier's own equipment and dispatched over its own system to another locality. Sometimes called transfer freight.

19. **Manifest.** A list of freight transported.
20. **Order notify bill of lading.** Document used when the shipper desires a bank or third party to collect charges on a shipment before delivery is made.
21. **Outbound freight.** Freight received by the carrier in the local area and dispatched over its system to some other locality.
22. **Peddle freight.** Freight loaded in customer order for delivery directly from the loaded vehicle.
23. **Pickup sheet.** A listing of freight picked up, usually showing shipper, consignee, destination, weight, and number of pieces in the shipment.
24. **Pickup truck.** A truck used for local pickup and delivery work. Also known as bobtail, cub, or city liner.
25. **Side aisle.** Trucking or movement aisles running the length of the dock.
26. **Stacking.** The orderly building up of a load or storage of freight.
27. **Stripping.** The unloading of a truck and sorting by shipments and destinations.
28. **Tow conveyor, also called a towline or dragline.** A moving chain, rope, or cable to which carts are hooked and pulled or dragged.
29. **Travel distance.** The distance freight must move on a dock.
30. **Tying.** Binding by the interlocking action of one package on another.
31. **Unit load.** Two or more articles which are grouped together in such a manner that they may be moved and handled as one unit.
32. **Waybill.** A list of goods sent by a common carrier.
33. **Way-station loading.** See Block loading.

Planning Truck Terminal Facilities

SITE SELECTION. The first step in selecting a terminal site is to compute the amount of land that will be required for present business and future expansion. The plot must be large enough for the truck dock, apron, and driveways, and if possible for a shop, parking area, and office. Consideration should be given to future expansion.

The following factors should also be considered:

1. Proximity to pickups, deliveries, and connecting carriers.
2. Accessibility to traffic arteries.
3. Traffic congestion and such obstructions as bridges and railroad crossings.
4. Transportation for employees.
5. Availability of power, water, sewage connections, and other utilities.
6. Cost of the land.
7. Construction costs for drainage, grading, and excavating.
8. Zoning regulations.

The terminal should be close to the locations of major customers so that trucks will not have to travel far before beginning productive work. Travel distances from alternate sites can be compared as follows: For each site, determine the average distance to and from each pickup and delivery route and each connecting carrier, cartage company, and warehouse. Multiply the distance by the tonnage involved. Compare the total ton-mile figures for the respective sites.

LAYOUT OF TERMINAL AREA. Although layout of a terminal area is influenced by shape and size of plot and other local conditions, certain general rules should be observed:

1. The **long axis** of the dock should run in the direction of the prevailing winds. Claims and rehandling are less if the closed end faces the wind, rain, and snow.
2. Provision should be made for **expansion.**

3. The **office** should be accessible to customers.
4. The **layout** should permit one-way circulating traffic, with no cross traffic.
5. Space nearest the entrance should be assigned to **operations of greatest activity.**
6. **Maintenance, repair, and gasoline facilities** should be located away from dock operations and the main traffic flow.
7. **Parking areas** for pickup trucks and road trailers should be convenient to shop and dock but should not interfere with movement of vehicles.
8. **Employee and customer parking** should be separate from truck and trailer parking.
9. **Trailer weighing scales** should be located so that the dial is visible from or in the office.

Pickup, cartage, and customer trucks, should be assigned to the street side of the dock because of the rapid turnover of equipment. Road trucks carry more freight and remain at the dock longer, and therefore should be assigned to the side away from the street.

Adequate **apron space** must be provided for maneuvering trucks and trailers. Requirements depend on (1) length of tractor-trailer units, (2) width of position allowed at dock for each vehicle, and (3) turning radius of the tractor. Tests by the Fruehauf Trailer Company with standard equipment handled by experienced drivers indicate space requirements, as shown in Fig. 1, for one maneuver into or out of dock position.

Length of Tractor-Trailer	Width of Position	Apron Space
35 ft.	10 ft.	46 ft.
	12 ft.	43 ft.
	14 ft.	39 ft.
40 ft.	10 ft.	48 ft.
	12 ft.	44 ft,
	14 ft.	42 ft.
45 ft.	10 ft.	57 ft.
	12 ft.	49 ft.
	14 ft.	48 ft.

Fig. 1. **Space requirements for one-maneuver operation into or out of dock position.**

The **yard** should be **graded** for escape of surface water, since vehicles lose traction in mud or ice. Sharp grades on yard or apron, however, may cause difficulty in loading, unloading, coupling, or pulling away from the dock.

A **shop** for maintenance and repair should be located nearby, especially if maintenance inspections are made after each run, but it should not interfere with yard requirements or cause traffic congestion. Labor costs for shifting and spotting increase with the distance between dock and shop.

The size of the **parking area** needed can be calculated from a determination of the maximum number of trucks that must be accommodated there at one time. Locating the area close to the dock will speed shifting of trucks and tend to reduce pilferage.

Since ruts and holes in the yard strain equipment and cause freight to topple, good **paving** saves money on repairs and claims. Paving should be designed for

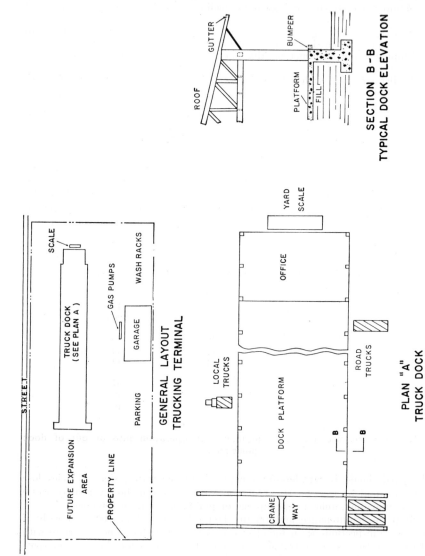

Fig. 2. Typical truck terminal and dock layout.

local soil and wheel-load conditions. In the absence of specific information, paving for 18,000-lb. axle loads on most topsoils should be not less than a 6-in. thickness of 2,000-lb. concrete, reinformed with 6 × 6-in. No. 8 wire mesh, with expansion fillers on 30-ft. centers. Eight inches of crushed rock or clean road gravel and 1½ in. of hot or cold asphalt topping may also be used, with concrete provided where the trailer landing gear contacts the surface.

Many operators have found it economical to install their own yard **scales** because of the travel cost and service charges for using public facilities.

Fencing protects loads parked overnight. It should be high enough so freight cannot be thrown over it and sufficiently heavy so it cannot easily be cut. To keep trucks from backing into the fence, bumpers should be constructed at a distance from the fence equal to that from rear wheel to rear of body, plus an allowance for safety. Heavy timbers or utility poles may be used, mounted on vertical supports of heavy pipe or sections of rail.

Fig. 2 is a typical terminal and dock layout.

DOCK DESIGN AND CONSTRUCTION. Operating efficiency of a dock can be improved by careful planning of columns, dock and ceiling heights, flooring, lighting, and other construction features.

Vehicle Positions. The first consideration in planning a dock is the space to be provided along the edge of the platform for each vehicle. Vehicle positions **12 ft. wide** are now standard for the following reasons:

1. The 12-ft. width permits centering a 12-ft. cross aisle on each two positions, with two rows of 32 × 40-in. pallets on each side of the aisle.
2. It allows platform space at each unloading position for two pallets being worked, and a stack of empty pallets.
3. It allows adequate apron space for maneuvering of vehicles. Spotting is faster and there is less danger of scraping and damage than in narrower positions.
4. It permits routine maintenance of trailers at docks.

Columns. If properly planned, columns need not be an obstacle to good operation. They should be on **24-ft. centers** along the edge to provide two 12-ft. vehicle positions between two columns. They should be **along the edge** because space outside the columns is largely wasted. To extend the platform sets up a cross current of traffic, exposes men to the weather, and creates safety hazards.

The ideal dock should be free of columns except along the edge. It is practical to construct a dock 60 ft. wide with conventional trusses, eliminating columns. Construction plans should be studied with the architect to minimize column interference and yet stay within reasonable building-cost limits. Columns that are necessary in the working area should be constructed of steel or concrete and not of wood.

Dock Height. The height of the platform should approximate truck-bed heights (distance from pavement to floor of truck body). The recommended platform heights in truck terminals are 48 in. for pickup trucks and 52 in. for road units. The best height for a particular dock, however, should be determined by measuring the equipment used there and standardizing on equipment that conforms to the established height. The two heights can be provided by ramps or depressions in some of the positions.

Bumper guards of heavy timber, steel-capped to withstand wear, prevent damage to the dock. Sections should be attached by countersunk bolts so that they can be replaced.

Differences between dock and vehicle height can be overcome by **dock plates,** which range in type from pieces of boilerplate to hydraulic leveling mechanisms built into the dock or pavement. Specifications for a plate should include the following. The plate should:

1. Be strong enough to support the handling medium plus the freight—⅜ in. for fork trucks and ¼ in. for 2-wheeled hand trucks.
2. Be light enough to be moved easily. Steel-reinforced aluminum and magnesium are the lightest, but expensive.
3. Be of sufficient length for an 8-in. overlap on both ends.
4. Be 48 in. in width.
5. Have a checked surface for traction.
6. Have a device to hold it in position, since a loose plate is dangerous.

Floors. Reinforced **concrete** is most practical for a dock floor. It is durable, fire resistant, easily cleaned, and will withstand weather. A fine float finish obtained by troweling and brushing provides a good surface for fork trucks. Carborundum or metal filings used as surfacing material add to longevity and improve traction. **Wood** floors are not recommended for new buildings, but powered materials handling equipment can be used on them. The surface can be improved by applying mastic flooring over the wood. Recommended **floor-load capacity** is 200 lb. per sq. ft. for 2,000-lb. fork trucks and 250 lb. for 4,000-lb. trucks.

Ceiling Height. The proper ceiling height is determined from the amount of freight to be stored and the methods of storage. Provision must be made for storage even if freight is set down only briefly for assembly awaiting final movement. Fire and safety regulations prescribe that 18 in. be left between the top of a stack and the lowest ceiling obstruction. If **manual** methods are used, stack heights will run up to 7 ft., which is as high as a man should normally stack. The ceiling should therefore be at least 8½ ft. above the floor.

If **fork trucks** are used, the minimum provision should be for stacks 9 ft. high, or a ceiling of 10½ ft. This permits stacks 2 pallets high. For stability, a loaded pallet should normally be no more than 4½ ft. high, 4 ft. of freight and 6 in. for the pallet. If the amount of freight necessitates higher stacks, at least 12 ft. of stacking height should be provided by insuring an over-all ceiling clearance of 13½ ft.

Lighting. The advantages of good lighting are:

1. Greater accuracy in reading markings; fewer misdirected shipments and less rehandling.
2. Increased production.
3. Improved morale.
4. Fewer accidents.

Overhead lighting on a **dock** should provide at least 10 foot-candles throughout the working area. Although skylights may be adequate during the day, most terminals work at night and require artificial illumination.

Lighting requirements in the **interior of trucks and trailers** are much higher than for the dock, for markings must be read accurately. The simplest lighting aid is the lamp on an extension cord, but it takes time to set up, is costly to maintain, and makes the stripper work in his own shadow. A practical type of illumination for stripping and stacking is the **spotlight** attached to a dock column with flexible conduit; it can be directed into the interior of the vehicle and swung out of the way when not in use. Well-protected **dome lights** installed in vehicles are useful both at terminals and on the road. They should be wired to operate from batteries or terminal current.

Other Considerations. The **canopy** or roof overhang should be as wide as possible, consistent with sound building practice. It shields the working area from the weather and thereby safeguards freight, improves working conditions and morale, and protects against such hazards as slippery floors.

Doors should be 10- or 20-ft. overhead units if columns are on 24-ft. centers. Doors are not necessary if freight is cleared at the end of the day and not subject to pilferage or damage by weather.

Dock scales, located in the pickup unloading area where they will not impede traffic, should be provided because many shippers fail to include weights on bills of lading.

Installation of a **crane or hoist** may be advisable for heavy lifts. The type may vary from a stationary mechanical hoist to a two-way travel, electric bridge-type crane, depending on the extent to which manual operation is to be used to keep investment low.

If gasoline-powered handling equipment is used, **ventilation** must be obtained from open doorways or by installing fans along the sides of the dock or in the roof.

Since most operations are carried on with open doorways, it is not practical to **heat** a dock even in cold climates. If freight subject to freezing must be stored, a heated area should be provided for it. **Refrigeration** facilities are necessary if perishables are handled. The cold room should be located apart from the general area if the volume is small.

Such facilities as **lunchrooms, drivers' quarters, and toilets** should be on the second floor or basement and not encroach on dock-level space. Many terminal operators believe a lunchroom improves morale and saves time employees would spend going to an outside facility. Some terminals set up sleeping quarters for drivers in order to avoid hotel expense and have drivers available when loads are ready; others believe terminal noise makes this practice inadvisable.

LENGTH OF DOCK. The best dimensions for a dock can be determined from estimates of the number of vehicles to be worked and space requirements for storage and operations. Estimates can be made by keeping a few simple records and analyzing them carefully.

Provisions for Peak Loads. The general rule for space is that there must be enough to accommodate what will normally be the peak load. What constitutes a **normal peak** is somewhat a matter of judgment. If records are examined for several years and it is found, for example, that 1,000,000 lb. of freight were handled each week during the busiest seasons, it would be justifiable to call that figure the normal peak. It is not advisable to plan to accommodate an abnormal peak, that is, one that occurs only once in several years, for that would tie up capital in space rarely used.

However, the dock must be planned not for the freight handled in the past, but for the **future**—the next 5 or 10 yr. or until the facilities can be expanded. A projection or forecast, based on the growth of the business, must be made of what the peak will be. For illustration, it may be assumed that the peak is 1,200,000 lb. a week. As it is expensive to keep road equipment waiting for a spot to load or unload, the dock must be long enough to accommodate all vehicles at the peak period of a week when 1,200,000 lb. will be handled.

The peak business **during a week** can be ascertained by keeping a record for one or several weeks, by half-hour intervals, of all vehicles backed up to the present dock or waiting to back in. The record should show whether the vehicle is loading or unloading and the weight of the freight. Assume the total for a week is 800,000 lb. The peak to be planned for is 50 percent more than that, so final figures must be adjusted upward by that percentage.

Area for Unloading. To find the number of spots needed for unloading, select the hour when the most freight was unloaded. Assume it to be 50,000 lb. from 20 vehicles, or an average of 2,500 lb. from each. If no other factor is available, a productivity rate for unloading of 7,500 lb. per man-hour may be used, although a highly skilled unloader may outstrip this rate by as much as 80 percent. Thus the average vehicle can be worked in 20 min. (⅓ hr.). Add 10 min. shifting time, for a total of 30 min. per vehicle. Each spot can accommodate 2 trucks per hr. With 20 trucks to be unloaded, 10 spots are needed. Apply the 50 percent increase, and the result is a planning figure of 15 spots. Each should be 12 ft. wide; a total of 180 ft. of dock length is therefore required for unloading at the anticipated peak hour.

This procedure must be modified if the unloading rate of 7,500 lb. per man-hr. can be improved by methods analysis, better planning, training, or supervision. Whether one week's record is representative may also be questioned. A statistician could develop a scientifically accurate sample, but the cost is seldom worth while in a terminal. The week's record is usually enough to disclose such characteristics of freight as the proportion inbound and the average weight of shipments; a week-by-week total for several years is needed to show maximum volume.

Area for Loading. Dock space for loading can be calculated in the same manner as for unloading. In the absence of better information, a rate of 8,500 lb. per man-hour may be used for continuously worked vehicles. A spot must be provided for each vehicle worked intermittently. Allowing 12 ft. for each vehicle, the total of loading and unloading doorways required simultaneously determines the length of a single-sided dock or the perimeter of an island dock for loading space.

WIDTH OF DOCK. Once the length has been established, the width of a dock must be determined from requirements for working and storage space. To provide an area for loading and unloading vehicles as well as for lengthwise travel, an aisle should be planned to run along each edge of the dock. The standard width for this aisle is 12 ft. If space is at a premium, it may be narrowed to 10 ft. 8 in. on the pickup side and 8 ft. on the road-equipment side.

Storage Provisions. Requirements for adequate storage and assembly space on a truck dock are often overlooked. All freight which must be floored constitutes storage and should be provided for accordingly. From the standpoint of space requirements, layout, and handling, it makes no difference whether the freight rests in storage a few hours or for months. The amount of storage space needed depends on:

1. Methods of storage and handling.
2. Volume of freight to be stored.
3. Characteristics of the freight and operations.

A common **method of handling** in truck terminals is that which makes use of fork trucks and pallets. With dock-edge columns on 24-ft. centers, a cross aisle in every 24-ft. bay is recommended. The usual pallet size is 32 in. (stringer length) × 40 in. If pallets are stored two positions deep on each side of the cross aisle, total pallet length in the bay is 10 ft. 8 in., leaving an aisle of 13 ft. 4 in. Better utilization of space results when pallets are stored three positions deep on one side of the aisle and two on the other, with an aisle of 10 ft. 8 in. To store three pallet positions deep on each side reduces the aisle to 8 ft., which is acceptable only for short emergency periods. A 32 × 40-in. pallet will require floor space of 32 × 44 in., to allow 4 in. between pallet rows for easier in-and-out movement.

If a **tow conveyor (towline)** is used, the center of the line should be 14 ft. from the edge of the dock. Platforms of standard carts are 40 in. long and 32 in. wide. A 5-ft. passage aisle for carts should be provided (2 ft. 6 in. on each side of the center of the line), leaving a working area 11 ft. 6 in. wide from this aisle to the dock edge. Storage space for each cart should be 48 in. long and 36 in. wide. In each 24-ft. bay there is space for six rows of carts (widthwise) and a 6-ft. aisle. With a **2-wheeled hand truck** system, 6-ft. cross aisles should be provided.

The second consideration in determining the width of the dock, **volume of freight stored,** can be measured by keeping a record for a week of the pallet or cart loads in storage every half hour. The maximum count should be increased by a percentage to allow for future growth of business, and the result is the storage that must be planned for in terms of pallet or cart loads.

The third consideration, **characteristics of freight and operations,** is primarily applicable to a fork truck pallet system. It will indicate whether pallets can be stored one, two, or more deep, and one, two, or more high. Towline carts can usually be stored three deep.

If each shipment must be loaded in a particular **sequence,** so the vehicle can drop one at each stop, the ideal layout will be one pallet high and one deep. Then the fork truck can pull out a shipment with only one approach. A storage pattern like this usually takes too much space, so pallets must be doubled up, both in height and depth. If shipments are **block-loaded,** each block can be stored together, two or more pallets high and two or more deep, without disadvantage.

Space Requirements for Operations. A rough calculation of space requirements for operations can be made by multiplying the maximum number of pallets or carts to be stored by the space required for each. To find the width of the dock required for storage, divide the total storage area required by the length of the dock. Add the storage width to the operating aisles to determine the over-all width of the dock.

In rough computations of this nature, space for cross aisles must be included in the storage area. For example, for a **pallet operation,** assume (1) five pallet positions between each two cross aisles, or three positions on one side and two on the other; (2) 32 × 40-in. pallets; (3) 10 ft. 8 in. cross aisles; (4) 24-ft. bays; (5) pallets stored two high. The floor area marked off for one pallet position would be 32 × 44 in. (including 4 in. between pallet rows), or 9.8 sq. ft. Counting in the cross aisle, five pallet positions would require an area of which one dimension would be 44 in. and the other 24 ft. (5 times 32 in., plus the 10 ft. 8 in. aisle). This is 88 sq. ft., or 17.6 sq. ft. per pallet position. The 17.6 sq. ft. must then be divided by the number of pallets in height to find the square footage per pallet. In this example, it would be divided by 2, or 8.8 sq. ft. per pallet to be stored.

For a **towline operation,** an area 4 ft. × 3 ft., or 12 sq. ft., is needed for a cart position. Counting in the cross aisle, the standard layout is six cart positions and a 6-ft. aisle in a rectangle 3 ft. 7 in. × 24 ft. This totals 86 sq. ft., or 14.3 sq. ft. per cart to be stored.

REPAIR AND MAINTENANCE SHOP. A complete shop should have the following facilities:

1. Tractor repair.
2. Trailer repair.
3. Tire repair and storage.
4. Tractor and trailer washing.

5. Parts storage.
6. Machine shop.
7. Washroom.
8. Office.

Painting may be accommodated in a separate building. The layout of a complete shop is shown in Fig. 3.

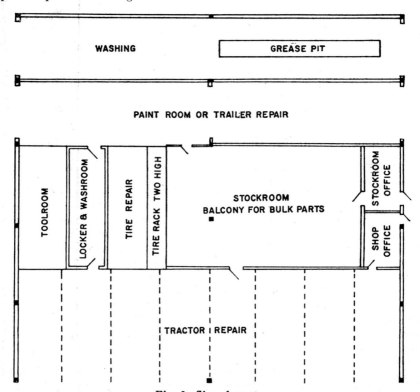

Fig. 3. Shop layout.

DOCK LAYOUT. Once doorway and space requirements have been computed, as covered in the previous discussion of Length of Dock and Width of Dock, a layout of the dock can be prepared, using factors similar to the ones given under those subjects.

Examples. Fig. 4 is a layout for **maximum accessibility** of stock. There is a cross aisle for almost every vehicle, and each pallet faces on a cross aisle. This layout can be used only when storage requirements are light. Columns are on 24-ft. centers, at the edge of the platform only, and provision is made for 12-ft.-wide vehicle positions. Pallet positions shown indicate maximum dock storage. Tonnage handled is approximately 600,000 lb. per day.

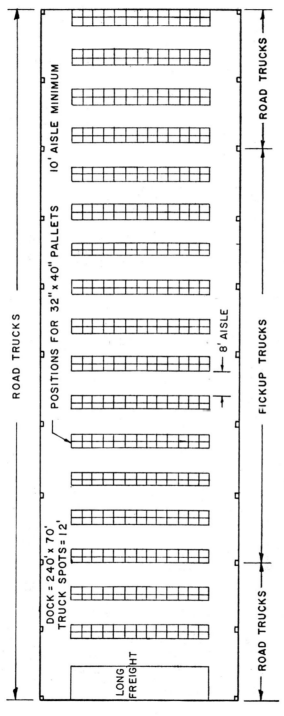

Fig. 4. Storage layout for peddle order loading.

The layout in Fig. 5 provides **more storage space,** for pallet depths are doubled on **one side** of each aisle. Tonnage to be handled is approximately 250,000 lb. per day. The pallet positions shown are the maximum required. It should seldom be necessary for all pallet positions to be filled. Inbound shipments should be stored close to pickup equipment to reduce travel distance. Outbound storage should be close to road equipment.

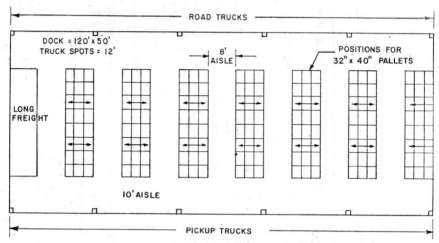

Fig. 5. Storage for combination peddle and way-station loading.

The layout in Fig. 6 makes **maximum use** of available storage space, since pallets **can be three positions deep** on each side of a cross aisle. Storage to this depth is satisfactory for freight to be block loaded or way-station loaded in trucks. For loading in peddle sequence, too many pallets would have to be moved to get at the desired shipment. Tonnage to be handled is approximately 300,000 lb. per day.

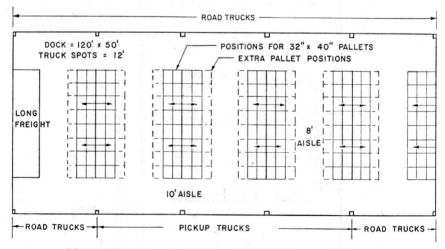

Fig. 6. Storage and aisle layout for efficient use of area.

CONTROLS. Before any layout can work properly, administrative controls must be planned. The first is a **locator record.** Freight should never be stored without a record of its location so it can be found when it is to be loaded out. Second is **housekeeping.** An orderly storage area will hold as much as 40 percent more freight than a disorderly one. Aisle lines should be painted, and pallets stored square and facing the aisle from which they will be removed.

Selecting the System: Computing Equipment Needs

FACTORS TO BE CONSIDERED. The factors in selecting a handling system are:

1. Mission of the terminal.
2. Tonnage to be handled.
3. Size of dock.

Mission of the Terminal. The mission governs the volume of freight that must be floored. The simplest operation is **transfer,** which involves unloading, sorting or checking, and reloading directly to another station. Each outbound vehicle has a single destination. No freight is floored, because it can be loaded on vehicles in any sequence. Although some freight must be held temporarily for proper weight distribution in trucks, handling is essentially continuous from one vehicle to another. At the other extreme is the **distribution** operation, in which mixed freight is unloaded and reloaded in stop sequence. Almost all shipments must be floored. Between these extremes is the unloading of mixed freight and reloading in **station sequence.** At least one station can be loaded directly. The rest of the freight needs to be separated only by station.

All operations fall into some combination of these missions. The proportion of total tonnage that must be stored and the degree to which the identity of each shipment must be maintained determine the importance of the storage factor. In the transfer operation there is no storage, but in the distribution operation the handling system must include efficient storage methods.

Volume of Handling. The volume to be considered is only that handled over the dock. "Loaded to ride" or "direct" tonnage should be subtracted from total terminal tonnage for this purpose.

Dock Size. Travel distances increase with the size of the dock and must be considered in selecting a handling system.

COMPARISON OF SYSTEMS. Selection of the handling system will have an overriding influence on all other planning decisions. To find the system best suited to a particular operation, the cost of each system should be estimated; the one chosen should be one that will result in the most economical operation. The system may make use of hand trucks, fork trucks, tractors, tow conveyors, roller conveyors, or a combination of these and other means of conveyance. The three main methods are those based on (1) 2-wheeled hand trucks, (2) fork trucks and pallets, and (3) tow conveyors and carts.

Two-Wheeled Hand Trucks. A 2-wheeled hand truck system should be used if volume is small, travel short, and storage unimportant. Aisle and working-space requirements, as given above under Width of Dock, are at a minimum. However, the loads transported are smaller (about 125 lb. average) than by pallet or cart, two additional handlings are required for floored freight, and it is not practical to store freight more than 6 ft. high. If the daily volume is 50,000 lb.

or less and not more than five men are employed, 2-wheeled hand trucks should be adequate.

Fork Trucks and Pallets. Compared with the 2-wheeled hand truck, the fork truck handles a load about three times as large, since one shipment averaging 380 lb. is usually accommodated on a pallet. It eliminates rehandling of stored freight; it is faster, permitting earlier dispatch of vehicles; it stacks higher and makes better use of storage space. About 90 percent of miscellaneous freight crossing a dock can be palletized. As a rule, the introduction of a fork truck is justified if it will reduce the work force by two men.

Compared with a **tow conveyor**, the fork truck system is more efficient on a dock **less than 200 ft.** long, the conveyor if the dock is **longer than 400 ft.** This difference arises from the fact that **travel costs** are less for a towline than for a fork truck. On a long dock, travel is the most important element. On a short dock, the governing factor is that it takes longer and costs more for men to hook and unhook carts than for a fork truck to pick up and set down a pallet. On docks from **200 to 400 ft.**, the choice between fork truck and towline will rest on the amount of freight to be stored and the volume moved in and out of storage.

Pallets can be stacked but carts cannot, so the fork truck system makes better use of storage space. On the other hand, as the volume to be moved increases, operating costs increase more than proportionately with a fork truck system and less with a towline. As more fork trucks are used, control is more difficult and delays more frequent, while a towline system can handle more volume without substantially greater cost.

If fork trucks are used, a key question is the **size of pallet.** In plants and warehouses, building characteristics such as column spacing have a bearing on pallet size. In truck terminals, however, characteristics of the freight are almost the sole governing condition. The 32 × 40-in. pallet has been adopted as standard in the industry because it conforms so well to size of shipments. The face is just under 9 sq. ft. For stability, freight should be stacked not over 4 ft. high on it. Thus the maximum capacity is just under 36 cu. ft., and the normal capacity, allowing for spaces caused by odd-dimensioned pieces, is about 30 cu. ft. Freight averages 30 to 35 lb. per cu. ft., so the average full pallet load this size will weigh about 1,000 lb.

Although shipments range from 10 to 10,000 lb., the extremes are rare. Averages vary, terminal to terminal, from about 200 to more than 500 lb. Therefore most shipments can be accommodated on one pallet. The large shipments that take more than one pallet are offset by the small lots that can be combined on one.

With 32 × 40-in. pallets, and 80 to 90 percent of the loads less than 1,000 lb., fork trucks of 1,000- or 1,500-lb. capacity are adequate for most lifts. One 3,000-lb. truck for every four or five smaller trucks should usually be provided for heavier loads.

Tow Conveyor. This is a conveyor with a powered chain or cable that runs overhead or in the floor and pulls carts from one truck spot or area to another. It can be adjusted to operate at various speeds and is an economical method of transport, since the only operating cost is for current.

The recommended size for **cart** platforms is 42 in. long by 36 in. wide. Wheel diameters should be limited to 4 or 5 in. to keep the platform as low as possible. Trailers that can be coupled to carts may be provided for large shipments.

In the **layout of a towline system,** the line may run around the perimeter of the dock or down the center. Working space must be left between the line and the dock edge, but it should be held to a minimum because every cart has to be pushed from the line to the edge and back. If the line is around the perimeter, for direct transfer from pickup to line-haul vehicles, the recommended distance from the edge is 14 ft.

There are several methods of providing for peddle-freight storage. The freight may be stored inside the towline. Another method is to run the line down the center of the dock and work freight from the center outward to loading spots; in this case, the area should be large enough to take care of the entire peddle volume. Clear areas should be left across each end of the dock for bulky or long freight not suitable for carts.

The **capacity of a towline** is the number of shipments that can be handled by the line in an hour, which is the same as the number of carts that pass a given point in an hour. Capacity is determined by the speed of the line and the

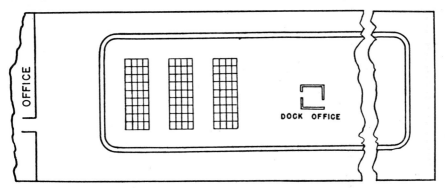

Fig. 7. Layout for tow-conveyor operation—central pallet storage.

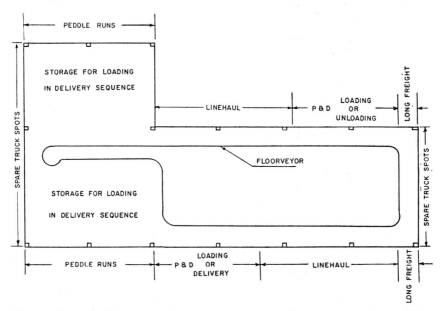

Fig. 8. Layout of fork truck tow-conveyor operation—varying dock widths.

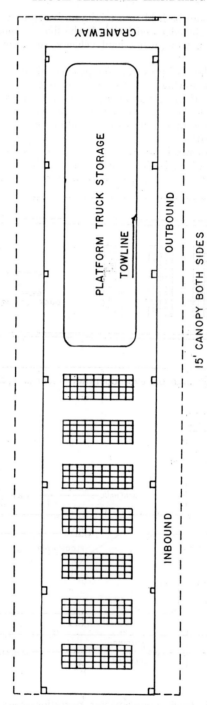

Fig. 9. Layout of fork truck tow-conveyor operation—segregated pallet storage.

spacing of carts. A line that runs 120 ft. per min. with carts every 10 ft. has a capacity of 720 carts (shipments) per hr. A towline should be capable of handling all shipments in the hour of heaviest volume.

It is usually recommended that the towline be installed to operate at variable speeds from 100 to 150 ft. per min. The speed to be used should be the fastest at which personnel can couple and uncouple carts safely, and will vary with the quality of personnel. The speed should be about 125 ft. per min. for personnel of average ability. Carts normally should be spaced every 10 ft., with every fourth chain-dog omitted for passage across the line.

The towline is best suited to transfer of freight direct from the pickup to the outbound line-haul vehicle. When there are peddle runs, carts may be pulled from the line and placed in the storage area, or freight may be placed on pallets on the carts and stacked by fork truck. Chainmen should be provided to service strippers and loaders. They remove empty carts from the line and furnish them to strippers. They take off loaded carts and push them to loaders or storage. This procedure reduces the time strippers and loaders would spend getting their own trucks.

Combining Tow Conveyor and Fork Trucks. Three layouts for combining towline and fork truck systems are shown in Figs. 7, 8, and 9.

TRACTOR-TRAILER TRAINS. In a long terminal where the amount of storage precludes a towline, tractor-trailer trains may supplement the fork truck system. Tractors and trailers are more economical than fork trucks for travel over 300 ft.

The operation should be set up as follows:

1. It should be palletized.
2. Trailer loading and unloading stations should be located every 120 ft. along the dock.
3. The coupling and uncoupling of trailers should be done not by the tractor operator but by an employee whose function it is to line up the trains.
4. Fork trucks should load and unload pallets from carts.
5. Freight moving less than 300 ft. should be transported by fork truck.

COMPUTING EQUIPMENT REQUIREMENTS. The materials handling equipment used on a large truck dock represents a substantial capital investment. Requirements should therefore be carefully computed before equipment is purchased. The requirements should be determined from a forecast of the amount of work to be done and an estimate of the time for performing each work unit. The data assembled are illustrated in Figs. 10 to 14.

Type	Shipments
Inbound	
Stored	75
Not stored	25
Outbound	
Stored	30
Not stored	150
Total	280

Fig. 10. Freight handled per day.

Fig. 10 indicates the **amount of work** to be done by fork trucks in a small operation. The volume is broken down by inbound and outbound shipments, stored and not stored. In this example, requirements are computed for fork trucks needed to handle outbound freight that is not stored (150 shipments per day). The next step, Fig. 11, is to determine the **average travel distance** in feet for each type of shipment. For outbound freight not stored, the distance is 120 ft. —pickup truck to road vehicle. Fig. 12 shows the computation of **fork truck time** for this type of freight, and Fig. 13 the **time for other types**. As the total time is 5.64 hr. per day, and the operation runs 8 hr., one fork truck is required. Fig. 14 illustrates the method of computing **pallet requirements**.

Type	Feet
Inbound	
Stored	80
Not stored	70
Outbound	
Stored	140
Not stored	120

Fig. 11. **Average travel distance.**

Operation	Minutes
Pick up pallet	0.10
Run loaded (120 ft.)	.45
Set down pallet	.10
Run empty (120 ft.)	.30
Total	0.95
Rest and delay (20%)	.19
Total per shipment	1.14
Total per day (150 shipments)	171.00

Fig. 12. **Handling outbound shipments—not stored.**

Type	Minutes
Inbound	
Stored	95.3
Not stored	21.3
Outbound	
Stored	51.0
Not stored	171.0
Total	338.6
	(5.64 hr.)

Operation runs 8 hr. per day.
One fork truck required.

Fig. 13. **Fork truck time per day.**

Operation		Pallets
Dead freight stored (20 shipments)		20
Pallets for outbound working		
Pickup trucks worked at once	10	
Pallets per truck for working	15	
Total		150
Outbound freight stored		30
Total		200

Fig. 14. Pallet requirements—outbound.

Intercommunication Systems

IMPORTANCE OF COMMUNICATION. It is often necessary to summon personnel, speed the flow of documents, record pickup requests, transmit information between terminals, permit central checking, and signal fork truck operators.

Central Checking. The equipment used for central checking provides two-way voice communication between checkers in a checking office and freight unloaders working in vehicles spotted at the platform. It incorporates a signaling system for calling fork truck operators to take away pallet loads from vehicles being unloaded.

One or more central stations are provided. Each has 10 positions connected to voice circuits that run to unloading doors, dispatchers, foremen, scales, or other checkers. There has been a tendency to adopt the 10-position equipment as standard. Remote stations are provided for unloaders to call checkers or to signal fork truck operators. One or more remote stations may be provided for convenience of foremen. Reserve equipment should be provided as a safeguard against interruption of service.

Switchboard or Patchboard. If there is more than one checker or 10 remote circuits, a switchboard or patchboard must be provided to connect central and remote stations. It should be mounted near checkers' desks, so that changes in connections can easily be made by any checker.

Standard Remote Stations. One standard remote station is provided for each unloader, up to the maximum number working at any one time, plus one to three additional stations as standby equipment.

Special Remote Station. A special remote station may be necessary for dock workers accepting freight from shippers, draymen, or interline drivers, because of the fact that this work calls for constant movement between a number of receiving doors, and the standard station equipment is too heavy to carry around for communication purposes. The special station may consist of a telephone-type handset with a call button inserted in the grip. This station can be carried in the worker's pocket when not in use.

Fork Truck Signal System. The fork truck signal system consists of a colored signal light for each unloading door, each light independently controlled by a switching arrangement consisting of the following equipment:

   1. A signal light mounted directly opposite and above the center of the door to which it refers, high enough not to interfere with fork trucks.

2. A fork truck operator's switch of the lavalier type, actuated by a pull cord within easy reach of the fork truck operator as he approaches the tail gate of a vehicle. A short 6-in. length of spring is inserted in the pull cord about 1 ft. from the lower end to absorb the shock of quick pulls on the cord and to act as a counterweight.
3. An unloader's switch of the normal type located in the remote-station control box.
4. Relays, if used, should be of standard heavy-duty design, easily procurable and replaceable.

Checking Office or Booth. The checking office or booth should be considered in its relationship to other related dock and terminal office functions, as well as for its construction and equipment.

1. The central checking office should be located convenient to other dock clerical functions so that the flow of inbound and outbound bills is as simple and direct as possible. Pneumatic tubes may be included to transmit documents. Since these processes vary with the individual line and terminal, no standard methods have been developed and put into use.
2. Central checking booths should be provided for each central checker within the dock office, the number depending on peak volume of freight, whether both inbound and outbound freight is centrally checked, and on clerical practices of the line and terminal. Each booth should be enclosed on three sides, walls and ceiling being lined with acoustical material to reduce noise level. Each booth should contain a sloping counter about 4 ft. 6 in. wide and 2 ft. 6 in. deep, the exact size depending on the location of speaker stations and the arrangement of bills for loads being checked. A chair or stool should be provided. The booth should be well lighted and ventilated, and bill cases should be placed within easy reach of the checker.
3. Miscellaneous central checking equipment includes devices for holding bills during the checking process, such as clip boards and alphabetical sorters. A form of bulletin board should be provided for posting papers constantly referred to, and a rack should be provided for rubber stamps.

OTHER EQUIPMENT. On a large dock, two-way, conveniently located **loudspeakers** or some other call system is needed to summon personnel and transmit information. **Pneumatic tubes** may be used to expedite delivery of shipping documents to the office for processing. The **TelAutograph** is a good means of transmitting written information and is especially useful for recording routine telephone requests for pickups. **Teletype** equipment is used for messages between terminals. It provides advance information on inbound freight, helps in tracing OS&D (Over, Short, and Damaged) freight, and provides written records to avoid misunderstandings (see Section **8,** on communications, for additional information).

Truck Terminal Handling Procedures

SPOTTING OF EQUIPMENT AND MANPOWER. It is necessary to set up adequate procedures for carrying on the work of a truck terminal. One of the important procedures is that for the spotting of equipment and manpower.

Assignment of Doorways. The doorways to which vehicles are assigned determine the distances over which shipments must travel from one vehicle to another. Up to 20 percent of dock operating man-hours is spent in transporting freight over the dock. The larger the dock, the more important spotting becomes. Heavy runs should be spotted in the center and light runs on each end. Unloading should be directly opposite heavy runs.

Spots assigned to unloading **inbound road vehicles** should be concentrated directly opposite the loading of delivery trucks. For loading outbound, at least one spot should be assigned to every regular schedule and two adjacent spots for heavy multiple-load routes. Loaded **local pickup trucks** should not be spotted along the whole length of the dock; they should be spotted at a few doorways directly opposite heavy outbound runs. More spotting will then be necessary, but it is cheaper to respot a truck than to move the load piecemeal on the platform. Fig. 15 shows spotting at one terminal dock **before planning**, Fig. 16 **after planning**, and Fig. 17 gives a **comparison** of travel distances and savings.

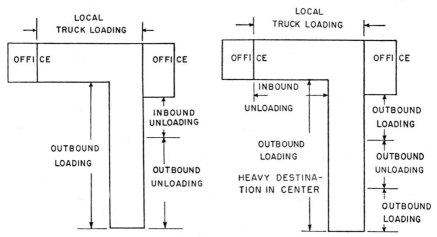

Fig. 15. Spotting arrangement before   Fig. 16. Spotting arrangement after
          planning.   planning.

Type of Freight	Before Planning, Travel Distance in Feet	After Planning, Travel Distance in Feet	Percent of Total Freight	Total Travel Before Planning	Total Travel After Planning
Outbound	99	62	52	5,148	3,224
Inbound	167	83	32	5,344	2,656
Intraline	108	129	16	1,728	2,064
Totals				12,220	7,944

Reductions in travel = 4,276 ft. daily, or 35 percent.

Fig. 17. Travel distances at an existing terminal before and after planning the spotting.

Manpower Assignment and Spotting. Assignment of labor must be considered with equipment spotting to keep stripping and loading in balance. A good ratio of loaders to strippers is 3 to 4, provided the strippers have no checking duties. To keep freight from accumulating in working areas, all tonnage being stripped should have an outlet—either to storage or to other trucks and trailers.

A **stacker** should load 6,000 to 8,500 lb. per hr. and may be able to load several light runs at once. Freight should be banked ahead of him so there is always work for him to do. When a stacker falls behind because of a heavy run for his units, the foreman should shift men to even up the work.

Example of Spotting. Assume the eight outbound schedules in **Fig. 18** are to be loaded in 4 hr., with simultaneous unloading of pickups. **Fig. 19** indicates the proper spotting of vehicles so that each of six loaders will handle 7,800 to 9,000 lb. per hr. For the balance of the operation, four pickup trucks should be unloaded at once to maintain the 3 to 4 ratio of loaders to strippers.

Schedules	Pounds
1	36,000
2	33,000
3	32,000
4	32,000
5	26,000
6	21,000
7	10,000
8	10,000
Total	200,000

Fig. 18. Outbound vehicle loading schedules.

Spotting Order of Schedules	Pounds	Manpower
8	10,000 ⎱	...................Loader
5	26,000 ⎰	
4	32,000	..................Loader
1	36,000	..................Loader
2	33,000	..................Loader
3	32,000	..................Loader
6	21,000 ⎱	...................Loader
7	10,000 ⎰	

Fig. 19. Spotting and manpower assignment.

STRIPPING OR UNLOADING. Dock productivity depends largely on the efficiency of stripping or unloading trucks. Clear and accurate marking by the stripper is an aid in moving shipments and finding them in storage. Marking systems should be simple, using abbreviations, short numbers, and symbols. If fork trucks are used, markings should be on the side of the load facing the operator.

A very skilled stripper should **unload an average of 9,000 lb. per hr.** To reach that figure, his work must be continuous. He therefore must be provided with empty equipment—pallets or carts. In a palletized operation, there must be some arrangement, such as a signal system, for a fork truck to remove pallets as they are loaded, or a roller conveyor or a dolly may be provided so that pallet loads can be pushed out of the way.

An inbound load often has many shipments for the same destination or route. The stripper may put small shipments to one side until he gets a pallet load for the same territory, then put them all on one pallet to increase the fork truck "payload." This practice means double handling by the stripper, but the increased cost will be more than offset by savings in transport if the fork truck run is over 80 ft. The principle can also be followed on outbound shipments, with small shipments moving from a pickup truck to one road unit.

Fork trucks can get a better "payload" for cross-dock movement by **stacking two pallet loads** if the bottom shipment is small and well trimmed to provide a flat surface for the upper pallet. If destinations are different, the bottom pallet can be dropped at one doorway and the top picked off and moved to another. If pallet loads are to be stacked in storage, strippers must trim them carefully, or the load will have to be rearranged for stable stacking. Packages that can be handled by fork truck without a pallet should be positioned by the stripper so that the fork truck can pick them up in one movement. If 2-wheeled hand trucks are used, the stripper should put the largest or heaviest piece on the bottom of each stack. Strippers should cross tie packages on 4-wheeled hand trucks for safe riding.

If the vehicle floor will not support a fork truck, the stripper may place the pallet on a dolly for shifting to and from the tail gate. The dolly should be on rollers, since casters may go through the floor. Conveyor sections may prove handy for strippers to move out many uniform pieces or to handle nose freight over heavy loads which are to be left in the rear.

CHECKING. Checking is the operator's protection against dishonesty and error. Since checking can constitute as much as 30 percent of dock handling cost, it should be simplified as much as possible. A checker should check 27,000 lb. per hr. of average-run freight.

Outbound Freight. The pickup driver should make the first check of outbound freight against the bill of lading at the shipper's platform. The second check should be made at the terminal when the pickup truck is unloaded. A third check may be made when freight is loaded on road equipment. However, there is not much chance for a shipment to become separated while crossing the dock, so the third check is suggested only for long hauls or when more than one schedule is run to a destination. If the run is short enough for a mistake to be corrected the following day, customer service is not impaired. If multiple schedules are run, some operators want the equipment number on bills for easier tracing. The bill must therefore accompany the shipment across the dock.

Inbound Freight. It is suggested that inbound freight be checked against a manifest rather than against waybills, so there is only one paper to work with and waybills can at the same time be sorted by city routes. If a blind check is used for inbound freight, the stripper must identify shipments by marks and keep each shipment together. Some terminals do not check intrasystem loads, reasoning that freight will arrive intact if properly loaded.

Central Checking. One way to reduce checking expense is for strippers to blind check and report each shipment over a speaker to a checker in an office. A central checker can check more than 40,000 lb. per hr. He can work 6 pickup trucks at once, eliminating two men, and strippers are not bothered with papers. Communication is by 2-way microspeakers. The location of the central checking office is immaterial; it may be at the end of the unloading area or suspended over the platform.

When an inbound load arrives, papers are delivered to the central checker. Bills are sorted by destination and put in trays or compartments to be readily located. As a stripper unloads a shipment, he calls the checker and gives consignee, shipper, and number of pieces. The checker finds the bill, verifies the count, and assigns the outbound route number to be marked on the shipment and bill. For peddle or station loading, a coding and marking system must be used to identify shipments. Central checking is advantageous because code sheets can be controlled by the checker and identifying numbers tied in with locations or flooring sequence on the dock.

Locator System. When freight is floored, a record must be kept of the location so it can be quickly found. Each bay or section of the dock should be given a letter-number designation, using a grid system with letters to designate lengthwise areas and numbers widthwise. For example, a shipment marked D/2 would be found in the second section, back of the fourth doorway.

STORAGE. Two principles of storage in a truck terminal are that:

1. Space should be effectively used.
2. Every shipment should be stored so that it can be easily found and moved from storage with minimum handling.

The storage system should be planned at the time the layout is made. If **pallets** are used, they should be stored and removed from cross aisles, unless the limits on working space dictate use of 4-way pallets. If freight is to be loaded in block or station order, pallets can be stored three deep from cross aisles, keeping the shipments for each station together. For peddle-sequence loading, pallets can be stored two deep, although rehandling will then be necessary; numbers of buried shipments should be marked on the shipment facing the aisle.

If carts or 4-wheeled hand trucks are used, the long axis of the cart should be perpendicular to the dock edge. Dense freight should be left adjacent to cross aisles to be loaded on the floor of vehicles. Aisles are passageways and must be kept clear so as not to impede traffic.

LOADING. A loader should handle 6,000 to 8,500 lb. per hr. if enough work is supplied to keep him continuously busy. Keeping a bank of work ahead of the loader will step up his pace. If freight is coming from vehicles being unloaded, a loader may be assigned to load more than one unit, depending on the flow of freight for each load. Shipments should be delivered into the unit if possible, or placed on dollies if the unit is long.

When a vehicle is loaded from freight stored on the dock, one loader should be assigned to each load, and the freight should be delivered to him in loading sequence. If shipments are palletized, one fork truck should serve two loaders. Each shipment should be kept together for ease of checking and assembly. For way-station loading, each block should be separated from the others. Pieces of burlap or paper may be used as separators. **Heavy shipments** should be placed on the bottom of the load and distributed over the body area to avoid concentration of weight and reduce damage and sway. The load should be built up to avoid shifting and axle loads should be distributed evenly. Unusually heavy shipments should be brought to the attention of the dock foreman for decision on placement.

Loaders should be trained to get full use of vehicle space. One operator, by training loaders, increased weight per load 8 percent and reduced truck-miles 2,000 per week.

Terminal Management

COST CONTROL. A cost control system aids efficient operation by signaling declines in productivity or evidences of mounting costs. **Productivity** can be measured by applying man-hours against tonnage handled. For example, if 10 men are employed full time for a 9-hr. working day to handle 225,000 lb., productivity is 2,500 lb. per man-hour. To obtain the figures, a record must be kept of weights crossing the dock and working time of laborers.

PERSONNEL. All man-hours spent in handling and supervising on the dock should be counted. For example:

1. **Supervision**—foremen, leadmen, or those under any other category whose duties include supervision of work on the platform.
2. **Dockmen**—checkers, strippers, loaders, truckers, fork truck operators, coopers, or any other classification whose duties include the handling or movement of freight on the dock. Building or equipment maintenance men engaged in work related to dock operations such as chocking or bracing should be included.
3. **Drivers or helpers** who may spend part of their working day on the platform loading, unloading, handling, or checking freight should be included for the portion of time spent in platform activities.

EQUIPMENT. If the operation is mechanized, equipment costs must be added to labor costs. Depreciation, maintenance, fuel or power, and insurance costs should all be considered in arriving at an hourly equipment cost.

TONNAGE. The dock operation should be credited with only the volume handled there, excluding all "loaded to ride" freight not passing over the dock. Inbound tonnage should include local, interline, and transfer or intraline freight. Outbound tonnage should include pickups and freight brought to the terminal by customer, cartage, or interline trucks. Fig. 20 is a sample daily dock operation report.

LABOR COST. The payroll cost for supervisory and handling personnel on the platform is the **dock labor handling cost** for the terminal. As a rule of thumb, this cost per hundredweight of freight handled should not exceed 5 percent of the hourly wage rate if there is considerable storage. For example, if pay scales average $1.50 per hr., the dock labor cost should not be more than 7½ cents per cwt. For a direct vehicle-to-vehicle operation with little storage, the cost per hundredweight should not be more than 3½ percent of the hourly wage rate, or, on the $1.50 per hr. basis, 5¼ cents per cwt. If costs are greater than these percentages, the need for improvement in operations is indicated.

WORK MEASUREMENT. Although few terminals have attempted to measure productivity of individual workers, a complete work measurement system may in some instances provide more detailed production and cost control data.

ASSIGNMENT OF MANPOWER. Theoretically, the number of men required can be determined by dividing total freight by the work one man can do. In practice, however, any such simple formula is precluded by problems like the peaks and valleys in volume, nature of freight, and whether volume is continuously available.

Work Load. To measure the work load, data must be accumulated on where the freight comes from, where it goes, by hour, in what quantities. Time limits must be set for inbound and outbound shipments. For example, if pickup trucks arrive from 5:00 P.M. on and the outbound freight must be loaded by 10:00 P.M. to meet schedules, the work must be done in 5 hr.

Productivity. In determining production per man-hour, allowance must be made for the volume handled a second time. Production rates will vary, depending on whether the volume is being loaded or unloaded. Loading outbound freight

---

SAMPLE DAILY DOCK OPERATION REPORT

Terminal _____

Date _____

Shift _____

Freight Handled per Day

Type	Over-the-dock Weight
1. Inbound	
2. Outbound	
3. Total weight	_____

	Chargeable to Dock			
Labor	Hr.	$	Hr.	$
4. Dock force				
5. Drivers				
6. Supervisors				
7. Equipment cost				
8. Total (4 + 5 + 6 + 7)				
9. Dock cost per cwt. (8 ÷ 3)				
10. Total hours (4 + 5 + 6)				
11. Production per man-hour (3 ÷ 10)				

*Dock Foreman's Signature*_____

*Terminal Manager's Signature*_____

Fig. 20. Daily dock operation report.

on a road unit usually takes more time than unloading it from a pickup truck, especially if the driver who picked it up unloads it. However, if checking onto road equipment is eliminated, the loading rate should approximate the stripping rate.

Calculating Requirements. Peaks and valleys of volume should be leveled as much as possible to prevent excess of manpower at periods of low volume. If peaks are unavoidable, it may be possible to use part-time labor; overtime is not recommended because of the extra cost. Work force requirements for surge periods should be calculated from the highest hourly production figures; for other periods, rates should be at least 20 percent lower. Fig. 21 is a manning table for a fork truck operation with an average daily volume of 230,000 lb., where 90 percent of the outbound freight is loaded in peddle sequence and must be coded, docked, and rehandled before loading.

ADMINISTRATION. Supervision is the key to an efficient dock operation. Without good supervision to keep operations at a reasonably high level, the work may tend to slow down and inefficiencies will rapidly develop.

Hour of Day	Description of Freight	Weight of Freight	Supervisors	Checkers (Central)	Fork Truck and Operators	Loaders and Strippers	Spotter *	Total Labor
A.M.								
8–9	Inbound	10,000	1		1	4**		6
9–10	Inbound	6,000	1		1	2**		4
10–11	Inbound	3,000	1		1	1		3
11–12	Inbound and Outbound	3,000	1		1	1		3
P.M.								
12–1	Outbound	3,000	1		1	1		3
1–2	Outbound	3,000	1		1	1		3
2–3	Outbound	3,000	1		1	1		3
3–4	Outbound	3,000	1		1	1		3
4–5	Outbound	6,000	1	1	1	1		4
5–6	Outbound	40,000	1	1	2	7**	1	12
6–7	Outbound	50,000	1	1	2	10**	1	15
7–8	Outbound	40,000	1	1	2	7**	1	12
8–9	Outbound	10,000	1		1	2	1	5
9–10	Outbound	10,000	1		1	2	1	5
10–11	Outbound	10,000	1		1	2	1	5
11–12	Outbound	10,000	1		1	2	1	5
A.M.								
12–1	Inbound	10,000	1		1	2	1	5
1–2	Inbound	10,000	1		1	2		4
Total		230,000	18	4	21	49	8	100

Inbound freight handled per day = 40,000 lb.
Outbound freight handled per day = 190,000 lb.
Production per man-hour = 230,000 lb. ÷ 100 = 2,300 lb. per hr.

* Spotter helps on dock work.
** Include pickup drivers working on dock.

Fig. 21. Type of dock manning table.

The **dock superintendent or foreman** is responsible for movement of the work load within the time limits set by management, enforcement policy and discipline, assignment of manpower, improvement of methods, and for working conditions on the dock. He decides whether shipments should be delivered direct or moved over the dock, and whether road or pickup trucks should make volume pickups. He manipulates manpower to meet peaks and places workers on the dock from knowledge of the amount of work to be done at each point. Since his principal duty is supervision of dockmen, he should spend most of his time with them, and be relieved of paper and telephone work.

The **dispatcher** is the next most important individual. He must have the ability to deal with customers over the phone, and a knowledge of the territory, customers' docks and business habits, rates and revenues, the men working for him, and company policy respecting schedules. His desk is the nerve center of the terminal operation. He must make decisions promptly and know what is going on on the dock in order to answer customers' questions.

Maintenance. Coordination between dock and shop is necessary to prevent tying up for maintenance those vehicles needed for service. **Inspection and maintenance schedules** should be specified. Most difficulties between dock and shop arise because vehicles are overdue for attention and take more time for repair than if preventive-maintenance schedules were followed. It is especially important to assign responsibility for inspection of trailers that are shuttled between terminals. Floors, sides, and roof are common sources of trouble in trailers.

Preventive maintenance is also important for materials handling equipment. If out-of-service time is unduly long, manpower requirements may increase. Keeping equipment in good condition is an aid to morale and safety.

Training. Systematic training of employees is necessary if they are to become proficient quickly in the best methods of handling freight. The first step is to insure that every prospective employee is **physically fit for dock work.** An individual with an infirmity can be a hazard to himself and others. Constant demands for identifying freight require that dock workers be able to read easily, and aptitude tests for reading should be given. The nature of the job, hours, pay, company policies, and working conditions should be explained. Upon reporting for duty, a new man should be schooled in the fundamentals of his job by the foreman or an assistant. Periodic meetings should also be held for a review of this instruction and re-emphasis of basic points.

Safety. Accident hazards are a constant challenge to dock supervision. Compensation insurance rates vary by state, but a typical standard rate for truck terminals is $5.30 per $100 of payroll. Depending on the safety record of the terminal, the actual charge may be from 30 percent above to 30 percent below the standard. Whether the terminal is charged a premium because of numerous accidents or is granted a credit because of its good safety record is largely under control of the operator. In addition to direct costs of accidents, **secondary costs** must be considered, such as damage to equipment and materials, loss of an experienced worker and breaking up of a team, time lost by other workers when an accident occurs, and bad morale resulting from a high accident rate.

Accidents to hands and feet occur frequently on truck docks, but protection against them by work gloves and safety shoes should be provided. Many companies sell these items to employees at cost or less to prevent such accidents. Aisles should be clearly marked and kept clear. Stored freight that projects into an aisle is a safety hazard. Faulty stacking in storage areas is another hazard. Employees should be trained to trim pallets and stacks so that there is no danger from falling packages.

Housekeeping. The attention that is given to housekeeping is a good indication of the caliber of supervision. Scatterings of waste paper, strapping, dunnage, and sweepings indicate carelessness. The condition of drinking fountains, toilets, lunchrooms, and locker rooms has a bearing on worker morale.

Good housekeeping can result in an increase of storage and working space. For example, tests at outbound loading doorways of a terminal where 4-wheeled trucks were used showed the storage potential could be increased 30 percent by proper alignment of trucks as against putting them in at random.

Floor maintenance is also an aid to efficiency. Accumulations from leaking containers, broken packages, and sweepings should be removed. Oil and chemical deposits should not be allowed to remain on floors. Wooden floors should be inspected to insure that spikes are not exposed.

Driveways should be kept clear of waste dunnage and blocking so that a driver does not have to leave his cab to move debris before spotting his vehicle. Chock blocks chained to the under side of the dock help to eliminate the accumulation of dunnage used for chocking and save the time of a driver trying to find a block.

RAILROAD TERMINAL HANDLING

CONTENTS

CONTENTS *(Continued)*

RAILROAD TERMINAL HANDLING

Designing the Handling System

ENGINEERING THE HANDLING PROCEDURES. The railroads of the nation each year transport millions of tons of mail, express, and less-than-carload freight, all of which must be put through terminals at origin and destination, and in many cases through transfer terminals as well. Expeditious handling of this tonnage is one of the highly important services the railroads offer.

The first step in terminal planning and operation is to engineer the handling system on the basis of such factors as the volume of traffic, number of assorts, and train schedules. So far as possible, the facility should be planned to accommodate the selected handling system, although if the terminal is already constructed,

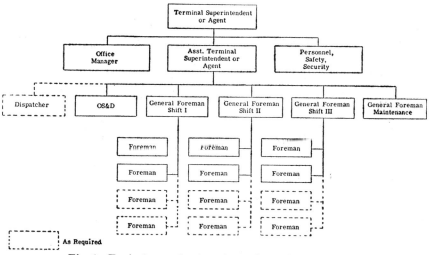

Fig. 1. Typical organization chart of terminal personnel.

compromises may have to be reached through modifications in both the system and the structure. Communications systems should be installed, and detailed operating procedures and maintenance, safety, and housekeeping practices established. A well-qualified supervisory staff, such as shown in Fig. 1, must be organized and trained. Work standards should be set and related to traffic volumes and schedules to develop a manning table so that management can control operations and give the prompt low-cost service that is the distinguishing mark of a good terminal.

FACTORS TO BE CONSIDERED. Before an improved handling system can be set up for any freight or mail-handling operation, six factors must be analyzed, namely, volumes to be handled, number of assorts to be made, time available to make assorts, characteristics of freight, physical facilities, and potential economies.

Volumes To Be Handled. The volume of freight, in pieces and pounds, to be moved and stored in any operation must be tabulated. This freight should be classified into **inbound, outbound, and transfer volumes.** It is also advantageous to break these classifications down further according to regular car and truck routes. Each classification should be tabulated according to week, day, and hour for periods long enough to establish definite patterns, and normal and abnormal peaks in the flow of materials to be handled. It is generally known by local managements that freight moves in cycles, but the volume to be expected during any specific day or hour is not usually known.

Because the volume of freight to be moved determines the size of the labor force and the amount of equipment required, this ability to forecast volumes with reasonable accuracy makes it possible better to utilize the services of men and machines. After volume figures are tabulated and before decisions are made on an improved handling system, every effort should be made to level off peaks and valleys in material flow. The reasons for any existing fluctuations should be uncovered and, if possible, the causes should be eliminated. Volume figures tabulated on the basis of past or present activities do not necessarily indicate what amounts may be handled in the future. Management must therefore estimate these amounts according to the closest possible **forecasts of future activity** during the period in which the contemplated handling system may be in operation.

Number of Assorts To Be Made. Assorting shipments for proper checking and routing is a primary function in freight handling. Consequently, the number of assorts that will have to be made should be tabulated and analyzed to determine the best time and place to do the assorting. Freight, mail, and express shipments are often **assorted while they are being unloaded** from railroad cars and trucks, for two reasons:

1. To expedite the movement of shipments into outbound cars, when the time to make the transfer is short; this kind of assorting occurs most frequently in passenger sheds when mail and express are being unloaded from head-end cars.
2. To reduce rehandling.

These reasons should never be the only considerations in determining where assorting should be done. Assorting during unloading slows down that operation and takes up an unwarranted amount of space on railroad platforms. L.C.L. (less-than-carload) and express shipments average approximately two pieces per shipment, so it is uneconomical to move the shipments through the terminal as individual units. Shipments are generally consolidated by routes or destinations to make up larger unit loads. If shipments are **assorted to pallets** or 4-wheel warehouse trucks, there are limits to the number of assorts that can be made within the car or truck—only one or two at the most and none when the car is full. Consequently, the pallets or trucks are usually arranged around the car door or truck tail gate. The larger the number of assorts being made, the more pallets or trucks required and the more space used. The travel distance from the interior of the car to the pallets may be excessive; with 12 to 14 assorts it may average as much as 50 ft. This method is also disadvantageous when rail cars are worked from track-level platforms and high wheelers are used.

The alternate assorting method for use during unloading is **central assorting,** i.e., bringing the freight into the building and making all necessary assorts there. In many terminals central assorting is done by peddling shipments from one short warehouse truck to others arranged in a circle or in rows. In some mail-assorting operations, mail is put in large piles on the floor; employees pick it up, piece by piece, from the piles and assort it into 4-wheel warehouse trucks arranged in rows.

These methods may be satisfactory for small-volume operations, but the walking distances are often excessive. Setting up **mechanical assorting stations** equipped with gravity or powered conveyors, or both, will reduce walking and cut down manual handling. The number of assorts must be known so as to design the assort conveyor properly. The number of ultimate assorts to be made within outbound cars and trucks should also be calculated. Assorting during loading slows down the operation, and it may necessitate restowing to reduce the risks of damage in transit. The relative costs of assorting at the originating and receiving stations should likewise be calculated to explore the possibilities for savings in time and labor.

Time Available To Make Assorts. The arrival and departure times of trains and trucks determine the time available for unloading, assorting, and reloading freight, the methods to be used, and the size of the work force needed. Arrival and departure times of scheduled cars and trucks, and the volumes of cargo that they normally carry, should be listed, and the resultant available working time should be computed. The **arrival pattern of nonscheduled trucks** should be ascertained by plotting arrival times for several weeks. The pattern may vary from day to day, but generally it is similar on the same days of the week. The combined patterns of scheduled and nonscheduled cars and trucks should then be studied, and an effort should be made to level the work load by eliminating extreme peaks and valleys. Arrival and departure schedules may have to be changed. Working agreements with outside carriers may be arranged, whereby they may reschedule arrivals and departures of their equipment at more desirable hours. It is sometimes beneficial to backlog work for periods of low activity by delaying the unloading and loading of drop trailers and cars which are to be held over.

Characteristics of Freight. The characteristics of materials to be handled influence the kind and capacity of the equipment to be used, as well as the amount of space required for handling and storage. First, it is necessary to determine the average **weight per piece.** If the number of pieces handled during a given period and their gross weight are known, the average weight per piece can be obtained by dividing the gross weight by the number of pieces. This figure can be used only if the difference between the lightest and heaviest pieces is not very great. Another and more nearly accurate way for ascertaining average weights is to weigh approximately 1,000 pieces of cargo selected at random and analyze the results statistically. Average weights in various ranges may be ascertained in this way. Second, compute the average **weight per shipment** to find the proportion of shipments large enough to travel through the facility as a unit. Shipment weights are available on manifests and bills of lading.

It is also important to ascertain **sizes of the freight to be moved** so as to set up equipment specifications and requirements. This information should be obtained by measuring the length, width, and height of a sufficient number and variety of units under shipment to make a statistical analysis. In both L.C.L. and express shipments one kind of transportation equipment probably will not handle all the different weights and sizes of freight. A study should likewise be made of the **number of pieces per shipment,** if it is desirable to maintain regulation over shipments. The number of pieces per shipment can generally be determined from lot stickers, manifests, and bills of lading.

Other characteristics which must be studied are **fragility, crushability, and perishability** of the shipments. Each of these factors may demand the application of different handling methods and equipment, or at least some modification in the system used for general freight.

Physical Facilities. The fifth factor to be analyzed is that of the physical facilities. Limitations in terminal layout, internal transportation systems, service installations, etc., will be decisive factors in the selection of the handling system. The **arrangement of tracks and platforms,** and the **size of platforms,** may make some kinds of handling devices, such as tow conveyors, unfeasible. Tracks and platforms may require alterations to permit the use of the best systems.

The **distances** over which shipments must be transported throughout the terminal influence the selection of equipment and methods and have a direct bearing on handling costs. In a multistory building the question arises as to the use of elevators versus other methods of vertical movement. Platforms and floors must be of sufficient strength to support heavy mechanical equipment and permit ready operation of mobile equipment such as industrial trucks. The **strength of floors and platforms** also determines the allowable concentration of stored shipments. The existing facility should also be examined closely for present and potential **storage space.** Most freight operations have to "floor" freight at one time or another.

Potential Economies. Before any handling system is selected for installation, its cost in capital outlay and operating expense must be weighed against potential savings. The contemplated system must also be weighed against alternate systems. An engineering economy study is therefore essential. The relative advantages and disadvantages of each system under consideration should be reduced to a dollars-and-cents basis. Intangible benefits should also be considered.

TYPICAL SYSTEMS. There are many systems in use in the various railroad terminals and many kinds of equipment to serve their respective needs. The following representative classes are those in general service:

Chutes and Gravity Conveyors. Straight or spiral metal chutes are useful for transporting certain kinds of freight to lower working levels. Their use, however, is restricted to sack mail and package freight which is neither fragile nor crushable.

Gravity roller conveyors, both portable and fixed, are widely used for transporting package freight over short distances. Lightweight, **portable conveyors** are particularly useful when loading and unloading trucks and railroad cars. The advent of reversible curved sections and accordion-type sections has further increased the value of gravity roller conveyors in freight-handling operations. Gravity conveyors are also used as accumulation sections, or "fingers," in conveyorized assorting arrangements. To reduce the cost of long conveyors, **alternate sections of powered and gravity conveyor** have been successfully used. The uneven pressures built up, as nonuniform packages push each other across gravity conveyors, often cause damage.

Use of gravity roller conveyors is restricted to short-distance transportation because of the incline required to move most parcel post, L.C.L., and express packages. Gravity conveyors are not well adapted to the handling of many types of freight, mail, and express that are handled by railroads; sack mail, bales, bags, and large bulky items are best handled with other equipment. When portable conveyors are used in trucks and rail cars, space must be left at the door for removal of such items by hand or powered truck.

Powered Conveyors. Where travel distances are long and the flow paths are fixed, powered conveyors are an economical means of transportation for a high percentage of mail and package freight. Of the two general kinds most commonly used, the powered belt conveyor is less costly than the powered roller conveyor and will accommodate a wider variety of freight.

The **weight of material** is a determining factor in deciding whether a belt or a roller conveyor is to be used. The latter has a higher load capacity than the former. Belt conveyors may have a slider or roller bed, the roller bed being used for the heavier loads. The necessity for pushing packages off a conveyor at right angles to the direction of travel will determine which kind of conveyor to select. It is easier to push materials off rollers than off belts, although smooth-top canvas belts have worked satisfactorily in some installations. Cleated cases, bags, and soft bales may not ride on roller conveyors without the use of glider boards. Rope and twine from packages may get caught in rollers, and wire and steel strap may cut belting at push-off points.

Where a powered conveyor is to be used to elevate or lower freight to another working level, the newer **grip-top belts** will permit steeper slopes and shorter conveyors than can be attained with rollers. With slopes greater than 25 to 30°, it may be necessary to add flights to the belt to prevent some types of freight from sliding or rolling down. Many conveyor installations **combine belt and roller types** so that advantage may be taken of the good features of both. This is the case in the setups currently used in many terminals for sorting and transporting parcel post and express packages. Short portable sections of powered conveyor have been used successfully when the flow pattern is not fixed and flexibility is required. Such portable sections are usually about 20 ft. in length, are mounted on large, locking-type casters, and have independent drives.

Warehouse Trucks. Two-wheel hand trucks are still of value in freight-handling operations, particularly where volumes are light, distances short, and stacking for temporary storage is not required. Although the average load carried on a hand truck is not much over 125 lbs. the hand truck requires less maneuvering space than other kinds of equipment. Consequently, a **hand truck** is often suitable for transporting bulky shipments between trucks or rail cars and platforms. Two-wheel hand trucks should not be used for long hauls, because travel time will be excessive, nor should they be used for a series of short hauls, because the picking up and setting down of shipments make hand trucks uneconomical.

A 4-wheel warehouse truck, while requiring more maneuvering space, will transport larger loads and can be obtained in a wide range of sizes and capacities. An 8-ft. long by 2½-ft. wide truck, equipped with roller-bearing wheels, will carry a 2-ton load and can be pushed along a smooth, level floor by one man. When such trucks are equipped with end racks and side racks or chains, freight can often be stacked 6 ft. high on these trucks. They can also be equipped with couplers for movement in tractor-trailer trains, or with hooks or pins for use on a tow conveyor.

Motorized Fixed-Platform Trucks. The motorized fixed-platform truck, sometimes known as a burden or load carrier, is a powered 3- or 4-wheel warehouse truck used extensively in rail terminals and is available in walkie or rider types in capacities up to 6,000 lb. The advantages of this equipment over hand-pushed warehouse trucks are reduced operator fatigue and increased speed of transportation. These trucks are useful where relatively small volumes are moved to many different destinations; they are also useful as utility trucks for shipments which cannot be readily moved by other equipment. Their biggest disadvantage lies in the idle time of equipment and operator during loading and unloading and the fact that shipments must be rehandled for storage. Another disadvantage is that the one-way movement of materials in a rail terminal results in dead-heading.

Platform Lift Trucks and Skid Platforms. The skid platforms most generally used in rail terminals are those of the standard 4-ft. by 3-ft. ironbound type. Longer skid platforms may be used for large, bulky shipments. The skid platforms are transported on hand or powered platform lift trucks and are loaded into trucks and rail cars.

Skids have been used in preference to pallets, even though their initial cost is considerably higher, because their sturdier construction gives them greater load-bearing capacities and longer maintenance-free life. Skid platforms, however, cannot be stacked as readily as pallets, and a platform lift truck will not pick up freight from a car floor in the way that a fork truck with chisel forks can. The two systems may be combined, pallets being used for light package freight and skids for heavy, bulky shipments.

Fork Trucks and Pallets. While fork truck and pallet systems are extensively used for handling operations carried on in small and medium-size truck terminals, they are not necessarily the best for rail terminal service where large volumes of materials must be transported. First, the average shipment passing through a rail terminal is of relatively light weight, and individual pieces are not always uniform in size. Second, travel distances are generally greater in rail than in truck terminals, and fork trucks are uneconomical for hauls over 200 ft. Fork trucks and pallets in conjunction with such equipment as tractors or tow conveyors, however, can be worked into well-organized handling systems.

Tractor-Trailer Trains. Tractor-trailer trains present probably the greatest potential for savings in terminal facilities where the average haul is greater than 200 ft. and where existing platforms will not accommodate a tow conveyor. Four-wheel warehouse trucks, equipped with couplers, can be pushed into trucks and rail cars by hand for loading or unloading and are transported about the terminal facility in trains pulled by gas or electric tractors. Thus, the system combines the advantages of 4-wheel trucks with an economical method of transportation.

This system is not advisable on a **narrow-island platform,** or in a facility consisting of several island platforms not connected by bridges or a head-end platform. Open-end platforms must be sufficiently wide to permit two-way traffic, otherwise considerable congestion and damage to freight will result. The width of aisles, particularly at turns and intersections, determines the number of trailers that can be safely pulled; in general, eight should be the maximum in one train. When open-end platforms are too narrow to permit a 180° turn of the train, trailers can be dropped off on the downward trip and picked up on the return.

Tow Conveyors. Tow conveyors are probably the most economical means for transporting loaded carts or trucks over long distances between relatively fixed points. The only operating cost is for power, and maintenance costs are normally low. The initial cost is high, however, and the construction features of some existing terminal facilities make the installation difficult and costs prohibitive. A tow conveyor, however, should always be considered as a possible installation when planning a large new facility.

Care must be taken that possible savings are not lost because of poor planning of layout and operation. Some kinds of freight cannot be transported by tow conveyor, and aisle space must be provided between the towline and the platform or dock edge. The distance from tow conveyor to platform edge, however, should not be so great that time is lost in pulling the carts into position. On a narrow platform it is advisable to **omit every fifth or sixth chain dog** so that freight can be moved by hand truck or fork truck through these gaps.

One danger of the tow conveyor is that it can degenerate into merely a device for providing storage in motion, because of poor planning by management. A tow conveyor will pull only as many carts as the chain has dogs. If filled carts are not removed from the line as fast as empties are being put on the line, the line eventually becomes loaded, and the men assigned to attach carts will remain temporarily idle. Conversely, if filled carts are removed from the line faster than empties are fed into the line, men will be idle while waiting for empty carts.

Combinations of Systems. Because of the nature of rail terminal operations, it is unlikely that the handling system will be based on only one kind of transportation equipment. The problem is to select the equipment best adapted to handling each of the classes of freight passing through the terminal, then to integrate these classes into a handling system.

Two-wheel hand trucks, platform trucks, or fork lift trucks may be used for transporting cross-platform freight. Other shipments are often loaded onto 4-wheel warehouse trucks within the railroad cars. Shipments to be stored temporarily may be palletized on 4-wheel warehouse trucks. The 4-wheel trucks may be pulled to storage, assorting areas, outbound cars, or motor trucks by tractor or tow conveyor.

Shipments which are palletized and moved to storage areas on 4-wheel trucks may be stored and removed from storage by fork trucks. Shipments to be assorted for routing may be removed from trucks by hand, assorted on an arrangement of conveyors, and returned to 4-wheel trucks for further transport to outbound cars and trucks. The entire transporting and assorting of materials may be done on conveyors, as is done with sack mail.

ESTIMATING THE QUANTITY OF EQUIPMENT NEEDED.
Calculating requirements for equipment is a necessary part of planning any handling system. When equipment is procured by "hunch" rather than by calculation, the tendency is to overprocure, to be on the safe side. Buying equipment with capacities greater than those required increases the initial capital outlay and reduces economies because the equipment is never fully utilized. On the other hand, managements which purchase on price alone usually end up with inadequate equipment which is soon overloaded. Overloading increases maintenance costs and may cause an otherwise well-planned system to break down.

Chutes and Conveyors. Three factors must be known in designing a chute. First, the determining factor in the width of a chute is the **width of the widest piece** the chute will have to convey. Second, the **slope** of the chute must be determined. This slope is dependent, not only on the relative elevations of the two working levels, but also on the friction between the materials and the slide. Since there are wide variations in the package freight passing through L.C.L., mail, and express terminals, the slope can be determined only by test. The slope is important, not only from the standpoint of capacity to handle the volume, but also because of the space the chute will occupy. Third, the **weight to be carried** by the chute must be estimated. It is good practice to assume that the chute will be completely filled from top to bottom. Under the above assumptions, the width of the chute, in feet, should be multiplied by its length, in feet, to determine the total load-bearing area. Divide this area by the area covered by the average-size package to calculate the average number of packages it may be expected to hold. Multiply this average number by the average weight per package. The result will be the total weight which the chute must support. An important point to cover when planning to use chutes in rail terminals is to plan alternate routes and provide special equipment for freight which cannot be transported on chutes.

Fig. 2 illustrates a typical transfer sorting conveyor layout. A "Christmas tree" picking conveyor is shown in Fig. 3.

Standard conveyor sections should be used whenever possible because of their economy and flexibility. The design of special-purpose conveyors should be assigned to competent equipment manufacturers. The following is the information which management must supply:

1. The **length of the conveyor** required must be determined from the layout of the proposed system. It is governed by the distances over which the freight must travel by conveyor and by physical obstructions in the layout of the terminal which must be by-passed.

2. The necessary **width of the conveyor** is determined by the width of the freight transported and is influenced by the inclusion of push-off points. Normally, a straight, powered conveyor does not require side rails to keep freight from falling off. Consequently, the conveyor can be narrower than the widest piece it is to carry. When freight is to be pushed off across the conveyor, the conveyor should be no wider than 36 in., and preferably less. It is almost impossible for the average-size man to push freight off a conveyor wider than 36 in. without using a pole or stick. When **turns** are incorporated into conveyor systems, the width and radius of each turn are dependent upon the length of the longest pieces which must make the turns. Conveyor manufacturers can usually supply charts showing the widths and radii required to handle the various sizes of packages to be transported.

3. The **height of the conveyor** above floor level will depend upon whether the conveyor is merely transporting freight or whether manual operations are being performed on moving freight. When freight is being loaded onto a conveyor by hand, the best height at the loading point is 18 in. above floor level. If shipments are to be routed and marked on the conveyor, the height at the marking point, and at push-off points, should be no less than 24 in. and no more than 30 in. Where freight is being picked off by hand, the height of the conveyor at the pick-off point should be approximately 14 in.

4. The **speed at which the conveyor operates** governs its capacity in pieces moved per minute. To find the required capacity in pieces per minute, divide the total pieces to be transported by the minutes available for moving that number. To get the required speed of the conveyor in feet per minute, multiply the pieces per minute by the average length per piece. Some allowance should be made for deviations from normal activity. If routing and marking are to be done on the moving conveyor, the ability of the routers to sort the moving freight will be the governing factor in determining the conveyor speed. Routers can mark freight moving at 100 ft. per min. That speed will give a conveyor capacity in excess of 2,500 pieces per hr. of package freight handled through L.C.L., parcel post, and express facilities.

5. To enable equipment suppliers to calculate the **power requirements** and belt specifications for a conveyor, they must know the speed at which the conveyor should run and the weight it will have to transport. The weight can be determined by dividing the length of the conveyor by the average length of the pieces handled. This figure is the average number of pieces the conveyor will carry at one time and should be multiplied by the average weight per piece to get the

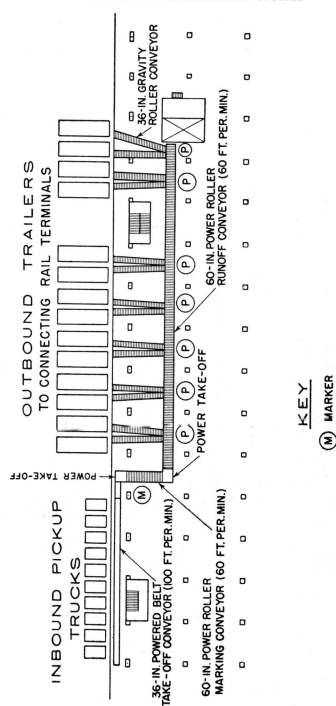

Fig. 2. Transfer sorting conveyor layout.

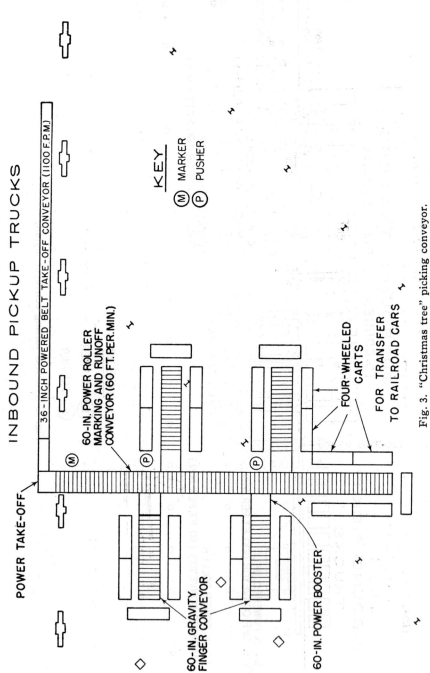

Fig. 3. "Christmas tree" picking conveyor.

total weight capacity of the conveyor. It is also desirable to know the size ranges of the pieces to be transported, as well as the load per square foot that the conveyor will have to support. These figures are used to calculate the diameter and center distances of conveyor rollers.

Warehouse Trucks. Computations for 4-wheel warehouse trucks, like computations for most handling equipment, start with the volumes to be moved and stored on trucks. Besides volumes, it is necessary to know the average sizes and weights of the pieces. The size of the trucks used is most often determined by the amount of space available in which to maneuver them. To avoid the use of different sizes of trucks, and the difficulty of getting the right size at the right time, most companies standardize on the kind of truck which will accommodate the widest variety of shipments. That size is generally the 2½ by 6-ft. or the 2½ by 8-ft. truck. This truck can be obtained in capacities from 1 ton up.

To compute the **number of trucks required,** it is necessary first to determine the average number of pieces a given-size truck will hold. The potential storage cube on the truck can be calculated by multiplying its length by its width and by the height to which the freight can be stacked (6 ft. high is about the maximum). Next divide the storage cube on the truck by the cube of the average-size piece handled. This calculation will give the average number of pieces that a truck will carry. Multiplying the number of pieces a truck will carry by the average weight per piece will indicate the necessary weight-bearing capacity of the truck. This is average weight; maximum weight could be twice as great.

It is necessary to determine how long it will take for **one truck to make a round trip** (this is travel time, plus loading and unloading time, plus an allowance for unavoidable delays). The number of trips per hour times the number of pieces a truck will carry gives its hourly capacity. Dividing this figure into the volume that must be moved in the peak hour will give the number of trucks required to move a given work load. To this number must be added the number of trucks holding freight in temporary storage and the number of trucks involved in assorting arrangements. The minimum number of trucks required is calculated by adding together the number needed in each of the above categories. To insure flexibility, one extra truck should be added for each assort being made and each car or truck being worked during a peak period.

Motorized Fixed-Platform Trucks. The same method as is used for computing warehouse truck requirements is used for computing motorized fixed-platform truck requirements. Because of its relatively high cost, however, this type of equipment would not be used for storage or in assorting arrangements.

Skid Platforms and Platform Lift Trucks; Pallets and Fork Trucks. When a skid platform or pallet operation is contemplated, the first step in computing equipment requirements is determining the size of the pallet or skid platform to be used. To keep the number of lift trucks required to a minimum, unit loads should be as large as can be safely handled. The limiting factors are the space available for storing loaded pallets and the aisle space for maneuvering the lift truck equipment. When large volumes of freight are stored on pallets or skid platforms, the clear space between columns in the storage area is a governing factor on pallet size. Pallets are often used which leave 2 to 3 ft. of floor width wasted in every bay. The larger the pallets or skid platforms used, the larger the equipment required, and the wider the aisles required to accommodate the equipment. The economics of space lost in aisles must be measured against the economics of larger unit loads.

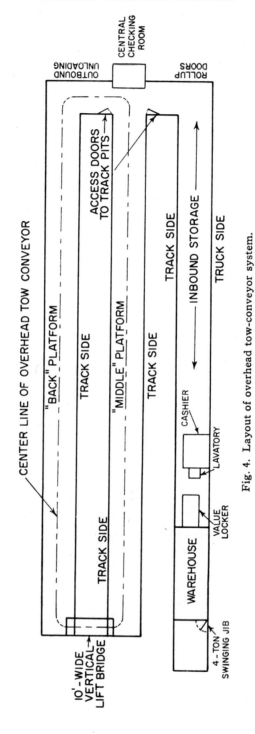

Fig. 4. Layout of overhead tow-conveyor system.

To compute the **number of pallets or skid platforms required,** compute the available cube on the pallet or skid platform. Divide this figure by the cube of the average-size piece of freight handled. The result will be the average number of pieces in a unit load. Then determine the average turnover time of a pallet, that is, the time from start of loading the pallet to the time it is returned empty for reloading. The number of trips a pallet can make in 1 hr., multiplied by the average number of pieces per pallet load, when divided into the number of pieces to be moved in 1 hr., will give the minimum number of pallets required. Add to this the number which are holding freight in storage. The sum is the minimum number of pallets required. Because control is difficult to maintain, it is advisable to add 5 to 10 pallets for each truck and rail car being worked simultaneously.

Platform and fork lift truck requirements are based on the weight of the load and the size of the pallet or skid platform. A fork lift truck with a capacity of 2,000 lb. at a 24-in. load center will handle at least 80 percent of the freight passing through a rail terminal. In operations requiring only one truck, its capacity should be at least 4,000 lb. so as to handle the small percentage of shipments weighing over 2,000 lb. Where more than one truck is required, only one in five needs to have a capacity greater than 2,000 lb.

To determine the **number of fork lift trucks required,** it is necessary to know how many pallet loads must be transported in a given time and the distances those pallets must be carried. The number of fork trucks required is arrived at by dividing the hourly volume in pieces by the average number of pieces per pallet. The average number of pieces can be arrived at only by measurement. Because travel and lift speeds vary according to make of equipment, it is best to use the speeds given in the manufacturer's specifications. Add an allowance, from 20 to 50 percent depending upon local conditions, for unavoidable delays.

Tractor-Trailer Trains. The method of computing the number of trailers or 4-wheel trucks required has already been explained. The layout of an overhead tow conveyor system is illustrated in Fig. 4. If tractors are to be used, the capacity and number of such tractors required must be determined. First, establish the number of trailers that can be safely towed in the existing facility. The average number of pieces those trailers will carry, times the average weight per piece, will give the pay load. Add the weight of the trailers and an allowance for friction in the trailer wheels. (The latter value can usually be obtained from the manufacturer of the trailers.) This is the total load to be pulled. If there are any slopes to be negotiated by the tractor-trailer train, the slope of the steepest grade must be used to determine the required capacity of the tractors.

To calculate the **number of tractors required,** the distances to be traversed and the speed of the tractors must be known. These figures will give the travel time, to which must be added allowances for coupling and uncoupling. From the elapsed time per trip and the number of pieces hauled per trip, the number of trips necessary to move a given volume in a predetermined time can be ascertained, and the number of tractors required can be determined.

TOW CONVEYORS. After the route of a proposed tow conveyor has been established, determine the **spacing of chain dogs,** the speed of the conveyor, and the weight the chain will have to pull at the desired speed. The spacing of the chain dogs will depend upon the length of the carts, the radii of curves, and the speed of the conveyor. The dogs should be far enough apart so that a cart being pulled by the conveyor will not be hit by the following cart. With a chain moving at 100 ft. per min. and pulling 6-ft. carts, the dogs should be 10 ft. apart.

The **speed required** to move a given volume of cargo in a given time is computed, first by reducing the volume, in pieces, to cartloads. The volume in pieces, divided by the average capacity of the carts, in pieces, will give this figure. Next, divide the number of cartloads by the number of minutes available to make the move. This figure will give the cartloads per minute which must be moved. The latter figure, multiplied by the distance between the chain dogs, will give the speed of the conveyor in feet per minute. Speeds in excess of 150 ft. per min. should be avoided because of the difficulty in removing carts and the tendency for carts to whip around the turns in the conveyor.

Knowing the total number of dogs on the tow conveyor, assume each one to be pulling a loaded cart. The total number of carts which can be pulled at once, multiplied by the average weight of a cart and its load, will give the maximum net weight which the conveyor must be able to pull at the speed desired. The equipment supplier will use these figures to calculate the size of the drive required.

Introducing Improvements

ANALYZING EXISTING FACILITIES. One of the factors to be analyzed before an improved handling system is selected is the physical facility or surroundings in which the handling system must operate. The following factors are those which must be considered and studied:

Location. The location of the facility with relation to allied operations is important because of transportation and communications costs. Managements of L.C.L. freight stations and rail-express terminals are often responsible for such operations as working cars on team tracks some distance away from the freight house or express terminal. Because many of these outlying operations are only part-time activities, they present problems in assigning and control of personnel. The railroads must assume the cost of transporting mail between their local facilities and the local government post offices. Consequently, the relative locations of these two facilities determine the methods and costs of transportation.

Rail terminal operations must be accessible by rail and by street and highway. They must be accessible to the public as well as to employees. The distance between the terminal and pickup and delivery areas influences arrival and departure times of vehicles and pickup and delivery costs. The arrival and departure times of vehicles and rail cars determine the work-load pattern for the operation. Finally, the distances between the operation and classification yards and passenger stations affect switching costs; this factor can delay the working of inbound cars which arrive in the yards and are switched to the freight house.

Layout. Up-to-date drawings of operating facilities should be obtained and critical dimensions checked, not only because of possible errors, but also because changes and improvements are often made on rail facilities by using detail sketches, without correcting master tracings.

1. **Over-all layouts.** An over-all drawing showing terminal trackage or sidings, building sites and sizes, bridges, platforms, and other major structures is required. The usual scale for such drawings is 1 in. = 50 ft., since a drawing of ordinary size will encompass a relatively large area. Track numbers, names of major areas and buildings, viaduct locations, and other pertinent information should be inserted on these drawings. Drawings are used for visualization of the area, marking major flow lines, and planning changes in track and building locations.

2. **Detailed layouts.** Detailed drawings of all buildings, floors, individual platforms, or other areas requiring consideration should be prepared. The minimum

scale to be used is 1/16 in. per ft., although 1/8 in. or 1/4 in. per ft. is preferable if the drawings are not very large. Use of architectural scales is customary because available building drawings are usually based on this system, and contractors and equipment suppliers are used to it. Detailed plan drawings should show tracks; platforms; trucks docks; assorting, storage, and office areas; aisles; obstructions; present truck and car spots when identifiable; and routes of freight, express, or mail moving through the operation. Legends, notes, or other suitable means should be used to include such information as overhead clearances, dock heights, and delivery route locations required for detailed analysis. Where conveyor installations or building changes are contemplated, or where multistory operations are involved, **detailed elevation drawings** should be prepared. Electrical layouts, plumbing and heating diagrams, and other special-purpose drawings may be required.

Services. The type, adequacy, and conditions of various building services should be checked, for they contribute to proper work patterns and reduction in loss and damage.

1. **Lighting.** Proper lighting is a requisite, particularly where routing, reading for destination, checking, and similar operations are performed. All **fixtures** should be checked for suitability, cleanliness, condition of reflective surfaces, and glare. **Illumination** at working levels should be checked with a **light meter.** In the absence of specific work tables or similar devices having definite heights, the working level is usually taken as 30 in. above the floor. If a light meter is not available, the local power company can probably supply one.

Of importance in providing proper light are the **color and cleanliness of walls** and ceilings. Surfaces should be painted a light color, but one which does not cause excessive glare. Light grey or green is often recommended for walls, ceilings, and other overhead surfaces. Aluminum paint has been used for overhead structures with success. All surfaces should be painted to permit easy cleaning.

2. **Power supply.** The amount and kind of electric power available should be determined. If new conveyors or other equipment will be needed, or additional lighting or heating demands may be made, additional power will probably be required. Data on voltage and cycle characteristics are needed so as to specify the correct kinds of electrical equipment.

3. **Heating and weather protection.** The terminal or dock heating system should be examined. Proper temperatures must be maintained in warm rooms, offices, locker and lunchrooms, and other clerical and service areas. Examination should be made of means of protecting traffic and personnel from rain, snow, and sleet. Closing off unused vehicle or rail spots by means of overhead doors, provision of roof overhangs where possible on rail and truck docks, and use of canvas tents to protect car-door openings aid in preventing undue exposure.

4. **Service areas.** Adequacy of all service areas should be determined in terms of size, location, and condition. Lunchrooms, locker rooms, and toilets should conform to state laws and local ordinances. If hot or prepared meals are served, **lunchrooms** should be equipped with steam tables, means for disposing of refuse, dishwashers, etc. **Lockers** should be well-ventilated, and locker-room floors should be easily cleaned. **Toilet facilities** should be planned for the peak usage at shift-change hours.

If service facilities are very far from work areas, time and production output are lost. If too close, they may interfere with the movement of traffic through the terminal. One solution is to locate these services on mezzanines where they will be out of the way but still available.

Warm room, cold room, value room, settlement room, and similar areas should be given adequate attention. By watching the flow of traffic or personnel through these areas, it is often possible to increase their capacity while reducing the floor area required. Their locations may have to be changed, or there may not be sufficient working area around some of the facilities, and a relayout of entire areas may be necessary. Effectiveness and coverage of public address systems, pneumatic tubes, phone systems, and other **means of communication** should be examined, as well as the location, capacity, speed, and dimensions of elevators, location of stairwells, chutes, and other **means of transferring personnel** or traffic from floor to floor.

IMPROVING EXISTING FACILITIES. It is necessary not only to analyze existing facilities but also to improve these facilities for higher efficiency. Among the possible improvements the following changes offer opportunities for further betterment:

Layout. Many facilities used for freight, mail, or express handling were not designed for that specific purpose but have been converted from some other use. Although it is difficult to secure the highest performance in space not designed for an operation, intelligent planning of building alterations and flow patterns will reduce terminal costs.

Traffic Movement Through an Operation. Flow patterns in a terminal should be as simple and direct as possible. Unnecessary travel, cross hauls, and back hauls should be eliminated. Service areas should be removed from the operating floor to mezzanines or unused space wherever possible. Constrictions in flow, such as low or narrow doors, unnecessary corners or bends in aisles, movement from floor to floor, and low capacity of bridges or docks should be corrected.

Consideration should be given to providing **one-way aisles,** particularly on narrow, finger-type rail docks or in operating areas in the house. It is sometimes impossible to widen these areas to provide adequate two-way aisles, but often alternate routes can be developed which will allow all traffic in narrow aisles to move in one direction.

Flow consideration should not be restricted to horizontal movement. In many large terminals, traffic must be moved by means of **elevators or ramps.** Scheduling and restriction of direction of flow will often substantially speed up terminal operations. Elevator bottlenecks usually are obvious. They can be determined by measuring the delay encountered by station trucks or other equipment when waiting for the cage. Ramps also cause delays in traffic flow, especially if the ramps are too narrow, steep, slippery, or have sharp turns.

Aisles. Minimum widths of two-way aisles, including doorways and other constrictions, should be 10 ft. If building design holds aisles to widths which are materially narrower than this figure, one-way aisles should be instituted. If fork trucks of greater than 2,000-lb. capacity, or other larger materials handling equipment are used, aisle widths must be increased to accommodate them. The best information on aisles required for specific machines can be obtained from manufacturers' data, or they can be computed from the formula: length of the pallet, plus distance from the heel of the forks to the center line of the front axle, plus the turning radius of the machine, plus 6 in. Other machines, such as cranes and tractors, vary in widths and characteristics so that no formulas are in common use for determining aisle widths. When fork trucks and industrial cranes are under consideration, heights of door openings and other obstructions should also be checked. Low clearances may have to be raised before using machines of these kinds.

Truck and Car Spots. Radical improvement can often be made in the operation of a rail terminal by alterations in rail and truck facilities and handling methods. Most efficient car loading and unloading can be done on house tracks, that is, tracks whose platforms form a part of the terminal building. In general, the most efficient kinds of facilities are separated island platform tracks, then team tracks. The poorest facilities are head-end operations.

Generally, the simplest means of improving car loading and unloading is by maximum use of house tracks through scheduling of car switching. Scheduling should be aimed at maximum utilization of the best spots. An approach toward improvement in the use of house tracks is through the preparation of a **car-spot utilization chart** showing the hours of the day across the top, and the days of the week along the side. Each day is subdivided into lines for car spots. Occupancy of each spot for each hour is indicated by a line. Posted immediately adjacent to that line is the car designation, or the train number from which the car is received or to which it will be consigned. Next to this information is the number of pieces or pounds of traffic loaded to, or unloaded from, the car. If variable crews are used, the number of men in the crew during each hour can also be indicated. By means of this chart, together with a listing of the cars received and dispatched daily, and the average footage or amount of traffic in each, it is possible to determine when house-track car-spots are not in use, when loading or unloading can be speeded up to release car spots, and what other cars can be placed on these tracks each hour of the day.

To assure best performance, facilities should be improved to the fullest extent. Inadequate **platforms** should be lengthened and widened. Platform widths should be no less than 10 ft. and preferably should be 16 ft. to provide for a line of 4-wheel trucks on each side of a two-way aisle and to simplify turning around at the platform end. Lengthening platforms will permit more car spots. Platforms should be roofed to protect against inclement weather and floors should be strengthened when necessary. The utility of island platforms—those not physically connected to the house but adjacent to it—can be improved by connecting them to house platforms. This connection is made by installing fixed or portable **bridges** as required. Stub-track installations usually can use the fixed type of bridges; the elevating or portable type is required for double-end tracks. Typical **truck dock heights** are 48 in. above the apron for pickup vehicles and 52 in. above the apron for tractor-trailer units. These dimensions vary according to the characteristics of the trucks to be serviced. If trucks unload onto a conveyor, the top of this line should be as close to truck-bed height as possible. The conveyor should be of the raised type, with no side guards or other protrusions on the dock side.

PLANNING NEW FACILITIES. As a final step it is advisable to plan new facilities to keep in step with new trends and betterments. Changes in product design, the advent of new products, gradual elimination of former kinds of products, and the development of improved equipment for the production of newer products all bring about significant changes in materials and production or fabrication methods.

Calculating Dock and Platform Requirements. After the handling system has been decided upon, the first step in laying out a terminal is to block in each of the working areas, storage areas, and other facilities required by the proposed operation. From this point on, the process is one of steady refinement, with each step adding more of the details required, until the **final layout** is prepared. The final layout is a complete functional plan of the operation, including column spacing, floor loading required, overhead clearances, and all the other items required by the architect so that he can prepare complete building plans. Within the limits imposed by economical construction, column spacing and size are functions of multiples of the unit storage quantity and of the spatial requirements of the sorting process. A storage bay, for example, should contain a given number of 6-ft. platform trucks—if these are the basic storage and handling unit for the operation—plus necessary aisle area, without wasting space. If a conveyor arrangement for sorting is decided upon, bay sizes should be such that columns will not interfere with proper layout of the conveyor, including working room required. In a facility using two or more handling systems, bay and column sizes will represent a compromise between the demands of each system.

Assorting Areas. Areas in which traffic is assorted are the centers around which mail, express, and L.C.L. terminals are focused. Although the purpose of these centers is the same for all rail terminals, the means customarily employed vary.

In large **mail-handling facilities,** traffic usually flows from the post office and from cars via belt conveyors to a primary assorting table. Sacks empty onto this table and are moved across it by assorters and lowered to one of a series of conveyors which underlie the table surface. Each of these conveyors connects to a secondary sorting station. At the secondary sort, sacks empty onto a table and assorters place them on 4-wheel trucks, one for each car of each train. When these trucks are loaded, they are towed by industrial tractors to the proper cars.

At modern **express terminals,** traffic from pickup vehicles, transfer vehicles, and cars is often dumped onto a "Christmas tree" assorting conveyor where it is routed and shunted to the proper finger of the assorting conveyor. From this point it is placed on 4-wheel trucks, one for each assort. When these trucks are loaded, they are towed by industrial tractor to the proper cars.

L.C.L. terminals usually have provisions for checking and assorting traffic as it is unloaded from cars. The fork truck and pallet or tow conveyor systems are used to transfer assorted shipments to the other side of the dock for loading into delivery trucks.

One of the principal methods of improving existing assorting areas is by clearing away all floor-type heaters, small cages or offices, lavatories, and other obstructions. Often in older terminals these areas gradually have been constricted by alterations until operations and flow paths have been impeded. By removing such obstructions and revising the operation, substantial performance improvements can be realized.

Service Areas. Each terminal service area has one or more unique features which must be incorporated into its design. A **warm room** is required in all express facilities and in those mail docks which are not heated. This area should be large enough to handle animals and also perishables. It is impractical in most cases, however, to provide a room of sufficient size to handle seasonal peaks of such semiperishables as citrus fruit and vegetables. Walls in the room, at least for the lower 6 ft., should be of glazed tile or other material which can be easily washed. The floor should be of concrete, sloped slightly, and equipped with a drain at the low point to permit washing. The room should also be provided with running water and a sink, so that livestock can be watered. Since livestock crates and other containers for perishables are large and of irregular shape, it is not practical to provide bins or other storage aids. A telephone connecting with the terminal circuit and built-in benches along one wall for preparing feed and taking care of smaller animals are recommended. Room doors should open in a direction away from drafts to avoid damage to animals. Ordinarily two doors are provided—a small door for personnel and a door to permit entrance and exit of platform or station trucks. The cargo door opening should be at least 5 ft. wide and 9 ft. high.

A **small cold room** is required in express terminals. It is usually located next to the ice-making machinery, and a portion of the insulated area can be used for storing flake ice until needed. The cold room itself is often compartmented to allow storage at several temperature levels. Slatted false flooring and walls are installed to allow even distribution of cold air around the periphery. Beside the ice-making machine, a concrete-floored area, provided with a drain, is located for re-icing perishables. Usually this area is arranged to include one or more truck backup spaces so that perishables can be brought from rail cars directly to this area, re-iced, and loaded into delivery vehicles. Express terminals also must be provided with a **value room** and a **settlement room**. Since these rooms are subject to special security provisions, their design and construction should be developed with the proper Railway Express Agency departments.

Toilet facilities should be provided reasonably near major work areas. They may be placed on mezzanines or in other areas where they will not interfere with operations. The number of toilet fixtures is ordinarily governed by state and local regulations, but if none exist, a minimum of one toilet fixture to every 20 persons should be provided, with at least two in each location. Closets should be housed in separate booths, formed of partial steel panels. **Washrooms** should be separated from toilets, and sufficient sink capacity should be provided for all workers. **Locker rooms** should be provided, with a locker for each employee. Lockers should be raised from the floor and should be provided with screening or other means of ventilation. All floors and walls should have a glazed or tile surface and should be cleaned daily. **Facilities for women workers** also are covered by state and local regulations. Requirements are similar to those for men, but rest rooms are almost invariably required.

Either a piped **chilled-water system** or individual water coolers should be provided. Fountains should be placed within a convenient distance of all personnel concentration areas.

Terminal office space should be provided in the portion of the building adjacent to the line of public access to the facility. General offices are customarily located at one end of a dock, or on mezzanines or upper floors, so as to prevent interference with operations. For planning purposes, it is customary to calculate office space on the basis of 100 sq. ft. per office employee. This figure includes corridors and is a basic allowance. It must be increased whenever provisions are required for conference rooms, file rooms, reception rooms, and similar extras. Corridors must be at least as wide as the width of the smallest exit door, although it is customary to make them approximately 6 ft. wide to accommodate two-way passage without crowding. A convenient scale for laying out office space is $\frac{1}{4}$ in. to the foot. Templets of desks and other equipment can be procured or drawn to this scale, which permits easy visualization of layouts by nontechnical executives.

Receiving, on-hand, and similar areas in express and freight terminals should be placed at the dock edge adjacent to the main office and to the terminal floor. They should be accessible to the general public. Sufficient customer parking spaces should be reserved next to those areas so that customer vehicles will not interfere with movement of regular traffic.

In large terminals, it may be necessary to provide **track offices, vehicle offices, supervisory offices,** and similar space in locations remote from main offices. These rooms are generally partitioned off from the terminal floor in locations convenient to the operations that they serve but out of the way of traffic flow.

General Factors. Certain facilities are necessary for efficient operation and adequate service.

Lighting. Two types of lights are used in terminals—fluorescent and incandescent. If a terminal has, or is planned for, direct current for lighting circuits, incandescent lights are preferable in all areas, since fluorescent lamp life and illumination efficiency are reduced in d.c. installations. **Incandescent bulbs** should be used in all open areas. As ambient temperature drops, regular fluorescent lamps lose efficiency, have reduced life, and may flash on and off if glow-switch-type starters are used. There are special low temperature lamps for temperatures below 32° F. However, these have reduced life and, like regular fluorescents, must be enclosed to shield them from drafts. **Fluorescent lighting** is recommended only for enclosed areas which are heated in winter. For offices, warm rooms, etc., fluorescents have advantages of economy, appearance, and reduction of glare. **Recommended minimum illumination levels** in various terminal areas are shown in Fig. 5.

Area Illuminated	Foot-Candles Maintained in Service
Office—Tabulating, accounting, business machine operation, transcribing, drafting, etc.	50
Office—General office area, private offices, file rooms, mail rooms, etc.	35
Office—Reception rooms, lobbies, stairways, washrooms, and service areas	20
Dock—General terminal storage and handling areas	15
Dock—Marking, routing, and sorting areas where labels of documents are read	35
Shop—Maintenance, automotive equipment, and coopering areas	30

Fig. 5. Minimum foot-candles to be provided at working height, or 30 in. above floor level; these are not initial design figures.

Heating. Express and mail terminals should be maintained at temperatures in excess of 32° F. to prevent spoilage of semiperishables, such as citrus fruits, seedlings, etc. L.C.L. freight docks should be kept above 32° F. wherever possible to assist in maintaining crew efficiency. Warm rooms, terminal offices, rest rooms, and similar areas should be heated according to their uses. Dock heating usually is by means of steam heaters, although natural gas, hot air, or electric heaters are often used. Unit heaters should be located off the floor to eliminate wasting dock area. They should be designed and located so that blasts of warm air are not directed at piles of freight, mail, or express. Offices and service areas are usually heated by steam radiators. Care should be taken to prevent excessive temperatures in checkers' booths, track offices, and other areas which dock personnel enter and leave during the course of their work. Steam for heating is ordinarily supplied from central terminal steam plants.

LAYOUT OF SURROUNDING AREAS. Proper attention should be given to the layout and arrangement of surrounding areas so as to facilitate operations.

General Rules. The site selected should be provided with **access roads.** Ideally, each truck dock should have entrance and exit by means of separate paved roads. If more than one truck dock is planned for a facility, each dock should be accessible to the others by paved roads. A terminal should not be located on a heavily traveled street. Preferably, access roads should carry no other traffic but that generated by the terminal.

Each truck dock should be provided with a **paved apron,** sloped to provide natural drainage away from the dock edge. With the recommended 12-ft. truck spots, the apron width required will vary according to the over-all length of the vehicles to use it. If gross tractor-trailer length is 40 ft., the apron width required is 44 ft.; if the tractor-trailer length is 45 ft., the apron width required is 49 ft. These dimensions will allow an experienced driver to back into a 12-ft. spot in one maneuver. Aprons must be unobstructed. Width should be calculated starting at the dock posts or at the front end of maximum-length vehicles parked at the dock. Before deciding upon apron width, local and state requirements for gross vehicle length and type should be ascertained. Truck aprons should be designed to accommodate vehicles of the maximum legal length, even though immediate plans call for using shorter trucks.

A paved or prepared-surface **parking area** should be provided adjacent to the truck dock. Its capacity should be sufficient to accommodate all vehicles which cannot back into the dock at rush hours. If trucks are garaged at a separate location, the parking area can be somewhat smaller than when it is expected to hold all units, but there still should be space to permit off-street parking of all vehicles which must wait before they can be spotted at the dock. Off-street parking for customer and employee passenger vehicles also should be provided.

When possible, the entire terminal area should be **fenced.** Vehicle and pedestrian access should be only by gates at which there are check points. This precaution will prevent unauthorized entry and minimize pilferage.

SITE SELECTION. A factor almost as important as the internal design of a rail terminal is the location of the facility itself. Although securing the proper site is often complicated by factors of existing land availability and present building location, a complete analysis should be made in each case so that the advantages and disadvantages of each location may be particularly considered in relation to the following:

Plot Size and Dimensions. The area selected should be of a size sufficiently large to permit locating the terminal so that truck and rail docks do not face the normally prevailing wind. There should be enough area to provide for expansion in a logical pattern, as well as for working and storage—rail tracks, truck aprons, parking lots, office area, maintenance shop, and similar facilities. The proportions of the plot should permit erection of all structures according to a logical pattern of flow.

Transportation. Freight terminals should be located near the facilities which they serve. Mail facilities and the post office should be adjacent to the passenger station, to permit of easy head-end operations. Express terminals should be near the passenger station. Each of these units should be near passenger-car storage yards so as to be able to obtain a supply of cars. L.C.L. freight terminals should be located adjacent to freight classification yards. A freight terminal should always be located where sufficient rail sidings and storage tracks can be installed, and where the cars can be readily transferred to and from the main line. The location, of course, should be well within the switching limits of the rail line.

Express and L.C.L. terminals should be erected in areas which it is convenient for customers to reach. In all instances, terminals should be approachable by public transportation. Lunchrooms should be provided unless there are one or more good restaurants in the immediate neighborhood. Terminals should also be placed as near as possible to the **center of the delivery limits** served by them. If, however, much of the traffic flows to another facility, a terminal should be placed near that facility.

In many cases these requirements can be met only by selecting and purchasing a terminal plot near the main business district of a community and paying the necessarily high acquisition costs and yearly taxes. In such cases the increased cost of the land should be weighed against the possible economies obtainable at each site. Because of the many variables affecting site selection, it is impossible to set up a standard formula. The advantages and disadvantages of each prospective site should be weighed against those characterizing the other sites, and the site offering the greatest conveniences and economies should then be selected for the terminal.

COMMUNICATION SYSTEMS. An effective communications system is necessary for the efficient operation of a terminal. Operating instructions and information must be transmitted clearly and rapidly between the office and the platform areas. Instant communication permits better utilization and control of the work force and equipment. Time lost in waiting for handling equipment can be reduced, truck and conveyor utilization can be increased, and men and equipment can be reassigned more quickly to meet emergencies and changes in work load. Rail terminals are usually so large that effective coordination of operations is difficult without some form of two-way communication. Radio transmission of instructions to pickup and delivery equipment in the transportation system results in faster handling and prompter service to the customer.

There are many kinds of communication and intercommunication systems now available, including paging, public address, telephone, intercommunication, mobile radio, signal light, pneumatic tube, TelAutograph and Teletype systems. These and other means of communication as applied to materials handling are described in detail in the section on Communications.

Administration

ORGANIZATION. Effective management of a terminal requires an organization tailored for its particular needs. The accompanying chart, Fig. 1, shows a general organizational pattern for terminal operation. A terminal superintendent or agent is in charge of all activities. Reporting to him are an office manager, in charge of all office activities, and an assistant terminal superintendent or agent, in charge of all physical activities. Provisions are made for a third person to handle the personnel, safety, and security problems of the terminal.

Reporting to the assistant terminal superintendent or agent are three general foremen, each in charge of a shift, and a general foreman in charge of maintenance. An OS&D (over, short, and damaged) man is shown at the general foreman level to insure cooperation by operating personnel in reducing freight claims. A dispatcher will be required where a terminal has pickup and delivery truck operations. The **number of foremen** reporting to each general foreman will depend on the size and kind of operation. Enough good, first-line foremen should be provided to maintain strong supervisory control over operations.

TRAINING. A systematic training program for supervisors will:

1. Provide a better understanding of the organization, its policies, and operating procedures.
2. Delineate responsibilities and duties of supervisors.
3. Acquaint them with better operating methods for more economical and safer operation.
4. Give them a better understanding of good human relations and benefits to be derived therefrom.
5. Develop supervisors for promotion to important jobs in the organization.
6. Teach them proper methods of training new employees.

COST OF OPERATION. To control the cost of operation, a standard of productivity must be set and actual production must be compared with it. Work load, productivity, and time available to do the job will determine the number of men required.

Work Load. Work load can be determined by tabulating the volume of freight being handled.

Productivity. Productivity is the rate of doing work, expressed in pounds or pieces of freight handled per man-hour. To determine whether or not an operation is efficient, work standards must be set. Standards are units of measurement against which performance is compared, and they should be determined scientifically by time study. By recording the hourly performance of handlers over a period of time, management has a check of performance against scientifically set standards.

Preparation of Manning Table. After ascertaining the volume of traffic and setting work standards, the number of men for each position must be determined from the ratio of volume of work to the standards. A manning table is a chart of an operation showing the number of employees necessary to run the operation at target efficiency. It lists the number of men needed to perform each operation at a given volume. By using a manning table, a supervisor can determine when to start his operation and with how many men. Since the work load varies hourly, the manning table should indicate manpower requirements at varying work loads. It will show how to distribute men to various positions corresponding to changes in work load. An example of a sample manning table for an outbound operation in a rail terminal is developed below.

In the development of the manning table, assume the following **hypothetical conditions:**

1. Eight-hour operation with 1 hr. lunch.
2. Target for unloading is 150 pieces per man-hr.
3. Maximum capacity of unloading belt is 1,200 pieces per hr.
4. Hourly volume of arriving traffic:

1400–1500	250 pieces	1900–2000	1,225 pieces
1500–1600	475 pieces	2000–2100	1,075 pieces
1600–1700	725 pieces	2100–2200	825 pieces
1700–1800	925 pieces	2200–2300	450 pieces
1800–1900	1,050 pieces		
		Total volume	7,000 pieces

5. Unloading is done by drivers, not terminal men; therefore the table will not include any vehicle unloading.

6. Operation will include markers to check destinations and mark the outbound code on the packages; pickers to remove from the belt and load onto station trucks; spotters to position empty trucks at the loading edge; tractor drivers to move the station trucks to the car positions in the yard, and car-loaders.

7. Targets determined by means of a time study:
Tractor: Capacity, four trucks of 25 pieces each; speed, 200 ft. per min.; round trip, 1,000 ft.; time to make up train and drop empties, 2½ min. Therefore, time per trip equals 5 plus 2½ min., or a total of 7½ min. This means 8 trips per hr. At 100 pieces per trip, the driver moves 800 pieces per hr.

8. Spotter can position 30 trucks per hr. at the loading edge. At 25 pieces per truck, his target is 750 pieces per hr.

9. Other targets:

Marker .... 630 pieces per **hr.**
Picker .... 150 pieces per hr.
Car loader .... 150 pieces per hr.

10. Based on an unloading target of 150 pieces per man-hr., the number of vehicles which can be unloaded by hour will be:

2   3   5   6   7   8   7   6   3

to correspond to the above hourly arrivals.

11. The manning table is then set up as shown in Fig. 6.

To correspond with the hourly arrivals above expressed in vehicles unloaded, the crew tabulated in Fig. 6 by hrs., will be required, as shown in Fig. 7.

This table is only a sample. All targets are hypothetical and are not to be accepted as actual work standards. It is important that the assigned targets be correct and that they should be determined by study.

A study of the manning table will disclose that the **number of vehicles being unloaded** controls the table since it determines the hourly volume on which the size of the crew is based. Data taken over a period of several weeks will help to determine how many vehicles are being unloaded each hour. It will also give the average number of pieces unloaded per man-hour per vehicle.

MANNING TABLE

Outbound

Number of vehicles unloading simultaneously	8	7	6	5	4	3	2
Volume in pieces per hr. (at 150 pieces per man-hr.)	1,200	1,050	900	750	600	450	300
Position *Target*	*Number of Men Required*						
Marker 630	2	2	2	1	1	1	1
Picker 150	8	7	6	5	4	3	2
Spotter 750	2	2	1	1	1	1	1
Tractor driver.. 800	2	1	1	1	1	1	1
Car loader 150	8	7	6	5	4	3	2
Total crew	22	19	16	13	11	9	7
Pieces per man-hr. ...	54.5	55.2	56.2	57.7	54.5	50.0	42.9

Fig. 6. Manning table for unloading vehicles.

Number of vehicles unloading simultaneously	2	3	5	6	7	8	7	6	3
Markers	1	1	1	2	2	2	2	2	1
Pickers	2	3	5	6	7	8	7	6	3
Spotters	1	1	1	1	2	2	2	1	1
Tractor drivers	1	1	1	1	1	2	1	1	1
Car loaders	2	3	5	6	7	8	7	6	3
Total crew for each volume	7	9	13	16	19	22	19	16	9
Pieces per man-hr	42.9	50.0	57.7	56.2	55.2	54.5	55.2	56.2	50.0

Average productivity $\dfrac{477.9}{9} = 53.1$

Total crew .... 130 man-hr. of labor required.

Average crew for outbound operation .... $130 \div 8$, or approximately 16 men required.

(NOTE: When terminal employees do any of the unloading, they should be added to the manning table.)

Fig. 7. Crew required, by hours, for the unloading job in Fig. 6.

When all supervisors have mastered the mechanics of preparing manning tables for their respective departments and understand how to use them to the fullest advantage, the tables will aid management in setting up an over-all manning table that will cover all operations. The table thus constructed will aid in dovetailing operations. For example, in one terminal the outbound operation is usually completed by 2200 hr., at which time inbound unloading is started. The men on the outbound operation do not finish their shift until 2400 hr. For the last 2 hr. of their shift, they are transferred to inbound work. The over-all terminal manning table picks up these loose hours and weaves them into a solid pattern of manning that practically eliminates lost manpower.

Labor Pool. The use of a labor pool provides a controlled medium for shifting men from department to department as needed. It is a progressive method of adjusting manpower to the work load, aimed at the eventual elimination of over-manning, at which time there is no further need for the pool. By analyzing the pool records, a pattern for the utilization of the manpower can be worked out. The labor-pool supervisor can then set up a daily chart for assigning men to such departments as may need them.

The pool should be located close to the center of operations and should be connected by telephone or intercommunication system with other work areas. Supervision of the pool should be assigned to a **supervisor** on each shift. He should be required to keep a daily record of the men sent to the pool, which supervisor released them, the hour they came to the pool, and what disposition is made of the men. If they are assigned to such nonproductive work as coopering, housekeeping, and maintenance, their time should be charged to the labor pool. If they are released to productive work, the record should show to which supervisor they have been released, the operation involved, and the time of release. At the end of his tour of duty, the labor-pool supervisor sends his day's report to the terminal agent.

The **terminal agent** should keep a daily record of the labor pool, showing the number of men sent to the pool on all three shifts and the total number of man-hours spent in the pool. Periodically, the labor-pool records should be studied by the local management to determine whether the force should be cut down in size to meet changing conditions and, if so, how many man-hours can be saved. For example, if the labor pool shows a regular pattern of an average of 16 man-hr. spent in the pool daily, the indications are that possibly two jobs can be abolished. A study of the daily records may show that one job can be eliminated from the night shift and one from the morning shift. By the proper use of the labor pool, overmanning will eventually disappear and the supervisors will be able to maintain high levels of productivity at lower operating costs.

MAINTENANCE. Benefits to be derived from a sound maintenance program include better service to customers, decreased cost of operation, increased productivity, higher machine utilization, increased safety of operation, and better employee morale. Inspection and maintenance schedules should be established under which the equipment can be kept in good operating condition. Complete maintenance records are necessary for proper cost control and forecasting of future maintenance requirements.

Maintenance of Equipment. Money spent on preventive maintenance to keep equipment in good condition is soon repaid in reduced operating cost and increased economically useful life. Excessive equipment breakdowns caused by neglect of needed repairs may bring about unexpected delays in operation and result in overburdening of manpower and handling equipment. Planned maintenance should be supplemented by an economically sound policy for equipment replacement.

Maintenance of Facilities. A planned program for maintenance of facilities will help to keep maintenance costs down. Properly maintaining adequate lighting facilities and good floor conditions usually helps in increasing productivity, decreasing the accident rate, and generally improving employee morale.

SAFETY. Safety consciousness is necessary at all times to aid in preventing accidents. Safety training should be an integral part of all employee training programs. Proper instruction in correct operational methods will do much to cut down the accident rate, reduce insurance costs and the direct cost of accidents, and minimize damage to equipment and material.

Accidents fall into three broad classifications, namely:

1. Mechanical causes.
2. Physical condition of the men.
3. Mental attitude of the men.

Accidents listed under the classification of **mechanical** include those resulting from the careless operation of equipment, poor condition of machinery or accessory equipment, lack of machine guards, breakdown of vehicles, etc. Accidents attributable to the **physical condition of the men** include those caused by lack of ventilation, temperatures too hot or too cold, faulty lighting, fatiguing work, and excessive overtime operations. Accidents resulting from **mental attitude** are usually caused by the ignorance, carelessness, emotional instability, or disobedience of the men regarding instructions.

Management has a direct responsibility for practically eliminating—or at least drastically reducing—those causes within its power of the accidents falling into these three classifications. Maintenance of equipment, good ventilation, adequate lighting, and good housekeeping will practically eliminate the first two classifications—mechanical causes, and physical condition of the men. The third—mental attitude of the men—can be controlled by positive leadership and by enlisting the cooperation of the employees—singly and as a company. Close supervision is required to keep employees safety-conscious at all times.

The following **suggestions** will help promote safety:

1. Set a good example.
2. Emphasize the importance of safety when training new employees.
3. Make certain that equipment is in good condition; report any need for safety devices and guards.
4. Check and report at once any failure of lighting, equipment, sanitary facilities.
5. Correct at once any unsafe practices; teach the men correct methods of using equipment and handling freight.
6. Try to help the employee who seems worried; most accidents happen when a man is in an emotional state.
7. Keep aisles, doorways, and stairways clean and clear.
8. Report accidents promptly and fully.

To enlist and maintain the employee's interest and cooperation in safety, the training program should never be relaxed. The best method of training is to explain the "why" of safety rules and to demonstrate the correct manner of carrying them out.

HOUSEKEEPING. As in the matter of safety, good housekeeping is a result of intensive training and close supervision. If the terminal itself is clean and orderly, most potential hazards in handling freight can be eliminated. Unclean water fountains, toilets, and locker rooms lower morale and discourage the fullest employee cooperation in sanitation. If careless housekeeping habits are permitted to prevail, carelessness soon spreads to methods of operation and safety, with costly results.

Cargo Handling Operations

SPOTTING TRUCKS AND RAIL CARS. An important factor in rail terminal operations is the spotting of trucks and rail cars to facilitate handling and control operations.

Factors Governing Assignment. Organized procedures are set up to carry on the work of car and truck loading so as to expedite incoming and outgoing shipments.

Truck backup spots. Delivery truck spots should be assigned so that the heaviest assorts or routes will be hauled the shortest distance on the dock. **Truck routes** should be analyzed by volume handled and dock locations should be assigned for the heaviest routes closest to the operation or storage point. In an L.C.L. dock, the heaviest routes should be placed along the center of the truck-loading edge, with lighter routes or destinations on each side.

When trucks unload outbound or pickup freight onto **conveyors,** the number of vehicles being worked at one time should be restricted so that the average unloading rate is somewhat less than the capacity of the conveyor. If more traffic is unloaded than the conveyor can handle, drivers or unloaders are delayed and the conveyor often is jammed and must shut down. **Maximum conveyor capacity** is simply calculated by multiplying conveyor speed in feet per minute by the average number of units or containers placed across the conveyor width, and dividing this product by the length in feet of the average unit or container. Average conveyor capacity is reduced from this maximum figure by the ability of the sorting crew at its other end to remove traffic from the line and by the need to have sufficient open area on the line to allow unloaders to empty trucks, without double decking traffic on the conveyor and without delay.

In **L.C.L.** terminals where fork trucks or tow conveyors are used, the more heavily laden vehicles are placed in the middle of the dock. It is important in this operation also to avoid unloading too many vehicles at a time, since both fork truck and conveyor systems have ultimate capacities. Although this problem can be partially overcome by dumping traffic on the dock, floored freight increases the cost of dock operation since it requires an additional handling and increases the difficulties of checking.

Rail car spots. After the car-spot utilization chart is prepared, it is possible to set up specific rail car spots. The general principle of minimizing travel distance is applied in several ways in typical terminal operations. When **finger-type rail docks** are used in mail and express services, it is sometimes possible to incorporate a power conveyor into the platform. Rail cars are connected to it by gravity roller conveyors or portable power belts which extend from the pile in the car, through the car door, to the main conveyor line. These installations, when used for handling express traffic, are complicated by the need for removing bulk traffic which cannot be placed on the conveyor. For mail handling, the main conveyor is the power-driven belt, while express traffic is better suited to the slat conveyor.

Another practice sometimes used when cars are spotted for unloading on **house tracks** is to use portable conveyors to connect the cars directly to the sorting system. This practice should be discouraged except where extremely high volumes must be unloaded from such cars in a very short period.

At L.C.L. terminals using the fork truck and pallet system, cars should be **spotted in accordance with volume,** the most heavily laden cars being placed in the center of the dock. This principle also can be used in the case of mail and express cars which are worked on house or platform tracks. However, switches are ordinarily made by groups of cars, and the locations of individual cars may not be ideal.

Problems Encountered. Improper switching of cars is a major source of difficulty in terminal operation. If there is a delay in spotting cars, unloading, assorting, and loading are delayed through lack of traffic. The solution lies in cooperation with railroad-operating officials. When the car dock is narrow or has columns along the edge, cars must be spotted precisely. Car doors should be directly opposite house doors, with cars spotted so that doors are between columns. If permanent conveyor lines are used to transfer traffic into the house, car doors should be directly opposite the entrance ends of the conveyors. In some older terminals which have inside car docks, it may be necessary to open the doors of refrigerator cars prior to shifting these cars into the house if platforms are too high to allow the doors to slide over them.

CAR UNLOADING. Cargo in cars is unloaded in various ways according to the nature of the shipments.

Head End. Mail and express must often be removed from cars while the train is standing in the station. Ordinarily these cars are semiassorted, that is, traffic for the city is either in the doorway or in a designated location in the car. If there are track-level platforms, station trucks are used. If elevated platforms are used, regular warehouse-type, 4-wheel trucks are employed. In either case, one or more trucks are placed at the car door. When several separations are made at this point, one of the trucks is marked for each. Traffic is unloaded by hand, assorted, and piled on the proper truck. On a passing train, it is customary to unload through one door and load through another. When full, trucks are made up into trains and towed to the house assorting area, or to other tracks when direct transfer to another train must be made.

Team Track. Team-track car unloading is similar to head-end work, except that assorts are made into highway trailers or trucks. Sometimes these tracks are equipped with island platforms, in which case vehicles are spotted on one side of the platform and cars on the other. Gravity or portable power conveyor lines are often set up to carry traffic from a car being unloaded to the trucks.

House Platform. Cars at house platforms are unloaded onto conveyor lines, warehouse-type 4-wheel trucks, pallets, or tow conveyor carts. Basic assorts are made at this point. When conveyors are used, crews carry traffic from the pile in the car and place it on the conveyor line. When 4-wheel trucks are employed, they are lined up adjacent to the car door, traffic is placed on them, and they are either pulled into the house by warehouse tractor or pushed by hand. If pallets are used, a pallet for each assort is placed outside the car door, and the unloading crew walks freight from the car and sets it on the proper pallet. When loaded, pallets are transferred to delivery truck spots by fork truck. The tow conveyor process is similar. When a cart is filled, it is pushed to the conveyor and attached to it.

MAIL HANDLING. Mail of various classes is unloaded and sorted according to organized procedures.

Storage Mail. Unloading and sorting of storage mail (bulk mail other than first class) is done by two principal methods. The first method is to unload storage mail from cars, **sorting it by primary destination** at the car door. Sacks are placed on 4-wheel trucks, one for each primary sort. Loaded trucks are hauled to secondary sorting areas where sacks are taken from trucks and dragged by hand to a series of 4-wheel trucks spotted around the elevated sorting platform. One or more of these trucks is allocated to each destination (train, other railroad, or city). Train mail is seldom separated by car; sacks are usually peddled from car to car.

An improved method in use at some rail terminals involves **bulk unloading** of rail cars onto 4-wheel trucks or onto a conveyor system. Sacks are transferred to a primary separation area where they are separated and placed on conveyors, each of which leads to a secondary separation area or the city table. At secondary assorts, sacks are **sorted by individual cars** rather than by train. At the city table, sorts are made for the post office, for the PTS (Postal Transport Service), and for transfer to other terminals in the city for further forwarding. This transfer operation may be done either by the post office or by the railroad under separate arrangement with the post office. **Outside parcels** (those which are not sacked) are unloaded from rail cars in the same manner as sacked storage mail and should be handled with sacked mail.

Some companies are large originators of **catalogues and similar mail,** and often have branch post offices on their property. Mail processed through these post offices is delivered to the rail terminal by company trucks. After such mail is unloaded, it becomes regular storage mail and is handled as such. A conveyor is often used to carry these sacks to the primary assort. Large quantities from a single originator—notably **publications**—are sometimes shipped to a rail terminal by rail freight car. The magazines are then distributed to the addressees by the post office system. When a carload of such traffic is received by a rail terminal, a post office employee accepts it at the freight car door as it is unloaded. From this point on, this category enters the regular storage mail assorting system.

RPO Mail. First class mail is sorted en route in RPO (railway post office) cars. Upon arrival at a terminal, each pouch is passed to a post office employee, who reads the label, calls out the destination, and hands the pouch to a railroad employee who places it on one of a series of 4-wheel trucks spotted at the car door. Trucks are taken to the post office or to other trains for further movement. Although a truck ordinarily contains pouches for a single train, sometimes traffic for several trains is moved on one truck to the platform, where it is peddled to the cars involved. An improved method, employed in some rail terminals, involves sorting out post office or city mail and pouches for trains having an early departure. The balance is bulk-unloaded and placed on the rail terminal conveyor system for assorting and further movement in the same manner as for parcel post. **Preferential mail** is given expeditious handling and does not enter the assorting system. Mail which travels under guard is either handled or guarded by post office employees while it passes through the terminal.

EXPRESS HANDLING. Express shipments are also handled by several methods, according to the sizes and shapes of the packages or containers under transportation.

Regular Shipments. In some terminals, the router attached to the car-unloading team marks each piece for destination at the car door. **Primary assorts** are made to a series of 4-wheel trucks surrounding the car door. Traffic for outbound trains is peddled to the trains, transfer shipments for other terminals are moved to the transfer trailers for loading, and inbound express is brought to the city delivery floor for peddling to routes.

Other operations split up outbound traffic for trains departing immediately after unloading, other outbound and transfer shipments, and inbound express for city delivery. Truckloads of each of the latter two categories are hauled to an **assorting conveyor system,** on which traffic is routed, assorted, and directed to transfer trailers, outbound cars, or city delivery routes. In a few cases, all traffic from cars is unloaded directly onto a conveyor line. This line carries the express to a main sorting conveyor, where both primary and final assorts are made.

It is customary in express terminals for routers to mark the destination of each piece by means of a numerical code, one number per destination. This code covers all destinations which are served by a terminal, or, where traffic for a distant point must pass through an intermediate terminal transfer or assorting operation, all of such terminals are numbered. Routes are chalked on pieces.

Bulk Shipments. Shipments which are too large to handle on sorting conveyors, or are too heavy for hand handling, are considered bulk. They are unloaded by fork truck or microlever dollies from cars; moved to a bulk area by fork truck, 4-wheel truck, or 2-wheel hand truck; sorted; and transported to outgoing cars, trucks, or city delivery vehicles. This operation is ordinarily performed separately from the regular car unloading and sorting process.

L.C.L. FREIGHT. Freight generally is unloaded from rail cars by a crew consisting of one or two freight handlers and a checker. The checker calls out the "block number" of the car to which each shipment is to be sent, after reading the label and checking the bills. Each shipment is placed on a pallet, 2-wheel hand truck, 4-wheel hand truck, or tow conveyor cart and moved to the proper location for loading into another car or truck.

LOCAL CHECKING AND CENTRAL CHECKING. Two methods are employed in L.C.L. terminals to check shipments: local checking and central checking. In local checking, a checker is stationed at the door of each car being unloaded. As freight is brought past him, he checks it against the bill. At the same time, he marks the block number or car designation on the shipment or on the 4-wheel truck.

When the central checking system is installed, checkers are removed from the carside and placed in a central checking booth, which is connected by a two-way communication system with each car spot. As a shipment is removed from a car, one of the freight handlers signals the checker in the booth. When the checker is ready, he replies. The freight handler calls out the shipment identification and the number of pieces. The checker compares this information with the bill, and if the right number of pieces has been given, he calls out the block number, which the freight handler chalks on the shipment.

Outbound freight is checked by the receiving clerk against shipping orders. This procedure is carried out as each shipment is unloaded from the pickup vehicle. Since express moves as individual shipments, methods comparable to these used for L.C.L. freight are not required. However, labels are read for destination at every assorting operation. Mail also is assorted rather than checked.

HOLD-OVER TRAFFIC. Both L.C.L. and express terminals must contain facilities for storing hold-over traffic. This class of shipments includes C.O.D.'s and traffic undeliverable because of strikes, holidays, and consignees not open for other reasons. In L.C.L. terminals, such shipments are stored separately. A locator system is used, based on the "pro number" (the last three digits of the freight bill number) to identify each shipment.

In **express operations,** hold-overs are retained at the terminal. They are segregated in separate piles and identified by the name of the consignee. Normally, hold-overs are the responsibility of the receiving clerk. They are retained in the terminal for a period of approximately 5 days and then transferred to the on-hand department. Undeliverable traffic is offered for delivery a second time and, if refused or if delivery cannot be made, shipments are then transferred to the "on-hand" designation. Since the railroad's responsibility for mail is limited to moving it from post office to post office, no such problem exists in a rail terminal for this class of traffic.

On-Hands. Express and L.C.L. terminals usually handle the "on-hands" class of business in an area separated from the regular terminal operation. These shipments usually consist of **"will calls,"** export shipments waiting for documents, and bonded freight waiting for customs clearance and duty payment. In addition, L.C.L. terminals handle freight on Order Notify Bills of Lading, which are C.O.D.'s with both cost of freight and cost of merchandise collectible by the carrier. Handling of this class of traffic in L.C.L. terminals is similar to that used for hold-over shipments. "Will calls" in an express operation normally are kept at the terminal for 5 days and then transferred to "on-hand." Export shipments by express are tagged with a red baggage check which lists the name and voyage of the vessel, as well as the identification of the shipment.

When traffic arrives in an express "on-hand" operation, notification is sent to the consignee. This notification normally is by post card, although telephone calls, telegrams, or air mail are used for livestock, citrus fruits, and other perishable shipments. Shipments are identified by serial number or by the storage bin location number. As railroads do not retain mail, but deliver it directly to the post office, they have no mail "on-hand" problem.

LOADING PROCEDURES. There are several methods for loading carriers, according to the nature, size, and shape of the shipments.

L.C.L. Cars. Cars handling less-than-carload shipments are loaded by teams of two or more men. Ordinarily the cars are stacked solidly, with no separations being made. In cases where rapid transfer to another train at an intermediate point is to be made, however, traffic is often separated—the transfers having been placed in the car door and the balance of the freight in each end. Also, there are cases where transfer freight is placed in one end of the car and local delivery in the other end.

L.C.L. Trucks. Freight for delivery by railroad trucks is stacked in truck bodies in delivery sequence.

Express Cars. As many as eight separations are made in freight-type cars, although four separations per car are more common. Twelve or more splits can be made in messenger cars. Car loaders read the destination on each shipment and stack it in the car in accordance with a previously established **loading pattern.** Carloading crews consist of two or more men. In station or team track operations, truckloads of traffic are peddled from car to car on a train, with pieces in each car being removed by that car's loading crew. Occasionally, where the shipment load for a train is not too heavy and where more than one car is involved, a single loading crew, assisted by a truck puller, will be assigned to several cars on the train. Livestock and extreme perishables are moved in messenger cars. Semiperishables, such as fruits, vegetables, seedlings, etc., are moved in freight-type cars.

Express Trucks. It is normal practice for city delivery drivers to load their own trucks. They check shipments against bills as they are loaded, the trucks being loaded in delivery sequence. A second method sometimes employed is for dock labor to load delivery vehicles in advance of driver reporting times. This loading is done by setting up an **advance loading plan** (which dock labor can follow) for each delivery route. To assist in the loading, truck bodies are sometimes marked into sections by means of lines painted on the floor and sides. Each of these sections is then filled with shipments for a particular part of the route.

Mail Cars. Storage mail cars are ordinarily loaded in bulk, with no separations. This work is done by railroad personnel. RPO cars are loaded under the direction of a post office employee.

Mail Trucks. Although it is not always a railroad function, trucks for star routes, transfer, highway post offices, and air mail are sometimes loaded by rail personnel. Separations and loading methods are directed by post office employees in each case.

Car Loading for Safe Transit

FACTORS IN CAR LOADING. Industrial purchasers expect the articles they buy to be in good condition when they receive them. This requirement necessitates good materials handling on the part of both the producer and the railroad. Railroad cars constitute materials handling equipment and should be designed to transport shipments safely to destination. The cars themselves should then be handled carefully. But even when the carrier company fulfills these obligations satisfactorily, most kinds of freight will not reach the consignee in the best of shape unless the shipper loads his product onto or in the car in the proper manner. To help the shipper do a good job of loading, carriers have published many materials handling manuals which show car loading methods for innumerable types of commodities. In addition, most of the larger railroads have on their payrolls loading experts whose main duty is to help the shipper solve his loading and packaging problems.

The **railroad's first step** in assuring a shipment safe transport is to furnish **cars suitable**—as to type and mechanical condition—for the shipment. No specific freight car, even when brand new, is likely to be suitable for all the kinds of commodities which can be loaded in or on it. And, as the car ages, it deteriorates: truck springs begin to set, wheels may flatten somewhat, side walls or floors may be damaged, and many other defects may occur. If a properly packed shipment reaches its destination in a damaged condition, it is frequently because of some **defects in the car.** It is necessary, therefore, that both shippers and car loaders should know not only what kinds, capacities, and dimensions of car they need, but also what the **general condition of the cars** should be. The local railroad agent or yardmaster, or the conductor of the local freight train which switches the car into the plant, should have the same information so that he may meet the shipper's requirements to the best of his ability.

Especially during periods of car shortages, the shipper may seldom get cars precisely suited to his needs. In many cases, however, defects in cars may be overcome by a little **ingenuity on the part of the shipper.** Just how far he can reasonably be expected to go in preparing such cars to take his freight is an open question. When necessary, the shipper usually removes steel strapping, anchor plates, and nails from floors and sidewalls, covers rough floors or floor racks (in refrigerator cars) with paperboard, and makes other minor adjustments. Some shippers go far beyond this. But shippers should not be expected to be qualified car inspectors, able to spot such mechanical defects as a flat wheel on a car.

There are, however, some defects which the shipper can learn to spot fairly easily. For example, a shipper of expensive furniture should learn to **spot defects in the boxcar,** such as leaky roofs, doors that will let in snow or rain, holes in side- or end-wall lining, etc. Cars having serious defects should be turned back to the railroad as unfit for the loading of the material in question. The loader should bear in mind that he can refuse to accept any car, but he should use discretion in doing so and should have specific reasons for any rejections.

PREPARING CARS TO RECEIVE SHIPMENTS. Even when the loader has done what he can to compensate for defects in the car, further steps may be necessary before the actual loading can begin. The Association of American Railroads' Freight Loss and Damage Prevention Section publishes **pamphlets** showing what should be done to prepare closed cars to receive loads of various kinds of commodities. The pamphlets also give loading instructions. The Mechanical Division of the A.A.R. prepares regulations and loading requirements for open-top equipment—gondolas, flats, etc.

If the shipper needs help in his loading problems, he should contact the **agent of the carrier** serving his plant, who may assist the loader in surmounting his difficulties. If the load is to be placed in or on an open car, the agent will have a car inspector of his road recommend the method of loading and bracing. If the shipment is to be moved in a closed car, he may ask the carrier's loading experts to devise a loading method. It is perhaps not generally known that most of the larger railroads have such personnel on their staffs. The Loss and Damage Prevention Section of the A.A.R. also has a staff of **loading specialists** who may be called on for help, either directly, or preferably through one of the railroads.

Planning Loads. In planning any given load for a car, the shipper must remember that the freight will be subjected in transit to longitudinal (length-wise), vertical (up-and-down), and lateral (sidewise) forces or **shocks.** The severity of these shocks depends on many factors, such as the condition of wheels, springs, and draft gear, the condition of the road-bed (track), sharp starts or stops of the train or of switching engines, and other causes. These are all factors over which the railroads have some degree of control. Practically, however, the control is not complete for many reasons. The shipper, therefore, must think in terms of these shocks when loading his freight in the car, realizing that he must block or brace the load so that it will withstand at least all but the worst of such shocks. Customers may be lost because of damaged loads. In spite of the fact that the carriers do pay legitimate claims for damage, the shipper really pays his own claim. Certain kinds of shipments need protection against vertical oscillation, almost all freight needs some bracing against longitudinal (horizontal) shocks, and some shipments need protection against side sway. At least one example of protection against each type of shock will be presented in this discussion.

Detailed literature is available which will help the loader—whether experienced or inexperienced—to solve his difficulties and do a good job in loading his cars. To avoid confusion and save a lot of time, however, loading-platform men should be equipped with one or more copies of the "Dictionary of Standard Loading Terms for Use in Describing Loading and Bracing Methods for Shipments of Commodities in Closed Cars," published by the Association of American Railroads, Freight Loss and Damage Prevention Section. By means of this guide the shipper can make the most effective use of the various loading pamphlets available from the Association. On open-top equipment, the Mechanical Division of the A.A.R. has published a **series of pamphlets,** numbered MD-1 to MD-6, each of which deals with the loading of a specific commodity or group of commodities. (An exception is MD-5, which covers the field of "miscellaneous commodities.")

REDUCING FREIGHT DAMAGE CLAIMS. In the last few years, claims paid by the Class I railroads for loss and damage to freight have been close to or greater than $100 million per year. This huge amount represents neither all the loss and damage nor the extent to which the railroads were responsible for the damage. Many claims for concealed damage are paid because the railroad cannot prove that it did not damage the freight. A recent report published by the Fiber Box Association (Transportation and Packing Survey) and the railroads indicates that a very high percentage of claims filed are for damage for which the shipper is responsible.

Claims paid for damage to carload shipments of food products in cans or packages (not including frozen foods) in the first six months of a recent year amounted to more than $4.3 million. Of this amount a substantial portion of the payment was for damage to canned goods. Nevertheless, with shipper cooperation, the railroads are making progress in reducing damage to canned goods shipments.

For **damage-free shipping of canned goods,** the condition—and preparation —of the car are very important. If a boxcar is to be used, the car should be clean; it should have level floors, and end and side walls which are straight, even, and without holes. If floors are rough, they should be covered with a layer of used fiberboard to keep the cartons from snagging if there is any lengthwise movement of the load. Then the actual loading can be done.

PATTERNS FOR LOADING. For loading canned goods, the best loading pattern is that of the bonded block. Speaking before the Freight Claim Division of the A.A.R., E. A. Olson, general traffic manager of Libby, McNeill & Libby, one of the world's largest canners, said that the bonded-block method of loading had helped substantially to reduce damage to canned goods shipped by his company. According to E. J. Kraska, canned-goods specialist of the A.A.R., the "substantial" reduction mentioned by Olson amounted to 74 percent (Railway Age, June 16, 1952). Both the Freight Claim Division and the Freight Loss and Damage Prevention Section of the A.A.R. have, among many other pamphlets, literature available showing how canned commodities in fiberboard boxes should be loaded.

The **bonded-block type of load** apparently is much more successful than other methods for reducing damage losses because most damage to canned goods is caused by "sawtoothing" brought about by tipping of the load. Bonded-block loading prevents the tipping. It has been calculated that a four-box block, six boxes high, is roughly ten times more resistant to tipping than a straight stack six boxes high. This loading method, therefore, is favored by the carriers and by many shippers.

There are many varieties of the bonded-block load, each type designed mainly for boxes of certain dimensions. For example, the bonded-block load pattern for fiberboard boxes containing the No. 2 regular cans is considerably different from the one for the 8-oz. tall can. The pattern for the boxes of No. 2 regular cans is shown in Fig. 8.

The **loading diagram** shown in Fig. 8 is based on a refrigerator car whose inside length is either 32 ft. 8 in., or 33 ft. 2¾ in., while the inside width is about 99 in. (8 ft. 3 in.). The car is intended for the loading of 256, 258, or 261 boxes per layer. Loaders should know the difference between layers, rows, and stacks. If the dimensions of the car differ somewhat from those given above, the loader will have to be guided by the extent of the difference. For example, in a slightly wider car more slack will have to be allowed at the points indicated on the drawing. Above all, loads should be tight against the side walls of the car. Loads should also be tight—but not joined—lengthwise.

Loads of canned goods may be damaged if the end walls are not square to the side walls, i.e., if the end is bulged outward. Sometimes the shipper may get a car where one or both end walls are bowed, i.e., bulge outward or away from the inside of the car. In that case the loader should "true up" the defective end by means of a **gate or bulkhead.** A bulge of several inches gives the freight a chance to start moving lengthwise inside the car, thus causing another possibility for damage.

Loading cars according to the bonded-block method may seem to be much more expensive than loading all cartons with their long axes either crosswise or lengthwise of the car. Many shippers who have given both methods a fair trial, however, state that there is little or no difference between the two costs of loading, and that the savings in damage more than make up for any slight additional costs. The cost of handling (filing, etc.) a claim alone will in many cases exceed the extra expense of interlocking the cartons.

Many shippers of canned goods make use of so-called **stop-off cars,** i.e., cars in which parts of the load are for two or more consignees. The bonded block should still be the loading pattern, but the portions of the load for each consignee should

APPROXIMATE OUTSIDE DIMENSIONS OF BOX
13 7/8"L x 10 1/2"W. x 9 9/16" H.

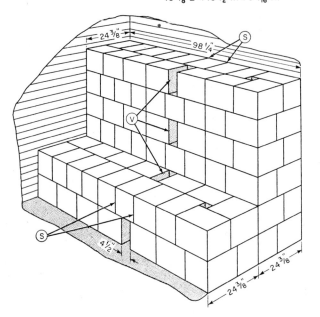

NO. OF LAYERS	HEIGHT OF BLOCK	TOTAL NO. OF BOXES IN BLOCK
6	57 3/8	96
5	47 7/8	80
4	38 1/4	64
3	28 3/4	48
2	19 1/8	32
1	9 5/8	16

PERSPECTIVE VIEW OF LOAD,
ILLUSTRATING FIRST BLOCK
AND PARTIAL SECOND BLOCK

1	2	3	4		5	6	7
8	9	10	11	12	13	14	15	16

PLAN VIEW OF FLOOR LAYER
OF FIRST AND SECOND BLOCKS
ILLUSTRATING BLOCK PATTERN
AND ALTERNATE BLOCK PATTERN
TOTAL OF 16 BOXES PER LAYER PER BLOCK

NO. OF BLOCKS	LENGTH-WISE SPACE OCCUPIED	NO. OF BLOCKS	LENGTH-WISE SPACE OCCUPIED
1	24 3/8	9	219 3/8
2	48 3/4	10	243 3/4
3	73 1/8	11	268 1/8
4	97 1/2	12	292 1/2
5	121 7/8	13	316 7/8
6	146 1/4	14	341 1/4
7	170 5/8	15	365 5/8
8	195	16	390

Fig. 8. Loading diagram for No. 2 regular, 24–18-oz. cans.

be separated and held firmly in place so that when any portion of the load has
been removed, the other part, or parts, will stay in place. One way of doing
this is to secure a gate or bulkhead against the load by means of steel straps, as
shown in Fig. 9. The other way, increasingly used by both shippers and railroad
men, is to employ the paper-tie method of holding such loads in place, as illustrated in Fig. 10. By wrapping the end sections of the load with a paper binder,
the containers in these sections remain intact during transit and act as floating

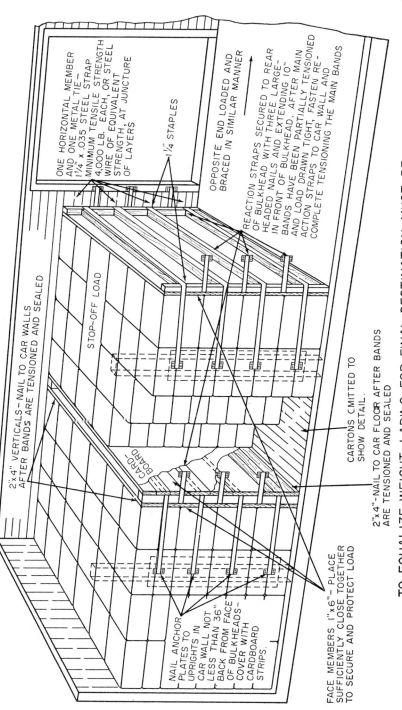

ONE HORIZONTAL MEMBER AND ONE METAL TIE— 1¼" x .035 STEEL STRAP MINIMUM TENSILE STRENGTH 4,000 LB. EACH, OR STEEL WIRE OF EQUIVALENT STRENGTH, AT JUNCTURE OF LAYERS

1¼" STAPLES

OPPOSITE END LOADED AND BRACED IN SIMILAR MANNER

REACTION STRAPS SECURED TO REAR OF BULKHEAD WITH THREE LARGE-HEADED NAILS AND EXTENDING 10" IN FRONT OF BULKHEAD. AFTER MAIN BANDS HAVE BEEN PARTIALLY TENSIONED AND LOAD DRAWN TIGHT, FASTEN RE-ACTION STRAPS TO CAR WALL AND COMPLETE TENSIONING THE MAIN BANDS

2"x4" VERTICALS—NAIL TO CAR WALLS AFTER BANDS ARE TENSIONED AND SEALED

STOP-OFF LOAD

CARD-BOARD

CARTONS OMITTED TO SHOW DETAIL.

2"x4"—NAIL TO CAR FLOOR AFTER BANDS ARE TENSIONED AND SEALED

NAIL ANCHOR PLATES TO UPRIGHTS IN CAR WALL NOT LESS THAN 36" BACK FROM FACE OF BULKHEADS— COVER WITH CARDBOARD STRIPS.

FACE MEMBERS 1"x6"—PLACE SUFFICIENTLY CLOSE TOGETHER TO SECURE AND PROTECT LOAD

TO EQUALIZE WEIGHT, LADING FOR FINAL DESTINATION MUST BE LOADED IN ENDS OF CAR, STOP-OFF FREIGHT IN CENTER OF CAR

Fig. 9. Gate or bulkhead secured against load by steel straps.

1. Start paper on car floor approximately 6 ft. from doorway; bring paper up ends of car to a point a few inches above the top of the load; roll up paper and tack to end wall.

2. Load containers by bonded-block method; stow containers in first two blocks to full height; stow containers in next two blocks to half height of load. Then roll paper tightly over the containers and bring the ends forward along the floor as illustrated.

3. Continue stowing the remainder of the load in bonded-block units, so as to hold the paper tightly in place.

4. The above cross-section of the completed load shows the position of the retaining paper. All containers are loaded tightly together in bonded-block units. The lading in the doorway area must be protected from contact with the doors or doorposts by flush-type doorway protection.

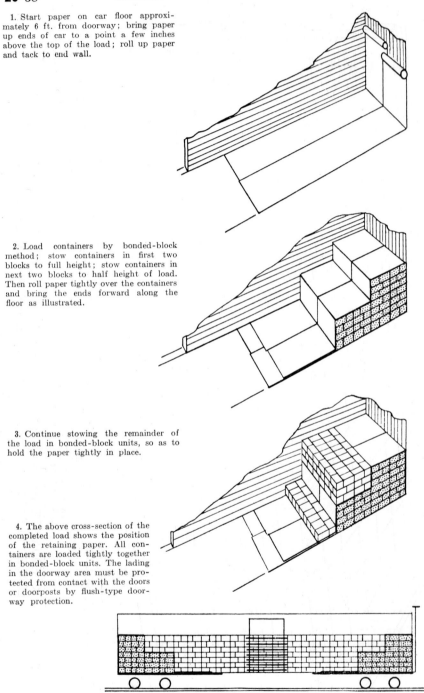

Fig. 10. Paper-tie method of holding unitized loads in place.

bulkheads to protect the goods against damage and disorder. The Retaining Paper Method of Unitized Loading has been successfully used in many loads. Duplex reinforced paper is used for this purpose, such as two sheets of 40 lb. Kraft tough pliable paper with approximately 40 lb. asphaltum lamination impregnated between the sheets to hold in position reinforcing fibres. Rolls of paper are usually available in various convenient widths to fit load requirements.

Canned goods shipped in mixed loads of different-sized outer containers frequently sustain heavy damage. Where the top and bottom edges of one size of box come against the side of another size of box, action similar to "sawtoothing" occurs while the car is in transit. In making a load for two or more sizes of containers, the bonded-block method can be used for each different size of box, but the divisions of the lading should be separated by sheets of corrugated fibreboard. Also, the different sections of the load should be made approximately of the same height.

If it is necessary to stow a **partial layer** at the very top of the load, as it frequently is, the bonded-block pattern should be followed as closely as possible, with the freight placed tightly against one end wall of the car. If the top portion of the load is to be composed of two sizes of boxes, each portion of that layer should be loaded against an end wall. The place to put these remaining boxes is over the main body of containers of the same size. Each section of the load in the top layer should be held in place, and the procedure is relatively simple. If a narrow wooden "gate" is used for this purpose, the height of the gate should be slightly more than the height of the containers being held in place. Cleats, steel strapping, or steel wire should be used to hold the gate in place. These procedures can be followed readily by consulting the A.A.R. Freight Loss and Damage Prevention Section's Pamphlet No. 13.

BLOCKING AND BRACING. Many firms go "all-out" to produce a fine product, and then do a poor job of loading the product in a railway car, the result being that the freight sometimes reaches the consignee in a badly damaged condition. Frequently the damage occurs because little or no blocking and/or bracing is applied to a load that really needs it.

The shipper may not realize what goes on inside a freight car when the car is either in a train traveling, say, at 60 m.p.h. or is being switched back and forth in a railroad yard. As previously stated, freight in transit is subject to shocks of varying intensities and in different directions—vertical, lateral, and longitudinal. "Sawtoothing" is caused by longitudinal shocks, although vertical shocks also help to bring it about.

Mention already has been made of loading freight solidly against the side walls of the car. If this were not done, considerable room would be left against one side wall. Cartons—especially those on the top of the load—would tend to move away from the rest of the load and keep bouncing against and off the wall. One or more cartons might even fall down between the load and the side wall and be badly crushed as the rest of the load was pushed against it. Where a fallen carton made contact with other boxes, it would crease the cartons and perhaps damage their contents.

Most of the damage chargeable to the railroads can be laid to **longitudinal shocks,** frequently caused by so-called rough handling. A series of shocks in one direction, produced by overspeed coupling in switching and/or by "slack" action when the car is in a train, would tend to jam the cartons against one of the end walls, producing a crushing action at the one end of the car. Springs in the draft gear, to which the coupler is attached, provide a certain amount of protective slack or cushioning action. Unfortunately, however, springs wear out, or the pull or push may be so violent that the draft gear cannot absorb all the shock. Much of the shock which cannot be absorbed by the draft gear is thus transmitted to the lading in the car. The shocks will not necessarily all be in one direction, but most shocks will, and, as a result, considerable space develops between the load and the end of the car opposite the one at which the jam occurs. Then, if a reverse shock is experienced, some cartons will fall from the top of the load down into the space between the end wall and the rest of the freight. Further shocks in that "reverse" direction will tend to crush the carton or cartons in that space, and also damage the cartons that crush it. This is the reason why the shipper is told to make a **tight load,** so that there is the minimum space between cartons.

Cartons in the **top layers of the load** tend to do the most moving. The nearer the carton is to the car floor, the less it moves under impact, because the weight from above tends to hold in place the boxes in the lower layers. It is this uneven movement of the layers of the load which creates the "sawtoothing" action mentioned above.

Vertical shocks (oscillations) cause perhaps the least damage to canned goods. This is not so with some other commodities packed in fiberboard containers. Vertical shock does most of its damage to more fragile commodities—those not so resistant to crushing as the "tin" can. Nevertheless, vertical shock does help damage those cartons of canned goods which are on the bottom of the stacks nearest an end wall against which the rest of the load shifts.

PROTECTION AT THE DOORWAY AREA. There is one other important cause of damage to canned goods. Many shippers forget what occurs at that very important place in the freight car, the doorway area. Frequently the carloading crew will do a fine job in loading the car, until they reach the doorway area. Either with some sort of gate or by means of the paper tie previously mentioned, the loader will make a unit of the load extending from each end of the car to the doorway. Then the doorway area will be filled without, however, protecting the freight in that area against the doors themselves. When the car gets to its destination, much of the material loaded at the doorways may be found to have shifted against the doors. Then, as the consignee opens the door, frequently with great difficulty, those packages in contact with the door are torn and perhaps otherwise damaged. It is therefore highly important that some protection be given that portion of the load at the doorway.

There are a number of ways in which doorway protection may be provided. Probably the most effective method applied to loads of canned goods is the one using steel strapping. The Loss and Damage Prevention Section's loading pamphlets, previously mentioned, explain this method. One specific reference source is Pamphlet No. 14. In this method, one strap is placed across the doorway opposite each layer of canned goods. The strapping should be nailed, or secured by means of **strap anchors,** to the door posts. Then fibreboard sheets should be placed between the metal bands and the freight, and sheets of fibreboard nailed to the doorposts so that the sheets will not fall down. The fibreboard must cover the anchor plates. If the plates are left uncovered, they are likely to snag some of the cartons and tear them.

Bracings. Good lumber, properly seasoned, should be used in all bracings. Green lumber has two disadvantages. Under some conditions it will give off moisture which may be damaging to some commodities. More important, it does not have the strength or stiffness of well-cured lumber. In addition, lumber used in blocking and bracing, if it is to do its job properly, must be free from knots and knot holes, checks and splits, and cross grain. Lumber should also be stored so that it is protected from the elements, or else dry rot may set in, making the lumber practically useless for bracings.

One of the greatest single faults railroad men find with the way in which some shippers block their freight is the manner in which bracing, cleats, etc., are nailed to car walls. In a standard 40-ft.-6-in. boxcar, car posts containing nailing strips are spaced about 3½ ft. apart, on each side of the car. In most of the boxcars now in use, the lining is only ¾ to ⅞ in. thick. Nails driven into the side wall at a point between upright car posts generally will not hold, or if they do hold, large chunks of the lining are pulled out under impact as the load pulls against the bracing.

To insure that the load does not brush aside the bracing by pulling the blocking away from the wall, the A.A.R. recommends that cleats be extended to the doorposts or to the closest upright car posts, and fastened there with at least three 16-penny nails. Whenever possible, all nails used should be of the cement-coated variety, because their resistance to being drawn out of walls or floors is about 40 percent greater than that of common nails.

STEEL STRAPPING. Steel strapping in many cases has replaced lumber as a bracing and blocking material. Despite its relative ease of application, shippers frequently fail to apply strapping properly. Sometimes strapping will be improperly threaded through the strap anchors. More frequently, the strap will be anchored to the car wall just a few inches behind the face of the load which is being held in place by the strapping and gate. In no case should strapping be anchored less than 3 ft. behind the face of the load; and the strap anchor plate should always be nailed to a car post.

Where gates are being held against the face of the load by strapping, **hold-down cleats** should be used with the gates. Hold-down cleats bear down on the uprights at the ends of the gates near the side wall, and thereby keep gates from rising under impact or as slack develops in steel strapping. In so doing, the hold-downs play an important part in preventing the load—or any part of it—from moving in an uncontrolled manner.

WOOD BRACING. There are many commodities other than canned goods which are transported in closed car equipment. It is not always possible or advisable to use steel strapping as the material to hold the load in place. For some commodities and some types of loads, wooden bracing and blocking material still is best. Furthermore, no one type of brace is the best for all loads. For example, in some cases crib bracing may be a necessity. The knee and K-braces also are useful in many instances. It is not feasible to discuss here all the types of such bracing and their application to loads of various commodities. Pamphlet No. 14 in the A.A.R.'s series contains **detailed drawings** which show clearly the size of lumber to be used in all these different kinds of bracing, as well as other pertinent details. Pamphlet No. 14 is perhaps the most valuable of all the A.A.R. pamphlets. Some railroad men believe that a shipper with an intelligent loading crew could load most commodities very satisfactorily with the aid only of this one pamphlet.

Railroad cars are sometimes derailed and badly smashed up. In many such cases the freight in the cars is rendered almost completely useless. Sometimes these derailments are caused by failures of shippers' loading crews to **distribute the weight** of the lading properly within the car. Occasionally, for example, a heavy casting may be loaded in one corner of a car while another of similar weight is not placed in the opposite corner at the same end of the car. Then, in transit, the poorly balanced car, rounding a curve at high speed, may tip over. Or, a load that has not been properly braced may shift to one side of a car. For example, loads of pulpboard rolls in which the rolls do not extend the whole width of the car may shift in transit and cause derailments. A number of accidents in the last few years have been attributed to this very cause and commodity. In such cases, if the load is 18 or more inches less in width than the inside width of the car, the load must be arranged so that its extreme sides are equidistant from the side walls, and must be braced so that it will stay in that position. Generally, the steel

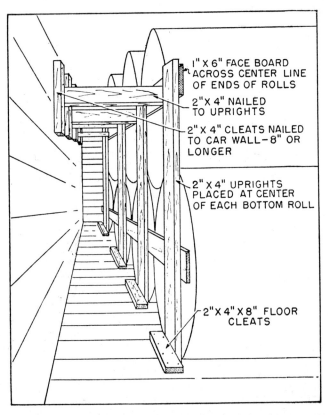

Fig. 11. **One method of bracing rolls at sides of car when excess crosswise space exceeds 18 in.**

strapping which is used to hold such a load in place against longitudinal shocks is not heavy enough to keep the load from **shifting sidewise.** Many shifted loads get through to destination in good or at least fair condition. But a single accident can be very expensive to shippers, their customers, and the carriers. Hence, financial expenditures sufficient to prevent such accidents would be a worth-while investment. Loading Pamphlet No. 38 of the Freight Loss and Damage Prevention Section contains all the details any shipper would need to be able to brace a load of pulpboard, in rolls, against sidewise movement. An example is shown in Fig. 11.

PERMISSIBLE MOVEMENT OF LADINGS. While the rigid load is perhaps the most commonly used method for securing freight in house-type cars, there are also methods for loading some commodities which permit some movement of ladings. These methods are variously known, and the name for one type of load has frequently—and incorrectly—been applied to one of the others. Thus, a snubbed load may be referred to as a floating load, and vice versa. A **snubbed load** permits a limited amount of longitudinal movement of the freight within the car, but, by some retarding device, the freight is held from moving more than a

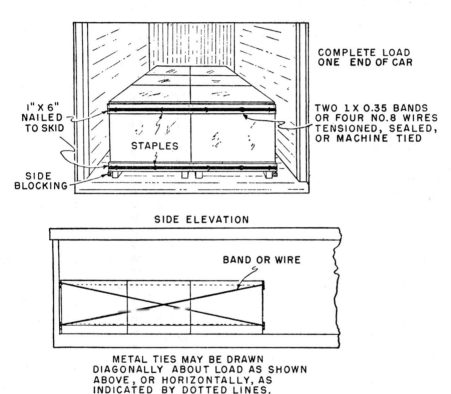

Fig. 12. Example of a floating load.

given distance. The **floating load** also permits the lading to move toward either end of the car, resistance to the movement being the friction between load and car floor. If loads are to be permitted some movement within the car, lading must of course be placed some distance from the ends of the car. There also is a load-type known as the **semi-floating load**, which permits lengthwise movement toward the center, or doorway area, of the car. The presumption is that the load is built up against one end of the car. Certain types of machinery and high-density freight whose shapes are regular are the types of commodities subject to these kinds of loading. Most commodities loaded so that they may move a bit are those which are rather vulnerable to sharp longitudinal shocks, or those extremely difficult and/or expensive to block and brace properly for rigidity.

Machinery of certain kinds is often subject to the snubbed load. A frequently used method of snubbing skidded machinery makes use of **lag screws** which stick through blocks alongside the skid, and extend on into the skid runners far enough to slow down—but not eliminate—longitudinal movement.

Paper on skids is a commodity frequently loaded in floating loads. In this case the commodity is extremely heavy and rather difficult to brace and block satisfactorily in a rigid manner. In spite of the best care in loading the paper on skids, the paper, when under impact, tends to leave the skid. Permitting both skid and paper to move in the direction of the impact eliminates the movement of one without the other. Fig. 12 shows an example of the floating load as it would appear in the car.

LOADS IN OPEN-TOP CARS. Considerable freight moves in non-house-type cars, on so-called open-top equipment, i.e., gondolas, hoppers, or flats. The rules governing the loading of freight in or on these cars are made by the Mechanical Division of the A.A.R. These rules are somewhat more strictly enforced by the carriers than are the rules for loading closed cars, for obvious reasons. Failure to observe the rules not only is likely to lead to damage to the lading, but also might cause a disastrous accident should freight fall from the car and onto tracks, perhaps in the path of an oncoming passenger train. Thus, safety plays an important part in determining the "prescriptions" in the open-top loading rules.

Preventing loss and damage to freight moving in or on open-top equipment is sometimes a matter of seeing that one has the proper car. An obvious example is that of loading coal in hopper cars. One would hardly wish to load a car whose slope sheets were so defective that sizeable quantities of coal could leak out. Floors of gondolas and flats should be examined to see whether they will bear the intended loads, especially if the loads are highly concentrated. Also, there are some commodities frequently loaded in, or on, open-top car equipment for which a relatively smooth floor is desirable, or—where a gondola is being used—requiring smooth side walls.

Railroad Line Clearances. Loading on or in open-top equipment is subject to another condition which must be observed, i.e., that of railroad line clearance.

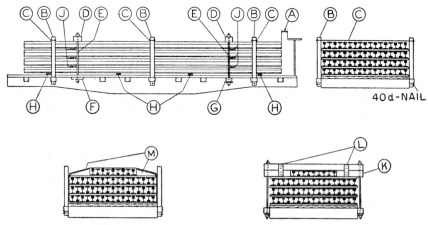

Fig. 13a. Stowing rails—flat or gondola cars.

Item (Fig.13a)	No. of Pcs.	Description
A	–	(Brake wheel clearance instructions.)
B	3 pr. per pile	Stakes, hardwood, extending not less than 3 in. above top of pile, and high enough to apply Items "C," when used.
C	1 ea. pr. Items "B"	4 strands, No. 11 ga. wire. Not required for loads less than 3 ft. high.
D	2 per pile	6 in. × 8 in., hardwood, length to suit. Use one bolt, ½ in. diam., crosswise, with washers, at each end to prevent splitting. Locate about 7 ft. from each end of load.
E	2 ea. Item "D"	1 in. diam. with washer, as close as possible to each side of load. Secure through Items "D," floor and Items "F," or to stake pockets through Items "G," also through Items "K," when used.
F	1 ea. Item "E"	4 in. × 4 in. × 18 in., hardwood, or ½ in. × 4 in. × 12 in. plate. Metal washer underneath this item should be as large as practicable.
G	1 ea. Item "E"	½ in. × 4 in. × 10 in. plate.
H	4	1 in. × 3 in., length equal to width of car. Locate end pieces about 3 ft. from each end of load and the others as far away from bands, if used, as practicable.
J	As required at 2 locations, as shown	1 in. × 3 in., length equal to width of load. Locate about 7 ft. from each end of load.
K	2	8 in. wide, length to suit, height equal to distance between top Item "J" and Item "D." Use one bolt, ½ in. diam., crosswise, with washers, at outer end to prevent splitting. Not required when top layer completely fills distance between Items "B" or when Items "M" are used.
L	2 ea. Item "K"	1 in. × 6 in. × 14 in. cleats. Secure each to Items "D" and "K" with eight 8d nails. Not required when top layer completely fills distance between Items "B" or when Items "M" are used.
M	2	6 in. wide, length to suit, tapered from height of rail to 1 in. at outer end. Wires must be secured to Items "M" with three 2-in. staples or nails with head bent over. Not required when top layer completely fills distance between Items "B" or when Items "K" and "L" are used.

Items "D," "E," "F," and "G" may be substituted with three 2 in. × .050 in. high tension bands, encircling load. Locate one band about 7 ft. from each end of load and the third one midway between the two.

Rails less than 12 ft. long on flatcars or above sides of gondola cars must have end and side protection consisting of boards 2 in. thick nailed to inside of stakes with side stakes spaced not more than 6 ft. apart. The height of such protection must be equal to height of load. When so protected, Items "C" to "M" inclusive, or their substitutes, may be omitted.

Material need not be secured when loaded below top of sides of gondola cars, with end gates raised and fastened, except as provided for in Rule 5.

See General Rules 4, 5, 9, 10, 12, 14, and 15 for further details.

Fig. 13b. Instructions for stowing an open-top load of rails as shown in Fig. 13a.

Not all roads can handle loads of the same dimensions. In the East, for example, the Erie Railroad can accept larger loads for movement between New York and Chicago than can any of the other roads, or any combination of roads serving the same two cities. When loading in, or on, open-top equipment it is always well to make sure before loading that the load will meet clearance specifications. The "Railway Line Clearances" publication is a valuable guide, but when there is doubt as to clearances for intended loads, it is advisable to check with the transportation line to be used. To a lesser extent, the problem of load weight—distribution particularly—is a factor, and the same source can be consulted in this case. The "Railway Line Clearances" contains information on the individual railroads in the United States, Canada, Mexico, and Cuba, and also handles the more commonly used interline routes between many points as units.

Longitudinal Shocks. Freight moving via open-top equipment is damaged mainly by longitudinal shocks. This fact, coupled with the necessity for keeping the freight from falling from the car, means that the main effort in blocking and bracing such freight must be to **anchor it tightly,** so that, even though it may be subjected to a series of longitudinal shocks, it will not move far. Thus, many kinds of loads such as rails, I-beams, etc., loaded on a flat-car must be secured with bolts, rods, plates, or other retainers (see Fig. 13), as well as by other bracing material. Where the use of heavy steel strapping or wire is permitted by the loading rules, the strapping or wiring must be stretched tight. Thus, with steel strapping, it is well to tension the bands once, let the load rest for a while, and then **retension the bands,** applying new seals when this has been done. This factor, incidentally, is more frequently forgotten by shippers of closed carloads than by those who ship on open-top equipment.

An actual description of any kind of load on open-top equipment seems superfluous here. In its place, a drawing and the accompanying instructions for stowing an open-top load of rails in flat or gondola cars are given in Fig. 13a and b.

The loading of freight cars, so as to prevent damage to the cars and their contents, is a serious—and in many respects complicated—undertaking. The following **recommendations,** therefore, may be of special aid to shippers.

1. Loading crews should be composed of intelligent and conscientious persons, not merely incidental employees from various plant departments.

2. In large plants, regular loading crews should be set up, with a foreman or superintendent fully as capable as any other foreman or superintendent in the plant.

3. Loading should not come under the supervision of the plant superintendent, who generally has his hands full with production matters and to whom the loading function is an unwelcome undertaking. If the company has a shipping, materials handling, or traffic department accustomed to dealing with the railroads, the loading function should be a part of this department's job.

4. Loading forces should be provided with the proper tools, including the A.A.R. loading pamphlets, with which to do the assigned work.

5. The loading experts of the railroad which handles the company's in and out shipments should be consulted on all problems connected with packaging, stowing cargo, etc. While these men may not always have broad experience, they can usually solve stowing problems to the mutual satisfaction of the shipping company and the railroad.

MARINE TERMINAL HANDLING

CONTENTS

MARINE TERMINAL HANDLING

ROLE OF THE MARINE TERMINAL. The ocean cargo terminal is important to the shipper of goods because it is the point of interchange for cargo being moved over a combination of land and sea transportation routes. Within the boundary of the terminal a consignment of cargo will be handled at least once and usually several times. The cargo must be weighed, measured, counted, and inspected and then may be stored for hours or days before being transferred to the hold of the vessel in which it will be transported to its overseas destination.

At the ocean terminal all handling of cargo is performed by employees of the steamship organization. The shipper does not have the same opportunity to protect his property as he has when loading a railroad car or an intercity truck. The terminal obviously must be operated efficiently in order to earn a profit for its owner. It must also be operated so that the interests of both the shipper and the owner of the goods under transportation will be safeguarded. The terminal must function simultaneously as a kind of warehouse and as a materials handling depot for the transfer of cargo.

COMPLEXITY OF MARINE TERMINAL OPERATION. To understand the techniques of cargo handling at a marine terminal, to envision the problems which must be solved, and to comprehend the nature of the mechanization practicable at the modern general-cargo marine terminal, it is important to examine the **methods of operation** and the **managerial processes** of the terminal organization. The cargo handled at the terminal is endlessly varied, consists of anything movable, originates in countless places, and cannot be packaged uniformly or stowed in neat, rectangular piles as in a warehouse or in a railroad car. Despite the great amount of materials handling equipment now used in modern marine terminals, a certain amount of manhandling of boxes, crates, and bags is unavoidable.

Complete **mechanization,** as found in an automobile assembly line, is impossible, since a certain uniformity and predictability are required for such mechanization. Furthermore, what is satisfactory packaging for one ocean trade is unsatisfactory for another. A container which may be of a size convenient for moving from the United States to a British port well-equipped with cranes or hoists may be beyond the handling capacity of the equipment at a small West African harbor. If a carrier should attempt to regulate too strictly the packaging procedures of the shippers who dispatch cargo on his vessels, he will quickly find that there are competing steamship lines which will accept cargo as offered by the shipper.

The problems of handling cargo at marine terminals are **managerial rather than mechanical.** Proper employment of men, acquisition of necessary kinds of equipment, adequate custody and care of cargo, the record-keeping essential to keep track of even the smallest item in a shipload of general cargo, and the ever-urgent requirement to have the ship ready to sail at the scheduled day and hour— all regulate the techniques of cargo handling. Materials handling equipment is used; in design and operation it is not peculiar to marine terminals, however, and the variety of machines employed is small. Improvements in handling have been gradually worked out over a long period of years, but marine occupational accidents are still the highest in the world. Newer and safer equipment has gradually been tried and adopted, but until the soundness and safety of new techniques can be proved, there will be a reluctance to introduce newer devices.

OWNERSHIP AND TENANCY. The details of ownership and tenancy of marine terminals are not of immediate concern to the shipper or receiver of goods except in so far as the shipper may be involved in claims filed against the carrier for damage to cargo. Occasionally terminals are under direct control of a **public port authority,** in which case permanent occupancy by either shipowner or stevedore is not permissible. At these installations, berthing space is provided for ships only as the need arises, and the stevedore is able to bring his equipment and laborers to the assigned terminal only when his services are required. This feature of impermanent occupation, resulting in the lack of a base for cargo operations, frequently results in slower, and occasionally in more hazardous, terminal operation.

Many terminals are owned by **private corporations,** such as railroads, terminal operators, or large industries which are the principal users of the port. Railroad-owned terminals customarily have rail tracks on the piers and wharves for maximum convenience in the transfer of railroad-borne cargo from shore to ship and vice versa. Very few railroads in the United States actually operate the marine terminals which they own, preferring instead to lease them to terminal operators, for example, to stevedore contractors. One of the modern terminals in Norfolk, Virginia, is leased to a major stevedore organization. This installation has wide aprons with two tracks on each side of the transit shed, and two tracks down the center of the shed. These tracks are spurs from the adjacent railroad assembly yards. Excellent lighting of the working area inside the transit shed, and the adjacent warehouses designed expressly to meet the needs of water-borne cargoes complete the establishment. Should a ship be scheduled to call at Norfolk, either on a regular or an occasional basis, these facilities are available through arrangement with the stevedore-tenant. Such lessees are intimately familiar with the physical layout of the terminal of which they make use, have equipment suited exactly to it, and employ a labor force which, from long experience in the terminal, can utilize the capabilities of the plant to the greatest advantage.

Certain major industries have found it to their benefit to build and operate marine terminals on scales sufficiently large to justify designation as "private" ports. A gigantic chemical processing plant in Texas City, Texas, has installed extensive water-front facilities to accommodate the vessels bringing in ingredients used in chemical processing, and to ship out the finished products. One corporation owns and operates in the New York area a coastal terminal equipped to handle the loaded railroad cars which make up the cargoes of its vessels. Little other shipping enters the port; hence there is no need for enlarged public wharves and sheds. Under conditions such as these the shipper and receiver of goods are sure of the best treatment of their cargoes, since the control of the port is vested in the industry most intimately concerned with its working.

Port Facilities

DESIGN AND LAYOUT OF TERMINALS. There are two basic kinds of marine terminals: finger piers and marginal wharves. The **finger pier,** as the name suggests, projects into the waterway at an angle to the shore line. Because it occupies the least amount of shore frontage and affords berthing to a maximum number of ships, it is the commonest kind of installation in American ports. The **marginal wharf**, on the other hand, is constructed parallel to the shore line and is found most often in ports where the waterway is too narrow to permit use of the finger pier. Regardless of the form, no marine terminal can be considered truly modern unless it can accommodate the newest kinds of ships and is constructed so that the most recent developments in materials handling equipment can be employed.

Cargo handling involves a specialized skill which must be acquired by the crews of every company engaged in marine transportation. As shipments are brought to terminals, the cargo must be sorted in conformity with the **ship's loading plan**, and all items which may endanger one another must be segregated and handled with special care. The methods of handling the consignments up to the time when they are placed aboard ship are similar to those employed in standard storage warehouses but are modified by the requirements of ships' stowage plans. Necessarily, marine terminal cargo handling has developed characteristics peculiar to the specialized skills and the nature of the stowage problems involved.

Today's high speeds in cargo handling have come about in response to the continuing effort of the shipowner to keep his costs below his revenues. Since he actually is paid only for moving the goods from one port to another and not for working his ship in port, whatever time is spent in handling cargo at terminals is not considered to be earning revenue. The need to reduce port time imposes a constantly increasing emphasis on **mechanization, palletization,** and **unit handling** of packages in large numbers, usually at the expense of more careful and precise methods of operation. The shipper must be prepared to offset, by sturdy packaging, these sometimes rough though not careless or thoughtless techniques, so that the shipment will not be returned to him for repacking or possible replacement because of damage.

TYPES OF SHIP BERTHS. In any port, ship berths will be of either the wharf or finger-pier type. The number of ship berths is limited along a wharf to the extent of water frontage available for development. At least one vessel may be berthed on each side of a pier; the number is limited only by the length of the structure. One of the longest piers in the world is Pier 6 at the Bush Terminal, in Brooklyn, New York, which has berths for three large cargo liners on each side of the pier. For an area limited in water frontage but unrestricted in width of waterway, the use of finger piers provides the greatest number of ship berths in relation to footage of land. This kind of structure has been adopted in most American ports and is the predominant form of terminal in the New York shipping area.

The essential **difference between pier and wharf** lies in managerial aspects rather than in structural fabrication. There is less confusion on a wharf, because only one ship can be worked at a berth, and all efforts are directed toward that one ship. There is no bottleneck at the entrance to the pier, since the entire side of the transit shed is available for use as an unloading or loading platform for cargo.

FACILITIES OF THE SHIP'S BERTH. The ship's berth should be at least **550 ft. long** and have adequate depth to accommodate the deepest-draft ships entering the port. The **slip**—the expanse of water lying between two piers —should be not less than 250 ft. wide unless it is proposed to berth two ships in the same slip, when a minimum of 350 ft. will be needed. The enclosed space inside the transit shed assigned to a ship should be 90,000 sq. ft., and the overhead clearance in the shed should be 20 or more ft. Doors must be sufficiently high to admit all the different kinds of cargo handling machinery used on the pier, and also to accommodate the large over-the-road trucks.

Herring (The Dock and Harbour Authority, vol. 35) states that the average dry-cargo ship will handle in a terminal port about 12,500 measurement tons of cargo. This quantity of cargo will occupy about 500,000 cu. ft. of space. If all cargo is palletized, it may be stacked 15 ft. high, thus fixing the minimum required floor space at 36,000 sq. ft. Allowing 25 percent of this figure for inevitable lost space brings the total requirement to 45,000 sq. ft. To provide truck berths, roadways, and working aisles, an additional 45,000 sq. ft. will be necessary.

Terminal Management. Terminal management—principally the technique of handling cargoes—has been affected greatly by the design of the sheds, piers, and wharves over which the cargo must pass. The old terminals generally had narrow transit sheds, small skylights, numerous stanchions supporting the roof, and an apron which was usually of no appreciable width. **Traffic congestion** became a major problem as the size of motor trucks increased. Adequate working space did not exist in which to pile cargoes and provide truck lanes and alleyways between the stacks. The increasing variety of ship's cargoes, the higher cost of owning ships, and the demand for faster turn-around of vessels have made shipowners, terminal managers, and shippers aware that the old piers and wharves are neither efficient nor economical to operate.

Recent terminal design reflects the significance of the motor truck in the inland transportation of goods in the United States. A growing percentage of export cargoes is delivered direct to terminals in trucks and to some degree has diminished the requirement for extensive rail facilities at the interchange between land and sea transport. The provision of adequate parking space for waiting trucks is now as much a part of design as is the installation of railroad tracks on the aprons or in the transit sheds. To assure quick dispatch for trucks it is considered necessary to handle an average of 15 trucks per hr. Since it requires 2 hr. to load a truck, not less than thirty berths must be available. These berths should be not less than 40 ft. long × 12 ft. wide, and adequate maneuvering space must be allowed for the trucks.

For the **design of specialized cargo terminals,** such as the banana handling facilities maintained in a number of coastal cities in the United States, the existence of direct connections to the major railroads serving the port is the single dominating factor. Trains of fruit must be moved as rapidly as the cars are filled and the greater the facility with which trains can be made up the more satisfactory will be the terminal. At the Weehawken Interchange Terminal in New Jersey, Herring (The Dock and Harbour Authority, vol. 35) states that 330 longshoremen can transfer 60,000 stems of bananas from a ship to railroad cars in a single 8-hr. day. Refrigerated meat terminals and citrus-fruit shipping points usually are adjacent to the freezing or cooling plants, so that there is no delay in handling which might warm the cargo and thus bring about compensation claims.

The **design of bulk-cargo terminals** has reached a point of interesting development in the shipment of bauxite and alumina. Stephenson (The Dock and Harbour Authority, vol. 36) describes the complete port construction made necessary for the prompt and completely mechanized transfer of alumina from the processing plant to the ocean-going carriers. The use of steel silos and conveyors has permitted the assembly of a ship's cargo in advance of the vessel's arrival, and loading requires only a matter of hours.

To accomplish the purpose of the marine terminal successfully, it is imperative that the transit shed **not become a storage warehouse.** Since cargo is transferred to bonded or free warehouses at the expense of the cargo, the proximity of the terminal to such warehouses reduces the cost of shifting the consignments. A noteworthy example of terminal design being integrated into warehousing facilities is Pier N, Norfolk, Virginia, which was built with two warehouses, each 100 ft. wide × 1,000 ft. long, connected to the transit shed by a covered passageway.

Mechanization has been facilitated by a reduction in the number of stanchions in transit sheds and by the **widening of the working area** available to a ship. Wide aprons, good illumination, and adequate ventilation of the transit sheds have combined to bring about more efficient handling of cargoes.

LAYOUT OF THE CARGO WORKING AREA. For easy access to the terminal the **marginal street** should be wide, with traffic moving in two directions. The street is maintained by the municipality, and control over it is not vested in the terminal. It is of interest to everyone concerned, however, that the street be maintained and the traffic on it regulated in such a manner that the shippers and consignees incur no inconvenience in coming to the terminal.

The **upland area,** or "farm," may be immediately adjacent to the transit shed. It consists of uncovered storage space where nonperishable cargo—lumber, brick, unboxed automobiles, and other similar items or products—may be deposited. For convenience and economy the closer the upland area is to the transit shed, the better it will serve the terminal operator. It should always be accessible to the materials handling equipment used in the transit shed. The **head house** is the control center of the terminal, and it shelters the terminal superintendent, traffic control office, security guard, receiving and delivery clerks, and customs representative. It should be considered as headquarters for all terminal activity and direction. It is the clearing house for the papers which must be processed as part of the routine of terminal management.

The **transit shed** is the shelter for cargo waiting either to be loaded on board a ship or to be delivered to a consignee. It is the area of greatest concentrated activity, for here cargo is accepted from the shipper, checked, recoopered, and otherwise made ready for loading. Cargo must move through this shed, and one of the constant goals of management is to prevent the transit shed from being used as a warehouse.

Transit sheds, which range in width from 75 to 600 ft., may be either **single or double decked.** Most modern terminals have single-decked sheds which are from 150 to 200 ft. wide. An advantage of the double-decked shed is that inward cargo can be discharged on the upper deck while outgoing cargo can be received and processed on the lower deck. The single-deck transit shed usually is covered with a roof containing many skylights, so that there is excellent visibility on the working floor. With the single deck there is less cargo handling than with double-deck sheds, and greater ease in planning how to use the available space. Modern design favors the **single-deck shed.** In Long Beach, California, the transit sheds are built with arched roofs and have a span of 200 ft. from wall to wall, without intermediate stanchions. New construction in Boston and New York has been predominantly of the single-deck type, with a minimum of stanchions. Materials handling equipment may be operated anywhere in the single-deck shed, and the benefits of mechanization are realized to the maximum.

Aprons are wide uncovered working platforms running the length of a transit shed; they make possible the delivery of goods by railroad car or truck directly to the side of the vessel. They also generally facilitate cargo handling, by reducing congestion and accelerating the movement of cargo to and from operations, since drafts of cargo may be deposited in a number of spots to await removal to the designated place of deposit. Piers built without aprons are less efficient, because each draft of cargo must be landed on a portable platform hung from the side of the transit shed by the stevedore after the ship is berthed. This temporary landing place, or sponson, is of sufficient size to accommodate a single draft of cargo, and until that draft is removed, no further activity can take place. The proper use of the tractor-trailer train is impossible under such circumstances, since trailers cannot be maneuvered under the ship's hook. **Aprons equipped with railroad tracks** make possible the shipside delivery of cargo without rehandling. There is no fixed pattern of design in such cases, some terminals having aprons with two sets of tracks, and others with only one set of tracks. Modern practice is to have the tracks set into the working surface so that vehicles of all sorts may be operated on the apron. Railroad-served aprons vary in width from 25 to 50 ft. Aprons for the exclusive use of **rubber-tired vehicles** may be as narrow as 15 ft.

Many transit sheds are equipped with **house falls,** which are cargo blocks shackled permanently to beams running above the door line of the shed. Through these blocks, cargo-runners may be rove and connected with winches either inside the shed or on shipboard. Drafts of cargo lifted by such rigging may be dropped much closer to the side of the shed than if ship's booms are used. Conversely, the wide apron may be spanned by means of the house fall if necessary.

LIGHTERAGE IN PORTS. Not all cities are so located that cargoes may be delivered by railroad cars directly to shipside. Nor are all ports so laid out that intraport transfers can be made economically by wheeled vehicles. Such limitations impose upon maritime centers the necessity for utilizing an extensive fleet of lighters. In London, for example, there are over 10,000 lighters, barges, and scows in daily service, linking the hundreds of berths, warehouses, and ships in the city. New York depends upon thousands of similar craft to transship cargo from the New Jersey railheads to piers and wharves in Manhattan, Brooklyn and Long Island City. Necessarily, the use of lighters involves extra handling of cargo and increases the expense of shipping through such ports. Competition with other ports often forces the railroads themselves to absorb the cost of lighterage, but the delay in transferring cargo, the threat of damage always inherent in any handling process, and the possibility of loss or pilferage are factors which must influence the selection of a port of this kind.

Lighterage operations are usually controlled by private firms engaged exclusively in such activities. Railroads providing free lighterage charter the required craft and then load and unload the lighters at their own expense. Frequently the railroads own and operate their own tugs and arrange to shift the lighters to suit the convenience of the cargo. Lighters are available to any person at a predetermined charge. They range in capacity from 50 to 500 tons and furnish an economical and flexible means of intraharbor transfer. Many shippers, in addition to the users of the railroads, find that lighters meet their needs perfectly. Nevertheless, despite the manifold advantages of such craft, their employment does entail additional handling, with consequent risk to the cargo.

Railroad Car Floats. A satisfactory but somewhat limited alternative to the transshipment process just described is to place the railroad car on a lighter (properly called a "car float") and to bring it alongside the ship. For cargoes such as bananas or coffee, which require segregation by characteristics of the lots being transferred, direct shifting of cargo from ship to railroad car is entirely practicable. The construction of the car float is such that packages must be transportable by one longshoreman from ship to car or vice versa. Occasionally it may be feasible to send a car float laden with gondola cars to a ship, to accept from it a considerable tonnage of bulk cargo, such as coal, ore, or ballast. This kind of handling, however, is rare; generally it is more satisfactory to route the vessel to a dump near the railhead where more rapid mechanized handling facilities are available.

ROADSTEAD PORT FACILITIES. The physical aspect of a port frequently is of greater importance to the shipper and importer of cargo than is the ownership of port facilities or the methods of intraport delivery. Cities like Norfolk and New York, located on landlocked bays, have been developed by human enterprise into ports with the most modern equipment. New Orleans and, in Europe, Bremen, situated well inland from the sea, are free from the hazards of wind and tide and thus are able to operate the year round. Other commercial communities, however, are not so fortunately positioned and depend almost completely for economic survival on the existence of marine transportation. Such ports must contend with many serious handicaps. Lacking harbors worthy of the name, they require the ships to lie in unprotected roadsteads, buffeted by winds, rolling and pitching. But cargo must be handled regardless of the movements of ship or lighter. Putting a piece of crated machinery weighing 7 tons or more on a restless little surfboat without endangering either package or boat requires skill, timing, and good luck. It is not always possible to avoid damage, and it is important for the shipper to inform himself in advance regarding conditions of handling which will be encountered at the port of discharge. The resources of the port and the sizes of surfboats or lighters should dictate the maximum size and weight of packages consigned to such destinations. Cargo losses in roadstead ports are noticeably high, because it is sometimes necessary to run surfboats or lighters through narrow openings in a reef or through the surf or to sand beaches where men, unaided by machines of any sort, must wade out a considerable distance to get their loads.

Terminal Organization and Procedures

SUPERVISION. The handling of marine cargoes, as a highly specialized activity, should be, and usually is, supervised by experts within the steamship company organization. The typical steamship terminal depends for its successful operation mainly upon two men: the terminal superintendent and the chief stevedore. As manager of the complex activities involved in loading and discharging ocean-going vessels, the **terminal superintendent** centers his attention on the proper and expeditious handling of cargo. Proper handling, from the carrier's viewpoint, means careful, methodical operations which result in keeping the cargo in the same condition in which it was received at the entrance to the terminal. Expeditious handling means the development of rapid, effort-saving technique for moving cargo from one point to another in the terminal and from ship to shore, or from shore to ship.

Terminal Superintendence. The terminal superintendent is responsible both for determining what work practices will give **maximum protection to cargo,** and for doing whatever may be required to insure that these practices are carried out. The actual supervision of the laborers who handle the cargo, and who are in a position to prevent damage or loss by their methods of working, is delegated to **foremen** who report directly to the superintendent. For the most part, terminal management is concerned with the care and handling of cargo prior to its being loaded aboard ship or after discharge and until the consignee accepts delivery. The range of this responsibility is emphasized when it is realized that in international commerce the ocean bill of lading is not an effective contract until the cargo is at the end of the ship's tackle, ready to go aboard ship, terminating when that cargo is released from the ship's gear at the discharging port. At all other times the **carrier is responsible for the cargo,** in the same manner as a warehouseman. Thus, as a matter of practice, the terminal manager is a highly specialized warehouseman whose techniques of handling and storing commodities are determined from beginning to end by the necessity of transferring the cargo into a ship, under the supervision of an expert in ship stowage, and who is answerable both to terminal manager and to shipmaster for the proper accomplishment of his duties in effecting the rapid and safe loading and unloading of cargo.

THE STEVEDORE. Few American shipowners handle their own shiploading operations. Instead, they engage a **stevedore contractor,** who provides all the equipment, labor, and supervision required to place the cargo aboard ship or to discharge it. The advantage of such an arrangement is that ships often carry unusual kinds and quantities of cargo, and additional men and machines may be needed to work the ship and keep her on schedule. Should the vessel carry less than normal cargo, equipment and men will be in part idle. The contracting stevedore, who usually has several contracts to service, shifts his equipment and man power around as required by the various ships he is servicing. By keeping equipment profitably employed, he is able to afford the proper kinds for the many assigned jobs and to make the equipment available to the shipowner at a reasonable cost.

The stevedore analyzes the **nature of the work** that he must perform, determines the equipment and man power needed, and estimates his cost on the basis of the number of tons of a given commodity he can handle per hour. The basic unit of computation is a **longshoreman gang,** which varies in size among the different ports. The productivity of the gang is a factor which depends upon the port, the commodity, and the equipment used. If the shipowner requests it, work is continued overtime. The stevedore earns no greater profit by reason of overtime activity, because he charges only the added difference in labor and related costs between straight time and overtime.

If a ship comes into a port with a load of 3,000 tons and has three days scheduled for unloading, the stevedore must set up his program to handle 1,000 tons per day. If the next ship comes in carrying 6,000 tons, the stevedore must expand his activity so that he will discharge 2,000 tons per day. Within limits, he can step up his labor force and its supporting equipment, and by working day and night rather than days only, he may be able to keep the unloading on schedule. Should a ship arrive with a 10,000-ton load, and the maximum number of men and machines practicable for unloading this kind of ship will handle only 2,500 tons of cargo in one day, it would be necessary for the operator to extend the vessel's stay by one additional day. The stevedore thus works in close association and consultation with the terminal superintendent, who is his contact with the management of the steamship company.

SHIP STOWAGE PLAN. The chief stevedore is the actual supervisor of shiploading operations. The stowage of cargo aboard ship follows a plan, always prepared by the chief stevedore but necessarily submitted to the vessel's master for approval before becoming effective. This plan is drawn up with due consideration for the safety of the ship and the characteristics of the different commodities to be loaded. The ship may be considered as a **mobile warehouse,** with her cargo to be handled under regular procedures. It is imperative to remember that a storage warehouse in a city is not subject to rolling and pitching, and that in such places commodities incompatible when in contact may be stored safely in the same area by the simple expedient of providing an air space or aisle between stacks. A ship, however, is in constant motion when at sea, and therefore, her holds must be filled so compactly that piles of cargo cannot topple to the deck, no matter how violent the motion of the ship. This, in itself, is a considerable achievement, requiring both great skill and long experience. Incompatible commodities must be stowed somewhere in the ship where they will not damage other cargoes. Hundreds of different lots of cargo must be kept separated for quick sorting and delivery at ports of discharge. The weight must be so distributed throughout the vessel that her **stability will be undisturbed** by the foreseeable hazards of the ocean voyage.

LOADING AND DISCHARGING PRINCIPLES. The placing of ten thousand tons of one kind of cargo in a ship is a relatively simple task compared with loading the same amount of cargo composed of a thousand different commodities in as many different kinds of containers. The five basic guiding principles given by Sauerbier (Marine Cargo Operations) are summarized as follows:

1. Stow in such a manner as to protect the ship.
2. Stow in such a manner as to protect the cargo.
3. Stow in such a manner as to obtain the maximum possible use of the available cubic space.
4. Stow in such a manner that rapid and systematic loading and discharging will be possible.
5. Always stow in such a manner as to provide safety for the longshoremen and crew.

Protection of the Ship. Protection of the ship is primarily a matter of **weight distribution throughout the hull.** The weight must not be concentrated too low in the hull, for such a **practice** condition makes a ship roll fast and to large angles. The weight must not be too high, because weight concentration at too high a point produces a very low range of stability; in other words, a ship loaded in such a way is unsafe in extreme weather or if she develops heavy leakage from any cause. A ship with the weight too low is called a **stiff ship;** where the weight is too high she is known as a **tender ship.**

Protection of the ship also involves **correct weight-distribution longitudinally along the hull,** so that excessive bending moments may not be produced. If the weight is concentrated in the ends, the ship tends to bend with the ends low, and this condition is called **hogging.** The opposite condition, with the weight amidships, causes the ship to bend with ends high and the middle of the ship low. This condition is called **sagging.**

Transverse distribution of weight offers no problem. If any concentration of weight occurs off-center transversely, the ship immediately notifies all hands by taking a discernible list. Besides being readily noted, off-center distribution is easily controlled by placing the cargo, piece by piece, on opposite sides of the keel and at equal distances from the center line.

Concentration of weights must be watched continually. Checking of concentration is simply a matter of making certain that the weight per unit of area does not exceed the limit of the ship. If it does, structural damage to the decks of the ship will result.

Cargo Protection. Protecting the cargo is primarily a problem of stowing only compatible cargoes together, using sufficient dunnage to protect the cargo from crushing damage, and securing the cargo in place by the use of toms, shores, and braces and/or suitable lashings.

Stowing cargo to obtain the maximum use of available cubic space is a problem in reducing **broken stowage.** Broken stowage is the space in a hold that is not occupied by cargo, such as that occupied by dunnage, or left unfilled. When not enough cargo is booked to fill the ship, broken stowage offers no problem. But care in planning stowage, and care in actually placing the cargo in position in the ship, should be exercised when the volume of the cargo booked exceeds the volume available for stowage. In this way the ship's revenue per voyage is increased.

Stowing cargo for rapid loading or discharging is simply a matter of keeping consignee blocks together so far as possible and avoiding stowage of cargo on top of other cargo that must be discharged first. This requirement can be met by means of proper planning.

Safety Precautions. The problem of providing **safety** for the longshoremen and crew with respect to the cargo involves planning to prevent the existence of high and unstable stacks of cargo near the working areas of either category of men. It also involves the removal of the debris produced by the loading or discharging operation. When discharging, for example, a large amount of dunnage and paper accumulates around the hold area. This tangle of wood and paper may cause accidents as the men attempt to work around it and, in some cases, in the midst of it.

Shiploading Operations. When loading commences, all hatches may be worked simultaneously, and cargo for a dozen different ports of call may be handled during a single hour. The **chief stevedore** places aboard the vessel a **ship foreman,** responsible to him for the proper performance of their tasks by all the laborers, who are divided into gangs under individual gang foremen. The **chief mate** watches the entire operation to see that the welfare of the ship, the accessibility of cargo, and the peculiarities of the individual commodities are given due consideration.

Ashore, under the supervision of an **assistant chief stevedore,** there will be numerous gangs of **pier men,** each under his own foreman. The function of these gangs is to collect the cargo from the places where it has been deposited and to bring it to the ship's side, there to make up the drafts which will be taken aboard. Approximately as many men are needed in the transit shed as on board ship. It is not unusual for the chief stevedore, as coordinator of all loading activities, to have between 300 and 350 laborers and perhaps 50 pieces of materials handling equipment at work during a single shift.

In appraising the **role of the chief stevedore,** it is appropriate to observe that the longshoremen who perform the arduous task of handling the cargo are, of necessity, highly skilled laborers whose background of experience is of the greatest value. Ships do not come and go absolutely on schedule, nor do they always carry the same amounts or kinds of cargo. Therefore it is not feasible for a single terminal organization to retain a continuing labor supply adequate to care for the peak demands of the ships. Hence, great dependence is placed on the existence of a labor pool which is flexible and can be drawn upon when and where needed. **Supervision** under such circumstances becomes of capital importance. Its importance is magnified by the highly developed trade unions to which practically all water-front labor around the world belongs. Union working agreements, with their complicated provisions for seniority, security, working hours, and limitations on what is to be demanded of laborers, must be understood by the supervisors, whose activities must fit within the framework of such agreements.

RESPONSIBILITY OF THE TERMINAL. The responsibility of the terminal for the care of the cargo begins when the cargo is received at the entrance to the transit shed. The supervisor of all activities relating to the acceptance of cargo and its location on the transit shed floor is the **receiving clerk**, a member of the permanent salaried staff of the terminal. Under him there is a force of inspectors, or **checkers**, who weigh, measure, count, and inspect for damage every individual package in any consignment accepted for shipment. The checker uses the shipper's dock receipt, which accompanies the consignment, as the basis for his inspection. The dock receipt is prepared by the shipper, and on it are found entered all the data significant to the checker: the name of the consignee, the identifying markings inscribed on the packages, the nature of the contents, the description of the container (bag, bale, box, or crate), the weight of each package, and the total number of containers in the consignment. From this receipt, the checker can verify the completeness of the shipment. He also measures every container, unless the entire lot is packaged uniformly, in which case a typical package is measured to determine the cubic size. Unless the container is very heavy, it will be weighed by the checker to make certain that the shipper has given the proper information. Where the package is so large and heavy that it cannot be placed on a scale conveniently, it is customary to rely on the weight given by the shipper as marked on the container. The checker's notations are placed on the reverse side of the dock receipt.

Under the watchful eyes of the checker the cargo is removed from the delivering conveyance—truck, railroad car, or lighter. In many terminals today, delivering vehicles do not enter the transit shed, and the entire checking operation takes place at the unloading platforms. Under such procedure the checker is responsible for directing the laborers who unload the vehicles as to where to stack the cargo to await loading. Proper marks and numbers for every lot of cargo help to reduce losses, since they facilitate identification of individual shipments and permit the taking of accurate inventories of the contents of the shed.

CHECKING OF CARGO. The necessity for proper checking of cargo cannot be overemphasized. Unless the carrier can show affirmatively that the package was received in damaged condition, it is assumed that there has been no exception to the statement that the cargo was "received in apparent good order and condition." Careful examination of the packages will show whether the statement applies uniformly, or whether there is damage which should be recorded at the time the carrier accepts the goods for shipment. The more complete and accurate the checker's description, the less occasion will there be for the carrier to be blamed for damage which he did not cause. Increasingly, carriers are insisting that their checkers make full entries as to the condition of cargo, since it has been found that a comment such as "damaged, leaking" is of no value in attempting to refute the charge that the carrier is responsible for damage.

Proper Checker's Notations. A few actual examples of proper notations on the condition of cargo will explain the technique now enforced by progressive terminal operators:

1 case hosiery, No. 224, marked wt.: 65 lb. Strap broken; actual wt.: 57 lb.

1 bale cotton ticking No. 56. Cover torn on end; three bolt ends soiled.

1 case cotton piece goods, No. 79. Poor second-hand case, nail racked.

1 crate filing cabinet. Insufficiently protected on back. Paper covering torn. Paint scratched in three places and dented near one corner. Due to paper covering, could not see other defects, if any.

Three bbl. medicinal extract, No. 1, No. 6, and No. 9 leaking. Recoopered and weighed. Wt.: 486, 477, and 430 lb. Marked wt.: 500, 498, and 491 lb. Bbl. No. 12 has lead patch on bung. Bbl. 3 has chime cracked. Bbl. 18 has stave slightly cracked. No evidence of leaking.

1,000 bags baby lima beans. 378 sunburned; 51 try holes resewn; 3 bags slack; wt.: 88, 80, and 72 lb.; marked wt.: 100 lbs. 31 patched sacks; weight correct.

1 planing machine on skids. Polished parts not greased, and slight rust thereon. Grease cups projecting and unprotected. Control lever bent.

RECOOPERING CARGO. Damaged cargo, particularly leaking containers, may be rejected for shipment. When the checker, notifying the receiving clerk of the condition of the cargo at the time it is brought to the terminal, reports some of the cargo in poor or bad condition, it is customary to communicate with the shipper and to attempt to have him substitute perfect containers for those which have been damaged. If the cargo has been delivered by a connecting carrier, such as railroad or barge line, from a remote point of origin, and it is impracticable to arrange a substitution, it is necessary for the carrier to protect his interests by rebuilding—or recoopering—the container as satisfactorily as possible. When this has been done, good practice is to affix a bright-colored sticker to the container, stating the container has been recoopered, and to make a notation to that effect on the dock receipt. If the container is broken, and there is reason to feel that the contents may not be intact or as listed on the dock receipt, most terminal managers will inventory the box. Before recoopering they will insert a copy of the inventory so that the quantity as received by the carrier will be made known to the consignee. The recoopered box then is marked conspicuously with the notation that the consignee must open the container only in the presence of a company representative if he intends to make a claim. Failure to observe these instructions may void the claim completely.

The labor for recoopering cargo is supplied by the terminal. Small jobs usually are handled at the expense of the terminal, regardless of who may have caused the damage. If the terminal is responsible for major damage, it must bear the costs of recoopering. If, on the other hand, the recoopering job is of considerable magnitude and clearly has not been caused by any fault on the carrier's part, the required work will be performed at the expense of the cargo, and a notation to that effect will be added to the bill of lading. It is virtually always to the carrier's interest to recooper all damaged containers before loading, in order to prevent the extension of liability and to facilitate stowage aboard ship.

PORT MARKS. To insure that the carrier will be able to discharge rapidly every piece of cargo headed for a given port, the custom has arisen of placing so-called "port marks" on every item accepted for shipment. These port marks follow a code established by the individual carriers, and each shape or color indicates a particular port of call. These marks may be applied to the upper left-hand corner of a box as it is faced by the checker. For example, a brilliant-blue square may signify Bombay; a red solid triangle may indicate Karachi; a white circle may mean that the cargo is to be discharged at Calcutta. The purpose of these port marks is to indicate to longshoremen who either are illiterate or do not read English, what cargo is to be handled in their port. Checkers must make sure that these vital port marks are applied as cargo is received.

Good terminal management demands that port markings be **conspicuous, distinctive,** and **permanent.** They should be made with paint or other substances which will not wash off, since the shipment may be exposed to rain, condensation, and salt spray before it reaches the consignee. Port markings must be applied to some portion of the package which will not be removed, either accidentally or otherwise. A final consideration of importance to the shipper is that the marking should not disfigure the package, because many manufacturers today rely in part on the package as an advertising medium, and consignees often resell the containers (if not scarred) to users in foreign ports.

MATE'S INSPECTION OF CARGO. When cargo is placed aboard ship, the chief mate usually will have made his own arrangements to inspect each container as it is received on deck. This procedure is necessary to determine what damage, if any, has been caused by the terminal in its handling of the cargo and what is the condition of the cargo when stowed in the ship. The **carrier's legal liability,** under the bill of lading and the laws regulating the carriage of goods by sea, is determined to some extent by the circumstances under which damage is caused. For instance, cargo which was crushed in the hold of a ship not reporting a storm or other fortuitous circumstance during the voyage, probably was damaged as a result of poor stowage, and hence the carrier may be liable. Cargo ruined by salt water leaking into a hold during a severe winter storm, on the other hand, presumably was damaged by forces beyond the vessel's control, and hence the carrier may be absolved from any responsibility.

CHECKING THE CARGO STOWAGE PLAN. The purpose of the shipboard inspection is not only to determine the condition of the cargo but also to verify the count of packages, to insure that port markings are on every package, and to make certain that cargo is stowed according to the loading plan. Since it often happens that not all the cargo can be delivered to the terminal in time to be put aboard ship, there may result a considerable difference between the proposed plan and the completed load. Many persons are concerned with knowing the exact distribution of cargo in the ship, and the preparation of an accurate diagram showing where each consignment has been placed is of great aid. It is the duty of the "plan clerk," who is an employee of the receiving clerk's office and is sometimes referred to as the "stowage clerk," to make up this plan. He compares the tentative shiploading plan prepared by the stevedore with the actual load and makes the appropriate changes. The final diagram reveals exactly where every consignment is placed and also shows the distribution of weight throughout the ship.

It is manifestly impossible to insert in the diagram the names of every consignee represented in the typical general-cargo load, and therefore the system of using **indicator numbers** in lieu of names on the diagram has been adopted. These indicator numbers refer to the detailed listing of consignments on the accompanying "stowage sheet," wherein the key number, the quantity and description of the shipment, and its weight are set forth. For the purposes of the terminal these data are sufficient for identifying the cargo and for keeping appropriate records of its disposition.

When the ship has been loaded, the **final plans,** complete in all details, are duplicated; and copies are furnished to the ship, the terminal manager, the stevedore, and the agents and stevedores at every port for which the ship is carrying cargo. Customarily, the **documents are sent by airmail,** to insure that they will precede the arrival of the vessel and permit the making of adequate plans for the proper and expeditious handling of the ship and her cargo. (A complete description of the process is given in this section under "Delivering Cargo.")

TRAFFIC CONTROL. An important detail of the work of the receiving clerk is the control of traffic in and around the terminal area. The modern trend is to provide **truck-handling platforms** at the entrance to or along the side of the transit shed and to unload and load all trucks and railroad cars at these designated points. One of the reasons for the development of this centralized loading area is the increasing size of intercity trucks, which require so much floor space inside the shed that they may interfere with the normal business of moving cargo from stack to shipside. Another reason is the greater security afforded by not allowing access to the cargo area to a number of possibly undesirable persons, which is an inevitable consequence of permitting trucks to drive into the shed. A third and perhaps more compelling reason is the **greater efficiency** which results when congestion is lessened inside the transit shed by allowing only terminal equipment there: cargo stacks may be much closer together; roadways do not have to be so wide, and it is not necessary to provide turn-around space for the trucks. Cargo is **supervised** more closely, because the working conditions on the truck platform are better than those at the cargo stacks. Checkers can be used for checking rather than as guides for trucks, and there is less time lost in giving men assignments.

The older terminals often do not have the facilities to permit handling trucks outside the transit sheds. Some operators claim that trucks working inside the sheds permit a reduction in the number of materials handling machines required to shift cargo from platform to place of rest and that the truck unloading time is less because there is no congestion at the various points in the shed where the trucks are busy. These proponents point out that bringing the truck to the stack involves no more handling than moving the cargo from the platform but that there is a reduced chance of breakage and loss if the cargo is taken out of the truck and placed directly onto the stack.

DELIVERING CARGO TO THE CONSIGNEE. Although the process of delivering cargo to the consignee theoretically should simply reverse the procedures of receiving it, there are significant differences which must be pointed out.

The arrival of the airmailed **shiploading plan** several days in advance of the vessel herself permits an orderly program of laying out the terminal to accommodate the different lots of cargo. Stacks of boxes, bags, and bales which have not been turned over to the consignees may be shifted to less congested working areas. Particular sections may be designated for a commodity requiring special handling, such as coffee. The number of longshoremen needed, the working hours available to the terminal if the ship is to sail on time, and the operations schedule may all be established well in advance—subject, of course, to alterations to fit unexpected changes in the ship's movements.

When the ship begins to discharge her cargo, her chief mate arranges to have each draft of cargo inspected for any **damage** which may have occurred during the voyage, for which the ship might be held to blame. The damage is described in the records, and where necessary the cargo is recoopered. In the case of commodities such as coffee, any bags which are stained, watermarked, or otherwise less than perfect are set aside, to be examined carefully at the first practical moment.

As the cargo comes out of the ship, it is **sorted and stacked** according to the prearranged plan, and an accurate record, by marks and numbers, is kept of the location of every consignment. The "location clerk" patrols the transit shed and notes where each lot is being placed so that he can compile his "location book," wherein will be shown the exact position on the shed floor of every shipment, no matter how small.

Notification of Consignees. The inbound freight section of the freight-traffic department is responsible for notifying every consignee listed in the ship's papers of the **approximate date** when the cargo will be ready for delivery. The consignee, who may obtain on request the assistance of members of the staff of the inbound cargo section, must make the necessary arrangements to clear his cargo through customs. If duty is payable, and there are other restrictions to be complied with, the consignee will not receive authority to pick up his property until all such requirements have been met. When the governmental authorities are satisfied, appropriate certificates releasing the cargo from customs custody will be issued. These certificates must be presented by the consignee to the carrier's freight cashier, who will compute and collect any charges which have been incurred by the shipment. Upon payment of these fees the carrier's **delivery order** will be issued, instructing the terminal department to permit the consignee to take possession of his goods.

Delivery of the Cargo. The delivery order may be presented to the **delivery clerk** by any authorized representative of the consignee. Like his counterpart, the receiving clerk, the delivery clerk is a permanent salaried member of the terminal staff, in charge of all deliveries of cargo to consignees. A particular responsibility of his is to verify that the person presenting the delivery order is in fact the authorized representative of the consignee.

When the delivery order has been verified, and the customs representative at the terminal approves the release of the goods, the delivery clerk assigns a **checker** to inspect the entire consignment as it is being loaded into the conveyance provided by the consignee. It is of the utmost importance that this final inspection be accurate and that all damage be noted, since the release of the cargo ends the carrier's responsibility as well as his ability to prove that the cargo is in a specified condition.

If the consignee resides in an inland city, and transshipment of cargo is required to complete delivery, it is mandatory that the checker point out to the representative of the connecting carrier any **damage** noted at the time the inland transportation agent assumes custody of the cargo. The careful adherence of checkers to this rule eliminates much discussion later as to who may be liable for certain damage.

When the inbound cargo is loaded, and the **consignee's agent** is ready to leave the terminal, he signs the "delivery book," thus making a matter of record of the name of the agent, the time and date when this agent took charge of the goods, and the goods which went away with him. This delivery book is a very simple document, recording only the delivery order number, the name of the consignee's inland carrier, the date and hour of departure from the terminal, and the name of the individual—truck driver, barge captain, or railroad-car-loader—who actually accepted the cargo.

In American ports, consignees are allowed 5 days of "free time," beginning the day after the vessel has completed discharge in that port. At the end of 5 days, the carrier is authorized to charge demurrage, usually an arbitrary assessment based on the weight of the consignment. This fee doubles after each succeeding

4 days, and is by design high enough to discourage the use of the terminal transit shed as a warehouse. The terminal manager must have an inventory made periodically to determine what cargo is subject to demurrage and also to seek cargo which has not been delivered to the consignees.

Over, Short, and Damaged Cargo Report. After a ship has completed discharge of cargo, all the notations of damaged cargo, shipments received with less than the stated quantity of goods, and cargo for which there are no papers (and hence may be presumed discharged in error) are assembled into the "over, short, and damaged" cargo report. This document is prepared under the direct supervision of the terminal manager, and it recapitulates all comments on cargo exceptions made on shipments to this particular port. Not only are the comments of the terminal shown, but the ship's reports and the notations from the loading port are also included so that exact determination of liability for any possible cargo damage may be made. Copies of this report are distributed to those officers of the operating department who are concerned and to the claims agents in the loading and discharging ports, the report becoming the basis for all future reference to damaged, overcarried, or short-delivered cargo and the basis for settling damage claims.

Delivery of Bulk Cargoes. Bulk cargo, such as iron ore, coal, or grain, is not subject to checking but may be sampled from time to time as the unloading progresses. **Lumber** must be checked to determine if the various grades are sorted correctly and to insure that damaged or broken pieces are segregated for such action as may be appropriate. Since most of these bulk cargoes move under charter, the liabilities for damage are covered by different laws and agreements.

Materials Handling in the Marine Terminal

MARINE CARGO HANDLING EQUIPMENT. The modern American marine cargo terminal, despite the great number of different commodities which it handles, has not introduced any noteworthy innovations in materials handling equipment manufactured by American industry. Very little use is made of the powered conveyor except for bulk cargoes in specialized loading or unloading operations. The terminal's principal reliance is on the **fork lift truck,** the **mobile crane,** the **tractor-trailer trains,** and the **straddle truck**—all of which are widely employed in other industries. The **gravity conveyor,** in 10- and 20-ft. lengths, is an important auxiliary in moving great numbers of uniformly sized packages over short distances, as, for instance, from a truck's tail gate to a cargo stack nearby. The most widely used piece of equipment, and the one perhaps used in the greatest numbers, is the **pallet.** While no standard size has been adopted by the marine industry, the one found in use most often is 6 ft. long × 4 ft. wide, and is usually constructed of 1-in.-thick lumber.

Other equipment employed in stevedoring is made to fit the particular needs of the jobs to be done. **Manila or wire-rope slings,** between 12 and 24 ft. in length and of such lifting strength as may be required, are used on every terminal. **Chain slings** are the customary device for handling steel beams. **Special slings of canvas,** reinforced by manila rope, are used in lifting bagged goods, particularly flour. Newsprint rolls, due to their great susceptibility to tears or cuts, are lifted with manila or woven (webbed) slings. The varieties of equipment are limited only by the imagination of the stevedore and the range and size of job which must be performed.

Handling of Various Commodities. No manual of equipment has been adopted by the stevedoring trades to show what is the "best" way to lift and position any given commodity. Necessarily, the decision as to which sling, net, or board to use must be determined by the experience of the stevedore, the characteristics of the item to be lifted, the amount of space available in the ship for stowage, and the personal preferences of the man actually supervising the work. To illustrate typical loading procedures, a few examples of commodities being moved through cargo terminals are described briefly below.

Coffee, because it is subject to chafing and squeezing when the unprotected wires of the sling are tightened, is being handled more and more by the canvas sling. This is about 3 ft. wide and about 10 to 12 ft. long. It consists of a piece of heavy canvas to which is sewn a manila sling 18- to 24-ft. long, one end of the canvas being much closer to the end of the sling than the other. When 12 to 20 sacks of coffee have been piled on top of the canvas, the long end of the sling is put through the short end, or eye, and dropped over the hook. When the lift is begun the canvas protects the bags from both chafing and squeezing and facilitates perfect outturn.

Cotton is practically immune to terminal damage and normally is loaded with manila slings, 2 to 4 bales being squeezed together in a single draft. The ordinary 24-ft. sling is used almost exclusively in cotton-loading ports.

Copper slabs, which are very heavy, are handled with a 12-ft. sling, and from 8 to 12 slabs are hoisted in a draft. **Tin ingots,** because of their great weight and small size, are dumped into heavy steel buckets which can accommodate about 3 tons of ingots and can be tilted to spill their contents. The hook of the lifting crane is inserted directly in the bail of the bucket.

Barrels and drums are lifted, usually 4 to 8 at a time, by means of hooks attached to the chimes. Chime hooks (also called "cant hooks" and "barrel hooks") may be rove on wire or chain slings, depending on the preference of the stevedore. **Packages** of every size and shape may be palletized and hoisted aboard ship. Shipowners have found the **pallet board** so adaptable that there is practically no limit to what may be transported on it. Canned goods, sides of frozen beef, boxes of refrigerated fruit, bales of rags, 10-gal. pails of paint, odd-shaped parcels of automobile body parts, sacked goods of all kinds, and kegs of nails are some of the commodities nearly always handled on pallet boards.

Large and heavy boxes, such as those enclosing machinery, usually are hoisted aboard ship by means of wire slings, which are generally equipped with spreaders to prevent crushing the top of the box. Slings are placed at the position closest to the ends of the container that the stevedore thinks will allow the best and safest lifting. Shippers' instructions, provided they are prominently displayed, are usually followed scrupulously in positioning the slings. Such instructions are very welcome to the stevedore, since they greatly reduce the possibility of both **damage to the item** being handled and injury to the **handlers.**

Discharging a **heavy container** from a tightly packed hold may require the use of "box hooks," steel pieces shaped like the letter "L," having a hoisting eye at the intersection of the two legs and interior faces studded with sharp points which bite into the wood. These box hooks are used to move the containers sufficiently to permit slings to be adjusted under the box or to shift its position to facilitate hoisting. The action of the hooks depends upon the compression exerted when the wire sling to which they are rove is tightened: the heavier the box, the greater the pressure on the container. A shipper who does not want to have such equipment used on his containers must mark his boxes very clearly to that effect.

COMMODITY SIZE LIMITATIONS. Commodities being loaded on a general cargo carrier must not exceed the linear limits of the hatchway, the weight limits of the gear used to hoist them on board, or the deck-load limits on which the commodities are to be stowed. For long, narrow lengths, the limit is the clearance between a hatch end and a far corner, or end, of the hold. On the average, the limit is about 50 ft., but some hatches can handle lengths nearly 70 ft. long. The openings into the holds average about 20 ft. by 40 ft., with a tendency recently toward wider hatches. The mariner-type ship has hatches approximately 30 ft. by 40 ft.

Weight limitations imposed by the capacity of the cargo gear depend upon the rigging of the ship. Normally the gear is capable of handling loads of 3 or 4 tons without any difficulty. If the load exceeds 3 tons with ⅝-in. diam. wire rope, or 4 tons with ¾-in. diam. wire rope, the gear must be modified in some way, as discussed under the section that follows—covering cargo handling gear. With slight modification the gear can be rigged to handle up to 8 tons safely. If the weight is beyond 8 tons, special equipment must be used. This special equipment includes the ship's own heavy-lift boom, or the services of a floating crane. Some ships are equipped to handle 60-ton weights. A few are capable of lifting 75 tons with their own equipment. Floating cranes, in some ports, can hoist 250 tons, but the limit is about 100 tons in most cases. If a floating crane is used to put a given load on a ship, it is important either that the load be placed on the ship so that the ship's gear can get it off or that another floating crane be available at the port of discharge.

Deck-load capacities average about 350 lb. per sq. ft. for the weather deck, about 450 lb. per sq. ft. for the upper 'tween decks, about 650 or 700 lb. per sq. ft. for the lower 'tween deck, and about 1,750 or 1,800 lb. per sq. ft. on the tank tops. If greater loads are placed on the upper decks, the decks may be made capable of supporting the loads by shoring up the load-carrying decks with large timbers down to the tank tops. Such shores should be about 12 in. square and cut to fit under the ship's beams. They should bear against a header on top and bottom and be made tight by the use of wedges. The shores should be spaced on 6-ft. centers, longitudinally and transversely. Such an arrangement will enable a weather deck on the average ship to carry about four times its normal load.

MECHANIZED MATERIALS HANDLING. Mechanization of cargo handling in the marine general-cargo terminal is limited by the endless variety of packages which pass across the transit shed. The principal machines used in the handling procedures are those described below.

Fork Lift Truck. Normally in the 2- to 3-ton-capacity class, the standard fork lift truck can pile cargo only about 9 ft. above the floor. Most of the trucks are gasoline powered, owing to the flexibility of this type of power plant. There usually are two trucks to a gang of longshoremen.

Mobile Crane. The stiff-boom crane, with a capacity of 3 tons, is found at every terminal, in numbers proportional to fork lift trucks, as dictated by the nature of the cargo handled. The stiff-boom crane is ideal in handling cargoes which normally fit into cargo nets, such as sacked goods, loose automobile tires, and baled material.

Shoreside cranes are standard equipment in many foreign ports. The older cranes are hydraulically powered, but those installed since 1920 are universally electrically powered. They usually have a capacity of 3 tons, adequate to handle anything not technically classed as a "heavy lift." Cranes are either full gantry in design, as in most European ports, and thus able to stand on two railroad tracks, completely independent of any structural walls; or they may be semi-gantry, with one leg resting on the side of the transit shed. The advantage of the **gantry crane** is that it may be some distance away from the transit shed and has a wide area in which to deposit its drafts. Its disadvantage lies in the amount of space which the two legs require on the apron. Even though the gantry may be one which will span a railroad car, the massive legs and supporting railroad trucks do absorb precious square footage. The **semigantry crane** requires that the transit-shed wall be of very sturdy construction to bear the heavy weight of crane and cargo. It requires less square footage on the apron and in many ways is more flexible than the gantry crane.

Shoreside cranes have not been generally adopted in the United States for several reasons:

1. The great expense of the installation and the limited capacity of the cranes.
2. The existence aboard practically all dry-cargo ships of cargo-gear, which has been found to be at least as fast as shoreside equipment.
3. Experience in handling the varied kinds of cargoes moving out of the United States, which indicates that cranes are not exceptionally well adapted to the needs of the stevedore.
4. The development since 1925 of materials handling equipment which permits rapid, extensive, and economical movement of cargoes around the terminal, thereby making less important the ability of the crane to place its drafts comparatively far away from the ship's side.

Stocker (Materials Handling) holds that efficient ship winches and booms, supported by adequate numbers of fork lift trucks, are more economical than shoreside cranes.

Floating Cranes. Lighters with heavy-duty booms or cranes mounted on them are referred to as floating cranes. They have a deck space in front of the hoisting machinery and can pick up a heavy item anywhere within reach in a harbor, bring it alongside a ship, and load it. The alternative method is to have the heavy load placed on a plain lighter and brought to the ship's side so that it can be loaded with the ship's equipment, or to bring it down to the pier apron by land transportation and lifted aboard by crane or hoist. The choice of what to do is simply a matter of economics. All kinds of methods are used. The factors that must be considered in making a decision are the cost per hour for the use of the floating crane, as opposed to the cost per hour for the plain lighter and the cost of rigging up the ship's heavy lift boom.

Tractor-Trailer Train. The tractor-trailer train, particularly useful in terminals equipped with wide aprons, which permit delivery of trailers directly to the side of the ship, offers great flexibility and economy to the operator who must haul each load of cargo over long distances.

Straddle Trucks. The nature of the straddle truck makes it invaluable for terminals that handle large quantities of lumber. It is not very common at other kinds of marine terminals.

Conveyors. Conveyors in many cases are used throughout marine terminals and on the ships. Their most extensive use is that of terminals where homogeneous cargoes are to be transported over fixed routes. For example, at the terminals and on the ships of the United Fruit Company and other similar transporters, full cargo loads of bananas are loaded, stowed, and delivered to their respective destinations. The ships load and discharge the bananas entirely by conveyors. Loading and discharging is done by means of an endless **canvas-pocket elevator** shaped like a flat-topped A. The cargo is discharged at the northern end of the voyage; the bananas—contained in polyethylene bags with small breather holes—are placed on shore by a curveyor. The **curveyor** is a type of conveyor in which the belt consists of pieces of a rigid material, like plastic, connected with a flexible attachment. The pieces measure about 4 to 6 in. along the path of the belt and about 18 in. across the path. They are curved pieces set with the concave side up and are capable of turning corners without breaking the belt. The stems of bananas are placed in the curveyor and roll from the ship's side down the dock face and eventually to the door of a waiting refrigerated railroad car. Eighty thousand stems, which is an entire shipload, can be discharged in 8 hr.

General cargo ships often travel over routes that are not fixed and may transport cargoes of a portable nature, such as packages, or loose, lightweight material. Short, endless **belt conveyors** are frequently used to assist in loading and discharging cargo from such vessels. The handling may be done through side ports or, where no side ports exist, may be carried on by raising cargo from a lower 'tween deck to an upper 'tween deck and thence off the ship.

Gravity roller conveyors are utilized in the hold of a ship to move single packages from the square of the hatch to the wings or in the opposite direction. These conveyors average about 2 ft. in width and 10 to 12 ft. in length and are able to handle loads of up to 100 lb. on each roller.

Handling Bulk Commodities

BULK COMMODITIES TRANSPORTATION. Transportation of bulk commodities is performed on such a large scale today that many terminal operators have developed special techniques for the efficient, expeditious, and economical loading and unloading of ships transporting these specific cargoes. It is impracticable here to attempt to describe the methods used for each and every type of commodity handled mechanically, but the procedures for such major items as coal, ore, grain, and sugar are described in order to indicate the lines along which such operations are carried on.

STOWING BULK COMMODITIES. No change in the layout of the ordinary dry-cargo hold is necessary for the transportation of bulk commodities such as grain and ore. In the case of bulk raw sugar, it has been found desirable to **sheath** the interior of the hold completely so that a smooth surface, without projections, exists.

Ships carrying bulk grain must be fitted with a longitudinal bulkhead along the center line to act as an **antishifting device.** The regulations for construction of these bulkheads are contained in a U. S. Coast Guard publication, Rules and Regulations for Bulk Grain Cargo, No. 266. Some ships have been equipped with so-called portable grain fittings. When grain is to be carried, these portable fittings may be broken out and erected with speed, and at a reduction in cost for **carpenter contracts.**

Without these shifting boards, as the centerline bulkhead is called, a hold partially or completely filled with grain is very dangerous to the safety of the ship. The **grain tends to flow like a very viscous liquid.** For example, wheat has an angle of repose of about 23°. Hence, if the ship rolls in a seaway to an angle even less than 23°, the grain will shift to one side. If the roll in the opposite direction is dampened by the off-center weight, then the next roll in the direction of the first shift will tend to shift more grain. Thus little by little the grain is flowing over to the low side of the ship. If there is enough space above the grain in the beginning, the ship may capsize. But even if the grain should pocket on one side, the ship is still in a dangerous condition, and with a heavy list caused by off-center weights. If heavy seas are running, the ship's hatches become more vulnerable to destruction, and eventual foundering becomes a possibility. There is also the problem of maintaining power in the propulsion plant when there is a bad list.

Prior to loading any bulk cargo in a typical dry-cargo hold, it is of great importance that the **drainage system** be prepared so that it will allow the drainoff of liquids but will not pass the bulk items into the system. This result is accomplished by covering the drain-well openings, or scupper drain-pipe openings, with two layers of burlap and then cementing down the edges of the burlap. As an added precaution, to protect the burlap covering, the opening should be covered with a box about 6 in. in height and sufficiently large to fit around the entire drain-well or drain-pipe opening. The bottom edge of this box should be notched to allow liquids to pass under without building up any pressure.

Ores have a large angle of repose—45° and greater; hence it is not considered necessary to erect center-line bulkheads to prevent shifting. However, it is a poor policy to carry the center portion of the ore much higher than that in the wings. In other words, the **ore should be trimmed down.** It need not be absolutely level, but it should be trimmed sufficiently to approach a safe curvature to the surface. If allowed to remain high in the center, when the ship takes a heavy roll, the already slanted surface of the ore may reach its angle of repose and a rapid movement of mass to one side may occur.

Bulk materials, such as bulk phosphates, bulk ores, or bulk limestones, are handled in huge quantities at ports and terminals where ships dock in approximately the same time and charge or discharge their loads directly into other ships. When cargoes are to be transported on ocean liners that are not specifically designed as bulk ore carriers, it is desirable to have long, elephant-trunk-type spouts at the ship end of conveyors to distribute the material evenly about the hold and prevent its coning up. Without such an attachment and in the absence of a mechanical trimmer of some kind, hand trimming should be employed.

Mechanization. The handling of bulk commodities, such as coal, ores, and grain, is usually completely mechanized in a modern, properly equipped port. This mechanization is practicable because a single commodity of known characteristics is to be handled in very large quantities, and there is urgent need for speed in loading or unloading ships.

Some ports handle only a **single commodity,** and the entire water-front activity of the city is dedicated to the efficient transfer of the cargo from shore to ship or vice versa. Such a port is Narvik, Norway, which exports great quantities of iron ore. A special ore-leading berth has been constructed at this port, and ships are able to take on thousands of tons of ore in a matter of only a few hours.

The great **ore-discharging terminals** of the Great Lakes ports of Conneaut and Lorain, Ohio, are built around wharves equipped with batteries of enormous Hulett unloaders, each capable of digging out a 20-ton bucketful of ore at the rate of 1,200 tons per hr. The Huletts empty their buckets into car-loading towers, and waiting gondola cars are filled as rapidly as they can be brought into position under the hopper. A very considerable area of land is needed in the vicinity of the ship berth since the inland distribution of the cargo depends upon the availability of railroad cars, often required by the hundreds.

Much bulk cargo is shipped or imported through cities which are not in themselves specialized ports. Through Philadelphia and Baltimore, for example, great quantities of iron ore are transported. Special sections of the water front are devoted exclusively to the facilities needed for handling this commodity. Millions of bushels of grain annually leave New Orleans and Houston, which are technically **general cargo ports.** Enormous, completely mechanized grain elevators have been installed in sections of these ports, and ships' cargoes are handled at high speed, whether they are loading full or partial cargoes of grain. Bulk ore and fertilizer cargoes are handled in a similar manner at the port of Bristol, England.

Certain industries which import or export large quantities of a particular commodity often find it economically feasible to build and operate their own waterfront facilities. In all such cases, the peculiar characteristics of the commodity in question will influence the design of the facility and usually determine the kinds of mechanical handling equipment to be installed.

Handling Coal. Coal shipments in and from the United States are handled by gigantic installations which elevate open railroad cars—one by one—to the level of the hopper and completely invert them, dumping the entire contents into the hopper. The empty car is then returned to the track and is replaced by another loaded car, which is put through the same operation. The coal moves from the hopper to the ship through a telescopic chute and is delivered into the ship's hold and spread out by means of a **trimmer.** The first layers of coal put into the ship must be laid down with care, in order to prevent breakage of the lumps: research has shown that fire hazard is reduced if lumps of coal are kept intact; new surfaces exposed to the air increase the possibility of spontaneous combustion. Coal dust also is much more combustible than solid coal.

The trimmer for leveling off the coal is lowered close to the deck, and the coal is delivered with a minimum of impact. Once a depth of 2 or 3 ft. has been laid down, the balance of the cargo can be poured in rapidly, since the cushioning effect of the first layers is adequate to protect the coal from breakage. Coal is trimmed across the ship rather than being piled, in order to prevent the accumulation of dust and to insure the cargo's being properly distributed for the stability of the ship. Trimming is accomplished by moving the chutes and the trimmer as directed by the loading supervisor.

Coal is **discharged** by grab buckets ranging from 5 to 20 tons in capacity. Normally the buckets are emptied into hoppers which in turn feed conveyor belts or other transportation equipment. In certain maritime trades coal is carried in self-unloading vessels, which depend upon an integrated system of conveyor belts and elevators to bring the coal from the bottom of the ship to the deck and transfer it to a conveyor operating on a boom which can be swung in an arc of 180° over the ship's side to the place where the coal is to be deposited.

Iron Ore. Iron ore is brought from the mine to the shiploading pier in railroad cars. The pier may be long, as in Duluth, Minnesota, where the maximum length is approximately 2,000 ft. On the other hand, it may be so short that it can accommodate only a single vessel. In either case the pier is built so that the railroad track runs along the top of the structure. At intervals there are openings through which the ore may be dropped from the railroad cars into the hoppers below the track. These **hoppers** have capacities up to 500 tons each and feed the ore to the waiting ship by means of open-topped telescopic steel chutes which permit the ore to slide down into the ship without hindrance.

Iron ore is not frangible and does not require any of the care needed in handling coal. Since the ore does not flow but rests where it falls, the chutes have to be moved from point to point so that the weight will be distributed properly throughout the cargo hold. On the Great Lakes, where ore-shipping has received the greatest attention, it is possible to deliver about 4,000 to 5,000 tons of ore to a ship in an hour. On very cold days the ore will freeze in the hoppers and clog in the chutes, necessitating the services of men with picks to break the jams.

At the port of discharge, the ore is dug out by grab buckets, either of the conventional type controlled by an operator in a traveling bridge, or of the **Hulett type,** installed at the major ports of the Great Lakes. The conventional grab buckets handle from 3 to 20 tons at a time and either dump their loads into hoppers for feeding to rubber conveyor belts or drop the ore into great stockpiles maintained close to the ship's berth. Hulett unloaders are gigantic electrically operated machines and are distinguished by the position of their operator, who rides just above the grab bucket. The capacity of the buckets is between 14 and 21 tons, and about one minute is required to complete a cycle. Normally, the buckets dump into a hopper which feeds waiting railroad cars.

Where iron ore is to be **transported by conveyor belt,** experience has shown that rubber belting, about 1 in. thick and from 36 to 42 in. in width, supported by rollers approximately 12 to 18 in. apart, is most satisfactory. The hopper has an automatic feeding device, which measures out the appropriate quantity of ore for the passing section of belt. It is possible to handle up to 1,000 tons per hr. with conventional grab buckets and conveyor belts and up to 1,200 tons per hr. per unloader when the Hulett machines are employed.

Grains. Grain, which includes oats, barley, wheat, and corn, is handled mechanically in practically all ports of the world. It moves in bulk. When a grain-filled railroad car is received at an elevator, it is placed on a **special car-unloader** which tilts the car to empty the contents. Approximately 5 min. are needed for this unloading process. The grain is poured through a funnel-shaped opening and is transported on a series of endless conveyor belts through a gallery to the storage towers, which are of either steel or concrete construction. As a ship is loaded, the grain moves by conveyor belt through a gallery running the length of the ship's berth, from which chutes slide the grain into the hold of the ship. Customarily, cylindrical telescoping pipes are installed from the gallery to the ship. The grain flows easily and is controlled by a loading master, who sees that the proper spaces aboard are completely filled. If trimming is required, it may be necessary to stop delivery while men are sent into the holds to move the grain into the proper spaces, but increasingly this is being done by centrifugal throwers which control the distribution. A mechanized operation such as this will load at least 30,000 bu. of grain per hr.

Discharging grain is a somewhat similar operation. It may be effected through a pneumatic sucker, which operates at the end of a long pipe; more often, though, a "marine leg" is used. This is a vertical elevator housing a bucket-equipped endless belt which digs into the grain and carries it to the overhead galleries, where it is conveyed on belts to the storage towers. This machine has to be supplied with additional grain as the piles of grain get low. Usually, men with shovels are assigned to the job of clearing the otherwise inaccessible portions of the ship in order to bring the grain within reach of the marine leg. The development of the versatile "payloader" type of mobile shovel has made practicable the mechanization of this part of the operation.

Sugar. Until recently, raw sugar was transported exclusively in large burlap bags, ranging in weight from 100 to 300 lb. per sack. These bags were difficult and expensive to handle and slow to empty but they required no special equipment in the process. Choker slings of manila rope were used to hoist drafts consisting of 7 to 12 sacks. New and up-to-date techniques have been perfected within the past 10 yr. which now make it feasible to load sugar directly from the refinery into vessels, using many of the principles applied in grain handling. In Hawaii, for example, raw sugar is brought to the loading point in trucks and dumped into bins, whence it moves by conveyor belts to a gantry loading machine seven stories high. The conveyor belt is secured to this gantry and delivers the bulk sugar to tubes leading directly into the ship's hold. At the end of the tube is the **trimmer**, which sprays the sugar wherever the operator directs, thus making a proper distribution of the cargo throughout the area.

At the discharging point in California a **device similar to the marine leg** is lowered into the bulk sugar, and the cargo is dug out mechanically. The sugar is drawn to the marine leg by scrapers, operated through a system of blocks and cables. From time to time the leg is shifted, as may be required, to dispose of new piles of sugar. When the sugar is picked up by the buckets of the leg, it is lifted to a point where contact is made with a conveyor belt, which carries the sugar into bins at the refinery. Along the Atlantic coast of the United States, shipment of bulk raw sugar has started within the recent past, and a less elaborate system of discharging has been put into use. **Large grab buckets,** very similar in size and operation to those employed in handling coal, are employed for digging out the sugar. Scraping is accomplished by means of mobile power scrapers rather than by drag-bucket equipment such as used on the Pacific coast.

The transportation of bulk sugar was long considered feasible only where the volume was very great and the extremes of weather encountered in passage were not excessive as in the Hawaii-California trade. The technological improvements in handling have been such, however, that it is now common practice to haul bulk sugar across the North Atlantic Ocean. One British shipowner has built a fleet of vessels for the specific purpose of transporting bulk sugar to England. Reports on this operation have been very satisfactory.

Marine Cableways. At many terminals throughout the world, equipment using a wire cable with some kind of trolley carrying a hook or a bucket or skip, out over the ship or over a hopper leading to the ship, is used for loading. In some instances this equipment has been used to discharge cargo.

An example of this kind of apparatus, known as a marine cableway or ropeway, is used on the south coast of Cyprus for loading ships at a berth a mile or so at sea. This particular ropeway has an ultimate capacity of 200 tons per hr. Details of cableway construction are discussed in the section on fixed cranes and towers.

The **Tigris Ropeway-Transporter** handles loads up to 53,000 lb. gross weight and has a length of 42 ft. The Cypress ropeway has a length of 1,650 ft. and spans a river which has a springtime channel of 1,250 ft. and an accelerated current of 12 knots.

An example of a **combination** of dock cranes and a ropeway 5,070 ft. long, used to handle tonnage up to 250 tons per hr., is the installation at Avonmouth, England. The capacity of the system, by weight, varies with the product handled. When handling zinc concentrates in this installation, the capacity is 250 tons per hr.; when handling phosphate, 190 tons per hr.; when handling coal, 98 tons per hr.; and when handling superphosphate, 95 tons per hr. There are 96 skips with a capacity of 3,400 lb. each, and they are spaced at about 37 yd. and at intervals of 24 sec. The supporting rope is of the locked-coil type and has a circumference of 6 in. on the incoming side and 5½ in. on the outgoing side, with breaking strengths of 126 and 103 tons, respectively. The haulage rope is Lang's lay and has a circumference of 2⅜ in. with a breaking strength of 20.4 tons. It is driven by a 50-hp. motor. The general layout of the ropeway is shown in Fig. 1.

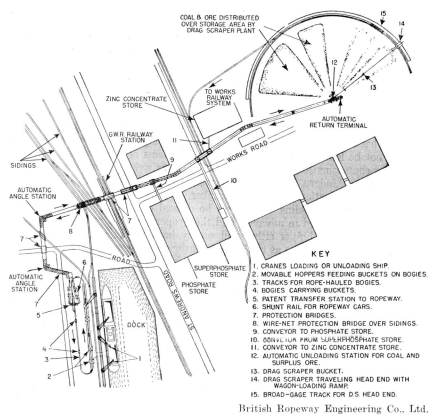

KEY

1. CRANES LOADING OR UNLOADING SHIP.
2. MOVABLE HOPPERS FEEDING BUCKETS ON BOGIES.
3. TRACKS FOR ROPE-HAULED BOGIES.
4. BOGIES CARRYING BUCKETS.
5. PATENT TRANSFER STATION TO ROPEWAY.
6. SHUNT RAIL FOR ROPEWAY CARS.
7. PROTECTION BRIDGES.
8. WIRE-NET PROTECTION BRIDGE OVER SIDINGS.
9. CONVEYOR TO PHOSPHATE STORE.
10. CONVEYOR FROM SUPERPHOSPHATE STORE.
11. CONVEYOR TO ZINC CONCENTRATE STORE.
12. AUTOMATIC UNLOADING STATION FOR COAL AND SURPLUS ORE.
13. DRAG SCRAPER BUCKET.
14. DRAG SCRAPER TRAVELING HEAD END WITH WAGON-LOADING RAMP.
15. BROAD-GAGE TRACK FOR D.S. HEAD END.

British Ropeway Engineering Co., Ltd.

Fig. 1. Layout of a combination dock-crane and ropeway installation.

Kinds of Cargo Requiring Special Handling

WET CARGO FOR BOTTOM STOWAGE. Liquids in barrels and drums usually are loaded at the bottom of the ship. Leaking barrels should not be accepted by the terminal and customarily are refused by the ship. **Extra dunnage** for proper stowage is normally required. Depending upon the weight of the liquid, the number of tiers of barrels will be fixed by the stevedore and the master after consideration of the season of the year and the characteristics of the ship. In loading such containers it is necessary that ample provision be made to prevent shifting of the barrels or drums.

Long Steel, Timbers, or Other Pieces for Bottom or Wing Stowage. The schedule for arrival of this kind of long cargo must provide for direct handling from the delivering conveyance to the ship. In a port such as New York long steel is delivered by lighter directly to the ship's side and loaded from the floating platform. In Baltimore, railroad cars are brought on aprons to the ship's side, and the long pieces are lifted from these cars. The stevedore must be notified in time to provide adequate shoring and strapping material for use in securing the cargoes. Recent practice in the movement of long steel beams has been to employ steel strapping, secured to eyes in the ship and crimped by machine when adequate pressure has been exerted to guarantee stable loading. Plans for loading such cargoes as these must be coordinated with the marine department to insure that the ship nominated for the lift will be able to accommodate the pieces in question. Structural changes, individual peculiarities, and, occasionally, prior cargo commitments often affect the availability of the **requisite space** for such items.

Odoriferous or Obnoxious Commodities for Special Stowage. If the packages of odoriferous or otherwise obnoxious commodities are dry, they must be placed so that they will not spoil other commodities and must be located so that they will not be loaded inadvertently with other items of cargo which could be affected by contamination. If such commodities are wet, as for example, green hides, Leeming (Modern Ship Stowage) recommends that the greatest care be exercised in the selection of dunnage lumber. No oaken boards may be used with green hides. A pickling solution to be doused over the hides as they are loaded must be prepared in advance, and the proper grade of salt must be provided. Normally, the shipper either will supply both the brine and the salt or will give explicit instructions as to the specifications for these indispensable items. Loose wet hides are stowed perfectly flat, and each layer is salted uniformly before being doused with the pickling solution. Piles of hides must be level throughout the hold so that the liquid will not be drained off. The closest supervision by the stevedore and the ship's officers is required to insure proper stowage. Discharge is just as difficult an operation, since precautions must be taken to prevent damage from slings, longshoremen's hooks, and projecting beams in the hold.

Heavy Lifts. Advance information on all heavy lifts which have been booked for the ship must be supplied to the terminal at the earliest feasible date. **Floating cranes** are the most satisfactory equipment for handling these lifts, but to insure their availability, use of them must be scheduled well in advance. High-capacity shore cranes are less flexible than floating cranes and often cannot be used without a considerable waiting period. Rollers, snatch blocks, and special shoring timbers, as needed, must be provided in advance. If a **heavy lift contractor** is employed, it is customary for him to supply a complete crew of workmen to handle the entire operation of slinging, hoisting, lowering, and unslinging the package. The ship remains responsible for proper stowage, however, and the heavy lift contractor takes orders from the mate and the stevedore as to the exact location in which to place the cargo.

If the **heavy lift gear** of the ship is to be used, the master must be notified of this intention at the earliest practicable hour so that arrangements may be made to rig the gear. This is a time-consuming operation, usually requiring the services of the cargo winches at two hatches; hence it has been found economically undesirable except in ports where there are no shore facilities available. Should the heavy lift cargo consist of **unboxed railroad rolling stock**, it may be necessary to make special provisions in the ship's holds by installing lengths of track on which the wheels will sit. This step will require the services of welders, and owing to the fire hazard implicit in welding, adequate safeguards for ship and cargo must be provided. Obviously such a movement requires the most **meticulous and complete planning** on the part of the marine department, the stevedore, the heavy lift contractor, and the traffic department.

Hazardous Cargoes for "On Deck" Stowage. Acids, explosives, and other "special stowage" commodities must be handled according to certain regulations promulgated by governmental and private bodies. The dangerous nature of the commodity requires that the ability of the ship to transport the item in question be ascertained, that the regulations be known and be fully up to date, and that all the inspecting and surveying agencies concerned be notified early enough so that they can make the required inspections. It may be necessary to shift the vessel to a special area of the port in order to handle the cargo. This step involves coordination between the terminal, the stevedore, and the marine department on the one side and the special port area authorities on the other. Above all, the requisite safety precautions must be learned, and all concerned be instructed minutely in their observance. To insure absolute enforcement of the safety precautions it may be necessary to hire additional supervisors, checkers, and guards. Nearly always these requirements result in much slower cargo handling.

Refrigerated or Perishable Cargo. Chilled or frozen meats must be scheduled very carefully for time of arrival and stowing. The ship's cold lockers must be cleaned, sweetened, and made ready well in advance of the arrival of the first consignment. Few terminals have frozen lockers in which to store **meat.** Usually it is brought by refrigerator cars or trucks directly to the ship. Time is critical, and a sufficient number of operators must be on hand to move the meat quickly into the ship. Whenever possible, meat should be in sizes which can be handled by one man without undue difficulty. Meat normally is chilled or frozen in warehouses close to the ship's berth and transferred to the ship as rapidly as circumstances will permit. Upon discharge from the ship it moves to refrigerated warehouses, frequently on trailers brought through side ports in the ship directly to the refrigerated stowage spaces. Except for the fact that the workers are employed in subfreezing temperatures and require protective clothing and gloves, normal working methods may be employed in handling such cargoes.

Refrigerated **fruit** is handled in a manner quite different from meat. It is cooled rather than frozen, and hence it has little resistance to surrounding heat. It must be moved rapidly from one refrigerated space to another; therefore it is customary to accept deliveries only a short time before actual transfer to the ship begins. In many cases it can be **handled mechanically,** as previously described for bananas and citrus fruits. In winter, the problem is reversed, because then the fruit must be safeguarded from freezing. It may be stored in specially prepared warming spaces, either in a large room where the temperature is controlled thermostatically or in a section of the transit shed curtained off by tarpaulins and heated to a temperature guaranteed not to permit freezing or induce spoilage.

Refrigerated fruit is a particular target of **pilferers,** and care must be taken that checkers and guards are alert to prevent breaking of boxes. Also, since fruit containers are not especially sturdy, longshoremen must be watched to prevent rough handling, which will damage either the boxes or the contents.

Glass and Other Fragile Goods. In handling goods which are by nature fragile, the problem of the marine terminal is to attempt to anticipate where and when the damage may occur and to plan to prevent it. Longshoremen must be informed of the proper procedures to be followed, and supervisors and checkers must make sure that proper markings indicating fragility are conspicuously applied. Shippers should package their fragile goods with full awareness that there will be many handlings between point of origin and final destination. Sturdy, rigid crates or boxes, padded and braced, must be provided.

In recent years the use of **large steel containers,** generally about 6 ft. sq. × 7 ft. high, has become quite common as a means of providing the necessary security for fragile cargoes. The carrier receives the packages of fragile goods and places them inside the steel container. When the container is filled the contents are shored so that no movement is possible, and then the container is sealed. It is lifted as a unit, stowed aboard ship without further handling of the contents, and discharged at port of destination as a unit, to be unsealed by the terminal at the time delivery is made to the consignee. Results from this method of operation have been most encouraging, and many shippers today are using the container directly, placing their cargoes inside these steel boxes themselves. The terminal, of course, finds this method a most satisfactory solution to the problem, because there is no individual handling of fragile cargo.

Cargoes Which Sift or Dust. Flour, unless overpackaged with heavy paper bagging, will sift through cloth and affect a large area of the hold. Lampblack is equally objectionable, for the same reason. Such cargoes must be loaded by the stevedore so that there will not be any damage to other cargoes in the same hold. Adequate advance notice of such cargo bookings usually is sufficient to insure that the ship will be loaded correctly, and no claims will result.

SAFE HANDLING OF CARGO. Terminal management is directed toward the proper and safe handling of cargo, because damaged cargo results in dissatisfied shippers. The entire process of checking cargo is the foundation of damage prevention, since it shows where the damage occurs and permits **correction of any improper or careless practices** thus brought to light. The careful and systematic inventory will reveal any instances of poor stacking, improper palletization, water leaks, and other hazards which might later cause claims. **Constant supervision** by the stevedore and the ship's officers is mandatory to enforce the loading plan and to insure proper handling of cargo into and out of the ship. This is particularly important when there is a great deal of cargo to be handled and time is pressing. Laborers sometimes have to be slowed down, lest in their haste they cause damage to the goods they are handling rapidly.

Cargo damaged by terminal handling is repackaged by the carrier, and every effort must be exerted to insure that the coopers do a correct job, and that the finished work will be satisfactory for the sea voyage. Much cargo is received by the carrier in domestic-type packaging and is accepted because of competition from other carriers. Domestic packaging, however, is dangerous to the carrier because of the great likelihood of damage. The terminal can notify the shipper that the packaging, while acceptable because of trade conditions, is not such that perfect outturn can be guaranteed. He can then be urged to package more acceptably for the succeeding shipment. Finally, in preventing damage, the terminal manager can supervise the **layout of the transit shed,** making certain that there is adequate space to handle the expected cargoes, that there is no crowding, and that instructions for the correct handling of the anticipated cargoes have been issued to all supervisory personnel.

Records and Documents Used in Marine Terminal Operation

CARGO ENGAGEMENT SHEET. The cargo engagement sheet is prepared by the outward freight department's booking clerk, and a copy is sent to the terminal. The layout of the transit shed and the preliminary shiploading plan are prepared from this engagement sheet. Cancellation of reservations or lack of ship's space for a particular kind of cargo will influence the operation of the terminal.

The **delivery permit** is issued by the booking clerk's assistant, the permit clerk, and is sent to shippers of consignments that are greater than carload lots. It is a schedule for the arrival of cargo at the terminal and is an effective means of **controlling the flow of traffic** to the terminal. For difficult cargoes, such as heavy lift items, odd shapes, and commodities requiring special handling, the terminal usually informs the permit clerk when it will be convenient to receive the shipment.

The **dock receipt** is the carrier's acknowledgment to the shipper that goods have been received in a described condition. Until loading aboard ship can be accomplished the goods are held in a warehouse status. Legally, the terminal's dock receipt is a **bailee's contract,** and the provisions of the bill of lading do not apply. Practically, the dock receipt is used to determine how the bill of lading shall be freighted, and what exceptions to the statement of "apparent good order and condition" will be made. The dock receipt is **signed by the terminal receiving clerk** after the cargo has been weighed, measured, and checked by the checker. A copy of the dock receipt always is retained by the receiving clerk.

The **bill of lading** is filled out by the shipper but freighted by the manifesting department after comparison with the dock receipt. Legally, it is the carrier's contract of affreightment and is effective in foreign trade from the end of the ship's tackle at the loading part to the end of the ship's tackle at the discharging port, under the terms of the Carriage of Goods by Sea Act, 1936. Practically, the bill of lading shows the names of the shipper and consignee and gives a complete description of the goods, including marks and numbers and any exceptions which may be agreed upon after comparison with the dock receipts. Copies of the bill of lading normally are supplied to the ship for information but do not get to the receiving clerk.

Hold-on-dock cargo is cargo received by the terminal on which complete export papers have not been received. This cargo legally cannot be loaded and must be held pending issuance of all appropriate documents. It must be segregated from other consignments; and a record of what is on hand, where it is stored, and changes in its status, must be kept current at all times.

The **outward cargo manifest** is a recapitulation of the vessel's total cargo by ports of discharge and lists all pertinent data from the bill of lading. It is a convenient document for reference and for planning the handling of cargo at the ports of discharge. It is very useful to the terminal in determining whether a complete consignment of cargo has been discharged from a ship.

The **delivery book** is maintained by the delivery clerk and contains the data relative to discharge from the carrier's custody to the consignee's possession of every item on the bill of lading. The name of the consignee's truckman or lighterman, the bill of lading number, and the hour and date of the pickup, together with the signature of the truckman or lighterman, are shown. Normally, cargo is loaded on the consignee's conveyance under the supervision of a checker, who must make certain that all cargo damage is noted, in order to prevent claims from the consignee for **damage not caused by the ocean carrier.**

The **over, short, and damaged cargo report** is a list of every item of cargo damaged, every consignment received in less than the specified quantity, and every item of cargo for which the port had no papers. It is prepared after each ship has completed discharge in the port, by and under the direction of the terminal manager. This report shows the exceptions made at the time of cargo delivery; the damage caused by the terminal, as recorded in the ship's comment on the condition of the cargo at the time it was put aboard; the damage resulting from handling while in the care of the ship, as recorded by the reports of checkers who examined the cargo as it was discharged from the vessel; and the final condition at the time of delivery to the consignee, as recorded by the checker's sheet compiled while cargo was being placed in the consignee's conveyance. Properly prepared and maintained, the over, short, and damaged cargo report is a running record of cargo handling experience and is the first source of information when a claim for damage is received by the carrier.

Cargo tracers are prepared by the claims division of the traffic department. They are based on the same information, for an individual shipment, that will be found for all shipments in the over, short, and damaged cargo report.

Demurrage accounts are prepared by the delivery clerk after inventories of the transit shed are made subsequent to expiration of "free time" for cargo. In most United States ports, "free time" is 5 working days after the ship completes discharge. The **inventory** is used to notify the inward freight department of the consignees who have not picked up cargo and indicates what cargo interests need assistance from this department. The inventory must be made regularly, if the transit shed is not to become a warehouse. As a matter of practice, inventories are made daily because of the constant movement of goods.

AIR TERMINAL HANDLING

CONTENTS

AIR TERMINAL HANDLING

Terminal Operations

HANDLING OF AIR CARGO. The development of comprehensive systems for the handling of cargo in air terminals has been retarded by a number of factors, many of which have not been introduced under the direct control of terminal operators. The fact that terminals are owned by municipalities and other agencies, public and private, and not by the terminal operators themselves, affects the ability of the operators to install any elaborate kinds of fixed equipment even where the installation would be justified as to savings in cost and reduction in the time of loading aircraft. Even where cargo-handling operations are centralized in a specific cargo-loading area, each airline and each forwarding company controls its own cargo-handling activities. Where the volume handled by one company justifies the use of special equipment, problems relating to the handling of cargo takes second place to problems of flight operations and of passenger service.

With these inherent difficulties facing them, there are few airline companies or forwarding companies which have not given considerable study to this problem. The result is that new systems and new kinds of equipment are being considered to supersede former less efficient methods. Thus the industry as a whole is extremely receptive to new ideas. Most of the new systems proposed are concerned with the problem of bridging the gap between the terminal-dock level and the deck level of the plane. The other major opportunity for improvement lies in the development of preloading techniques and devices. Along with the development of pallet use, the cargo system described in this section is a major advance in this field.

FUNCTIONS OF AN AIR FREIGHT TERMINAL. In all kinds of terminals there are a certain number of standard activities which must be carried on. As these activities multiply and become more complex, it becomes increasingly difficult to identify clearly the basic functions which are essential for the movement of cargo to the prime carrier. Essentially the basic functions of an air freight terminal are to:

1. **Receive shipments of cargo** from the consignor. This step involves the tailgate unloading of trucks which may have collected the cargo throughout the city or local trade area. The truckers are interested in unloading their cargoes in the shortest time possible, because this is nonproductive time for these men.
2. **Weigh individual packages,** prepare documentation, and sort according to destination or to outgoing flight. Unless procedures are carefully planned, each package will probably be handled an unnecessary number of times before it is finally deposited in the proper storage area.
3. **Retain packages in temporary storage** until the times comes for the flight. During this time other increments are often added to the shipment. The amount of space required depends upon the amount of cargo to be shipped and the frequency of flights to that destination. Theoretically, there should be no

handling of cargo during this stage and there should be no direct labor costs involved.

4. **Load cargo into plane.** This step is the culminating function at the air terminal. Other functions should have been performed in such a way to expedite this last step. The critical time at this point is the time required to load the cargo into the airplane and secure it ready for flight. In many cases all other considerations are subordinated to the task of reducing the terminal time of the plane.

Determinants of Terminal Handling and Layout. In planning the layout for a new terminal, or in evaluating the use of alternate handling systems for existing terminals, there are certain kinds of information that must be assembled. Frequently, terminal operations for a specific carrier, or even for the cargo handling activities of an entire airport, start out successfully at a modest scale but finally develop into a large, unwieldy, and costly handling operation before management realizes that such a situation has come about.

The factors in such a situation call for a thorough study to organize the operations and develop standard procedures. The following factors require thorough investigation:

1. **Volume of cargo.** Volume or tonnage of cargo to be handled is, of course, one of the first determinants in the selection of the handling system and in planning the layout. Buildings and permanent kinds of equipment should be amortized over a reasonable number of years. Provision must be made for expansion of terminal facilities so as to meet the anticipated operating needs for 5 to 10 yr. If a large **increase in volume** is expected, the kinds of handling equipment installed should be of a standard kind to which additional units can be added when needed.

Fluctuation in volume of cargo, and the importance of being able to assemble and ship out large loads during **peak periods** of demand have considerable influence over the kinds of equipment selected. The equipment should be of a kind that will permit lowered manpower requirements during **slack periods.** Some kinds of handling equipment involve capital investments which can be amortized only by a constant use of planes at a high rate of activity. As volume increases and sustained high loads of activity can be maintained, these specialized kinds of equipment will become more feasible.

2. **Size of the individual package.** The size, shape, and weight of the individual package must be taken into account. Recent studies have shown that there is less variation in the size and weight of packages than is commonly supposed. Immer (Materials Handling) points out that there has been a steady increase in packages of small size. **Uniformity** in size of packages offers some advantages from the standpoint of handling, but the fact that larger or unusual-size packages may be expected at any time precludes the use of handling equipment designed only for packages of small size.

3. **Nature of the package.** The nature of the package is also a problem. Shippers do not hesitate to send fragile products in **very light packages** which offer scant protection if roughly or carelessly handled. In fact, the **smaller amount of protective packaging** required for air shipments is one of the more important economic arguments for airplane shipments in preference to land-transport shipments. More care is thus required in handling cargo shipped by air than by railroad, steamship, or truck, and this care adds to both the cost and time of processing the shipments.

Consideration must be given to the handling of **special shipments** such as ladies' ready-to-wear clothing, orchids, perishable foods, baby chicks, and other light cargo. In some instances, special attention of the airline crews to the handling of this type of cargo has led to the growth of a substantial business in such items. Because of the nature of most air cargo shipments, therefore, special care and prompt delivery are usually required in their handling. When the breakdown of some special and expensive machine necessitates securing a replacement part in a hurry, or when some other special emergency develops, or when dealers' shelves are depleted of some product in heavy demand, it is very convenient to wire a dealer and receive on the next day a shipment of the items desired. In any case, shipments can usually be ready and waiting for the first flight out, and delivery by air is the quickest and most satisfactory medium to meet such emergencies.

4. **Frequency and timing of flights.** An adequate number of loading sites must be provided for the maximum number of aircraft which may be expected to be concurrently loaded or unloaded. Failure to make such provisions results in delay in loading the planes or holding trucks in stand-by areas until they can be run to the loading dock for transfer to outgoing planes.

Adequate space must also be available for the accumulation of cargo for each flight, for a number of practically concurrent flights, or for a large number of destinations. The timing of these flights is also an important factor. Obviously, space requirements will be greater if arrivals and departures are concentrated rather than being distributed as evenly as possible throughout the working period of the terminal.

MOVEMENT OF CARGO. The movement of cargo through an air terminal must be checked from the time it enters the air terminal area up to the time it is secured in the cargo plane. Not only must the cost of each specific handling be considered, but also possibilities of prepositioning, palletizing, containerizing, and other steps must be considered which will decrease handling costs as much as possible throughout handling operations.

The greatest operating economy will be obtained under a system which reduces the physical handling of cargo to a minimum. To accomplish this objective the system of handling utilized must provide for the **continuous movement** of cargo, **"live" storage** or merely **temporary retention** of cargo, and **mechanical handling** by equipment. Mechanical handling usually leads to use of the unit-load system and the application of some kind of unitizing agent. Factors in the case are continuous movement of cargo, a live storage system, and a container or pallet system.

Importance of Keeping Cargo Moving. The most desirable system for moving air cargo through a terminal is one which provides for continuous movement of all the cargo. Material would be unloaded directly from incoming trucks to a conveyor on the loading dock. Cargo would be carried on the conveyor through the scales and through a documentation area where waybills and other documents would be prepared. Necessary papers would be affixed and the cargo would move into a sorting area where it would be sorted as to respective destinations and according to scheduled flights. On each of the **conveyors** branching out from the main conveyor, the cargo for specific flights would be collected. As the flight is called, that conveyor would be set in motion and the materials would be moved out to the loading area, where the conveyor system would be extended to the waiting aircraft, and the cargo would be moved into the plane without any other handling. Portable, lightweight, extendable conveyors within the plane would complete the movement almost to the exact point of stowage.

Live Storage System. Live storage refers to a system or method by which materials held in storage, or temporary retention of any kind, can again be put into movement without any physical handling. It does not include a complete system of handling but in practice can be a modification of either a conveyor system or a fork truck system utilizing pallets.

As applied to a **conveyor system,** this method consists of a number of conveyors branching out from a main conveyor. Each branch conveyor represents a flight. These conveyors are activated to advance a short distance each time packages are delivered to it. When the cargo for a particular flight is to be sent out, the carriers or boxes on that conveyor would be fed to the conveyor leading to the loading dock.

As applied to a system involving pallets, the retention or storage areas consist of sections of **gravity roller conveyors** set up on the floor, with a slight slope away from the feeding or incoming area. Each pallet, when set down on the conveyor for its flight, would roll to the far end where it would be picked up by other fork trucks at flight time and delivered to the proper plane.

Container or Pallet System. This system involves the use of containers, skids, pallets, or other devices to permit the handling of a number of packages or items at one time. Depending upon the kind of truck-pickup arrangement employed, it becomes possible in many instances to have the container or pallet in the truck so that the packages can be removed from the truck at the incoming dock by a fork truck as a unit.

After the container or pallet load is weighed, waybills are affixed, the containers are sorted, and the cargo is again accumulated on pallets or in containers and is retained in a temporary storage area until time for loading for its respective flight. **Fork trucks** are used both to carry these units to the storage area and from this area to the plane, for loading. The load is elevated to the level of the cargo compartment where it is either pushed into place manually or maneuvered into place by a hand-operated fork truck.

Cargon Air Freight Handling System. The Cargon system consists basically of large-wheeled pallets which are designed to replace the conventional cargo floor

Fig. 1.   Preloaded Cargon is rolled into the fuselage of a Bristol 170 from trailer in seconds.

of freight-carrying vehicles. It replaces the sectionalized floor of the vehicle in the factory, warehouse, or terminal where time and facilities permit a more efficient job of loading and tying down. Developed in New Zealand primarily for use with the Bristol freighter and highway trucks and trailers, it has been perfected over a period of five years of operational experience. In the United States the tray dimensions of the Cargon are controlled by the standard 40 × 48-in. pallet as a modulus. The general purpose Cargon has a width of 96 and a length of 80 in.

Design requirements are similar to those already considered for air terminals, such as truck-bed height, constant section, and level floor. In addition, straight-in end loading is a feature of all general-purpose highway vehicles. This same feature is contained in the design of such military aircraft as the C-119, C-123, C-130, C-132, and the C-133. In the field of commercial air transports, the Safri, a new design being readied for production by the Frye Corporation, is designed specifically for the Cargon system (Fig. 1).

Equipment and Facilities

USE OF WHEELED VEHICLES IN HANDLING CARGO. Wheeled vehicles of various kinds are generally used to transport cargo across terminal floors and into plane-loading areas. Fork trucks are widely used because of their flexibility and adaptability to the changing requirements of air terminal operations.

Four-Wheel Trailer. The 4-wheel trailer is the one most widely used for handling air cargo. Various kinds of lightweight trailers have been developed especially for airport operations. They are usually designed for use as individual baggage trucks or as components of a train pulled by a tractor.

In the storage section of the terminal, cargo can be accumulated on loaded pallets, according to flight, on separate trailers. A number of these trailers can be pulled out to the plane loading area by an **industrial tractor unit.** Some kinds of trailers are so designed that they can be elevated by a fork truck to the height of the plane deck so that the only handling required is that of unloading the loaded pallets from the trailer to the deck of the plane for final stowage. Four-wheeled units of this kind usually have an **automatic braking device** which locks the wheels and prevents the moving of the truck when the handle is in the "up" position.

Tractor Train and Trailer System. In certain cases small compact **industrial tractor units** are used to move a number of loaded trailers at one time. These trains are quickly assembled in terminal storage areas, hauled as much as several hundred yards to the loading area, and then released so that the tractor can return for another set of trailers. The tractors are also used to move loaded trailers of passengers' luggage and other miscellaneous cargo going out on passenger flight.

Fork Lift Truck. The fork lift truck has become an indispensable piece of equipment for air-terminal operations. **Palletized cargo** is being received for air shipment in increasing quantities each year. It is generally desirable to keep materials on pallets when being transported in shipments. A fork lift truck is used to unload them from the highway truck, deliver them to the terminal floor for checking and sorting, and finally deliver them into the plane. This sequence is followed in reverse at the receiving airport. Where larger quantities are involved and the distance from the terminal to the plane is too great, a fork truck is used to load the pallet onto a trailer and another fork truck is used at the loading site to remove the pallet from the trailer and elevate it into the plane. It is also common practice to use the fork truck to elevate trailers to plane-deck height to facilitate loading from trailer to plane.

High Platform Truck. The door sills of the DC-4, DC-6A, and the 1049H planes are all 9 ft. above the ground. Where terminals have a high loading platform on the plane-loading side, a high platform truck has been used to bridge the gap. Cargo is assembled on top of the truck. When the plane is in position for loading, the truck is driven alongside the cargo-door opening and the cargo is rolled across to the deck of the plane at the same level.

Lift Platform Truck. In most airport operations cargo must be loaded to docks and to decks of planes at a variety of heights from the ground. The high platform truck described above is useful only for certain kinds of planes and where a high loading dock of the same height as the plane floor has been provided.

The lift platform truck has a movable platform which can be elevated from 4 ft. to 10 ft. from the ground. Therefore it can be used for different kinds of planes, for the different cargo-door openings—at different heights from the ground—on the same plane, and where the height of the terminal loading dock is different from any of the plane deck heights. The most important disadvantage is that which applies to all powered carriers—loads cannot be retained on the platform for any length of time because the trucking unit is needed elsewhere for other loading operations. Thus, in times of greatest activity, trucks cannot be preloaded so as to be ready for plane loading. Loads are also exposed to the elements in inclement weather.

Two-Wheel Hand Truck. The 2-wheel hand truck is still the standby of small terminals where more expensive handling equipment may not be justified. Even in larger terminals this equipment still serves a useful purpose for standby service. Although very **little investment** is required to purchase these trucks, **direct labor costs** in the use of this equipment are extremely high. Therefore, even in small airline terminals, it is usual to provide at least one powered fork truck. This equipment usually justifies its use by the savings which it makes in the terminal time of the plane and by savings in other tasks for which the fork truck may be used at other times. In addition, it can handle loads which are beyond the capacity of small hand trucks.

Crane Boom Mounted on Truck. Although the fork truck is used for most lifting jobs in terminal handling, materials are sometimes received for which a crane of some kind is required. In larger air terminals, cranes are frequently used for lifts up to 5 tons. For heavier lifts, or where cranes are not available, outside crane service must be contracted for. The cranes used are generally of the industrial fixed-boom type, although cranes of the **front-swivel boom type** are sometimes purchased because of their flexibility, wider range, and higher load capacity.

USE OF CONVEYORS IN AIR TERMINAL HANDLING. Conveyors can be used at air terminals as complete systems of handling or as equipment to take care of some specific handling problem which may, or may not, tie in with other equipment in the handling system. There have been few completely conveyorized handling systems installed in air terminals for the handling of cargo.

The greatest use of conveyors has been for such specific operations as the unloading of packages from a plane.

Belt Conveyors in Fixed Positions. Belt conveyors are used at air terminals principally for movement of cargo through receiving, weighing, documentation, and on to temporary storage areas. A more extensive system has been installed at the Los Angeles terminal of American Shippers, Inc. (Air Transportation, vol. 26). This installation consists of a belt conveyor system running along the dock outside the terminal and extending along the full length of the building. The system has eliminated bottlenecks and has been estimated to save approximately 300 man-hr. per week.

Portable Belt Conveyors. Portable belt conveyors have been mounted on motor trucks to provide mobile conveyor units capable of being moved from one plane to another; such units can be set up in an operating position without delay. One or two men (or more) are used to move the cargo in the plane, while another man is required to remove cargo from the lower end of the conveyor, when the latter is used for unloading. Packages removed from the lower end of the conveyor are stacked on trailers for removal from the loading area by tractor train.

Chutes. Wooden or metal-lined chutes are used in some companies to unload package cargo. Use is limited to unloading operations, and some kind of mobile supporting frame must be provided for the chute. Since the portable belt conveyor noted above serves the same purpose, and can also be used for loading the plane, its use is generally preferred.

Gravity Roller Wheel Conveyors. Gravity roller and **skate-wheel** conveyors are frequently used in receiving, sorting, and transporting operations. Their use has also been considered for more comprehensive systems. A system such as that shown in Fig. 2 can transport packages through an entire terminal from receiving

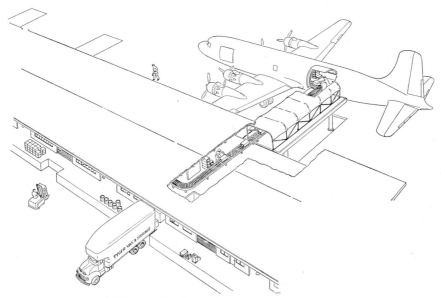

Fig. 2. Gravity roller conveyor system.

at the truck dock to stowage in a plane. **Wheel-conveyor systems** must be readily adjustable and have **power-booster sections**; at least power must be supplied to the rollers in some way. Portable and lightweight sections of skate-wheel or roller conveyors are also used for plane-loading operations. Portable sections are quickly set into place and permit rapid movement of packaged items.

Overhead Trolley Conveyor System. A system of handling which has been effective in lowering terminal handling costs for warehouses and rail and truck terminals employs an overhead trolley conveyor system to guide 4-wheel trailers or carts along a prescribed path. The system involves a high first investment, requires a high volume of operation, and offers its greatest advantages where packages from a number of different sources must be sorted and delivered to, or reclaimed from, storage. An installation of this kind is more suitable where all the cargo-handling operations of an air terminal can be centralized. It is not an economical arrangement for a small installation.

In the terminal studies made by Lockheed Aircraft Corporation, attention was given to the installation of various kinds of conveyor systems. The first arrangement considered was referred to as a "closed loading system," i.e., **late shipments could not be inserted easily into the conveyor line.** Also, it does not permit of sorting according to flight, which is an important terminal function. In the "open loading system," which is based upon the conveyor towing system, it is easy to sort to a large number of flights. This latter conveyor system is illustrated in Fig. 3.

NEW YORK CITY'S INTERNATIONAL AIRPORT. The newer air cargo terminal at the New York City International Airport is not only one of the most recent air cargo terminals constructed but also illustrates some of the many problems of planning for internal handling and for site location within the airport area. The type of construction and the plan were the result of considerable research on the part of the Aviation Department of the Port of New York Authority, which constructed the terminal and leases space to the individual airlines. This fact, in itself, had a certain effect upon the plan finally developed.

The **interrelationship of the site** of the cargo terminal and the many other operating functions of the New York International Airport is shown in Fig. 4. The site was selected so that access would be possible from the various arterial parkways without actually entering that portion of the airport used for passenger and for aircraft-servicing functions. The peripheral taxiway system and service road is of use to aircraft used for mixed passenger-cargo flights. Vehicle traffic on 150th Street will pass under the runways and feed directly into the passenger terminal area.

As the **four cargo buildings are leased out** to over 26 domestic and foreign flag airlines, they must be adaptable to a wide variety of operations because the cargo-handling activities of the carriers vary from one company to another. Although the total tonnage passing through the terminal is impressive, the volume handled by any one line is relatively small compared to the volume of cargo processed by other kinds of terminals, such as truck or rail terminals. This fact had an important bearing in selecting the kinds of materials handling equipment that would be most economical for use in an operation of this size; this fact also limited the use of specialized handling equipment which, for example, has been effective in lowering handling costs in rail and truck terminals.

Each cargo building is 750 ft. × 80 ft. The basic rental module is a section of the building 150 ft. × 80 ft., each module having its own aircraft-parking area

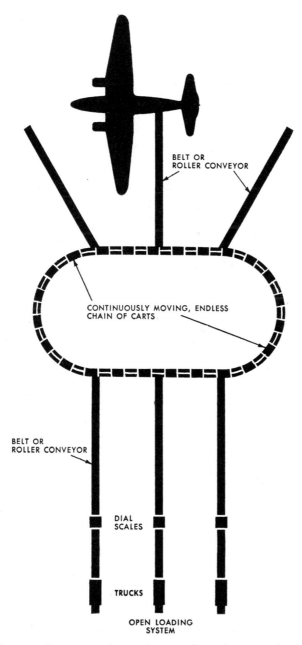

Fig. 3. Open loading system for sorting cargo to a large number of flights.

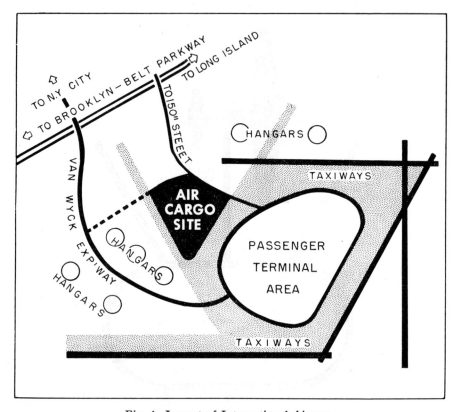

Fig. 4. Layout of International Airport.

(150 ft. × 160 ft.), truck-loading area (150 ft. × 60 ft.), and vehicular parking area for customers and employees. This arrangement is shown in Fig. 5.

Centered between the four cargo buildings is a 2-story **Cargo Service Building,** which provides space and facilities for freight forwarders, customs brokers, and the various federal agencies concerned with cargo movement. The truck-loading dock is raised 3 ft. 6 in. above grade so that trucks can back up to the building, and the cargo can be rolled directly into and through the building and on out to the aircraft apron.

The **basic building shape** was arrived at as the result of a questionnaire which was sent to prospective tenants. The buildings are of steel-frame construction with steel and block facing, with a built-up roof on metal decking, and insulation carried on open-web steel joists. The floor is concrete, designed to carry a load of 250 lb. per sq. ft. Each tenant installs interior partitions, provides his own materials handling equipment, and develops his own work-place arrangement.

THE AEROBRIDGE. Rausch (Terminal Planning for the Air Freight Age) describes the Aerobridge developed by the Lockheed Aircraft Corporation. This structure is a **portable dock or bridge,** adjustable as to length and height, used to span the gap between the loading dock of the terminal and the deck of the plane to which the cargo is to be loaded. The basic model has an unobstructed

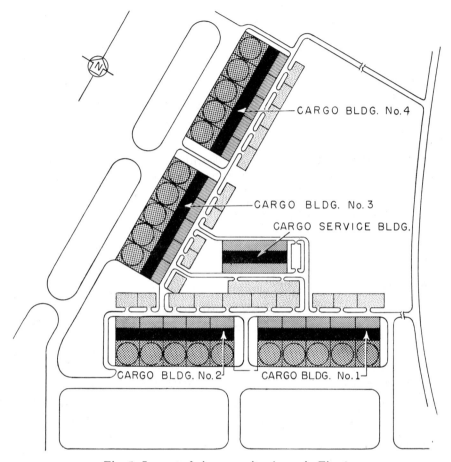

Fig. 5. Layout of air cargo site shown in Fig. 4.

width of 8 ft. and a basic length of 70 ft., with an extendable section of an additional 15 ft. on the airplane-end of the ramp. It is self-powered for a rotation through an arc of 180° and also for movement along the face of the air terminal.

The **bridge** consists of a main span and a telescoping span supported by two towers mounted on carts or dollies. The inner dolly is designed so that its rotary motion is accomplished by the power-and-steering mechanisms installed in the outboard dolly. A supplementary power unit is also installed in the inner dolly for adjustment along the face of the dock when the bridge is extended and in position for loading and unloading. The outboard end of the bridge is attached to the supporting tower, and a cable hoist supports and guides rollers to permit raising and lowering. The unit is extended or retracted by means of the telescopic action between the two main sections of the bridge.

The bridge is equipped with a **removable canvas canopy** for use during inclement weather. This canopy extends the entire length of the unit and moves out or retracts with the bridge units. A dock board spans the gap between the outboard end of the bridge and the loading deck of the plane. The entire operation of the bridge is controlled by one operator from an electric panel mounted at the outboard end, where he has full vision and control over all movement.

The **height** of both the inboard and the outboard end of the bridge can be adjusted from 4 ft. to 9 ft., thus making it possible to handle material through the entire terminal system on a level. Hackney (Air Cargo Loading on the Level) reports that an analysis made of the savings made possible by this feature in one large terminal with six DC-4 Airfreighters daily, showed a saving of $21,000 a year in direct labor alone at this one installation. It was further estimated that, with experience, an additional saving of 25 percent would result. There was also a slight reduction in plane-loading time.

RESEARCH STUDIES. Studies made within recent years by the Lockheed Aircraft Corporation on the design requirements of freight-terminal operations have resulted in a number of observations on the handling of air cargo which provide a sound basis for terminal design. The result of these studies was a building plan which has been called the "Lockheed Plan." This plan, which was released in 1949, has had considerable influence on the planning of later terminals.

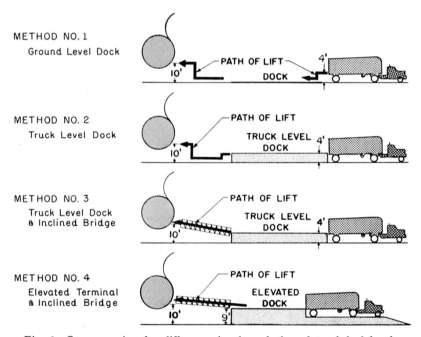

Fig. 6. Compensating for difference in plane-deck and truck-bed levels.

Effects of Deck Heights on Loading Operations. First studies of air freight terminal requirements resulted in agreement on the necessity for an elevated design. Experience with rail and truck facilities in other industries showed that properly designed docks for these transportation services must be elevated to the **height of the carrier bed.** From the standpoint of trucks bringing freight to the airport, the terminal should be elevated to truck-bed height, which is between 40 in. and 48 in. The problem is treated in the following manner by Rausch

(Terminal Planning for the Air Freight Age) and is graphically illustrated in Fig. 6:

Method 1. With a ground-level dock, each pound of cargo must be lowered 4 ft. and raised 10 ft. to the height of the plane deck. A load of 35,000 lb. will require a lift of 490,000 ft.-lb. (35,000 × 14) of lift before loading of cargo is completed.

Method 2. Although the dock in this second layout is now at truck level, cargo must still be lowered to the ground before being elevated, so the foot-pounds of lift remains the same.

Method 3. The installation of a bridge, conveyor, or high lift truck at the 4-ft. dock height reduces the lift to 210,000 ft.-lb.

Method 4. In the final method, a completely elevated terminal floor, 9 ft. high., is used. A ramp is provided to run trucks up to dock level and a bridge is used to move cargo into the plane. As the vertical lift is now only 1 ft., the lift is only 35,000 ft.-lb.

Preliminary Plans. The basic problem undertaken in the development of a layout for a representative terminal was to provide a maximum ramp area and the largest number of airplane-loading stations for a given warehouse and dock area. Studies of existing freight docks showed that at least three times as much ramp area is needed as for dock and warehouse area.

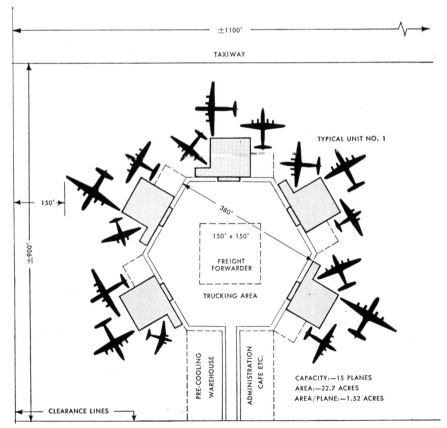

Fig. 7. Hexagonal layout for spotting three planes at each loading dock.

The first layout plans developed consisted of eight buildings arranged in the form of a modified octagon, with all truck activity working from the inside of the octagonal area. The principal disadvantage of this plan was that only two airplanes could be spotted at each loading dock. In the modified arrangement, shown in Fig. 7, five units were combined in the form of a hexagon in such a way that three planes could be spotted at each loading dock.

Still another layout, shown in Fig. 8, provided for a straight-line arrangement of building units. This arrangement has the advantage that the open layout permits the unlimited addition of units to the original design.

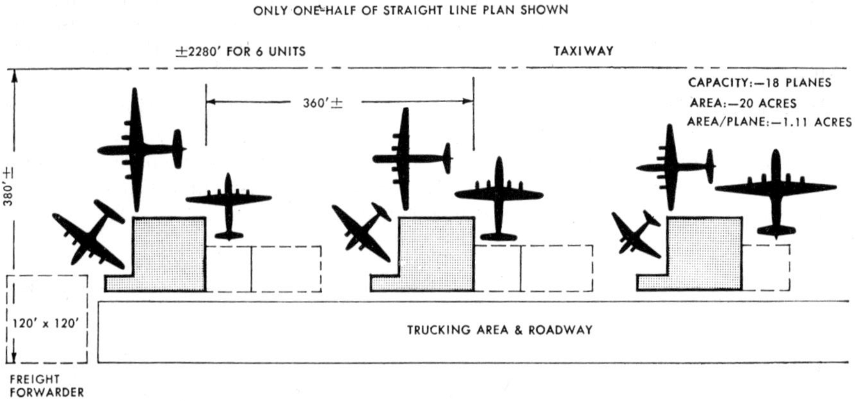

ONLY ONE-HALF OF STRAIGHT LINE PLAN SHOWN

Fig. 8. Straight-line arrangement of building units.

The Lockheed Plan. In the plan finally selected by Lockheed, described by Hackney (Planning the Air Terminal) and shown in Fig. 9, space is provided for loading seven planes at one time. For greatest economy in construction, the plan involves two rectangular structures of standard industrial dimensions as to building width and length. These structures are 50 ft. by 100 ft. in dimension and are set at an angle of 120° to one another. Each wing of the building provides 5,000 sq. ft. of enclosed warehouse area and necessary office space. Because several of the larger planes contain over 1,000 sq. ft. of floor area, the warehouse area is not excessive for that number of loading docks. This plan includes the high elevated platform shown in Fig. 10.

LOADAIR DEVICE. The Loadair device, developed by the Whiting Corporation, consists of three trucks whose tops are flush with the airport pavement, and which travel on rails imbedded in the ramp surface, and at right angles to the terminal building. Each truck supports one wheel of an aircraft's landing gear. The purpose of this device is to **bring the plane in close to the terminal.** Although the device had been under study and experimentation since 1941, the first actual installation was made at Baranquilla, Colombia, in 1951. A second device was installed later at the New York International Airport. The latter installation included passenger-handling facilities and a **conveyor system** for handling light cargo. According to Rausch (Terminal Planning for the Air Freight Age), it has been estimated that the first device, operated in connection with a conveyor system, resulted in a 50 percent reduction in average cargo airplane turn-around time. Average loads of 8,578 lb. were removed from C-46's in 9.2 min. by an average crew consisting, in effect, of 5½ men.

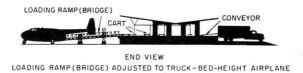

END VIEW
LOADING RAMP (BRIDGE) ADJUSTED TO TRUCK-BED-HEIGHT AIRPLANE

END VIEW
LOADING RAMP (BRIDGE) ADJUSTED TO HIGH CARGO FLOOR AIRPLANE

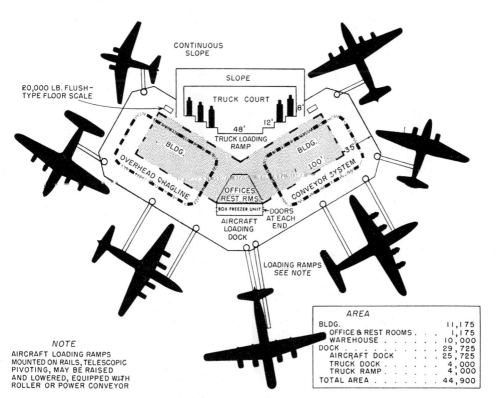

Fig. 9. Loading seven planes at one time.

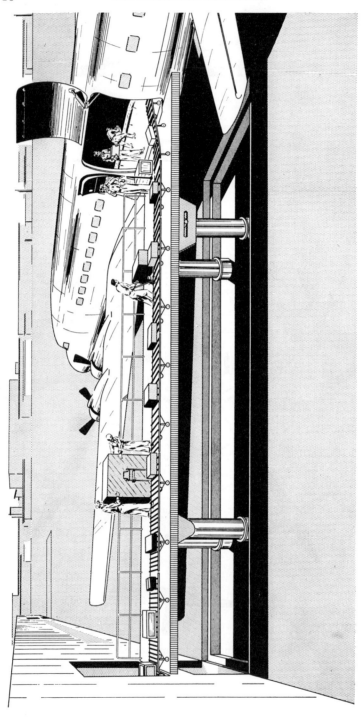

Fig. 10. Adjustable loading dock.

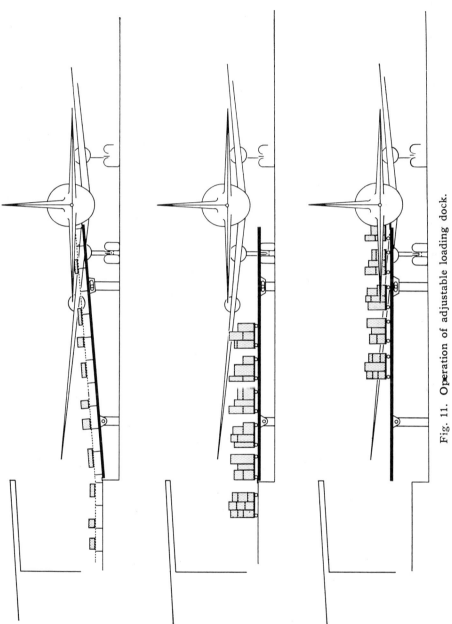

Fig. 11. Operation of adjustable loading dock.

ADJUSTABLE LOADING DOCK. The adjustable loading dock, developed by Douglas Aircraft Company, Inc., is a hydraulically operated platform used to provide a means of bridging the gap between the air terminal dock and the deck of the cargo plane. As shown in Fig. 10, the **platform is supported by four hydraulic jacks in two sets.** Each set is operated independently, thus permitting the platform to be leveled to the terminal dock at one end and to the plane deck at the other end. The length of the platform is governed by the **wing-span of the planes.** For the DC-4 and the DC-6A, a 60-ft. length will clear the wing tip by 5 ft. A 15-ft. width has been suggested to permit the simultaneous use of a roller conveyor and wheeled equipment, such as a fork truck. Where the terminal dock level is lower than the plane deck, loading and unloading can be accomplished as shown in Fig. 11.

AIR DOCK. The **air dock** developed by United Air Lines is intended for passenger terminals only. Basically, the system involves a two-level terminal in which the aircraft are towed into and out of the loading position. It provides for a **complete separation of the functions of passenger loading and cargo loading.** While passengers are disembarked at the upper level, passenger luggage is unloaded at the lower level to a conveyor belt which ends at a mechanically revolved sorting table. Mail, express, and freight are next unloaded, in that order. In the meantime the plane is serviced and refueled from fixed sources of supply, thus eliminating a large number of vehicles which otherwise would have to serve the plane. For outbound loading, the **conveyor belt** carries preloaded and pre-weighed conveyor carts to the docked plane. On arriving at the correct place beside the fuselage, the carts trip off hydraulic hoists. Controlled by cargo handlers, the **hoists** raise the carts to levels which facilitate loading of fore, aft, and belly pits.

The **principal advantages of the air dock** are:

1. Complete separation of passenger and cargo loading activities.
2. Protection from the terminal to the plane for both passengers and cargo in inclement weather.
3. Eliminates use of ramps and stairs for loading of passengers.
4. Fixed facilities permit the immediate refueling of the plane as soon as it is brought into position on the dock. This eliminates the need for gasoline trucks and other service vehicles. By means of fixed elevated platforms, mechanics and refuelers have immediate access to the wing areas of a plane without the need for ladders and other paraphernalia.

The air dock was developed to **speed up the handling of baggage,** to reduce the number of vehicles required to service planes, and to provide shelter for passengers boarding the planes. A full-scale mock-up of the air dock was constructed at the Denver Operating Base of United Air Lines.

Air Cargo Stowage

PREPARATION OF CARGO FOR AIR SHIPMENT. The general problem of air cargo packaging is outside the scope of this Section of the Materials Handling Handbook. However, since proper packaging will assist measurably in the proper handling of a shipment by air, certain cautionary remarks are given here.

Shipments moving by air are not usually exposed to the shock loads to which they are subjected in surface shipping. Rough roads, car humping, vibration, and similar impacts are notably absent in an airplane. Loading procedures, because of the nature of an airplane, are also more carefully controlled and subject the shipments to less shock. Consequently, lighter packaging may safely be used.

The following rules may be used as a guide when packaging for air shipment:

1. Boxes or cratings should be light, but strong, and capable of reasonable stacking.
2. Manufacturers' load limitations on pasteboard or fiberboard cartons should be complied with.
3. Reasonable consolidation of small packages will assist in better over-all packaging and handling.
4. Over-all package size limitations for the type of aircraft on which shipments will move should be complied with.
5. Floor loading limitations for the aircraft should be considered and proper skids or load spreading devices should be supplied, when required.
6. Heavy crating is not required for large items of machinery, furniture, etc. In many cases paper wrapping is all that is necessary.
7. Protruding parts of machines, etc., should be wrapped or protected by some suitable framework, whenever possible, to prevent impact damage.
8. Sharp-edged castings or miscellaneous small metal parts should not be packed in burlap bags; boxes provide much better protection.
9. Light metal tubing and similar items should also be boxed.
10. The center of gravity of a package or crate should be kept as low as possible.
11. Airline tariff restrictions on items not acceptable for air transportation should be complied with; certain items require a specific type of packaging.
12. Since the cargo must be tied down in the aircraft, proper cargo tie-down attachments must be available and utilized. The following unit of this Section covers tie-down restraint criteria.
13. When in doubt as to size, weight, type of packaging required, etc., contact the local airline representative.

LOADING AND SECURING CARGO. Proper loading and securing of cargo is required for all shipments, whether the carrier moves on the highway, on the railroad, on the water, or in the air. The securing of cargo, because the airplane moves in a three-dimensional medium, and because of its lighter construction, is more critical in air transport than in other forms of transportation. Aircraft loading crews are faced with a dual problem:

1. The airplane must be so loaded that its **center of gravity** falls within relatively closely defined limits. Failure to observe these limits results in a poorly balanced aircraft that will be difficult to control, will fly more slowly, and may be, in extreme cases, unsafe to operate.

2. All cargo loaded aboard an aircraft must be **tied down** to prevent shifting in flight caused by rough air conditions or airplane attitude. Cargo restraint criteria established by civil air regulations provides that all cargo must be secured as follows:

Forward load restraint	$9.0G^*$
Sideward load restraint	$1.5G$
Upward load restraint	$2.0G$
Downward load restraint	$4.5G$

* "G" refers to one unit of gravitational force. A weight of 100 lb., when subjected to a down load of 2G, would have an effective weight of 200 lb.

Aircraft loading crews must, therefore, secure all cargo loaded aboard an aircraft in conformance with the above-listed criteria. Cargo aircraft floors and walls contain numerous **tie-down fittings** which are used in conjunction with tie-down devices to secure cargo to the aircraft structure. (See dimensional and loading data charts in section on air carriers.)

Cargo Tie-Down Devices. The devices used to tie down or secure cargo vary among the respective airlines and in the military services. Some of the more commonly used units include:

1. A strong **woven-duck strap** 2 in. wide, with attachment hooks at each end and a take-up and tensioning device. Designated by the Air Force as Type A-1A, it has a usual capacity of 1,250 lb.
2. A **compound unit** similar to the Type A-1A, but with a nylon or dacron web strap and heavy forged fittings, is available with capacities ranging from 5,000 to 15,000 lb.
3. Another type consists of a **flexible steel cable** generally 7/32 in. in diam., with an attachment hook at one end and a mechanism for attaching, adjusting, and tensioning at the other end. It is known as Type B-1A and its usual capacity is 5,000 lb.
4. A commercial three-piece **flexible steel cable unit** with capacities of 2,000–7,000 lb. One is a piece of steel cable with a hook at one end and a loop at the other. The second consists of a steel cable and hook assembly with sliding beads for initial adjustment threaded on the cable. The third is an over-center locking device for final tensioning, with a hook at one end which engages the loop of the simple cable, and a slot that engages the beaded cable assembly at the other.
5. Another type is made up of a **flexible steel chain and a turnbuckle,** each with a hook at one end. The turnbuckles also contain a slot and locking lug, which receives and retains the chain in making initial adjustment. Final adjustment is made by means of the turnbuckle screw. Units of this nature come in capacities ranging from 14,000 to 50,000 lb. (see Fig. 12).

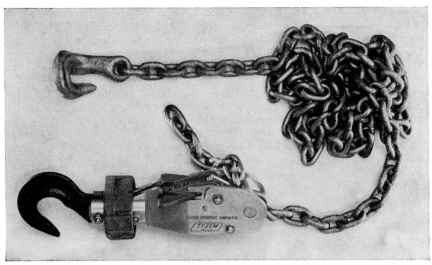

Eastern Rotorcraft Corp.

Fig. 12. Modified C-2 tie-down device.

Use of Tie-Down Devices. Tie-down devices such as have been described are generally used on fairly heavy pieces of cargo, which may be tied down individually or in small groups. The number of tie-down devices used will depend on the weight of the piece or pieces, the type of tie-down unit being used, and the securing criteria being applied. Airplane floor-fitting or wall-fitting strength must also be considered, and the type and number of tie-down devices matched to the aircraft's fitting strength.

The method of attaching the tie-down device to the cargo will also be a factor in deciding the number of tie-down units required. Passing the tiedown over or around the cargo has the effect of doubling its effective strength, just as a double strand of rope will support twice the weight that a single strand will hold.

For example, a 1,000-lb. box must have a 2G or 2,000-lb. upward restraint to meet civil air regulations. If one Type A-1A tie-down unit (capacity 1,250 lb.) is passed over the top of the box and secured to floor fittings on each side, restraint criteria will be met, since each section or leg of the tie-down will be capable of restraining the full capacity of the unit, in this case 1,250 lb., for a total of 2,500 lb. (see Fig. 13). Floor-fitting capacity must equal or exceed the tie-down strength.

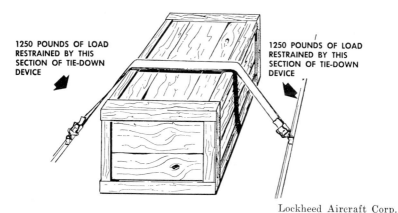

1250 POUNDS OF LOAD RESTRAINED BY THIS SECTION OF TIE-DOWN DEVICE

1250 POUNDS OF LOAD RESTRAINED BY THIS SECTION OF TIE-DOWN DEVICE

Lockheed Aircraft Corp.

Fig. 13. Use of 1,250-lb. tie-down device to restrain 2,500 lb.

Similarly, the forward restraint required for this box will be 9G, or 9,000 lb. One B-1A unit (capacity 5,000 lb.) will be sufficient if it is passed around the forward end of the cargo and each of its ends is secured to the rear. In this case the strength of each floor fitting would have to be at least equal to 4,500 lb., because under the 9G condition, each leg of the tie-down device would bear a load equal to this figure.

If it were not practical to pass the tie-down unit around the cargo, then the device would have to be hooked between the rearward end of the cargo and the floor. In such a case, two B-1A units would have to be used to meet the required restraint of 9,000 lb., because one unit would be subject to a direct pull of 9,000 lb., which would exceed its allowable capacity of 5,000 lb.

The tie-down devices described above may also be used to **restrain cargo in more than one direction.** If the restraint device is fastened to the cargo and angled to the side and rear, one tie-down, if of proper strength, may be sufficient for both side and forward restraint (see Fig. 14). In cases of this nature, care must be exercised in the selection of the device and the angle of pull-off to which the floor fitting is subjected, particularly since the strength of some fittings will vary radically with the direction of pull.

Some tie-down devices are fitted with "riders" which make use of the principle that a double web will double the strength of the tie-down unit. Devices of this nature are particularly useful when it is not practical to pass the tie-down around or over the piece of cargo, and it is desired to minimize the weight of the securing devices.

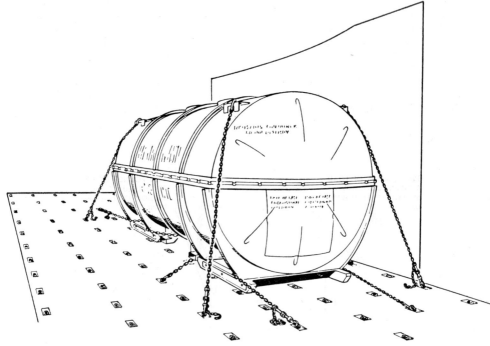

Lockheed Aircraft Corp.

Fig. 14. Multiple directional restraint of cargo.

Cargo Nets. Light and bulky cargo is more easily restrained in an aircraft by means of cargo nets. The flexibility of the nets makes them especially useful to cover cargo on the floor, to form bulkheads, to form walls for side aisles, to end off-loads, or to segregate cargo by destinations.

Nets in general use are manufactured from light steel cable, ⅜-in. manila rope, and nylon or dacron webs. A popular size is 100 in. × 100 in., with hooks and keepers at 20-in. intervals on all sides of the net. The hooks allow the nets to be attached to floors, walls, or other nets, in any desired combination. Final securing of the load is accomplished by pulling the net tight with a tie-down device such as the A-1A, the flexibility of the net allowing it to conform to irregularly shaped loads. Tie-down devices may be built into the net if desired.

A 100-in. × 100-in. net made of ⅜-in. **manila rope**, woven and interlocked in a 7-in. × 7-in. diamond pattern, will secure a distributed load of 6,000 lb., when the net is secured at 20 or more equally spaced points.

Nylon nets and dacron nets—especially dacron nets—may be made in capacities of 15,000 lb. and up. Their flexibility and ability to restrain a load in all directions simultaneously have resulted in an increasing use of such nets for heavy pieces that formerly were tied down individually.

MATERIALS HANDLING SYSTEMS WITHIN CARGO AIRCRAFT. Cargo materials handling equipment used within the airplane may be divided into two general sections:

1. Portable or removable equipment.
2. Built-in equipment.

Each of these classes of materials handling equipment has recently been receiving the comprehensive study and attention which the field deserves. In the past, practically all equipment utilized within an airplane was of a kind which had been designed for ground handling and was not entirely suited for aircraft applications. The vastly larger volumes of air cargo now being handled, however, make investment in materials handling equipment worth-while from the viewpoints of both the manufacturer and the user. Consequently a large number of devices have been developed and applied specifically for aircraft loading. Some are adaptations of old and common ground-type devices. Others are new in principle and use to the aircraft field. All such equipment has materially reduced the time required to load and unload aircraft.

A great many devices may be used within an airplane to assist in loading and unloading cargo. Only the latest and most important developments and the most commonly used equipment will be illustrated and explained here. No attempt will be made to describe all kinds of handling devices that could have an aircraft application.

PORTABLE EQUIPMENT. The various kinds of removable equipment applied in the handling of cargo aboard airplanes includes pry-bars, dollies, rollers, tackle, winches, pallet movers, and lifts.

Lever Dolly. Probably the first item of materials handling equipment used in an airplane was a pry-bar or the familiar "Johnson Bar." However, it was not one made of forged steel. A handy piece of pipe, or a short length of "two-by-four" probably served the loading crew and, in many cases, still does. Aircraft floors, however, are easily damaged by indiscriminate use of these devices, and rubber-tired lever dollies have now come into general use both on commercial airlines and in the military services. The standard steel-wheeled warehouse variety has been modified to incorporate **four rubber-tired wheels** in order to spread the load and to avoid scuffing the wood or metal aircraft floors with which most cargo aircraft are equipped.

Motorized Lever Dolly. A recent application of the "Johnson Bar" principle has been made in the "Tug-Bar." which may best be described as a motorized lever dolly. The unit consists essentially of a wheeled lever, electrically powered, used to push or pull cargo loads weighing up to 4,000 lb.

The 28-v. or 110-v., ½-hp. motor is mounted on four wheels, with the lever "lip" mounted in front of the motor. The conventional lever is mounted in back of the rear set of wheels and has a "dead-man"-type switch at the upper end. The ratio of handle load to cargo load reaction is 9 to 1. A flexible power cable connects the motor to the power source. Power from the motor drives a dual set of 6-in. rubber-tired wheels attached to the front axle.

Its use corresponds to that of the conventional lever dolly. The lip is placed under the cargo, which is lifted slightly by means of the lever. Cargo is moved by pressing either the forward or reverse switch on the handle. Free-running speed is 35 ft. per min., and 18 ft. per min. when hauling a 4,000-lb. box or package. Intermittent overloads up to 7,000 lb. may be satisfactorily handled. Fig. 15 shows such a motorized lever dolly or tug-bar.

Western Gear Works

Fig. 15. Tug-bar.

Airborne Dolly. The airborne cargo dolly is a small, lightweight device, designed for moving light-to-medium-weight cargo within an airplane. It is constructed of aluminum, and one model is 19½ in. wide and 20 in. long. This particular unit was designed to ride on the lips of the longitudinal magnesium floor sections of the Lockheed R7V-1/1049D cargo aircraft. The dolly rides on four 1¾-in.-diam. roller-bearing wheels, one of which is installed in each corner of the unit. Side rails of the dolly extend below the lip of the floor extrusions of the airplane and therefore act as guides during fore-and-aft movement of the dolly. The lips are purposely extended below the bottom of the rollers to prevent the unit from being used on the ground. Its lightweight construction adds little weight penalty to the aircraft. Capacity is 4,000 lb. per unit.

A similar unit has been designed incorporating two large rollers across each end of the dolly to allow its use in aircraft with flat wooden or metal floors. Many airline personnel have improvised units of this nature by using a short length of conventional roller conveyor, with the side rails extended upward, if necessary, so that the cargo will clear the rollers when it is placed upon the dolly.

Roller Conveyors. Conventional warehouse roller conveyors have been widely used in aircraft, particularly in loading or unloading large numbers of small, easily handled packages. Both gravity and hand-powered systems have been used. Some airlines carry roller conveyors within the aircraft and use them in conjunction with a power-operated belt conveyor at the door, to materially decrease the manpower required for unloading operations.

Gravity systems, particularly in level-floor aircraft, introduce some problems because of restricted cabin heights within the airplanes in common use. The heights of the successively shorter conveyor legs required to give an adequate slope to the system sometimes introduce clearance problems which are inconvenient, though not necessarily insurmountable.

Block and Tackle. Like the "pry" or "Johnson Bar," the block and tackle was one of the earliest devices used for moving heavy cargo within an airplane. It is still in wide use, either in single or compound hitches. Cargo tie-downs are generally used as points of attachment, but care must be taken to avoid overloading the fittings. The earlier airplanes with relatively light tie-down fittings have a sad history of failures resulting from a husky cargo-handler giving a heave on a compound block. In some cases, radio racks and door jambs have also been used as anchors for blocks and tackles. The results have been uniformly disastrous.

Modern cargo aircraft in many cases have special attaching points for block and tackle, or high-capacity, permanent pulley blocks built into the floor structure. These block-and-tackle installations are usually located opposite door openings and at the ends of cargo compartments where they can be used in conjunction with various pulling devices to move cargo into, out of, or within the aircraft. Installations of this nature are incorporated in the Douglas C-124 and the Lockheed R7V-1. The C-124 pulleys, located in the rear of the aircraft, are used in conjunction with a ¾-in.-diam. steel cable for loading heavy vehicles or skid-mounted cargo into this aircraft. The pulleys are designed for a 30,000-lb. working load. A tie-down ring is incorporated in the pulley for holding down heavy cargo.

Portable Electric Winches. The need for a lightweight portable electric winch for handling heavy pieces of cargo has become more urgent with the advent of larger cargo aircraft. Convertible aircraft used by the military services for cargo, passengers, or litter patients have a particular need for devices of this nature. The Douglas Aircraft Company has recently designed an experimental 2,000-lb.-capacity unit. The winch incorporates a 28-v., d.c., vapor-proof electric motor driving a cable drum through a set of reduction gears. Incorporated in the base of the winch are facilities which permit the unit to be quickly attached to the seat studs installed in the cargo floor of the aircraft. An automatic over-running dry clutch protects the device against overloads, the clutch being set to release when loads in excess of 2,000 lb. are applied to the cable. A hand-held control switch with 25 ft. of control cable permits the operation of the unit from a remote position. The cable speed is 37 ft. per min. at full load of 2,000 lb. No-load speed is 74 ft. per min. and over-all weight is approximately 75 lb. Loads in excess of 2,000 lb. may be handled by the unit, by using a compound hook-up block and tackle system between the winch and the load to be pulled.

Portable Electric Winch and Capstan. Another approach to the cargo-handling problem within airplanes is incorporated in the "Bulldog Winch" illustrated in Fig. 16. This unit attaches to the airplane's cargo tie-downs and incorporates the following features:

  a. A 28-v., d.c., vapor-proof-shielded 6½-hp. motor driving a cable drum through a reduction-gear train. The drum contains 100 ft. of 9/32-in. flexible steel cable.
  b. A manually operated clutch which controls the drum or cable speed and allows the operator to select speeds ranging from 0 to 45 ft. per min. Maximum pulling force is 4,000 lb.
  c. A constant-speed capstan in addition to the cable drum. The capstan is designed for use with ¾-in.-diam. manila rope, and will develop a pulling force up to 3,000 lb. at speeds up to 55 ft. per min.
  d. The capstan and winch may be operated independently by one man at the same time, allowing him to maneuver items when a pulling force from two different directions is required.
  e. An on-off switch is provided on the base of the unit. A power cable is also provided for connection to the airplane's electrical system.
  f. Over-all weight of the unit is 198 lb.

Air Cargo Equipment Co.

Fig. 16. Bulldog air cargo winch.

Pallet Movers. Heavier cargo loads in aircraft are resulting in increasing study on the part of airline operators of ways and means for consolidating small packages into larger units. Consequently, palletization of cargo is becoming more and more common in military and commercial cargo terminals. Military Air Transport Service is now experimenting with lightweight wooden pallets which are shipped with the cargo and carry upwards of 1,500 lb. each.

Moving loaded pallets within an aircraft is therefore becoming a problem. Conventional warehouse pallet lifters with rubber-tired wheels are one solution to this requirement. The conventional units, however, need space to maneuver and, far too frequently, loaded aircraft do not have sufficient space for them.

The Palevator. A number of units are now being produced which combine the desirable features of direct lift and maneuverability in close quarters. A typical unit of this nature, the Palevator, produced experimentally by the General Logistics Corporation, is being evaluated by the military and various commercial airlines.

The Palevator is only 5 in. thick, which allows it to slip between loaded pallets or between a pallet and a side wall. Pallet forks swivel and are placed under the load after the lifting unit is in place; a hydraulic jack of 3,000-lb. capacity lifts the load prior to moving. In fore-and-aft movement, the Palevator moves on a large roller that forms its base. Locking the main roller permits traverse movement when interior balls built into the base bear on the floor.

Rol-A-Lift. Another somewhat similar device—the Rol-A-Lift—is proving adaptable to aircraft usage. Capacities range from 2,000 lb. to 10,000 lb. per unit. The Rol-A-Lift is mounted on dual rubber-tired, castered wheels that allow complete directional control of the lift and load. Width of the device has been held to a minimum to make the best possible use of available space.

Elevating Loading Platforms. The Douglas Aircraft Company has developed two types of semiportable loading equipment which may be attached to the door-sill of a Douglas C-118A/R6D-1 or Lockheed R7V-1. The units, which are used in loading cargo and litter patients, are known as the Douglas Cargo Lift and the Litter Lift. Both are self-contained and may be stowed within the aircraft for transport from stop to stop, or may be removed and held on the ground until needed.

The **Cargo Lift** shown in Fig. 17 is designed to handle light-to-medium loads, up to a total of 4,000 lb., from the truck bed to the floor of the airplane. In its main essentials, the device consists of a platform 50 in. × 74 in. supported by a frame assembly hanging from the doorsill of the airplane. Braces from the structure to the bottom of the fuselage provide stability to the entire unit. The frame not only supports the lifting platform, but also contains the motor, hoisting drum, cables, pulleys, etc. Maximum platform load is 4,000 lb. with a unit load of 200 lb./sq. ft.

Operation is through the airplane's electrical system, but preferably only when a ground power source is connected to the aircraft. Power for lifting the platform and load is supplied by a constant-speed, 26-v., d.c. reversible motor that incorporates a planetary gear system, overload clutch, electromagnetic brake, and thermal protection. The brake automatically engages whenever the unit is stopped or the power fails. An emergency manual release button may be used to lower the lift in the event of power failure.

The lift is controlled by a **hand-held switch** incorporating two spring-loaded control buttons for "up" and "down" movement, and an "on-off" switch for energizing the lift motor. Sufficient cable is provided to allow the unit to be operated either from the ground, or within the airplane.

Two special lift cables are provided in the top of the unit so that the device will lift itself into the airplane to its stowage position when the cables are connected to two fittings installed on the upper floor frame. The unit is lowered to operating position by reversing the process.

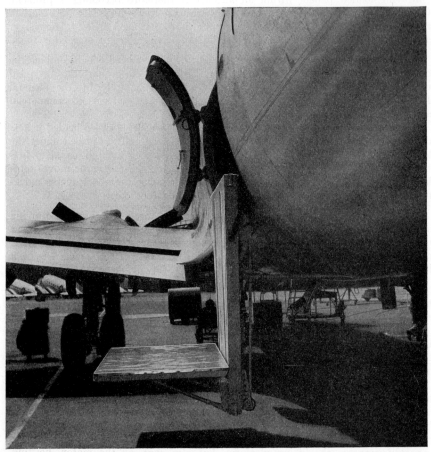

Douglas Aircraft Co.

Fig. 17. Cargo lift in operating position.

The **litter lift,** illustrated in Fig. 18, operates on a principle similar to the cargo lift but is a smaller unit both in size and capacity. This unit also attaches to the door frames of the Douglas C-118A/R6D-1 and the Lockheed R7V-1. A secondary attachment to the fuselage provides rigidity to the entire hoist when in operating position. It lifts itself into the airplane when the fuselage attachment is released and the platform arm is temporarily secured to the cargo deck.

The lifting unit consists of a welded tubular frame with a square aluminum platform which supports two litters with patients, or a 500-lb. maximum load. Hoisting drum, motors, and cable system are mounted on the bottom of the main support leg as shown in Fig. 18.

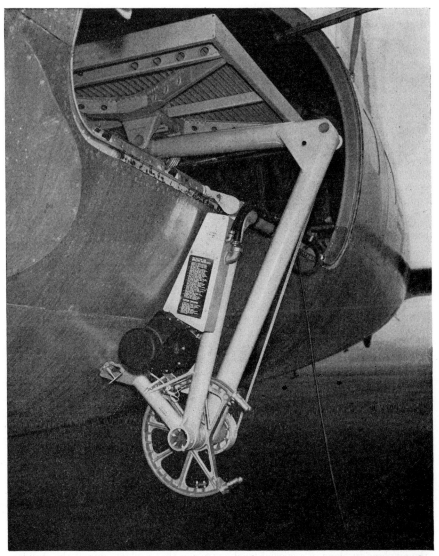

Douglas Aircraft Co.

Fig. 18. Litter lift in operating position.

BUILT-IN EQUIPMENT. Heavy materials handling requirements, particularly in military transports, have resulted in the design of built-in equipment with high lifting capacity and minimum increase in aircraft weight.

Overhead Traversing Crane Hoist. A crane hoist of this nature, installed in the Douglas C-124, is built by the O & M Machine Co., Inc., to Douglas Aircraft Company's specifications. The hoists may be used singly or in pairs. The crane will lift heavy loads vertically and carry them fore and aft in the airplane. Two units, normally installed in the airplane, also lift a large removable section of the aircraft floor (7 ft. 8 in. × 13 ft. 4 in.) which acts as an elevator for loading purposes. The crane is **electrically powered** from the airplane's electrical system, but is also equipped for emergency manual operation. A pendant control box provides for "Up" "Down" "Fore" "Aft" and "Emergency Stop" conditions. The crane beam is supported by rubber-tired trolleys riding on I-beams which extend the full length of the airplane. Electrically actuated limit switches prevent damage to crane or aircraft structure through inadvertent overtraversing.

The **maximum load** per unit is 8,000 lb. when two two-part lines are used. Two single lines will lift 4,000 lb. When the cranes are used in pairs, a maximum lifting capacity of 16,000 lb. is available. Maximum elevator capacity is 9,300 lb. Limit clutches automatically prevent overloads from damaging the hoisting unit. **Lifting time** is 60 sec. when hoisting 8,000 lb. 13 ft. Full-load traversing speed is 65 ft. per min. Total weight of hoist, trucks, power units, electrical equipment, and two snatch blocks is 405 lb.

Overhead Monorail Hoist. The Boeing C-97 series of cargo airplanes incorporate a built-in monorail hoist of simple design and rugged construction. The equipment consists of an electrically driven winch fastened to the forward bulkhead of the main cargo compartment. The **hoisting cable** runs from the winch to a traveling trolley and pulley block mounted on the monorail, which runs the full length of the cargo compartment. Fore-and-aft movement of the trolley is controlled by a separate traversing drum and cable mounted in the winch unit. Traversing and hoisting drums may be operated singly or in unison, so that cargo may be hoisted and then traversed the length of the cabin under power and full control.

The **motor** is a series-wound, reversible, 24v., d.c. unit. It draws its energy from the airplane's electrical system, and incorporates a built-in disc brake, a reduction gear system, a torque-limiting clutch, and an emergency hand-crank drive. **Operation** is controlled by a hand-held switch box equipped with 15 ft. of flexible cable and a quick disconnect plug. Three power receptacles are located in the cabin at convenient points for winch control. The control box incorporates pushbutton controls for "Up," "Down," "Forward," "Aft," and "Emergency Stop." The unit is energized only when the buttons are depressed. **Hoisting capacity** is 2,500 lb. with a single line and 5,000 lb. when a double line and snatch block are used.

Underfloor Conveyor. Lockheed Aircraft Corporation has equipped all R7V-1 cargo airplanes with an underfloor conveyor, the Aero-Trusty Conveyor, manufactured to Lockheed specifications by Weber Aircraft Corporation. The conveyor (see Fig. 19) consists of an endless and fixed chain running the length of the airplane fuselage in a special track extrusion that replaces one of the standard magnesium floor sections and maintains the same floor level.

Power for the conveyor is supplied by a power unit operated from the ship's 28v. power system, or from a ground power source. The power unit, motor, and gear train can provide a maximum of 4,000 lb. drawbar pull to the conveyor system. The motor system is equipped with a circuit-breaker in the ship's electrical system, thermal protection built into the motor, an electric brake, and a torque-limiting clutch built into the gear train. The power unit is also designed to provide a means of automatic slack-take-up for the endless chain when under load. In the interest of weight savings, the motor and power gear-train system is quickly removable from the aircraft.

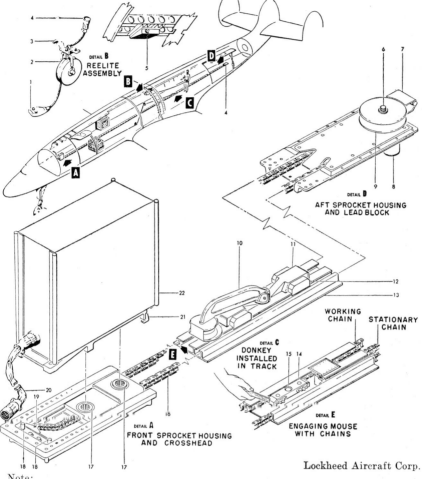

Lockheed Aircraft Corp.

Note:

1. When moving cargo, do not exceed the designed chain pull of 4,000 lb.
2. Do not attempt to insert mouse while conveyor chain is in motion. The operator inserting the mouse should be holding the hand control unit to prevent inadvertent chain movement.
3. Do not permit more than one mouse to be ejected at the forward chain sprocket guard at one time.
4. Do not operate from aircraft batteries. External source of power or auxiliary power unit is necessary.

Ref.	Part
1.	Hand control unit.
2.	Reel and extension cord.
3.	Reelite securing bracket.
4.	Reelite power plug.
5.	Reelite power receptacle.
6.	Pulley attaching bolt.
7.	Cable guard.
8.	Drain plug.
9.	Lead block pulley.
10.	Load hook (swivel).
11.	Donkey.
12.	End plates.
13.	Cargo conveyor track.
14.	Mouse.
15.	Donkey securing socket.
16.	Cargo conveyor chain.
17.	Power unit driveshaft engagement spline.
18.	Power unit housing positioning pin.
19.	Crosshead and tail chain assembly.
20.	Power cable.
21.	Power unit attachment.
22.	Power unit.

Fig. 19. Aero-Trusty Conveyor.

In operation, a submerged unit called a "mouse" is introduced into the conveyor chain system under the floor, and acts as an anchor block for the pulling or pushing unit, known as a "donkey." The donkey may be introduced at any desired point in the system, and therefore does not interfere with cargo already loaded. Since the conveyor is fully reversible, cargo may be pushed or pulled at the will of the operator. **Control** is achieved through a hand-held pendant switch and cord mounted on an overhead retractable reel. Sufficient cable is provided to allow the operator to walk to any part of the aircraft cabin. Operation is through two switch buttons, one for "forward" and one for "aft" motion.

An automatic brake in the power unit stops all movement and holds the load in any position. Loads may be "inched" to final position. Maximum chain pull is 4,000 lb., which will allow an 8,000-lb. load to be dragged on the metal floor installed in the airplane. Wheel-mounted loads of 20,000 lb. and up may be easily handled by the conveyor alone. Compounding may be accomplished through snatch blocks also supplied with the airplane. Weight installed—less motor, controls and other easily removed items—is 315 lb. Removable items total 125 lb.

Detachable Packs. In the original design of the Lockheed Constellation series, the weight-lifting capacity balanced the space provided in the fuselage. Successive increases in landing and take-off weights, however, increased the airplane's weight-lifting capacity to the point where, on shorter ranges, it could lift more payload than could be loaded in the fuselage. The Speedpak (see Fig. 20) was developed to meet this need, and constituted the first successful and only commercial application of the "pack" principle to aircraft design. It is used only on the 049, 649, and 749 series. No provision is made for the use of the Speedpak on Super-Constellations.

The Speedpak is a self-contained, quickly **removable container** of aircraft-type construction. It attaches to the underside of the airplane's fuselage and incorporates its own electrically powered winch which raises or lowers the unit by four cables. Emergency manual operation is provided for. Manually operated locks provide the final attachment.

When the pack is detached, loading is done from the top of the unit. When the pack is attached to the aircraft, a side door permits loading and unloading at intermediate stops. A zippered vinyl cover protects the contents from dirt and dust while on the ground, and rubber seals between the pack and airplane further protect the contents in flight.

Specifications for the Speedpak are as follows:

Design gross weight	10,000 lb.
Empty weight	1,800 lb.
Capacity load	8,200 lb.
Length	33 ft.–4 in.
Width	7 ft.–4 in.
Usable depth	3 ft.–2 in.
Usable volume	427 cu. ft.
Hoisting motor—reversible	3 hp., 24 volt

The unit also incorporates retractable rubber-tired wheels for ground towing, a built-in flush lighting system, a recognition lamp, and web nets and tiedowns for securing cargo in flight. A self-contained, thermostatically controlled electrical heating system provides heat for the protection of cargo. Smoke detectors and a CO_2 extinguishing system provide protection against fires. The electrical system incorporates the usual hoisting-limit switches and overload circuit-breakers.

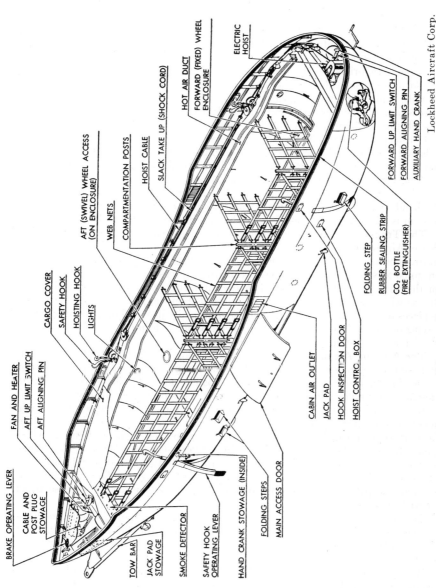

Lockheed Aircraft Corp.

Fig. 20. Speedpak details.

When the Speedpak is installed, the aircraft's speed is reduced 8 m.p.h. indicated air-speed at a given flying weight, the rate of climb is reduced 40 ft. per min., and the range is reduced 5 percent for a given amount of fuel. The "pack" does not affect the control characteristics of the airplane. The Speedpak was designed and built by Lockheed Aircraft Corporation.

Removable Aircraft Floors. A radical departure from conventional materials handling systems is incorporated in removable aircraft floors installed in all cargo airplanes. In principle, the floor is composed of large removable pallets, which are loaded and unloaded on the dock and then moved into the aircraft by means of rails, bridges, or similar devices. Locking the pallet to the basic aircraft structure completes the loading operation, as all cargo tie-down is accomplished on the dock before loading the movable floor section.

Considerable savings in aircraft loading and unloading time is achieved with a relatively small weight penalty on the aircraft. A number of such systems have been, or are being, developed, three of which are given below.

The Cargon, the first of such systems, has been illustrated in Fig. 1. Weight penalty on the aircraft is only 550 lb., and a maximum of 13,000 lb. of cargo may be handled at one time. Average turn-around time of the airplane with this system is 16 min. from take-off to touchdown, including time to load and unload.

The Trac-Pac system is a somewhat similar system developed by the United States Air Force at Wiesbaden, Germany, for use with their Fairchild C-119 aircraft. These units compromise flat or caged pallets, ranging in size from 40 × 48 in. to 60 × 84 in., which move on special wheeled legs engaged to tracks installed in the airplane. When positioned in the aircraft, the pallets are locked to the tracks with special cam-locking devices installed on the pallets. Since the system replaces much of the permanent equipment normally installed in the aircraft, a net saving of 255 lb. is achieved by this system. While still in the experimental stage, the Trac-Pac system shows considerable promise.

The Air Log Airail system, now under development by the Air Logistics Corporation, is an integrated materials handling proposal comprising a combination of loading and elevating devices, rails, pallet dollies, pallets, and tie-downs designed for universal use in and between all types of cargo transports.

Rails, which carry loaded pallets within the aircraft, are designed for attachment to the aircraft's floor tie-down points or may be bolted directly to the aircraft floor. Loaded pallets move on the rails to their final positions, at which point they are locked to the guide rails by four cam-engaging locks. Pallets are of standard 40 × 48 in. size or may be obtained in multiples of two and four times the size of the standard unit. Capacity per 40 × 48 in. pallet is 2,000 lb. If desired, the pallet dolly may also be used with a conventional warehouse pallet or with folding pallet boxes.

The system is designed for use in all current cargo transports, whether of high- or low-bed design, nose, tail, or side-loading. A turntable that turns and/or traverses between the tracks is part of the system used within side-loading transports.

When installed in transports with no floor modification, some weight penalty on the aircraft is involved. However, the rapid loading and unliading which the system makes possible, particularly between various types of airplanes, offsets some of the weight penalties involved. Permanent installation in an aircraft will also materially decrease the weight of the installation.

BELT CONVEYORS

CONTENTS

CONTENTS (*Continued*)

BELT CONVEYORS

BELT CONVEYOR DESIGN. Good belt conveyor design is a product of careful analysis and study, good judgment and experience, and sufficient technical knowledge for meeting basic engineering requirements. Experts are required to design installations such as a 2-mi.-long belt conveyor or an inclined conveyor that requires a 1,500 hp. drive, or to determine the accelerating or decelerating time for a system of conveyors handling, say, 6,000 tons of ore per hr.

No attempt is made to present a solution of the occasional or exceptional so-called long-center belt conveyor problem. An adequate solution becomes intricately involved in increments of acceleration, belt stretch, motor drives, and controls—all requiring specialized training, long experience, and availability of reference data assembled by engineers engaged professionally in belt conveyor design.

The belt conveyor consists essentially of an endless belt of sufficient longitudinal and transverse strength for supporting a load and onto which material is placed for transportation. The roadbed over which a belt travels may consist of a slider trough for the handling of light, clean material or a series of flat or troughed idler rolls for handling heavier articles or bulk material. Because a belt can be made of materials suitable in width, strength, and construction to each kind of material to be handled, the belt conveyor is one of the most widely used and efficient kinds of materials handling conveyors.

Types of Belt Conveyors

FLAT BELT CONVEYORS. Flat belts are used for transporting:

1. Small parts on assembly conveyors.
2. Small pieces or parts in crates or boxes, packages, bundles, etc., in manufacturing, shipping, warehousing, and merchandising operations.
3. Mail bags, bundles, baggage, etc., in post-office and terminal operations.
4. Some bulk materials, such as foundry sand and cottonseed where slider beds can be used.
5. Personnel, logs, other large objects.

TROUGHED BELT CONVEYORS. In the handling of bulk materials, troughed belts are used:

1. For obtaining greater carrying capacity than flat belts.
2. For handling material that would slide or roll off flat belts.

The problems in the application of troughed belts are concerned with the wide variation and range of sizes, weight, and condition of bulk materials; speeds; capacities and lengths of conveyors; the many factors determining the grade, type, and construction of the conveyor belt; and availability of various types of idlers.

NORMAL BELT CONVEYORS. The great majority of troughed belt conveyors used in industrial plants or transporting operations are employed to move material from one location to another within the plant or operation. Such belt conveyors might be called "normal"—or **"transfer"**—conveyors. The distances moved are relatively short, paths are straight-line, and horizontal or inclined belt stresses are well within the limits of standard cotton fabric belts. In general, for a conventional belt conveyor, the total weight of the belt and idlers on the carrying and return runs, together with the weight of the conveyed material on the fully loaded belt, is relatively small, as indicated by low belt stresses well within the safe tension limits of the selected belt. The additional force required to start the conveyor and to bring this relatively small mass up to operating speed is provided by the reserve capacity contained in the belt, the drive pulley, and the drive. Belt stretch is not an important item, and starting stresses are ignored.

As an approximate arbitrary division line, a belt conveyor should not be considered a normal conveyor when its operating belt tension exceeds 75 to 80 percent of the rated maximum operating tension, as given later in Fig. 1. Starting stresses should be figured to assure ample drive pulley and take-up capacity to prevent the belt from slipping on the drive pulley during starting. A conveyor cannot be classed as normal when its path is a combination of horizontal and inclined motion with a vertical transition curve connecting the two sections, or a combination of decline and horizontal motions. The minimum radius of a concave transition curve is determined by the belt tension at the curve and the weight per feet of the belt. Unless starting stresses are provided against, the belt may rise up from the idlers during starting. Both empty and loaded belt tensions must be taken into account, the radius of the curve being based on the less favorable condition.

LONG-CENTER CONVEYORS. There is no sharp line of demarcation between a normal and a long-center conveyor. A long-center conveyor may be defined as one in which the belt tensions may become critical, perhaps to the extent that:

1. Excessive stretch becomes a factor, and high-tension cord or special fabric belts are required, not only for greater strength but also for less belt stretch.
2. Well-designed, gradual-starting control is necessary for keeping the accelerating forces and the belt stretch within allowable limits during starting.

BELT CONVEYORS AS TRANSPORTATION MEDIA. Long-center belt conveyors may be used for jobs such as:

1. Transporting the output of a mine across rough country to a processing plant located where rail or water transportation is available.
2. Bringing coal or ore from underground or open-pit mining operations onto the surface.
3. Operating over long distances (by means of a series of conveyors) over paths that are a combination of incline, decline, and horizontal sections, following the natural contours of the ground.
4. Stripping, mining, or construction operations.

Such conveyors must be competitive with other means of transportation in cost per ton-mile, and the problems presented are economic ones, as well as those inherent to complex design. There must be sufficient over-all quantities to be handled to justify the original cost of a belt conveyor. Whether there is any final salvage value depends on the wear and tear of the conveying operation.

The availability of material at the feed end and its disposal at the discharge end must be such that the material can be handled in a constant, continuous stream at a rate that will permit a competitive cost per ton-mile, covering amortization, power and light, operating and maintenance labor, supplies, repairs, and belt replacement. The belt is the largest single item of cost in the original installation as well as the main item of replacement. The belt selected will determine the maximum conveyor centers and thus the number of conveyor units in a conveyor transportation system.

Each transfer of material from one belt to another not only wears the belt but also presents an operating hazard, particularly in the handling of material that may be wet and sticky. Such material may build up and clog at transfer points and damage the belt seriously. An attendant may be stationed at each transfer point to keep the material flowing, but this provision adds to the operating cost. Longer belts require fewer transfers, but the savings in transfers must be weighed against the increased cost per foot of belts of higher tension for conveyors with longer belt centers.

Belt Conveyor Components

CONVEYOR BELTING. The great majority of belt conveyors handling bulk material use some type of rubber-covered conveyor belt made up of a carcass having longitudinal strength for pulling the load, transverse strength for supporting the load, and protected from damage by a rubber cover, which varies in thickness and wear resistance according to each application.

TYPES OF BELT CONSTRUCTION. Woven or stitched canvas belting is more widely used for package and piece handling than for handling bulk material. Belts of this kind can be made with special coatings, impregnations, or insulations for resisting acids and fumes and high temperatures in the handling of bulk material in various special applications.

Cotton-fabric ply-constructed belting is the most widely used kind of rubber-covered conveyor belt, in which the carcass is made up of a number of layers or "plies" of woven cotton fabrics of various weights. These fabrics have been impregnated with a rubber compound known as "friction" rubber, which, after vulcanizing, binds the plies together. Fig. 1 gives the permissible operating belt tensions and pulley diameters for cotton-fabric ply-constructed belts.

Cord belts, with a carcass made up of longitudinal fibers or steel cords imbedded in rubber and enclosed in an envelope of belt ducking, to which the outer rubber covering is attached, provide greater strength, more flexibility, and somewhat greater impact resistance than ply-constructed belts. The steel-cord belt has the further very desirable characteristic of low stretchability, making possible ever-increasing conveyor centers and capacities.

Special **high tensile fabrics** provide strengths comparable to the fabric cord belts. Belts with **special weaves** are designed to give greater transverse strength when handling unusually heavy coarse material or to give better troughability, which permits the use of thicker belts, or to have greater resiliency to impact for unusually severe applications.

Belt covers made of special wear- and impact-resisting rubber compounds with cord breaker strips imbedded in tough rubber to bind the cover to the carcass are designed to protect an expensive belt carcass at loading points when a sharp, heavy lump material is being handled under adverse loading conditions.

The regular **breaker strip,** included in the cover in the top grades of belt, is an open weave fabric known as "cider cloth," which is imbedded in the rubber cover to bind it more firmly to the carcass and to resist the stripping of the cover.

No attempt is made here to cover the technology of the design and construction of the various types of conveyor belting: this would require a handbook

Permissible Operating Tensions (lb. per in. per ply)			Weight of Fabric	Minimum Pulley Diameters in Inches										Percent Permissible Operating Tension
Type of Belt Splice				Number of Plies in Belt										
Metal	Vulcanized 2L/S*													
	Less than 2	More than 3		3	4	5	6	7	8	9	10	11	12	
26	30	35	28 oz.	18	24	30	36	42	48	48	54	60	66	100
			and	16	20	24	30	36	42	42	48	54	60	80
				12	16	20	24	30	30	36	36	42	48	60
30	35	40	32 oz.	12	16	16	20	24	24	30	30	36	36	40
35	40	45	36 oz.	20	30	36	42	48	54	60	60	66	72	100
			and	18	24	30	36	42	42	48	54	54	60	80
				12	16	20	24	30	36	36	42	48	48	60
40	50	55	42 oz.	12	16	18	20	24	30	30	36	36	42	40
†	60	70	48 oz.		30	36	42	48	60	66	72	72	84	100
					24	30	36	36	48	54	60	60	66	80
					20	24	24	30	36	42	42	48	54	60
					20	20	20	24	30	30	36	36	42	40

* $2L/S = 2 \times$ conveyor centers/Belt speed (F.P.M.); for 450 ft. centers at 300 F.P.M. $2\ L/S = 900/300 = 3$. The 100 percent tension for a 7-ply 32-oz. belt with a vulcanized splice would be 40 lb. per in. per ply, and a pulley 42 in. in diameter should be used. If the belt tension is 80 percent of the maximum permissible, or 32 lb. per in. per ply, a pulley 36 in. in diameter could be used.

† Metal splices are not recommended for 48-oz. fabric.

Fig. 1. Permissible operating belt tensions and minimum pulley diameters for cotton-fabric ply-constructed rubber conveyor belts.

devoted to belts alone. It is good practice to consult belt and equipment manufacturers in regard to the best grade and type of belt to be used in an installation, particularly where belt stresses are such as to require the maximum in the regular cotton fabric ply-constructed belt. A fabric cord or high-tensile fabric ply-constructed belt of less thickness may prove to be better, not only because it would be more flexible, giving better troughing, but also it might be more economical. A special cover or special transverse strength might increase considerably the tonnage a given belt might handle.

The ply-construction belt, because of its wide, general use and its particular construction and application, has become practically standardized and well known. The characteristics of this belt can be quite definitely defined.

The application of this kind of belt is based on the number of plies and the weight of the duck used to make up the carcass of the belt. The **maximum number of plies** that can be used to make up the carcass depends upon the width of the belt and the weight of the duck used. The combination must be such that the belt will be sufficiently flexible transversely to form a trough that will conform to the shape of the troughing idler and maintain adequate contact with the horizonal center roll of the troughing idler. The center-roll contact provides the guiding effect to the belt. A belt that is so stiff that it touches only on the inclined rolls will not train properly (keep centered on the line of travel), and the restricted contact with the inclined rolls concentrates the wear of the rubber cover to a narrow strip toward each edge of the belt.

The **minimum number of plies** that can be used also depends on the belt width and the weight of the duck used. There must be enough plies to give the belt sufficient body to train properly and to support the material it is to convey. The heavier and coarser the material, the more the plies and the heavier the duck required. See Fig. 16 for minimum and maximum plies.

Quality of Carcass and Cover. Five weights of cotton duck, which determine the allowable maximum operating tension, are normally used. These weights are 28, 32, 36, 42, and 48 oz. for a piece of duck 36 in. long and 42 in. wide. Fig. 1 gives **allowable unit operating tensions,** which means the number of pounds tension permitted for each ply 1 in. wide. These operating tensions are based on the ultimate strength of the fabric, on the percent of elongation, and on the strength of the splice that makes the belt endless.

There are several choices in the selection of a 36-in.-wide belt: 6 ply 28 oz., 5 ply 32 oz., or 4 ply 42 oz. Each supports about the same load and has about the same tension capacity. The belt with the lesser ply of heavier duck is generally preferred because it is more flexible, both in troughing and in going around terminal pulleys, and may be lower in cost.

The quality of the carcass is measured by the **grade of the friction-rubber** compound with which the fabric plies have been impregnated and which determines the extent of adhesion keeping the plies together. Friction is designated by the pull in pounds required to strip a 1-in.-wide piece of ply from the carcass of the belt. The carcass quality is increased by the use of a **skim coat** of rubber between the plies—a thin film of rubber that adds to the flexibility or **"flex life,"** of a belt in passing around terminal pulleys.

Cover quality is based on the **blending** of rubbers to produce covers best suited for each grade of service, according to the experience and best judgment of the belt manufacturer. The **first grade** belt has a cover made of a rubber that will provide maximum abrasion resistance for the handling of **very abrasive material,** with a breaker strip (regular or special, depending on the severity of service), the highest "friction" (20 lb.), and a skim coat of rubber between the plies. The **second grade** belt has a cover of a different rubber in order to provide the necessary resistance in handling an **abrasive** material whose lumps may not be as large, hard, and sharp as those of very abrasive material. The cover is provided with a regular breaker strip and the carcass has a 16-lb. friction, usually with a skim coat between plies. The **third grade** can be used for handling **nonabrasive** or **mildly abrasive** materials. It does not have a breaker strip in the cover. It has a 12-lb. friction, but no skim coat between plies.

Belt Splices. The **metal splice** is a butt splice, in which the carefully squared ends of the belt are joined by some kind of metal fastener, generally a bolted plate type, of which the "Flexco" fastener is typical. Because it is relatively simple to install, there is a tendency to use this splicing wherever possible on the "normal" type of conveyor. It is limited in the amount of full belt strength it will develop, and allowable unit belt stresses are consequently reduced when a metal splice is used. It is subject to damage because of the loosening of bolts and plates and should have frequent inspection. It interferes with the scraper type of belt cleaners unless the rubber cover is far enough removed to permit the fasteners to sit directly on the carcass, and the entire joint is covered with a rubber compound that can be vulcanized into place. This makes not only a smooth surface but a highly desirable seal against the entrance of moisture into the joint.

Some operators prefer the metal splice over the vulcanized splice because it can be used in emergencies with a minimum of shutdown time. Low starting torque is recommended when there are metal splices on highly stressed belts. Metal splices are limited to ply-constructed belts.

The **vulcanized belt splice** is a stepped, lapped splice in which the several plies of the belt are vulcanized together to make a joint of a strength almost equal to that of the solid belt and allowing higher operating belt tensions than for the metal splice. The joint is completely sealed and presents a smooth surface for various kinds of belt cleaners. This splice, of course, is more desirable than the metal splice; but technical skill and experience, time, and vulcanizing equipment are required for making it. This generally limits it to the larger installations. Detailed data are supplied by the belt manufacturer.

Belt Cleaners. Considerable effort is being spent by equipment manufacturers to develop better cleaning devices, and these manufacturers should be consulted in this regard. No cleaning device will succeed if installed in a location that cannot be readily reached for inspection, cleaning, adjusting, and repairing, nor can it give successful service if allowed to become fouled with an accumulation of dirt.

Belt Care. Regular general inspection and periodic detailed inspection should be made to detect and repair any injury to the belt covering as soon as possible after it occurs. Edge wear due to side interference should be watched for and corrected, because ply separation quickly develops with edge wear. Splices, and particularly mechanical splices, should be carefully maintained. Any defect that permits moisture to get into the carcass causes rapid belt deterioration.

A conveyor belt is exposed to wear and tear at the loading point, and to possible damage caused by gouging, edge wear, and other hazards. Every precaution should be taken against any such damage that could result from poor design, construction, and maintenance.

A poorly selected belt may handle many more tons of even a coarse abrasive material than the most carefully selected belt operating on a poorly designed conveyor if the former is operated at the proper speed and belt tension over freely turning idler rolls properly spaced and kept in good alignment, with well designed drive and terminals, and suitable loading and unloading facilities.

BELT CONVEYOR IDLERS. Conveyor idlers determine to a great extent the efficiency of a belt conveyor. They must be accurately made and provide a rigid framework that will maintain permanent alignment of well-balanced, smooth-running, easy-turning idler rolls.

Pressure lubrication is applied, in general, to individual or groups of ball or roller bearings. "One-shot" lubrication or "sealed-for-life" bearings are advocated as desirable installations to minimize lubrication. Properly lubricated, a well-designed and constructed idler roll, which has adequate protection against the entrance of dirt and grit into the ball or roller bearings, may require additional lubrication only once a year. This lubrication is not so much to provide needed grease as to give slight movement to the grease in the bearings and housings in order to remove any dirt particles that may tend to collect at the entrance to the bearing.

More idlers are overgreased than are undergreased. Bearings may be handicapped and prevented from free and easy turning by packing grease too tightly.

The correct grade and kind of grease has an important bearing on idler performance; grease recommendations should be made by the equipment manufacturers or by an oil company expert.

Kinds of Carrying Idlers. There are, in general, three kinds of belt-carrying idlers which are used in handling bulk materials and which influence the cross sectional load on the belt:

1. The flat-belt idler, used for granular-type material having an angle of repose of not less than 35°. Generally used where low capacity requirements warrant only a simple, low-cost conveyor, or where it is desirable to plow a suitable material from the belt for distribution into hoppers (foundry sand, wood chips, cotton seed, for example). Handling pulpwood logs in the paper industry is an important application for the flat-belt conveyor.
2. The 20° troughing idler, used for handling all kinds of bulk materials, permits the use of heavy ply-constructed belts—well-standardized in the conveyor industry and the most widely used.
3. The 35° and the 45° troughing idler, used for handling small-particle light-weight-material, such as grain, cottonseed, wood chips, and also for heavier medium-sized lumps like crushed stone, gives deeper trough, greater cross-section, greater capacity than the 20° troughing idler; requires thinner ply-constructed belts or the more flexible synthetic fiber or cord belts to conform to the deeper trough.

Idler Modifications. Various modifications have been made in the design of idlers for specific purposes. There are **self-aligning idlers,** which are used in the carrying and return runs to compensate for lack of permanent- and fixed-belt alignment, unbalanced loading, and other factors that would cause the belt to run out of line. A belt should be installed to run in line without the use of self-aligning idlers, the latter acting only as a means for preventing the belt from getting too far out of alignment. These idlers are spaced at about 150-ft. centers in both runs. Rubber-covered **impact idlers,** closely spaced at loading points, cushion the impact of heavy lumps and are good belt protection at all loading points. Closely spaced regular idlers are adequate to keep the belt snug against the loading skirt plates when handling small-size free-flowing material. **Transition idlers** are used for highly stressed belts. These are troughing idlers with provision for regulating the angle of the inclined rolls in order to provide a gradual transition from a fully troughed section of the belt to a flat-faced pulley. This transition eliminates high stress concentrations in the belt.

Idler Rolls. Concentricity and uniformity of wall thickness are necessary for smooth-running idler rolls. The rolls may be made of heavy steel or other metal for unusually severe service. Cast-iron rolls may be used where corrosive conditions exist. Particularly in the handling of coke, return-run idler rolls wear rapidly and are often made of heavy-wear-resisting steel or covered with a thin rubber sleeve. Rubber discs or rubber spirals replace the smooth return rolls of belts handling sticky material, in order to avoid the buildup of material on a smooth return roll.

Diameter of Idler Rolls. Except for special applications, such as for underground conveyors and portable conveyors, the following diameters of idler rolls are considered adequate for the services noted:

4-in. diameter idler rolls....Belt speeds up to 300 f.p.m.
    20-in. belts and less ......No limitations on material suitable for belt
    24-in. belts ....50 lb. per cu. ft. maximum weight of material
    30-in. belts ....Small material up to 2 in., 100 lb. per cu. ft. and under

Average Idler Spacing in Feet				Weight of Revolving Parts of Idler Rolls*		Width of Belt (in.)	Minimum Belt Tensions at Loading End of Conveyor for 2% Sag Limitation											
Troughing Rolls							50 Lb./Cu. Ft. Material				100 Lb./Cu. Ft. Material				150 Lb./Cu. Ft. Material			
Weight of Material per Cu. Ft.			Return Rolls	Trough Rolls	Return Rolls		Idler Spacing			Load on Belt (lb. per ft.) ϕ	Idler Spacing			Load on Belt (lb. per ft.) ϕ	Idler Spacing			Load on Belt (lb. per ft.) ϕ
Up to 50 lb.	Up to 100 lb.	Up to 150 lb.					5 ft.	4 ft.	3 ft.		4½ ft.	4 ft.	3 ft.		4 ft.	3½ ft.	3 ft.	
5½	5	5	10	25	21	16	400	350	300	7	500	450	400	14	650	550	500	21
5	5	4½	10	26	23	18	450	400	350	9	650	550	450	18	800	700	600	27
5	4½	4	10	29	25	20	500	450	400	11	800	700	500	22	950	850	750	34
5	4½	4	10	33	29	24	700	600	500	17	1,200	1,000	850	34	1,500	1,300	1,100	51
4½	4	4	10	48	43	30	1,100	900	700	27	1,900	1,600	1,200	54	2,300	2,000	1,700	81
4½	4	3½	10	55	50	36	1,600	1,300	1,000	39	2,500	2,200	1,700	78	3,200	2,800	2,400	117
4½	4	3½	9	64	57	42	1,800	1,400	1,100	54	3,000	2,400	2,000	108	3,600	3,000	2,600	162
4	4	3½	9	71	65	48	2,300	1,800	1,300	74	4,000	3,000	2,300	148	4,500	4,000	3,500	222
4	3½	3	8	78	72	54		1,900	1,400	95		3,500	2,500	190	5,000	4,500	4,000	285
3½	3½	3	8	86	79	60		2,000	1,500	120		3,800	2,800	240	5,500	5,000	4,500	360

* Weights of idler roll parts (from Link Belt Co. Catalog No. 900) are based on (1) 5-in. diameter steel rolls, 16- to 24-in. belts inclusive; and (2) 6-in. diameter steel rolls, 30- to 60-in belts inclusive. For belts 48 in. and over handling 100 lb. per cu. ft. material and over, check on the advisability of using heavy-duty idlers, whose weights will be about 55 percent higher than those shown.
Idler weights are subject to variation according to roll construction.
Load on belt in pounds per foot is based on the capacities listed in Fig. 4.

Fig. 2. Idler spacing, weights of revolving parts, and minimum belt tensions as in 20° troughing idlers.

5-in. diameter idler rolls.... Belt speeds up to 500 f.p.m.
24-in. to 36-in. belts ...... Up to 10-in. material, 100 lb. per cu. ft. and under

6-in. diameter idler rolls.... Belt speeds up to 800 f.p.m.
36-in. belts and over ..... Handling all manner of normal material
48-in belts and over ..... Heavy-duty idler rolls for coarse, heavy lumps

7-in. diameter idler rolls.... Heavy-duty idler rolls for extra-heavy belts handling coarse, heavy lump material

In general, return idler rolls are of the same diameter as for the carrying run of the belt.

Idler Spacing. For the "normal" belt conveyor, troughing and return-run idlers are spaced as indicated in Fig. 2. Since the permissible idler spacing is a function of the belt tension, a graduated spacing could be used, increasing the spacing as the tension increases. This step is seldom taken, however, except on long conveyors. By dividing the conveyor into **zones** and increasing the spacing in each zone in accordance with definite increases in belt tension, a saving in the

Width of Belt (in.)	Maximum Permissible Tension (lb.)	Permissible Belt Tension at Entry to Curve					
		Radius of Curve in Feet					
		20	30	50	75	100	125
24	3,600	1,800	2,400	2,800	3,100	3,200	3,300
	4,800	2,400	3,200	3,800	4,100	4,300	4,400
30	5,400	2,000	3,100	4,000	4,500	4,700	4,800
	7,200	2,700	4,200	5,400	6,000	6,300	6,500
36	8,600	2,200	4,300	6,000	6,800	7,300	7,500
	11,500	2,800	5,700	8,000	9,200	9,700	10,000
42	10,000		4,100	6,500	7,600	8,200	8,600
	12,000		5,000	7,800	9,200	9,900	10,300
	15,000		6,200	9,700	11,500	12,300	12,900
	18,000		7,500	11,700	13,800	14,800	15,500
48	14,000		4,600	8,400	10,200	11,200	11,700
	20,000		6,600	12,000	14,600	16,000	16,800
	23,000		7,600	13,800	16,800	18,400	19,000

Fig. 3. Maximum operating belt tensions for convex vertical curves.

number of troughing idlers can be made. A 6-ft. maximum is considered to be a practical limit, even though belt tensions might indicate a still greater spacing. When a **vertical convex curve** is used in passing from an incline to a horizontal section, the belt tensions are limited (as indicated in Fig. 3), and the troughing idlers are spaced at about one-half of the normal spacing (indicated in Fig. 2). Where belt stresses are at a maximum for the curve, a spacing of four-tenths of normal is advisable.

CONVEYOR PULLEYS. As a conveyor belt passes around a **terminal or bend pulley,** the plies of a ply-constructed belt are elongated, in proportion to the distance from the center of rotation of the pulley. Consequently there is a slight movement of one ply upon the other. This movement must be taken up by the "friction" rubber than binds the plies together. The larger the pulley. the less strain on the "friction" and the less tendency to ply separation. A "skim coat" of rubber between plies relieves the strain on the "friction" rubber and tends to permit higher belt tensions or pulleys of smaller diameter.

Fig. 1 shows **minimum pulley diameters** for various percentages of permissible operating belt tensions, with ply-constructed belts. Generally, **crown-face pulleys** are used. Where belt stresses are so high as to become critical, **straight-face pulleys** are used at the points of maximum tension to reduce the areas of stress concentration in the belt. For belts up to 42 in. in width, the pulley face is generally 3 in. wider than the belt. For the wider belts the pulley face is 4 to 6 in. wider than the width of the belt. **Cast-iron pulleys** are generally superseded by welded-steel pulleys with closed ends, which contribute to safety. **Welded-steel pulleys** are lighter in weight and less subject to breakage. **Magnetic pulleys** are used on belts ahead of crushers and grinders for removing pieces of iron and steel.

Rubber lagging is used on pulleys to increase the friction between belt and drive pulley. It is also advantageous on snub and bend pulleys that contact the "dirty" side of the belt. The rubber lagging on a drive pulley is of harder rubber (55 to 65 durometer) than that used on snub or bend pulleys, where a softer rubber (40 to 50 durometer) is used to form a pliable pulley surface that will be easy on the belt and prevent the buildup of material on the pulley face. Drive-pulley lagging is about ½ in. thick. A ⅜-in. thickness of soft rubber lagging on a snub or bend pulley makes a soft, pliable cover. The lagging may be grooved to make the surface more pliable and self-cleaning.

For the heavier belts, 30 in. and over, a **snub pulley** is used to bring the belt in line with the return idler rolls, even though not required for drive-pulley contact. Such a pulley may be of small diameter to replace the first return idler. **Access space** should be provided beneath the pulleys for cleaning and inspection purposes, to provide space for belt cleaners, and for the disposal of the drippings from the belt cleaners.

DRIVES FOR BELT CONVEYORS. Practically all belt conveyors are driven by an **electric motor** directly connected to a **speed-reducer** unit through a flexible coupling. The reducer may be directly connected to the drive shaft of the conveyor through a flexible coupling or by means of a chain drive. Direct connection of reducer to drive shaft is used mostly in the heavier drives or where space permits, by extension of the drive in a direct line from the center of the conveyor.

Most conveyors are driven at the **head shaft** where the material is discharged from the conveyor, and where space is often restricted. Here the chain-connected drive permits the reducer and motor to be set to the best advantage—alongside, above, or in front of the conveyor. The heavy flexible coupling is replaced by a precision-steel roller chain and sprockets, the speed reduction in the chain drive permitting the use of a smaller reducer and if desirable, making possible a change in the speed of the conveyor by a simple change of the drive sprocket of the chain drive.

Ball- or roller-bearing pillow blocks on terminal pulley shafts are advantageous, not so much for the reduction of friction in the bearings, which is relatively unimportant, but owing to a considerable reduction in maintenance compared to plain sleeve bearings.

For inclined conveyors a **hold-back device** must be provided to prevent possible backward movement of the conveyor. For this purpose a brake may be installed on the motor, but preferably a more direct device should be mounted on the end of the drive shaft, opposite the drive, so that it will lock with the least backward movement of the belt. A differential band brake, a post brake, or a device such as the "Wonway Clutch" will provide the necessary protection.

Motors and **controls** are important to the operation of a belt conveyor, and particularly in the case of the long belt conveyors previously discussed, they should be specified under the direction of an electrical engineer experienced in their application to belt conveyors.

TRANSFER TERMINALS. The transfer of materials from one conveyor to another—and particularly a right-angle transfer—is one of the most critical kinds of operations. To save height and space the **transfer chute** may be restricted, the drive may be crowded against the conveyor, a snub pulley and belt-cleaner may be installed underneath the belt—all to such an extent that good operation house-keeping, inspection, and maintenance are practically impossible.

Transfer chutes must be of the size, shape, and slope best suited to the flow-ability and size of the material to be moved, and to the speed of the belt and the diameter of the discharge pulley, which determine the path or trajectory of the material as it leaves the belt, and where the material will land in the chute. If it lands in a restricted area, such as the corner of the chute, it "fights" itself in trying to get away, which may cause buildup, particularly in the case of sluggish or coarse material. Dry, free-flowing material will move in valley angles of 35 to 40°; sticky material, such as wet fine coal, may build up and clog in 50 to 55° valley angles. Stainless-steel liners help the flow of material; loosely attached sheets of tough impact rubber help to prevent buildup when sticky material strikes the side of a chute.

Provision must be made for the **disposal of the drippings or scrapings** from belt cleaners. If the drippings or scrapings are to be dropped into an extension of the discharge chute coming in underneath the belt cleaners, liberal height must be allowed, particularly for sluggish material that will flow down only on steep slopes. Sometimes, in order to reduce height, small auxiliary conveyors are placed under the belt cleaner to return the scrapings into the flow of material. Belt scrapers used with magnetic pulleys should be located out of the magnetic field of the pulley.

Power plants handling large quantities of fine wet coal over magnetic pulleys find that considerable quantities of coal cling to and drop off with the magnetic refuse at belt scrapers, thus presenting a major clean-up problem. A small vibrating screen onto which the magnetic refuse can drop will separate out the coal, which can then be put back into the flow, leaving only the magnetic refuse to be disposed of.

LOADING AND UNLOADING DEVICES. Various chutes, feeders, trimmers, plows, and trippers are employed to deliver materials to and remove them from conveyor belts.

Direct chute from dump hopper, bin or storage pile. Such an installation is limited to delivering free-flowing materials directly to the belt conveyor. The volume of delivery can be controlled by a regulating gate, usually of the quadrant type. Size of material is limited to that which will not arch over a gate opening set to suit the capacity of the belt to which it delivers.

Chute from a Feeder. The volume of material is controlled by the feeder delivering to the chute. The function of the chute, particularly in the handling of large lumps or coarse abrasive material, is to deliver the material centrally onto the belt as evenly and gently as possible. Side boards, or skirt plates, extending

6 to 8 ft. along the belt, should be rigidly attached to the conveyor structure in order to maintain a central position on the belt and a fixed clearance above the belt. Skirt plates are spaced at two-thirds of the width of the belt for belts up to 36 in. in width and to three-quarters of the belt width for wider belts. Rubber strips are attached to the inside edge of the skirts in order to contact the belt and to keep material from getting in between the rigid edge of skirt plates and the belt where it is supported by the closely spaced idlers at the loading point.

Reciprocating Plate Feeder. This feeder is a simple, rugged kind of feeder that can place the material onto the belt with the least drop and requires only minimum headroom. The main objection to such a feeder is that it has a tendency to discharge the material in surges, giving an uneven loading on the belt. Such surge can be minimized by using two or more feeders properly synchronized.

Apron Feeder. Feeders of this kind vary in construction. In the usual short-center feeder, the type consisting of two or more strands of chain attached underneath formed-steel or cast manganese-steel pans, the chain and pans are supported by a series of large diameter independent rollers of a rugged construction and subject to only a minimum amount of wear. Chains of 6-in. and 9-in. pitch and pans varying in ruggedness to suit each particular application are used. The shorter the pitch, the less the headroom required, the less the drop of material to the belt, and the more uniform the discharge from the feeder. Due to its rugged type of construction the apron feeder can take the heavy impact loads of material dropping directly upon it and can support a column of coarse abrasive material and pull it out from under a large bin opening in a continuous and fairly uniform stream.

Belt Feeder. Since a rubber belt is vulnerable to ripping and tearing it is not generally used as a feeder where material may drop directly onto the feeder, or where material is pulled out from under a large bin opening—especially where the material is sharp and jagged. The feeder installed in such cases should be protected from the direct impact of heavy, coarse material and adapted to control the flow from a liberal-size opening in a bin or loading hopper. Owing to low belt tension, the smallest pulleys listed in Fig. 1 can be used. The belt feeder, when properly installed and equipped with rubber belts designed for feeder service and supported on closely spaced impact idlers, is often preferred to the apron feeder because of lower maintenance cost, cleaner operation, and uniformity of discharge.

Plow. The plow, used to unload a conveyor belt, consists of a rubber-tipped blade extending across the belt at an angle of about 60° for a one-side discharge or a V-shaped blade for a two-side discharge. The belt must pass over a flat slider plate at the plow to permit close contact between the belt and the rubber-tipped blade, pivoted above the belt so that it can be raised out of the flow of the material. The plow may be adjusted to control the percentage of material leaving the belt at its location. Because of the flattening of the belt, the plow is limited to the handling of material with a high angle of surcharge, which will stay on a flat belt, and of smooth granular particles, which will flow along the plow blade and off the belt. Rough, irregularly shaped particles of hard material, such as crushed stone, do not successfully plow off the belt. This kind of discharge is used where material is deflected at fixed points along the belt. Its most common application is in conveying prepared foundry sand to a series of hoppers.

Belt Tripper. A belt tripper is an unloading device made up of two pulleys supported in a fixed or movable frame. The one pulley serves to elevate the belt a sufficient height from the carrying idlers to permit a discharge chute to be set in under the pulley. This chute receives the material flowing over the pulley and discharges it to either or both sides of the belt. The belt passes back and around the second pulley and beneath the chute, in order to resume its position on the carrying idlers. A soft rubber cover on the lower pulley helps to prevent the buildup of sticky material.

Fixed Trippers. Fixed trippers, where the pulleys are supported on a fixed frame, may be used to discharge the material at a number of fixed points. In this case each tripper chute is provided with a bypass gate in order to permit the material to pass through and back onto the belt and to be carried on to the selected discharge point. Since flexing of the belt around pulleys has a detrimental effect on the life of the belt, it is desirable to hold the number of pulleys to a minimum. The additional bend pulleys required for a series of fixed trippers therefore tend to be objectionable. Where material may be discharged only at fixed points, perhaps widely separated, a series of fixed trippers provides a solution.

A **movable tripper** has two pulleys and a chute supported on a frame, with wheels that run on rails alongside the conveyor. These rails must be rigidly supported on the conveyor frame or in some cases, on external supports, in order to maintain alignment and a fixed position in relation to the conveyor belt.

The diameter of the tripper pulleys should be proportioned to the maximum operating stress on the belt (see Fig. 1), which may be the same as that for which the drive pulley has been selected. The upper pulley should be set high enough to permit the installation of a chute of sufficient size and slope to discharge successfully the kinds of material being handled. Standard trippers may have pulleys of a diameter that is adequate for the majority of conveyors handling a normal material and operating within normal belt stresses; but for highly stressed belts or for sluggish materials, a standard tripper may be inadequate, and one with certain modifications may be desirable. Unless special precautions are taken, a tripper handling sticky material may be a source of considerable operating trouble.

Movable trippers may be **self-propelled** by a friction drive so arranged that by means of a reversing lever, the driven friction wheel can be made to engage a driving friction wheel on either one of the tripper pulley shafts, thus obtaining both forward and backward travel along the belt.

A simple, self-propelled, friction-driven tripper should have a manually operated reversing lever accessible from an operator's platform attached alongside the tripper frame. Such a tripper is generally limited to belts up to 36 or 42 in. in width and where material is discharged into a series of adjacent piles by manually setting the reversing lever in neutral position and applying track clamps to hold the tripper stationary until the pile is completed. The track clamps then are released, and the frictions are engaged for forward or backward movement to the next location. Self-propelled friction-driven trippers have been made to be automatically self-reversing, but, in general, this kind of drive has not been sufficiently positive to be thoroughly reliable, and its use for automatically self-reversing application is generally discouraged.

Motor-propelled and rope-propelled trippers are recommended for **automatic self-reversing service.** So-called "bedding trippers," used for spreading material evenly into a bunker or pile, are of this type. **Motor-propelled trippers** have the objectionable feature of requiring a cable reel or trolley wire to bring current to the motor on the tripper. Under critical dust conditions and when confined in a housing over a bunker, the trolley wire may be a liability, because of possible dust explosions. The **rope-propelled tripper** is moved by means of a reversible endless cable along each side of the conveyor, the cable being attached to the tripper frame and passing around a motor-operated cable-puller at one end and around an idler-sheave at the other end of the tripper travel. The cable-puller may be enclosed in a separate dust-tight housing. In each kind of installation, limit switches or other devices reverse the travel at each end of the tripper travel, and overtravel switches are provided as additional safety features.

Special Tripper Applications. Short cross-belts, receiving material directly from an upper tripper pulley, may replace the tripper chute when handling sticky material. The cross-belt may be lengthened and made reversible or may be made as a movable shuttle conveyor, supported on the tripper frame, for making wider piles from a conveyor operating on an overhead structure. Enlarged and specially designed units built on the tripper principle, with inclined balanced boom belts extending to each side or with an inclined boom belt mounted on a rotating base to spread material into piles on both sides of a conveyor operating at ground level, are known as **"stackers."** Boom belts mounted on crawler bases, with feeders delivering material from dump hoppers into which a shovel or drag-line can discharge overburden, are also known as "stackers" and are used in mining, reclaiming, and construction operations.

Shuttle Conveyors. A belt conveyor completely contained on a frame equipped with a series of wheels in order to form a movable unit is known as a "shuttle conveyor" because it can "shuttle" back and forth over a specified distance. It is generally a reversible conveyor that can pass in either direction under a central loading point and discharge over either end within a distance that is approximately twice the length of the conveyor. Since it must contain a drive and motor for operating the belt and will require a cable reel or trolley, it is generally motor propelled. Where the conveyor becomes so long that sufficient traction cannot be obtained by a drive to an axle of the conveyor, a rope drive or a special type of chain drive is used.

Weighing Devices. Weighing the material in transit is done by passing the loaded belt over a series of idlers mounted on a frame suspended or balanced, in several ways, according to the varied designs of such equipment. The installation is located at the loading end where belt tensions are lowest and distance of travel least. Its proximity to the loading zone is determined by the manufacturer when he constructs the particular device. Data on such devices must be obtained from the manufacturer of the weighing equipment or through a conveying-equipment manufacturer.

CONVEYOR STRUCTURES. Conveyor supports are generally separate from the main structural supports. Supports for the usual kinds of conveyors generally consist of 5-, 6-, or 7-in. channel stringers (depending on the width of the belt) with supporting legs to the main structure, to the floor, or to piers. For long conveyors, where the immediate conveyor supports amount to a sufficient tonnage, standard lightweight truss sections are available that permit longer spans and more economical construction.

The conveyor-supporting frame must have sufficient rigidity to maintain belt alignment, clearance at least sufficient to prevent damage to the edge of the belt on its return run, and adjustments for aligning shafts. A decking which not only protects the return run of the belt but also lends lateral stiffness to the conveyor-supporting structure is generally placed on top of the stringers.

Design for Handling Bulk Materials

MATERIALS HANDLED. The proper design of a belt conveyor for handling bulk materials is governed largely by the characteristics of the materials to be handled, particularly **consistency** and **size**.

Materials Suitable for Handling on a Belt. Some sticky materials may be handled successfully on a belt if proper precautions are taken. Sticky iron ore is handled by eliminating as many transfers as possible and transferring directly from one conveyor to another by conventional transfer chutes, using only side skirt plates to guide the material. On its return run the belt carries along sticky material, which not only builds up on the return idler rolls and snub pulleys, causing the belt to run out of line, but also drops off and accumulates under the return belt, thus creating not only operating problems but also clean-up and maintenance problems. A method of turning the return belt over immediately after it leaves the discharge pulley so that the clean side of the belt contacts the return idlers has worked out successfully but may not always be applicable.

Power-driven revolving **belt-cleaning brushes** tend to wear rapidly and, particularly if the material is wet, to fill up and become solid. Fixed and hinged **scrapers** of various kinds, also having objectionable features, have been most commonly used. Where temperatures permit, spraying a fine liquid on the belt just before loading may tend to prevent material from sticking to the belt.

Belt trippers generally should not be installed when the equipment is handling sticky materials. Shuttle conveyors are suggested instead. If it is necessary to use a belt tripper, one of special design should be used, conforming with the recommendations of the equipment manufacturers.

Conveying Hot Materials. Heat is detrimental to the rubber and cotton fiber which make up the carcass of a belt. Cotton fiber chars and loses its strength at around 300° F. unless protected or strengthened by some means. Operating temperatures above 125° to 150° F. are not recommended

Closely packed material, such as hot foundry sand, holds the heat against the belt and causes more rapid deterioration than a coarse, loose material, such as coke. Sustained heat is most destructive. Cooling intervals are highly desirable and add to the life of the belt or permit materials or products at somewhat higher temperatures to be handled. Special rubber compounds and carcass constructions are recommended by the rubber-belt manufacturers. Stitched canvas belts with various impregnations and insulations are said to handle material as hot as 300° to 450° F. Glass fabric is being used in belts for hot materials.

Chemical Action on Conveyor Belts. Special compounds for rubber belts and impregnations and coverings for stitched canvas belts—all of which resist certain chemical actions—are available. Helpful data on special belts which will resist heat and chemical action can best be obtained from belt manufacturers when a complete description is given of the material to be handled, the conveyor centers, speed of belt, hours of operation, and the surrounding conditions under which the belt is to operate.

Size of Material. The size of pieces or lumps in the material that is to be handled may determine whether or not a belt conveyor is applicable. If the material contains pieces too large for the belt to handle:

1. Some other method of handling may be necessary.
2. The material may be crushed to a size that can be handled.

| Maximum Size of Material (in.) | | | Maximum Belt Speeds in Feet per Minute | | | | Width of Belt (in.) | Capacity in Tons (2,000 lb.) per Hour of Material Weighing 100 Lb. per Cu. Ft. Multiply by 0.30 for 30 lb./cu. ft. Material, 0.50 for 50 lb./cu. ft. Material, 1.50 for 150 lb./cu. ft. Material | | | | | | | Cubic Yards per Hour at 100 Ft./Min. Belt Speed |
| Coarse Lump | | Small Lump, Unsized | Granular Material 1/8 to 3/4 in. (sand, coal, grain, wood chips) | Coarse-Lump Nonabrasive Material (such as coal, earth) | Coarse, Crushed, Abrasive Material (ore, slag, etc.) | Heavy, Large, Abrasive Material (ore, slag, stone, etc.) | | Belt Speed in Feet per Minute | | | | | | | |
Sized	Unsized							100	200	300	400	500	600	700	
3	4		450	400	400	400	16	42	84	126	168	210			31
3	4		450	400	400	400	18	54	108	162	216	270			40
3	5		550	450	450	400	20	67	135	202	270	337			50
5	8	2	600	450	500	400	24	100	200	300	400	500	600		74
6	10	3	800	500	550	450	30	160	324	486	648	810	972	1,134	120
8	15	4	800	550	600	500	36	235	470	705	940	1,175	1,410	1,645	174
10	18	5	800	550	600	500	42	325	650	975	1,300	1,625	1,950	2,275	240
12	21	6	800	600	600	550	48	440	880	1,320	1,760	2,200	2,640	3,080	326
14	24	8	800	600	600	550	54	570	1,140	1,710	2,280	2,850	3,420	3,990	420
16	26	10	800	600	600	550	60	720	1,440	2,160	2,880	3,600	4,320	5,020	530
Average thickness of top rubber cover			1/8 in.	3/16 in.	1/4 to 5/16 in.	5/16 to 3/8 in.		For flat belts use 50% of the above capacities.							

Bottom rubber cover varies from 1/32 in. for light nonabrasive material to 1/8 in. for severe operating conditions. 1/16 in. is normal.
Suggested operating speeds:

Minimum for average or normal operation..................	300 to 400 ft. per min.
For heavy fine material such as cement..................	250 to 300 ft. per min.
For light fluffy material such as soda ash, pulverized coal, or where degradation is harmful..................	200 to 250 ft. per min.
For material such as soap chips..................	150 to 200 ft. per min.
Where discharge plows are used..................	150 to 200 ft. per min.

(Using 20-degree troughing idlers.)
Speeds of 300 fpm or more are suggested for better discharge of material which may tend to adhere to belt.

Fig. 4. Maximum size pieces, maximum belt speeds, and average belt conveyor capacities.

3. The material, if containing only a small amount of oversize pieces, may be passed over a grizzly screen to separate and discard the oversize pieces, or some auxiliary means may be used for this purpose. This occurs usually in stripping operations.

Lump-Size Material Classification. In Fig. 4, two categories, "Sized" and "Unsized," are given under the heading "Maximum Size of Material." For belt-conveyor purposes, "unsized" material may be considered as being composed 10 percent of maximum to half-maximum size lumps and 90 percent ranging uniformly in size from half maximum to fines. "Sized" material may be considered as being 20 percent maximum to half-maximum size lumps, and 80 percent ranging uniformly from half-maximum size to fines. Owing to the larger proportion of coarse lump, the maximum-size lump is less for sized than for unsized material. "Small lump" material has the same proportion of coarse lump to fines as unsized material, with the maximum lump sizes restricted to those shown in Fig. 4.

Owing to its small lump size, "small lump" material loads onto a belt much better than large lump material, forming a more uniform and compact load of greater cross section.

TYPES OF MATERIAL AFFECTING CROSS-SECTIONAL LOAD-ING. Different materials determine the cross-sectional load on a belt by the maximum angle of surcharge to which they can be loaded onto the belt. According to the Link-Belt Co., these materials may be divided into the three groups listed on page **23·18** (see cross-section diagrams in Figs. 5a and 5 b).

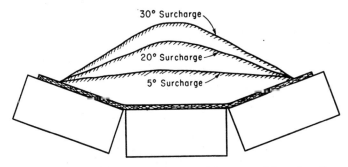

Fig. 5a. Twenty-degree troughing idler—equal-length rolls.

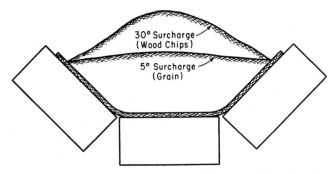

Fig. 5b. Forty-five-degree troughing idler—equal-length rolls.

1. Those having a 5° maximum angle of surcharge. Flat slump or semifluid material which is very free flowing, having an angle of repose of less than 30°, such as very dry or very wet sand, whole grain, dry material finely ground or pulverized (such as cement, lime, soda ash). Flat belts are not recommended for this class of material.

2. Those having a 20° maximum angle of surcharge. Coarse lump material having an angle of repose of between 30° and 40°, with lump-size limitations (as in Fig. 4), such as coal, stone, and ore.

3. Those having a 30° maximum angle of surcharge. Sluggish material maintaining an angle of repose of over 40°, such as damp sand and earth, fibrous materials, wood chips, cottonseed, and small-lump material having an angle of repose of between 30° and 40°. Lump-size limitations as given in Column 3 of Fig. 4.

Fig. 6 shows belt conveyor capacities based on the foregoing types of idlers and types of material. This table gives what may be considered conservative capacity limits. With expert design, operation, and maintenance, the wider belts are known to offer considerably higher capacities than are listed in this table.

Fig. 4 shows what may be considered normal capacities of conveyors handling normal material having an angle of repose between 30 and 40° with limits in speeds and lump sizes. The capacities given have been widely used over the years, recognizing that they are conservative. It is considered conservative to use the lower capacities given in Fig. 4, because of variable conditions, such as method and regularity of feed, and changes in the "flowability" of the material which may affect the cross-sectional loading of the belt. Conservative design will use the higher capacities in Fig. 6 for power requirements, so that for a 30-in. belt conveyor which is to handle 650 tons per hr. of 100-lb.-per-cu.-ft. material at 400 ft. per min. (as in Fig. 4), the power requirements and machinery design would be based on 180 tons per hr. at 100 ft. per min., or 720 tons per hr. (see Fig. 6).

Capacities at 100 Ft. per Min. Belt Speed

20° Troughing														Bushels per Hour 5° Surcharge		
Cubic Yards per Hour			Cubic Feet per Hour				Tons per Hour (100 lb./ cu. ft.)			Width of Belt (in.)	Area of Cross Section (sq. ft.)			Type of Troughing Idler		
Degree of Surcharge			Degree of Surcharge				Degree of Surcharge				Degree of Surcharge			20° Equal-Length Rolls	45° Equal-Length Rolls	45° Un-equal-Length Rolls
5	20	30	5	20	30	30*	5	20	30		5	20	30			
19	33	40	516	900	1,100		26	45	50	16	0.086	0.152	0.184			
25	44	54	684	1,180	1,460		34	59	63	18	0.114	0.197	0.244			
33	53	58	882	1,428	1,580		44	72	79	20	0.147	0.238	0.263			
50	81	90	1,350	2,180	2,400		67	109	120	24	0.225	0.363	0.402	1,100		1,600
84	133	145	2,260	3,590	3,920	5,400	113	180	196	30	0.377	0.599	0.654	1,800	2,900	2,600
124	196	217	3,360	5,310	5,870	8,000	170	266	293	36	0.560	0.886	0.978	2,700	4,250	3,300
175	280	300	4,740	7,500	8,160	11,600	237	375	408	42	0.790	1.250	1.360	3,800	6,000	4,600
223	370	400	6,300	10,000	10,980	14,900	315	500	550	48	1.050	1.670	1.830	5,000	8,400	6,300
298	470	513	8,040	12,700	13,860	19,300	400	636	693	54	1.340	2.120	2.310			
364	580	635	9,840	15,600	17,160	24,300	490	780	858	60	1.640	2.600	2.860			

* Forty-five-degree equal-roll troughing idler.

Fig. 6. Conservative capacity limits of belt conveyors at various loadings.

Capacities of flat belt conveyors handling foundry sand and similar materials are rated on the basis of half those of troughed belts, as listed in Fig. 4. Belt speeds range from 150 to 200 ft. per min.

Flat Belts for Handling Pulpwood Logs. The width of belts for handling pulpwood logs is influenced largely by the method of loading the belt uniformly or in surges. In general, side loading is preferred. The carcass of the belt should be of at least 6-ply 32-oz. duck with 3/16- to 1/4-in. top rubber cover with breaker strip and 1/16-in. bottom cover. Sorting belts are of 6- or 7-ply construction and are made of 36-, 42-, or 48-oz. duck to give ample body to the belt, depending on the maximum size of logs handled. The top rubber cover should be 1/4 to 3/8 in. thick with a breaker strip to keep the pics from piercing the carcass.

Belts are run at speeds of 300 to 400 ft. per min. because at these speeds the load is more evenly distributed. There should not be much differential between belt speed and that of the logs striking the belt at a properly controlled loading point. The logs rolls off the belt as soon as they contact the unloading plow. Standard 6-in. diameter flat-roll idlers on 1 1/4-in. shafts are used for belts up to 42 in. wide, spaced 3 1/2-ft. centers for 4-ft. wood and 4 1/2-ft. centers for 5-ft. wood. For 48-in. and wider belts heavy duty 6-in. diameter rolls on 1 7/16 in. shafts in ball-bearing pillow blocks are used. Belts 30, 36, and 42 in. wide are used for 4-ft. wood, depending on the number of cords per hour and the diameter and number of sticks per cord. A 48-in.-wide belt should never be used for 4-ft. wood, because it would be too close to the length of stick that might get crosswise of the belt and wedge between the skirt plates alongside the belt. A 54-in., but preferably a 48-in., belt should be used for 5-ft. wood.

A conveyor to handle 80 cords per hr. of nominal 5-ft. wood (5 1/4-ft.-long sticks) from 7 to 12 in. in diameter would carry about 80 sticks per cord or 6,400 sticks per hr. At 5 1/4 ft. per stick the rate of flow would be about 33,600 linear ft., or 560 linear ft. per min. At a belt speed of 300 ft. per min. the handling would approximate 2 linear ft. of wood per ft. of conveyor, or 2 sticks of wood continuously on the conveyor. If the maximum sticks are 12 in. in diameter, the belt should be at least 2 1/2, but preferably 3, sticks wide to take care of surges. A 30-in.-, or preferably a 36-in.-wide belt is recommended. A rate of flow of 80 cords per hr. at 6,000 lb. per cord is 8,000 lb. per min. At a belt speed of 300 ft. per min. the load on the belt would be about 27 lb. per ft. of belt; from these data, power, belt tensions, etc., can be computed.

CONVEYOR PATH. A belt conveyor can handle any suitable material on a horizontal path and on inclines and/or declines that are kept within operating limits. Where necessary, particularly in long-distance conveying, the path may be made up of a number of horizontal, inclined, and declined sections joined by concave transition curves, bend pulleys, or convex transition curves. Fig. 7 lists maximum inclines for typical materials, expressed in degrees of slope.

The concave transition curve, passing from a horizontal to an inclined section or from a declined section to a horizontal section, should have a minimum radius, determined by the belt tension at the entrance to the curve and by the weight of the empty belt on the curve, to assure that the belt will not lift off the idlers, flatten out, and spill material at the curve. (See Fig. 8.)

The transition from an inclined to a horizontal section (or horizontal to declined section) may be made by an abrupt bend over a pulley, but a fully loaded belt will spill material when flattening out in order to pass over any normal-size bend pulley. The normal cross-sectional load on the belt can be maintained on the curved section by placing closer-spaced idlers on a curved section—called a

convex transition curve. To avoid overstretching of the edges of the belt in passing over the curved section, the curve should have a minimum radius, as indicated in Fig. 3. (See "Idler Spacing" in this section.)

Anthracite Coal		Concrete		Rock and stone	
Fines	20	6-in. slump	12	Plus 4 in.	
Lump (screened)	16	4-in. slump	20	Sized	15
Run of mine	16	2-in. slump	24	Unsized	16
		Earth	20	Minus 4 in., plus ⅜ in.	
Bituminous Coal		Grain (whole)	15	Sized	16
Fines	20	Gravel		Unsized	18
Lump (screened)	16			Fines, minus ⅜ in.	20
Run of mine	18	Unsized	18		
		Sized	15	Sand	
		Sized and washed	12	Wet, from dewatering	
Beans (whole)	8	Saturated gravel and			11 to 15
		sand	12	Bank run	20
Coke		Ore		Dry	under 15
				Foundry, prepared	24
Run of oven	18	Hard, coarse crushed	17		
Screened	18	Hard, recrushed	20		
Breeze	20	Soft, mixed	20	Wood chips	27

Fig. 7. Maximum incline for typical materials (incline expressed in degrees of slope).

Weight per Foot of Empty Belt	Maximum Belt Tension at Approach Point of Curve*							
	Radius of Curve in Feet							
	150	200	250	300	350	400	450	500
3	350	480	600	720	840	960	1,080	1,200
4	480	640	800	960	1,120	1,280	1,440	1,600
6	720	960	1,200	1,440	1,680	1,920	2,160	2,400
8	960	1,280	1,600	1,920	2,240	2,560	2,880	3,200
10	1,200	1,600	2,000	2,400	2,800	3,200	3,600	4,000
12	1,440	1,900	2,400	2,900	3,300	3,800	4,300	4,800
15	1,800	2,400	3,000	3,600	4,200	4,800	5,400	6,000
18	2,200	2,900	3,600	4,300	5,000	5,800	6,500	7,200
21	2,500	3,400	4,200	5,000	5,900	6,700	7,600	8,400
25	3,000	4,000	5,000	6,000	7,000	8,000	9,000	10,000
30	3,600	4,800	6,000	7,200	8,400	9,600	10,800	12,000
40	4,800	6,400	8,000	9,600	11,200	12,800	14,400	16,000

* Based on $R = T/w$, or $T = Rw$

where T = belt tension
w = weight per foot of empty belt
R = radius of curve in feet

Tabulated tensions are 80 percent of formula: $T = Rw$

Fig. 8. Maximum empty belt tension for concave vertical curves for gradually accelerated belts.

Many mistakes in belt-conveyor design can be corrected with little trouble; but very little, if anything, can be done to correct a conveyor that has been installed on too steep a slope. It is therefore of extreme importance that inclined or declined conveyors have their slope angle kept within safe limits. This requirement necessitates a thorough study of the material to be handled.

Flowability of Materials. The readiness with which a material flows—its flowability—determines the angle of slope at which a belt will handle that material successfully. Flowability is determined by the moisture content of the material, by the size and shape of its particles and lumps, by the smoothness of their surfaces, and by the proportion of fine particles and lumps present.

The angle of incline on which a given material can be conveyed should be from 5° to 10° less than the angle at which the material will slide or roll on the belt. Whether it will be 5° or 10° depends on the material and whether there may be some variation at times in its flowability. Large lumps held in a bed of fine material will carry on a steeper slope than uniformly sized material. Irregular, rectangularly shaped lumps will carry on a steeper slope than rounded lumps. A conveyor carrying a full cross-sectional load will carry on a steeper slope than a faster-moving conveyor with less cross-sectional load.

Damp fine coal or sand can be carried safely on a 22° slope; thoroughly dried sand will flow like water. The capacity of an inclined conveyor successfully carrying damp fine coal may be materially reduced if the coal becomes extremely dry, because there will be excess slip of the fine dry coal on the belt at the loading point.

Possible changes in a material from time to time, affecting its flowability, should be taken into consideration when establishing the slope of a conveyor. The slope depends on the importance of the conveyor and its capacity and the importance of temporarily reduced capacity and spilled material. Whether or not the slope of the conveyor should be set for an unfavorable condition depends on how often the unfavorable condition may occur. Flatter slopes, of course, mean longer conveyors must be used for the same amount of lift of the material. Important conveyors handling large amounts of material should be held to conservative inclines. In large power plants the conveyors handling mine-run coal to the breakers or crushers are generally limited to a maximum incline of 16°.

Individual **tests** are recommended to establish safe slopes for conveyors handling formed particles, such as briquettes, pellets, and nodules. The regularity in the size and shape of such particles, and the roughness or smoothness of their surfaces—the factors that establish their flowability and thus the safe slope of a conveyor—are subject to considerable variation.

Even where a well-loaded inclined conveyor belt has been installed, a certain amount of material, depending on its condition and the slope of the conveyor, may roll back as the belt empties itself. It is a minor matter if this rollback occurs only a few times per day. If it occurs several times per hour, however, there may accumulate a considerable amount of objectionable spill which, with some forethought, may be reduced or eliminated.

WIDTH OF CONVEYOR BELT. The proper width and proper slope of a belt conveyor are basic requirements for successful operation, and in most cases once they are established they can hardly be changed. Provided a material is suitable for handling on a belt conveyor, the belt must be wide enough so that the maximum size lump to be handled can be loaded onto the conveyor so that it can sit there securely among the other lumps. This basic requirement establishes the minimum belt width that should be used (as indicated in Fig. 4).

SPEED OF BELT CONVEYORS. The belt conveyor is a relatively high-speed conveyor, and this high speed should be used to advantage wherever possible. A belt should carry a full cross-sectional load for most efficient service. If the size of the lump or the nature of the material is not a determining factor, a narrow belt carrying a full cross-sectional load at a higher speed is more efficient than a wider belt at a lower speed.

Whether full advantage of minimum width and maximum speed should be taken in designing a conveyor depends on the application it will have. For permanent, long-range applications some reserve capacity may be advisable. Fortunate is the power plant that can speed up its conveyor system to handle the additional coal necessary for new high-pressure boilers meeting increased power-load demands. Only heavier drives, not new conveyors, are necessary.

Some materials should be handled at slower speeds, as indicated in Fig. 4; but unless otherwise limited, a belt speed of at least 300 ft. per min. is recommended. Speeds up to 400 ft. per min. are good loading speeds. Such speeds are sufficiently high to effect a good discharge of damp material, to give enough trajectory to the material over the discharge pulley, to permit the installation of a good design of transfer or discharge chute, and to keep within the rather restricted discharge-chute limits of the usual standard tripper.

Maximum belt speeds, as indicated in Fig. 4, are for the most part influenced by the loading of the material onto the belt. A granular free-flowing material of small particle size can be made to flow onto the belt smoothly and evenly, so that the belt need accelerate the material only a very little, thus keeping belt wear at the loading point down to a minimum. It is difficult, however, to control the flow of coarse, abrasive material. Sharp, heavy, irregularly shaped lumps striking the belt must be speeded up or slowed down to belt speed, with consequent scuffing and gouging of the belt. Maximum size heavy lumps have a pounding effect as they pass over the troughing idlers. The accelerating and pounding effect of loading heavy lumps increases with belt speed. It is mainly for these reasons that limitations in belt speeds are recommended, as indicated in Fig. 4.

BELT CONVEYOR CAPACITY. The capacity of a belt conveyor is determined by the cross-sectional load of material on the belt and the speed of the belt. The cross-sectional load on the belt will vary with (1) the type of carrying idler used, which determines the amount of troughing or absence of troughing given to the belt; and with (2) the nature of the material being handled, which determines the quantity of material that can be safely loaded into a given cross section.

Horsepower of Belt Conveyors

BELT CONVEYOR HORSEPOWER. Power is the rate at which work is done. When a force of 1 lb. acts through a distance of 1 ft., 1 work unit, or 1 ft.-lb. of work, is done. The power unit of 550 ft.-lb. per sec., or 33,000 ft.-lb. per min., is known as one "horsepower." The unit of 1.341 hp. is a unit known as a "kilowatt." If a conveyor belt is pulling 330 lbs. and traveling 100 ft. per min. it is requiring 330×100, or 33,000 work units per min., or 1 hp., to move the belt.

Effective Horsepower Pull, E. As explained later, the 330-lb. force in the belt is not the belt tension but rather only that part of the belt tension which causes the belt to move. It is quite commonly known as the "effective horsepower pull," designated by the capital letter E. If a belt moves at a speed of S ft. per min. as the result of an effective horsepower pull, *E*, the required horsepower is designated by the formula:

$$\text{Hp.} = \frac{E \times S}{33,000} \tag{1}$$

The effective horsepower pull is the algebraic sum of all the frictional and gravitational forces that oppose or assist the movement of the belt. Frictional forces tend to retard movement of the belt; gravitational forces tend to retard belt movement on inclines and assist belt movement on declines.

For a **horizontal conveyor,** *E* is determined by the length of the conveyor, by the weight per foot of the load on the conveyor, by the weight per foot of the belt and rotating parts of the idlers, and by the frictional resistance offered against the movement of the belt and its load. For an **inclined conveyor,** *E* is determined the same way except that the gravitational forces necessary to elevate the belt and the load on the carrying run will offer additional resistance to the movement of the belt, and the gravitational forces on the return run, because of the weight of the belt, will assist the movement of the belt. For a **declined conveyor,** the gravitational forces caused by the weight of the belt on the return run will oppose movement of the belt, while the weight of the belt and load on the carrying run will assist the movement of the belt. These gravitational forces in some cases may exceed the frictional forces, to the extent that power may be generated and the movement of the belt down the slope must be controlled.

Normally, the difference between the actual length of the conveyor on the incline or decline and its horizontally projected length is not sufficient to affect the power requirement appreciably, and, for simplicity, the horizontally projected centers are generally used.

Factors Affecting the Effective Horsepower Pull, *E*. Gravitational forces are constant, according to the weight of the belt and its load, but frictional forces are subject to considerable variation. The **frictional forces** that offer resistance to movement can be readily determined for a flat belt sliding on a flat surface, because the coefficient of sliding friction between a given type of belt and type of sliding surface is known or can be easily determined and, with proper maintenance of the belt, is fairly constant.

The **frictional resistance** to the movement of a troughed belt is not so easily determined, because of the several factors—besides the rolling friction of the idler rolls—that enter into the over-all friction factor. Modern troughing and return idler rolls, fitted with ball or roller bearings, when well made and properly lubricated, will rotate with an ease that is difficult to measure but which can be greatly lowered by poor construction, improper greasing, and misalignment.

The belt sags between the troughing idlers to some extent, depending on the load on the belt, the spacing of the idlers, and the tension in the belt. As the belt sags, it tends to allow the load to flatten the belt between the idlers. The internal friction in the load, as the particles rub against one another while the belt reshapes itself and the load in passing over each troughing idler, builds up resistance against the movement of the belt. To keep this belt sag from having an appreciable effect on power requirements, an arbitrary limit of 2 percent of the idler spacing has been considered reasonable for the allowable belt sag between the idlers. This limit means that the belt tension at any point in the carrying run of the conveyor should be no less than that necessary to limit the sag to 2 percent of the idler spacing:

$$\text{Minimum belt tension} = 6.25\,wl \tag{2}$$

where w = wt. per ft. in lb. of the belt and its load
l = idler spacing (expressed in ft.)

Fig. 2 gives minimum belt tensions for limiting belt sag.

The tendency for a conveyor belt to shift sideways because of a poor splice, a crooked belt, or the misalignment of the belt idlers on the conveyor frame, builds up resistance to the movement of the belt. Skirt-board drag and the acceleration or deceleration of the material at the loading point, bearing friction at the terminal pulley shafts, bending of the belt around the pulleys, initial troughing of the belt—are all intangible items that are somewhat independent of conveyor centers but contribute to the resistance to belt movement that builds up horsepower requirements.

FRICTION FACTORS. The factors affecting the frictional forces in a belt conveyor are influenced by:

1. **Conveyor design:** spacing of troughing idlers; proper belt tension to prevent excessive sag; proper size pulleys; rigidity and clearances of conveyor structure; and loading of the belt.
2. **Construction and maintenance:** quality and accuracy of idler rolls and freedom with which they rotate and continue to rotate because of the use of proper lubricants, proper lubrication methods, and inspection; and continued alignment of belt and idlers.
3. **Conveyor length:** as length increases the belt tension increases, reducing belt sag and flattening of load, so that for long conveyors with high belt tension, idler friction tends to approach the friction factor of the ball or roller bearing. The influence of the intangible items decreases with increase in conveyor length.

Tests made on a long, well-designed, and properly constructed belt conveyor indicated that a friction factor of 0.0175 for the weight of the belt and idler rolls and 0.02 for the weight of the material on the belt gave close checks on the actual power requirements. Tests on other long, well-designed, and well-constructed conveyors gave an over-all friction factor of 0.022. It is evident that the friction factor is influenced by conditions subject to determination only in a general way, and that it may vary somewhat from one installation to another. It is therefore necessary to adopt a reasonably safe over-all friction factor. This **over-all friction factor,** to be used in belt conveyor design, must recognize the effects of possible variations in the class of design, construction, and maintenance, and be based on at least two conveyor classifications. Each of these classifications indicated below should have provision for including those intangible power-consuming factors that are somewhat independent of conveyor length. Accepted practice has been to add a length factor, commonly known as L_0, to the conveyor centers in order to include the intangible items.

For the "normal" conveyor in average industrial applications using high grade antifriction idlers properly spaced to limit belt sag to 2 percent of idler spacing:

Friction factor = 0.030
Length factor (L_o) = 150 ft.

For well-designed, constructed, and maintained long conveyors using high grade antifriction idlers properly spaced to limit belt sag to 2 percent of idler spacing:

Friction factor = 0.022
Length factor (L_o) = 200 ft.

For either kind of conveyor application, for providing against the backward movement of an inclined conveyor or for the retarding of a declined conveyor:

Friction factor = 0.010

Entirely different friction factors must be used when considering the limitation of backward movement of inclined conveyors, because of power failure or other causes or in controlling forward movement of conveyors carrying materials down an incline. Tests have shown that an idler-roll friction of as low as 0.01 to 0.015 actually may exist under field conditions. If an inclined conveyor design has been based upon a safe friction factor of 0.022 in order to determine the friction forces to overcome in bringing the material up the slope, more inherent friction may have been attributed to the incline than it could actually supply to retard the backward movement of the conveyor. Likewise, in the decline conveyor a safe minimum friction value must be used in the basic calculations for frictional retarding forces.

DETERMINATION OF HORSEPOWER AND OF EFFECTIVE HORSEPOWER PULL, E. Belt conveyor horsepower as such is necessary mainly for electrical requirements and for such drive equipment as may be rated by horsepower capacity. For the mechanical parts of the conveyor, such as shafts, pulleys, holdbacks, and for the belt to provide sufficient tension capacity to pull the load, the effective horsepower pull or belt tension, E, is the basis of design. There are **two methods** of approach: (1) the algebraic summation of forces, (2) determination of horsepower by formula to obtain E.

In order to determine the algebraic sum of all the frictional and gravitational forces that must be considered in designing the conveyor, the conveyor may be regarded as a free body acted upon by **tensions** at the ends and **frictional resistances and gravitational components** along the belt. This approach is particularly advantageous where a conveyor is made up of two or more sections—horizontal to incline, decline to horizontal, decline to incline, etc. Each section can be considered a free body, and the end tensions can be determined for each section for the design of transition curves connecting the sections and for establishing minimum tensions throughout the entire conveyor to limit belt sag. For any conveyor where acceleration must be considered, this method provides the details necessary for determining the maximum allowable starting belt stresses and the proper location and design of take-up.

For the majority of belt conveyor applications, where belt tension and belt stretch are not critical, the horsepower determined from an established formula provides a quicker and easier method for arriving at belt stresses necessary for establishing operating belt tensions that determine the required belt strength, diameter of shafts and pulleys, and other mechanical parts. Using the horsepower figure obtained by this method:

$$E = \frac{\text{hp.} \times 33,000}{\text{Belt speed in ft. per min.}} = \frac{\text{hp.} \times 33,000}{S} \qquad (3)$$

The Goodyear formula, developed by the Goodyear Tire and Rubber Company, of Akron, Ohio, is one of the oldest and best known formulas for determining belt conveyor horsepower. The general formula for the total power for the belt is the algebraic sum of the power items (tripper included), as follows:

$$\text{Total horsepower} = \frac{C(L + L_o)(0.03QS)}{990} + \frac{C(L + L_o)T}{990} \pm \frac{TH}{990} \qquad (4)$$

The first item is empty-belt horsepower; the second item, horsepower to convey the load horizontally; the third, horsepower to elevate the load (added) or to lower the load (deducted). When a tripper is used, the additional lift required by the tripper is added to the third item.

In this formula:

C = the friction factor
Q = the weight of the moving parts of the conveyor, in pounds per foot of center-to-center distance, carrying and return runs (idler-roll weights from Fig. 2; belt weights from Fig. 9.)
L = the center-to-center distance, in feet, between head and foot pulleys
L_o = the length factor
S = the belt speed in feet per minute
T = tons per hour of material handled (1 ton = 2,000 lb.)
H = vertical height in ft. through which material is raised or lowered, including rise at tripper.

Because of the length factor, the Goodyear formula gives higher values for short-center and lower values for long-center conveyors than does a formula based on a proportion of power and length.

Weight of Fabric	Thickness per Ply (In.)	Total Thickness of BOTH Rubber Covers (In.)	Weight in Pounds per Inch of Width per Foot of Length									
			Number of Plies									
			3	4	5	6	7	8	9	10	11	12
28 oz.	0.045	3/16	0.176	0.201	0.225	0.250	0.274	0.299	0.324	0.348		
		1/4	0.210	0.235	0.259	0.284	0.309	0.333	0.358	0.382		
		5/16	0.244	0.269	0.293	0.318	0.343	0.367	0.392	0.416		
32 oz.	0.053	3/16	0.184	0.211	0.238	0.265	0.292	0.319	0.346	0.373	0.400	
		1/4	0.218	0.245	0.272	0.299	0.326	0.353	0.380	0.407	0.434	
		5/16	0.252	0.279	0.306	0.333	0.360	0.387	0.414	0.441	0.468	
36 oz.	0.056	3/16	0.188	0.216	0.245	0.273	0.302	0.330	0.359	0.387	0.416	0.444
		1/4	0.222	0.250	0.279	0.307	0.336	0.364	0.393	0.421	0.450	0.478
		5/16	0.256	0.284	0.313	0.341	0.370	0.398	0.427	0.455	0.484	0.512
		3/8	0.290	0.318	0.347	0.375	0.404	0.432	0.461	0.489	0.518	0.546
42 oz.	0.063	3/16	0.196	0.227	0.259	0.290	0.321	0.353	0.384	0.415	0.447	0.478
		1/4	0.230	0.261	0.293	0.324	0.355	0.387	0.418	0.449	0.481	0.512
		5/16	0.264	0.295	0.327	0.358	0.389	0.421	0.452	0.483	0:515	0.546
		3/8	0.298	0.329	0.361	0.392	0.423	0.455	0.486	0.517	0.549	0.580
48 oz.	0.069	3/16		0.238	0.272	0.306	0.340	0.374	0.408	0.442	0.476	0.510
		1/4		0.272	0.306	0.340	0.374	0.408	0.442	0.476	0.510	0.544
		5/16		0.306	0.340	0.374	0.408	0.442	0.476	0.510	0.544	0.578
		3/8		0.340	0.374	0.408	0.442	0.476	0.510	0.544	0.578	0.612

EXAMPLE: Find weight per ft. and thickness of belt 36 in. wide, 6 ply, 48-oz. duck, with a 1/4-in. top and a 1/8-in. bottom rubber cover.

Total thickness of covers: 1/4 + 1/8 in. = 3/8 in.
Total weight per ft.: 36 × 0.408 = 14.68 lb. per ft. of belt.
Total thickness of belt: 6 × 0.069 + (1/4 + 1/8) = 0.789 in.

For weight of belting having other thickness of rubber cover, allow 0.017 lb. for each 1/32-in. thickness of cover.

Fig. 9. **Weight of cotton-fabric ply-constructed rubber conveyor belt.**

EFFECT OF BELT SPEED ON HORSEPOWER REQUIREMENTS.
The speed of a belt affects only the **empty-belt horsepower** requirement. While an increase in belt speed increases the empty-belt horsepower, this horsepower increase may be more than compensated for by the decrease in the belt tension

required for moving the load, because the increased speed puts a thinner load on the belt for a given capacity, that is, less weight of load per foot. This factor is important in selection of the belt. By increasing the belt speed within the limits given in Fig. 4, thereby reducing unit belt stress, it may be possible to use a lower-cost belt with relatively little increase in power cost.

Belt Width	Q	Horizontal Conveyor Centers in Feet											
		100	200	300	400	600	800	1,000	1,200	1,400	1,600	1,800	2,000
Friction Factor, 0.03; Length Factor, 150 Ft.													
16	14	0.31	0.44	0.57	0.69	0.94	1.20						
18	15	0.34	0.47	0.61	0.75	1.02	1.28						
20	19	0.42	0.59	0.76	0.93	1.27	1.61						
24	23	0.53	0.74	0.95	1.16	1.59	2.00	2.43	2.86				
30	33	0.75	1.05	1.35	1.65	2.25	2.85	3.45	4.05				
36	41	0.93	1.30	1.67	2.04	2.79	3.53	4.27	5.02				
42	51	1.15	1.62	2.08	2.54	3.47	4.39	5.32	6.25				
48	63	1.42	2.00	2.56	3.13	4.27	5.41	6.55	7.69				
54	76	1.72	2.41	3.10	3.79	5.17	6.55	7.93	9.31				
60	86	1.95	2.73	3.51	4.29	5.85	7.41	8.97	10.5				
Heavy-Duty Idlers													
48	79	1.75	2.45	3.15	3.85	5.25	6.65	8.05	9.45				
54	93	2.12	2.97	3.82	4.67	6.37	8.07	9.77	11.4				
60	102	2.30	3.22	4.14	5.06	6.90	8.74	10.5	12.4				
Friction Factor, 0.022; Length Factor, 200 Ft.													
16	14	0.27	0.36	0.45	0.54	0.72	0.90						
18	15	0.30	0.40	0.50	0.60	0.80	1.00						
20	19	0.36	0.48	0.60	0.72	0.96	1.20						
24	23	0.45	0.60	0,75	0.90	1.20	1.50	1.80	2.10	2.40	2.70	3.00	3.30
30	33	0.66	0.88	1.10	1.32	1.76	2.20	2.64	3.08	3.52	3.96	4.40	4.84
36	41	0.82	1.09	1.36	1.64	2.18	2.73	3.27	3.82	4.36	4.90	5.46	6.00
42	51	1.02	1.36	1.70	2.04	2.72	3.40	4.08	4.76	5.44	6.12	6.80	7.48
48	63	1.26	1.68	2.10	2.52	3.36	4.20	5.04	5.88	6.72	7.56	8.40	9.24
54	76	1.50	2.00	2.50	3.00	4.00	5.00	6.00	7.00	8.00	9.00	10.00	11.00
60	86	1.71	2.28	2.85	3.42	4.56	5.70	6.84	7.98	9.12	10.26	11.40	12.54
Heavy-Duty Idlers													
48	79	1.58	2.11	2.63	3.16	4.22	5.27	6.32	7.37	8.43	9.48	10.54	11.59
54	93	1.86	2.48	3.10	3.72	4.96	6.20	7.44	8.68	9.92	11.16	12.40	13.64
60	102	2.04	2.72	3.40	4.08	5.44	6.80	8.16	9.52	10.88	11.24	13.60	14.96
		100	200	300	400	600	800	1,000	1,200	1,400	1,600	1,800	2,000

$$\text{Hp.} = \frac{CQ(L + L_o)S}{33,000} \quad \text{or} \quad \frac{C(L + L_o)(0.03\ QS)}{990}$$

Multiply values from this table by $\dfrac{\text{Belt speed in ft. per min.}}{100}$

EXAMPLE: 24-in. belt, 800-ft. ctrs., 350 ft. per min. Friction factor, 0.03; length factor, 150 ft.

$$\text{Hp.} = 2.00 \times \frac{350}{100} = 7$$

Fig. 10. Empty-belt horsepower.

Figures 10, 11, and 12, prepared from the Goodyear formula and using friction and length factors given under the previous heading of "Friction Factors," provide a quick method of determining horsepower requirements used either as the basis of design for normal conveyors or for checking and complementing the determination of E by the algebraic summation of forces. The Q value used is given in Fig. 10 for empty-belt horsepower. Variations in Q will, of course, change horsepower requirements.

C	L_o	Horizontal Conveyor Centers in Feet											
		100	200	300	400	600	800	1,000	1,200	1,400	1,600	1,800	2,000
0.03	150	0.76	1.06	1.36	1.66	2.27	2.88	3.48	4.09				
0.022	200	0.66	0.88	1.10	1.32	1.76	2.20	2.64	3.08	3.52	3.96	4.40	4.84

$$\text{Hp.} = \frac{C(L + L_o)T}{990}$$

Multiply values from this table by $\dfrac{\text{Tons per hr.}}{100}$

EXAMPLE: Friction factor, 0.03; length factor, 150 ft. Convey 350 tons per hour 800 ft.

$$\text{Hp.} = 2.88 \times \frac{350}{100} = 2.88 \times 3.5 = 10.88$$

Fig. 11. Horsepower to convey material horizontally.

Horsepower per 100 Tons per Hour To Raise or Lower											
Vertical Height in Feet											
5	10	15	20	30	40	50	60	70	80	90	100
0.51	1.01	1.52	2.02	3.03	4.04	5.05	6.06	7.07	8.08	9.09	10.10

$$\text{Hp.} = \frac{TH}{990}$$

T = Tons per hour (1 ton is 2,000 lb.)
H = Vertical height in feet

Multiply values from this table by $\dfrac{\text{Tons per hr.}}{100}$

EXAMPLE: Elevate 350 tons per hour through 50 ft.
Hp. = $5.05 \times 350/100 = 5.05 \times 3.5 = 17.66$.

Elevate 175 tons per hour through 25 ft.
Hp. for 100 TPH through 20 ft.. 2.02
Hp. for 100 TPH through 5 ft.. 0.51
Hp. for 100 TPH through 25 ft.. 2.53
Hp. for 175 TPH through 25 ft.: $2.53 \times 175/100$................. 4.43

Fig. 12. Horsepower due to vertical height (lifting or lowering.)

Conveyor Belt Tension

BELT TENSION. Whether arrived at directly as the summation of forces or derived from the horsepower formula, the effective horsepower pull, E, is the force that must be transmitted from the drive pulley to the belt.

There are three sets of belt tensions necessary in arriving at the final full-speed operating tension in the belt: fixed tension, starting tension, and operating tension.

Fixed Tension. The term "fixed tension" is applied to the tension in the belt when the empty conveyor is at rest and is put into the belt by a device known as a "take-up" primarily to provide the necessary slack-side tension for driving the conveyor under all conditions but also to maintain a minimum "sag" tension throughout the carrying run of the conveyor. Fixed tension includes the weight of the belt for inclined or declined conveyors. For a belt weighing 10 lb. per ft., a conveyor with a 30-ft. lift would have a weight tension of 10×30, or 300 lb., in each run of the belt. Where slack tension is critical, return run friction must be included in fixed tension.

Slack-Side Tension, T_2. To get sufficient pressure between the belt and the drive pulley so that it can transmit the effective horsepower pull to the belt, there must be a certain tension in the belt as it leaves the drive pulley. This "leaving tension," or "slack-side tension," is commonly designated as T_2. With the rotation of the drive pulley as power is applied, the T_2 tension in the belt makes possible the development of a greater tension, T_1 in the belt as it enters into contact with the drive pulley.

The possible increase in belt tension from T_2 to T_1 is dependent on the coefficient of friction between the belt and the drive pulley and on the arc of contact of the belt on the drive pulley. The relationship between T_1 and T_2 is expressed mathematically by the equation $T_1 = T_2 \times 10 \,(0.00758fa)$ in which f is the coefficient of friction between the belt and the drive pulley, and a is the arc of contact between the belt and drive pulley, expressed in degrees. The difference between T_1 and T_2 is the effective horsepower pull, E, that is available for moving the belt:

$$E = T_1 - T_2 \tag{5}$$

$$T_1 = E + T_2 \tag{6}$$

The second equation above indicates that for a required effective horsepower pull, E, the larger belt stress, T_1, depends on how much T_2 is required. Since the amount of T_2 depends upon the friction between the belt and the drive pulley, and the arc of contact of the belt on the drive pulley, the design of the drive pulley arrangement determines the operating strength which a belt must have in order to deliver a given effective horsepower pull.

Fig. 13 indicates the relationship between E, T_1, and T_2. For an effective horsepower pull of 4,000 lb., a lagged drive pulley snubbed to a 210° arc of contact (*LPS*210) would require a belt sufficiently strong for 5,500 lb. of operating tension, with 1,500 lb. of T_2, with a 240° arc of contact (*LPS*240) for 5,200 lb. with 1,200 lb. of T_2 tension. With a tandem or dual pulley drive (*LPS*420), the belt tension would be only 4,320 lb., with 320 lb. of T_3 tension.

A 240° **belt contact** is about the maximum for a single pulley drive, and large drive and snub pulleys are required to have that much contact. Tandem or dual drives lose their effectiveness as the "fixed" tensions exceed the required slack tensions. If in the above example the fixed tension were 1,200 lb., the *LPS*420 drive would have no advantage over the *LPS*240 drive.

It is always necessary to determine the **minimum T_2 required.** The required sag tension and/or the weight tension may exceed the minimum T_2 requirement in order to develop a certain E, in which case the fixed tension becomes T_2 and adds to the operating strength requirement of the belt by its excess over the minimum T_2 requirement. Whether the T_2 tension sufficient at the drive pulley will be sufficient throughout the run of the conveyor to provide the necessary **sag tension** at all critical low-tension points of the carrying run, depends upon the amount of T_2 required, the location of the take-up mechanism, and the incline of the conveyor.

The tension in the carrying run is least at the foot, or loading end, of most conveyors. Closely spaced idlers are always placed directly under the loading

Degree of Belt Contact	Type of Drive	Operating Belt Tension, T_1		T_2 for Single-Pulley Drive T_3 for Dual-Pulley Drive		T_1/T_2 for Single-Pulley Drive T_1/T_3 for Dual-Pulley Drive	
		Bare Pulley	Lagged Pulley	Bare Pulley	Lagged Pulley	Bare Pulley	Lagged Pulley
180	Plain	1.85E	1.50E	0.85E	0.50E	2.19	3.00
200	Snubbed	1.72E	1.42E	0.72E	0.42E	2.39	3.39
210	Snubbed	1.67E	1.38E	0.67E	0.38E	2.50	3.61
215	Snubbed	1.64E	1.36E	0.64E	0.36E	2.55	3.72
220	Snubbed	1.62E	1.35E	0.62E	0.35E	2.61	3.83
240	Snubbed	1.54E	1.30E	0.54E	0.30E	2.85	4.33
360	Tandem	1.26E	1.13E	0.26E	0.13E	4.80	9.02
380	Tandem	1.23E	1.11E	0.23E	0.11E	5.25	10.19
400	Tandem	1.21E	1.09E	0.21E	0.09E	5.72	11.51
420	Tandem	1.19E	1.08E	0.19E	0.08E	6.25	13.00
450	Tandem	1.16E	1.07E	0.16E	0.07E	7.12	15.27
500	Tandem	1.13E	1.05E	0.13E	0.05E	8.86	21.21

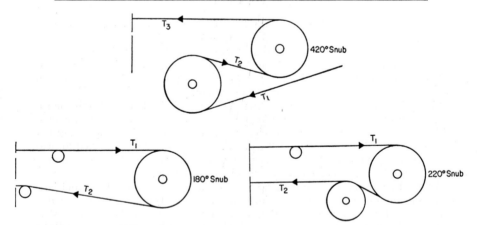

The above values are based on a coefficient of friction between belt and pulley of 0.25 for bare iron or steel pulleys and 0.35 for rubber lagged pulleys.

IMPORTANT NOTE: The ratio T_1/T_2 or T_1/T_3 is very important in determining whether the belt will slip on the drive pulley. The ratio given in the last two columns should never be exceeded **for operating belt tensions; for starting tensions only** these ratios can be increased 50 percent.

Fig. 13. **Design data for belt conveyor drives.**

point, but beyond that, the tension in the belt must be sufficient to keep the belt sag within proper limits. It is important to check the necessity of **additional take-up tension** to insure against excessive belt sag at any point in the carrying run, or of placing idlers closer.

For a complex conveyor whose path may consist of a combination of horizontal, inclined, or declined sections, **low tension points** may occur at one or more of the transition curves connecting these sections. This condition requires a detailed analysis of the frictional, gravitational, and inertia forces in the belt, both in starting and under full-load operating conditions, with empty belt and various conditions of loading being checked for the most unfavorable condition.

Starting Belt Tension. The starting belt tension is the maximum belt tension, T_M, and is the sum of the fixed belt tensions, the effective horsepower pull, E, and of all the additional forces required to bring the belt to full operating speed. These additional forces are the "inertia forces," which may be designated as the i forces. Their magnitude is determined by the total weight of the load and moving parts of the conveyor that must be accelerated and the force available for acceleration.

Operating Belt Tension. The additional forces that have been required to start the conveyor disappear as the conveyor reaches full operating speed, and the operating tension becomes T_1, the sum of the "fixed tensions" and the effective horsepower pull, E. The operating strength of the conveyor belt, as given in Fig. 1, is based on this operating tension.

INERTIA FORCES. Assume that a conveyor operating at 300 ft. per min. and requiring 38 hp. for full-speed operation is driven by a 40 hp. 1,800-r.p.m. motor with 200 percent starting torque capacity. The horsepower available for acceleration is 42-hp. $(40 \times 2.00 - 38 = 42)$. At a 300-ft.-per-min. belt speed, the total available linear accelerating force is

$$\frac{42 \times 33,000}{300} - 1,620 \text{ lb.}$$

Part of the 42-hp. torque will be used to overcome the **rotational inertia**, WK^2, of the motor and drive and bring them up to full rotational speed. The remainder, in the form of linear forces at the belt, will be available to bring the conveyor and its load up to full linear speed. To determine the proportioning of the 4,620-lb. available linear force at the belt, rotational inertia is expressed in a form that makes it equivalent to a proportion of the total weight of the moving parts of the conveyor. For convenience and simplicity the rotating terminal pulleys, being of little influence in the total result, are included as part of the weight of the conveyor in linear motion. Because of weight distribution, 65 percent of the weight of the rotating part of troughing rolls and 75 percent of the return rolls are included in the weight of the carrying and return runs.

The rotational inertia of the motor, WK^2, can be expressed as an **equivalent weight** at the conveyor belt line and at the belt speed.

$$\text{Equivalent weight of motor} = \frac{WK^2 \times (2\pi)^2 \times (\text{motor r.p.m.})^2}{(\text{Belt speed in ft. per min.})^2}$$

The additional "equivalent weight" for the drive is generally considered to be about one-sixth that of the motor. The WK^2 of motors must be obtained from motor data sheets.

For the conveyor under consideration:

Equivalent weights:

Carrying run (material, belt, and idler rolls)............................	32,300 lb.
Return run (belt and idler rolls)..	6,000 lb.
Pulleys (5 at 300 lb. each)...	1,500 lb.
Equivalent weight of motor ($WK = 11$)...............................	16,000 lb.
Equivalent weight of drive (approx. $\frac{1}{6}$)...............................	2,650 lb.
Total	58,450 lb.

Unit accelerating force: $\dfrac{4,620}{58,450} = 0.079$ lb. per lb.

Inertia force distribution:

Carrying run	32,300 lb. at 0.079....................	2,550 lb. (i)
Return run	6,000 lb. at 0.079....................	475 lb. (i)
Pulleys	1,500 lb. at 0.079....................	120 lb. (i)
Motor and drive..............	18,650 lb. at 0.079....................	1,475 lb. (i)
		4,620 lb. (i)

Inertia forces, like friction forces, retard movement of the belt.

A high-tension, low-stretch belt, such as a wire cord belt, is required for long conveyors used as transportation media. All the tension capacity built into such higher-cost high-tension belts must be utilized as operating tension to justify the long centers. Any additional tension required to start the conveyor must be kept within the maximum overload allowance specified by the belt manufacturer.

For the force required to accelerate a given mass:

$$F = Ma \qquad (7)$$

If W is the weight in pounds to be accelerated:

$$M = \frac{W}{g} \qquad (8)$$

Factor g represents the acceleration caused by gravity (32.16 ft. per sec. per sec.). Factor a is the rate of acceleration in feet per second per second. If v_o is the initial and v the final velocity in feet per second, and t is the time in seconds to change from v_o to v, then:

$$a = \frac{v - v_o}{t} \qquad (9)$$

When starting from rest,

$$a = \frac{v}{t} \qquad (10)$$

A certain 30-in. inclined-belt conveyor with 1,750-ft. centers handling 670 tons per hr. of ore at a belt speed of 550 ft. per min. requires the full allowable operating tension of 19,500 lb. of a wire-cord belt. The necessary additional starting forces must be kept within 40 percent of the maximum allowable operating tension.

The total weight of material on the fully loaded belt, plus the weight of the belt and rotating parts of idler rolls on the carrying and return runs is 143,000 lb.:

$$M = \frac{W}{g} = \frac{143,000}{32.16} = 4,400$$

If the rate of acceleration, a, is 1 ft. per sec. per sec., the required accelerating force is $F = Ma = 4{,}400 \times 1 = 4{,}400$ lb. The velocity of the belt is $550/60 = 9.16$ ft. per sec. With 1 ft. per sec. per sec. acceleration, the 4,400-lb. accelerating force will bring the belt from rest to 550 ft. per min. in 9.16 sec. For the belt under consideration the controls were designed to bring the belt up to speed in from 8 to 10 sec.

Effect of Inertia Stresses. In general, inertia forces, whether they are considered in stopping or starting a conveyor, are calculated in order:

1. To check the T_1/T_2 ratio at the drive pulley for starting a conveyor or for stopping a conveyor by braking.
2. To check belt stresses at a transition curve in order to provide a proper radius curve to maintain belt contact with the troughing idlers under all conditions.
3. To provide control to keep the maximum starting tension, T_1, within prescribed limits, and to check minimum sag tension at critical points.

For the normal belt conveyor, inertia forces are disregarded.

Excessive stresses cause slipping of the drive pulley, surging of the gravity take-up, and excessive elongation of the conveyor belt, which may result in a drawing out, or narrowing, of the belt.

T_1/T_2 Ratio at the Drive Pulley. The last two columns of Fig. 13 indicate the effectiveness of various drive-pulley arrangements as discussed under Slack-side Tension, T_2. This ratio is of prime importance in the effective operation of the conveyor.

For a lagged drive pulley snubbed to 215° of belt contact (symbol *LPS*215), this table indicates that $T_1/T_2 = 3.72$. This value means that 100 lb. of T_2 tension can develop an operating tension, T_1, of 372 lb., and the effective horsepower pull available will be $372 - 100$, or 272 lb. The inertia, or i, forces required to bring the belt up to operating speed, change what may be a proper operating ratio of 3.72 to 1, to one in which the available T_2 may not be sufficient to permit the drive pulley to start the belt, and the drive pulley slips. The slippage occurs because the inertia forces that resist the starting of the carrying run of the belt make necessary an increased tension in the belt as it enters into contact with the drive pulley, while those that resist movement in the return run of the belt reduce a T_2 tension sufficient only for operating purposes.

The limit to which this ratio can be increased is 50 percent, so that, for starting only, 100 lb. of T_2 will provide 558 lb. of **starting tension.** ($T_1/T_2 = 3.72 + 3.72/2 = 5.58$). If the inertia forces in the return run amount to 10 lb., decreasing T_2 to 90 lb., then

$$\frac{T_1}{100 - 10} = 5.58$$

and T_1 is limited, $5.58 \times 90 = 502$ lb. at starting. Based on 372 lb. of T_1 **operating tension,** the inertia force in the carrying run would be limited to $502 - 372 = 130$ lb. If the inertia forces were 150 lb. in the carrying run and 10 lb. in the return run, the **starting ratio** would be

$$\frac{372 + 150}{100 - 10} = 5.80$$

This ratio exceeds the allowable starting ratio of 5.58, and the drive pulley would tend to slip and fail to start the belt.

To use the same drive and to keep the starting ratio within the allowable 5.58, it is necessary to increase T_2 by an amount t, that would make the ratio less than 5.58, say 5.50. To keep the forces balanced, t must be added to T_1 and T_2:

$$T_1/T_2 = \frac{372 + 150 + t}{100 - 10 + t} = 5.50, \text{ from which } t = 6.$$

If 10 lb. are added to T_1 and T_2:

for starting

$$T_1/T_2 = \frac{372 + 150 + 10}{100 - 10 + 10} = 5.32$$

for operating

$$T_1/T_2 = \frac{372 + 10}{100 + 10} \cdot \cdot \cdot = 3.47$$

Both of these ratios are within allowable limits.

Radius of Concave Transition Curve. Since the radius of a concave transition curve is determined by the tension in the belt at the curve and by the weight per foot of the belt, it may be important to investigate the most unfavorable conditions, which exist generally when starting the conveyor when the belt is loaded up to the curve but empty on the curved section. (See under "Conveyor Path" in this section, and see Fig. 8.)

Unless taken into consideration, and provided against, additional starting tension may cause the belt to lift off the idlers. All conditions of loading should be checked. Gradual acceleration is recommended for all conveyors with concave transition curves.

Acceleration and Belt Stretch. Any belt will stretch to some extent when its tension is increased and will pick up its load progressively from head end to foot end according to its stretch characteristic. For a **short conveyor,** in which belt tensions are so low as to cause little elongation of the belt when increased from "fixed" tensions to "starting" tensions, practically the entire conveyor and load is accelerated as soon as power is applied. Belt speed is almost uniform throughout because of the slight change in belt length, and pulleys B, C, D, and E (see Fig. 14) start rotating about as soon as the drive pulley A.

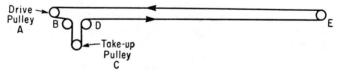

Fig. 14. Belt stretch.

This fact can be illustrated by a conveyor 175 ft. center to center using a normal conveyor belt, driven by a 30-hp. 1160-r.p.m. motor at a belt speed of 300 ft. per min., requiring a starting belt tension (T_M) that causes the belt to stretch 1.6 percent (0.016) in the carrying run at the head end. The "fixed" tension in the belt at the foot end has caused the belt to stretch 0.6 percent (0.006). The expected stretch in the carrying run at starting would be

$$\frac{0.016 - 0.006}{2} \times 175 = 0.875 \text{ ft.}$$

Under this slight belt stretch the motor comes up to full load speed under practically full load conditions, lengthening its period of acceleration. If it makes 20 turns before arriving at full load speed and makes 4 turns per foot of belt travel, the belt travels $20/4 = 5$ ft. in coming up to operating speed. The belt stretch (0.875 ft.) is taken up by the time the motor reaches 17.5 percent of full load speed $(0.875/5 = 1.75)$. After the motor has made $3\frac{1}{2}$ turns (20×0.175) the entire conveyor is moving. Where **long centers** increase belt tensions to the extent that a steel-cord belt is required, the combination of longer centers and low stretch characteristics of the steel-cord belt may be such that the higher belt tension in the steel-cord belt will produce belt elongation proportional to that of the short conveyor with the higher stretch belt, and **belt movement** will be as nearly uniform throughout the long center as for the short-center conveyor. The mass to be accelerated, however, will be in proportion to the longer centers. As long as speeds are nearly uniform throughout the conveyor, the entire mass of the conveyor and its load must be considered as being accelerated, and controlled acceleration may be necessary to keep the starting tension within the overload limit of the steel-cord belt.

Whether a belt with high- or low-stretch characteristics is used, when the combination of belt stretch and conveyor centers is such that maximum starting tension, T_M, causes belt elongation to the extent that the drive pulley can reach full speed before the entire conveyor is under way, controlled acceleration has a two-fold purpose:

1. To keep **starting tensions** within specified limits.
2. To hold the motor at **reduced speed** until all the belt is under way, so that with the entire conveyor load on the motor, final acceleration is slow, and there is little additional stretch in the belt in reaching full operating speed. This condition allows the belt-stretch to be taken up gradually as it slowly develops in the belt, giving a smooth action to the travel of the take-up as it takes up the belt stretch and maintains a constant T_2 starting tension on the drive pulley.

If there is no control of the belt stretch and drive pulley A is allowed to reach full operating speed before the entire conveyor is under way, the belt at pulley B may be at full speed before the belt at pulleys D and E starts moving. The take-up pulley C will be traveling downward to take up the belt being payed off the drive pulley A. When all the stretch is taken out of the belt and the belt at pulley D suddenly starts moving at full operating speed, the downward travel of take-up pulley C will be suddenly reversed, with consequent surging of the take-up and the introduction of violent stresses which have been known to cause a belt permanent damage.

For a 1,000-ft.-center conveyor driven by a 125-hp. 1750-r.p.m. motor at a belt speed of 550 ft. per min. requiring a starting tension T_M, that causes the belt to stretch $2\frac{1}{2}$ percent (0.025) in the carrying run at the head end and a "fixed" tension that has caused the belt to stretch 1 percent (0.01) at the foot end, the expected stretch in the carrying run of the belt is

$$\frac{0.025 - 0.01}{2} \times 1,000$$

or 7.5 ft. If the motor makes 3.2 turns per ft. of belt travel, it would require 3.2×7.5, or 24, turns to put the expected stretch in the belt. If the motor comes up to full speed in 8.3 turns, only about one-third of the conveyor would be moving when the drive pulley reached full operating speed.

Belt Take-up. For the great majority of belt conveyor applications, the "normal" belt conveyor, belt stretch is incidental, and the generally accepted rule is to allow 2 percent of the conveyor centers for the amount of take-up travel. The take-up, however, has an important function besides taking up belt stretch, and that is to maintain the proper "fixed" tension so necessary to successful operation of the belt conveyor. It must provide sufficient initial or "slack" tension to the drive pulley and must also maintain a proper "sag" tension. The take-up tension must be no greater than necessary, because it influences the operating tension which determines the strength and therefore the cost of the belt.

Screw-Type Take-ups. For the short-center conveyor (with centers up to 150-ft.), in which belt tensions are low, the necessary T_2 tension is likely to be less than the minimum "sag" tension required at the foot end of the conveyor, as indicated in Fig. 2. Screw-type take-ups with 24- to 36-in. travel are sometimes used with such conveyors, by means of which sufficient tension is put into the belt, so that it operates without noticeable belt sag, according to the best judgment of the operator. Screw take-ups are generally limited to horizontal conveyors with centers under 150 ft. Screw take-up tensions are very likely to be excessive, but since the belt for a short conveyor is generally selected for width or ply thickness to support the load, belt tension is not an important factor.

Gravity-Type Take-ups. Gravity-type take-ups are recommended for conveyors in general because they can maintain a constant and predetermined tension in the belt at all times, and their length of travel can be made to suit most conveyors. For extremely long-center conveyors, the belt stretch of even a high-tensile fabric or fabric-cord belt may be too much for any reasonable take-up device, so that a low-stretch wire-cord belt may be used because of stretch rather than strength.

A gravity take-up must be so placed that the necessary T_2 tension is immediately available at starting, so there will be no belt slip caused by slack accumulation at the drive pulley. If a gravity take-up is placed at the foot end of a long horizontal conveyor, with the drive pulley at the other end, slack will tend to accumulate in the return run at starting because of frictional and inertia forces in the return run, and T_2 tension will be reduced or lost at the drive pulley. The same condition applies to inclined conveyors where the incline is not sufficient to provide gravitational forces to overcome the frictional and inertia forces in the return run, to the extent that full take-up tension can be maintained at the drive. For such conveyors, the gravity take-up is preferably located adjacent to the drive pulley at the head end. If conditions are such that the take-up must be placed at the foot end, excess counterweight to the amount of the frictional and inertia forces in the return run of the belt will be necessary. Where belt tensions are critical, this additional tension might call for a heavier belt, in which case it might be well to consider a foot-end drive, and avoid the excess counterweight.

For conveyors inclined at slopes sufficient for the gravitational forces to exceed the frictional and inertia forces of the return run, a **horizontal gravity take-up** can be used at the foot end. Where the gravitational forces caused by the weight of the return-run belt exceed the sum of the frictional and inertia forces of the return run and the required T_2 tension, a horizontal gravity take-up can be used at the foot end, but its only loading would be to maintain the required "sag" tension in the belt.

The horizontal type of gravity take-up is best adapted to the foot end of a conveyor. Where used anywhere in the run of the conveyor it requires at least one more bend pulley than would a **vertical-type take-up.** The vertical type is preferred where space permits.

Belt Conveyor Design Calculations

PROCEDURE. The development of the data and order of calculations is illustrated by the solution of the following typical problem:

To convey and elevate 400 tons per hr. of unsized coal with 12-in. maximum-size lumps and weighing 50 lb. per cu. ft. The horizontal distance is 300 ft., the vertical lift 50 ft. The drive is at the head end.

Step 1. Determine the suitability of the materials for handling on a belt.

Step 2. Compute the angle of incline.

Rise per 100 ft.: 50/300 = 16.6 ft.

Fig. 15 shows this slope to be between 8 and 10°. The maximum slope for run-of-mine coal is 16° (see Fig. 7).

Step 3. Determine the width of the conveyor belt. Fig. 4 shows that a belt 36 in. wide is the minimum for handling unsized material containing 12-in. maximum lumps.

Step 4. Determine the speed of the conveyor. Fig. 4 indicates that 550 ft. per min. is the maximum speed for a 36-in. belt for coarse-lump coal.

Step 5. Determine the capacity of the conveyor belt. 400 tons per hr. of 50-lb. material is equal in volume to 800 tons per hr. of 100-lb. material. According to Fig. 4, a 36-in. belt at 300 ft. per min. handles 700 tons per hr. of 100-lb. material. The required belt speed is:

800/700 × 300 = 343, say 350 ft. per min.

Slope Angle in Degrees	Rise in Feet	Incline Center	Slope Angle in Degrees	Rise in Feet	Incline Center
4	6.99	100.24	16	28.67	104.02
6	10.51	100.55	18	32.49	105.14
8	14.05	100.98	20	36.40	106.41
10	17.63	101.56	22	40.40	107.85
12	21.26	102.24	24	44.52	109.47
14	24.93	103.06	26	48.77	111.26

EXAMPLE: What are the required horizontal distance and incline centers of a conveyor that is to rise 38 ft. on an incline limited to 16°?
Rise for 100-ft. horizontal distance on 16° incline = 28.67 ft.:

$$\frac{38}{28.67} = 1.3254$$

Horizontal distance:

1.3254 × 100 = 132.54 ft.

Incline centers:

1.3254 × 104.02 = 137.87 ft.

Fig. 15. Rise and centers per 100 ft. of horizontal distance for inclined conveyors.

Step 6. Determine the horsepower of the belt conveyor (based on an 0.03 friction factor and a 150-ft. length factor). Fig. 6 shows that a 36-in. belt at 100 ft. per min. can handle at least 266 tons per hr. of 100-lb. material or 133 tons per hr. of 50-lb. material. At 350 ft. per min. it can handle at least 133 × 3.5, or 465, tons per hr. Base the figure for horsepower on 460 tons per hr. for conservative design, for possible overloads.

The following values are found in the figures indicated:

Fig. 10: Horsepower to drive the empty belt:

$$1.67 \times 350/100 = 5.85$$

Fig. 11: Horsepower to convey the material:

$$1.36 \times 460/100 = 6.32$$

Fig. 12: Horsepower to elevate the material:

$$5.05 \times 460/100 = \underline{23.48}$$

$$35.64 \text{ hp.}$$

Use 35 hp. for further calculations.

Step 7. Determine the effective horsepower pull, E.

Formula 3:

$$E = \frac{35 \times 33,000}{350} = 3,300 \text{ lb.}$$

Step 8. Make a preliminary determination of the operating belt tension. Assume an LPS215 drive (a lagged pulley snubbed to obtain 215° of belt contact). From Fig. 13:

$$T_1 = 1.36 \times 3,300 = 4,500 \text{ lb.}$$

This is a "net" T_1 and does not include "fixed" or "operating belt" tensions.

Step 9. Determine the required "slack" tension at drive pulley.

$$T_2 = T_1 - E = 4,500 - 3,300 = 1,200 \text{ lb.}$$

Step 10. Make a tentative belt selection. Fig. 16 shows that for handling 12-in.-lump coal a 36-in. belt requires:

a. A minimum of 6 ply of 28- or 32-oz. duck. (Eight ply is maximum.)
b. A minimum of 6 ply of 36-oz. duck. (Seven ply is maximum.)
c. A minimum of 5 ply of 42-oz. duck. (Six ply is maximum.)

Step 11. Check the approximate unit belt stress.

For a 6-ply belt:

$$\frac{4,500}{6 \times 36} = 20.8 \text{ lb. per in. per ply}$$

For a 5-ply belt:

$$\frac{4,500}{5 \times 36} = 25 \text{ lb. per in. per ply}$$

Fig. 1 shows the permissible belt stress (pounds per inch per ply):

28-oz. duck: 26 lb., using metal splice
42-oz. duck: 40 lb., using metal splice

The 42-oz. belt is considerably stronger than necessary; the 6-ply 28-oz. belt has sufficient strength even with a metal splice and is well under the maximum ply for troughing. Reference to Fig. 4 shows a 3/16-in. top rubber cover and a 1/16-in. bottom cover. The lump size indicates the second grade of cover.

Step 12. Determine the unit weights. The following values are found in Fig. 9: a 36-in. 6-ply 28-oz. belt and a 1/4-in total cover. Therefore:

$$36 \times 0.284 = 9.22$$

The belt load per foot is:

$$\frac{100 \, T}{3 \, S} = \frac{100 \times 460}{3 \times 350} = 44 \text{ lb.}$$

Grouping: columns under *Light Materials*, *Minus 4 in. Coal…*, *Minus 20 in. Coal…*, and *Coarse Ores…* are **Minimum Plies To Support Load**; columns under *20° Troughing Idlers* and *45° Troughing Idlers** are **Maximum Plies for Troughing**. All sub-columns are **Weight of Duck**.

Width of Belt (in.)	Light Materials (grain, wood, chips)		Minus 4 in. Coal / Minus 3 in. Stone / Minus 1½ in. Ore / Sand and Small Gravel / Coke				Minus 20 in. Coal / Minus 8 in. Stone / Minus 6 in. Ore / Earth Stripping					Coarse Ores or Other Heavy Material (large lumps)				20° Troughing Idlers					45° Troughing Idlers*				
	28	32	28	32	36	42	28	32	36	42	48	32	36	42	48	28	32	36	42	48	28	32	36	42	48
16	3	3	4	4												4	4								
18	3	3	4	4	3	3										4	4	3	3						
20	4	4	4	4	3	3										5	5	4	3						
24	4	4	4	4	4	4	5	5	4	4	4					5	5	5	4	4	3				
30	4	4	5	5	5	4	6	6	5	4	4	6	6	5	5	6	6	6	5	5	4				
36	4	4	6	5	5	4	6	6	6	5	5	7	7	6	6	8	8	7	6	6	5	4			
42	4	4	6	5	5	5	7	7	6	6	6	8	7	6	6	9	9	8	8	7	5	4	4		
48	4	4	6	5	5	5	8	7	7	6	6	9	8	7	7	10	10	10	9	9	6	5	5	4	4
54				7	6	6		8	7	6	6	10	9	8	8		12	12	11	11	6	6	6	5	5
60				7	7	6		8	7	6	6	10	9	8	8		13	13	12	12					

* Because of the steeper angle of the troughing rolls making a greater bend in the belt to form the deeper trough, thinner belts are necessary for 45° troughing idlers, to avoid longitudinal breaks in standard ply-constructed belts. Where greater strength is required, cord belts or special weaves may be used. Consult belt supplier for recommendations.

Fig. 16. Maximum and minimum plies for cotton-fabric ply-constructed rubber conveyor belt.

Step 13. Compute the minimum belt tension (sag tension) at the foot end.
(See "Factors Affecting Effective Horsepower Pull, E" and "Fixed Tension" in this
section.)

Using Formula 2, minimum tension is 6.25 w l. Using the values given in Fig. 2:
idler spacing, l, for a 36-in. belt for 50-lb. material is 4.5 ft. The weight of the belt
and load, w, is 9.22 + 44, or 53.22. The minimum or sag tension is therefore:

$$6.25 \times 53.22 \times 4.5 = 1,500 \text{ lb.}$$

Referring to Step 9, the required slackside tension is seen to be 1,200 lb.

Step 14. Determine the total "fixed" belt tension. (See "Fixed Tension.")

The tension caused by the weight of the belt in 50 ft. of vertical
   height is 50 × 9.22... 460 lb.
Sag tension 1,500

Total "fixed" tension (not including return-run friction).............. 1,960 lb.

Where slack-side tension is critical return-run friction must be considered. See discussion under "Fixed Tension" and "Gravity-Type Take-ups."

Step 15. Determine the total operating tension in the belt. (See "Operating Belt
Tension" and "Effect of Inertia Stresses.") This is the sum of the "fixed" tension
and the effective horsepower pull, E, or 1,960 + 3,300 = 5,260. Therefore, the unit
belt stress is:

$$\frac{5,260}{6 \times 36} = 24.5 \text{ lb. per in. per ply}$$

The permissible operating tension using a metal splice, (see Fig. 1) is 26 lb. per in.
per ply. The maximum permissible operating unit stress is 35 lb. for a vulcanized
splice. The ratio of operating stress to maximum permissible stress is:

$$\frac{24.5}{35} = 0.70$$

Since operating stress is only 70 percent of the maximum permissible stress, this conveyor is classed as "normal," and starting stresses need not be considered. (See "Normal Belt Conveyors.")

Step 16. Check the drive-pulley ratio, T_1/T_2. (See "T_1/T_2 Ratio at the Drive
Pulley.")

Total operating tension, T_1.................... 5,260
Total "fixed" tension, T_2...................... 1,960
Drive ratio:

$$\frac{T_1}{T_2} = \frac{5,260}{1,960} = 2.7$$

Fig. 13 shows that for an LPS215 drive pulley the permissible $T_1/T_2 = 3.72$ for operating. This can be increased 50 percent for starting, or to 5.58. The drive ratio is well
within safe limits.

Step 17. Determine the minimum pulley diameters. The operating stress at the
head end is 70 percent of the maximum permissible. According to Fig. 1, for a 6-ply
28-oz. belt, the minimum pulley diameter is 30 in. The operating stress at the foot
end is:

$$\frac{1,960}{6 \times 36} = 9 \text{ lb. per in. per ply}$$

The minimum pulley diameter is 20 in.

Step 18. Determine the size of the head drive shaft. Because of the snubbing of the belt around the drive pulley, the total belt pull on the shaft is not equal to the sum of T_1 and T_2 but is the resultant of these two forces, which when combined with the weight of the drive pulley, gives the total load on the two bearings of the headshaft (not considering the weight of the headshaft). Assuming that the resultant of T_1 and T_2 combined with a 600-lb. pulley is 7,200 lb. and that the moment arm (the center line of bearing to the nearest pulley hub) is 12 in., the bending moment in the headshaft is:

$$\frac{7,200}{2} \times 12 = 43,200 \text{ in.-lb.}$$

The torsional moment is $(5,260 - 1,960)\ 15 = 49,500$ in.-lb.

Charts based on combined torsional and bending moments indicate installation of a shaft with a $4\frac{7}{16}$-in. diameter. It is good design to use the next-larger size of shaft, in order to minimize shaft deflection. Excessive deflection in wide-face pulley shafts tends to cause pulley failure or to cause the belt to exert excessive transverse pressure or movement at the pulley. The **diameter** of the shaft determines shaft deflection, not the material from which the shaft is made.

Bend-pulley, take-up, and foot-pulley shafts are designed for bending only. The bending moment of such shafts is the product of the moment arm and the resultant of the entering and leaving belt tensions and the weight of the pulley.

Step 19. Check for holdback. If the fully loaded conveyor stops because of power failure or other trouble, the load on the belt will tend to cause the belt to move backward, piling material at the foot end. The force of gravity that causes this backward movement is the 44 lb. of material per ft. of belt passing through 50 ft. of vertical height, or $44 \times 50 = 2,200$ lb. The resistance to this force is the force contained in the frictional resistance of the idlers caused by the weight of the material on the belt, the weight of the belt, and the weight of the rotating parts of the idler rolls. The holdback friction factor is 0.01, to assure ample safety.

In Fig. 2, the weight per ft. of 36-in. troughing rolls is shown to be $55/4.5 = 12.2$ lb. The weight per ft. of 36-in. return rolls is $50/10 = 5.0$ lb.

Weight of material on belt...........................(300 + 150)44 = 19,800 lb,
Weight of belt (carrying run)..................   ....(300 + 150) 9.2 = 4,200
Weight of troughing rolls.............................(300 + 150)12.2 = 5,500

                                                                     29,500 lb.

Weight of belt (return run)..........................(300 + 150) 9.2 = 4,200
Weight of return rolls...............................(300 + 150) 5.0 = 2,250

                                                                     6,450 lb.

(*Note:* 150 is the length factor.)

The resisting force $(29,500 + 6,450)\ .01 = 360$ lb., say 400 lb. The possible belt pull at the head pulley is $2,200 - 400 = 1,800$ lb. For a head pulley 30 in. in diameter (2.5 ft.), the holdback device should have a torque capacity of:

$$\frac{1,800 \times 2.5}{2} = 2,250 \text{ ft.-lb.}$$

Closed-Belt Conveyors

DEFINITION. In a closed-belt conveyor the belt, instead of being merely troughed, is **wrapped completely around its load of material.** It is, in effect, a moving conduit with material and casing walls moving together. Thus it differs basically from the en masse conveyor, which has a stationary casing with material sliding through it.

ADVANTAGES OF CLOSED-BELT CONVEYORS. The principal advantages of the closed-belt conveyor are:

1. Ability to handle fragile materials gently and **without degradation.**
2. Ability to handle corrosive or abrasive materials **without contamination.**
3. Versatility in layout.

Closed-belt conveyors are especially suited to handling materials like fragile carbon black or ceramic pellets that would break down if subjected to pressure, impact, or rubbing; and chemicals or products that must be maintained at a **high degree of purity,** particularly with respect to absence of metal particles. Where circumstances require that material be conveyed through a circuitous route in a single unit, the closed belt offers exceptional possibilities. Its running qualities are unusually smooth and quiet.

Closed-belt conveyors do not compete in **cost** with types such as ordinary screw conveyors and centrifugal bucket elevators in applications where these would give satisfactory results. Since the material-carrying conduit of a closed-belt conveyor moves with respect to feed and discharge chutes, **complete dusttightness is not practical** as it is in an en masse conveyor where the stationary conduit can be continuous with the connecting chutes. The closed belt is not adapted to handling **sticky materials** that would adhere to the rubber surfaces.

BELT CONSTRUCTION. Although closed-belt conveyors have been manufactured in various forms, the most practical to be marketed so far is the type known as the **Zipper conveyor.** A section of the Zipper belt is shown in Fig. 17.

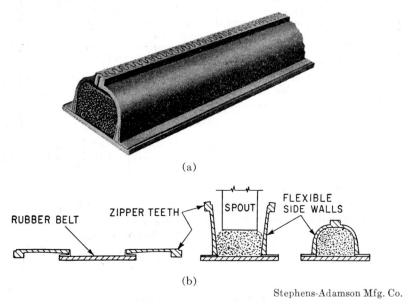

(a)

(b)

Stephens-Adamson Mfg. Co.

Fig. 17. The endless Zipper belt (a) loaded and closed and (b) in section, showing how load is completely enclosed.

It consists of a flat base belt with two flexible side walls hinged to its edges. The outer edges of the side walls are provided with teeth which may interlock to form a complete enclosure. The base is of rubberized fabric plies to provide body and tensile strength, while the side walls are solid rubber with **teeth molded integrally.** The hinges are of special synthetic fabric. Details of the opening and closing mechanism are shown in Fig. 18.

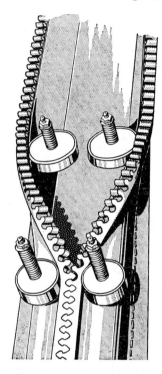

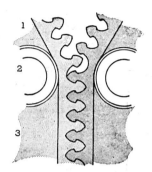

ABOVE — Enlarged diagram shows; (1) the normally spaced teeth on both sides of the Zipper belt; (2) the teeth spread to open the spaces between teeth, and permit free meshing; and (3) the teeth locked, and belt securely closed for conveying.

LEFT — Drawing shows how Zipper belt teeth are automatically spread, meshed, and locked by means of ball bearing rollers—as the belt travels past the closing station. Belt is automatically opened in reverse manner.

Stephens-Adamson Mfg. Co.

Fig. 18. Diagram showing spreading, nesting, and locking of teeth.

The Zipper belt is driven by means of ordinary pulleys, as in the case of a belt conveyor. For engaging pulleys the belt is in the flat condition (as in *A*, Fig. 1). In the closed condition (*C*) the belt can be carried around bends on a series of rollers. The **minimum radius** for such a bend is about 18 times the over-all depth of the closed belt whether the bend is made with base toward center or with the base toward the outside. Also, the belt may be twisted in a straight run of a length at least 30 times the over-all depth of the closed belt for every 90° of twist.

CONVEYOR SHAPES. In view of the ability of the closed belt to travel around bends and to take a twist, the possible paths are almost limitless and include shapes in more than one plane. As with all versatile types of conveyors, the simplest practical layout will lead to the most satisfactory results and the more complex shapes should be adopted only where actually necessary. Fig. 19 shows several common shapes. It is always essential that the belt be fed at a point where the slope is well below the angle of slide of the material.

SPEED, SIZE, AND TONNAGE. Up to the present time only one size of Zipper belt has been available. It has a base belt 7 in. wide and an over-all depth

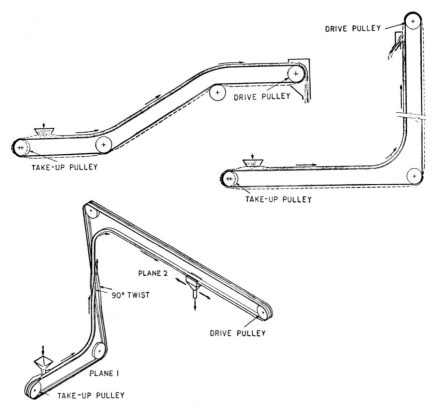

Fig. 19. Shapes of Zipper conveyors with feed and discharge locations.

when closed of approximately 4 in. The volume carried by the Zipper belt is 0.07 cu. ft. per lineal ft. of closed belt. Normally there is no appreciable slippage between the belt and the conveyed material. Therefore **volumetric capacity** can be calculated as follows:

$$C_v = 0.07 \times S$$

where C_v = cu. ft. per min.

S = belt speed (in ft. per min.)

Capacity by weight is:

$$C_w = 0.0021 \times W \times S$$

where C_w = tons per hr.

W = weight of material (in lb. per cu. ft.)

The belt should not run over 200 ft. per min. but can run at any lesser speed. The speed should be suited to the capacity so that the belt will be well filled, especially if prevention of degradation is important.

POWER REQUIREMENT. Since there is no relative motion between material and the moving conduit, and since the belt travels on antifriction rollers, the power required is low in proportion to tonnage. The approximate power required at the conveyor drive shaft is:

$$\text{Hp.} = \frac{(A + 150) \times S}{30,000} + \frac{B \times T}{16,000} + \frac{C \times T}{500}$$

where A = horizontal projected length of entire belt (in ft.)
B = horizontal projected length of loaded portion of belt (in ft.)
C = vertical projected length of loaded portion of belt (in ft.)
S = belt speed (in ft. per min.)
T = tons handled per hr.

LENGTH OF CONVEYOR. The practical length of a closed-belt conveyor is limited by the working strength of the base belt. There is considerable latitude possible in weight of fabric and number of plies which go to make up the base, provided pulley diameters are kept in correct relation. The rules governing design of ordinary belt conveyors will apply in general. **Weight of the Zipper belt** with 7-in.-wide base is 3½ lb. per lineal ft. assuming 5 plies of 42-oz. fabric. An additional limitation exists where the belt makes a bend in which the carrying side faces the center of curvature. Because of bowing of the base belt between the edge-supporting rollers, the **tension** in a 5-ply 42-oz. base should not exceed 700 lb. for a normal curve.

FEEDING AND DISCHARGING. Material enters the belt when it is in the condition shown in B, Fig. 17. Beyond the feed inlet chute the side walls are brought together between rollers and interlocked to give condition C. **Self-feeding** from a hopper or bin is feasible with free-flowing nonaeratable materials, such as grain.

The belt may be discharged over the head pulley (as in A in Fig. 19) or in a vertical run (as in B). To discharge at a point along a horizontal run (as in C) the belt must be in an inverted position, so that when it is opened, the material can flow out readily. A feature of the closed belt conveyor which is often useful is its adaptability to having the **discharger movable** along an entire horizontal run.

CLEANOUT. If any portion of the carrying run slopes steeper than the angle of slide for the material, special provision must be made to cause that portion to be **self-emptying** when the feed is cut off. A large majority of installations do not require the self-emptying feature. Where a **complete cleanout** is necessary, the cleaning can be accomplished by means of vanes attached to the base. The vanes fill the cross-section of the closed belt and act as partitions to prevent the backward flow of the material. For shape B in Fig. 19, the vanes can be rigid, but when the belt is to run over the pulleys in inverted position, they must be flexible, in order to allow the base belt to wrap on to the pulleys. The flexible vanes require some maintenance.

WEAR AND MAINTENANCE. The service life of the Zipper belt depends to a great extent on the correct adjustment of the rollers that guide the rubber walls and especially those that control the meshing and unmeshing of the teeth. Assuming careful adjustment and periodic checking, the belt as well as the machinery will have the same long-lasting characteristics as an ordinary belt conveyor.

Throwers

DEFINITION. The term "thrower," as used in materials handling, refers to a device for projecting bulk material through the air in an unsupported stream. Generally the stream is directed upward on an angle from 10 to 45° above horizontal. The material then follows a natural curved trajectory and comes to rest in the pile as it is formed.

Throwers are used for filling bins, making storage or refuse piles, loading cars, and trimming ships. Their chief advantage lies in their ability to **distribute materials** over considerable areas from a central point. As compared to conveyors capable of a similar range of distribution, throwers are simple, compact, portable, and inexpensive.

CENTRIFUGAL BELT THROWERS. Although throwing devices have been built using several different basic principles, such as impellers and air jets, the most successful and widely used type is the **centrifugal belt.** It consists of a short endless flat belt running on pulleys, with a portion made to follow a concave curved path by means of discs engaging the edges, as shown in Fig. 20. Material is fed onto the belt at the beginning of its curved portion, then travels with the belt and between the discs. Where the belt makes a convex bend onto the pulley, the material leaves because of its momentum, thence following its trajectory.

Usually, though not necessarily, the entering material is traveling more slowly than the belt but acquires belt speed before reaching the point of discharge. Greater speed is imparted from belt to material through friction, which is greatly augmented because of the centrifugal force of the material traveling in the curved

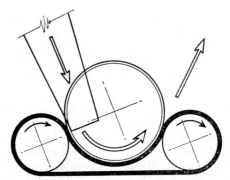

Fig. 20. Diagram of centrifugal belt thrower.

path. It is evident that if the entering stream engages the belt smoothly at a point where the belt and material are traveling in the same direction, all the initial velocity of the entering stream is preserved. Thus it is possible that **material may enter and discharge at belt speed,** the only function of the thrower then being to change direction of the stream.

The graphs in Fig. 21 show theoretical trajectories for a variety of discharge velocities and angles. Because of air resistance, actual trajectories fall short of those shown in the graphs by widely varying amounts according to certain conditions. The **effect of air resistance** is greater as material is lighter and drier, as particle size is finer, as discharge velocity is greater, and as tonnage is smaller. For instance, half-inch crushed rock discharged at 4,000 ft. per min. would follow the theoretical trajectory quite closely even at small tonnages. Damp sand discharged at 4,000 ft. per min. and 100 tons per hr. would be only slightly affected by air resistance. If the sand were dry, the main stream would conform approximately to theory, but the fringes of the stream would fall short. If the tonnage

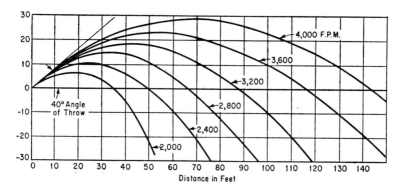

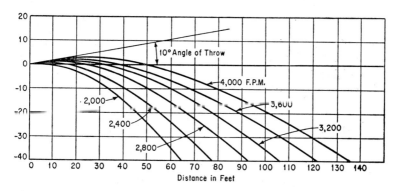

Fig. 21. Theoretical trajectories for discharge velocities and angles.

of dry sand were reduced to 10 tons per hr., the average throwing distance would probably be less than half of that shown in the graph. Dry bran discharged at 4,000 ft. per min. would fall far short even at 100 tons per hr. If the bran were discharged at 2,000 ft. per min. and 100 tons per hr., most of it would go close to the full distance, but with tonnage reduced to 10 tons per hr. the entire stream would fall short.

CAPACITY OF THROWERS. There is **practically no limit to the tonnage capacity** of throwers, provided the size and strength of the equipment are made proportional to the service requirements. The feed chute must be large enough to pass the required number of cubic feet per minute without danger of clogging. Greater density of material and higher entering velocity, as well as larger dimensions of thrower, will increase the rate of tonnage handled. Illustrating the relationship of equipment size to tonnage, a ship trimming thrower capable of handling 1,500 tons per hr. of ground rock with a discharge velocity of 2,700 ft. per min. has an over-all width of 4 ft., length of 6 ft., and height—exclusive of feed chute—of 6 ft. A piler capable of throwing grain at a speed of 3,000 ft. per min. and 50 tons per hr. is shown in Fig. 22.

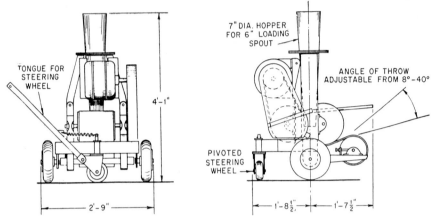

Stephens-Adamson Mfg. Co.

Fig. 22. Portable flexible thrower.

Capacity is also dependent on the power of the motor driving the belt. Power is consumed (1) in increasing momentum of the material, (2) in friction between belt and material, and (3) in running the equipment, that is, belt-flexing and bearing friction. The approximate motor horsepower may be determined from the formula:

$$hp. = \frac{B \times V_2}{40,000} + \frac{T(V_2{}^2 - V_1{}^2)}{150,000,000}$$

where B = belt width (in in.)
T = tons per hr.
V_1 = velocity of material entering thrower (ft. per min.)
V_2 = velocity of discharge = belt speed (ft. per min.)

In most thrower applications the material acquires its **entering velocity** by falling through the feed chute. Although arrangements are feasible in which the material may remain in engagement with the belt through an arc of nearly 270°, such arrangements are rare in industrial practice. For the simple case shown in Fig. 20 the arc will lie between 100 and 135°. Discharge speeds of the order shown in the graphs of Fig. 21 can then be obtained only if the material is able to drop a considerable distance. The Fig. 23 table provides some data on minimum drop for materials such as grain. The values given may be reduced slightly for materials having a higher friction factor.

METHODS FOR SWIVELING. Nearly all applications of throwers used for filling and piling involve some means for swiveling the unit on a vertical axis. By such means the stream is pointed in various directions to produce the distributing effect, which is generally the main objective. One method is to mount the thrower on wheels so arranged that it can be moved from place to place like a cart or allowed to remain in one location and turned on its wheels about an axis through the center of its feed chute. This latter arrangement is shown in Fig. 22.

Discharge Velocity (F.P.M.) (Assumed Same as Belt Speed)	Minimum Drop for Discharge Angle of 10° (Ft.)	Minimum Drop for Discharge Angle of 40° (Ft.)
1,600	3	2
2,000	5	3
2,400	7	5
2,800	9	6
3,200	11	7
3,600	14	9
4,000	17	12

Fig. 23. **Minimum drop for materials such as grain.**

Another method is to mount the thrower on the lower end of a chute containing a swivel joint, as exemplified in the apparatus shown in Fig. 24. Still another method is to suspend the thrower from a cable attached to a cross member on the center line of the feed chute. Thus the unit may be fed from a stationary chute adjacent to the supporting cable while the thrower and its feed chute are rotated. Fig. 25 illustrates this latter arrangement.

Forming Storage or Refuse Piles. An effective application for the forming of storage or refuse piles is the use of a swiveled thrower mounted at the end of an extensible conveyor. The swiveling may be controlled from a remote point,

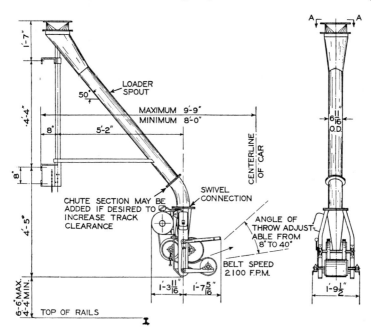

Stephens-Adamson Mfg. Co.

Fig. 24. **Thrower mounted on swivel joint.**

by either hand- or power-driven equipment. By such means it is entirely practical to obtain a tenfold increase in pile volume over the same conveyor setup minus the thrower. Another possibility is the forming of a pile beyond the range of conveyor supports for ease of later reclaiming.

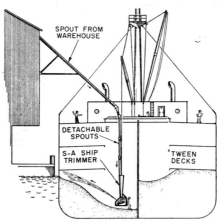

Fig. 25. Thrower suspended from cable.

A simple addition to the thrower mechanism permits movement of the outer pulley to vary the angle of throw in the vertical plane. This adjustment is useful in regulating the height of pile, as in car-loading, where ideal depth of load would vary with type of material. It is seldom if ever advantageous to vary belt speed in order to regulate throwing distance. The reason is that the crest of the pile begins at the far end and automatically follows the trajectory inwardly as it is formed.

MAINTENANCE COST. The principal item of maintenance cost is the thrower belt. Expressed in terms of cost per ton of material handled, it is generally a negligible amount, but under certain adverse conditions it may be prohibitive. **Belt life** tends to be shorter as material of relatively higher abrasiveness is being handled, as lumps are larger and more angular, as belt speeds become higher, and particularly as speedup of material between entry and discharge is greater. Other conditions of an unpredictable nature have a significantly negative effect on belt life. They include improper training of the belt, which may result in quick and serious damage. Any condition which causes the entering stream of material to impinge on the belt at an oblique angle will greatly increase the rate of belt wear.

If the nature of the material handled is such as to cause rapid wear on the normal belt, the cost of belt replacements per ton can be reduced by installing belts made of thicker covers and higher-quality rubber. As a typical example of belt life, a ship-trimmer handling coke required a new belt after loading 50,000 tons. Maintenance cost was approximately $0.002 per ton. For nonabrasive materials such as grain or meal there is no appreciable wearing of the belt cover. Assuming correct machine adjustments and no occurrence of accidents, belt maintenance cost is then almost nil.

ELEVATING CONVEYORS

CONTENTS

CONTENTS *(Continued)*

SECTION **24**

ELEVATING CONVEYORS

———

Bucket Elevators

CLASSIFICATION OF BUCKET ELEVATORS. Bucket elevators are broadly classified into **two general types:** (1) spaced-bucket elevators, and (2) continuous-bucket elevators. These two types of elevators are further subdivided as follows.

Under spaced-bucket elevators four classes are included: (a) centrifugal-discharge elevators, (b) positive-discharge elevators, (c) marine-leg elevators, and (d) high-speed elevators for handling grain and similar nonabrasive materials. Continuous-bucket elevators likewise are subdivided into (a) regular continuous-bucket elevators (b) supercapacity bucket elevators, and (c) internal-discharge bucket elevators.

Bucket elevators, in general, are especially useful where **moderate capacities of materials** are handled and where **space is limited.** They are recommended because of their simplicity and relatively low cost. Material being handled in these elevators must be free. In most cases particle size should not exceed 2 to 3 in., although standard supercapacity buckets may handle up to 12-in. sizes, depending on factors such as percentage of lumps and bucket size. Normal lifts range up to 100 ft., but by special construction the lift can be increased to as much as 300 ft. Above this height, chain or belt tensions develop that are beyond the economical range of this type of equipment.

SPACED-BUCKET, CENTRIFUGAL-DISCHARGE ELEVATORS. The spaced-bucket centrifugal-discharge elevator is the type most frequently used. It employs malleable iron buckets of various designs adapted to particular industrial conditions. These elevators are also furnished with Salem buckets for lighter service, and special high-speed buckets are available for handling grain and similar materials. The buckets are spaced on the chain or belt line to allow free flow of material at loading and discharge points, and the **operating speed** of this type of elevator is higher than that of the continuous type of bucket elevators. The holes for the attachment of these buckets to the belt or chain are placed near the top of the elevator bucket. This arrangement gives a stronger attachment for the buckets digging in the elevator boot, and also improves the centrifugal action when the material is thrown out of the bucket at the discharge point.

There is a definite ratio required between the **bucket speed** and the **head-wheel diameters.** This ratio is based on giving a combination of good centrifugal discharge and good bucket pickup conditions. Fig. 1 shows recommended head-wheel diameters for different bucket speeds. Depending on the nature of material handled, the speed and head wheel sizes may be varied after checking the discharge trajectory.

Caution must be used if bucket speeds are increased over those listed in Fig. 1. At higher speeds **"fanning" action** may develop because of centrifugal force of

24·1

buckets passing around the foot wheel. This action results in underfilling the buckets and necessitates increasing the height of the loading chute. Excessive speed at the head shaft will also cause the material to leave the buckets earlier than it should for correct discharge, and will allow part of the material to fall back down the elevator leg instead of being thrown out through the discharge opening.

Head Wheel Diameter (in.)	For High-Speed Grain Elevators		For General Industrial Purposes and Low-Speed Grain Elevators	
	R.P.M. of Head Wheel	F.P.M. of Belt	R.P.M. of Head Wheel	F.P.M. of Belt or Chain
12			55	180
15			50	200
18			47	230
24	69	427	42	270
30	61	479	38	305
36	56	527	35	335
42	52	573	32	355
48	49	615	29	370
54	46	650	28	400
60	43	675	27	425
72	40	754	25	480
84	37	813		
96	34	855		

Goodyear Tire & Rubber Co.

Fig. 1. Recommended speeds for spaced-bucket elevators and diameters for head wheels.

Types of Buckets. Several types of buckets are used with this centrifugal-discharge type of elevator, the most common being malleable iron style A or style AA buckets. These are cast round-bottom units. The AA buckets with the reinforced digging lip are preferred because, at a small increase in cost, substantially longer service can be obtained. The AARB buckets have reinforced backs to provide more substantial attachment to the chain. Style B malleable iron buckets have a lower front than style A buckets and are used to better advantage for handling coarsely broken or more abrasive material such as coke, ore, stone, and similar materials on inclined elevators. Style C malleable iron buckets have flat fronts and are used to handle materials which tend to stick or pack in other types of buckets. Salem-type buckets are used for lighter and less abrasive materials. Also available are specially designed high-speed buckets used for discharging materials such as grain at high speeds. Sometimes these speeds range between 700 to 800 ft. per min., and these special buckets can discharge at this speed without throwing the material against the back of the preceding bucket.

There is a wide range of standard units from which the bucket elevator best suited for the particular service can be selected. In general, the unit selected should have ample capacity for all peak tonnage conditions, and the buckets should be of a kind that will discharge the particular material properly. Materials that are sticky have the characteristic of building up in the V- or round-bottom type of buckets. This calls for buckets with **reserve capacity** in the original selection, and there must be a practical means of periodically cleaning the buckets. Steam jets are sometimes directed into the buckets as they leave the discharge position. This treatment, used intermittently, is effective for cleaning out certain raw sugars.

Operating Speeds. The usual speeds for spaced-bucket centrifugal-discharge elevators vary between 200 and 335 ft. per min. To deliver the rated capacity and give satisfactory performance, bucket elevators should be fed at a **uniform rate.** Grain and similar materials flow freely, and the volume of flow can be regulated by means of a gate or valve. Materials more difficult to handle, and which are less uniform in flow characteristics, should be fed to the elevator boot under definite control, preferably by means of pan- or belt-type feeder. These feeders, which are manufactured in many designs, are also used to take the surge condition out of the conveying system. Such a provision is highly desirable in almost all processing operations.

Materials Handled. The materials handled in these elevators are limited in size, and the spaced bucket-type centrifugal-discharge elevator is seldom used where individual particles are larger than the equivalent of $4\frac{1}{2}$-in. cubes. For average industrial work, the capacity of the spaced-bucket type of elevator is seldom over 150 tons per hr. This type of elevator offers an inexpensive, compact apparatus for raising materials in processing operations. The buckets are mounted on either chain or belt, the choice being based on the type of material to be handled.

Manufacturers have prepared tables, based on many years of experience in the application of bucket elevators, showing where chain or elevator belt is recommended in handling specific materials. Fig. 2 gives such a listing. The headings to the columns in the table are explained as follows:

1. CLASS OF MATERIAL: "A" indicates that the material is abrasive, "NA" that material is nonabrasive.
2. TYPE OF ELEVATOR: "S" indicates spaced-bucket or centrifugal-discharge type, "C" indicates continuous-bucket type, "P" indicates positive-discharge type, and "SC" indicates supercapacity type. For the larger capacities and heavier service where continuous-bucket elevators are recommended, use supercapacity type.

POSITIVE-DISCHARGE BUCKET ELEVATORS. Positive-discharge bucket elevators are a special type of spaced-bucket elevator. They have a **knuckle shaft** under the head shaft. The sprockets of this knuckle shaft invert the buckets, and the material is poured from the buckets as they pass over the discharge spout. This discharge condition does not depend upon centrifugal force. Positive-discharge elevators operate at comparatively slow speeds—usually about 120 ft. per min.—and they have a very definite field of application for materials that would otherwise give trouble when being discharged. The impact of the chains as they engage the knuckle sprockets has a slight jarring effect which aids in freeing the material from the buckets when the latter are in an inverted position. The buckets are end mounted between two strands of matched chain. The buckets dig the material in the boot when loading, very much as they do in the spaced bucket centrifugal-discharge type of elevator.

Material	Class Material	(b) Av. Wt., Lb. per Cu. Ft.	Elevator Type	Elevator Class
Acid phosphate (pulv.).....	A	60	C, (h) S, P (h)	Chain
Alum. (lumpy)	NA	55	C, S	Chain or Belt
Aluminum chips	A	15	C	Chain or Belt
Aluminum oxide	A	120	C	Chain or Belt
Ashes	A	40	S (a)	Chain or Belt
Asphalt (crushed)	A	45	C, S	Chain or Belt
Bakelite (powdered)	NA	35	C, P	Chain or Belt
Baking powder	A	55	C (h) S, P	Chain or Belt
Barley (d)	NA	38	S	Chain or Belt
Bauxite (aluminum ore)....	A	80	S (a) C, SC	Chain or Belt
Beans (d)	NA	50	S	Chain or Belt
Bones (crushed)	NA	40	S (a)	Chain or Belt
Borax (powdered)	A	53	S	Chain or Belt
Bran (d)	NA	16	S	Chain or Belt
Brewers' grain (dry) (c)....	NA	28	S (c)	Chain or Belt
Brewers' grain (wet)	NA	55	S	Chain or Belt
Carbon black (pelletized) ..	NA	25	C (h) S (a)	Chain or Belt
Cement clinker	A	75–80	C, SC	Chain or Belt
Cement (fluffed)	A	65–70	C, S (a)	Chain or Belt
Chalk (crushed)	A	90	C, S	Chain or Belt
Charcoal	A	15–34	C (h) P	Chain or Belt
Cinders, blast furnace	A	57	C, S (a)	Chain or Belt
Clay (dry)	A	63	C, S	Chain or Belt
Coal	NA	50	C, S, SC	Chain or Belt
Coffee beans	NA	25–30	C, S	Chain or Belt
Coke	A	25–40	C, S	Chain or Belt
Cork	NA	12–15	C, P	Chain or Belt
Corn (shelled) (d)	NA	45	S	Chain or Belt
Corn meal (d)	NA	40	S	Chain or Belt
Cottonseed (dry)	NA	25	S	Chain or Belt
Cottonseed meal	NA	38	S	Chain or Belt
Dolomite (crushed)	A	95	C, S, SC	Chain
Feldspar (ground)	A	75	C (h) S (a)	Chain or Belt
Flaxseed (d)	NA	45	S	Belt
Flour (d)	NA	35	S	Belt
Fuller's earth (raw)	NA	40	S	Belt
Fuller's earth (burnt)	A	40	C (h) S	Belt
Fuller's earth (oily) (c) (f) .	NA	60	S (a)	Belt
Glass batch	A	90	C, S	Belt
Grain	NA	30–40	S	Chain or Belt
Gravel	A	100	C, S, SC	Chain or Belt
Gypsum (crushed)	A	100	C, S (a) SC	Chain or Belt
Hops, spent (dry)	NA	35	S	Chain or Belt
Hops (wet)	NA	50	S	Chain or Belt
Ice (crushed)	NA	35–40	C, S (a)	Chain
Iron ore (crushed)	A	110–150	C, SC	Chain or Belt
Lime (ground)	A	64	C, S, SC	Chain or Belt
Lime (hydrated)	NA	40	C (h) P (h)	Chain
Limestone (pulverized)	A	70	C (h) S, SC	Chain or Belt
Limestone (crushed)	A	96	C, SC	Chain or Belt
Malt, whole (dry)	NA	20–30	S	Chain or Belt
Malt (wet) (c)	NA	60–65	S	Chain or Belt
Oats (d)	NA	26	S	Belt
Phosphate rock	A	75–85	C, SC	Chain or Belt
Plastics	NA	...	C, S, P	Chain

The Jeffrey Mfg. Co.

Fig. 2. Elevator selection table (continued on next page).

Material	Class Material	(b) Av. Wt., Lb. per Cu. Ft.	Elevator Type	Elevator Class
Quartz (crushed)	A	100	C, SC	Chain or Belt
Rice (hulled) (d)..........	NA	45	S, P	Chain or Belt
Rice (rough)	A	36	S	Chain or Belt
Rubber (ground)	NA	23	C, S, P	Chain or Belt
Rye (d)	NA	45	C, S	Chain or Belt
Salt (coarse) (c)	NA	45	S (a)	Chain or Belt
Salt (cake) (c)	NA	85	S (a)	Chain or Belt
Salt (fine) (c).............	NA	80	S (a)	Chain or Belt
Sand (dry)	A	100	C, S	Chain or Belt
Sand (damp)	A	120	C, S	Chain or Belt
Sand (foundry)	A	100	S (a)	Belt
Sand (silica)	A	100	C, S	Belt
Sawdust	NA	12	S	Chain or Belt
Shale	A	92	C, S	Chain or Belt
Slag, furnace	A	70	C, SC	Chain or Belt
Soda ash (heavy)	A	60	C (h) S	Chain or Belt
Soda ash (fluffy)..........	A	30	P (h)	Chain
Soybeans (cracked) (j)....	A	32–36	S	Chain or Belt
Soybeans (whole) (j).......	A	45–50	S	Chain or Belt
Soybean (cake)	A	42	S	Chain or Belt
Soybean flour	NA	27	S	Chain or Belt
Soybean meal	NA	40	S	Chain or Belt
Starch (d)	NA	45	S	Chain or Belt
Stone (crushed) (m).......	A	100	C, SC	Chain or Belt
Sugar (raw)	NA	60	S (g)	Chain
Sugar (refined)	NA	55	S (a)	Chain or Belt
Sulphur	NA	90–125	S (a)	Chain or Belt
Tanbark (ground) (c)......	NA	55	S (a)	Chain
Wheat (d)	NA	48	S	Chain or Belt
Wood chips	NA	10–30	C, S (a)	Belt

a A fixed bearing boot is recommended where material is lumpy or tends to pack, cake, or build up in the boot.

b The weight per cubic foot of material varies widely, depending upon the size of material and condition (moisture content, etc.); therefore the weight per cubic foot should be determined as accurately as possible. The weights listed here are average weights most frequently encountered.

c When handling foods or corrosive materials, chain and buckets, either specially plated or made from special materials, as well as specially prepared belts, may be required to protect chain and buckets and to prevent contamination of food.

d Light-gage steel Salem elevator buckets may be substituted for the malleable iron buckets and the number of plies in the belt reduced when handling materials of this nature.

f Use canvas belt for oily fuller's earth.

g Use style C malleable iron buckets.

h While positive-discharge elevators are usually recommended for handling light fluffy materials such as soda ash, hydrated lime, a centrifugal-discharge or a continuous-bucket elevator may be used, in which case the manufacturer's engineering department should be consulted as to rated capacity, speed, and bucket spacing. Type DH buckets should be used on type C elevators.

j Soybean hulls are extremely abrasive.

m Use class S elevator for crushed stone only when the material contains lumps not over ½ in.

Fig. 2. (Concluded.)

MARINE-LEG BUCKET ELEVATORS. The marine-leg type of centrifugal discharge elevator is used for unloading bulk cargoes from ships or barges. It consists of a vertical elevator leg which digs into the bulk cargo and usually discharges onto a horizontal conveyor. This conveyor takes the material to the dock for warehousing or processing. These elevators are supported on a pivoting boom frame so that the elevator can be raised or lowered as it digs into the bulk cargo at the varying positions of the cargo in the hold and under varying tide conditions. The elevators are usually arranged so that they can be moved thwartwise across the hatch openings. Their usefulness depends upon their being able to dig at the full rating of the elevator, and this requirement means that the material under the decks has to be brought to a position where the elevator can reach it.

Arrangements have been worked out so that power shovels or bulldozers working in the ship continually crowd the material to the boot of the elevator. **Drag scrapers** operating between the elevator boot and the skin of the ship have been designed with remote-control points located on deck. These remotely controlled drag scrapers are frequently operated by compressed air, by means of electrically actuated air valves. This arrangement gives excellent flexibility in the control of the scraper buckets, which operate between blocks placed on pad eyes on the frames of the ship and blocks mounted on the lower part of the elevator casing. The elevator buckets are of the high-speed design. They are usually mounted on a heavy precision elevator chain, and the drive is arranged for an **operating speed** of 350 to 400 ft. per min.

For complete flexibility, these marine-leg elevators have been mounted on **traveling gantry frames** so that they can dig from the several hatches without having to move the ship. Marine-leg gantry elevators with this complete flexibility are used to unload bulk cargoes of raw sugar on both the Atlantic and Pacific seaboards. Complicated structural steel design problems must be solved to provide stability for the elevator and structure in all operating positions, and to withstand gale winds when the hinged boom is in the stowed position. The boom is usually balanced by a counterweight system which is designed to pick up the correct amount of counterweight for all the operating positions of the boom and elevator.

		Bucket Data				Belt Width W (in.)	Head Wheel Diameters (in.)							
							18	24	30	36	42	48	54	60
							Corresponding R.P.M. of Head Wheel							
							47	42	38	35	32	29	28	27
							Corresponding Belt Speed F.P.M.							
Type	Length and Projection (in.)	Depth Along Belt (in.)	Average Weight (lb.)	Struck Volume (cu. in.)	Space Center to Center (in.)		230	270	305	335	355	370	400	425
							T — Peak Capacities in Tons per Hour							
Malleable style A or AA	6×4	4¼	2.5	55	12	7	8	10	11	12	13	13	14	15
	8×5	5½	4.5	115	14	9	15	17	20	22	23	24	26	27
	10×6	6¼	6.5	204	16	11		27	30	33	35	37	40	42
	12×6	6¼	7.5	246	16	13		32	37	40	43	44	48	51
	12×7	7¼	10.0	332	18	13		39	44	48	51	53	58	61
	16×7	7¼	13.5	467	18	18		55	62	68	72	75	81	86
	14×8	7½	15.0	509	20	15			61	67	71	74	79	84
	18×8	7½	20.0	668	20	20			80	87	93	97	104	111
	24×8	7½	30.0	887	20	26			105	116	123	128	138	147
	18×10	10½	30.0	1,053	24	20				115	122	127	137	146

Peak Capacities in Tons per Hour — T

Goodyear Tire & Rubber Co.

Fig. 3. Spaced-bucket elevators handling materials weighing approximately 50 lb. per cu. ft., with a few representative sizes and styles of buckets.

A moderate-size marine-leg elevator has a capacity of somewhat less than 250 tons per hr. of free-digging grain or raw sugar.

Typical Data on Spaced-Bucket Elevators. Data on spaced-bucket elevators handling materials weighing, respectively, 50 lb. and 100 lb. per cu. ft. are given in Figs. 3 and 4 for a few representative sizes and styles of buckets. Data on the proper number of belt plies for elevators are given in Fig. 5 on a minimum ply

							Head Wheel Diameters (in.)							
							18	24	30	36	42	48	54	60
		Bucket Data				Belt Width W (in.)	Corresponding R.P.M. of Head Wheel							
							47	42	38	35	32	29	28	27
							Corresponding Belt Speed F.P.M.							
Type	Length and Projection (in.)	Depth Along Belt (in.)	Average Weight (lb.)	Struck Volume (cu. in.)	Space Center to Center (in.)		230	270	305	335	355	370	400	425
							T – Peak Capacities in Tons per Hour							
Malleable style A or AA	6×4	4¼	2.5	55	12	7	16.5	19.4	22	24	25	27	29	30
	8×5	5½	4.5	115	14	9	30.0	35.0	39	43	46	48	51	55
	10×6	6¼	6.5	204	16	11		54.0	61	67	71	74	80	85
	12×6	6¼	7.5	246	16	13		65.0	73	80	85	89	96	102
	12×7	7¼	10.0	332	18	13		78.0	88	97	102	107	115	122
	16×7	7¼	13.5	467	18	18		110.0	124	136	144	150	162	172
	14×8	7½	15.0	509	20	15			121	133	141	147	159	169
	18×8	7½	20.0	668	20	20			159	175	186	193	209	222
	24×8	7½	30.0	887	20	26			211	232	246	256	277	294
	18×10	10½	30.0	1,053	24	20				230	243	254	274	291

Peak Capacities in Tons per Hour — T

Goodyear Tire & Rubber Co.

Fig. 4. Spaced-bucket elevators handling materials weighing approximately 100 lb. per cu. ft., with a few representative sizes and styles of buckets.

Bucket Data			Maximum Lumps (in.)	Proper Plies for Materials of Maximum Lump Size							Proper Plies for Materials Composed of Fines Only						
				Lift in Feet – H							Lift in Feet – H						
Type	Projection (in.)	Space (in.)	Mixed with Fines	40	50	60	70	80	90	100	40	50	60	70	80	90	100
Malleable style A or AA	4	12	1½	5	5	5	5	5			4	4	4	4	4		
	5	14	1½	6	6	6	6	6			5	5	5	5	5		
	6	16	2	7	7	7	7	7	7		6	6	6	6	6	6	
	7	18	2½	8	8	8	8	8	8	8	6	6	6	6	6	6	6
	8	20	3	9	9	9	9	9	9	9	7	7	7	7	7	7	7
	10	24	3	10	10	10	10	10	10	10	8	8	8	8	8	8	8

Goodyear Tire & Rubber Co.

Note: Plies underlined are needed for tension in handling 100 lb. per cu. ft. material. Based on 35-oz. duck, lagged-head pulley, and screw take-up.

Fig. 5. Proper number of belt plies for elevators in Figs. 3 and 4.

basis. Weight of material to be handled should be considered in using the latter table.

CONTINUOUS-BUCKET ELEVATORS—USUAL TYPE. Continuous-bucket elevators are used where judgment indicates a slow-moving operation, usually about 50 percent of the speed of centrifugal-discharge elevators of the spaced-bucket design. This ratio brings the **speed of the continuous-bucket elevator** to a range of 100 to 175 ft. per min. These bucket elevators are better suited for handling lumpy, abrasive material than are the centrifugal-discharge elevators. Steel buckets are used in most installations, and they are mounted on a chain or belt, with a loading arrangement that chutes the material directly into the buckets. Thus the buckets are not required to dig the material out of the boot. With good design, these elevators are more economical than centrifugal-discharge elevators, although the first cost is somewhat higher. They are run at slower speeds and are not subject to the same wear at the loading boot. These elevators, in many instances, operate vertically. For outdoor service in stone plants, and on construction work, they often operate on inclines of 60 to 70° from the horizontal. Where the elevators operate on an incline, they rarely have enclosed casing.

In this type of elevator, the steel buckets are placed almost touching one another on the belt or chain. As each bucket discharges onto the back of the preceding bucket, the material slides away and thus does not depend upon centrifugal action for discharging. The holes for attaching the buckets to the chain or belt are placed in the bottom half of the bucket, thus allowing the lip of the bucket to rise as it goes over the head pulley or sprocket. This action delays the discharge slightly and allows the preceding bucket to come into position for correctly unloading the elevator.

SUPERCAPACITY CONTINUOUS-BUCKET ELEVATORS. Supercapacity elevators are a special type of continuous-bucket elevator. Instead of mounting the buckets on the chain or belt through bolts in the back of the buckets, they are end-mounted between two strands of chain. Usually a high-grade roller or steel side-bar bushed chain is required for this kind of elevator, and the buckets utilize the space both above and below or in front and back of the chain line. These elevators have guides on the frame for carrying the roller chain on the up-run; the down-run is also guided.

These elevators can be used for handling materials up to 10 to 12 in. in size, and they have been built for **handling capacities** ranging up to 1,000 tons per hr. The larger elevators usually run on inclines which vary between 30 and 70° from the horizontal. This special type of continuous elevator runs at speeds varying from 100 ft. per min. in the small sizes down to 40 to 50 ft. per min. in the very largest sizes. Elevators of this design have been built with buckets 6 ft. long.

INTERNAL-DISCHARGE, CONTINUOUS-BUCKET ELEVATORS. The internal-discharge bucket elevator operates at slow speeds and is suitable for handling free-flowing, nonabrasive materials. The buckets are internally loaded from a chute extended through either side of the casing. Discharge can also be made on either side of the casing. The elevating medium consists of an endless series of overlapping continuous buckets with inner openings. These buckets are supported on double strands of steel roller chain. Movable guides in the lower section provide automatic adjustment for the chain and bucket line. The casings are of steel and are built with internal guides for the chain.

Peak Capacities in Tons per Hour — T

Type	Length and Projection (in.)	Depth Along Belt (in.)	Average Gage	Average Weight (lb.)	Struck Volume (cu. in.)	Space Center to Center (in.)	Belt Width W (in.)	Inclined 15° to 30° Buckets 75% Full Speed F.P.M.–S 100	150	200	250	Vertical Buckets 60% Full Speed F.P.M.–S 100	150	200	250
								T — Peak Capacities in Tons per Hour							
Steel	10×5½	8¾	16	5	220	9	12	19	29	38	48	15	23	31	38
	12×8	11¾	14	12	550	12	14	36	54	72	90	29	43	57	72
	16×8	11¾	14	14	730	12	18	48	71	95	120	38	57	76	95
	20×8	11¾	10	29	920	12	24	60	90	120	150	48	72	96	120
	24×8	11¾	10	33	1,100	12	28	72	107	143	179	57	86	114	143
	16×10	15¾	10	35	1,150	16	18	56	84	113	141	45	68	90	113
	20×10	15¾	10	40	1,440	16	24	70	106	141	176	56	85	113	141
	24×10	15¾	8	54	1,730	16	28	85	127	170	212	68	102	136	170
	30×10	15¾	8	63	2,160	16	34	106	159	212	267	85	128	170	213
	16×12	17¾	10	41	1,660	18	18	72	108	144	180	58	86	115	144
	20×12	17¾	10	51	2,070	18	24	90	135	180	225	72	108	144	180
	24×12	17¾	8	70	2,500	18	28	109	163	218	272	87	130	174	218
	30×12	17¾	8	80	3,100	18	34	135	203	270	338	108	162	216	270
	36×12	17¾	8	91	3,700	18	40	161	242	322	403	129	194	259	323
	36×16	23¾	¼	190	6,600	24	40	215	322	430	537	172	258	344	430

Goodyear Tire & Rubber Co.

Fig. 6. Continuous-bucket elevators handling materials weighing approximately 50 lb. per cu. ft., with a few representative sizes and styles of buckets.

These elevators provide a means for the continuous, gentle **handling in bulk of relatively small articles** such as stampings, castings, plastic chips, pellets, bolts, nuts, rivets, and similar materials. A special type can be furnished with double head shafts operating in fixed bearings. This construction provides a longer interval for discharging the material from the buckets and greater capacity than the type with the single head shaft.

Typical design data on continuous bucket elevators are given in Figs. 6 to 9.

Type	Projection (in.)	Gage	Space (in.)	Maximum Lumps (in.) Mixed with Fines	Proper Plies for Inclined Elevators Buckets 75% Full — Lift in Feet H 40	50	60	70	80	90	100	Proper Plies for Vertical Elevators Buckets 60% Full — Lift in Feet H 40	50	60	70	80	90	100
Steel	5½	16	9	2	6	6	6	6	6			6	6	6	6	6		
	8	10	12	4	8	8	8	8	8	8	8	8	8	8	8	8	8	8
	10	8	16	5	9	9	9	9	9	9	9	9	9	9	9	9	9	9
	12	8	18	6	10	10	10	10	10	10	10	10	10	10	10	10	10	10
	16	¼	24	8	12	12	12	12	12			12	12	12	12	12		12

Goodyear Tire & Rubber Co.

Based on 35-oz. duck, lagged-head pulley, and screw take-up and capacities shown in Fig. 6.

Fig. 7. Proper number of plies in belt.

Peak Capacities in Tons per Hour – T

Bucket Data							Belt Width W (in.)	Inclined 15° to 30° Buckets 75% Full				Vertical Buckets 60% Full			
								Speed F.P.M.–S				Speed F.P.M.–S			
Type	Length and Projection (in.)	Depth Along Belt (in.)	Average Gage	Average Weight (lb.)	Struck Volume (cu. in.)	Space Center to Center (in.)		100	150	200	250	100	150	200	250
								T – Peak Capacities in Tons per Hour							
Steel	10×5½	8¾	16	5	220	9	12	38	57	76	96	31	46	61	77
	12×8	11¾	14	12	550	12	14	72	107	143	179	57	86	115	143
	16×8	11¾	14	14	730	12	18	95	143	190	238	76	114	152	190
	20×8	11¾	10	29	920	12	24	120	180	240	300	96	144	192	240
	24×8	11¾	10	33	1,100	12	28	143	215	288	360	115	172	230	287
	16×10	15¾	10	35	1,150	16	18	112	169	225	281	90	135	180	225
	20×10	15¾	10	40	1,440	16	24	141	211	282	352	113	169	226	282
	24×10	15¾	8	54	1,730	16	28	169	254	338	423	136	203	271	339
	30×10	15¾	8	63	2,160	16	34	211	316	424	527	169	254	338	423
	16×12	17¾	10	41	1,660	18	18	144	216	288	360	115	173	230	288
	20×12	17¾	10	51	2,070	18	24	178	268	357	446	142	214	285	356
	24×12	17¾	8	70	2,500	18	28	215	323	430	539	172	259	350	431
	30×12	17¾	8	80	3,100	18	34	268	402	536	670	214	321	428	535
	36×12	17¾	8	91	3,700	18	40	320	480	640	800	256	384	513	640
	36×16	23¾	¼	190	6,600	24	40	430	645	860	1,075	344	516	690	860

Goodyear Tire & Rubber Co.

Fig. 8. Continuous-bucket elevators handling materials weighing 100 lb. per cu. ft., with a few representative sizes and styles of buckets.

Bucket Data				Maximum Lumps (in.)	Proper Plies for Inclined Elevators Buckets 75% Full							Proper Plies for Vertical Elevators Buckets 60% Full						
					Lift in Feet – H							Lift in Feet – H						
Type	Projection (in.)	Gage	Space (in.)	Mixed with Fines	40	50	60	70	80	90	100	40	50	60	70	80	90	100
Steel	5½	16	9	2	6	6	6	6	6			6	6	6	6	6		
	8	10	12	4	8	8	8	*8*	*9*	*10*	*11*	8	8	8	8	8	*8*	*9*
	10	8	16	5	9	9	*9*	*9*	*10*	*11*	*13*	9	9	9	9	*9*	*10*	*11*
	12	8	18	6	10	10	*10*	*12*				10	10	10	*10*	*11*	*12*	
	16	¼	24	8	12	*12*						12	12	*12*				

Goodyear Tire & Rubber Co.

Based on 35-oz. duck, lagged-head pulley, and screw take-up and capacities shown in Fig. 8.

Fig. 9. Proper number of plies in belt.

BUCKET-ELEVATOR COMPONENT PARTS. The elements of a bucket elevator are simple. They are made up of:

1. The head shaft with pulley or sprockets.
2. The driving mechanism, consisting of motor and speed reducer. In this driving mechanism, or on the head shaft of the elevator, a holdback is recommended to prevent the reversal of the bucket line in case of power interruption.

3. The foot shaft with take-up arrangement and pulley or sprockets. In certain cases elevators can be furnished with fixed boot shaft with the take-up at the head end. Such design is sometimes preferred when handling food products or where the material has a tendency to pack in the elevator boot. This design is also preferred where lumpy material is being handled.
4. The elevator buckets, mounted on belt or chain.
5. The enclosure of the elevator.

Elevator Enclosures. Elevators are enclosed to control the dust, and the enclosing casing also serves to control the drop of the buckets in case of belt or chain failure. In addition to the enclosure, access ladders to the head-shaft driving mechanism are required, and there should be a sufficient working platform at the head shaft or driving level for maintenance and service requirements.

For **inclined elevators** the enclosure is often omitted because of the problems resulting from the sag in the return run of buckets. If the return run is guided by angle tracks in the casing, the buckets must have two strands of end-mounted chain attachments. The alternative plan would be to build a casing enclosing the sag in the return run, but this awkward type of construction is used infrequently.

The design of the enclosure must include an arrangement for successfully feeding the material to the bucket line. The design of the discharge end must be such that the material can be carried away freely from the elevator casing.

SELECTION OF BELT. After the correct selection of the buckets has been made, the selection of the correct belt is of prime importance. If a belt elevator is indicated, the total tension that will be developed in the belt must be calculated. This tension is computed as follows:

The total tension in an elevator belt as it goes on to the head pulley of the elevator is the sum of the following components:

1. Tension due to horsepower pull $= T_1$
2. Tension due to weight of empty buckets and belt on one run $= T_2$
3. Initial or slack side tension $= T_3$

$$T_1 = \text{Hp.} \times \frac{33.000}{S}$$

where $S =$ speed of elevator in feet per minute

and $\text{Hp.} = \dfrac{T(H + H_o)}{990}$

where $T =$ capacity of elevator in tons per hour
$H =$ height of elevator in feet
$H_o = 30$ for all spaced-bucket elevators
$H_o = 10$ for all continuous-bucket elevators

$$T_2 = BH + \frac{12\,bH}{D}$$

where $B =$ weight of belt in pounds per foot
$H =$ height of elevator in feet
$b =$ weight of each bucket
$D =$ spacing of buckets in inches (center-to-center distance)

$$T_3 = T_1 \times K$$

where $K = 1.00$ for bare-drive pulley with screw take-up
$K = 0.84$ for lagged-drive pulley with screw take-up
$K = 0.64$ for bare-drive pulley with counterweight take-up
$K = 0.52$ for lagged drive pulley with counterweight take-up

The sum of T_1, T_2, and T_3 equals the maximum tension to which the elevator will be stressed under normal operating conditions. The proper number of plies to carry this tension is one calculated according to the following formulas, in which W = width of belt in inches:

$$\frac{\text{Maximum tension}}{W \times 27} = \text{number of plies for 28-oz. duck belt}$$

$$\frac{\text{Maximum tension}}{W \times 30} = \text{number of plies for 32-oz. duck belt}$$

$$\frac{\text{Maximum tension}}{W \times 33} = \text{number of plies for 35- and 36-oz. duck belt}$$

$$\frac{\text{Maximum tension}}{W \times 41} = \text{number of plies for 42-oz. duck and heavy rayon belt}$$

W is usually 2 to 4 in. wider than the elevator buckets. It is good practice to specify that the elevator belt have protective rubber covers on both sides of the belt. The thinner cover goes on the bucket side and the heavier cover is in contact with the pulleys.

SELECTION OF CHAIN. In elevators using chain, the chain tension is the sum of T_1 and T_2. T_3 does not apply because the K factor equals zero.

Manufacturers' ratings for elevator chains should be used and a selection made where the working load is well within the theoretical calculations obtained above. This **working load** is based on a factor of at least six to one in relation to ultimate strength. Judgment is required in the selection of the proper chain. If the selection is good, the chain installed should provide several years of operation without replacement or unusual maintenance.

Combination-type chains, ley-bushed chains, steel sidebar bushed, and roller-type chains are four types of chain with wide ranges of usefulness in elevator service.

Motor Horsepower for Driving Elevators. The horsepower of the motor selected for driving elevators can be computed, in most instances, from the following formulas:

$$\text{Hp.} = \frac{H \times T}{500} \text{ for spaced-bucket elevators with digging boot}$$

$$\text{Hp.} = \frac{H \times T}{550} \text{ for continuous-bucket elevator with loading leg}$$

$$\text{where } T = \text{tons per hour}$$
$$H = \text{vertical lift in feet}$$

Obviously these two formulas become progressively conservative for elevators with high lifts, as there is no difference in drive efficiency in high- or low-lift elevators. Hence the greater reserve capacity of the drive is available for loading conditions at the boot and for starting the elevator from rest with a full load in the buckets.

CAPACITY FORMULA. The capacity formula for either spaced- or continuous-bucket elevators is as follows:

$$T = \text{peak capacity in tons per hour}$$
$$S = \text{speed in feet per minute}$$
$$M = \text{weight of material in pounds per cubic foot}$$
$$s = \text{distance from center to center of buckets in inches}$$
$$V = \text{struck volume of each bucket in cubic inches}$$
$$T = \frac{VMS}{6400s} \text{ with buckets 75\% full}$$

or

$$T = \frac{VMS}{8000s} \text{ with buckets 60\% full}$$

BELT CARE AND SPLICING. The B. F. Goodrich Company ("Care, Maintenance and Installation of Elevator Belting") recommends the use of rubber bucket washers between the buckets and the belt. On larger buckets, rubber padding is advised as a cushion between the buckets and the belt.

Elevator Belting of 4 or 5 Ply. Metal clamps are often used for belting in light duty service. These clamps are made from two pieces of 1 × 1 in. or larger equal leg angle iron cut about 1 in. shorter than the belt width. Sharp right angle outside corners, which will be against the belt, should be rounded by grinding or filing. One leg of each angle piece and the belt ends are drilled with mating holes for $\frac{1}{2}$ in. bolts on about 2.0 in. centers. Ends of belt fold up with pulley sides facing and are sandwiched together for bolting between the drilled angles. The clamp is on the bucket side of belt and the undrilled angle legs will be against the belt when tension is applied so that no part of the clamp touches the pulleys.

The **overlap type splice**, which is next explained, is also used on 4- or 5-ply belting.

Elevator Belting of 6 or 8 Ply. The **overlap type of splice** is common. The overlap of the belt ends should extend under three to five buckets. This splice can be made with the bucket bolts extending through both thicknesses of belt. A separate row of bolts should also anchor each end of the belt. This splice should be operated in a direction so that open end of pulley side overlap trails. With relatively thick belting, this trailing end should be chamfered to obtain smoother operation over the pulleys.

Elevator Belting over 6- or 8-Ply Thickness. The **butt-type joint** is commonly used for thick belts. There are two types of this joint:

1. One type uses a pad the same width as the belt and approximately 24 in. long. The pad material may be the same as the elevator belt or may be made from a thinner, more flexible material. The bucket spacing is interrupted at this pad with no buckets placed over the pad. The elevator belt ends butt under the midpoint of the pad. Elevator bucket bolts of $\frac{3}{8}$ in. diameter can be used to fasten pad to belt. The total number of bolts is suggested to be approximately $1\frac{1}{2}$ times the belt width in inches and $\frac{1}{2}$ of this total number is placed in a staggered pattern with three rows on each side of the butt joint. Two-plate type of belt fasteners have also been used in place of the bolts, with the longer dimension of the plate fasteners placed transversely.

2. A common type of butt joint uses a pad of the same material as the belt over the butt ends. The elevator buckets are then bolted over and through the pad and belt. The length of the pad should be such as to accommodate two to four buckets. In addition to the bucket bolts, one row of $\frac{3}{8}$ in. bolts should be placed through belt and pad at each end of pad and also over each butted end of the main belt.

Other Fastening Methods. Elevator belt splices can also be simply made with regular metal fasteners. The two-plate type is most common. The overlap or butt-strap type of splice gives more strength.

Recently, more thought has been given to the use of **vulcanized splicing.** The usual elevator does not provide much take-up movement nor is it very easy to remove part of the casing to provide space for the stepping-down and vulcanizing operation. Vulcanized splices have been giving good service on some jobs where the belt was initially installed with an overlap-type bolted splice. After an operating period during which time initial belt elongation was removed, the joint was vulcanized. This involved having available working space and the stepping down of the overlapped ends containing numerous bolt holes. The bolt holes in the steps are filled with splicing gum during making of the splice.

Bucket Elevating Conveyors

PIVOTED-BUCKET ELEVATING CONVEYORS. The pivoted-bucket type of elevating conveyor consists of a line of malleable iron buckets end-mounted between two strands of heavy-duty precision roller chain. The pivoted bucket carrier is a massive, slow-moving conveyor unit which can convey both vertically and horizontally, or in a path combining horizontal and vertical conveying. This carrier in past years had wide acceptance in power-plant design, where the amount of coal to be conveyed was under 150 to 175 tons per hr., and where there was a demand for a combined coal- and ash-handling unit. The modern trend in **central power-plant coal-handling equipment** is toward increasingly larger hourly capacities. These capacities now range all the way to 2,000–2,500 tons of coal per hr. Within the last ten years, the central power plants have usually specified coal-handling equipment with capacities over 200 tons per hr., and the belt-conveyor system is preferred for these large hourly tonnages.

For **industrial power plants** handling under 75 tons per hr., standard bucket elevators or the en masse type of conveyors are often used because of the lower first cost of this type of equipment in comparison with the pivoted-bucket carrier. This trend has resulted in a narrowing of the field of application for the pivoted-bucket carriers in the power-plant industry. Where economic factors indicate the use of such conveyors, however, they provide a very substantial type of unit, and operate for many years with extremely low operating and maintenance charges. They have the further advantage of being able to handle both coal and ashes in the same conveyor. These conveyors are also used in cement mills, the ceramics industry, and to a small extent in stone-crushing plants.

The pivoted buckets are kept in the horizontal position except when passing over **fixed or movable trippers.** These trippers either turn the buckets over

Size of Bucket (in.)	Pitch (in.)	Capacity in Tons per Hour—T		Speed (ft. per min.)	Weight of Chain and Bucket per Foot, (lb.—W_E)	Weight of Load per Foot (lb.—W_L)		Diameter of Bucket Cross Rods (in.)
		Coal (50 lb. per cu. ft.)	Stone* (100 lb. per cu. ft.)			Coal (50 lb. per cu. ft.)	Stone (100 lb. per cu. ft.)	
18×15	18	15- 20	30- 40	30-40	97	16.6	33.2	$^{15}/_{16}$
18×21	18	22- 30	44- 60	30-40	106	24.5	45.0	$^{15}/_{16}$
24×18	24	40- 50	80-100	40-50	110	44.5	89.0	$1^{3}/_{16}$
24×24	24	50- 62	100-124	40-50	117	55.5	111.0	$1^{3}/_{16}$
24×30	24	70- 87	140-174	40-50	137	78.0	156.0	$1^{3}/_{16}$
24×36	24	90-112	180-224	40-50	147	100.0	200.0	$1^{3}/_{16}$
30×24	30	78- 96	156-192	45-55	166	86.5	173.0	$1^{7}/_{16}$
30×30	30	100-125	200-250	45-55	185	111.0	222.0	$1^{7}/_{16}$
30×36	30	125-150	250-300	45-55	215	138.0	276.0	$1^{7}/_{16}$
36×36	36	175-210	350-420	50-60	278	194.0	388.0	$1^{15}/_{16}$

Stephens-Adamson Mfg. Co.

Based on material 1½ in. and under in size.

Fig. 10. Table of capacities, speeds, and weights.

completely or tilt them sufficiently to discharge the material, after which the bucket drops back into the horizontal position. These massive conveyors are usually protected by shear-pin hub design drive. Further protection is added by a mechanism that will prevent the loaded buckets from reversing and running back in case of power failure. At the bend corners, cutout switches are installed which will stop the conveyor if the buckets do not ride properly.

The **chain** used with these carriers is a bushed roller-type chain with a pitch usually of 18 in., 24 in., 30 in., or 36 in. The 18-in.-pitch chain has an allowable working load per strand varying between 11,000 and 22,000 lb. The 24-in.-pitch chain has an allowable working load per strand varying between 11,000 and 30,000 lb. The 30-in.-pitch chain has an allowable working load per strand varying between 22,000 and 56,000 lb. The 36-in.-pitch chain has an allowable working load per strand varying between 28,000 and 76,000. In Fig. 10 the range of capacities, speeds, and weights of some of these pivoted-bucket carriers are given.

The formulas presented in Fig. 11 give an accurate method of determining the maximum chain tensions and horsepower requirements of bucket-elevating conveyors.

To FIND SIZE OF CHAIN. With size of bucket, speed, and capacity determined from Fig. 10, the size of chain on which to mount the buckets can be selected as follows:

Compute Maximum Chain Tension P from following formula—using maximum capacity and greatest horizontal and vertical distances over which the material is to be carried. The result is the maximum pull on each strand of chain for an installation including four bend corners as indicated in the middle diagram. For each additional bend corner, add 5 percent to total pull thus obtained. From the maximum chain tension table above, select the size of chain with a rated working strength equal to or greater than the maximum tension P obtained.

$$\left(\begin{array}{c}\text{Maximum chain}\\\text{tension on 1 strand}\end{array}\right) \text{(Vertical component)} \qquad \text{(Horizontal component)} \qquad \text{(4 Bends)}$$

$$P = \frac{H(W_E + W_L)}{2} + \frac{(2L \times W_E) + (L_U + L_L)W_L}{20} \times 1.2$$

To FIND SIZE OF MOTOR. The power required to drive a pivoted bucket carrier is the total of the following components and can be computed from the formula given below.

1. As the empty vertical runs (buckets and chains) balance each other, the power necessary to move them is simply that required to elevate the load at normal operating speed.
2. The power required to move the horizontal runs is only that necessary to overcome rolling friction of the loaded and empty runs of buckets and chains at normal speed.
3. The formula below also includes the power needed to pass the chains around corner sprockets in the normal 4-bend installation shown in the top diagram. For each additional bend, add 5% to the hp. obtained by the formula

$$\text{hp.*} = \frac{(W_L \times H \times 10) + (2L \times W_E) + (L_U + L_L)W_L}{330,000} \times S \times 1.2$$

* This formula gives the hp. required at the drive shaft.

P = Maximum chain tension or pull on 1 strand of chain
hp. = Running hp. required at head shaft (extras must be added for drive losses)
T = Tons of material handled per hour, see Fig. 10
S = Conveyor speed in feet per minute
L = Total horizontal length, in feet

L_U = Length of upper horizontal loaded run in feet
L_L = Length of lower horizontal loaded run in feet
H = Total vertical lift in feet
W_E = Weight of chain and buckets (empty) per foot, from Fig. 10
W_L = Weight of load in pounds per foot, from Fig. 10.

Fig. 11. Methods for calculating maximum chain tension and horsepower required for pivoted-bucket conveyors (continued on next page).

4. Additional horsepower for drive losses between motor and drive shaft. The usual allowance is 5% for each cut gear, or roller chain reduction, 5% for each helical gear speed reducer and 10% for each cast tooth gear reduction. If other types of reducers are used, be sure to use manufacturers' efficiency ratings.

The total of the above components gives the horsepower required to run the conveyor, and a motor of equal or greater power must be used. If the conveyor is to be started under load frequently, a motor of high starting torque is recommended.

Three main classifications of drives for pivoted bucket carrier installations. From these three diagrams, in Fig. 11 horsepower and chain tension can be figured for practically any installation.

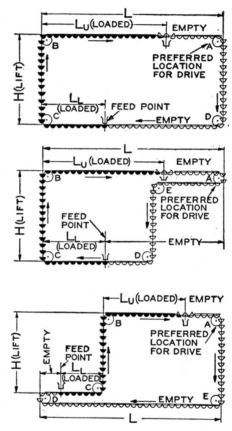

Stephens-Adamson Mfg. Co.

Fig. 11. (Concluded.)

Figs. 12 and 13 illustrate an arrangement of a pivoted-bucket carrier for bulk materials.

Steel plate enclosures are recommended for all parts of the conveyor except where open construction is required for loading and discharge. These enclosures confine the dust that is generated by this type of equipment and the enclosures also provide guide rails for the roller-type chain. The chain is usually guided on both sides of the rollers in the vertical path of the conveyor.

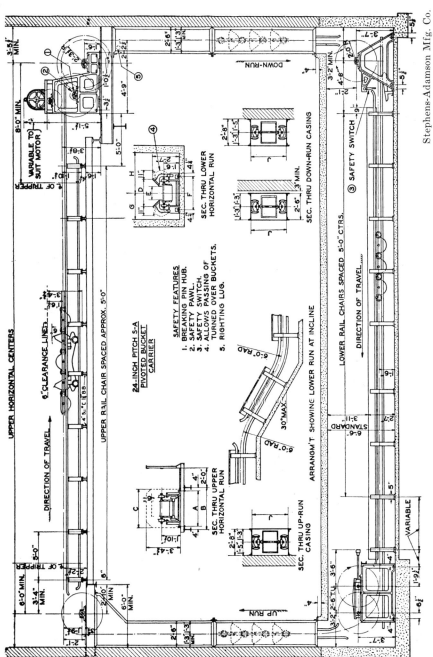

Fig. 12. Pivoted-bucket carrier for bulk materials.

The drive shown in the upper right-hand corner is very seldom used now. In place of this it is common to use an enclosed gear reducer.

Stephens-Adamson Mfg. Co.

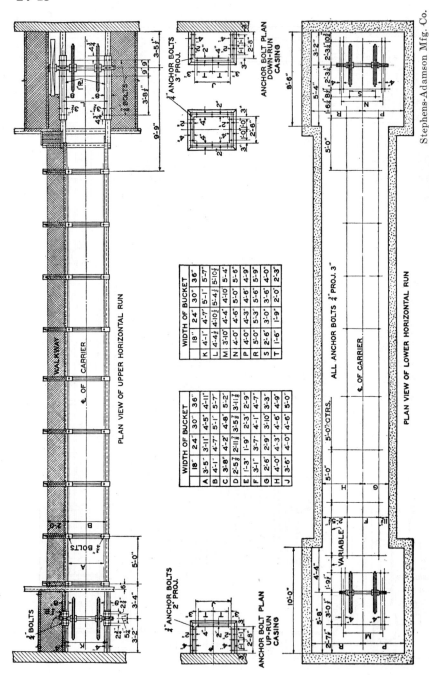

WIDTH OF BUCKET			
	18"	24"	30"	36"
A	3-5"	3-11"	4-5½"	4-11"
B	4-1"	4-7"	5-1"	5-7"
C	3-8"	4-2"	4-8"	5-2"
D	2-5⅞"	2-11⅞	3-5⅞	3-1-11⅞
E	1-3"	1-9"	2-3"	2-9"
F	3-1"	3-7"	4-1"	4-7"
G	2-6"	2-9"	3-10"	3-3"
H	4-0"	4-3"	4-6"	4-9"
J	3-6"	4-0"	4-6"	5-0"

WIDTH OF BUCKET			
	18"	24"	30"	36"
K	4-1"	4-7"	5-1"	5-7"
L	4-4½	4-10½	5-4½	5-10½
M	3-10	4-4	4-10	5-4
N	4-0"	4-6"	5-0"	5-6"
P	4-0"	4-3"	4-6"	4-9"
R	5-0"	5-3"	5-6"	5-9"
S	2-6"	3-0"	3-6"	4-0"
T	1-6"	1-9"	2-0"	2-3"

Stephens-Adamson Mfg. Co.

Fig. 13. Plan view of upper and lower horizontal runs of conveyor shown in Fig. 12.

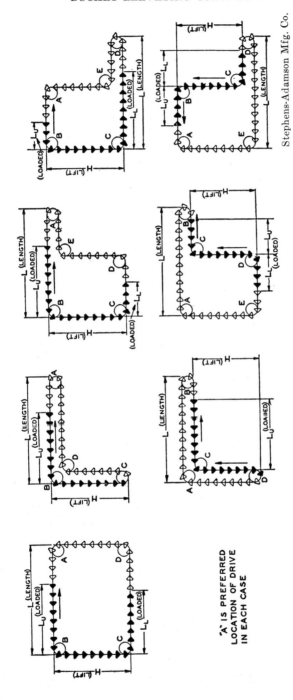

"A" IS PREFERRED
LOCATION OF DRIVE
IN EACH CASE

Stephens-Adamson Mfg. Co.

From these diagrams, horsepower and chain tension can be figured for practically any installation.

Fig. 14. Typical arrangements for gravity-discharge conveyors.

GRAVITY-DISCHARGE ELEVATING CONVEYORS.

The gravity-discharge elevating conveyor was originally designed both to elevate and to distribute sized coal to overhead bunkers in power plants. The use was later developed to handle coal in retail coal pockets and at railroad coaling stations. This type of conveyor is now used rather widely in handling other nonabrasive lumpy materials.

The conveyor consists of V-shaped buckets, end-mounted between two strands of heavy roller chain. These buckets carry the material on the vertical run and act as scrapers moving the material through the horizontal distributing trough. This type of conveyor costs appreciably less than the pivoted-bucket type of conveyor and has a useful range of service, handling materials such as coal at capacities up to 100 or 125 tons per hr. **Roller-type chains** are used for mounting the buckets, and in many cases the long-pitch, steel sidebar, bushed roller chain of 9-in., 12-in., or 18-in. pitch is recommended. The drop-forged rivetless chain is also used for supporting these V-buckets.

Typical arrangements for gravity-discharge conveyors are given in Fig. 14. The conveyor is usually run at 75 to 125 ft. per min. Fig. 15 gives the bucket

Bucket Size (in.)			Vol. Level Full (cu. ft.)	Gage of Bucket	Weight of Bucket (lb.)	Maximum Sized Material (in.)	Maximum Unsized Material (in.)		Minimum Bucket Spacing (in.) for Maximum Lump
Width	Length	Depth					Not to exceed 50% (in.)	Not to exceed 10% (in.)	
12	12	6	0.229	12	14	2	3	5	18
12	16	6	0.308	12	17	2	3	5	18
15	16	7½	0.488	10	28	2½	4	7	18
15	20	7½	0.613	10	31	2½	4	7	18
15	24	7½	0.739	10	35	2½	4	7	18
20	20	10	1.100	³⁄₁₆"	60	3	5	10	24
20	24	10	1.325	³⁄₁₆"	69	3	5	10	24
20	30	10	1.662	³⁄₁₆"	82	3	5	10	24
20	36	10	2.002	³⁄₁₆"	95	3	5	10	24
24	30	12	2.400	¼"	133	4	6	12	24
24	36	12	2.890	¼"	150	4	6	12	24
24	42	12	3.380	¼"	167	4	6	12	24
24	48	12	3.870	¼"	184	4	6	12	24

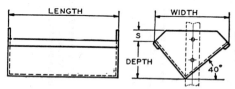

Stephens-Adamson Mfg. Co.

The bucket shape and method of mounting shown above is standard—other shapes can be used if desired. The 40° slope of one side of bucket permits good discharge while the flat slope on opposite side makes possible good loading of bucket at feed point.

Fig. 15. Standard V-bucket capacities, weights, spacings, and maximum lumps handled.

Type of Chain	Pitch of Chain (in.)	Number of Chain Which Can Be Used	Weight of Chain per Foot (lb.)	Friction Factor F	Allowable Working Load at 100 F.P.M. (lb.)
Malleable Iron Roller	6	#1,130	7.6	0.2620	4,000
	6	#1,131	11.5	0.2380	5,500
	6	#8,061	12.0	0.1090	2,800
	6	#8,062	16.0	0.1125	4,000
	6	#8,063	18.0	0.1250	5,300
(S.B.R.) Steel Bushed Roller	9	#8,091	12.0	0.1125	4,000
	9	#8,092	14.0	0.1250	5,300
	9	#8,093	17.0	0.1310	6,800
	9	#8,094	31.0	0.1225	10,800
	12	#8,121	14.0	0.1310	6,800
	12	#8,122	25.0	0.1225	10,800
	12	#8,123	37.0	0.1130	12,800
	12	#8,124	47.0	0.1420	22,400
Rivetless Drop Forged	6	#678	6.5	0.4180	10,000
	6	#698	11.4	0.4200	16,666
	9	#998	10.2	0.4400	16,666
	9	#9,118	16.0	0.4500	26,666

Stephens-Adamson Mfg. Co.

Fig. 16. Typical chain used with gravity-discharge conveyor elevator.

Size of Bucket (in.) Mounted on Roller-Type Chain	For each 100-Ft. Horizontal Run						For each 10-Ft. Lift		
	Empty, with Buckets Spaced			Loaded, with Buckets Spaced			With Buckets Spaced		
	18 in.	24 in.	36 in.	18 in.	24 in.	36 in.	18 in.	24 in.	36 in.
12×12×6	2.66	2.5	2.32	4.46	3.9	3.22	0.30	0.23	0.15
12×16×6	2.81	2.6	2.4	5.31	4.4	3.6	0.42	0.30	0.20
15×16×7½	3.32	3.0	2.67	7.22	5.9	4.57	0.65	0.48	0.32
15×20×7½	3.47	3.1	2.74	8.37	6.8	5.24	0.82	0.62	0.41
15×24×7½	3.66	3.25	2.83	9.56	7.65	5.83	1.00	0.73	0.50
20×20×10	...	3.58	3.09	...	10.18	7.49	...	1.10	0.73
20×24×10	...	3.89	3.26	...	11.79	8.56	...	1.30	0.90
20×30×10	...	4.36	3.57	...	14.26	10.17	...	1.65	1.10
20×36×10	...	4.82	3.88	...	16.82	11.88	...	2.00	1.33
24×30×12	...	5.72	4.47	...	20.12	14.07	...	2.60	1.60
24×36×12	...	6.22	4.81	...	23.52	16.31	...	2.89	1.91
24×42×12	...	6.72	5.15	...	26.92	18.65	...	3.70	2.25
24×48×12	...	7.23	5.46	...	30.43	20.86	...	3.87	2.57

Stephens-Adamson Mfg. Co.

Fig. 17. Approximate horsepower required to run gravity-discharge conveyor elevators.

capacities, weights, spacing, and size of materials handled in this type of equipment. The data are based on V-buckets, where the V angle equals 100 deg. When figuring capacities of a gravity-discharge conveyor, use 80 to 90 percent of level full volume for handling sizes of material recommended in Fig. 15. If larger lumps are to be handled, use larger buckets or make further reduction in capacity. Figs. 16 and 17 give data on typical chains and approximate horsepower requirements for these conveyors.

Gravity-discharge elevating conveyors should be enclosed except at the points where the material is fed to and discharged from the unit. This enclosure controls the dust incident to handling dusty materials and is furnished with angle-iron gudes to control the path of the elevating chain.

En Masse Conveyors

CHARACTERISTICS OF EN MASSE CONVEYORS. En masse conveyors are so called because they convey materials by causing them to flow in a

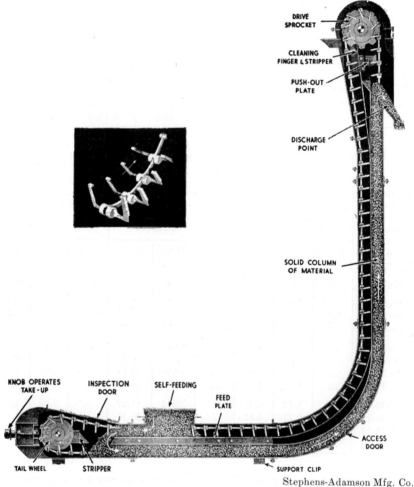

Stephens-Adamson Mfg. Co.

Fig. 18. Redler en masse conveyor using skeleton-type flights.

compact and unbroken stream through a conduit. The conveyor consists of a stationary conduit or casing and a moving, articulated element which is pulled through it. The moving element, comprising a series of flights, occupies only a fraction of the space inside the conduit, the remainder of the space being filled with the material that is being conveyed. Assuming correct design, a flowable material like grain or dry cement will move with the moving element rather than remaining stationary and allowing the flights to pass through it.

Advantages of En Masse Conveyors. The chief advantages of en masse conveyors are:

1. They are inherently enclosed.
2. They are versatile as to layout.
3. They are relatively small in cross section.
4. They are self-feeding.

Wherever a conveying problem calls for **tightness against leakage of dust, liquid, or gas,** en masse conveyors should always be considered. Wherever arrangement is difficult or space is limited, en masse conveyors will often provide the best, and sometimes the only feasible, solution. En masse conveyors do not

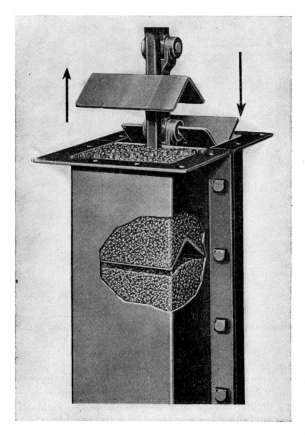

Link-Belt Co.

Fig. 19. Section of Bulk-Flo elevator using double-sloped vanes for discharging.

compete with belt conveyors or bucket elevators in the fields of handling coarse mineral products or large tonnages over long distances.

TYPES OF FLIGHTS. The flights on en masse conveyors may be **vanes** which approximately cover the cross section of the casing or they may be of **skeleton type,** consisting of relatively narrow bars shaped to sweep a majority of the perimeter. In either case the spacing, or pitch, of flights must be kept within a certain limit; for best results, pitch should not exceed average cross-sectional

Chain Belt Co.

Fig. 20. Tilting-vane-type flights. One flight shown tilted for discharging.

width of casing. Skeleton flights were used in the prototype of the en masse conveyor (known as the Redler conveyor, named after the inventor) and have continued to be a popular design in the conveyors which have been marketed under this classification. The cutaway view of a Redler conveyor in Fig. 18 shows the skeleton-type flights. An example of rigid vane-type flights is shown in the cutaway view of a Bulk-Flo conveyor (Fig. 19). Still another type uses **flat vanes pivotally mounted on a chain** and a device to tilt the flights when passing a discharge outlet. Fig. 20 shows a portion of the moving element from an elevator of the latter type.

The casing may be rectangular or circular in cross section. Manufacturers generally prefer the rectangular shape because of the greater ease in fabrication for bend sections, for casings with renewable liners where access to the interior is necessary.

CONVEYOR SHAPES. A wide variance is possible in the path and shape of the conduit—one of the greatest assets of the en masse conveyor. However, a basic limitation exists wherever the path of the material-carrying portion of the casing slopes steeper than the angle of slide for the material. The shape must then be such that material enters where the slope of the casing is well below the angle of slide. While a path in more than a single plane is possible, such a conveyor

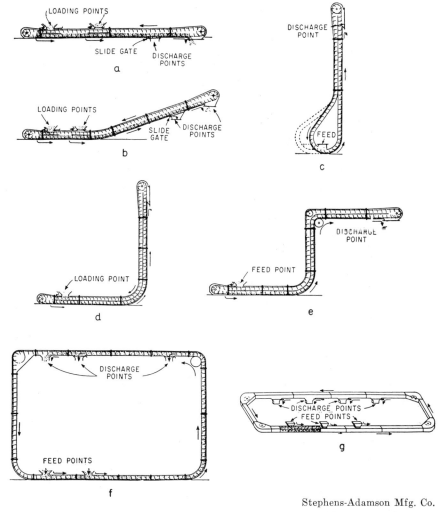

Stephens-Adamson Mfg. Co.

Fig. 21. Typical common shapes of en masse conveyors and elevators.

requires a universally flexible or double-articulated moving element. Conveyors of this kind have generally been found troublesome and are shunned by most manufacturers.

In Fig. 21 (illustrations *a* to *g* inclusive) are shown a variety of common shapes. The shapes marked *a, b, c, d,* and *e* have the return run of the chain parallel to the carrying run, while shapes *f* and *g* are circuit types. Parallel return-run casings are generally integral with carrying-run casings. The two runs

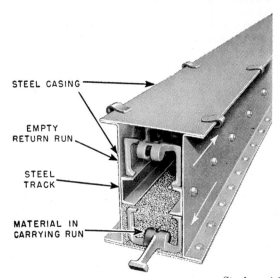

STEEL CASING

EMPTY
RETURN RUN

STEEL
TRACK

MATERIAL IN
CARRYING RUN

Stephens-Adamson Mfg. Co.

Fig. 22. Double-run casing with open return-run tracks.

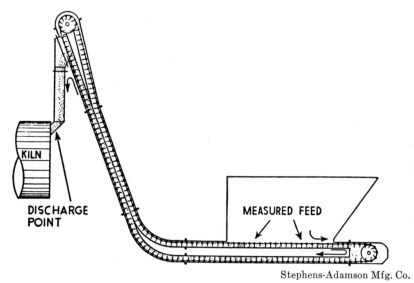

KILN

DISCHARGE
POINT

MEASURED FEED

Stephens-Adamson Mfg. Co.

Fig. 23. Parallel runs in separate casings.

are necessarily separated by a partition in portions that slope above the angle of repose. In horizontal or gradually sloping portions the runs may be partitioned off, but more often they have the return-run flights carried on tracks with center open, as in Fig. 22. Even where the runs are parallel, they also may be in separate casings, as shown in Fig. 23.

Shape c (Fig. 21) is referred to as a **loop-boot** elevator, shape d as an L-type elevator or conveyor-elevator, shape e as a **Z-type,** f as a **vertical closed circuit** or a **run-around,** and g as a **horizontal closed circuit.** The loop of shape c may have an alternate shape in which there is a short horizontal portion at the base, as shown by dotted lines.

In shapes such as e and f, where the carrying run makes a bend at the top of a vertical or steeply sloping portion, it is usual to provide a "drum-bend corner." The moving element and material bear against the rim of a rotatable drum, thus reducing sliding friction. Both of the circuit types have the ability to **recirculate any material that is not discharged**—a feature of particular importance in the horizontal closed-circuit elevator-conveyor.

HORIZONTAL CLOSED-CIRCUIT CONVEYORS. Fig. 21g, previously referred to, shows one of the possible shapes of an en masse conveyor of the horizontal closed-circuit type. A typical cross section through one run of such a conveyor is shown in Fig. 24.

Stephens-Adamson Mfg. Co.

Fig. 24. **Typical cross section through a horizontal closed-circuit conveyor.**

These conveyors have the unique ability to **receive material from multiple open inlets,** taking no more than enough from each to acquire a normal load, and to discharge through multiple open outlets, giving out just as much to each as is needed to keep each receiving chute filled. Such characteristics are exceedingly useful and the applications are many. An example is the drawing of coal from any of several bunkers and delivering it to a number of stoker hoppers, automatically keeping them supplied under varying demands. Another common application is the supplying of a line of packaging machines from one or more supply bins. A principal advantage attending this operation is the ability of the conveyor to **return undelivered material to the feed point,** where only enough new material is added to complete a full normal load.

OPERATING SPEED. Rate of conveying in terms of volume per unit of time depends on cross section of the casing, on speed of the moving element, and on a **capacity factor** Q, which expresses the ratio of average speed of the stream of material to that of the flights.

Standard casing sizes, as listed by manufacturers, range from about 0.07 sq. ft. of cross section to about 1.7 sq. ft., with some eight or nine sizes in this range. Since designation of sizes is not systematized among manufacturers, it is not feasible to list the various sizes accurately. Fig. 25 shows approximate sizes in terms of casing widths. These sizes correspond roughly to commercially available conveyors. Depth of casing runs from 85 percent of width in the smaller sizes to 60 percent in the larger sizes.

Casing Width (In.)	Cross-Section Area (Sq. Ft.)
4	0.07
6	.15
8	.3
10	.4
12	.6
14	.8
16	1.0
18	1.3
20	1.7

Fig. 25. Casing widths and cross-sectional areas.

Chain speeds are limited by a rather complex set of factors. These factors include:

1. Running qualities of chain on sprocket.
2. Ability of the particular material to enter and leave the conveyor at the conveying speed.
3. Tendency of the material to fluidize with too rapid motion.
4. Considerations of wear and maintenance.

As a general guide to maximum allowable speeds, free-flowing, nonabrasive materials such as grain can be handled with chain speeds up to 100 ft. per min. For aeratable materials like cement or pulverized starch, chain speeds should be kept below 50 ft. per min. Stringy, flaky, sticky, or sluggish materials require handling at slower speeds according to the nature and extent of their unfavorable properties, generally keeping well under 50 ft. per min. For limiting rate of wear and reducing maintenance requirements, chain speed is only one of a large array of considerations. Where the material handled is abrasive, such as coke, chain speed is seldom over 30 ft. per min.

CAPACITY FACTOR. The capacity factor Q, defined above, is usually 1.0 for horizontal conveyors. For elevating, Q varies from 0.85 for granular materials loaded close to the bend, to 0.50 for loose powders. Values are higher as the horizontal casing length from loading point to bend is greater. If conditions are such that Q tends toward the smaller values, it will also tend to be variable and uncertain.

Volumetric capacity may be determined from the formula

$$C = A \times Q \times S$$

where C = capacity in cubic feet per minute
A = cross-section area, square feet (see **Fig. 25.**)
Q = capacity factor
S = chain speed, in feet per minute

Capacity by weight, or tonnage, may be determined from the formula

$$T = \frac{W \times A \times Q \times S}{33}$$

where T = capacity in tons per hour
W = weight of material in pounds per cubic foot

Surges. The fact that en masse conveyors may be self-feeding has led to an erroneous idea that they are basically incapable of handling surges. Actually, where they are expected to handle a **variable rate of flow** from another conveyor or from a processing machine, they can be designed to convey at a rate in excess of any expected surge. They will then handle any lesser amount also, just as is the case with belt conveyors or bucket elevators. Size and chain speed should be selected to allow not only for surges but also for uncertainties in the capacity of factor Q and weight per cubic foot. Since en masse conveyors, unlike centrifugal-discharge bucket elevators, have a wide latitude in workable speeds, it is quite easy to make corrections in capacity after installation. To this end, speeds should be assumed below the maximum that would be allowable, and drive equipment should be designed for easy change of ratio.

POWER CONSUMPTION. Although the power needed to operate en masse conveyors is greater than that for the belt conveyor or bucket elevator, it is not generally large enough to be a serious deterrent to their use. The accurate determination of power requirement, especially for shapes having bends, must take into account the characteristics of the material handled. Since the properties which affect performance of en masse conveyors are often of an intangible nature and are recognizable only as a result of experience, it is well to have horsepowers checked by manufacturers in any case where power requirement might be a critical factor.

Power consumption may include two or more of five main components:

1. Sliding friction of material on casing walls.
2. Sliding friction of conveying element in return run.
3. Overcoming of gravity in case of lift.
4. Friction of moving element on curve plates of bends.
5. Internal friction in material at bends.

The more common basic shapes of en masse conveyors are shown in Fig. 21. The following approximate formulas give motor horsepowers for the various shapes.

Fig. 26 lists weights per cubic foot for numerous materials handled by en masse conveyors and numerical factors to be used in the formulas for calculating horsepowers for the various shapes of these kinds of conveyors.

$$\text{For shape } a, \text{ hp.} = \frac{ELT}{1,000}$$

$$\text{For shape } b, \text{ hp.} = \frac{ELT + HT}{1,000}$$

$$\text{For shape c, hp.} = \frac{GT\,(H + C/2)}{1,000}$$

$$\text{For shapes d, e, and f, hp.} = \frac{(FL + GH + K)T}{1,000}$$

$$\text{For shape g, hp.} = \frac{JDT(1 + 0.07N)}{1,000}$$

where C = casing width, inches
D = distance around horizontal closed circuit, feet
H = height of loaded run, vertical or steep slope, feet
L = length of loaded run, horizontal or gradual slope, feet
N = number of corners in horizontal closed-circuit conveyor
T = tons per hour
E, F, G, J, K = factors from Fig. 26.

Material	Weight (Lb. per Cu. Ft.)	E	F	G	J	K
		(for Units 5 In. Wide)				
Beans, dry	54	1.3	2.5	3.9	1.0	100
Bran	26	3.3	6.6	3.4	2.3	0
Cement, dry Portland	85	2.5	6.0	5.2	2.0	0
Coal, dry slack	50	2.1	3.8	3.6	1.6	40
Coal, wet slack	55	2.8	4.7	4.4	2.0	40
Coffee, ground	28	1.9	3.9	2.9	1.4	20
Corn flakes	12	2.9	6.0	2.1	1.8	0
Flour, wheat	35	2.6	5.6	3.2	1.8	0
Lime, dry burned, small lumps and dust	50	2.8	4.2	6.1	1.8	200
Salt, dry granulated	80	1.7	3.3	5.0	1.4	80
Starch, lump	30	1.7	3.2	3.4	1.2	90
Sugar, dry granulated	50	2.3	4.8	7.9	1.8	160
Wheat, dry, fairly clean	48	1.5	2.7	4.5	1.1	40
Wood chips	25	2.7	5.1	2.5	1.7	40

Fig. 26. Factors for various representative materials (for use in formulas for calculating horsepowers for the various conveyor shapes).

Numerical factors for various materials handled by en masse conveyors are listed in Fig. 26. A comprehensive list of such materials would be impractical; therefore, only familiar, representative kinds are included. Each material listed has a well-defined and distinctive set of properties. Factors for other materials may be assumed to be the same as for the materials in the table having similar properties.

The formulas are based on "fed loads." That is, they assume the material drops through the inlet at a controlled rate such that it is never allowed to back up into the supply chute. Many en masse conveyors, however, are **self-feeding**. The inlet is then "choked" and the moving stream of material in the casing has to slide out from under the stationary mass of material in the supply chute, hopper, or bin. Obviously, more power is needed for a choked feed than for a fed load. To allow for the additional horsepower, it is necessary to increase the value of L by four times the length of the choked inlet. If the inlet is in the return run, as in Fig. 23, five times the length of the choked inlet should be added to the loaded length of the carrying run.

LIMITATIONS OF LENGTH AND HEIGHT. The limiting factor in length and/or height of en masse conveyors is the working **tensile strength of**

the moving element. A standard design is offered by each manufacturer. This design is a compromise between excessive cost for short units and undue limitation of lengths. Some manufacturers also offer an **extra strong chain** at a higher cost. This chain is specified when the combination of horsepower pull and height-weight factor is too great for the standard element. While the cost of a conveyor on a per-foot basis is less as the length increases within the limit of a standard chain, the cost per foot will suddenly rise as the length goes into the class requiring high-strength chain. As length is further increased, a point is reached where an adequate chain would be impractical in size and prohibitive in cost.

For most shapes of conveyors the **length limitation** refers to the carrying run only. However, since it is assumed that a horizontal-circuit conveyor should be capable of carrying a full load completely around the circuit, the limit for this type refers to total chain length. An offsetting factor is the possibility of dual drives for horizontal circuits, which double the length allowable with one drive. Fig. 27 is a guide to maximum conveyor lengths that are feasible.

Shape of Unit	Maximum Length for Standard Chain, ft.		Maximum Length for High-Strength Chain, ft.	
	Wheat	Cement	Wheat	Cement
Straight horizontal	300	110	450	170
Straight vertical	110	80	180	130
Horizontal followed by equal length of vertical..........	90	45	160	75
Horizontal closed circuit with one drive	320	120	–	–

Fig. 27. Allowable lengths of chains for en masse conveyors.

Allowable lengths as given in Fig. 27 may be increased in the case of the solid-flight type by regulating the relation of feeding rate to chain speed so as to reduce the cross section of load. In the case of the skeleton flight this can be accomplished only by going to a smaller size unit. However, if conveyor lengths are thus carried far beyond the normal limits, the economic setup becomes questionable. Attempts have been made to produce a moving element having an extreme tensile capacity by use of high-strength alloys. Generally, experience has shown that the metal with a lower yield point and greater ductility is more reliable and more resistant to fatigue.

FEED INLETS. The feed inlet consists of an opening in the upper wall of a portion of casing that is horizontal or sloping at an angle less than the angle of slide of the material. Where **rate of feed** is controlled by means independent of the conveyor, as for material flowing from a continuous drier, there is usually no special problem concerning the inlet. However, most installations take advantage of the unique ability of en masse conveyors to feed themselves at just the correct rate without any extra equipment. The choked feed inlet, although basically sound, has certain limitations.

Since material above the inlet is relatively compact and quiescent, some types of products, like soap chips, may arch across the opening. Therefore, since the effective width of inlet cannot be greater than the width of the moving element, the selection of conveyor size may depend on necessary **width of inlet** to prevent arching, rather than on tonnage requirement.

Often an inlet is made as long as the length of a bin or hopper, thus saving important space. In operation under a full bin, the material below the inlet is under much more than normal pressure. Not only is wall friction thus increased, but also the moving stream must be sheared from the stationary material above it. The chain load per foot of choked inlet is approximately five times as great as it is per foot of covered casing.

With shapes having double-run casings it is customary to feed into the upper, or return, run, as illustrated in Fig. 21. This simple construction is not suitable for all materials. In materials containing lumps, some of the lumps will tend to catch between the edges of flights and the end of the inlet, thus causing excessive chain loads and possible bending or breaking of parts. This difficulty can be avoided by feeding the material into the carrying run where flights are of the skeleton type. With construction as shown in Fig. 28, it is evident that lumps cannot become jammed between flights and inlet.

 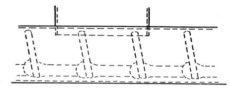

Stephens-Adamson Mfg. Co.

Fig. 28. Construction of inlet to avoid jamming of lumps.

Handling Finely Divided Dry Materials. Many finely divided dry materials may become aerated in handling and will then behave much like liquids. Typical examples occur in the case of cement and pulverized starch. Such materials do not require any special treatment in horizontal conveying, but in any kind of uphill path, where gravity opposes motion of the moving element, a fluid material will tend to stand still or run back in a conveyor of standard design. By certain refinements in construction, however, this difficulty can be overcome to such an extent that **fluidity** in any degree is no bar to successful handling in any direction.

The only special layout requirement is that the **material must enter in a horizontal or downhill section** and the casing must be straight for several chain pitches on each side of the inlet. The flights must form complete barriers covering the cross section of the casing. The clearance spaces between periphery of flights and casing walls must be so small that the material in its most fluid condition cannot flow back through them at a rate anything like that at which the flights are moving it forward. Preventing this backflow may increase manufacturing costs considerably. In conveyors using the skeleton type of moving element, special flights called **web flights** are inserted at intervals to provide barriers.

FRICTIONAL RESISTANCE AT BENDS. The great versatility in layout of en masse conveyors is due largely to their ability to **carry materials around bends**. It is always desirable, however, to avoid bends if practical, the alternative usually being to use two separate units instead of one. In each case it is necessary to decide whether the advantage of a single unit will offset the limitations imposed by a bend.

Additional friction is caused in bends by:

1. Pressure of the flights against the inner wall resulting from component forces of chain tension.
2. Internal shifting of material.

The friction resulting from rubbing of flights on a bend is greater in proportion to chain tension at the point where the bend occurs. Thus a bend near the feed point may be of little consequence, while the same bend located far beyond the inlet may be quite serious. As the flights advance around a bend, the chain tension builds up cumulatively because of friction. Therefore the total increase of tension is greatly dependent on the **angle, or degree, of a bend,** but is not affected by the **radius of curvature.** While the increase in chain tension is reflected in higher power requirement and need for a stronger chain, the bend friction also may create a wear problem. Whether or not the problem is so serious that a contemplated conveyor layout becomes impractical depends on numerous factors, as discussed later under the subject of "Wear." No hard and fast rules can be stated.

Internal friction in material results from the shifting of particles from their normal positions when the stream changes from straight to curved and then back to straight. Some materials, such as flour, offer little resistance to internal movement, while others, such as granulated sugar, offer so much resistance that a bend may become a major factor in **determining power and chain tension.** Unlike friction of flights on the casing, internal friction in material is independent of chain tension and also of bend angle beyond 20 or 30°, but it does vary inversely with the radius of curvature. Bend material friction is greater in a bend followed by a vertical run than in a bend from vertical to horizontal.

For bends from vertical or steeply sloping runs to horizontal or gradual slopes it is practical to substitute a rotating drum for the stationary inside curve plate. Thus most of the friction of flights on the casing is eliminated. The saving is of considerable importance because the chain tension tends to be high at the top of a vertical run. Dribble of material through operating clearances around the drum is disposed of by running it into the return run. Since this method is not usually feasible in a bend at the base of a vertical run, drum-bend corners are generally specified only in Z-type or run-around shapes. (See types *e* and *f* illustrated in Fig. 21.)

DISCHARGE OF MATERIALS. Discharge is effected through an outlet in the bottom of a horizontal or sloping portion of casing or in any wall of a vertical casing. Free-flowing nonsticky materials are **discharged by gravity.** Although such materials will tend to flow out of the spaces between flights through an opening in a vertical wall, a portion resting on any surface of the moving element that slopes less than the angle of slide will be carried beyond. Various devices are employed to prevent flights from carrying material past an outlet, or at least from carrying over the head sprocket and into the return run. Bulk-Flo flights are sloped two ways, as shown in Fig. 19. In some other makes, flights are pivoted and are caused to tilt by means of a cam opposite the outlet. Skeleton flights do not have flat surfaces large enough to carry appreciable quantities of material, but web flights hold considerable amounts which are poured off as the flights are tilted in passing around the head sprocket. Whatever system is used, little difficulty is experienced with free-running materials.

Special problems of discharging arise with materials that are sticky, stringy, or sluggish. Outlets comprising two, three, or four walls of the casing and lengths greater than standard may be a solution where these properties exist in moderation. If skeleton-type flights are used, a **push-out plate** may be installed to force material out of the area inside the flights. Thus sticky materials can be handled successfully that could not be discharged by gravity alone. A particularly favorable arrangement for feeding and discharging difficult materials is the vertical circuit (**Fig. 21f**) equipped with skeleton flights. The material can enter and leave the casing through the open side of the flights, thus encountering no obstruction to its free passage.

An important advantage of en masse conveyors is their **adaptability to multiple feed and discharge points.** In general, only a simple slide gate is needed to start or stop the process of feeding or discharging at any location along the path of a conveyor. For discharging, the gate may be used to reduce the discharge to a very low rate. A partial discharge, adjustable as to amount, may take place at several points simultaneously. These methods are feasible because the flights continually pass over the outlets and prevent arching over the narrowest openings.

CLEANOUT. In a few conveyor applications it is essential that the conveyor be able to clear itself of material. Some types, such as belt conveyors, naturally clear themselves completely by running for a short time after the feed is stopped. Others, like screw conveyors and bucket elevators, clear themselves except for a residue in the trough or boot. Since the latter types of conveyors will not eliminate the residue by any amount of running, they may be unsatisfactory for some kinds of service. An example is the handling of a material that would be subject to spoiling or infestation if allowed to remain in the conveyor during a shutdown period.

Among the conveyors that are completely enclosed, the en masse types have excellent **self-cleaning ability.** Where they are horizontal, or on slopes below the angle of repose of the material, the cleanout action is inherent even with standard designs. Since the flights tend to bear directly against the casing bottom as the bulk of the material is swept out, the removal of remnants is nearly complete. The addition of wiper strips along the edges of several flights will insure cleanout of the last vestiges.

Conveyors having portions of the carrying run vertical or steeply sloping present a special problem regarding cleanout. When the feed is stopped and the casing below the bend has been emptied, normal conveying above the bend ceases. Fine materials start to drop back through the clearance spaces between flights and casing walls. If the rate of backward flow is less than the conveying rate, a portion of the vertical casing will be cleared. However, any material leaking past the flights will remain in the conveyor unless it is removed by some means other than the normal en masse action. Minimum clearances that are practical with ordinary manufacturing procedures are bound to **permit appreciable leakage** with most materials, even where wiper flights are used in conveyors having vertical or nearly vertical runs.

In certain makes of en masse conveyors all or part of the flights may be made of a type that will elevate and discharge a quantity of material without the benefit of a supporting column of material underneath. A special construction is also necessary in the head section in cases where it discharges on the vertical. This provision is made to insure that the carrying flights will so discharge their load that none of it falls back into the up-run casing or is carried over into the down-run casing. When fed at a normal rate the material is propelled in a solid stream. As soon as the feed is stopped, the cleanout action commences and continues until practically all material has been discharged from the casing. The **time required for cleanout** varies from 1 min. to 20 or 30 min. according to the height and speed of elevator and character of the material.

Complete cleanout assumes nonsticky material that does not cling to the chain or flights. Although many sticky materials are successfully handled in en masse conveyors, complete self-cleaning in such cases is out of the question.

PROBLEMS OF WEAR. With most en masse conveyors wear is no problem. Even when handling abrasive materials en masse conveyors can show good economy if properly specified and designed. The places where wear may occur, the conditions which cause or increase wear, and the steps that may be taken to offset wear must all be recognized.

Even under adverse conditions, **covers and return-run casings**, where there is no positive pressure of the flights against the surfaces, are not subject to wear. Carrying-run surfaces not under positive pressure from the flights are only slightly affected if the material, even though abrasive, is fine grained or pulverized. For example, in handling fine sand, there would be practically no wear on any of four sides of a vertical carrying run or on the sides or top of a sloping or horizontal carrying run.

Surfaces that have rubbing contact from the flights under positive pressure are subject to wear, even in return runs and in handling relatively nonabrasive materials, but the tendency increases with the abrasiveness of the material. If preventive measures are not taken, wear may occur, for example, in the **return-run tracks** of horizontal conveyors, in the **partition plate** supporting the return chain of a sloping elevator, in the bottom of the carrying run of a horizontal or sloping unit, and in the bottom of the horizontal carrying run of an L-type elevator. To a still greater degree, wear may occur in the inside **curve plate** of a loop boot, in any of the curve plates of a bend section (although primarily in the inside curve plate of the carrying run), and in the curve plate at the base of an elevator head section. The rate of wear on curve plates decreases as the radius of curvature of the plate increases and as the tension in the chain at the curve is less. Therefore, the curve-plate wear of an L-type elevator is less as the length of horizontal run decreases.

Wear on the **casing walls** of carrying runs is greatly increased when large, hard lumps become wedged in the clearance spaces between flights and casing. This wear may occur not only in all the regular wearing areas but also in the four walls of a vertical carrying run and the sides of a sloping or horizontal carrying run. The rate of wear will increase in proportion to the hardness, roughness, size, and number of the lumps in the material being conveyed.

In general, casing wear due to wedging of lumps is not accompanied by corresponding wear in the flights. However, casing wear due to rubbing contact from the flights, as on curve plates and return tracks, is also accompanied by a tendency to wear the **flight surfaces** that make the rubbing contact. For example, the tops of flights are subject to wear on the curve of an L-type elevator, while both the tops and bottoms of flights are subject to wear on horizontal conveyors in which part of the carrying run may occasionally operate without load.

Methods for Increasing Wear Life. To combat wear in en masse conveyors, the following methods may be used:

1. The chain speed may be reduced by using a larger conveyor.
2. The wearing parts may be made thicker.
3. The wearing parts may be made of harder materials.
4. The parts subject to wear may be made easily renewable.

Although each of these measures will add to the first cost of the equipment, each will increase the wear life per dollar of initial cost.

COUNTERACTING THE EFFECTS OF HIGH TEMPERATURES. En masse conveyors are well suited to handling hot materials or to operating in hot surroundings. Their heat-resisting ability particularly surpasses that of conveyors that have vital parts made of rubber, such as belt conveyors, belt elevators, and certain types of vibrating conveyors. Up to about 300° F. no special problems are encountered. Higher temperatures may bring about any or all of the following effects unless provided against in the design:

1. Breakage of casing or fastenings caused by expansion.
2. Buckling or overstressing of chain induced by unequal expansion between chain and casing.
3. Permanent weakening of chain resulting from changes in grain structure of metal.
4. Rapid corrosion.
5. Chain breakage or stretching because of lowered strength at the high temperature.

Expansion of casings may be allowed for by use of telescoping sections, which allow terminals and chute connections to remain fixed, or by sliding supports, which require that at least one terminal shall move. Unequal expansion between chain and casing may be compensated for by gravity or spring take-ups, which will add 10 to 20 percent to normal chain load.

Danger of **embrittlement of the chain** from heat begins at about 500° F. for malleable iron, at 800° F. for heat-treated malleable iron, and at 900° F. for the lower steel alloys. Higher alloys are obtainable which are stable up to the highest practicable operating temperatures.

Temporary **loss of strength** from excessive heat for all metals begins at about 700°, with a reduction of 50 percent at 900°. Above 900° only metals designed for elevated temperatures should be considered. Many of these are available, each suitable for a given set of conditions and all being much more expensive than the common steel alloys. With some metals, temperatures as high as 1,200° F. are possible.

PROTECTION AGAINST EXPLOSIONS. For safety in the bulk handling of materials containing flammable vapors or dust, a primary requisite is that the conveyor be vapor- or dust-tight. Assuming total enclosure, certain other characteristics are also needed:

1. Inability to produce sparks.
2. Minimum enclosed space that could contain an explosive mixture.
3. Means for relieving pressure before a destructive bursting can take place.

En masse conveyors are adapted to the prevention of explosions in all of the ways above noted.

1. **Sparks** may be caused by accumulation of static electricity or by friction. If all parts of an en masse conveyor are made of metal, which is usual, and the casing is **grounded,** the possibility of static sparks may be ruled out. Friction sparks are unlikely in the normal operation of any type of conveyor, but are always possible as the result of an accident. In the case of a sudden jamming, sparks are less likely to occur as the speed of the moving element is slower, and as the materials from which the conveyors are constructed contain less iron or steel. The relatively low speeds of en masse conveyors favor safety, and the speeds may be kept even lower than normal by using conveyors of larger sizes for a given capacity. **Nonsparking metals** such as manganese bronze are sometimes used for chains and sprockets. Some kind of device—such as shear pins, for quick relief of load if jamming occurs—is essential if there is a chance of friction sparks causing an explosion.

2. A design in which there was no space at all that could contain an explosive mixture would be impractical in any type of conveyor. Although en masse conveyors necessarily contain **vacant spaces** in the return runs and terminals, the volume relative to conveying capacity is less than in other types such as bucket elevators and screw conveyors. If, in spite of small vacant space and measures to prevent sparking, explosions present a great hazard, it is advisable to fill the casing with an **inert gas** such as carbon dioxide.

3. A simple way to prevent serious damage in the event of an explosion occurring in the casing of an en masse conveyor is the inclusion of **pressure relief panels**. These panels are located at convenient points in the walls of the return run or terminals. They may consist of flanged openings covered with a durable and easily replaceable material, such as rubberized fabric, which will burst and relieve the pressure long before any deformation would occur in the body of the casing. In considering the advisability of relief panels it should be noted that an explosion may originate outside a conveyor and travel into it through the connecting chutes.

NOISE REDUCTION. Under most circumstances en masse conveyors run quietly, sometimes to the point where no sound will reveal whether they are running or stopped. Under certain other circumstances they may be noisy to an objectionable degree. The noise, usually an uneven squeal, is nearly always produced by rubbing of moving parts against the casing in the presence of a conveyed material having certain noise-potential properties. The vibration may be transmitted through the entire casing so that its source is difficult to locate.

In general, the property that promotes noise may be described as "chalkiness." It is found to high degree in talc and soda ash, and to a moderate degree in cellulose acetate. Materials such as cereals, especially if oily, like soy-bean meal, do not produce any noise.

If noise-producing materials are to be handled in a location where noise would constitute a serious disturbance, it may be the determining factor in the design and selection of conveyors. Shapes should be chosen which cause only a minimum of rubbing between moving element and casing. A loop elevator (Fig. 21c) would be much more suitable for installation than an L-shaped conveyor (Fig. 21d).

Noise may be eliminated, or satisfactorily reduced, by use of various nonmetallic surfaces at the points of rubbing on the casing. Manufacturers of en masse conveying equipment are in a position to furnish data on effectiveness, wear resistance, and cost of noise-prevention materials to suit any given set of circumstances. The main objective is not to overlook the question of noise if it appears to be possible and objectionable.

COMBATING CORROSION. Attention should be given to any possible corrosive effect between the conveyed material and the surfaces with which it comes in contact. The effect of corrosion is generally more pronounced wherever there is rubbing that would tend to scour off the corroded surfaces and continually expose new metal to the corrosive action. The alternate **rusting** and **scouring** away of the rust is especially severe in the handling of wet coal for boiler-plant use. Not only does the coal from open cars or outside storage average high in moisture, but also it is common practice to run coal conveyors intermittently and allow them to remain full of wet material while stopped. Under these conditions a casing made of mild steel of ordinary thickness may have a life much too short for good economy.

Two methods are available for combating corrosion: increasing thickness of parts, and making them of metals or materials more resistant to the particular type of corrosion. In specifying **greater thickness,** it is unnecessary to use the heavier material for covers, return runs, or portions of terminal sections not coming in contact with the moving stream of material. But the affected parts may well be several times normal thickness, since cost in this case increases but little in proportion to weight.

Although there is a wide selection of materials of construction which resist corrosion, the list is greatly narrowed when cost and economy are taken into account. For example, to install stainless steel or brass equipment for the handling of boiler-house coal would increase the cost of equipment out of proportion to the benefit gained. Galvanizing is of little advantage for coal-handling equipment since the surfaces subject to rubbing are soon denuded. **Steel alloys,** however, which provide much greater over-all economy than ordinary steel, are available for construction of conduits. They contain small percentages of alloying elements such as chromium, nickel, and copper, which increase conveyor cost less than 7 percent and produce metals that last approximately twice as long as mild steel of equal thickness.

Corrosion from conveyed materials or from gases and/or elevated temperatures involves a wide variety of chemical reactions which may be controlled or minimized by use of suitable materials of construction. Materials used for casings may include stainless steel of various types, stainless-clad steel, brass, cast iron, bakelite, numerous kinds of plastics, and ordinary steel galvanized, metalized, or coated with vitrified enamel. For moving elements, stainless steels of S. A. E. types 302, 304, and 316 are commonly used, as are manganese bronze and Monel metal, as well as malleable iron or steel, galvanized or metalized. If possible, specifications for corrosion-resisting construction should be based on previous experience by the prospective user, because manufacturers of equipment do not always have a knowledge of corrosive action equal to that of producers or users of the particular material to be handled.

PROTECTION AGAINST OVERLOADS. Accidental shutdowns or damage to equipment are generally caused by overloads, foreign materials, or choked outlets. Overfeeding is normally impossible in en masse conveyors, but excessive chain pulls may result from a change in the character of material; for instance, an increase in moisture content. Such overloads usually build up gradually, and an ordinary **thermal relay** will generally give adequate protection to the motor. The sudden jamming that would occur, however, if foreign material—say a steel bar—should drop between a moving flight and the edge of the feed inlet would not be adequately relieved by an overload relay. The reason is that the inertia of the high-speed elements of the drive would be more than the chain could absorb under a sudden stop. It is essential, therefore, to have some device, such as **shear pins,** located in the low-speed portion of the drive to give instantaneous relief. Fluid or friction couplings are not suitable because they are too expensive, if large enough to serve at low speed, and fail to eliminate the effects of inertia when installed at the high-speed end of the drive.

En masse conveyors, in common with nearly all other types, **cannot withstand choking of the final outlet.** While it is true that material backing up into the head section will ultimately cause a shutdown through the motor overload relay or the shear-pin device, the conveyor may be seriously damaged before it stops. The reason is that when the chain running onto the head sprocket is buried in material, it may "climb the teeth." When this happens the entire chain—return run as well as carrying run—may be put under tension enough to start cracks or cause permanent distortion before the drive torque builds up sufficiently to cause the shear pins to act. Therefore, devices to prevent backing up of material into the drive terminal are essential for trouble-free operation.

DIAGRAM OF REPRESENTATIVE INSTALLATION. A typical layout of a storage and reclaiming system using en masse conveyors is shown in Fig. 29. The truck delivery point is shown in the right-hand view, and the

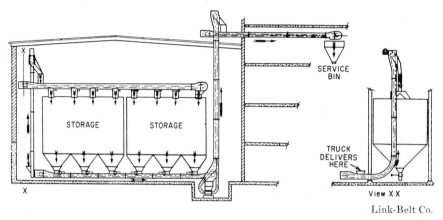

Link-Belt Co.

Fig. 29. Layout typical of storage and reclaiming system using en masse conveyors.

general layout of the storage bins and the conveyor system is diagrammed in the left-hand view. Incoming bulk material is distributed overhead to the various storage bins and reclaimed from them through the lower conveyor line. It is then fed into an elevating conveyor and delivered by a horizontal conveyor to the service bin.

CHAIN CONVEYORS

CONTENTS

CONTENTS (*Continued*)

CHAIN CONVEYORS

GENERAL DEFINITION. A chain conveyor consists of one or more **endless chains** that travel the entire conveyor path. Loads are carried directly on the chain links or on specially designed elements attached to the chain. These conveyors are classified according to the type of load-carrying arrangement used: apron and pan conveyors, slat conveyors, crossbar conveyors, carrier conveyors, and car-type conveyors. **Trolley conveyors,** which also employ endless chain, are treated in another section of this Handbook. These and other definitions presented in this section follow those specified by the Conveyor Equipment Manufacturers Association.

Apron and Pan Conveyors

DEFINITIONS. An apron conveyor consists of one or more endless chains or other linkage to which overlapping or interlocking plates or shapes are attached to form a continuous moving bed for bulk materials, packages, or objects. A pan conveyor is similar to an apron conveyor, but the interlocking plates or shapes are equipped with vertical ends to form pans.

APRON AND PAN CONVEYOR APPLICATIONS. Apron and pan conveyors are used extensively in practically all modern mining, manufacturing, and processing industries. They are particularly suited to the handling of incoming raw materials, in-process materials, and finished materials; they also find wide application in industrial and municipal power and heating plants.

Generally, apron and pan conveyors are used to perform the heavy duties of conveying large quantities of **bulk materials** such as coal, coke, ore, slag, rock, stone, gravel, clay, clinker, and foundry sand.

They are frequently used as **supply feeders** for large crushers, breakers, pulverizers, grinders, and similar machines; as feeders to other units; from processing machines, storage and supply hoppers; as prime movers or transporters for conveying purposes over long horizontal hauls or at inclines and declines (Fig. 1). They are flexible in arrangement and can conveniently be arranged to follow a combined horizontal and inclined path to suit conditions of varying elevations as shown in Fig. 2.

The maximum horizontal and inclined **conveyor centers** that can be used are dependent on the type of conveyor chain selected. All chains have a normal allowable maximum working tension rating. This rating should not be exceeded; thus it limits conveyor length and lift conditions.

Apron and pan conveyors operate at relatively **slow speeds,** quietly and without appreciable vibration. Slow speed promotes long life, requires minimum maintenance, and prevents material degradation. **Minimum lump breakage** is particularly important to the coal-mining and coke-processing and similar industries in which the prevention of degradation of sized materials is important.

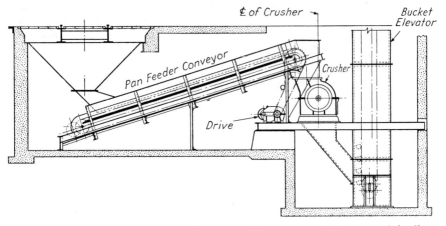

Fig. 1. Pan feeder conveyor receiving material from a track hopper and feeding to a crusher.

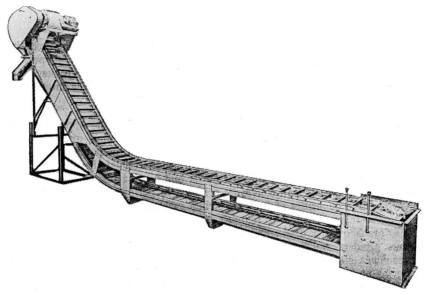

Fig. 2. Shop view of a pan conveyor. Pans are equipped with pushers to assist in moving material up steep inclines.

APRONS AND PANS. Aprons and pans are made in various types. Selection of type is dependent on material to be handled. Most **common types** are made of formed steel, with front and rear edges beaded so that one overlaps the next to form a continuous surface or trough. The overlap must be maintained in flexing over sprockets to guard against leakage between or jamming of adjoining aprons or pans. The styles illustrated in Fig. 3 are described below.

1. **Style A** aprons and pans are used for horizontal and low-incline (20–25 deg.) service. Both types in short pitches are used for feeders; pans, in medium or

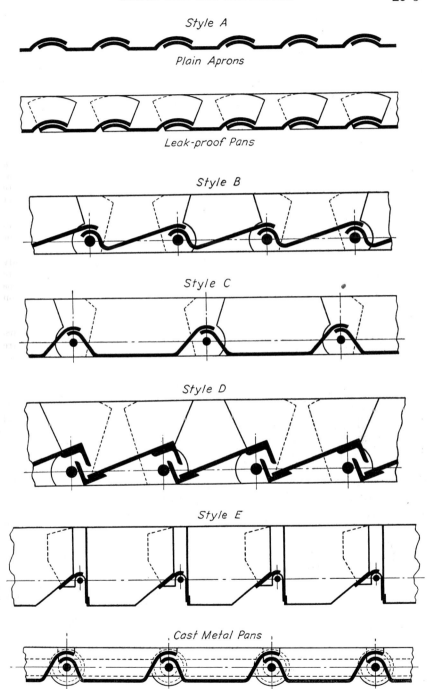

Fig. 3. Cross sections of aprons and pans.

long pitches, for conveyors. This style is suitable for most bulk materials, including hot, dusty, abrasive materials such as shake-out sand in foundries, limestone in cement mills, and ores in mining.

2. **Style B** pans are designed to provide free and easy discharge and, consequently, low drop of material. This style is especially suited to handle lump material which should not be broken. It is also suitable for wide conveyors and can be used for inclined conveying up to 30 deg.

3. **Style C** pans are used for large capacities of fines and lumps and inclines up to 30 deg. They require a higher discharge point than style B. They are suitable for use as feeding, picking, sorting, and lowering conveyors.

4. **Style D** pans are similar to style B. Built of angles and plates, they are of very strong and rigid construction. These pans are capable of carrying large quantities of material such as coal, rock, and castings. The pans have complete discharge with very little drop and breakage of lumps. They have good impact resistance under loading point.

5. **Style E** pans are super-capacity pans for handling fine, crushed, or lump materials in very large quantities. They can be used for horizontal conveying or inclined conveying as steep as 45 deg.

6. **Cast-metal** pans are usually made of gray or malleable iron, and are commonly used for handling hot, gritty materials. When special corrosive materials are to be handled, pans can be made of corrosion-resistant materials. Shallow pans are limited to inclined conveying under 25 deg.; deep pans can be used on inclines as steep as 45 deg.

End Plates. Fig. 3 illustrates aprons equipped with end plates to form pans. Common practice is to weld end plates to aprons. For cast pans the end plates are cast integrally with the aprons. The purpose of end plates is to permit the carrying of a deep bed of material without spillage and thus obtain greater capacity.

Leakproof Pans. This is one of the more common types in general use. The arrangement of closely overlapping aprons and end plates is particularly advantageous when handling fine materials. Note the direction of conveyor travel in Fig. 4. When material discharges over the head end of the conveyor, the material cascades past the overlapping joints. If the conveyor were operated in a reverse direction from that shown in Figure 4, the material would get into the overlapping joints and develop a binding condition that would distort the pans. Also, reverse operation would contribute to excessive spillage.

Shallow Pans. Shallow pans are used for horizontal and low inclines (20–25 deg.) service. Retarding cleats can be attached to pans to prevent material from sliding back. These pans may be used in feeders or conveying units and are suitable for carrying any loose (but not sticky) bulk material, such as coal, ore, slag, clay, coke, rock, stone, gravel, clinker, foundry sand, cement, and hot castings. The cast metal pan in Fig. 3 is typical.

Deep Pans. Deep pans are used for handling large quantities of various bulk materials in such applications as feeders and picking, sorting, and lowering conveyors. They are excellent for handling very hot bulk materials and will carry materials on inclines up to 30 deg. Fig. 5 shows a **headshaft assembly** with a section of a deep-type overlapping cast-metal pan conveyor. In this installation deep pans have equalizing-saddle mounting on steel roller chain equipped with rigid through rods, and renewable outboard traction rollers. This type of pan is used for steeply inclined conveyors. The pan cross section is similar to that of the cast pan in Fig. 3.

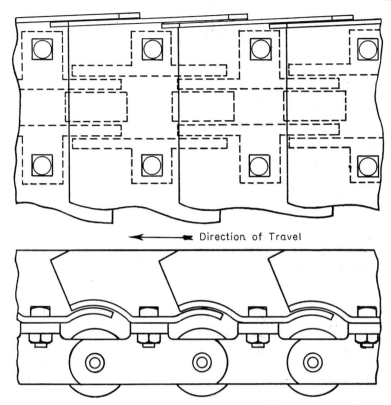

Fig. 4. Leakproof-type pans mounted on roller conveyor-type chains.

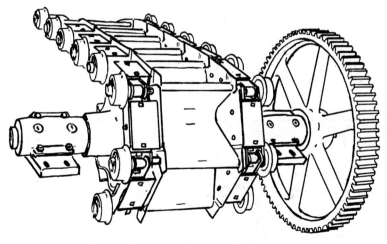

Fig. 5. Typical conveyor with deep pans.

Hinged Pans. Hinged pans find extensive use for conveying metal scrap, chips, trimmings, turnings, etc., or carrying small parts out of quench tanks or through washing tanks. The conveyor assembly shown in Fig. 6 illustrates the type of construction used on hinged pans.

Direction of Travel

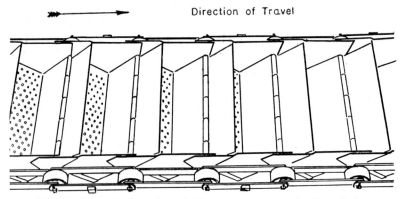

Fig. 6. Assembled section of hinged pans on steel roller chains.

These pans are made in several forms. Openings at articulations, common in other styles, are absent in this style. The profile or path of conveyor travel can be adapted to meet practically any requirement.

Cast Pans. Cast pans are used for handling hot, gritty, corrosive materials, such as hot rock, ashes in power plants, hot clinkers in cement mills, and hot lime. The very generous proportions of the cast pans made of gray iron, steel, or malleable iron give ability to withstand high temperatures, and a reasonable heat transfer for cooling is provided. Figs. 3 and 5 illustrate cast pans.

Pan Reinforcements. Long pans, when heavily loaded or subjected to heavy impact due to large lumps dropping directly on them, can be reinforced, as shown in Fig. 7, by:

1. Underside stiffeners.
2. Additional chain strands between main strands.
3. Rollers or shoes instead of additional chain strands.

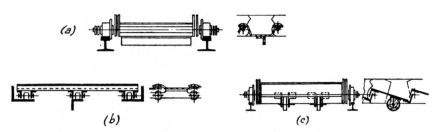

Fig. 7. Pan reinforcements.

Special Types. The foregoing is indicative of the broad use of this type of conveying medium. Consequently, apron and pan conveyors and their related types can be classed as both general-purpose and special-application conveying mediums. The many special application types are too numerous to be illustrated in these pages.

In some instances a special type of apron conveyor has been developed and used for certain applications. As its use becomes more extensive and covers a broader field, it ceases to be considered special and becomes a standard for a particular industry. An example is the cast-metal pan conveyor using four-compartment overlapping pans (Fig. 8). Pans are mounted on two strands of steel roller chain. This conveyor is used for taking ingots from melting furnaces. Molten metal is poured into the pans. The ingots thus formed cool in the conveyor and are automatically discharged over the head end.

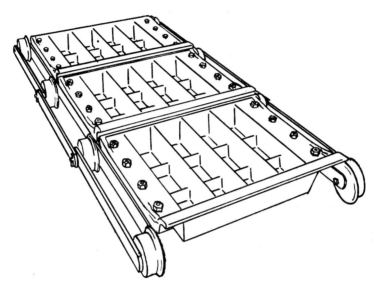

Fig. 8. Ingot-casting conveyor.

Slats. In sugar mills **beaded aprons** are usually referred to as slats. The common types of slats used on apron conveyors in the sugar-mill industry are shown in Fig. 9 and described below.

1. **Style K** slats are deep-beaded for added stiffness and strength, generally mounted on short-pitch chains of approximately 3-in. pitch. These slats are specially designed for use on intermediate carriers between sugar-cane rolls. The usual practice is to operate these slats with the large bead trailing. The larger bead acts as a crowding means to force cane into the cane rolls.

2. **Style AD** slats are made with a lip extension to insure a minimum of leakage of knifed cane, and with a center corrugation the length of each slat to insure rigidity. This style is rapidly replacing some of the older-style slats in the sugar-mill industry. Its special design gives it maximum rigidity and extremely good sealing qualities between slats.

3. **Style AC** slats are designed with center corrugation the length of each slat to insure maximum rigidity and strength. Where leakage is not a major problem, this type of slat can be used with extremely good results.

4. **Style AA** slats are die-formed with lip extension to prevent cane from dropping through the carrier when it flexes over sprockets. On this type of slat the center corrugation is eliminated; the carrying capacity is thereby increased, but the rigidity is reduced.

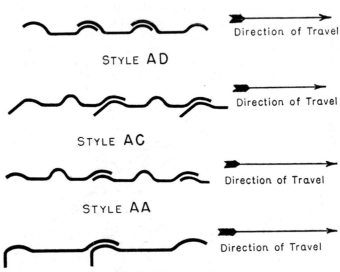

Fig. 9. **Types of slats.**

CHAIN ATTACHMENTS. Attachment links are links having suitable projections (lugs) or holes to which aprons and pans, etc., may be fastened. The projection or lug is called the attachment. Attachments are identified by type, and each type is designated by a letter or a name. The three most common types are: the *A* attachment, the *K* attachment, and the equalizing-saddle attachment.

The A Attachment. As shown in Fig. 10 an *A*-type attachment is on only one side bar of the chain link. This causes a concentration of load on one line of side bars resulting in a tendency for chain to tip toward the loaded side and misalignment of chain rollers. When *A*-type attachments are used, it is recommended that the **factor of safety** for chain selection employed be increased to nearly double the normal. The use of rigid through rods, illustrated in Fig. 12, will help to reduce eccentric chain loading.

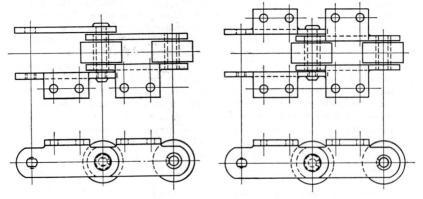

Fig. 10. *A*-type attachment. Fig. 11. *K*-type attachment.

The *K* Attachment. The *K*-type attachment is illustrated in Fig. 11. Symmetrical attachments of this type provide equal distribution of load through both inside and outside lines of chain side bars with true alignment of chain rollers. The only tendency for the chain to tip is that caused by apron or pan deflection. The use of *K* attachments and rigid through rods permits stressing of chains to normal rated capacity.

The Equalizing-Saddle Attachment. This construction is shown in Fig. 12. **Outboard rollers** and **rigid through rods** can be employed to permit use of full allowable chain working tension in design. The loads resulting from the weight of material conveyed and the chain weight and apron or pan weight (but not chain tension load) are carried by the larger-diameter outboard rollers. The

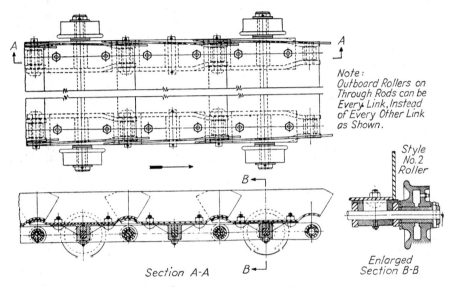

Fig. 12. Equalizing-saddle attachment.

chains used are subjected only to the tensions encountered plus the lesser amount of joint wear, because owing to the infrequent engagement with sprockets, there is minimum chain roller rotation. Minimum maintenance is provided by the larger diameter, low rolling friction on outboard rollers, longer chain life, and accessibility of parts. Outboard rollers and sleeves on which they rotate can be replaced without uncoupling the chains.

Through Rods. Rigid through rods, used either at mid-pitch or at the chain joint, offset unequal chain loads and distribute them equally on all four lines of the side bars. When located at mid-pitch, they extend through the chains and serve as axles for the outboard rollers. When used at the chain joint, they replace the regular chain pin. Fig. 12 shows through rods assembled in a conveyor.

FEEDERS. Apron-conveyor-type feeders provide positive and uniform feeds of material to other conveying or processing units (Fig. 13). Primarily they are used to control the amount of material to be delivered and are the medium through which a batch or storage material is converted into a **continuous-flow material** for handling or processing requirements.

Usually feeders of the apron-conveyor type receive material from a hopper or storage pile and deliver it to other machines at a uniform controlled quantity rate.

When required, material can be fed long distances, either horizontal or inclined; thus the materials handling medium serves not only as a quantity control but also as a conveyor.

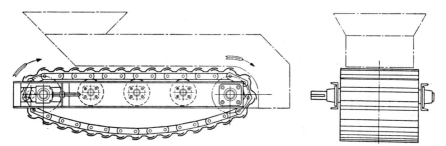

Fig. 13. Heavy-duty self-contained apron feeder. Roller-supported chain belt is used.

SELECTION OF EQUIPMENT. Proper selection of the type of apron or pan conveyor best suited for a particular application is most important for obtaining a completely satisfactory installation.

Apron and pan conveyors have certain characteristics which make them preferable to other types of conveyors. Because of their heavier construction, apron and pan conveyors are capable of handling heavy, lump, or abrasive materials which would damage lighter types of conveyors within a short time. Practically any type of bulk material can be handled by these conveyors, as noted previously. It is possible to install them in horizontal or steeply inclined paths or a combination of such paths. When stationary skirt plates of different heights are used, the conveyor capacity can cover a wide range.

When component parts for a complete apron or pan conveyor are being selected, the problem should be approached progressively as follows:

1. Type of apron or pan.
2. Thickness of aprons and pans.
3. Type of chain and mounting.
4. Sprockets, style and size.
5. Skirt plates, if required.
6. Frame cross section.

Factors that apply specifically to pan and apron conveyors are discussed below. Other considerations of more general applicability are treated under Principles of Conveyor Component Selections.

Type of Apron or Pan. The more common types of aprons and pans have been described and illustrated earlier. Some of the more common materials that the various types are best suited to handle have also been mentioned along with suggested types for certain applications.

The selection chart in Fig. 14 can be used as a convenient reference for selection of apron or pan type. The various materials listed are only a very few of those frequently encountered in materials handling. Many other materials have similar characteristics, and those listed are intended to serve only as a guide.

Material Handled	Style of Apron or Pan										
	A	AA	AC	AD	B	C	D	E	K	Cast	Hinged
Castings	•										
Cement clinker											
Hot										•	
Crushed	•				•						
Clay											
Bank run	•				•		•				
Coal											
Mine run					•	•	•				
Sized	•				•		•				
Lignite	•				•						
Coke											
Lumps	•										
Fines					•	•					
Corrosive										•	
Cullet											
Glass	•										
Earth											
Common loam	•										
Lumps loam	•				•	•	•				
Gravel											
Bank run	•				•	•	•				
Sized	•				•	•	•				
Hot										•	
Extreme										•	
Mild	•				•	•	•				
Limestone											
Quarried	•										
Sized	•										
Metal											
Chips											•
Small parts											•
Turnings											•
Trimmings											•
Ore											
Light	•				•	•	•	•			
Heavy	•				•	•	•	•			
Rock											
Lumps, large					•	•	•				
Sized	•				•	•	•				
Sand											
Dry	•				•	•	•				
Hot						•	•			•	
Slag											
Furnace	•				•	•	•			•	
Granulated	•				•	•	•				
Stone											
Lumps, large	•				•	•	•	•			
Sized	•				•	•		•			
Sugar											
Cane		•	•	•					•		
Bagasse	•	•	•						•		

Fig. 14. Apron or pan selection chart.

Thickness of Aprons and Pans. When selecting thickness of metals from which aprons or pans are to be made, the more general considerations are:

1. Total weight that each pan must support, so that deflection is limited to a minimum and thus binding between overlapping pans is prevented.
2. Impact of falling lumps that may cause deformation.
3. Abrasiveness of materials handled.
4. Corrosion and resistance to chemical reaction.
5. Life expectancy.
6. Limits of economical fabrication.

Recommended metal thickness of aprons and pans for various conditions are:

Apron or Pan Thickness	For Handling
No. 10 gage or 3⁄16 in.	Lightweight materials that are only mildly abrasive; also where corrosion is no factor.
¼ or 5⁄16 in.	Medium-weight materials with probable corrosion and abrasion considerations; also where moderate impact is to be encountered.
3⁄8 or ½ in. and heavier	Heavy-weight materials that are highly abrasive, corrosive; also where impact may be severe.

Protective coatings are available for aprons or pans that are subject to rapid deterioration caused by corrosion or chemical reaction. Aprons and pans can also be made of alloyed metals for such applications and for prevention of contamination of the material handled by the aprons or pans.

Skirt Plates. When deep loads are carried on a conveyor, some arrangement must be provided to confine the material. **Stationary plates** that perform this function are called skirt plates. Generally the stationary skirt plates are attached to the frame of the conveyor. The height range that skirts can have to increase conveyor capacity can be varied to suit conditions. Heights of 12 to 48 in. are common, but greater heights, especially for feeders, are frequently used. The conveyor cross sections in Figs. 15 and 16 show skirt plates.

A **general rule** to follow for determination of height of skirt plates follows:

$$\text{Depth of material} = \tfrac{2}{3} \text{ skirt-plate height}$$

For relatively fine and small lump material, the amount of free board allowed can be decreased without danger of spillage.

TYPICAL CONSTRUCTIONS. The **equalizing-saddle type** of attachment illustrated in Fig. 15 is one of the most popular. It can be used for both horizontal and inclined conveyors of any length within the limitation of the chains, and with or without stationary skirt plates. Stationary skirt plates permit handling of loads of greater depth, as for feeder service.

Style A aprons, mounted on K-type chain attachments, extend across the top of the two strands of chain. This construction should be used only on horizontal or inclined conveyors of **short centers**, because of sliding return run, as shown in Fig. 16. Most bulk materials can be handled satisfactorily, but free-flowing materials will creep laterally between the aprons and stationary skirt plates.

When style A pans are mounted on A-type chain attachments and through rods are used, the return run rolls on the chain rollers. Thus, conveyor centers can be maximum, in keeping with allowable chain tension capacity.

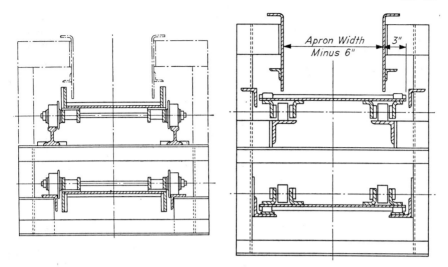

Fig. 15. Style *A* pans, leakproof type, mounted on equalizing-type chain attachments.

Fig. 16. Style *A* aprons mounted on *K*-type chain attachments

Slat Conveyors

DEFINITION. A slat conveyor consists of one or more endless chains to which nonoverlapping, noninterlocking, spaced slats are attached to form a moving support for the packages or objects being conveyed. This type of conveyor is sometimes called an **apron slat conveyor** or a **platform conveyor,**

APPLICATIONS. Slat conveyors are used extensively in many different industries. A few typical industries and materials handled are:

Industry	For Handling
Food-packing plants	Meats, clean corn, canned foods, etc.
Foundries	Flasks, castings
Wire mills	Coils of wire
Automotive plants	Machined and assembled parts
Refineries	Barrels, boxes, crates
Processing plants	Bales, packages, sacks

General use includes: as a transportation medium for materials or objects; as a traveling work table; as a ramp conveyor between stock or shipping rooms and truck or railroad-car loading platforms, etc. Slat conveyors can also readily be adapted to a combination of processing and transportation functions. They provide a steady and orderly flow of materials through a plant.

Slat conveyors will carry all kinds of parts and packages, light, heavy, or bulky (see Fig. 17). They operate on the horizontal, on inclines, or a combination of both. The Escalator or moving stairway is a familiar type.

Maximum length between centers for slat conveyors, either horizontal, inclined, or a combination of both, is limited only to the maximum allowable working tension of the chains to which the slats are attached. Chain tension ratings should not be exceeded.

Conveyor width is the length of the slats. When objects are to be loaded promiscuously, the conveyor width should equal the diagonal dimension of the largest object to be carried plus approximately 4 to 6 in. for minimum clearance.

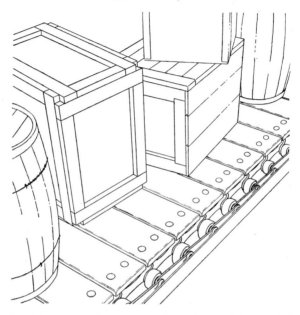

Fig. 17. Slat conveyor handling various sizes and types of objects.

When used for **inclined conveying,** slats are usually equipped with **pusher cleats** spaced at regular intervals. The cleats prevent slide-back of the articles being conveyed. Generally, if the article being handled presents a flat surface to the conveyor slat and if the conveyor inclination is not greater than 10 deg., pusher cleats are not required. Plain slats are generally used for horizontal conveying.

Special fixtures for supporting certain units on which work operations are to be performed can be fastened to the conveyor slats. An assembly conveyor is an example.

Slat conveyors can be designed to assist specifically in the manual handling of materials. For example, when loading or unloading platforms are at a different elevation from shipping or receiving floors, slat conveyors, inclined, can be used to negotiate the change in elevation. This type is called a **ramp conveyor.**

SLATS. The most common slats are plain flat slats, usually made of wood, and flanged metal slats. For most purposes, plain wood slats made of any well-seasoned hardwood, preferably maple or oak, are used. Wood slats are frequently **armored** with steel plates when articles being handled will cause excessive abrasion. For heavy-duty conveying, the slats are usually made of steel plates, flanged for stiffness, or structural channel shapes. Figs. 18, 19, and 20 show typical slats.

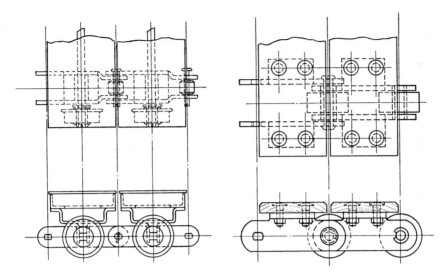

Fig. 18.   Reinforced   steel   slats   on   equalizing-saddle attachment.

Fig. 19. Wood slats on K attachment.

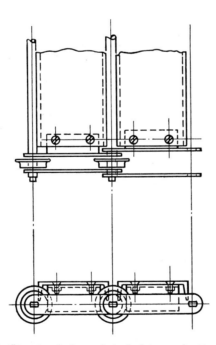

Fig. 20. Structural channel steel slats on A attachment.

CHAIN ATTACHMENTS. Attachment links for slat conveyors are similar to those described and illustrated for apron and pan conveyors. They are the equalizing-saddle type, the K type, and the A type and are as shown in Figs. 18, 19, and 20. Each type is treated in greater detail under the discussion of Apron and Pan Conveyors.

SELECTION OF COMPONENTS. When selecting a slat conveyor, the requirements of the particular application must be analyzed to obtain a completely satisfactory installation. A slat conveyor is selected particularly to handle units, packages, parts, etc., and consequently all component parts of the complete conveyor must be designed and selected for the specific application. Variations of the typical **slats** shown in Figs. 18, 19, and 20 are frequently designed to accept irregular-shaped items. The latter are frequently called **cradles** and may be designed for such special applications as handling engine blocks through machining and assembly operations. Principles of **chain, sprocket,** and **frame** selection are similar for all conveyors and are discussed later in this section.

Skirt plates, guide rails, etc., are required only if the parts, packages, or objects being conveyed have a tendency to slide laterally off the conveyor. When units being conveyed are of irregular size and shape and are loaded onto the conveyor indiscriminately, it is necessary to use restraining skirt plates or guide rails. Also, if loading is at an angle to the receiving conveyor, skirt plates or guide rails prevent objects from sliding across and off the conveyor.

Typical Constructions. Choice of **slat mountings** involves much the same factors as for pans and aprons. Equalizing-saddle mountings are again the most popular. The chains have outboard traction rollers. They can be used for both

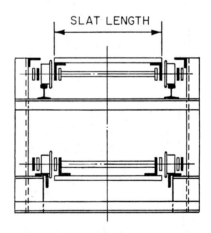

Fig. 21. **Cross section of conveyor with slats mounted on type-A attachments.**

horizontal and inclined conveyors of any length within the limitation of the chains. Slats mounted on K-type attachments on all-steel roller-type chain extend across the top of the two strands of chain. This type of construction should be used only on horizontal or inclined conveyors of short centers, because of sliding return run.

A cross section of a conveyor with slats mounted on A-type attachments of all-steel roller-type chain is shown in Fig. 21. This construction permits the return run to roll on the chain rollers.

Crossbar Conveyors

DEFINITION. A crossbar conveyor consists of a single or double strand of endless chain supporting spaced, removable, or attached "sticks" or cross members from which materials are hung or festooned while being processed.

APPLICATIONS. Crossbar conveyors may be used for unit conveying and elevating of individual objects, such as bags, boxes, and bales in inter-departmental movement, to or from loading and receiving docks, in shipping rooms and warehouses. They are also used in a wide range of process applications such as dipping, quenching, washing, spraying, bleaching, drying, and assembly.

In addition to their extensive application in the metal and lumber industry, crossbar conveyors are also frequently used in breweries, food-packing plants, and by large-volume dispensers of packaged and boxed products.

Crossbar conveyors can be arranged to provide travel in a variety of paths. **Contours** may be horizontal only, inclined only, or a combination of both.

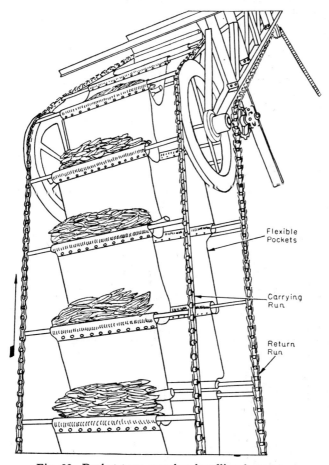

Fig. 22. Pocket-type crossbar handling bananas.

Maximum total length centers and **maximum lifts**, for conveyors that are horizontal, inclined, or a combination of both, are limited only to the maximum allowable working tension of the conveying chains. Chain tension ratings should not be exceeded. Balanced **intermediate drive stations** can be incorporated to permit extension of total conveyor length; they should be so spaced as not to develop a working chain tension beyond rated capacity.

TYPES. Various types of crossbar conveyors are in use in many different industries. Those employing only a single strand of conveyor chain are frequently identified with trolley conveyors.

The following types are most commonly used:

1. The **pendent conveyor** employs a single strand of conveyor chain and a single hanger bar projecting down through the chain. The lower end of the hanger bar can be equipped with a single hole, a hook, or a crossbar for supporting the objects being conveyed. Some authorities classify this type as a **trolley conveyor.**

2. The **pocket conveyor,** shown in Fig. 22, employs two strands of conveyor chain having crossbars that support a continuous series of pockets formed of a flexible material. The pockets are festooned between the crossbars and serve as hammocks for support of the material being handled.

3. The **mesh deck conveyor** employs a continuous wire-mesh surface attached to and supported between two strands of chain. Frequently used for conveying oily products, it permits the oil to drip off through the mesh. It is also used for conveying fruits, vegetables, and other articles to be washed prior to packing or processing. Some authorities class this conveyor as a **belt conveyor,** the wire-mesh deck being referred to as a chain selvage belt.

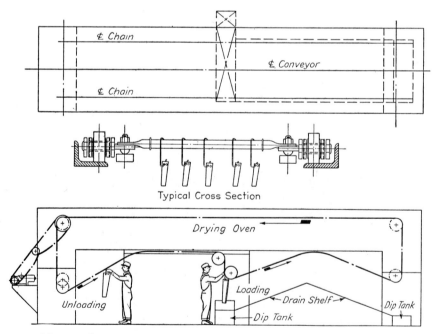

Fig. 23. Crossbar conveyor used in painting and drying operations.

4. The **removable-crossbar conveyor** employs two strands of conveyor chain with special attachments for loosely supporting crossbars.

5. The **fixed-crossbar conveyor** employs two strands of conveyor chain with regularly spaced attachments to which crossbars are permanently attached. The objects to be conveyed can be supported on or suspended from the crossbars (Fig. 23).

SELECTION OF COMPONENTS. Chain-mounting attachments, hangers, crossbars, etc., are generally designed for the particular requirements of the installation. General principles of chain selection, sprocket design, and frame construction apply to crossbar conveyors as well as to other types.

Carrier Chain Conveyors

DEFINITION. Carrier chain conveyors consist of one or more endless chains or other linkage to which may be attached any of many different attachments for the purpose of conveying loose materials or objects or of providing securements or supports for objects being conveyed.

APPLICATIONS. Carrier chain conveyors have an extremely broad application in conveying and elevating parts, pieces, objects, assemblies, subassemblies, etc. They are used by practically all the basic **fabricating and processing industries** having materials handling requirements; for this reason they are the most widely used single type of chain conveyor. They can be applied for the handling of incoming materials, of in-process materials, and of finished materials or products. They can be arranged to provide conveyor travel in a variety of paths in horizontal, inclined, or combination patterns. Almost any contour can be accommodated and an attachment design selected for the purpose, as is evident from the number of different designs currently in use.

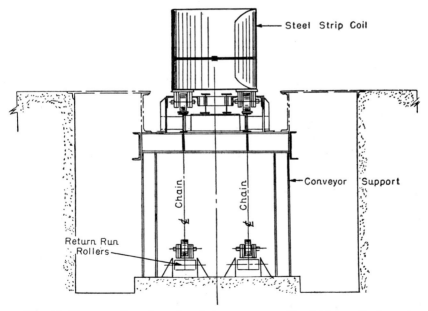

Fig. 24. Cross section of carrier chain conveyor with platform attachment.

For many applications, principally horizontal, an attachment is not required. There is usually sufficient friction between the object being conveyed and the carrier chain to propel the object along at the same speed as the carrier chain. Maximum total length centers and maximum elevating lifts, for conveyors that are horizontal, inclined, or a combination of both, are limited only to the maximum allowable working tension of the conveying chains used.

TYPES OF CARRIER CHAIN CONVEYORS. Although there are many different types of carrier chain conveyors, they can be classified into two basic types, namely: rolling-type carrier chain conveyors, and sliding-type carrier chain conveyors.

Each type can be constructed with special features and attachments to suit a particular application. Both types may use single or multiple strands of chain.

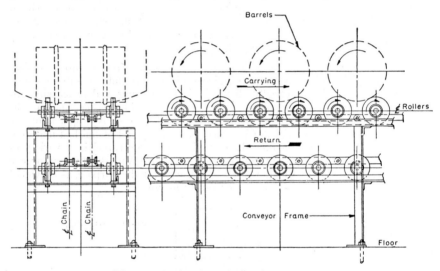

Fig. 25. Typical barrel-pitching conveyor.

Rolling-Type Carrier Chain Conveyors. This type consists of one or more endless chains equipped with rollers. Some utilize rollers mainly to effect a minimum amount of friction and are equipped with pusher- or platform-type attachments for contact with, or support of, objects being conveyed. Fig. 24 shows the cross section of a carrier chain conveyor with platform-type attachments.

Other conveyors of this type employ rollers for the support of the objects being conveyed, and the conveying chain serves as a connecting and propelling medium for the rollers. The rollers may be shaped to accommodate the objects being conveyed, or they can be flat-faced for the movement of boxes or other objects with flat surfaces.

Another application of roller attachments is illustrated by the barrel-pitching conveyor in Fig. 25. Rollers are designed to accept the piece axis placed at a right angle to the chain axis. With the cylindrical piece resting on two rollers of each chain strand, the piece is rotated when the chain is in motion.

Sliding-Type Carrier Chain Conveyors. This type consists of one or more endless chains (without rollers) on which packages or objects are carried. The conveyed package or object rests directly on the chain. The chain slides on a track, a surface, or in a trough. Because of sliding friction, this type of carrier chain conveyor requires greater chain tensions than the rolling type. Care must be exercised so that the allowable working tension of the chain is not exceeded.

The sliding carrier chain conveyor is widely used in lumber mills and warehouses for conveying lumber, boxes, barrels, crates, and similar objects.

Fixtures and attachments or specially designed chain links may be used and spaced to suit conditions. A typical application without special fixtures is shown in Fig. 26.

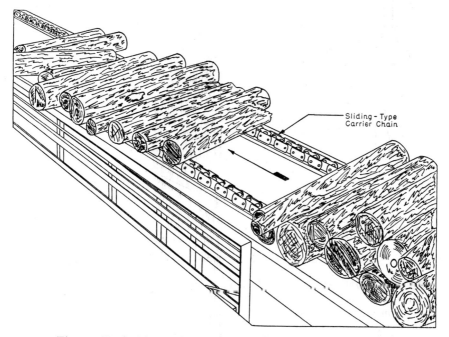

Sliding - Type
Carrier Chain

Fig. 26. Typical log deck handling logs in a pulp and paper mill.

Flat-Top Chain Conveyors. These conveyors can be of either the rolling or the sliding type, as preferred, and are particularly adaptable to the controlled high-speed production encountered in the processing industries, such as food canning and bottling.

Various types are being used extensively, such as hinged-joint continuous flat-top sliding type, plate-top sliding type, plate-top rolling type; crescent-shaped plate top for multiplaner or carrousel-type operation; and double flex chains.

Flat-top chain conveyors are designed to present to the objects being conveyed a continuous **level moving table** capable of supporting extremely small objects without spillage. Fig. 27 shows such a conveyor with crescent-shaped flat-top chain for a carrousel operation. This type can be designed for multiplaner operation. Plates can be designed in a variety of shapes. One type frequently used in the bottling and canning industry is shown in Fig. 28. The carrying strand is supported on continuous tracks or "ways" that can be made of metal, hardwood, or plastics. When the application is of the sliding type, a lubricant is used to maintain minimum friction.

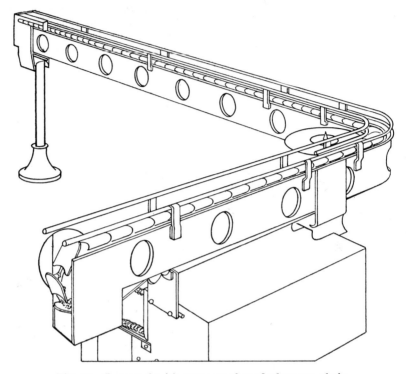

Fig. 27. Carrousel with crescent-shaped plate-top chain.

SELECTION OF EQUIPMENT. Like most other conveyors, a carrier chain conveyor is designed to suit a particular application. The general approach to component selection outlined later in this section applies. Care must be used to make certain that all component parts are designed properly for the application, and that the construction used provides ample structural strength to absorb the impacts and support the loads imposed.

Types of Pushers, Platforms, Roller Attachments, and Lugs. Some indication of the variety of attachments and chain designs used with carrier chain conveyors has been given in the preceding descriptions of this class of conveyor. The varieties are nearly as numerous as are their applications. A few types, such as pusher lugs for handling logs and lumber, have become standard through long usage.

Details of some typical attachments are shown in Fig. 29. The **platform type** of attachment is used with the conveyor in Fig. 24. The **concave roller faces** are designed to accept pipes and tubes which are placed lengthwise on the rollers parallel to the axis of the chain. As the chain moves, the turning of the rollers applies an additional propelling force on the piece, resulting in a piece velocity twice that of the chain. The same principle may be applied to carriers with **flat-faced rollers** used in conveying boxes. The third type shown is a **lug** incorporating rollers which is also used in conveying pipe or tubing. Conveyors with this type of attachment usually have multiple strands. Pipes or tubes are placed across the strands and between the lugs and are rolled along the conveyor track.

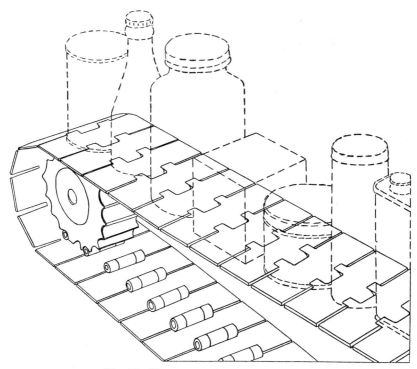

Fig. 28. Flat-top carrier chain conveyor.

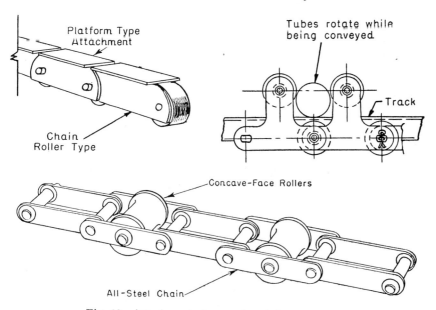

Fig. 29. Attachments for carrier chain conveyors.

Car-Type Conveyors

DEFINITION. A car-type conveyor consists of a series of cars attached to and propelled by an endless chain or other linkage which operates in a defined path. This type is frequently called a **carrousel conveyor** or a **pallet-type conveyor**.

A typical layout is shown in Fig. 30. Car design and path of travel in nearly all instances are determined by the particular application, such as size and weight of object being handled, distance to be traveled, and time requirements.

APPLICATIONS. Car-type conveyors have wide fields of application, primarily in such industries as foundries, steel mills, and paper mills, where they are used for carrying such items as molds for castings, coils of steel strip, rolls of paper, and many similar items including contained loose materials.

In addition to the function of **transportation,** car-type conveyors can also be used for the performance of necessary **processing operations** during transport. Strip-steel coils can be cooled, molten metal in molds can solidify and cool, assembly operations can be performed, etc.

Car-type conveyors are generally arranged for operation in a **horizontal** plane, but can also be used to negotiate **moderate inclines** to effect reasonable changes in elevation. In plan, they can be arranged to travel almost any **straight or irregular path.** They can be arranged to deliver to unloading stations, to receive at loading stations, to deliver to and take away from processing stations, to travel into and through cooling areas, to provide live storage and thus save floor storage space. For example, in a foundry these conveyors can be arranged to carry completed molds through the pouring areas, then through a cooling area either inside or outside of the building, to the shake-out area when after shake-out the flasks can again be placed on the cars for return to the molding area. With this type of arrangement, equipment such as the flasks and weights can be in constant use with practically no dead storage required; thus savings in handling and floor space are effected.

Essentially, car-type conveyors are used for transporting objects that are large and relatively heavy or for transporting contained loose material. **Relatively slow speeds** are generally necessitated by the nature of the objects being conveyed or by the processing operations required, such as cooling and solidifying.

Maximum total **conveyor length and lift** for conveyors that are horizontal or a combination of horizontal and inclined is limited only to the allowable working tension rating of the endless chain or other linkage used to propel or connect the cars.

TYPES. In general, cars are **permanently connected** by the chain or cable connecting and propelling medium. The section through the car-type conveyor in Fig. 31 shows the location of the connecting and propelling chain.

Another type having cars without interconnection is shown in Fig. 32. In this case the cars are propelled by **pusher dog attachments** on the propelling chain that engage lug devices on the cars.

Many other types designed for specific applications have been used.

Drive Arrangements. When cars are permanently connected by the chain-propelling medium, a separate drive chain, often called a **caterpillar drive,** is used. This arrangement, in which the powered auxiliary drive chain engages and actuates the conveyor chain by means of lugs, is described and illustrated in the section on trolley conveyors.

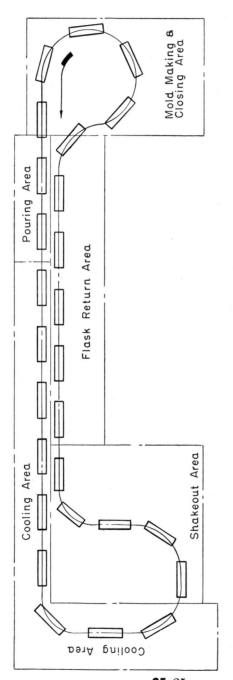

Cooling Area

Pouring Area

Flask Return Area

Mold Making & Closing Area

Cooling Area

Shakeout Area

Cooling Area

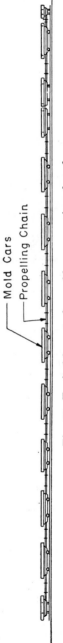

Mold Cars

Propelling Chain

Fig. 30. Typical layout of a mold conveyor in a foundry.

An **air-cylinder drive** is occasionally used when the cars are permanently connected by the propelling chain. The air cylinder engages the chain on the forward stroke, disengages during the return stroke, and re-engages on the following forward stroke to complete the cycle.

Car Types. Four-wheel cars as shown in Figs. 31 and 32, are generally used. For a special application, 2-wheel and other wheel arrangements can be embodied in the car chassis designs.

The **car wheels,** or rollers, can be equipped with plain or antifriction bearings. The wheels can be either flanged or flat-faced. Flanged wheels assist in guiding

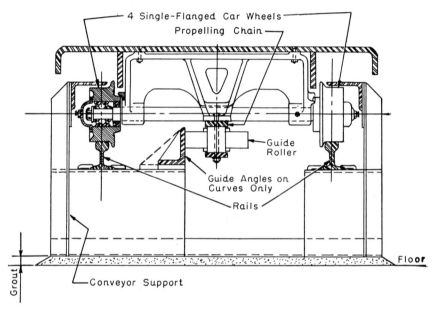

Fig. 31. **Cross section through car, 4-wheel type.**

the cars along the carrying rails and eliminate the need for other means of guiding them along straight runs. A **guiding roller** (Fig. 31) and guide track are commonly used at the curves to relieve the strain against roller flanges. When flat-faced rollers are used, it is generally necessary to provide retaining **guide tracks,** on both straight runs and curves, that control the path of travel.

LOADING AND DISCHARGE. Cars are usually loaded on a unit basis manually or by means of automatically timed loading equipment.

To assist in unloading, and particularly for heavy objects, the car tops can be equipped with free-turning rollers. Automatic discharge or unloading mechanisms can be employed and placed at predetermined locations along the conveyor travel. The automatic unloading can be accomplished through the use of cams, air-cylinder pushers, guides, or rollers and can be arranged to transfer objects to other conveyors in synchronized operation to unloading platforms or areas on either side or alternate sides of the car.

SELECTION OF COMPONENTS. Like other systems, car-type conveyors are generally designed to suit a particular application, and the same principles of

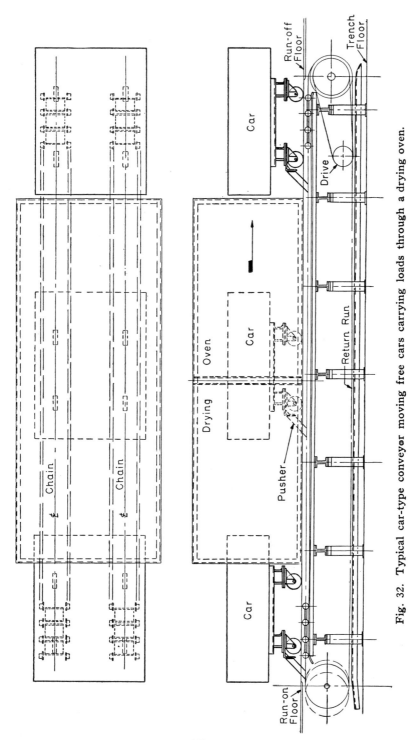

Fig. 32. Typical car-type conveyor moving free cars carrying loads through a drying oven.

component selection should be applied. **Cars** and **car platforms** also are usually designed to suit a specific application. Applications are so varied and insufficiently repetitive to permit standardization to any great degree.

A consideration peculiar to this type of conveyor is the **car turn.** For practically all car-type conveyors incorporating such turns in the installation layout, care must be used to provide adequate **radii** for best operation. Mostly because of space limitations, a tendency prevails to make turns as sharp as possible. This practice may result in a radius so small that interference between cars occurs and operation becomes jerky. The latter is the result of the speed differential between straight-line distance between cars and the lesser chordal distance between cars on the turn.

Each installation must be carefully laid out in sufficient detail so that a maximum radius can be used.

Engineering

CONVEYOR TYPE SELECTION. Probably one of the most difficult problems encountered in the handling of materials is the selection of the proper type of conveyor to be used.

Although some standards have been established through frequent use, there are many instances in which the proper selection can be made only after a very thorough study and analysis. Important considerations in selecting type and style of conveyor are:

Purpose
1. Work to be done.
   a. Contour (plan and elevation) through which material is to be conveyed.
   b. Loading and discharge points.
   c. Desired flow of material.

Operation
1. Is installation to be temporary or permanent?
2. Cycle.
   a. Hours per day.
   b. Days per year.
3. Preference for:
   a. Light equipment.
   b. Medium equipment.
   c. Heavy equipment.

Material To Be Conveyed
1. Condition of material.
   a. Dry, moist, plastic, sticky, corrosive, chemically active.
   b. Temperature range: hot, cold, or variable.
   c. Special characteristics.
2. Weight.
   a. Bulk materials per cubic foot: settled, solid, or fluffed.
   b. Unit material—weight per unit. Is grouping, bunching, or stacking a possibility?
3. Size.
   a. Bulk materials. Measure uniform lumps in inches. If unsized, measure minimum and maximum lumps in inches and approximate proportions of the different sizes.
   b. Unit materials. If uniform, use cube dimensions. If variable, use probable minimum and maximum cubes.

Capacity Requirements
  1. Average: tons or units per hour.
  2. Maximum: momentary or surge-tons or surge-volume per unit of time.
  3. Possible future requirements.

Loading
  1. Will bulk materials be fed direct from crusher? direct from bin or hopper? from a feeder—what type? from another conveyor—what type?
  2. Will loading of unit materials be controlled with units spaced? from a processing machine—what type? from another conveyor—what type? by hand? not controlled?

Length and Lift
  1. Horizontal and vertical shaft centers.
  2. Contour.
  3. Possible future extension.

Fig. 33 presents in tabular form some recommended selections of conveyor types according to the material to be handled.

Conveyor Type	For Handling
Apron and pan conveyors	Bulk materials such as coal, coke, ore, slag, rock, stone, gravel, sand, clay.
Slat conveyors	Objects such as barrels, boxes, crates, bales, packages, sacks, parts, coils of wire, flasks, castings.
Crossbar conveyors	Objects such as bags, boxes, bales for applications such as dipping, quenching, washing, drying, spraying, assembly.
Carrier conveyors	Objects such as parts, pieces, assemblies, subassemblies, tubes, rods, boards, slabs, slats.
Car-type conveyors	Molds for castings, coils of steel strip, rolls of paper, assemblies, etc.

Fig. 33. Suggested conveyor type selection.

Condition of Material Handled. In selecting the proper type of conveyor and its component parts, careful consideration must be given to the character and condition of the material to be handled. These factors affect capacity, loading, unloading, abrasion, corrosion, and life. Many materials may flow freely when dry but be sluggish when moisture is present. When damp or wet, the material may cling to the conveying medium, may not discharge freely, and thus may seriously decrease the conveyor capacity. In addition, added moisture affects material weight.

Conveyor Capacity. Capacity for a **conveyor handling bulk materials** is determined by multiplying the average cross section of the load by the conveyor speed during a given period of time. If bulk material is being conveyed in carrying units such as pans, the capacity is determined by multiplying the load in each carrying unit by the number of these units passing a fixed point in a given period of time.

The capacity of **apron conveyors** and **feeders** is calculated as follows:

$$E \times D \times S = \text{C.F.H.}$$

where E = effective width of conveyor, in feet; D = depth of material, in feet; S = speed, in feet per hour; C.F.H. = cubic feet per hour.

Capacities in Cubic Feet per Hour

Effective Width of Carrying Surface (in.) *	Depth of Material on Conveyor (in.) †														
	2	3	4	5	6	7	8	10	12	14	16	18	20	24	30
18	113	169	225	281	338	394	450	563	675	788	900	1013			
24	150	225	300	375	450	525	600	750	900	1050	1200	1350	1500	1800	
30	188	281	375	469	563	656	750	938	1125	1313	1500	1688	1875	2250	2813
36	225	338	450	563	675	788	900	1125	1350	1575	1800	2025	2250	2700	3375
42	263	394	525	656	788	918	1050	1313	1575	1838	2100	2363	2625	3150	3938
48	300	450	600	750	900	1050	1200	1500	1800	2100	2400	2700	3000	3600	4500
54	338	506	675	844	1013	1181	1350	1688	2025	2363	2700	3038	3375	4050	5063
60	375	563	750	938	1125	1313	1500	1875	2250	2625	3000	3375	3750	4500	5625

Fig. 34. Apron and pan conveyor capacities.

* The effective width is represented by the distance between pan sides, or the distance between stationary skirt plates, as the case may be.
† Refer to page 25·12 for relation of material depth to height of skirt plates.

The capacity table, Fig. 34, lists capacities for conveyors having various widths and a speed of 10 ft. per min. So that **momentary surge-loads** can be accommodated without spillage, the capacities listed are 75 percent of calculated actuals, a recommended practice. For speeds other than 10 ft. per min. use direct proportion. When calculating the **depth of the material** (D above), consider the irregular cross-sectional shape of the aprons or pans. If aprons or pans are shallow, their irregularity of cross section is not great. Deep pans may seriously affect calculations and must be considered.

If, in selecting a conveyor or feeder from the table, the capacity requirement does not fall within the initial size selection, a slight adjustment can be made to either the speed or the depth of material. When making such adjustments, use direct proportions.

Capacity for a **conveyor handling objects** is determined by multiplying the weight of each object by the number of objects passing a fixed point in a given period of time. If objects are variable in size and weight, an average can be used. The following equations may be used in determining capacities of slat, crossbar, carrier chain, and car-type conveyors:

1. **Quantity.**

$$E \times S = \text{C.P.H.}$$

where E = objects handled, per lineal foot; S = speed, in feet per hour; C.P.H. = capacity (objects per hour). Quantity considerations are required for processing and production calculations.

2. **Weight.**

$$\frac{P \times S}{2,000} = \text{T.P.H.}$$

where P = pounds handled, per lineal foot; S = speed, in feet per hour; T.P.H. = capacity, in tons per hour. Weight considerations are required for horsepower and chain tension calculations.

SIZE OF CONVEYING UNIT. If lump or object size is critical, care must be exercised to insure adequate conveyor size to permit satisfactory loading and discharge and to prevent spillage, choking, and possible interferences along the path of travel. If **lump sizes** in excess of permissible may be encountered, loading through restricted openings, such as a grate having fixed size openings, is recommended.

In determining the size of any chain conveyor or feeder, three factors must be known or established for every installation. They are based on over-all requirements such as process involved, plant capacity, production schedules, loading and unloading facilities, characteristics and size of material to be handled. These factors are:

1. Units in tons (T.P.H.), or objects, per hour to be handled.
2. Weight of material, in pounds per cubic foot (W.C.F.), or average of objects, in pounds.
3. Maximum lump or object size.

Pan and Apron Conveyors and Feeders. When bulk materials are to be handled, as in pan and apron conveyors, units are tons per hour, pounds per cubic foot, and lump size. The above factors are applied to determine:

1. **Cubic feet per hour.**

$$\text{C.F.H.} = \frac{\text{T.P.H.} \times 2,000}{\text{W.C.F.}}$$

2. **Depth of material** to be conveyed is determined on the basis of one or more of the following considerations:

   a. **Conveyor speed and width.** When depth is determined solely by lump size, these can be established at the most economical minimum.

   b. **Height of end plates** on pans, for conveyors and feeders without full-length stationary skirt plates. It is recommended that full-length stationary skirt plates be avoided, when possible, to effect economy in power requirement and maintenance cost. End plates on pans are generally either 4 or 6 in. high. Occasionally, for certain installations, they may be as high as 8 in. Selection of the 4-in. or 6-in. height will permit use of most manufacturers' standards.

   c. **Skirt plate height.** This is related to height of hopper opening. Hopper opening is determined either from lump size or from volume of material to be handled. See page 25·35.

   d. **Hopper opening height.** This height should not be less than 2½ times maximum lump size. Material flowing from a hopper onto a conveyor usually assumes a depth of 75 percent of the hopper opening height (see Fig. 35).

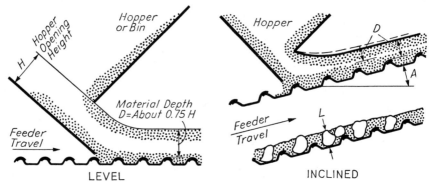

Fig. 35. Hopper openings and skirt plate height.

Example: Material with 8-in. maximum size lumps flowing from an opening 20-in. high usually assumes a depth of 15 in.

The foregoing applies to inclines up to the **critical angle,** at which material starts to slide back. A in Fig. 35 indicates critical angle; D, the depth of material above top of bead on pan or top of pusher cleat; and L, the maximum lump size. Values for each depend entirely on the material being handled. Rounded-type lump material, when agitated but slightly, will roll back more readily; therefore, A for such materials should be established at a conservative maximum.

3. **Conveyor or feeder width.** The width may be selected from the capacity chart, Fig. 34. Minimum width and speed give the most economical installation from the standpoint of first cost and long life and low maintenance cost.

4. **Conveyor speed.** Speed may be determined according to the following recommendations:

   a. **Feeder speeds** are generally slow, 10 ft. per min. being average for materials from dead storage, such as stockpiles, hoppers with long-length openings, when material is handled from rest. Higher speeds, usually 30 ft. per min. maximum, are frequently used for feeders when material flows onto the feeder. For example, from a chute or slide, feeder speeds, particularly for coal and ore, may operate at 4 to 25 ft. per min. and average 10 ft. per min.

   b. **Conveyor speed** depends on conditions. For the more common materials, 50 to 75 ft. per min. is average. Favorable conditions will permit an increase. For example, bituminous-coal-mine picking tables and loading booms average 60 ft. per min.

IMPORTANCE OF UNIFORM LOADING. To prevent overloading that may result in damage and possible failure to the conveying unit, the material being handled should be delivered to the conveyor at a uniform rate. A feeding device is recommended to provide the necessary control.

Chutes are often used in the loading and unloading of conveyors. It is especially important when bulk materials are being handled to give particular consideration to the design of the chutes. Because of the many different kinds and types of materials and conditions, only the roughest rules can be established. In general, therefore, the factors that influence chute design are:

1. Kind of material.
2. Lump size.
3. Moisture content.
4. Percentage of fines.
5. Angle of slide.
6. Whether material starts from rest, as from a bin, or flows through chutes, as when discharged from a feeder or other conveyor unit.
7. Kind of chute, its length, and the condition of its surface.

Conveyors for Unit Objects. In computing for sizes of slat, bar, carrier chain, and car conveyors, the three required factors listed above are measured in objects per hour, average weight of objects, in pounds, and cube size of objects. These values are used to determine:

1. **Average load in pounds per foot** of conveyor length is determined from the weight of the objects handled and their spacing on the conveyor. Spacing is dependent on size of objects or on design spacing for processing. For example, if an object weighs 200 lb. and is spaced on 2 ft. 0 in. centers along the conveyor length, the average material load per foot equals 100 lb.
2. **Conveyor width** must be great enough to accept the largest dimension of object placed on the carrying surface, plus 4 to 6 in. for clearance. The largest dimension is generally a diagonal measurement; it is used when objects are placed at random on the conveyor. Frequently the bases of objects being conveyed are much smaller than their over-all width. The conveyor need only be wide enough to accommodate the width of the base, but clearances on the sides must be great enough to permit free passage without interference. If items are to be hung from the conveyor, the design need only provide suitable clearance for the conveying medium, but space must be provided above, below, and on the sides for free passage of the object being carried. The most **economical installation,** from the standpoint of first cost, long life, and low maintenance cost is that with minimum width operating at minimum speed.
3. **Conveyor speed** is best determined by the specific requirements of each installation. Obviously, the speed must be slow if the objects to be conveyed are very heavy and if they started from rest. With light objects, the conveyor speed may be greater to obtain sufficient capacity. The speed should be as slow as will deliver the desired capacity and permit convenient loading and unloading. The following are average speed ranges for various **slat conveyor** applications:

Assembly conveyors	3–6 ft. per min.
Casting conveyors	6–10 ft. per min.
Baggage and interprocess conveyors:	
In industrial plants	20–60 ft. per min.
Ramp conveyors	20–60 ft. per min.
Pusher conveyors	40–70 ft. per min.

PRINCIPLES OF CONVEYOR COMPONENT SELECTION. In selecting the components of a conveyor of any type, careful attention must be given to the specific application for a completely satisfactory installation. Not only is one type of conveyor better suited to handle particular classes of material, but also, within each type, components should be selected or adapted for the item which it is to convey and the conditions under which it is to operate. Components peculiar to each type of conveyor have been described in general terms. Regardless of the type of conveyor to be installed, the following points should be considered in selecting appropriate components:

1. Load-carrying attachment, which must be structurally and mechanically designed to carry or support the item to be conveyed.
2. Type of chain and mountings.
3. Sprocket style and size.
4. Construction and design of supporting frame.
5. Skirt plates, guide rails, etc., if required.
6. Clearance requirements and safety considerations.

Various designs for load-carrying attachments have been discussed with the type of conveyor to which they apply.

Chains and Mountings. The chains most generally used are either all-steel roller type, malleable iron, or alloyed material. All-steel roller-type chains are generally preferred because of the greater strength and wear life they provide. Mountings vary according to the type of conveyor and the specific application. Chain selection is based on:

1. **Longest practical chain pitch** that will permit use of minimum diameter sprockets to suit space limitations. Long-pitch chains of equal working load tension capacity are less costly than shorter-pitch chains. Longer-pitch chains also permit more convenient mounting for aprons or pans.
2. **Allowable working load tension,** full consideration being given to service life, e.g., hours per day, years expected, live bearing pressure, class of service, and lubrication.
3. **First cost** and **maintenance.**

Sprockets: Size and Style. The most practical and economical selection is the smallest-diameter sprocket with the fewest teeth that will maintain smooth operation. In the case of **pan and apron conveyors** sprocket diameter and number of teeth must also be sufficient to maintain an overlap of pans and aprons as they flex around the sprocket.

For a given conveyor chain speed and a given chain tension, **smaller-diameter** sprockets permit use of minimum-size terminal equipment and minimum reduction between prime mover and conveyor drive shaft.

The principal advantage of a greater **number of teeth** in the conveyor sprockets is the smoother operation obtained. Chordal action of chain links when going around the sprockets imparts a pulsating motion to the conveyor chain that is more pronounced when sprockets with fewer teeth are used. When conveyor centers are short, the pulsation is least noticeable. Pulsation is most pronounced on slow-operating-speed conveyors with very long centers.

Conventional style sprockets are most commonly used. They can be made of a good grade of cast iron with chilled teeth to resist abrasive wear, of cast or fabricated steel for added strength and impact resistance, or of steel with hardened wearing surfaces and removable teeth for easy and economical replacement.

Frame Construction. Frame construction is also always custom-designed to suit the application. It must embody proper clearances for all moving parts, structural strength, and rigidity. The frame can be floor-supported, set below the floor, be ceiling-hung, or bracketed from a wall, as desired. Frame constructions of various design are illustrated with the treatment of each type of conveyor.

Skirt Plates and Guide Rails. These components are required only to confine bulk materials carried in depth, or if parts, packages, or objects being conveyed may have a tendency to slide laterally off the conveyor. Usually, when units being conveyed are of irregular shape and are loaded onto the conveyor indiscriminately, it is necessary to use restraining skirt plates or guide rails. Also, if loading is at an angle to the receiving conveyor, skirt plates or guide rails are used to prevent objects from sliding across and off the conveyors.

Takeups and Their Location. The most **common type** of takeups are those having an adjusting screw for proper positioning of the bearings mounted on the takeup shaft. **Bearings** can be of the fixed, sleeve, or antifriction type in keeping with the type used throughout on the terminal equipment of the installation.

By "positioning of the bearings mounted on the takeup shaft" is meant the location or position of the **takeup bearings** in relation to the conveyor and its **supporting structure.**

The original position established during installation layout is set to permit slack-off of conveyor chain for coupling and ample adjustment for initial stretch and subsequent wear.

Counterweighted-type takeups providing constant automatic adjustment are frequently used. They not only provide uniform constant chain tension, but also necessitate minimum maintenance attention. Counterweighted-type automatic takeups are a definite requirement for installations subject to wide ranges of temperature variations. As temperature conditions vary, the conveyor chains elongate and contract, and automatic-type takeups not only maintain constant chain tension but also prevent excessive chain tension.

Terminal Bearings. Either antifriction-type or sleeve-type bearings are used for bearings on the terminal shafts.

Sleeve-type bearings, although generally less costly on a first-installation basis, require much more frequent lubrication maintenance than do antifriction-type bearings. Sleeve-type bearings may require lubrication as frequently as once every 8 hr. of operation, whereas antifriction-type bearings, properly sealed to prevent escape of lubricant and entry of foreign material, may require relubrication once every 30 days or less frequently.

Care must be used when selecting bearings to stay within established allowable load ratings.

Power Units. The size of the power unit must be carefully considered for each installation. When making power unit selection it is necessary to include, in addition to the power required for normal operation of the conveyor, sufficient power for the following:

1. Starting from rest, particularly when fully loaded.
2. Uneven loading.
3. Possible surge-loading that establishes a peak condition.
4. Conditions, such as material spilled on tracks or hardening of materials in troughs.
5. Type of service, such as 8 hr. per day, 24 hr. per day, or frequent starts and stops.

CONVEYOR CHAIN PULL. The force or pull necessary to move conveyor chains results from:

1. Live load—material being conveyed—plus
2. Dead load—resistance of conveyor parts.

For carrier-type chain conveyors, usually only the friction of the loaded chains, or loaded carrying medium, need be considered. Depending on conveyor type and construction, the friction may be sliding or rolling friction on both the carrying and return runs, or rolling friction on one run and sliding on the other. Starting effort causes increased chain pull for which allowances must also be made.

	Approx. Coefficients, %	
	Dry	Lubricated
Sliding Friction		
Chain (flat-linked, nonroller) on rolled-steel track or trough	33	20
Coal (bituminous fines and lumps, mixed) in rolled-steel trough	33	—
Crushed stone, or dry sand, in rolled-steel trough	60–70	—
Cement in rolled-steel trough	80	—
Steel shaft on plain babbitted bearing, grease lubricated	—	1.7
Antifriction bearings on hardened races	—	0.25
Bronze on steel	—	15
Steel on steel	33	20
Cast ferrous metal on cast ferrous metal	50	30
Cast ferrous metal on hardwood	44	—
Hardwood on hardwood	48	—
Rolling Friction		
Chain with:		
1½-in.-diameter rollers		20
2-in.-diameter rollers		15
2½-in.-diameter rollers		12
3-in.-diameter rollers		9
4-in.-diameter rollers		8
5-in.-diameter rollers		7
6-in.-diameter rollers		6

Formula

$$\text{Rolling friction} = R \times \frac{d}{D} + \frac{B}{D}$$

where $B = 0.06$, metal on metal, average conditions;
　　　　$= 0.12$ for rough roller on rough track.
　　　$d =$ diameter of axle (pin or bushing), in inches.
　　　$D =$ diameter of roller, in inches.
　　　$R = 0.20$ for metal on metal, greased;
　　　　$= 0.33$ for metal on metal, not greased.

Fig. 36. Coefficients of friction.

Friction Coefficients. The coefficients of friction in Fig. 36 are expressed in percentages of the total loads carried. For all chain, they include the weight of the chain and carrying parts, and for roller chain they are based on an average axle diameter for a given roller diameter. The coefficients for all chain are based on average conditions, such as handling coal. For all chain handling gritty materials, they should be increased. If the chain is working under extremely good conditions and is well lubricated, the coefficients may be reduced. Cast-type roller chain introduces greater friction than steel chain having rollers that revolve on finished surfaces.

CHAIN PULL AND CONVEYOR HORSEPOWER. The formulas for chain pull and conveyor horsepower that follow apply generally to all types of conveyors treated in this section.

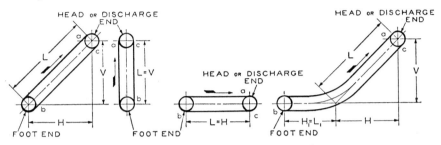

Fig. 37. Chain pull and horsepower designs.

Fig. 37 gives line diagrams of inclined, vertical, horizontal, and combined horizontal and inclined conveyors. Notations are explained as follows:

f = coefficient of friction of chain on runway.

H, H_1 = horizontal projection of conveyor, in feet.

L, L_1 = length of conveyor centers, in feet.

S = speed of conveyor, in feet per minute.

T = capacity of conveyor, in tons per hour.

V = vertical projection of conveyor, in feet.

w = weight of moving conveyor parts—chains and aprons or pans, chain and slats, chains and crossbars plus hangers, chains and attachments, or chains and complete cars in pound per foot.

W = weight of material handled per foot of conveyor centers, in pounds.

Y = resistance, pound per foot, caused by material load rubbing against stationary skirts (see below).

The formula below applies to practically all types of carrier chain conveyors except apron or pan feeders. Feeders involve additional chain pull and horsepower due to hopper loads and effort required to pull apart interlocking lumps, etc., at loading hopper. The latter values cannot readily be formulated.

For conveyors **without stationary skirts** total pull on chains equals the friction to be overcome due to the weight of:

Suspended Weight of Load		Load		Conveyor Carrying Run		Conveyor Return Run
↓		↓		↓		↓
$\dfrac{33.3TV}{S}$	$+$	$\dfrac{33.3TfH}{S}$	$+$	$w(V + fH)$	$+$	$w(fH - V) =$
WV	$+$	WfH	$+$	$w(V + fH)$	$+$	$w(fH - V)$

If V in the quantity $w(fH - V)$ exceeds fH, the conveyor return run would move down its runway, owing to gravitational pull overcoming the frictional resistance of the return run. When this is true, $w(fH - V)$ equals zero. If V is less than fH, the return run must be pulled along its runway. When this is true, the pull to move the return run is represented by the expression $w(fH - V)$, which must be added to compute the total chain pull.

When deep loads of material are moving between **stationary skirts of apron or pan conveyors,** an additional frictional pull is caused by side rubbing. This pull (Y) must be added to the chain pull obtained from the formula above; it is computed as follows:

Y (pounds per foot of length) $= h^2/K$, where $h =$ height, in inches, of the material against the sides (see Fig. 38).

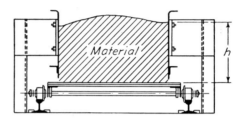

Fig. 38. Cross section of bulk material laterally confined by skirt plates.

K is a factor dependent on type of material conveyed and the nature of the skirt plate. K values for typical materials sliding against rolled steel plates are:

Materials	K
Cement clinker	8
Chips, pulpwood	48
Coal, fines and lumps mixed	30
Gravel or stone	8
Iron ore, crushed	4
Sugar cane	70

The basic formula for computing **horsepower** requirement is:

$$\frac{1.15S \, [\text{Total chain pull} - w(V - fH)]}{33,000}$$

In this formula 10 percent has been added for headshaft friction and 5 percent for footshaft friction. However, it does not account for the power necessary for the gear reduction, etc. The required adjustment is made by adding 5 percent for each belt, roller chain, or cut-tooth gear reduction, and 10 percent for each cast-tooth gear reduction. Percentages should be compounded.

The **driving power** is considered here to be applied at the head end, usually the delivery end of the conveyor. The required power is practically the same when applied at the foot end. The advantage of a head-end drive is that only one run of the chain is under maximum load. The foot-end drive puts both runs under heavy load, causes greater friction at the headshaft, and greater wear on the chains.

The expression $w(V - fH)$ used in the equation is considered only when V exceeds fH. The load then represents the excess of gravitational pull of the return run over its frictional resistance. This excess does not reduce the total chain pull, but balances a like amount of that pull, the unbalanced remainder being the horsepower pull.

In the diagram in Fig. 37, the force, **horsepower pull,** required to drive the chains is the difference between the pulls at a and c. The total or maximum pull is at a, while the pull at c is zero, or some value in the direction of rotation. In the latter case, the pull at c helps to reduce the driving force required at a by partially balancing the carrying-run pull.

On **horizontal conveyors** the friction of the return run increases the driving force required. On **inclined conveyors** the weight of return run may cause a pull at c, depending on the amount of friction between the run and its runway. If the friction exceeds gravitational pull, this run will not move of its own accord, and a pull at b will be required to move it.

When gravitational pull exceeds the friction, no additional pull will be required at b to move the return run. Then the pull at c equals the excess tendency of the run to move down.

TROLLEY CONVEYORS

CONTENTS

CONTENTS *(Continued)*

SECTION **26**

TROLLEY CONVEYORS

General Considerations

USES OF TROLLEY CONVEYORS. One of the most versatile types of conveyor is the trolley conveyor. This is primarily because it **functions in three dimensions,** whereas almost all of the other fundamental types of conveyors operate in a single plane. Its three-dimensional function gives the trolley conveyor an enormous basic advantage. Horizontal and inclined runs, vertical curves and horizontal turns can be put together in many combinations to follow complicated routes. There are few limits in length, and very few restrictions as to paths of travel.

The trolley conveyor can be used to carry almost any type of material through most kinds of operations or processes. **Loads** can be very large and heavy, or very light and small. Different sizes and weights of **materials** can be handled at the same time on the same conveyor. Materials can be hot or cold, and can be carried through processes such as cleaning and washing, bonderizing, painting, drying and baking, degreasing, sand blasting, and many others. It can be, and usually is, used as a storage conveyor at the same time that it functions as a processing and delivery conveyor. It can be a pusher or a towing conveyor. The same conveyor can be used for a combination of these functions. Except for carrousels, other conveyors have a fixed head and tail end, and an empty return run. Trolley conveyors are endless, and the entire length may generally be used. The recirculation of materials is often of tremendous advantage in manufacturing.

Additional advantages of trolley conveyors are low initial unit cost, long wear, low maintenance, and inexpensive repair and replacement. Salvage value is very high. Conveyors can be inexpensively taken down from one location and reinstalled in another. They can easily be altered in path, shortened, lengthened, combined, and divided into almost any desired combination. Spacing and types of loads can be changed easily. Another advantage is the small space taken up by the trolley conveyor.

TYPICAL TROLLEY CONVEYOR. In its most widely used form, a trolley conveyor consists of an endless drop-forged chain suspended from two-wheel trolleys that roll on the lower flange of an I-beam track. A typical assembly is shown in Fig. 1. Loads are suspended from **attachments** bolted to the trolley brackets. If the loads are light, they may be suspended from attachments bolted to the chain between trolleys. The loads are supported by a great variety of carriers, hooks and trays being the commonest.

There are **other types** of trolley conveyors. Some use wire rope cable instead of chain. Special chains are used in others. In one conveyor, the chain has rollers, and moves inside a formed track. Special conveyors, however, have special uses or limitations.

The **path** of the conveyor consists of straight runs which may be horizontal or inclined. The straight runs are joined together by horizontal turns and/or

26·1

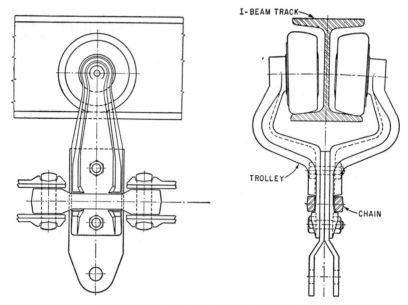

Fig. 1. Assembly of chain, track, and trolleys.

vertical curves to form an endless loop. The trolley conveyor may be **powered** by one or more drive units, or may take power from some other conveyor or machine.

The **basic components** of a trolley conveyor are:

1. Chain.
2. Trolleys.
3. Track and supports.
4. Horizontal turns.
5. Vertical curves.
6. Drives.
7. Take-ups.

Chain

RIVETLESS CHAIN. Drop-forged-steel chain (also called Keystone Chain) is ideal for trolley conveyors. It provides light weight with high strength at a

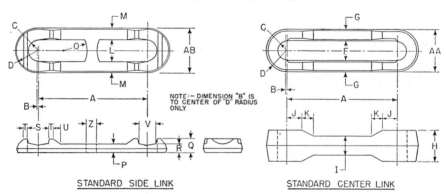

Fig. 2. Dimensions of rivetless chain (continued on next page).

relatively low cost. It can be flexed transversely on a comparatively short radius, and can be easily connected to trolleys without the use of special chain attachments. Construction is very simple. The chain is assembled from three parts: (1) side links, (2) center links, and (3) chain pins. It may be easily assembled and disassembled without tools. Detail dimensions of the rivetless chain may be seen in Fig. 2.

SIZES. Four sizes of chain are in common use. These are designated 228, 348 and X-348 and X-458, and 678. There is also a 658 chain, which is the

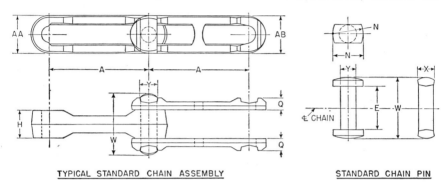

TYPICAL STANDARD CHAIN ASSEMBLY   STANDARD CHAIN PIN

DETAIL DIMENSIONS OF DROP-FORGED STEEL CHAIN (in.)

Chain	A	B	C	D	E	F	G	H	I	J	K	L	M	N
348	3	$\frac{1}{32}$	$\frac{17}{32}$	$\frac{17}{32}$	$1\frac{11}{32}$	$\frac{9}{16}$	$\frac{1}{4}$	$\frac{13}{16}$	$\frac{1}{2}$	$\frac{1}{2}$	$\frac{3}{16}$	$\frac{9}{16}$	$\frac{1}{4}$	$\frac{31}{32}$
458	4	$\frac{1}{32}$	$\frac{41}{64}$	$\frac{45}{64}$	$1\frac{5}{8}$	$\frac{23}{32}$	$\frac{11}{32}$	$1\frac{1}{64}$	$\frac{5}{8}$	$\frac{9}{16}$	$\frac{3}{8}$	$\frac{11}{16}$	$\frac{11}{32}$	$1\frac{7}{32}$
X-458	4	$\frac{1}{32}$	$\frac{21}{64}$	$\frac{45}{64}$	$1\frac{5}{8}$	$\frac{23}{32}$	$\frac{11}{32}$	1	$\frac{5}{8}$		$\frac{3}{4}$	$\frac{5}{16}$		$1\frac{7}{32}$
468	4	$\frac{1}{32}$	$\frac{25}{64}$	$\frac{15}{16}$	$2\frac{15}{32}$	$\frac{7}{8}$	$\frac{1}{2}$	$1\frac{1}{8}$	$1\frac{1}{8}$	$\frac{11}{16}$	$\frac{1}{4}$	$\frac{13}{16}$	$\frac{17}{32}$	$1\frac{11}{16}$
658	6	$\frac{1}{32}$	$\frac{21}{64}$	$\frac{45}{64}$	$1\frac{5}{8}$	$\frac{23}{32}$	$\frac{11}{32}$	$1\frac{1}{64}$	$\frac{5}{8}$	$\frac{9}{16}$	$\frac{3}{8}$	$\frac{11}{16}$	$\frac{11}{32}$	$1\frac{7}{32}$
678	6	$\frac{5}{64}$	$\frac{29}{64}$	1	$2\frac{1}{4}$	1	$\frac{1}{2}$	$1\frac{5}{16}$	$\frac{13}{16}$	$\frac{13}{16}$	$\frac{1}{2}$	$\frac{31}{32}$	$\frac{33}{64}$	$1\frac{7}{8}$

Chain	O	P	Q	R	S	T	U	V	W	X	Y	Z	AA	AB
348	3	$\frac{1}{4}$	$\frac{13}{32}$	$\frac{1}{4}$	$\frac{9}{16}$	$\frac{1}{8}$	$\frac{1}{4}$	$\frac{9}{16}$	$1\frac{27}{32}$	$\frac{17}{32}$	$\frac{1}{2}$	$\frac{3}{8}$	$1\frac{1}{16}$	$1\frac{1}{16}$
458	$\frac{3}{4}$	$\frac{5}{16}$	$\frac{15}{32}$	$\frac{9}{32}$	$\frac{23}{32}$	$\frac{1}{8}$	$\frac{1}{4}$	$\frac{21}{32}$	$2\frac{1}{4}$	$\frac{21}{32}$	$\frac{5}{8}$	$\frac{3}{8}$	$1\frac{13}{32}$	$1\frac{3}{8}$
X-458			$\frac{15}{32}$	$\frac{9}{32}$	$\frac{21}{32}$	$\frac{3}{32}$		$\frac{5}{8}$	$2\frac{1}{4}$	$\frac{21}{32}$	$\frac{5}{8}$	$1\frac{25}{32}$	$1\frac{13}{32}$	$1\frac{3}{8}$
468	$\frac{7}{8}$	$\frac{1}{2}$	$\frac{5}{8}$	$\frac{25}{64}$	$\frac{55}{64}$	$\frac{1}{8}$	$\frac{1}{4}$	$\frac{25}{32}$	$3\frac{9}{32}$	$\frac{25}{32}$	$\frac{3}{4}$	$\frac{1}{2}$	$1\frac{7}{8}$	$1\frac{7}{8}$
658	$\frac{3}{4}$	$\frac{5}{16}$	$\frac{15}{32}$	$\frac{9}{32}$	$\frac{23}{32}$	$\frac{1}{8}$	$\frac{1}{4}$	$\frac{21}{32}$	$2\frac{1}{4}$	$\frac{21}{32}$	$\frac{5}{8}$	$\frac{3}{8}$	$1\frac{13}{32}$	$1\frac{3}{8}$
678	1	$\frac{1}{2}$	$\frac{3}{4}$	$\frac{7}{16}$	$\frac{61}{64}$	$\frac{5}{32}$	3" R	$\frac{29}{32}$	$3\frac{1}{8}$	$\frac{59}{64}$	$\frac{7}{8}$	$\frac{5}{8}$	2	2

Jervis B. Webb Co,

Fig. 2. (Concluded.)

same as 458 except that it is 6-in. pitch. Another chain is 468 of 4-in. pitch. Specifications are given in Fig. 3. The prefix "X" designates an improved design of chain which is better proportioned and flexes transversely on a shorter radius. Types such as 348 and X-348 can be coupled together in the same conveyor, but must not be flexed transversely on a radius shorter than is allowable for the older form of chain.

These chains are so widely used, and so well known that they are often identified by number only, without other specifications.

STRENGTH. In the past, both heat-treated and untreated or green drop-forged chain have been available. However, trolley conveyors are frequently altered, with parts taken down from one conveyor to be used in another. Since it is no longer considered desirable to have both untreated and heat-treated chain in the same plant, conveyor manufacturers now tend to offer only heat-treated chain.

ALLOWABLE CHAIN PULL. The working load allowed on a trolley conveyor chain is much less than for the same chain used in other types of conveyors. The factors that limit the maximum chain pull are:

1. The pressure per square inch on the bearing area.
2. The track life at vertical curves due to trolley load plus chain reaction load.
3. Pin bending and/or pin bearing pressure at vertical curves.

There is no definite agreement between trolley-conveyor manufacturers on the proper values to use for maximum allowable chain pull. Ratios between ultimate strengths and allowable loads that are in general use are 16:1 for multiplane conveyors and 12:1 for monoplane conveyors. Larger values than the allowable loads given in Fig. 3 are sometimes used under very favorable conditions.

Chain No.	Approximate Pitch	Pin Diameter	Ultimate Strength (lb.)	Maximum Allowable Load (lb.)	
				*Multiplane	†Monoplane
228	2 in.	¼ in.	6,000	400	600
348 X-348	3 in.	½ in.	24,000	1,000 to 1,400	2,000
458 X-458	4 in.	⅝ in.	48,000	2,000 to 3,000	4,000
468	4 in.	¾ in.	70,000	4,000	5,000
658	6 in.	⅝ in.	48,000	2,000 to 3,000	4,000
678	6 in.	⅞ in.	85,000	4,000 to 5,000	6,000

* Multiplane indicates conveyors which have vertical (transverse) curves.
† Monoplane indicates conveyors operating in a horizontal plane only.

Fig. 3. Drop-forged chains—heat-treated.

RADII FOR TRANSVERSE BENDING. One of the most important factors in the selection of a chain and in trolley spacing is the minimum radius of vertical curves. Values for drop-forged chain are given in Fig. 4. These values conform to most manufacturers' recommendations but may vary with loads and operating conditions. Short-radius vertical curves and steep inclines can cause

Trolley Spacing in Inches	Minimum Vertical Radius in Feet*			†
	348	458	678	228
8 c. to c.		6		2
12 c. to c.	4		12	3
16 c. to c.		8		4
20 c. to c.				6
18 c. to c.	6			
24 c. to c.	8	10	15	8
30 c. to c.	10			
32 c. to c.		12		
36 c. to c.	12		20	
40 c. to c.		16		

Jervis B. Webb Co.

* To center line of I-beam track.
† To bottom of I-beam track.

Fig. 4. Radii of vertical curves for drop-forged chain.

operational limitations but are very desirable for plant layout purposes. They save valuable floor space. In the case of paint-dip and plating tanks, and similar dipping operations, they allow the use of smaller tanks. The use of short-radius curves also makes it easier to run the conveyors through floors. Another advantage of short-radius curves is that they facilitate the conveyors' entrance into and exit from ovens.

ATTACHMENTS. Loads are usually hung from trolleys. However, when light loads must be closely spaced, they may be hung from the chain. Attachments can be furnished as extensions to chain pins in styles similar to the attachments used with trolleys. See Fig. 5.

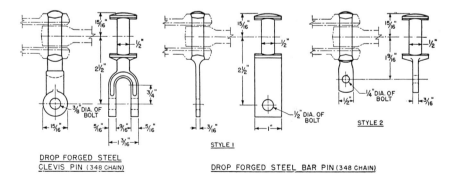

Fig. 5. Chain pin attachments (continued on next page).

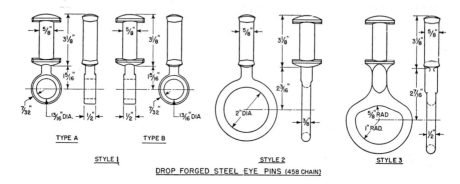

TYPE A   TYPE B

STYLE 1   STYLE 2   STYLE 3

DROP FORGED STEEL EYE PINS (458 CHAIN)

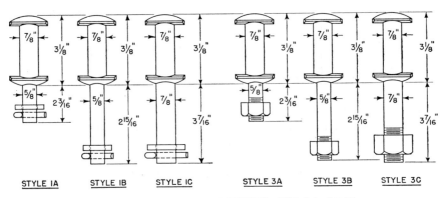

STYLE 1A   STYLE 1B   STYLE 1C   STYLE 3A   STYLE 3B   STYLE 3C

DROP FORGED STEEL EXTENDED PINS (678 CHAIN)

Fig. 5. (Concluded.)

Trolleys

TYPES OF TROLLEYS. There are many different types of trolleys, with different kinds of wheels, brackets or side arms, attachments, and methods of connecting brackets and wheels. The most popular type of trolley has heavy, machined, ball-bearing wheels, drop-forged brackets, and steel attachments, which may be fabricated, drop forged, or cast.

WHEELS. The wheel is the most important part of the trolley. The foremost manufacturers generally make trolley wheels to the following specifications:

1. The wheel tread is one-piece, heavy, and machined to run true and smoothly. The tread is also the outer race of the ballbearing.
2. The inner race is one-piece.
3. The ball bearing has large-diameter balls, accurately spaced by a metal separator.
4. The balls and ball races compare favorably with precision ball bearings in quality of metal and heat treatment. Ball races are ground.
5. Fit of bearing balls and races is purposely made loose so that there is a noticeable "rock" in the bearing. It prevents binding from changes in temperature

and allows the wheels to roll when lubricant cakes up or dirt gets in the bearings.

6. Seals are all-steel, labyrinth types, with very small clearances. (Some users whose plants are very clean prefer to omit seals and use an oil-mist spray for lubrication. This is a method also used in high-temperature-oven work.)

7. The side of the trolley wheel facing the I-beam track web is closed which makes a dust-and-grease-tight closure.

8. Wheels are cambered a few degrees to provide good tracking properties on the beam.

Trolley wheels which meet these specifications are used in 3-in., 4-in., and 6-in. systems.

Other Wheel Types. **Pressed-steel ball-bearing wheels** with two-piece ball races and without ball separators are somewhat lower in first cost but are not applicable to all types of service. **Precision-type ball bearings,** inserted in forged wheels, are also available. These bearings are frequently of the lubricated-for-life type and are therefore limited to moderate temperature applications. When used at high temperatures (without the lubricated-for-life feature), bearings with special trolley internal clearances are used. Wheels with **inserted ball races** and unmachined treads are also available. These ball races are usually of the commercial grade with unground races and without separators. These wheels are frequently lower in price than those having the eight features listed above.

Trolley wheels for use with 228 chain are **skate wheels,** such as used in roller skates. A wide variation in quality, load ratings, and performance may be found in different makes of these wheels. Special types of conveyors are made with **tapered roller-bearing flanged wheels,** for very heavy duty. For some types of service, trolleys with bronze bushings, textolite treads, and other variations are used. It is advisable to use standard types whenever possible.

Brackets. These are sometimes called side arms, and connect the wheels to the chain and load attachments. Brackets are usually drop-forged steel with wide, heavy ribs. Brackets are bolted or riveted to trolley wheels. Some brackets are made with integral machined trunnions which are riveted to the wheels. Stamped steel brackets are used for some makes of trolleys. However, better distribution of metal and greater strength are available in drop-forged brackets at little extra cost.

Attachments. The third important part of the trolley is the attachment. Some representative attachments are shown in Fig. 6. Commonly used types include:

1. I, or idler attachment—used when the trolley is connected to the chain only, and does not carry a load.

2. H, or clevis attachment—used more than all others, for suspended load carriers.

3. B, or rod attachment, used mostly for connection to load bars, and for oven sealing plates.

4. C, or pendent tongue attachment—used in the same manner as the H attachment, except that the clevis connection is on the load carrier.

5. P attachment—similar to the C attachment, but designed for rigid connection of load carrier to trolley.

6. J attachment—for use with rod-connected carriers, rotating loads, oven-sealing plates, etc.

7. T attachment—used almost exclusively for carrying load bars.

Numerous modifications of these basic types are available.

For all chains except the drop-forged chains the attachments and the trolley brackets are bolted to the top and bottom of the chain. This requires special

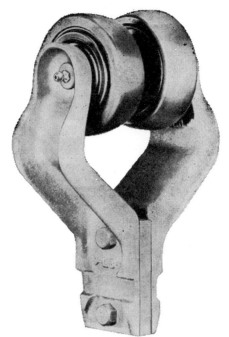

Link-Belt Co.

I-idler attachment.

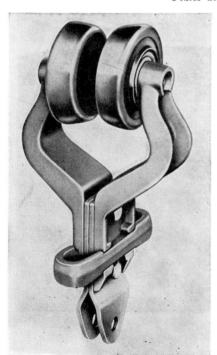

Mechanical Handling Systems, Inc.
H-clevis attachment.

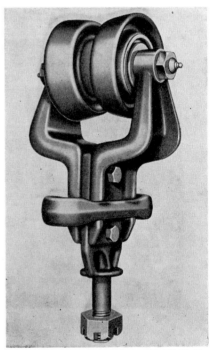

Jervis B. Webb Co.
B-rod attachment.

Fig. 6. Trolley attachments.

chain attachments, or special chain pins. Thus, the chain supports, and must be strong enough to carry, the loads. The open center links of the drop-forged chains allow the loads to be carried directly through the links from the attachments to the trolley brackets. The chain pulls the loads, but does not have to carry them.

DROP. The distance from the I-beam track to the center line of the chain is called the "drop." This distance is sometimes measured from the top of the I-beam, and sometimes from the bottom. It is an important dimension. It varies with different manufacturers, but trolleys can generally be obtained with commonly used drops. It is possible, and very desirable, to have a uniform drop throughout a plant. Conveyors can then be made interchangeable, even though obtained from several sources. It is also desirable that distances from the center line of the chain to the attachment bolt holes conform to a common standard.

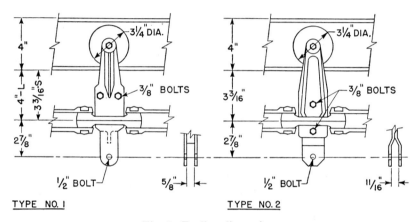

Fig. 7. Trolley dimensions.

Dimensions under discussion are shown in the diagram for 4 in. I-beam trolleys in Fig. 7.

TROLLEY LOADS. Trolleys must support two loads, (1) the suspended weight of the carrier and its live load, and (2) the load imposed on the trolley by chain pull at vertical curves where there is a change in elevation. When chain pull is large, or radius of vertical curves is small, the **imposed load** can become excessive. It should be calculated to be sure that the maximum trolley ratings are not exceeded (see Fig. 8).

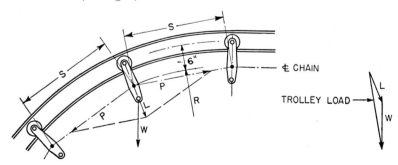

Fig. 8. Imposed load diagram.

Let L = imposed load on a trolley (lb.)
  P = chain pull (lb.)
  S = trolleys spacing (in.)
  R = curve radius at center line of **chain** (in.).

$$L = \frac{P\,S}{R}$$

If W = suspended weight of carrier (lb.), then $W + L$ = radial load on the trolley (Vector addition). In practice, arithmetical addition of $W + L$ is usually close enough.

The above formula is for uniform trolley spacing. When trolley spacing is not uniform, the average of the trolley spacing on each side of the loaded trolley should be used for S.

The modern type of trolley wheel is a large ball bearing with a very high load capacity. The track on which it runs cannot support nearly as great a load as the wheel can carry. Thus, the I-beam wear is the limiting factor in setting trolley load limits. Load ratings generally preferred are:

Size of I-Beam	Maximum Allowable Trolley Load	
	$W + L$	W
2⅝ in.	100 lb.	75 lb.
3 in.	400 lb.	250 lb.
4 in.	800 lb.	400 lb.
6 in.	1,600 lb.	1,000 lb.

LOAD BARS. When a trolley load exceeds the allowable rating of a single trolley, it can be hung from a load bar which is connected to two trolleys. Sometimes two load bars are connected by a third one so that the load is suspended from four trolleys. Load bars are necessary on steep inclines and vertical runs to hold the suspended loads away from the chain and to prevent the chain from kinking. A semirigid load-bar attachment is shown in Fig. 9.

Link-Belt Co.

Palmer-Bee Co.

Fig. 9. Semirigid load-bar attachments.

Track and Supports

TRACK. Many different shapes have been used for overhead trolley-conveyor track. These include I-beams, double angles, structural tees, double T-rails, steel bars, rods and pipe, and formed track similar to sliding-door track. I-beam track is the most frequently used. Standard sizes of I-beams are:

> 2⅝-in. I, 3.74 lb.
> 3-in. I, 5.7 lb.
> 4-in. I, 7.7 lb.
> 6-in. I, 12.5 lb.

Standard I-beam track is usually made of high-carbon steel. This is stronger and wears better than ordinary structural steel. I-beams should be straight, with webs both central and square with the flanges. Track must be installed plumb, otherwise the trolleys will ride to one side, which cuts the track and causes excessive wear on the trolleys due to eccentric loading.

Joints. Track joints are usually welded and ground smooth where trolley wheels make contact or must clear. Top flange joints are reinforced with angles. Sometimes track must be installed in places where there are fire hazards and where welding therefore is not permitted, such as paint-spray rooms, oil and paint storage, oil washing, and other flammable locations. In such locations track joints should be bolted. The joints should occur at or close to supports, and the track ends should be doweled together for alignment. This is usually a more expensive construction than welded joints.

Expansion Joints. Expansion joints in the track are used when a conveyor operates in an oven or where the temperature varies between wide limits or at building expansion joints. Long oven lines may require several of these joints. They prevent distortion, warping, and twisting in the track. The change in length of the track is determined by the following formula:

$$E = \frac{0.078\,TL}{1,000}$$

where E = expansion of track (in.)
T = range in temperature (° F.)
L = length of track affected (ft.)

Spans. I-beams are furnished in 20-ft. lengths, and supports may be as much as 20 ft. apart. When sag is excessive, intermediate hangers are added. Many plants specify shorter spans for the heavier loads. The simplicity and low cost of the single I-beam track are so desirable that any deviation from this construction should usually be avoided. There may be times when long spans are compulsory. In such cases, cap channels or extra supporting beams can be used in combination with the I-beam track.

SUPPORTS. Track loads include the weight of track, trolleys, chain, carriers, and live loads. In addition to these loads, when guards are used, their weight is usually carried by the track beam.

Loads. Track, trolleys and chain can be considered uniform loads. Carriers and live loads, if light and closely and evenly spaced, can also be considered uniform loads. When carriers and live loads are heavy or widely spaced (i.e., more than 24-in. centers), they should be considered concentrated loads. Hangers for guards are widely spaced and transfer the guard weight to the track as concentrated loads.

Hangers. Most trolley conveyors are suspended from ceilings, trusses, floor beams and slabs, and overhead structures. Hangers consist of light angles, rods, or steel bars, with clip angles for connection to the track, and clamps for connection to roof trusses and beams. Inserts or expansion bolts are used for connection to concrete ceilings and lag bolts or clamps for connection to wood.

Hangers over 12 in. long are usually braced and appear in a V-shape. One leg should be vertical, to simplify field work in aligning the track, both horizontally and vertically. Horizontal bends, drives, and take-ups are heavily braced; when they are long, the hanger frames are usually tower structures. The location and arrangement of the hangers is usually determined in the field by erection superintendents who know by experience how to hang and brace a conveyor to get the best results.

Floor Supports. Where the ceiling structure will not support the conveyor load, or in very high bays where hangers would be too long, or where overhead cranes or other conditions prevent the use of hangers, column floor supports are used. When it is necessary to use columns for floor supports, they can be selected by structural design methods for cantilever columns with eccentric loads. However, it should be noted that the length l, used in determining allowable loads for columns, is equal to twice the height A of such a column (i.e., $l = 2A$).

As floor support columns must be very stiff, bracing is seldom used. One column may even be used to support a corner turn, since the columns in the adjacent straight lines are usually sufficiently stiff to take the conveyor chain pull. A good anchorage is required, such as a wide base with large anchor bolts.

Superstructure. Any extra framing which must be installed at points where hangers cannot be directly connected to the building structure is called superstructure. This framing is usually clamped to the building steel so that it can be removed with the conveyor when changes are made, leaving the building in its original condition. It is customary to consider the superstructure as part of the conveyor, to be furnished and built on the job by the conveyor contractor.

Turns

HORIZONTAL TURNS. Horizontal turns are made at roller turns, at sprocket turns such as are used with sprocket drives, or at traction-wheel turns. Horizontal turns can be of short radius (compared to long-radius vertical curves), since the chain articulates at the joints. The radius is determined by the clearance between adjacent carriers or loads. Radii should be as large as possible, especially for heavy chain pulls, and near the points where chain pull approaches the maximum. However, it is better practice to use the same radius for all horizontal turns.

The minimum radius for standard roller turns (depending on pitch of the chain) is 15 in. Minimum diameter for traction wheels is 12 in. Most manufacturers have individual standards, and the radii or diameters may vary slightly. Standard angles for turns are 15 (kinker), 30, 45, 60, 90, and 180° and these are used wherever possible. When required by special conditions, turns can be made any angle or radius.

Roller Turns. For angles of 90° or less roller turns generally cost less and occupy less space than wheel turns of the same radius. A large-radius roller turn can be used around a corner or column where only a small-diameter wheel turn can be used. Some roller turns have been built with radii as large as 25 ft., for high-speed operation. Fig. 10 illustrates a typical 180° roller turn.

Jervis B. Webb Co.

Fig. 10. 180° roller turn.

Rollers. It is generally considered good practice to use double-row ball-bearing, roller-turn rolls, with hardened treads concentric with the ball races. The rolls should be spaced close enough to prevent bumping or pulsation of the conveyor chain. A typical roller-turn mounting is shown in Fig. 11.

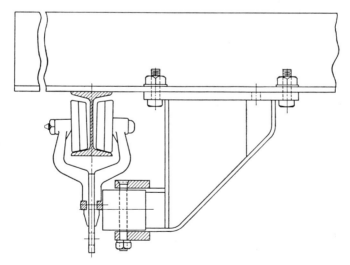

Jervis B. Webb Co.

Fig. 11. Roller-turn mountings.

Wheel Turns. Wheel turns are made with flat-face traction wheels and sprocket-wheels. The power loss at these turns is less than at roller turns of the same radius. For angles of 90° or more their cost is usually higher than corresponding roller turns. A 180° traction-wheel turn is shown in Fig. 12.

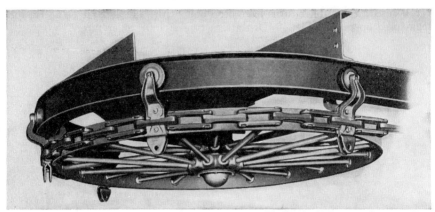

Mechanical Handling Systems, Inc.
Fig. 12. 180° traction-wheel turn.

Traction wheels are preferred in ovens, washers, degreasers, sandblast operation, foundries, and similar severe-duty locations where lubrication, maintenance, and wear must be reduced to a minimum. Traction wheels may be cast iron with finished or chilled treads, or have steel rims with welded pipe or rod spokes, or steel rims with rod spokes upset and riveted to the rims or plates with welded rims and either welded or removable hubs. Hubs may have either bronze bushings or roller bearings. In some cases, such as inside an oven, traction wheels have been fastened to rotating shafts with bearings located outside the oven.

Alignment. The center line of the chain should be slightly above the center of roller-turn rollers or traction-wheel treads to allow for chain sag between trolleys. Traction-wheel treads must be concentric with the bores, and both roller turns and traction wheels should be in proper alignment with the curved track. Otherwise, trolleys will be pushed or pulled to one side, resulting in excessive wear both on them and on the track.

VERTICAL CURVES. Changes in elevation are made with vertical curves. For each change, often called a "dip," one reverse curve or compound vertical curve is required. To go from a higher to a lower elevation requires a dip down, and the opposite requires a dip up. When the change in elevation is large, the top and bottom sections of the reverse curve are connected by an inclined straight section of track.

Forty-five degrees is the maximum inclination from the horizontal that is used in standard practice. Steeper inclines can be used, and conveyors have even been built with vertical runs, but these require special consideration. Heavy suspended loads on steep inclines tend to cock the trolleys and to kink the chain. Some users do not permit inclines exceeding 30°, but this prohibition sacrifices valuable space.

For layout purposes it is desirable to use the shortest possible radius and steep inclines for making vertical curves and changes in elevation. For optimum conveyor operation it is best to use the longest possible radius and gradual inclines. Therefore, it is advisable to check carefully the radii of vertical curves, the trolley spacings which determine those radii, and the angle of incline, for both new and existing conveyors. With floor space at a premium, changes in existing standards may pay big dividends. Formulas and values useful in curve computation are given in Figs. 13, 14 and 15.

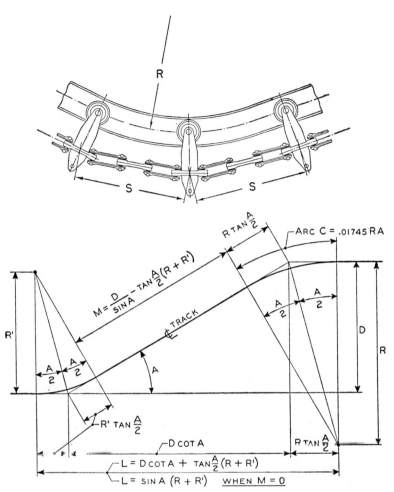

Fig. 13. Diagrams and formulas for vertical curves.

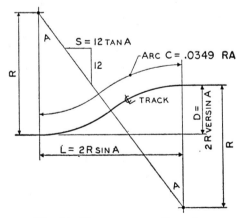

Fig. 14. Reverse curves formulas.

| Radius R | | | | | |
| 6'-0" | | 12'-0" | | 25'-0" | |
D	L	D	L	D	L
		0'-1⅛"	2'-1⅛"	0'-2¼"	4'-4⁵⁄₁₆"
0'-2³⁄₁₆"	2'-1"	0'-4⅜"	4'-2"	0'-9⅛"	8'-8³⁄₁₆"
0'-4⅞"	3'-1¼"	0'-9¹³⁄₁₆"	6'-2⁵⁄₁₆"	1'-8⁷⁄₁₆"	12'-11⁵⁄₁₆
0'-8¹¹⁄₁₆"	4'-1¼"	1'-5⅜"	8'-2½"	3'-0⁵⁄₁₆"	17'-1³⁄₁₆"
1'-1½"	5'-0⅞"	2'-3"	10'-1¹¹⁄₁₆"	4'-8³⁄₁₆"	21'-1⁹⁄₁₆"
1'-7⁵⁄₁₆"	6'-0"	3'-2⁹⁄₁₆"	12'-0"	6'-8⅜"	25'-0"
2'-2⁵⁄₁₆"	6'-10⅝"	4'-4⁵⁄₁₆"	13'-9³⁄₁₆"	9'-0½"	28'-8⅛"
2'-9¹¹⁄₁₆"	7'-8⁹⁄₁₆"	5'-7⅞"	15'-5⅛"	11'-8⅜"	32'-1¹¹⁄₁₆"
3'-6⁵⁄₁₆"	**8'-5¹³⁄₁₆"**	**7'-0⅜"**	**16'-11⅝"**	**14'-7¾"**	**35'-4¼"**
4'-3⁷⁄₁₆"	9'-2⁵⁄₁₆"	8'-6⅞"	18'-4⅝"	17'-10⁵⁄₁₆"	38'-3⅝"
5'-1⁷⁄₁₆"	9'-9¹⁵⁄₁₆"	10'-2¹³⁄₁₆"	19'-7¹⁵⁄₁₆"	21'-3⅞"	40'-11½"
6'-0"	10'-4¹¹⁄₁₆"	12'-0"	20'-9⁷⁄₁₆"	25'-0"	43'-3⅝"
6'-11⅛"	10'-10½"	13'-10⁵⁄₁₆"	21'-9"	28'-10⁷⁄₁₆"	45'-3¹³⁄₁₆"
7'-10¾"	11'-3⁵⁄₁₆"	15'-9½"	22'-6⅝"	32'-10¹³⁄₁₆"	46'-11¹³⁄₁₆"
8'-10¾"	11'-7⅞"	17'-9⁷⁄₁₆"	23'-2³⁄₁₆"	37'-0¾"	48'-3⁹⁄₁₆"
9'-11"	11'-9¹³⁄₁₆"	19'-10"	23'-8⅝"	41'-3¹³⁄₁₆"	49'-2⅞"
10'-11⁷⁄₁₆"	11'-11⁷⁄₁₆"	21'-10⅞"	23'-10⅞"	45'-7¹¹⁄₁₆"	49'-9¹¹⁄₁₆"
12'-0"	12'-0"	24'-0"	24'-0"	50'-0"	50'-0"

For S, over 45°, use

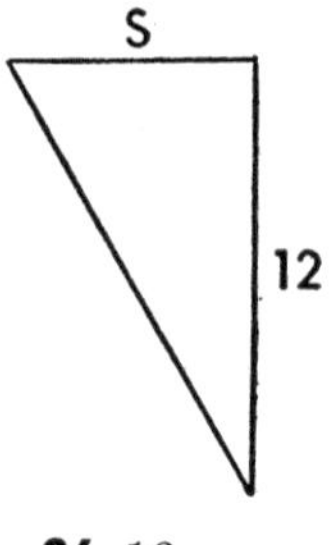

S

12

26·16

Fig. 15. Reverse curves—

A	S	2'-0"		4'-0"	
		D	L	D	L
5°	$1\frac{1}{16}$"				
10°	$2\frac{1}{8}$"	$0'-\frac{3}{4}$"	$0'-8\frac{5}{16}$"	$0'-1\frac{1}{2}$"	$1'-4\frac{5}{8}$"
15°	$3\frac{7}{32}$"	$0'-1\frac{5}{8}$"	$1'-0\frac{7}{16}$"	$0'-3\frac{1}{4}$"	$2'-0\frac{7}{8}$"
20°	$4\frac{3}{8}$"	$0'-2\frac{7}{8}$"	$1'-4\frac{7}{16}$"	$0'-5\frac{3}{4}$"	$2'-8\frac{7}{8}$"
25°	$5\frac{19}{32}$"	$0'-4\frac{1}{2}$"	$1'-8\frac{5}{16}$"	$0'-9$"	$3'-4\frac{9}{16}$"
30°	$6\frac{15}{16}$"	$0'-6\frac{7}{16}$"	$2'0$"	$1'-0\frac{7}{8}$"	$4'-0$"
35°	$8\frac{13}{32}$"	$0'-8\frac{11}{16}$"	$2'-3\frac{3}{16}$"	$1'-5\frac{3}{8}$"	$4'-7\frac{1}{16}$"
40°	$10\frac{1}{16}$"	$0'-11\frac{1}{4}$"	$2'-6\frac{7}{8}$"	$1'-10\frac{1}{2}$"	$5'-1\frac{11}{16}$"
45°	12"	$1'-2\frac{1}{16}$"	$2'-9\frac{15}{16}$"	$2'-4\frac{1}{8}$"	$5'-7\frac{7}{8}$"
50°	$10\frac{1}{16}$"	$1'-5\frac{1}{8}$"	$3'-0\frac{3}{4}$"	$2'-10\frac{1}{4}$"	$6'-1\frac{1}{2}$"
55°	$8\frac{13}{32}$"	$1'-8\frac{7}{16}$"	$3'-3\frac{5}{16}$"	$3'-4\frac{15}{16}$"	$6'-6\frac{5}{8}$"
60°	$6\frac{15}{16}$"	$2'-0$"	$3'-5\frac{9}{16}$"	$4'-0$"	$6'-11\frac{1}{8}$"
65°	$5\frac{19}{32}$"	$2'-3\frac{11}{16}$"	$3'-7\frac{1}{2}$"	$4'-7\frac{7}{16}$"	$7'-3$"
70°	$4\frac{3}{8}$"	$2'-7\frac{9}{16}$"	$3'-9\frac{1}{8}$"	$5'-3\frac{3}{16}$"	$7'-6\frac{3}{16}$"
75°	$3\frac{7}{32}$"	$2'-11\frac{9}{16}$"	$3'-10\frac{3}{8}$"	$5'-11\frac{1}{8}$"	$7'-8\frac{3}{4}$"
80°	$2\frac{1}{8}$"	$3'-3\frac{11}{16}$"	$3'-11\frac{1}{4}$"	$6'-7\frac{5}{16}$"	$7'-10\frac{9}{16}$"
85°	$1\frac{1}{16}$"	$3'-7\frac{13}{16}$"	$3'-11\frac{13}{16}$"	$7'-3\frac{3}{8}$"	$7'-11\frac{5}{8}$"
90°	0"	$4'-0$"	$4'-0$"	$8'-0$"	$8'-0$"

Note: For S, up to 45°, use

Method of interpolating: For any given angle, D and L are directly proportional to the radius.

From "Trolley Conveyors" by Sidney Reibel

values of D and L.

Reinforcement of Vertical Curves. The heaviest trolley loads occur at vertical curves because of imposed loads due to chain pull. Thus, the maximum wear and peening of track-beam flanges will usually occur at these points. Drives are strategically located (if possible) so as to reduce chain pull in vicinity of vertical curve.

Drives

TYPES. There are no general standards for trolley-conveyor drives except those which individual manufacturers specify. Drives are of two general types: sprocket drives and caterpillar drives. A floating sprocket drive and a caterpillar drive attachment are shown in Figs. 16 and 17.

Jervis B. Webb Co.

Fig. 16. Floating sprocket varipulley drive.

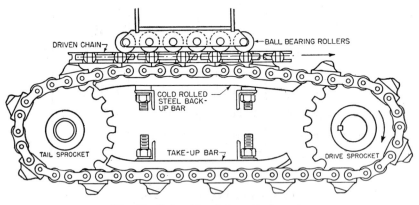

Fig. 17. Caterpillar drive attachment.

Headroom is usually very limited under ceilings, and side clearances are small because of piping, ducts, wiring, and other obstructions. Therefore, the various parts of a drive are usually arranged in a line and on about the same level. This arrangement makes a drive unit long but compact, with minimum height and width. The general arrangement of the drive machinery, from the motor to the drive shaft, is the same for both types. It is the manner in which the drives engage the conveyor chain which makes them different.

SPROCKET DRIVES. This type of chain conveyor drive has the conveyor chain wrapped around and driven by the sprocket on the drive shaft. A sprocket drive is usually located at a 90° or 180° corner turn, but, if necessary, may be located at turns of other angles. The sprocket drive is rated for chain pull at the head sprocket. Manufacturers' ratings of chain pull are usually based on the use of a 36-in.-pitch-diameter drive sprocket. These drives will have a constant torque rating; therefore, when drive sprockets other than 36-in.-pitch-diameter are used, the allowable chain pull will be inversely proportional to the pitch diameters of the sprockets.

CATERPILLAR DRIVES. The caterpillar drive employes a short loop of auxiliary drive chain alongside and parallel to the conveyor chain. Driving dogs on the caterpillar chain engage and drive the conveyor chain. Back-up bars on the caterpillar side and rollers on the driven-chain side confine the chains and prevent them from separating. A caterpillar drive can be located on any straight run of conveyor. The ratings of caterpillar drives are based on chain pull capacity.

Advantages of Caterpillar Drives. While sprocket drives are frequently used, caterpillar drives have many advantages:

1. The caterpillar drive can be located in the best place to take care of chain pull, such as the middle of a straight run.
2. If load conditions change, or if the conveyor is altered, a caterpillar drive is easier to move and relocate without changing the existing conveyor.
3. When chain pull is moderate to heavy, a caterpillar drive is usually less expensive than a sprocket drive, owing to the much lower torque requirements.
4. A caterpillar drive can be re-used on any conveyor, regardless of the requirements for clearance or of the radius or angle of horizontal turns. With a sprocket drive, the load clearance will be limited by the diameter of the drive sprocket.

CONSTANT AND VARIABLE SPEEDS. Both sprocket and caterpillar drives employ the same basic drive mechanism. These come in three different styles: (1) Constant-speed, (2) Varipulley with infinite speed variation up to 3:1, and (3) Full-variable with infinite speed variation up to 10:1 or even more.

Constant-speed drives use a V-belt drive from an electric motor to a vertical gear reducer. The output shaft of the reducer can carry the conveyor sprocket, or it may be mounted on a drive shaft connected through a spur gear reduction, preferably with antifriction bearings. This sprocket can be either the one which engages the conveyor chain, making a sprocket drive, or the drive sprocket of a caterpillar chain drive.

A varipulley drive unit is arranged the same as the constant-speed type except that a variable-pitch pulley unit is used instead of a V-belt drive between the motor and reducer. The ratio between maximum and minimum speeds is approximately 3:1.

In the third style, a full-variable transmission is introduced into the drive between the motor and reducer. Connection from the transmission to the reducer is by V-belt or silent chain drives and to the motor is by V-belt drives.

Speeds can be obtained from an imperceptible movement of a fraction of an inch per minute up to 150 ft. per min. Drives for very low or very high speeds and for very large chain pulls must be specially designed. Manufacturers' standard drives can usually meet other requirements. Drive ratings should have an allowance for short-period overloads without damage to the drive machinery.

CONSTRUCTION OF DRIVES. The use of trolley conveyors as vital installations in industrial plants places a duty on management to obtain, and on conveyor manufacturers to supply, drives of the utmost dependability. Drives with open gearing, or chain drives which are not an integral part of the reducer have in recent years been replaced by drives in which all reduction gearing is combined in a single unit, with all gears running in oil. These drives are specially designed for trolley conveyors. Even the bearings are incorporated in the reducers, so that there are no separately mounted outboard bearings at the reducer output shafts.

Motors. Drives for trolley conveyors are powered by individual electric motors. In many large manufacturing plants, where all operations are interdependent, only standard **stock motors** are used in trolley-conveyor drives. They are preferred because a stock motor can be replaced quickly in case of a motor failure. This prevents a long, costly shutdown while a damaged motor is being repaired. Motors with special windings, shafts, or other features, gear motors, and motors with built-in mechanical or electrical adjustable speed changers are generally not used because replacements cannot be made in a hurry.

The **a.c. constant-speed squirrel-cage motor** is most frequently used. Both motor and control are inexpensive and dependable. Under normal conditions they are easily obtained from stock. Across-the-line starting requires only simple wiring, which is inexpensive and easy to maintain. Direct-current motors are used for constant speed only where alternating current is not available. They can be either shunt- or compound-wound.

Variable-speed drives for trolley conveyors must hold to any set speed regardless of variations in loading or chain pull. Again, the a.c. constant-speed squirrel-cage stock motor is the one most frequently used, with a separate mechanical speed changer. Motors with built-in mechanical speed changers are also available but are seldom used in these drives. Changing the speed electrically has been the aim of many experiments and designs. The wound-rotor, adjustable-speed motor is not suitable as it has a range of only 2:1 and does not have inherently stable speed characteristics when chain pull varies. One successful development is a drive that uses a squirrel-cage motor which runs at a constant speed and an **eddy-current clutch** with a variable-speed output shaft. There is no mechanical connection between the input and output rotors of the clutch, the connection being made through a magnetic field at an air gap. The slip at the air gap can be varied by means of an electrical control to obtain any desired speed. The drive has stable speed characteristics.

The speed of **d.c. compound-wound motors** may be varied by armature or field control to about 50 percent below or 25 percent above full load speed, a total range of 2.5:1. A range of 8:1 or more can be obtained by variable voltage control. A total range of 20:1 is readily available with a Ward-Leonard system incorporating field weakening.

Motor horsepower may be calculated from the following formula:

$$\text{Motor horsepower} = \frac{\text{Chain pull (lb.)} \times \text{speed (f.p.m.)}}{33,000 \times \text{total drive efficiency}}$$

The **horsepower** required to drive a trolley conveyor is very small. As an example, for a heavy drive of 3,000 lb. used on a conveyor operating at a maximum speed of 35 f.p.m., (assuming 75 percent efficiency) the net horsepower required of the motor will be:

$$\frac{3,000 \times 35}{33,000 \times 0.75} = 4.24 \text{ hp.}$$

MULTIPLE DRIVES. When the chain pull of a conveyor is too great to be handled by a single drive, two or more drives are used. Additional drives can be added when a conveyor is lengthened or when the chain pull is increased. One conveyor, 11,000 ft. long, uses 14 drives at a constant speed. Another, 8,500 ft. long, uses 5 drives with variable speed.

The problem of **matching drive speeds** is complicated, even at constant speed. Long strands of chain of equal length will not have exactly the same number of pitches. Thus, a 1,000-ft. strand of 458 chain may have 2,970 pitches and the next 1,000 ft. only 2,950 pitches. The same length (measured in feet, not pitches) must pass each drive during the same time interval. But the drive sprockets (whether for sprocket or caterpillar drives), which have equal numbers of teeth and advance equal numbers of chain pitches per revolution, must therefore rotate at different rates. Thus, each drive turns a different number of revolutions for each phase and section of chain, and during any time interval the drives are revolving at different, varying rates. This requires a continuous "hunting" action of the drives so that they will keep in proper relationship and will not tend to tighten or loosen the sections of chain they pull.

In some cases there are wide **variations in chain pull** at any one drive, without corresponding changes in drive loading at the other drives. Then the problem of controlling the speed of the multiple drives on a conveyor becomes so complicated that electrical controls must be used to get workable installations.

Constant-Speed Multiple Drives. For constant-speed drives, high-slip, squirrel-cage motors are used. These slow down under heavy loads or tight chains, and regain speed under light loads or loose chains. Slip couplings of the fluid or particle type are frequently used for balancing of individual drives on a multiple drive system. If a large number of drives is required, it is advisable to keep chain pull under 2,000 lb. Wound-rotor and synchronous motor drives would not be satisfactory.

Variable-Speed Multiple Drives. The floating-type drive can be used for multiple-drive installations when the speed of the drives must be varied. When the speed is controlled manually, a change at one drive will automatically change the speed at the other drives within the range of the arm control. Beyond that limit, the drives must be adjusted individually. With mechanical or electric operation of the speed adjustment, it is possible to vary the speed over the entire range from a central point.

Eddy current clutch and direct current motor drives are frequently used on variable-speed multiple-drive conveyors, especially when the number of drives is three or more. These drives are almost a necessity when the load on an individual drive varies greatly and independently of the other drives. In addition both systems contain provision for balancing loads when physical considerations preclude accurate balancing by mean of location of the drive. Both systems offer remote control of the speed as a result of the control wiring to each drive.

DRIVE LOCATION. A drive should be located at the top of a drop, or just ahead of a take-up, to eliminate slack. Location just before a rise might allow the chain to bunch up and jam in a caterpillar drive or come off the sprocket in a sprocket drive. The portion of the building to which the drive is attached must be strong enough to sustain the chain pull as well as the conveyor weight. Location of multiple drives requires expert consideration and should be determined by the point-to-point calculation method. As an example, it can result in using only three drives where five drives at first appeared necessary. In one case, running a conveyor in one direction required two drives. Reversing the conveyor permitted the use of only one drive. Locations of drives for reversing service, and automatic loading and unloading are difficult problems. Ovens are poor locations for drives, but sometimes must be used.

OVERLOAD DEVICES. All drives require some form of mechanical device for protection to the drive and the conveyor in case of an overload or a jam in the line. The overload device is usually mounted on the variable-speed shaft of the speed changer, on the high- or low-speed shaft of the speed reducer, or on the final drive shaft; or it may be placed directly to oppose the chain pull. However, a mechanical overload device can be used at a motor, or on the drive from the motor to the reducer, only when the speed is constant. If the speed is varied, an overload device at the motor will furnish protection only at the high speed, and little or none at lower speeds.

Shear Sprocket. These sprockets consist of two halves: the sprocket half, not keyseated and free to turn on the driving shaft; and the driving-flange half, keyed and set-screwed to the shaft (see Fig. 18). The driving force is transmitted

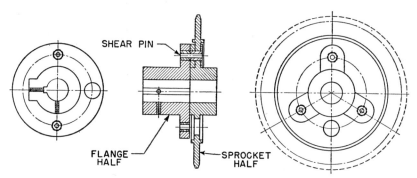

Fig. 18. Shear sprocket.

to the sprocket from the driving flange by a single cold-rolled-steel shear pin carried in a pair of hardened-steel bushings. The shear sprocket has the advantages of simplicity, economy, instantaneous reaction, and location which tends to protect all of the drive machinery. However, there are factors which can limit its application. Replacement of pins is sometimes inconvenient and time consuming. In addition there is a tendency of maintenance personnel to ignore the cause of repeated pin failure and replace the pins with alloy material, thereby limiting protection. Finally the failure of a pin does not normally shut off the motor and this can result in seizure between the stationary sprocket and the rotating member. This difficulty can be overcome by the use of an electric shear sprocket which turns off the drive motor or all motors on a multiple drive conveyor.

Floating Drive. The best overload device is one which will stop the motor (or motors when more than one drive is used) when an overload occurs, and will

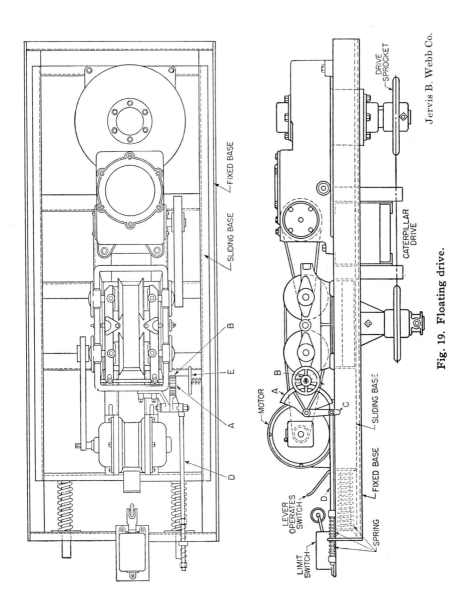

Jervis B. Webb Co.

Fig. 19. Floating drive.

allow the motor to be started again when the cause of the overload is removed. An overload device which does not require changing shear pins, or any other alteration to the drive, is desirable. Also, the overload device should be located in the drive as close to the load as possible, so that it will respond to the load quickly, and will not require a superfine adjustment or calibration. A drive that meets these requirements is the floating drive. It is made in both caterpillar and sprocket types.

The floating caterpillar drive is made up of a drive frame free to move in a fixed secondary frame to which the conveyor track is attached. The driving effort is resisted by compression-coil springs of suitable capacity and so arranged that the sliding frame will contact a limit switch to shut off the motor in case of an overload or jam on the line. The shut-off point can be adjusted to allow for different chain pulls. A shear pin is not required and, after the cause of shutdown has been corrected, the unit is at once ready to go back into service. The floating drive measures only the load between the conveyor and caterpillar chains. It does not protect the drive against misalignment or extraneous material in the caterpillar base. A floating drive is illustrated in Fig. 19. Sprocket drives can also be made the floating (pivoting) type, arranged so that the springs resist rotation.

When fitted with balancing speed control, two or more variable-speed drive units can be applied to a single chain. The balancing control consists of a gear pinion B, keyed to the adjustment shaft E of the variable-speed transmission. They are rotated by a gear segment A with an operating lever C, of adjustable length, pivoted on a bracket on the transmission frame. Rod D connects operating lever C to the fixed frame of the drive unit. Should the drive tend to take more than its proper load, the sliding frame will move back against the springs, producing a rotation in the gear pinion which automatically reduces the speed. Conversely, should this unit take less than its load, the sliding frame will move forward and speed up the drive. Where multiple drives are used, they will thus automatically maintain their proper proportion of the total driving effort regardless of load conditions, length of chain, etc., within the limits of movement of lever arm C. Limit switches may be interconnected so that, if one drive shuts down under overload, they will all be shut off, and signals can be arranged to show which drive shuts down first. Mechanical or electrical controls can be substituted for the hand wheels at E, so that the speeds on all the drives of a conveyor can be regulated at one time from a central point.

Fluid Couplings. These are not a reliable overload device but can be used to obtain smooth starts for heavily loaded constant-speed conveyors. They are also used as a load-balancing mechanism on multiple-drive constant-speed conveyors.

Slip Couplings. There are now available slip couplings which offer the advantage of smooth starts for heavily loaded conveyors, with little or no slip at full speed.

TAKE-UPS. Take-ups are usually used on trolley conveyors. However, a dip following a drive will take care of some slack in the chain and in some plants, where excellent maintenance facilities exist, the preference is to omit take-ups. Generally, ideal conditions for omitting take-ups do not occur and conveyors are installed with take-ups.

Level conveyors should have take-ups. Oven conveyors and outdoor installations with wide variations in temperature require counterweighted take-ups, unless the expected change in length is small, in which case spring take-ups may be used.

Types of Take-ups. There are five types of take-ups: track-type, screw take-ups, spring take-ups, air-cylinder take-ups, and counterweighted take-ups. Two types are illustrated in Figs. 20 and 21. **Track take-ups** are used only on very inexpensive installations. The track is provided either with inserted filler pieces, or expansion-type sliding joints. When taking up slack in the chain, the hangers are

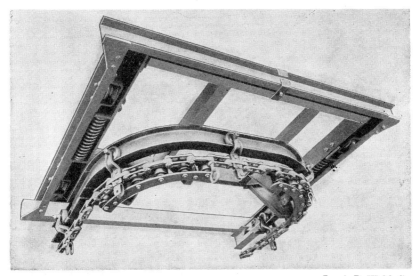

Fig. 20. Spring take-up.

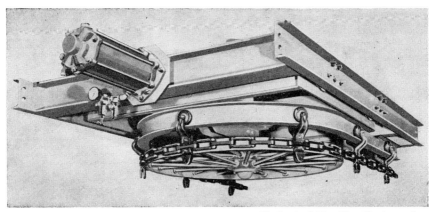

Fig. 21. Air-operated automatic take-up.

sprung. This type of take-up is used at 90° and 180° roller turns. **Screw take-up frames** are made to slide or roll in a fixed frame, and the tracks have expansion-type sliding joints. Adjustment is by a long screw or pair of screws. They may be used with either roller turns or traction wheels, at 90° and 180° turns. The screw take-up is used in conveyor installations where slack must be taken up but the turn must not move or float. These conditions are required in some multiple-drive installations and for the exact positioning necessary in automatic loading and unloading.

Spring take-ups have the same construction as the screw type, except that springs automatically adjust the take-up to maintain a tension on the chain. Screws may or may not be used for initial adjustment, or to release the take-up when removing slack in the chain. The **counterweighted** and **air-cylinder take-ups** are also similar to the screw type, except that they maintain a constant tension on the chain. All take-ups require attention. Otherwise, when excessive chain slack develops, they have lost their function, and they do not become useful until the slack is removed.

Whenever possible, **180° take-ups** should be used. They work better, and adjust for much more slack than **90° take-ups**. Sometimes, there is no place in the layout for a 180° turn. Then a 90° type is used. This has a single sliding joint, and the leg at right angles has a hinge, or the track is sprung. When the distance between the parallel lines at a take-up is greater than the diameter of the 180° turn, the take-up can be made of two 90° turns with a straight section between them. Thus a turn with two lines 6 ft. apart using 24-in.-radius roller turns would be a "24-in.-radius-roller-turn-180°-take-up with a 6-ft. spread."

Take-ups for Multiple Drives. Take-ups can be very useful in the control of multiple drives. If there are two drives on a conveyor, one can be the "master" and the second the "slave," controlled by the movement of the adjacent take-up. In some cases when drives are electronically controlled, the take-up following one drive is used to control other drives.

Location. Take-ups are located close to drives, on the slack side of the conveyor chain. A straight horizontal run or a short curve upward should follow a take-up, especially when it is the automatic (counterweighted or spring) type. The take-up should not be followed by a downward curve which will put a pull on it through the weight of the conveyor line. Sometimes a take-up must be located where there is a heavy chain pull, so that a drive pulls through the take-up. This requires a very heavy counterweight, or a screw take-up, and should be avoided.

Guards

REQUIREMENTS. The ideal guard not only should prevent a load from dropping on someone below but should allow enough room so that moving loads will clear a fallen load resting on the floor of the guard. In practice, there is seldom enough headroom to provide that much clearance, and the cost of the larger guard would be excessive. Clearances must be enough to keep swaying or tilted loads from hitting or dragging on the sides or bottom of the guard. Guards must be carefully laid out to provide these clearances. This is especially important at turns and dips.

TYPES OF GUARDS. Guards are usually made of woven-wire mesh, welded wire mesh, or expanded metal so as to offer the least obstruction to light, and to keep the guards light in weight. **Drip pans** are used to keep oil or dirt from dropping on workers or equipment. They are also used following paint or other dip-tanks to catch drip from loads and, if possible, to allow it to drain back to the tanks. Guards have also been made of spaced wood planks and of plywood. These are quite heavy and cut off a great deal of light.

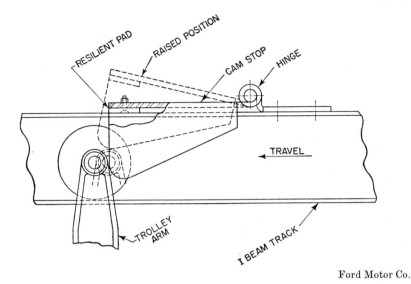

Ford Motor Co.

Fig. 22. Uphill safety stop.

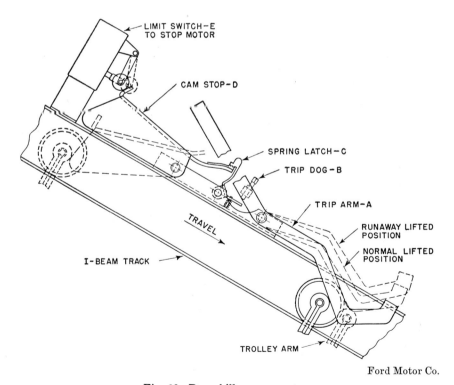

Ford Motor Co.

Fig. 23. Downhill runaway stop.

When a conveyor drops down to a work station, the guards follow the dips down from the high lines until the bottom clearance line of the guard framing is approximately 7 ft. above the floor. This **minimum height** is in general use, as it allows walking headroom under the conveyor. In some plants, where this is not considered sufficiently safe, additional protection is furnished by installing handrails around the lower curves of these dips. Then if any load falls on an inclined guard, it will roll down into a guarded space on the floor. Hand rails will also keep workers from walking into moving conveyor loads at the inclines. **Finger guards** are also used in some plants at low runs of conveyors. These cover the chain, trolleys, track, and turns to prevent hands or fingers from getting injured.

COST. Safety guards are quite expensive and have been known to equal the cost of the balance of the conveyor. The guard structure and mesh should be designed only for protection and not for structural rigidity. It is much cheaper to replace, infrequently, a piece of guard damaged by a falling load, than to build it strong enough to resist damage which will seldom occur, and then only in a few spots. It is advisable to make the construction as simple as possible and to see that guards are specified only where they are necessary.

STOPS. For conveyors on inclines, uphill and downhill stops are sometimes used to prevent a runaway of trolleys and loads if a chain breaks. An uphill safety stop may be seen in Fig. 22, while Fig. 23 shows a downhill stop.

Laying Out the Conveyor

PROCEDURE. There are no rules or definite methods that can be followed in laying out the path of a trolley conveyor. Some conveyors are easy to lay out. Others, because the route is long or irregular, will require the exercise of considerable ingenuity. The usual practice is to make the conveyor fit the layout of buildings and machinery, rather than vice versa.

Typical Example: A manufacturing plant has the departmental layout shown in Fig. 24a. Raw materials must go from Receiving Storage to Departments 1, 2, 3, and 4 and must be further processed in Department 5. The output of Departments 5, 6, and 7 must go to Department 8 for inspection and packing, and then to Shipping Storage. The problem is to lay out a single conveyor to handle materials in the proper order.

Step 1. From detailed department layouts locate on the plan, Fig. 24a, the points X where materials will be unloaded from the conveyor to enter each department, and the points O where they will be loaded back on the conveyor when they leave the department. Conveyor dips (vertical curves) will be required at each of these points. The direction of the conveyor line at the vertical curves must suit the department layout, and is now marked at each point.

Step 2. Join the points marked X in Departments 1, 2, 3, 4, 6, and 7. Also join the warehouse loading and unloading points, and connect with point O in Department 8 (Fig. 24b).

Step 3. Now join points O in Departments 1, 2, 3, and 4, and X in Department 5. Continue to O in Departments 5, 6, and 7, and to X and then O in Department 8 (Fig. 24c).

Step 4. Combine the layouts in Figs. 24b and 24c, as in Fig. 24d. Join O in Department 1 with X in Department 4, and O in the receiving warehouse to X in Department 6, taking care to make one run high and the other one low where the conveyor lines cross.

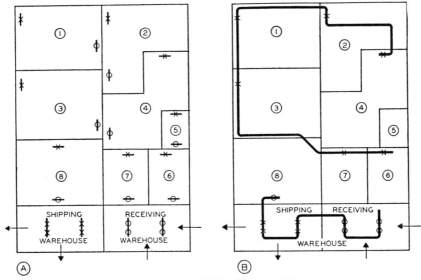

X—UNLOADING POINT FOR INCOMING MATERIAL
O—LOADING POINT FOR OUTGOING MATERIAL

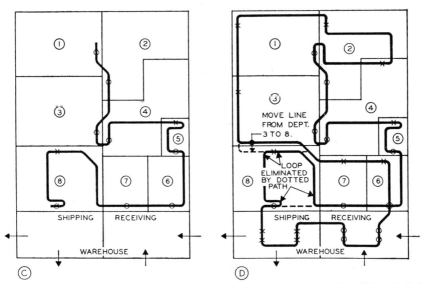

From "Trolley Conveyors" by Sidney Reibel

Fig. 24. Laying out the conveyor.

If more than one path can be drawn, try all possible arrangements. Select the one that is the shortest and has the least number of turns, provided it is satisfactory from the operating viewpoint. Try to see whether backtracking can be eliminated. A slight change in conditions may improve the layout. For instance, if raw, processed, and semi-processed materials can be loaded on the conveyor at the same time (either on the same or different carriers), and if the capacity is ample, a change can be made that will effect a considerable saving. In this example the dotted path in Fig. 24d will eliminate the backtracking loops in Department 8.

CLEARANCE DIAGRAMS. The path of the conveyor must allow for external clearance, such as headroom over aisles, workers, and machines, and under trusses, beams, piping, ducts, wiring, and lights. Horizontally, the conveyor must clear the same obstructions, as well as columns, walls, and other items. Guards for high conveyor lines add to the clearance requirements. Internal clearance must be provided so that carriers, loads, guards, and chain do not foul or interfere with each other. Fig. 25 shows the method to use in laying out clear-

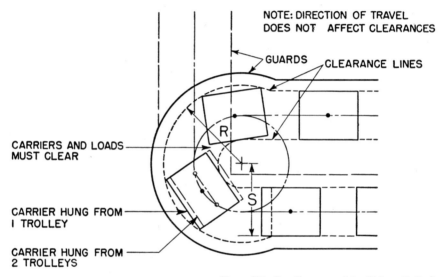

From "Trolley Conveyors" by Sidney Reibel

Fig. 25. Carrier and guard clearance.

ances at vertical curves. To lay out the bottom clearance line, determine first points D and H at the top and bottom of the curves, where the loads or carriers start to change elevation. Then with radius $CD = AB$, and radius $GH = EF$, lay out arcs DJ and HK. Join tangent points J and K, and the clearance line $DJKH$ is established. (Note that radius EF is not equal to AB.)

Fig. 26 shows the clearances that must be determined at horizontal turns. Clearance radius R is greater than dimension S. The clearance lines shown are for loads and carriers suspended from one trolley. When carriers are suspended from two trolleys, less clearance is needed at the outside, but more is required on the inside curve, and the spacing between loads may have to be increased so that they will clear each other.

Fig. 27 shows the clearance required between adjacent horizontal and vertical curves. The distance T between tangent points of the two curves should be not less than one trolley space. When trolley spacing is not uniform, use T equal to the largest trolley space. The space between horizontal and vertical curves prevents twisting of the chain, which would cause excessive wear on all the chain and trolleys, and on the track at this point.

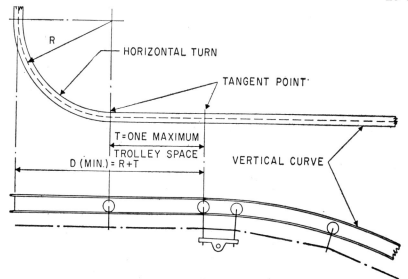

From "Trolley Conveyors" by Sidney Reibel

Fig. 26. Horizontal clearance.

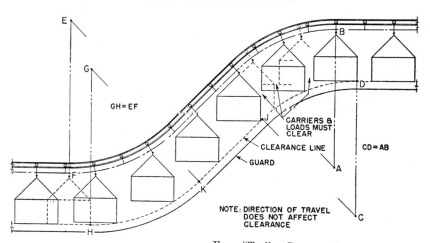

From "Trolley Conveyors" by Sidney Reibel

Fig. 27. Clearance between horizontal turn and vertical curve.

Calculating Chain Pull

BASIS OF CALCULATIONS. Calculations of the chain pull of trolley conveyors are based on determining the losses due to friction of the moving conveyor parts and loads, and the forces necessary for elevating loads. The method of calculation is the same whether the parts are carried or towed. Another load which adds to chain pull is that required to move parts through processes, from sliding sealing plates, etc. It will occur in washers, dip tanks, paint-spray and sand-blast cabinets and places where the parts are revolved. The power requirements for such cases except sealing plates are small, and the excess capacity of drives will usually be enough to take care of the extra loads.

Moving conveyor parts include trolleys, chain, carriers, and suspended live loads. The rolling friction will be due to the weight of these parts, which is carried by the trolley wheels. Additional friction is due to losses at horizontal turns and to imposed loads and bending losses at vertical curves. There is also the pull required when live loads, elevated at vertical curves, are not balanced by corresponding loads lowered at other vertical curves; such as when the conveyor is loaded going up and empty or partly empty going down. When loads are towed by mast attachments on trucks, the horizontal draw-bar pull at the trucks is added to the chain pull due to the weight of the conveyor chain, trolleys, and attachments.

Variable Factors. The factors which are the most difficult to determine are the amount of live load and the friction losses. The **variations in loading** to consider are:

1. Weight of loads:
   a. Maximum (for trolley capacity).
   b. Average (for chain-pull calculation).
2. Percentage of loading of carriers:
   a. With maximum loads.
   b. With average loads.
   c. Partly loaded.
   d. Empty.
3. Distribution of loads on the conveyor when:
   a. Conveyor starts empty and is gradually loaded.
   b. Variations in loading occur at different sections of the conveyor, during normal operation.
   c. The conveyor is unloaded for shutdown.
   d. Loads are not removed and are carried again around the circuit.

Friction factors vary considerably at different times, even on the same conveyor. They can be affected by the following conditions:

1. Trolley construction:
   a. Smoothness and roundness of treads—whether or not the treads are concentric with the bearings.
   b. Construction of trolley wheel bearings—accuracy, finish, and fit of balls and races.
   c. Ratio of tread diameter to mean diameter of bearing.
   d. Accuracy of alignment of trolley wheels and brackets and proper suspension of loads—whether wheels run true and carry equal loads.
   e. Condition of trolley wheels—new, partly worn, badly worn.
2. Lubrication:
   a. Type and efficiency of lubricant.
   b. Whether and how long the lubricant remains in the trolley bearing and on the chain. (Conveyors running through washers, degreasers, ovens, etc., may operate under widely different conditions varying from well-lubricated to dry.)
   c. Whether bearings are clean or dirty. (Contamination may be dust, dirt, water, etc., which enters from the outside, or burned lubricant inside a well-sealed bearing.)
3. Alignment and condition of the track:
   a. On straight runs.
   b. At vertical curves.
   c. At horizontal turns.

4. Conditions at roller and traction wheel turns, similar to those listed for trolley construction and lubrication.

The preceding list of variables indicates how impossible it is to make accurate calculations of chain pull for any trolley conveyor, no matter how good the design and layout, how well lubricated it is, how carefully loaded and operated, or how well maintained. The best way to handle this situation is to be sure that, under the worst possible conditions, the chain and trolleys will not be overloaded and the drive unit and motor will have ample capacity.

APPROXIMATE METHOD FOR CALCULATING CHAIN PULL.

1. Add the total weight of conveyor chain, trolleys, carriers, and live loads. In most cases, live loads are figured for the entire length of the conveyor. Even when part of the conveyor is expected to be empty, if there is any possibility at all that it may be loaded, it should be figured 100-percent loaded. Sometimes, part of the conveyor, or all of the carriers, definitely will not be loaded. This is taken into account when figuring the loading.

Multiply the total moving weight by:

For 2⅝-in. I-228 Chain Conveyor.................................4.00 percent
For 3-in. I-348 Chain Conveyor...................................3.00 percent
For 4-in. I-458 Chain Conveyor...................................2.50 percent
For 6-in. I-678 Chain Conveyor...................................2.25 percent

When operating conditions are good, and there are only a few turns and dips, as in a monoplane conveyor, slightly lower factors can be used. When operating conditions are bad (accumulated dirt, poor lubrication, etc.), or when there are a great number of turns and dips, the factors should be increased.

2. The chain pull which is due to change in elevation is ignored for ordinary dips on the same floor. For considerable changes in elevation (over 8 ft., or from one floor or another) and where loads are elevated without balancing descending loads, the chain pull equals the maximum live load per foot of conveyor multiplied by the difference in elevations (expressed in feet).

3. Add the values of 1 and 2 to get the maximum chain pull.

4. Motor hp. $= \dfrac{\text{chain pull (lb.)} \times \text{maximum speed (f.p.m.)}}{33,000 \times \text{drive efficiency}}$

For example, a conveyor follows the path shown in the diagram, Fig. 28, and has carriers spaced at 6-ft. centers. The maximum load on the carriers is 200 lb., but the average load is 135 lb. Not more than 80 percent of the carriers will be loaded. The carriers weigh 132 lb. Chain is 458, track is 4-in.I, trolleys are ball-bearing and spaced 24 in. center to center. Conveyor speed is 10 to 30 f.p.m. The chain and trolleys are well protected from the sprays in the washer. Determine the chain pull and the sizes of the drive unit and motor.

The data are as follows:

Total length of conveyor: 772 ft. (approx.)
Maximum lift: 21 ft.
Weight of chain (772 × 3) ....2,300 lb.
Weight of trolleys (772 ÷ 2 × 8) ....3,100 lb.
Weight of carriers (772 ÷ 6 × 132) ....17,000 lb.
Weight of loads (722 ÷ 6 × 135 × 0.80)........................13,900 lb.

    Total moving load ....36,300 lb.

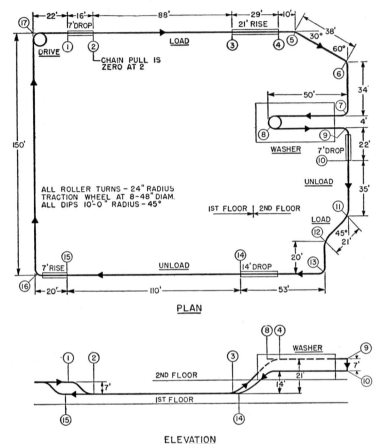

PLAN

ELEVATION

From "Trolley Conveyors" by Sidney Reibel

Fig. 28. Chain-pull calculations (continued on next page).

Calculations as follows:

Chain pull from rolling friction (0.025 × 36,300) .... 910 lb.
Chain pull from change in elevation (200 ÷ 6 × 21) .... 700 lb.

Total chain pull .... 1,610 lb.

Use a 2,000-lb. drive unit.

Assuming a drive efficiency of 75 percent, motor hp. $= \dfrac{1{,}610 \times 30}{33{,}000 \times 0.75} = 1.95$

Use a 2 hp. motor.

POINT-TO-POINT FOR CALCULATING CHAIN PULL. Quite often, the general method of calculating chain pull is not accurate enough. This is usually the case with long, heavily loaded conveyors that have high lifts and a great many horizontal turns and changes in elevation. Calculations must then be made from one point to the next, adding percentages by which the chain pull is increased at horizontal turns and vertical curves. An analysis can also be made by drawing a profile of the conveyor, which is very helpful in locating drives.

Conveyor Section	Horizontal Pull	Rise or Drop	Total Factor For Hor. Turn or Vert. Curve	Total Chain Pull lb.
2– 3	0 + (88 × .82)			= 72
3– 4	72 + (29 × .91) + (21 × 52)		= 1,190 × 1.05	= 1,250
4– 5	1,250 + (10 × .82)		= 1,258 × 1.02	= 1,283
5– 6	1,283 + (38 × .82)		= 1,314 × 1.03	= 1,353
6– 7	1,353 + (34 × .82)		= 1,381 × 1.04	= 1,436
7– 8	1,436 + (52 × .82)		= 1,479 × 1.05	= 1,553
8– 9	1,553 + (52 × .82)		= 1,596 × 1.04	= 1,660
9–10	1,660 + (22 × .49) − (7 × 29)		= 1,468 × 1.05	= 1,541
10–11	1,541 + (35 × .82)		= 1,570 × 1.025	= 1,609
11–12	1,609 + (21 × .82)		= 1,626 × 1.025	= 1,666
12–13	1,666 + (20 × .82)		= 1,682 × 1.04	= 1,750
13–14	1,750 + (53 × .49) − (14 × 29)		= 1,370 × 1.05	= 1,439
14–15	1,439 + (110 × .82)			= 1,529
15–16	1,529 + (20 × .49) + (7 × 29)		= 1,742 × 1.092*	= 1,902
16–17	1,902 + (150 × .49)		= 1,976 = 1.04	= 2,055

On the other side of the drive corner, there will be a negative pull:

17–1–2   [(22 + 16) × .49] − (7 × 29) = −184 ÷ 1.05   − =   175

Net pull at drive = 2,055 − 175 = 1,900 lb.

* 1.04 (for 90 deg. turn) × 1.05 (for rise) = 1.092.

Fig. 28. (Concluded.)

The **friction factors** for straight horizontal runs are lower than those given in the above description of the general method. The following friction factors, and percentage additions to make at horizontal turns and vertical curves, are used as a guide by Jervis B. Webb Co.:

Straight rolling friction:

3-in. ball-bearing trolley ....2.00 percent
4-in. ball-bearing trolley ....1.75 percent
6-in. ball-bearing trolley ....1.50 percent

Add at horizontal turns:
For 36-in.-diam. bronze-bushed traction wheel:

45° turn ....2.0 percent
90° turn ....3.5 percent
180° turn ....5.0 percent

For 24-in.-radius 348 and 458 chain, and for 36-in.-radius 678 chain—roller turns:

30° turn ....2.0 percent
45° turn ....2.5 percent
90° turn ....4.0 percent
180° turn ....6.0 percent

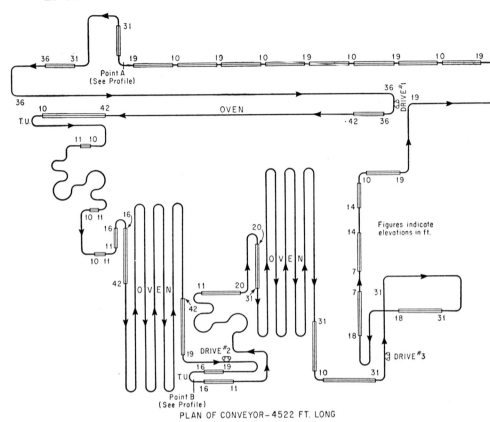

PLAN OF CONVEYOR—4522 FT. LONG

Fig. 29. Plan of conveyor.

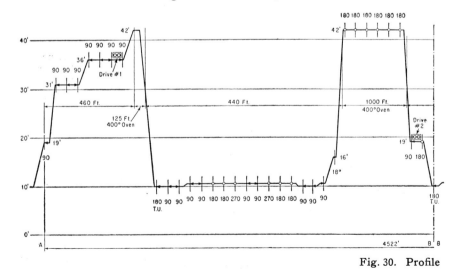

Fig. 30. Profile

Add at changes in elevation for a compound vertical curve (in addition to increase or decrease of chain pull from lifting or lowering loads):

15.0°	....2 percent
22.5°	....3 percent
30.0°	....4 percent
45.0°	....5 percent
60.0°	....6 percent

These percentages are for average, good operating conditions only. They must be increased when conveyors operate in ovens, washers, degreasers, foundries, and other places where conditions are not favorable.

Operating conditions determine the size of drive to use. If the worst condition will last only 15 to 20 minutes, and does not occur too often, a drive should tolerate **overload** if the motor is large enough. Drives are then selected on the basis of the chain pull resulting from normal operating conditions. However, such decisions should be made only when reliable operating information is available.

It is good practice to be liberal in the **selection of a drive** unit after determining chain pull. Quite often, conditions change, or the conveyor may be lengthened, increasing the original chain pull. Some users have minimum requirements of 2,000 lb. for the chain-pull capacity of a drive unit and 1½ hp. for the size of a motor. They have found that oversize drives are insurance against loss of production due to breakdown, or costly drive changes when a conveyor is altered. Also, when conveyors are taken down to be used elsewhere, the salvage possibilities of the larger-capacity drive units are much better.

The chain pull at the drive unit may not be the maximum. This is especially the case where the difference in elevations is large. The maximum chain pull in Fig. 28 is 1,900 lb. This is more than the net pull at the drive of 1,610 lb. The difference in pull on some conveyors may be much greater. It is not necessary to determine the maximum chain pull, except when it may equal or exceed the maximum allowable values for the chain and trolleys.

Profile Diagram. Heavily loaded conveyors with very high lifts or drops can be analyzed by making a profile diagram. Vertical lines can be used to indicate

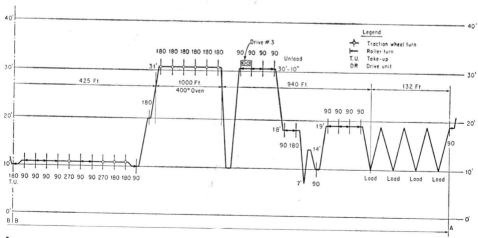

of conveyor.

each horizontal turn. **Symbols** can be used to indicate these turns, with circles representing traction wheels, and arrows for roller turns.

An actual installation is shown in plan in Fig. 29, and in profile in Fig. 30. The conveyor is so long that the profile had to be broken up to come within the limit of the page size. The conveyor is 4,522 ft. long. There are 30 changes in elevation and 63 horizontal turns. The conveyor live load is 22.5 lb. per foot, which is not considered a very heavy load. Drives are located to divide the load quite evenly, and take advantage of the helpful pull at the drops. They are also located in advance of the tortuous parts of the path to minimize the build-up of chain pull from percentage additions by keeping the chain pull low at these turns. The take-ups are located to allow for expansion and contraction of chain in the ovens as well as to take care of slack. While this appears to be a complex problem, it may be solved very quickly by using the profile analysis along with point-to-point calculations.

Power-and-Free Systems

APPLICATION. In many applications, trolley conveyors have been combined with machines and other equipment to form integral units. Some of these are well known and in general use, such as sandblast units, washers, degreasers, and ovens. Pusher conveyors, using the trolley conveyor for power, and monorail lines with nonpowered trolleys to carry the loads have been used extensively. This combination is necessary when loads must be switched off to branch lines, when load spacing must be different in various sections of the conveyor, when loads must be halted for storage, work, or inspection, and when any other condition does not permit the loads to be moved continuously, at a uniform rate, and at fixed spacing.

In this combination, the load trolleys are usually made to run on I-beam track or special monorail track. Pusher arms project from the load carriers and engage

Jervis B. Webb Co.

Fig. 31. Free trolley.

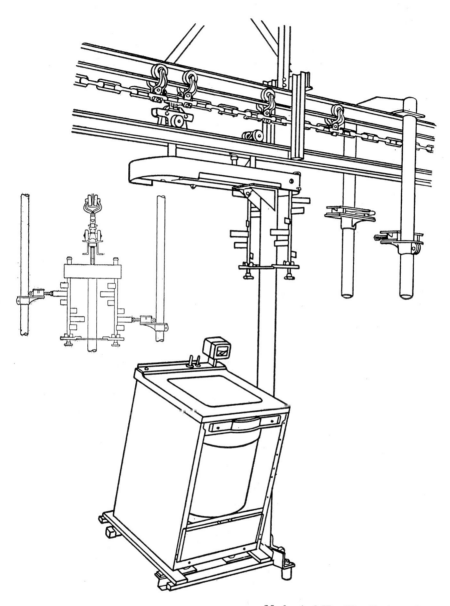

Mechanical Handling Systems, Inc.

Fig. 32. Power-and-free assembly.

with **pusher dogs** on the trolley-conveyor chain. The pusher dogs can engage or release the **carrier arms** at vertical curves in the trolley conveyor or at switch-track connections in the free-trolley track. The **side-pusher** combination must be arranged so that automatic switching is always done on the side away from the power conveyor pusher arms. This works quite well, until the layout becomes elaborate and loads must be switched to both sides of the power line, either at the same or at different switch points. Another combination must then be used, with the power-trolley conveyor directly above the free trolleys, which run in double-channel track. This construction is called **"power and free"** and is shown in Figs. 31 and 32.

The cost is considerable but has been justified in many plants where automatic dispatching, automatic switching and transfers, and other features have resulted in remarkable savings in labor and manufacturing costs. Power-and-free conveyor systems have revolutionized production methods in some of the automobile tire, engine, and body manufacturing plants. They have increased output and have reduced inventory of work-in-process. In foundries, they provide unusual flexibility of operation in the handling and cooling of molds, flasks, and castings. Other applications have been made in home-appliance manufacturing, textile mills, and elsewhere.

POWER (PUSHER) LINE. As illustrated in Fig. 33, this is a conventional 4-in. I-458-chain trolley conveyor. The pushers are inexpensive rigid attachments on the trolleys or chain, and pusher spacing can be any multiple of 8 in. They engage or disengage with the free trolleys by switching in the free track and by horizontal turns and vertical curves in the power line. The vertical curves need be only a 2- or 3-in. rise or drop, and about 3 ft. long. Thus **transfers** and changes in the pattern in which the power and free lines are combined may be accomplished in small distances, making a very compact design. Horizontal turns in the power conveyor are roller turns and can be given any radius to suit the requirements of the layout.

Drives can be either sprocket or caterpillar type. Take-ups are necessary. One advantage of the power-and-free combination is that the power conveyor often can be kept out of an oven, bonderizing unit, or other undesirable location.

FREE LINE. The free **track** usually consists of one of the following types of construction. In one method of construction the free track consists of two channels turned in, so that the four-wheel trolleys ride on the inside. In the second method, free track construction consists of two ship channels back-to-back with clearance between them. The four wheels of the trolley ride visibly on top of the channels with the sideguide rollers between the backs. In both methods the free track is suspended from the power line by a yoke arrangement.

The power operation of the switch may be by means of air cylinders supplied with compressed air or by means of mechanical power supplied by the power line.

Free track can follow **any path desired.** It can bend horizontally, curve down or up, branch out and combine again. The limitations on horizontal and vertical curves are the same as for trolley conveyors when the free is combined with the power line. Free track only is usually level or slightly inclined for gravity use, and horizontal curves are determined by load clearances and by the minimum radius the trolleys will operate on.

Free Trolleys. The construction of free trolleys is quite different from that of the ordinary monorail trolley is shown in Fig. 31. The trolley has four **load wheels** and two or more side **guide rollers.** Load wheels are regular, ball-bearing trolley wheels, such as are used on trolley conveyors. Lubrication is through Zerk fittings in the welch plugs. The side guide rollers center the trolley on the track channels, eliminate rubbing or drag, and prevent binding at the turns.

The two counterweighted **tilting dogs** are designed so that as the power pusher attachment engages the free trolley, it shoves one dog down to pass over it and engage the second dog. When the first dog is released, it tilts back into the upright position and becomes a holdback. Either tilting dog can be the pusher or holdback, depending on the direction of travel or incline. The trolley **frame** is designed with a single-hole load attachment.

Spacing can be varied at different sections of the same conveyor. Trolleys and loads can be spaced out in one section and bunched close together in another section. Trains of trolleys can be made up of various lengths and spacings with different and varying intervals between trains. The spacing combinations can be obtained in several different ways. These include the combination of power pushers at various intervals with variable spacing and timing of the feed of individual free trolleys or trains into the power-feed sections. Pusher dogs can be furnished on some trolleys, omitted on others. Almost any wanted feed and spacing of loads can be obtained.

SPRING PUSHERS. Spring-pusher conveyors permit the stopping of carriers while letting the conveyors continue to run. Thus live **storage banks** of loaded carriers may be accumulated in assembly or processing areas, or empty carriers may be banked at convenient points and automatically fed back into the main line conveyor as required.

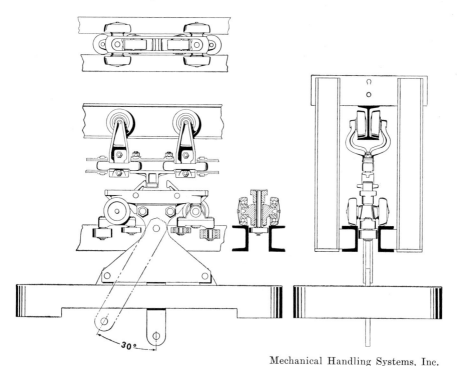

Mechanical Handling Systems, Inc.

Fig. 33. **Nonreversible spring pusher.**

The spring-pusher assembly has sufficient rigidity to push a loaded carrier to a manual or automatic stop, or against the last carrier in a bank of carriers, where the increased resistance compresses the spring and causes the pusher to slide over the dogs on the free trolley. Fig. 33 illustrates a nonreversing spring pusher.

The nonreversible spring-pusher conveyor is ideal for controlling the descent of loaded carriers down a vertical curve, as the dog on the free trolley is held back by the spring pusher on the power trolley. The spring-pusher assembly is designed so that the pusher cannot be deflected in the direction in which the conveyor is moving. It thus prevents loads from running away. The reversible spring-pusher conveyor may operate as a shuttle conveyor between two points. In such a case, the spring pusher is flexible in both directions.

Loaded carriers are accumulated at a stop, and the conveyor is then reversed for spacing the carriers properly along the free lines. When the operation has been finished on the parts, subassemblies, or complete units, the conveyor is again started, and pushes the carrier beyond the end of the spring-pusher conveyor to an automatic stop and feeder which feeds them back into the main line. This conveyor is designed for banking on level lines. Controls may be manual, push-button, or entirely automatic through electrical devices.

AUTOMATIC STOP AND FEEDER (ENTRANCE SWITCH). Proper functioning of the **power-and-free system** is dependent upon the mechanism which causes the free line trolleys to be moved into the power line. This

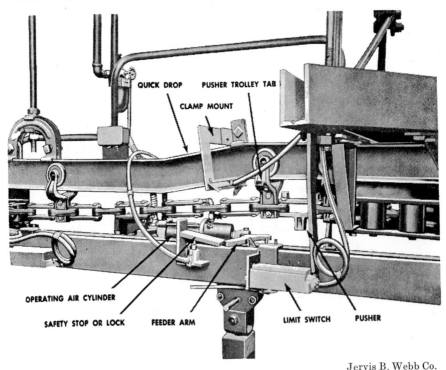

Jervis B. Webb Co.

Fig. 34. Automatic stop and feeder.

mechanism enables free line carriers to be moved automatically from a branch free line to a main line consisting of power and free. The movement is synchronized so the carrier will be engaged by the pusher on the power line when the pusher reaches the desired point above the carrier. Such mechanisms may be purely mechanical or may be operated by air cylinders controlled by electrical means.

The **mechanical entrance switch** consists of a mechanism with a chain which takes power from the power line and uses this same chain to propel the free line carrier into position to engage the power line pusher. The carrier is held in the free line waiting position until released by a mechanical linkage operated by an empty pusher on the power line. When the carrier is released it is engaged by the switch chain and is propelled at the same speed as the power line. It is moved into position to engage the power line pusher and continues its travel as a controlled carrier. The switch has a **mechanical lock** which prevents it from operating whenever a power line pusher is already moving a carrier. The automatic stop and feeder is another method for the movement of free line carrier into engagement with the power line.

SIZES. The size of the components of a power-and-free system is dictated essentially by the largest individual load. The load determines the cross section of the track and the spacing of the track hangers. In addition to track considerations it is necessary to investigate wheel loading. It is essential to check wheel capacity and the track wear due to wheel loading. Track wear is frequently the factor which will determine wheel size for the system. The wheels used are usually identical to the wheels used on trolley conveyors. These are the 3″, 4″, or 6″ trolley system wheels, with the majority of applications using the 4″ system.

ACCESSORIES. There are many important items of accessory equipment available for use in power-and-free systems. Elevators and lowerators can be used for vertical lifts and drops, either two-level or multiple-level. Power booster-units can be used to raise or lower free-track loads on inclines. Shuttle conveyors provide storage, transfer, and feeding of carriers on storage lines. Turntables and special track switches allow loads to be turned and switched as desired. Other accessories are constantly being designed to meet special requirements and become available for other, similar installations.

CABLE CONVEYORS

CONTENTS

CABLE CONVEYORS

Aerial Tramways and Other Cable Systems

NATURE OF AERIAL TRAMWAYS. An aerial tramway is a machine used to transport people and materials by the use of overhead cables and ropes, and is composed of one or more spans extending from a loading point to a discharge point up to several miles distant. Aerial tramways possess many inherent advantages. Some of these advantages are:

1. The shortest route can be taken between terminals. Tramways are independent of the contour of the ground. They cross over highways, railroads, rivers, mountains, and valleys. Their construction does not require bridges or tunnels.
2. The cost of operation is usually low as compared with other systems of transportation. Naturally, lower ton-mile costs prevail in tramways of heavier hourly capacity.
3. Wide varieties of materials can be handled, such as ores, sand, gravel, logs, sawed lumber, bananas, explosives, and glassware. Tramways are also used for transporting passengers.
4. Materials can be transported between given points without rehandling.
5. They are extremely flexible. The positive movement of carriers enables gradients to be safely and dependably overcome which would not be practical with other means of transportation.
6. They are not subject to interruptions in service because of extremes in weather conditions.
7. Loads can be automatically discharged at any desired point, thereby often eliminating an auxiliary plant.
8. It is simpler to acquire rights-of-way for aerial tramways than for any other system. The cables can be placed at heights necessary to clear highways, railways, buildings, and cultivated land.
9. Back freight, such as mine supplies, can be accommodated when provision is made for that service.

AERIAL TRAMWAY SYSTEMS. There are two distinct aerial tramway systems, the bicable and the monocable. The **bicable system** uses stationary high-tensioned cable or cables over which the loads are pulled by a moving traction rope. The **monocable system** uses a single, flexible rope—spliced endless—which both supports and moves the loads. Both systems may be designed and operated as continuous or as reversible tramways.

BICABLE CONTINUOUS SYSTEM. This kind of tramway consists of two stationary, high-tensioned track cables and one endless traction or pulling rope moving continuously in one direction. The loads move from the loading terminal to the discharge terminal, the empty carrier returning to the loading point on the light side of the line. The carriers are automatically attached to and detached from the traction rope at the terminal points. This is the most widely used system in the United States. Such systems are particularly adaptable to the greatest variety of local conditions and to the handling of many kinds of finished products and raw materials. They have been built in lengths from a few hundred feet to several miles, with capacities ranging from 1½ tons to more than 300 tons hourly. It is economically possible and practical to obtain increases in capacity by designing heavier single units in certain instances, or by building parallel tramways. The increase in length is limited only by the economic features of any particular transportation problem. **Long tramways** are divided into sections, and becomes a series of shorter tramways, the carriers being shunted on overhead rails from one section to the next without transferring the material. Design details and engineering factors are considered later in this section.

Rolling Stock for Bicable Systems. Rolling stock consists of carriage, hanger, bucket or carrier, and a grip for attaching to the traction rope.

The **carriages** are of either the 2-wheel or the 4-wheel type, the 4-wheel unit being used on heavier loads. The wheels on the 4-wheel carriage are articulated so as to equalize the load on each wheel. There is a definite relation between the load per wheel, the angle which the track cable makes under the wheel, and the tension in the track cable. It is good practice to keep the load per wheel under 2,000 lb. In addition to the loaded carrier, it is necessary to consider the downpull on the traction rope in determining the load per wheel. This is especially necessary when the carrier approaches a structure with a sharp breakover from one span to the next. It is conceivable that the downpull on the traction rope could exceed the loaded weight of the carrier in certain instances.

The **hanger** is the connection between the carriage and the bucket or carrier, and is the mount for the grip for attaching to the traction rope. It is necessary for the hanger to be exceptionally rugged to withstand fatigue at critical points.

Grips must be positive in action when attaching to or detaching from the traction rope. There are three basic designs in grips:

1. The **compression type** operates on the toggle principle. The toggles are mounted on a floating lever which acts against the resistance of a powerful spring. This spring provides automatic compensation for small differences in diameter of the traction rope as well as for the natural decreases in diameter of rope caused by stretch and wear. It is possible to pass through an automatic angle station without detaching from the rope with this type of grip.

2. The **screw type** brings the jaws together, as in a vise, and locks when the screw stops turning. This grip also provides good gripping power and compensates for reasonable differences in the diameter of the traction rope.

3. The **weight-operated grip** depends on the weight of the carrier for its gripping power. The weight of the carrier acting through a series of levers provides the holding force. This type of grip compensates for considerable variation in rope diameter and is particularly desirable in heavy-duty tramways of more than one section. When passing through a station or terminal where it is necessary to detach from the traction rope, the weight of the carrier is supported by a set of rollers mounted on the hanger which rides on rails in the structure, thereby removing the load from the gripping mechanism.

Grips are usually attached automatically, although the compression and screw types can be attached manually. All types of grips are always detached automatically.

The **carriers** in most cases are buckets. There are three basic types of buckets:

1. **Rotary dump buckets** are used in sizes under 30 cu. ft. capacity for handling such material as ore, crushed stone, and coal. They are supported on trunnions located below the loaded center of gravity so that they will overturn

easily in discharging the load. This kind of bucket can also be equipped with counterweights for ready self-righting.

2. **End dump buckets** are used for larger sizes and are well adapted for lump materials, such as mine waste or run-of-mine coal. This kind of bucket is commonly used when it is necessary to discharge the load from the cable. Such buckets are not economical for sizes under 20 cu. ft. capacity.

3. **Bottom dump buckets** are heavier—for the same capacity—than are other types. They are used for quick discharge into small hoppers, or for discharge of sludge or sticky materials from the cable.

There are many special types of carriers for transporting packages, bales, liquids, logs, sawed lumber, etc.

Loading. Material which is loaded from a **storage bin** is controlled by a bin gate or an electric vibrating feeder. Bin gates may be either hand- or power-operated. The undercut, curved gate-type of bin gate is well adapted for loading tramway buckets.

Power-operated loading devices are used on tramways equipped for automatic loading. The application of power to bin gates reduces the manual labor required for operations in a loading terminal. In one system of automatic loading the carriage comes to rest on a spring-mounted rail which starts the flow of material. When the bucket is filled to the proper point, the flow of material is automatically stopped. The bucket then rolls on graded rails toward the dispatching point, making way for the next bucket and a repetition of the operation.

Dispatching of buckets can be performed automatically by an electrically operated device which releases the loaded buckets from the loading terminal at

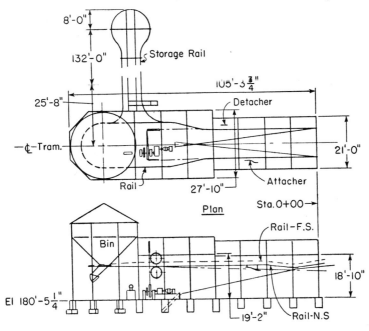

Fig. 1. Typical loading terminal.

regular, predetermined intervals, regardless of rope speed. Such a mechanism eliminates the hand pushing of buckets to the attaching point in the loading terminal, and enables every bucket to be attached at rope speed, thereby minimizing labor, assuring uniform bucket spacing, and reducing wear on grip-jaw liners and wire rope.

Loading Terminals. Loading terminals for bicable tramways consist of a loop of overhead rail for supporting the carriers and a means for loading the material to be transported. Hand-operated or power-operated bin gates, apron conveyors, or vibrating feeders may be used, or—for free-flowing materials—the loading may be automatic. Buckets detach from the traction rope, run on graded rails, and attach again after they are loaded. Detaching and attaching are automatic. Fig. 1 shows the layout of a loading terminal.

Discharge Terminals. Discharge terminals for continuous bicable tramways (Fig. 2) are of two principal types:

1. Those in which the carriers detach from the traction rope.
2. Those provided with large-diameter tail sheaves for automatic return of carriers without detaching.

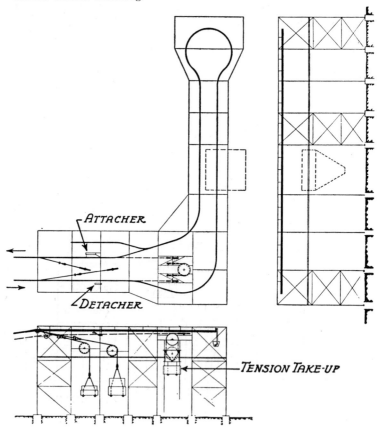

Fig. 2. Typical discharge terminal—bicable tramway.

In the first type the carriers—after they are detached—may be shunted to any point desired for discharging the loads. The drive, or traction-rope mechanism, or both, may be placed in a discharge terminal of this type. In the second, or automatic type, buckets may discharge either on the incoming or outgoing side, or while passing around the large-diameter tail sheave. No labor is required in a terminal of this kind.

Drives. Tramway drives consist of a suitable power unit, necessary shafting couplings, speed-reducing units, and the drive sheave.

Grip sheaves are used as driving sheaves when the friction developed by plain grooved sheaves is insufficient to transmit the required power. The rope engages toggle jaws mounted in pockets which are equally spaced around a segmented rim. They are usually made in 4-ft., 6-ft., and 8-ft. sizes, and transmit from 20 to 300 hp. The standard type of grip sheave is used for rope speeds up to 600 ft. per min., although special types have been developed which are capable of operating up to speeds of 1,500 ft. per min.

Drive sheaves with rubber-lined grooves for one-half rope lap have been used very successfully. It is most important that the diameter of the driving sheave be related to the rope diameter and the pressure of the rope on the sheave groove. Unit radial pressures up to 300 lb. per sq. in. have been successfully used. Rubber-lined sheaves have in many instances given exceptional rope life. **Speed reduction** between the power unit and the driving sheave is made by open gearing, enclosed speed reducer units, or V-belts.

REVERSIBLE BICABLE TRAMWAYS. Reversible tramways are constructed with: (1) a track cable, or cables, on which the carrier, or carriers, run; (2) a continuous traction rope, a bucket, or buckets; and (3) driving machinery to impart a reciprocating motion to the traction rope. The carrier, or bucket, moves back and forth between the loading and discharging terminals.

Double Reversible Tramway. The double reversible tramway is the most commonly used of the reversible-type tramways. These tramways are constructed with two track cables and two buckets. In some installations it is necessary to use two cables for each carrier, in which case the installation is known as a **twin-cable unit.** Reversibles are often the most economical system for relatively short hauls.

When one bucket is at the loading chute the other is at the discharge point. **Buckets** may discharge into a bin at the end of the tramway, or they may discharge automatically at any point along the cables. Only one man is required, regardless of the length or capacity of the system. Where automatic loading is used, no operating labor is needed. **Two bin gates** are used where the cables must be parallel at the loading terminal. It is possible in some cases to bring the two track cables close together at the loading terminal and spread the cables at an intermediate tower to permit passage of the two buckets.

To change the dumping point on a double reversible tramway, it is necessary only to change the position of one carrier on the traction rope. To facilitate this operation, one carrier is usually equipped with a clamp or grip while the other carrier is fitted with the usual clip connection. It is customary practice to change the position of the carriers frequently to help increase the life of the traction rope. The carrier may always be run to the outer end of the line, thereby eliminating necessity for changing its position.

In reversible tramways with **anchored-span track cables,** the G/t angle under the load is continually changing as the carrier moves along the line. This angle is at a maximum when the carrier is close to the supporting structures, at which time the track cables are approaching the empty-cable erection tension. This factor is an important consideration in determining the number of carriage wheels and selecting the size of track cables to be installed.

For reversible-type tramways, it is necessary only to provide for track-cable anchorage, traction-rope drive, loading chute, and a platform for the operator, thus constituting a very simple installation.

The **discharge terminal** for reversible tramways consists of a support for the track cable and a bucket tripper mounted over a bin or chute.

Single Reversible Tramway. The single reversible tramway differs from the double reversible type in that it uses only one track cable and one bucket. The choice between the single reversible and double reversible tramway is determined primarily by the **hourly tonnage** required, and to some extent by total capacity of the waste or storage piles.

Discharging the load in the span is accomplished either by a tripping frame hung on the track cable, which can be moved to the desired dumping point, or through an automatic device of some kind which is usually driven and operated by the carriage.

In properly designed reversible installations, buckets can be operated at **speeds** of 1,000 ft. per min. In clear spans it is possible to operate at speeds in excess of this rate. The speed, length of run, and size of bucket are closely related factors in the design of a reversible tramway. When dumping in the span, it is possible to increase the capacity by decreasing the length of run to meet peak load conditions.

Under certain conditions it is practical to handle over 500 tons hourly with a reversible tramway installation. Reversible tramways are particularly suited for waste disposal, stockpiling, and transporting materials over short distances.

MONOCABLE TRAMWAYS. Monocable tramways are the earliest developments of aerial wire rope tramways. One endless running rope is used for supporting as well as moving the tramway carrier. The rope may be run from loading terminal to discharge terminal at a constant speed, the empty and loaded carriers moving in parallel but opposite directions, or it may be run in a circuit, taking on loads at one or several points and discharging them at other points in the circuit. The rope passes around a **driving sheave** at one terminal and around a **plain groove sheave** at the other terminal. The latter sheave is mounted on a movable support and is counterweighted so that proper tension is applied to control deflection in the various spans and to compensate for changes in length due to stretch and temperature effects.

The **intermediate supports** are equipped with the proper number and size of rollers, which are designed to permit the passage of the grip carriage. These rollers are usually equipped with either ball or roller bearings since such mountings minimize the maintenance, labor, and cost of lubrication.

Monocable tramways are classified into **two general types:** (1) in which the carriers are permanently attached to the rope, and (2) in which the carriers are equipped with a rope-gripping device which permits shunting the loads to overhead rails in the terminals.

A typical installation using **permanently attached carriers** has been constructed in a 16,000-ft. circuit for transporting bananas from the field. The loads are light, weighing 60 to 80 lb., and are hung on light steel hooks, each attached to the rope by a clip so that it is free to swivel on the rope. Clips are restrained from sliding along the rope by buttons, which are attached after the rope is spliced and put under tension. The rope travels in a circuit at slow speed and the bunches of bananas are hooked on at numerous points at shoulder height while the rope is moving.

The **application** of this system to handling various commodities is apparent. Any unit load capable of being handled by a man can be loaded in the manner described. Heavier loads may first be hung on an auxiliary monorail temporarily supported on a swinging arm. The **length of rope** in such a monocable tramway system depends on difference in elevation, tonnage carried, number of supports, and the power that may be transmitted by a half lap on the driving sheave.

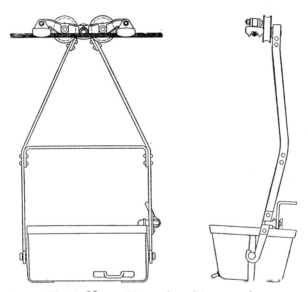

Fig. 3. Monocable carrier with rope grip.

The **second type** of monocable tramway utilizes a carriage, a hanger, and a bucket or other container for the load. The **boxhead-type carriage** (Fig. 3) consists of a frame containing toggles which grip the rope and obtain their holding power from the weight of the load. Two small wheels are also supported in the carriage which enable the load to be transferred from the moving rope to the overhead rails in the terminals or in intermediate stations. The hanger is pivoted in the framework of the carriage. The use of this type of grip is limited by the gradient at which sufficient holding power will be developed. There are **other types of gripping devices** which may be used on profiles having steeper gradients than may be negotiated by the toggle-type carriage grip.

Terminals. Terminal arrangements may be made as flexible as desired. The overhead rails may be erected so as to load from several chutes when different kinds of materials are to be transported. In the discharge terminal, the loaded carriers may dump their contents into a bin having either one or several compartments. Fig. 4 shows a typical monocable loading terminal, and Fig. 5 illustrates a typical monocable discharge terminal.

Construction. Angles may be turned in the alignment of a monocable tramway by running the carriers through an angle station equipped with overhead rails and large-diameter sheaves for deflecting the rope. In general, the **dimensions** for a monocable tramway are smaller and the structure lighter than those for the bicable system. For moderate capacities, the initial cost of a monocable tramway is less. It is satisfactory to use either steel or timber construction, depending on which proves more economical and desirable.

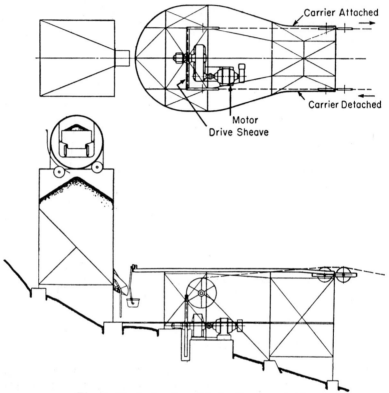

Fig. 4. Typical monocable loading terminal.

Monocable tramways of this kind have been constructed up to 21,000 ft. in a single section. The **length** is a factor related to the tonnage carried and the ground-profile characteristics. Under certain conditions it is practical to design a monocable installation for handling up to 175 to 200 tons hourly, although most have been of considerably lesser capacity. Most of the monocable installations have been constructed in foreign countries, since users in the United States to date have shown a preference for the bicable system.

MONORAIL TRAMWAYS. In the monorail tramway system, the carriers run entirely on suspended rails and are motivated by a wire rope. This type of tramway is particularly adapted to the distribution of material in large buildings, and to transportation over short distances which would be uneconomical for the installation of track cables.

Such installations are simple in operation and are capable of transporting a wide variety of products. These kinds of installations can be designed using either the continuous or reversible principle.

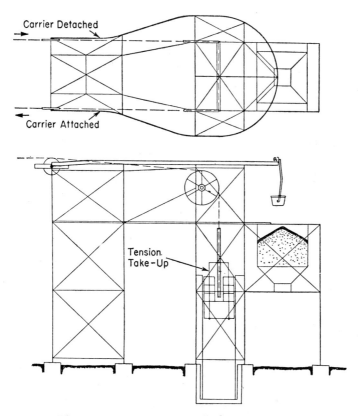

Fig. 5. Typical monocable discharge terminal.

LAWSON SYSTEM. The Lawson system differs from conventional bicable and monocable tramway designs in that the carriers run on parallel track cables in the same horizontal plane. One set of **track cables** is located above the other. The loaded carriers run on the top set and return on the lower.

The **carriers** have two or more wheels on each side and are connected to an endless traction rope by a clip, clamp, grip, wedge socket, or other means. The carriers are usually in the shape of a rectangular shallow pan. At each end of the tramway the traction rope passes around a sheave located in a vertical plane. The carriers are transferred from one set of track cables to the other by the wheels being guided in shaped rails located in planes parallel to the vertical sheave circumference, and having a proper radius of curvature, and with the same center as the vertical sheave. The carriers are **discharged** as they are inverted in passing from the upper set of track cables to the lower. They are **loaded** after continuing from the discharge point to the loading terminal, and return to the upper set of track cables in a righted position. The carriers are loaded on the fly. This tramway system usually operates at a slower speed than conventional tramways so as to facilitate loading and reduce spillage. Since loading is done while the carrier is in motion, this system operates better with material which flows freely. It operates at an **average speed** of about 400 ft. per min.

When heavier loads are imposed on the traction rope, it is usually preferable to divide the tramway into sections rather than resort to the use of a larger-diameter traction rope. In such a case, it is necessary to discharge each carrier into a hopper or bin at the end of a section and reload it into carriers in the next section. The performance of this type of tramway, as well as any other, is dependent on the thoroughness and adaptability of the design.

MISCELLANEOUS WIRE ROPE CONVEYORS. Conveyors employing an endless wire rope are used in most food canneries for moving empty cans. The cans run in a trackway and are moved by friction between the can and the moving rope, which is on the opposite side of the can from the trackway. The drive consists of a low-horsepower motor driving the rope around a multiple-groove drive sheave and idler which has a screw take-up. The rope is usually from $\frac{1}{4}$ to $\frac{3}{8}$ in. in diameter and of 6 or 8 strands. It is necessary to use on the rope a lubricant which will not soil the cans. Wire rope is used on other cannery conveyors for moving pans of fruit or produce being processed. The pans rest on the conveyor rope and are moved along the trackway by the friction between the moving rope and the pan. The same kind of drive is used as on the can conveyors.

Wire rope is often used for car spotting. It is operated by a single drum winch and has an attachment on the end of the rope for hooking onto the cars to be moved. It is also used extensively in logging, in most cases employing temporary rigging which provides the flexibility necessary in this type of operation.

Engineering Data

TYPES OF STRUCTURES FOR TRAMWAYS. While steel or concrete construction is undoubtedly the most durable for cable conveyor systems, a decision as to the kind of construction must take into account the relative costs of steel, concrete, and timber, climatic conditions, and the probable life of the installation.

Bins. Aerial tramways usually load from, and discharge into, bins. Storage facilities at both terminals provide for smooth, uninterrupted operation of the tramway. They also reduce the possibility of shutting the plant down on account of failure of the tramway system.

Bins are usually of the hopper or silo type. Various arrangements are used, depending on the classes and quantities of materials to be handled.

Steel or concrete construction has proved very successful for permanent installations. Timber construction is often used on temporary jobs. Heavy timbers, such as 3 in. x 12 in., placed on edge to the load, make a very sturdy structure.

Quantities to be stored have a direct bearing on size and number of bins. It is common practice to use several bins of small capacity rather than one large bin, in case large tonnages of material are handled. The type of material—whether it is free flowing or sticky—has a direct bearing on bin designs.

Towers. Towers vary from a single steel column with a bracket at the top to a completely built-up support type. For continuous **bicable** and reversible tramways, towers are equipped with saddles for the track cable and rollers for the traction rope. On **monocable tramways** the saddles are replaced by two or more large-diameter rollers. Steel masts up to 250 ft. in height are sometimes used as tail towers of reversible tramways.

Average weights of steel towers are shown in Fig. 6.

Height, ft.	8-ft. Gage, lb.	10-ft. Gage, lb.
15	3,500	4,000
20	4,000	4,500
25	5,000	5,500
30	6,000	6,500
35	7,000	7,500
40	8,000	8,500
45	9,000	9,500
50	10,000	10,500

Fig. 6. **Average weights of rocking saddle steel towers for bicable tramway.**

Saddles. When a decided change in vertical **cable angle** occurs at a structure, and the angle is too great for one rocking saddle, sometimes two or more saddles are supported in a structure having two or more **bents.** Such construction is usually more economical than building two or more towers close together, each with a single saddle. In cases where the vertical curvature is too great to be taken over a series of rocking saddles, a **stationary curved saddle** is used. The traction rope rollers are usually placed close under the rail so that the grip on the carrier will just pass over the rollers. This arrangement reduces the traction rope downpull to a minimum and thereby partially relieves the track cable of this load as the carrier approaches the structure.

Anchorage and Tension Structures. To maintain proper working tensions in track cables, under some of the conditions encountered in tramway design, it is necessary to counterweight them. **Counterweighting** provides constant tension and automatically compensates for variations in length caused by stretch and temperature changes, and the cable angle under the carriage wheels is practically a constant factor at all points in the span. Depending on the number of saddles, length of spans, and difference in elevations, the counterweighted sections may range from 3,500 ft. to 6,000 ft. in length. Sometimes one section of track cables is anchored while the other is counterweighted. For certain conditions of the profile, it is necessary to counterweight both sections of the track cable in one structure, hence the **double-tension structure,** shown in Fig. 7.

Angle Stations. Angle stations are used when a tramway cannot be run in a straight line between terminals. The traction rope is guided around the angle by suitable sheaves or rollers and the carriers pass through the station on overhead rails, without reducing speed or detaching from the traction rope. Since angle stations increase the initial cost, it is desirable to build a tramway in a straight line between terminals whenever possible. Angle stations also serve as **anchorage and tension stations** for the track cable.

Where there is space available, it is sometimes possible to build a portion of the tramway on the chords of a **long-radius horizontal arc.** In such a case, a small horizontal angle is made over each of several towers, and it is not necessary to build a special angle station.

Control Stations. When the tonnage, difference in elevation, and length of the tramway are such that the installation would require a traction rope of excessive size, it is desirable to divide the tramway into two or more sections. Common practice is to use traction ropes $1\frac{1}{8}$ in. in diameter and smaller on

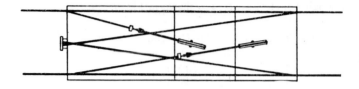

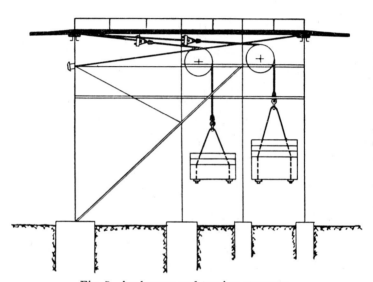

Fig. 7. Anchorage and tension structure.

bicable installations. In each station, the carrier automatically detaches from the moving traction rope, continues uninterrupted through the station on graded rails, and attaches automatically to the traction rope in the next section. Each section of the tramway requires a drive. These stations may also incorporate a horizontal angle. Fig. 8 shows a typical control station.

STRESSES IN SUSPENDED CABLES. Cable spans are divided into two general classes, **anchored spans** and **counterweighted spans.** In each of these divisions it is necessary to solve for stresses and deflections of uniformly loaded spans and also of spans supporting one or more concentrated loads. It is necessary to analyze the conditions of each problem, considering the following points:

1. Horizontal distance between supports.
2. Difference in elevation between supports.
3. Maximum allowable deflection measured vertically from chord to cable.
4. Length of cable between supports.
5. Weight per foot of cable plus any ice or snow load.
6. Maximum load to be supported by the cable.
   a. Uniform load over length of span.
   b. Single load at any point.
   c. Multiple individual loads.

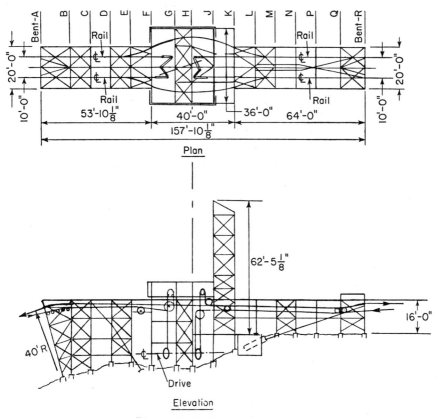

Fig. 8. Typical control station.

7. Is cable anchored at both ends or anchored at one end and counterweighted at the other?
8. Modulus of elasticity in tension.
9. Wind loads on cable and suspended load.
10. Changes in length of cable due to temperature.

Level Span: Uniformly Loaded, Anchored. The values used in the following computations are illustrated in Fig. 9.

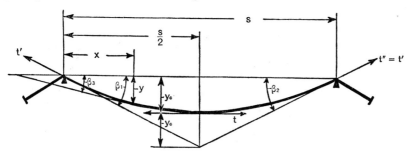

Fig. 9. Level span: Uniformly loaded, anchored.

When the tension is known, the **center deflection** is found from

$$y_c = \frac{ws^2}{8t} \tag{1}$$

where w = weight per foot of horizontal length.

The deflection at any point in the span is

$$y = \frac{wx(s-x)}{2t} \tag{2}$$

When the center deflection is known, the **horizontal component of tension** is found from

$$t = \frac{ws^2}{8y_c} \tag{3}$$

The tension at each support is

$$t' = t'' = t \sec \beta_1 = t \sec \beta_2 \tag{4}$$

The **cable slope** at either support is

$$\tan \beta_1 = \tan \beta_2 = \frac{4y_c}{s} \tag{5}$$

The cable slope at any point is

$$\tan \beta_3 = \frac{w}{t}\left(\frac{s}{2} - x\right) \tag{6}$$

When the tension is known, the **length of cable** is

$$L_1 \text{ or } L = s + \frac{w^2 s^3}{24t^2} \quad \text{(approx.)} \tag{7}$$

where L_1 = length along cable when only cable is supported and L = length along cable when a uniformly distributed load is suspended.

When the deflection is known,

$$L_1 \text{ or } L = s\left(1 + \frac{8}{3}k^2\right) \quad \text{(approx.)} \tag{8}$$

where k = ratio of deflection to span.

The **erection tension**, t_e, may be found by solving the following equation, using the trial-and-error method:

$$Pt_e + L - (Pt + s) = \frac{w^2 s^3}{24t_e^2} \quad \text{(approx.)} \tag{9}$$

where $P = L/AE$, A = net cross-section area of cable, and E = modulus of elasticity in tension.

Inclined Span: Uniformly Loaded, Anchored. The following formulas give the **increments of deflection and slope** resulting from inclination of the chord.

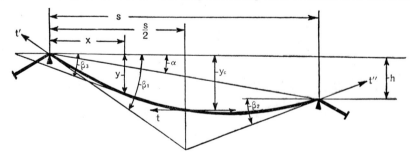

Fig. 10. Inclined span: Uniformly loaded, anchored.

"Down" slopes are considered as plus values and **"up"** slopes as minus values. The values are illustrated in Fig. 10.

$$y_c = \frac{ws^2}{8t} + \frac{h}{2} \qquad (10)$$

At any point,

$$y = \frac{wx(s-x)}{2t} \pm x \tan \alpha \qquad (11)$$

$$\tan \beta_1 = \frac{ws}{2t} + \tan \alpha \qquad (12)$$

$$\tan \beta_2 = \frac{ws}{2t} - \tan \alpha \qquad (13)$$

$$\tan \beta_3 = \frac{w}{t}\left(\frac{s}{2} - x\right) \pm \tan \alpha \qquad (14)$$

When center deflection is known,

$$t = \frac{ws^2}{8y_c - 4h} \qquad (15)$$

When deflection at any other point is known,

$$t = \frac{wx(s-x)}{2(y - x \tan \alpha)} \qquad (16)$$

$$t' = t \sec \beta_1 \qquad (17)$$

$$t'' = t \sec \beta_2 \qquad (18)$$

The length of cable is

$$L_1 \text{ or } L = \sqrt{s^2 + h^2} + \frac{w^2 s^3 \cos^3 \alpha}{24t^2} \quad \text{(approx.)} \qquad (19)$$

Level Span: Single Load at Center, Anchored. The **deflection** produced by a concentrated load suspended midway between two fixed points A and B forms two equal subchords, AC and BC (Fig. 11). The cable forms two catenary arcs

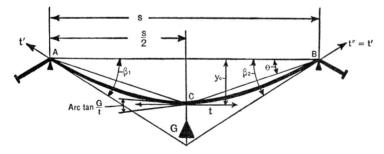

Fig. 11. Level span: Single load at center, anchored.

which intersect at C. The following formulas are based on the **parabola**, since the difference is negligible.

$$y_c = \frac{s(2G + ws)}{8t} \qquad (20)$$

$$t = \frac{s(2G + ws)}{8y_c} \qquad (21)$$

$$t' = t \sec \beta_1 = t \sec \beta_2 = t'' \tag{22}$$

$$\tan \beta_1 = \frac{G + ws}{2t} = \tan \beta_2 \tag{23}$$

$$L = 2\left(\sqrt{\left(\frac{s}{2}\right)^2 + y_c{}^2} + \frac{w^2\left(\frac{s}{2}\right)^3 \cos^3 \theta}{24t^2}\right) \tag{24}$$

Inclined Span: Single Load at Center, Anchored. This situation is diagrammed in Fig. 12.

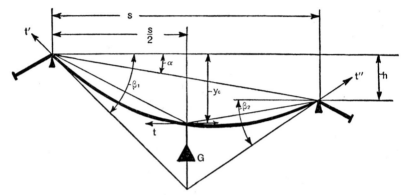

Fig. 12. Inclined span: Single load at center, anchored.

When the chord is inclined, the center deflection is found by adding $h/2$ to equation (20).

$$y_c = \frac{s(2G + ws)}{8t} + \frac{h}{2} \tag{25}$$

$$t = \frac{s(2G + ws)}{8y_c - 4h} \tag{26}$$

$$t' = t \sec \beta_1 \tag{27}$$

$$t'' = t \sec \beta_2 \tag{28}$$

$$\tan \beta_1 = \frac{G + ws}{2t} + \frac{h}{s} \tag{29}$$

$$\tan \beta_2 = \frac{G + ws}{2t} - \frac{h}{s} \tag{30}$$

Level Span: Single Load at Any Point, Counterweighted. In a constant-tension span the **deflection at the load** is determined from

$$y = \frac{Gx\,(s - x)}{st} + \frac{wx(s - x)}{2t} \tag{31}$$

The **deflection of the cable** may be determined for any point in the span, with the load at any point, x_1, y_1 being coordinates to the left of G and x_2, y_2 to the right (Fig. 13).

$$y_1 = \frac{Gx_1\,(s - m)}{st} + \frac{wx_1(s - x_1)}{2t} \tag{32}$$

$$y_2 = \frac{Gm(s - x_2)}{st} + \frac{wx_2(s - x_2)}{2t} \tag{33}$$

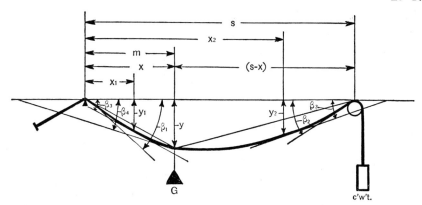

Fig. 13. Level span: Single load at any point, counterweighted.

The cable slope at left support, when $x_1 = 0$, is

$$\tan \beta_1 = \frac{G(s-m)}{st} + \frac{ws}{2t} \qquad (34)$$

The cable slope at right support, when $x_2 = s$, is

$$\tan \beta_2 = \frac{Gm}{st} + \frac{ws}{2t} \qquad (35)$$

When $x = m$, the slope at and to the left of the load is

$$\tan \beta_4 \ (\text{sloping to left of } G) = \frac{G}{t} - \frac{Gx}{st} + \frac{w}{t}\left(\frac{s}{2} - x\right) \qquad (36)$$

The slope at and to the right of the load is

$$\tan \beta_4 \ (\text{sloping to right of } G) = \frac{Gx}{st} + \frac{w}{t}\left(x - \frac{s}{2}\right) \qquad (37)$$

The **tangent of the angle** under the load is equal to $(36) + (37) = G/t$.

The **slope** which a moving load must climb is the tangent of an angle equal to one half the difference between the angles obtained from (36) and (37).

Level Span: Multiple Loads, Counterweighted. A cable supporting multiple loads, as in Fig. 14, forms a series of parabolic arcs between the loads. The

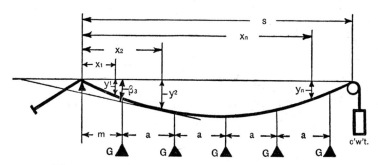

Fig. 14. Level span: Multiple loads, counterweighted.

formula for deflection at any point x,y of a span supporting n loads of uniform spacing and weight, the cable tension being constant, is

$$y = \frac{G}{t}\left[x\,(n-u) - m\left(\frac{xn}{s}-u\right) - a\left(\frac{bx}{s}-c\right)\right] + \frac{wx(s-x)}{2t} \tag{38}$$

where $b = n\dfrac{(n-1)}{2}$

$\qquad c = u\dfrac{(u-1)}{2}$

u = number of loads to left of x,y.

$$t = \frac{G}{y}\left[x\,(n-u) - m\left(\frac{xn}{s}-u\right) - a\left(\frac{bx}{s}-c\right)\right] + \frac{wx(s-x)}{2y} \tag{39}$$

The cable slope at any point may be found from the formula

$$\tan\beta_3 = \frac{G}{t}\left[(n-u) - \frac{nm+ab}{s}\right] + \frac{w}{t}\left(\frac{s}{2}-x\right) \tag{40}$$

Inclined Span: Multiple Loads, Counterweighted. Formulas involved in the situation diagramed in Fig. 15 are

$$y = \frac{G}{t}\left[x\,(n-u) - m\left(\frac{xn}{s}-u\right) - a\left(\frac{bx}{s}-c\right)\right] + \frac{wx(s-x)}{2t} + x\tan\alpha \tag{41}$$

$$t = \frac{G}{y-x}\tan\alpha\left[x\,(n-u) - m\left(\frac{xn}{s}-u\right) - a\left(\frac{bx}{s}-c\right)\right] + \frac{wx(s-x)}{2(y-x\tan\alpha)} \tag{42}$$

$$\tan\beta_3 = \frac{G}{t}\left[(n-u) - \frac{nm+ab}{s}\right] + \frac{w}{t}\left(\frac{s}{2}-x\right) \pm x\tan\alpha \tag{43}$$

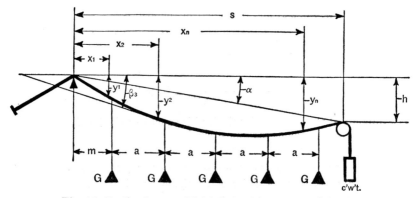

Fig. 15. Inclined span: Multiple loads, counterweighted.

STRESSES IN WIRE ROPES IN INCLINED PLANES AND SLOPES. There are two methods of designating the **grade or pitch of an inclined plane or slope.** One uses the angle of incline, and the other uses a percentage figure which is the ratio of the vertical rise to the horizontal distance.

To find the total pull on a rope **four factors must be evaluated.** They are: (1) gravity load, (2) car friction load, (3) rope friction load, and (4) stress due to acceleration.

The **gravity load** is equivalent to the total weight of loaded cars plus the weight of wire rope multiplied by the sine of the angle of incline.

Car friction is usually equivalent to the weight of the loaded car multiplied by 0.03 times the cosine of the angle of incline.

Rope friction is a widely variable factor. Consequently, a coefficient having at least twice the value of that used for car friction is commonly used. The rope friction would then be equivalent to the weight of the rope between the car and the drum, multiplied by 0.06 times the cosine of the angle of incline. In the interest of safety the minimum angle is used where there is more than one grade.

For ascending trips, friction loads are added to the gravity load; for descending trips they are subtracted.

A friction factor of 0.01 is commonly used in calculating bicable continuous tramway traction rope tensions and horsepower requirements.

To cover stress caused by **acceleration,** a 5 percent addition to the total stress in the wire rope is usually considered adequate for speeds under 500 ft. per min. A 10 percent factor should be used for speeds of 500 to 1,000 ft. per min. For higher speeds the stress caused by acceleration should be calculated.

TRACK CABLE AND TRACTION ROPE DATA. The modulus of elasticity of wire rope and cable varies according to construction and will vary throughout the life of the rope or cable. Some of the commonly used approximate values for moduli of elasticity for typical constructions are given in Fig. 16. Examples of the rope and cable considered are shown in Fig. 17.

Construction	Modulus of Elasticity
6 x 7 hemp center	14,000,000
6 x 19 hemp center	12,000,000
6 x 19 wire center	14,000,000
6 x 19 galv. wire core bridge rope	15,000,000
37 wire galv. bridge strand	18,000,000
Prestressed galv. bridge strands	24,000,000
Locked-coil track strand	19,000,000
Smooth-coil track strand	19,000,000

Fig. 16. Approximate moduli of elasticity.

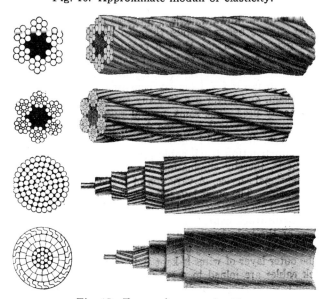

Fig. 17. Types of rope and cable.

Breaking Strengths and Weights. The breaking strengths and weights of traction and haulage ropes are shown in Fig. 18.

Diam., in.	6 x 7 Construction			6 x 19 Construction		
	Breaking Strength Tons of 2,000 lb.		Approximate Weight per ft., lb.	Breaking Strength Tons of 2,000 lb.		Approximate Weight per ft., lb.
	Improved Plow Steel	Plow Steel		Improved Plow Steel	Plow Steel	
⅜	5.86	5.10	0.21	6.10	5.31	0.23
⁷⁄₁₆	7.93	6.90	0.29	8.27	7.19	0.31
½	10.3	8.96	0.38	10.7	9.35	0.40
⁹⁄₁₆	13.0	11.3	0.48	13.5	11.8	0.51
⅝	15.9	13.9	0.59	16.7	14.5	0.63
¾	22.7	19.8	0.84	23.8	20.7	0.90
⅞	30.7	26.7	1.15	32.2	28.0	1.23
1	39.7	34.5	1.50	41.8	36.4	1.60
1⅛	49.8	43.3	1.90	52.6	45.7	2.03
1¼	61.0	53.0	2.34	64.6	56.2	2.50
1⅜	73.1	63.6	2.84	77.7	67.5	3.03
1½	86.2	75.0	3.38	92.0	80.0	3.60

Note: Wire center ropes add 7½ percent to the above breaking strengths and 10 percent to the weight.

Fig. 18. Breaking strengths and weights, 6 x 7 and 6 x 19 construction.

The breaking strengths and weights of track cables are shown in Fig. 19.

Cable and Rope Construction. Experience has proved that **Lang lay ropes** with hemp centers give the most satisfactory service for traction ropes on continuous bicable tramways and for haulage ropes on surface haulage systems. The greater wearing surface better enables them to resist external wear and gives them a **better gripping surface than a regular lay rope.** These ropes also usually give the most satisfactory service on monocable tramway installations.

The usual practice for traction ropes on bicable tramways in sizes from ⅜ in. to ¾ in. diam. is to use 6 x 7 Lang lay construction with hemp center, while for sizes ⅞ in. diam. and larger 6 x 19 Lang lay Seale construction with hemp center is customarily used. The same general rules apply to haulage ropes on surface haulage systems, except that the 6 x 7 Lang lay construction is often used in sizes of ⅞ in. diam. and larger.

Locked-coil-construction track cable provides a smooth wearing surface for the carriage wheels, thereby eliminating impact. In well-designed installations it has given exceptional service. A variation of the locked-coil construction is the **half-lock track cable.** The outer layer of wires consists of alternate round wires and shaped wires. This construction has not been so widely used in the United States. **Smooth-coil track cable** is made of all round wires, hence does not have the advantages of the locked-coil and half-lock constructions. Extreme caution should be exercised in the handling of all track cables to prevent unlaying and to insure that the outer layer of wires is kept tight.

When track cables are joined in a span it is necessary to use a **mechanical coupling** which is small enough in diameter to permit the carriage wheels to pass over it. These couplings consist of a shell, thimbles and wedges for socketing, and a screw plug for tightening. They are available for piecing two cables together, or for end attachments in sizes through 2 in. Zincked-type end fittings are also used.

Diam., in.	No. of Wires	Smooth Coil			Locked Coil		
		Tons of 2,000 lbs.		Approx. Weight per ft., lb.	B.S. in Tons of 2,000 lb.		Approx. Weight per ft., lb.
		Extra High Strength	High Strength		Special	Standard	
½	19	15.3	12.6	.55	–	–	–
⅝	19	22.3	19.2	.86	–	–	–
¾	19	32.5	27.6	1.24	31.5	25.0	1.41
⅞	19	44.4	37.6	1.69	41.5	32.0	1.92
1	19	58.0	49.2	2.20	52.5	42.0	2.50
1⅛	37	70.7	60.0	2.70	66.0	54.0	3.16
1¼	37	84.6	71.8	3.23	81.0	65.0	3.91
1⅜	37	105.0	88.8	4.01	100.0	78.0	4.73
1½	37	127.5	108.4	4.88	120.5	93.0	5.63
1⅝	61	146.0	124.0	5.63	140.0	108.0	6.60
1¾	61	171.0	145.8	6.59	165.0	125.0	7.66
1⅞	61	189.0	161.0	7.28	187.5	138.0	8.79
2	91	218.0	185.0	8.40	215.0	158.0	10.00
2¼	91	266.0	233.0	10.36	280.0	–	12.50
2½	91	335.0	285.0	13.10	345.0	–	15.20
2¾	–	–	–	–	420.0	–	18.30
3	–	–	–	–	500.0	–	22.20
3¼	–	–	–	–	580.0	–	25.60
3½	–	–	–	–	690.0	–	29.90
3¾	–	–	–	–	785.0	–	33.90
4	–	–	–	–	800.0	–	38.40

Fig. 19. Breaking strengths and weights of smooth- and locked-coil construction.

TRAMWAY DESIGN. To determine the preliminary **design data** and characteristics of a particular installation, it is necessary to have the following information:

1. Horizontal distance between terminals.
2. Difference in elevation of terminals.
3. Which terminal is at higher elevation.
4. Intermediate points on profile which are higher or lower than either terminal.
5. Size, weight, and nature of material to be carried.
6. Desired capacity.
7. Obstacles to be crossed, such as rivers, roads and power lines, and protection—if any—required.
8. Will proposed tramway run in a straight line, or will one or more angle stations be required?
9. Special features such as automatic loading.

While it is desirable to have an actual survey to work from, in the preliminary stages of analysis a **contour map** or an accurate sketch will usually suffice. Before actual design work commences, it is essential that an accurate survey be made of the line.

PRELIMINARY CALCULATIONS FOR BICABLE TRAMWAY.

The following example, supplied by the Columbia-Geneva Steel Division of the United States Steel Corporation, illustrates the method for making the preliminary calculations for a bicable tramway:

Requirements.

Horizontal length .... 3,975 ft.
Difference in elevation .... 616-ft. drop
Material: crushed limestone, fines to 7 in. at................. 100 lb. per cu. ft.
Required capacity .... 300 ton per hr.
Assume speed of tramway................................... 550 ft. per min.
Automatic loading and discharge required.

The **profile** for this tramway is shown in Fig. 20.

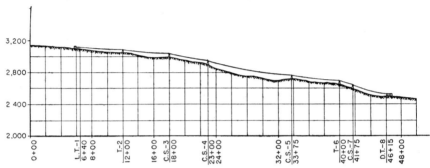

Fig. 20. Profile for tramway analysis.

Size and Spacing of Buckets.

Try 42 cu. ft.

Wt. of mat. $= (300 + 0.05 \times 300) \times 2000 = 630,000$ lb. per hr. (It is good practice to allow a 5 percent capacity margin.)

No. of buckets $= \dfrac{630,000}{42 \times 100} = 150$ per hr.

Time interval $= \dfrac{3,600}{150} = 24$ sec. (This is satisfactory; the minimum interval for good operation is usually 22 sec.)

Spacing $= \dfrac{550}{60} \times 24 = 219.98$ ft.

Wt. of 42 cu. ft. bucket and hanger $= 1,380$ lb.
Wt. of 4-wheel carriage $=\ \ 315$ lb.
Wt. of grip for $1\frac{1}{8}$ in. rope $=\ \ 100$ lb.

     1,795 lb.

Wt. of traction rope per bucket spacing $=\ \ 446$ lb.

     2,241 lb. empty

Wt. of load $= 4,200$ lb.

     6,441 lb. loaded

Wt. of cable empty $= \dfrac{2,241}{219.98} = 10.19$ lb. per ft.   and

Wt. of cable loaded $= \dfrac{6,441}{219.98} = 29.29$ lb. per ft.

Empty side: Use 1 in. diam. special-grade, locked-coil cable—maximum rolling load on 4 wheels = 2,538 lb.
This cable weighs 2.50 lb. per ft.
Using a safety factor of 2.85, the tension in the cable would equal 36,950 lb.

Loaded side: Use 1⅝ in. diam. special-grade, locked-coil cable—maximum rolling load on 4 wheels = 6,812 lb.
This cable weighs 6.60 lb. per ft.
Using a safety factor of 2.85, the tension in the cable would equal 98,300 lb.

To prevent excessive wear and fatigue in the track cable, it is good practice to limit the load per wheel to 2,000 lb. maximum and the angle under each carriage wheel to 0°58′ maximum. **Wheel loads** exceeding 2,000 lb. usually result in a unit bearing pressure between carriage wheel and track cable which is detrimental to the service life of the cable. The **cable angle** under the load is equivalent to the arc tangent G/t. The G/t angle under each carriage wheel in an articulated arrangement is equal to the total angle divided by the number of carriage wheels. The angle under each wheel measures the degree of bending in the cable. Maintaining the proper G/t ratio is very important to the service life of the track cable. Counterweighted spans differ from anchored spans in that the tension in the track cable remains constant as loads move along the line.

Location and Height of Towers. It is necessary to locate towers at such points, and have them at such heights, that adequate clearances will be maintained for the rolling stock when fully loaded, and so that the track cable will stay in the tower saddles under erection tension without any rolling load.

In preliminary layouts, the tentative heights and locations can be determined graphically. The profile (Fig. 20) is plotted to a scale of 1 in. equal to 100 ft. The loaded and empty cable curvatures applicable to the scaled-down profile are calculated as follows:

$$\text{Loaded} = \frac{98,300}{(29.29 + 6.60)100} = 27.1 \text{ in. radius}$$

$$\text{Empty} = \frac{98,300}{6.60 \times 100} = 151 \text{ in. radius}$$

Templates of these radii may be used to simulate the actual loaded and empty cables on the scaled profile. The best locations and heights of towers may then be determined.

Traction Rope Size and Horsepower Required. The traction rope sizes and the horsepower required to operate the system must next be calculated. In the case under discussion the calculations are as follows:

Loads down:
Gravity 29.29 × 616   = −18,042
Friction 29.29 × 0.01 × 3,975 = + 1,164
                              ─────────
                              −16,878 lb.

Empties up:
Gravity 10.19 × 616   = + 6,277
Friction 10.19 × 0.01 × 3,975 = +   405
                              ─────────
                              + 6,682 lb.

Difference in tension between loaded and empty sides:

$$T - S = -16{,}878 + 6{,}682 = -10{,}196 \text{ lb.}$$

$$\text{Horsepower} = \frac{-10.196 \times 550}{33{,}000} = -170 \text{ hp. (in this case developed)}$$

Assuming a drive efficiency of 85 percent, the hp. req. $= -170 \times 0.85 = -145$ hp. In practice, use 150 hp.

Tension Diagram of System. To assure proper operation of the tramway, it is necessary to have the counterweight of such size as will produce **adequate tension** at the point of minimum tension in the traction rope, as shown in Fig. 21.

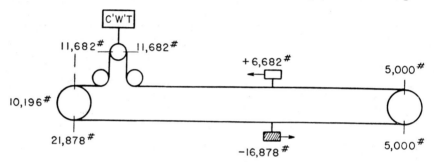

Fig. 21. Tension diagram of system.

In this case a 5,000-lb. tension is assumed. In the final calculation and design the minimum tension may be lower, but in a first trial it is good practice to be conservative. The counterweight would be 23,364 lb. The point of maximum tension (−21,878 lb.) is at the drive sheave in the upper terminal on the loaded side.

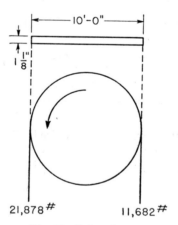

Fig. 22. Drive sheave.

Now $1\frac{1}{8}$ in. 6 x 19 improved plow hemp center traction rope breaking strength $= 105{,}200$ lb.

$$\text{Factor of safety} = \frac{105{,}200}{31{,}878} = 4.81$$

This safety factor is a little low for traction rope. It is good practice to maintain a minimum of 5.0.

Sheave Sizes. With a 10 ft. diam. rubber-filled drive sheave such as shown in Fig. 22:

$$\text{Unit radial pressure} = \frac{21{,}878 + 11{,}682}{10 \times 12 \times 1.125} = 248 \text{ lb. per sq. in.}$$ (O.K. Max. allowance based on experience = 250 to 300 lb. per sq. in.)

$$S_{min.} = \frac{10.196}{0.9} = 11{,}329 \text{ lb.}$$ (satisfactory for rubber-filled sheave with one-half lap)

Traction Rope Sheaves at Loading Terminal. Using a 5 ft. diam. cast-steel, flame-hardened sheave on the tight side, the maximum allowable unit pressure is 750 lb. per sq. in. (Fig. 23).

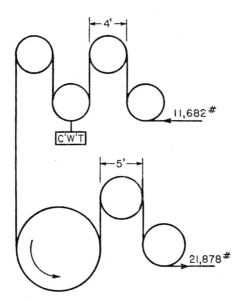

Fig. 23. Traction rope sheaves—L.T.

$$\text{Unit radial pressure} = \frac{2t}{D \times d} = \frac{2 \times 21{,}878}{60 \times 1.125} = 648 \text{ lb. per sq. in.}$$

Using a 4 ft. diam. cast-steel, flame-hardened sheave on the slack side:

$$\text{Unit radial pressure} = \frac{2 \times 11{,}682}{48 \times 1.125} = 432 \text{ lb. per sq. in.}$$

Empty Cable Angles. The formula for empty cable angles is as follows:

$$\text{Empty cable angle} = \tan^{-1} \frac{ws}{2t} = \tan^{-1} 0.0336 \text{ for 1,000-ft. span}$$

Values for spans of varying lengths are given in Fig. 24.

	Span	Tangent	Deg. and Min.
1	560 ft.	0.0188	1° 05′
2	600	0.0202	1° 10′
3	500	0.0168	0° 58′
4	1,075	0.0361	2° 04′
5	625	0.0210	1° 12′
6	175	0.0059	0° 20′
7	440	0.0148	0° 51′

Fig. 24. Cable angles when without load.

Load Angles. Factors in the load angle calculations below are illustrated in Fig. 25.

$$\text{Load angle:}\quad \frac{b + (b + a) + (b + 2a) \cdots (n - 1)}{\text{Span length}} \times \frac{G}{t}$$

$$\text{Loaded side:}\quad \frac{G_1}{t_1} = \tan^{-1}\frac{6.441}{98,300} = \tan^{-1} 0.0655 = 3° 45'$$

$$\text{Empty side:}\quad \frac{G_e}{t_e} = \tan^{-1}\frac{2.241}{36,950} = \tan^{-1} 0.0608 = 3° 29'$$

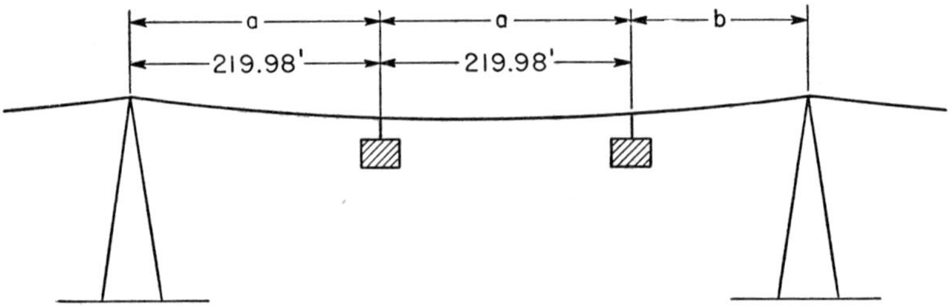

Fig. 25. Carrier and tower relation—load angle calculations.

Values for the spans in the present example (see Fig. 20) are given in Fig. 26.

Loaded span	Formula	Loaded Side	Empty Side
1–2	$\dfrac{460}{560} \times \dfrac{G}{t}$	3° 05′	2° 52′
2–3	$\dfrac{540}{600} \times \dfrac{G}{t}$	3° 22′	3° 08′
3–4	$\dfrac{340}{500} \times \dfrac{G}{t}$	2° 33′	2° 22′
4–5	$\dfrac{2,100}{1,075} \times \dfrac{G}{t}$	7° 20′	6° 48′
5–6	$\dfrac{590}{625} \times \dfrac{G}{t}$	3° 32′	3° 18′
6–7	0	0	0
7–8	$\dfrac{220}{440} \times \dfrac{G}{t}$	1° 52′	1° 44′

Fig. 26. Load angles.

Summarizing the Data. Data developed from the profile and the preceding calculations may be summarized as in Fig. 27.

1 Struct.	2 Sta.	3 Elev.	4 Diff. Elev.	5 Span	6 Tan α Col. 4 ÷ 5	7 α	8 Chord ∠ Over Struct.	9 Empty Cable ∠	10 Chord ∠ + Empty Cable ∠	11 Load ∠ L.S.	12 Load ∠ E.S.	13* Total ∠ L.S.	14* Total ∠ E.S.	15 Type of Struct.
L.T.#1	6+40	3110					+5°-06'	1°-05'	+6°-11'	3°-05'		13°-01'	12°-32'	L.T. #1
			50	560	.0893	5°-06'								
#2	12+00	3060					+1°-05'	1°-10'	+3°-20'	3°-22'	2°-52'	17°-17'	16°-18'	Stat. Saddle Tower #2
			65	600	.1082	6°-11'								
#3	18+00	2995					+2°-54'	0°-58'	+5°-02'	2°-33'	3°-08'	18°-27'	17°-30'	" #3
			80	500	.1600	9°-05'								
#4	23+00	2915					+0°-57'	2°-04'	+3°-59'	7°-20'	2°-22'	21°-22'	20°-07'	" #4
			190	1075	.1768	10°-02'								
#5	33+75	2725					-2°-01'	1°-12'	+1°-15'	3°-32'	6°-48'	19°-37'	18°-19'	" #5
			88	625	.1408	8°-01'								
#6	40+00	2637					+0°-45'	0°-20'	+2°-17'	0°	3°-18'	9°-34'	9°-04'	Rocking Saddle Tower #6
			27	175	.1542	8°-45'								
#7	41+75	2610					+6°-00'	0°-51'	+7°-11'	1°-52'	0°	16°-33'	15°-53'	Stat. Saddle Tower #7
			116	440	.2635	14°-46'								
D.T.#8	46+15	2494					-14°-46'		-13°-55'		1°-44'	-11°-03'	-12°-11'	D.T. #8

* Note. To obtain total angle over structure, add angle equal to one G/t for Rocking Saddle Towers and two G/t for Stationary Saddle Towers.

Fig. 27. Preliminary profile notes and calculations.

Traction Rope Tensions. The traction rope tensions at each tower are calculated from the equation:

Tension at any point = Tension due to load + Friction load + Minimum tension

Values for the system in the preceding example are given below:

	Loaded Side		Empty Side	
Tower No. 7	116×29.29	$= +\ 3,398$	116×10.19	$= +\ 1,182$
	$29.29 \times 440 \times 0.01$	$= -\quad 129$	$10.19 \times 440 \times 0.01$	$= +\quad 44$
		$+\ 3,269$		$+\ 1,226$
Tower No. 6	143×29.29	$= +\ 4,190$	143×10.19	$= +\ 1,460$
	$29.29 \times 615 \times 0.01$	$= -\quad 180$	$10.19 \times 615 \times 0.01$	$= +\quad 62$
		$+\ 4,010$		$+\ 1,522$
Tower No. 5	231×29.29	$= +\ 6,765$	231×10.19	$= +\ 2,353$
	$29.29 \times 1,240 \times 0.01$	$= -\quad 363$	$10.19 \times 1,240 \times 0.01$	$= +\quad 126$
		$+\ 6,402$		$+\ 2,479$
Tower No. 4	421×29.29	$= +12,331$	421×10.19	$= +\ 4,289$
	$29.29 \times 2,315 \times 0.01$	$= -\quad 677$	$10.19 \times 2,315 \times 0.01$	$= +\quad 236$
		$+11,654$		$+\ 4,525$
Tower No. 3	501×29.29	$= +14,674$	501×10.19	$= +\ 5,105$
	$29.29 \times 2,815 \times 0.01$	$= -\quad 825$	$10.19 \times 2,815 \times 0.01$	$= +\quad 287$
		$+13,849$		$+\ 5,392$
Tower No. 2	566×29.29	$= +16,578$	566×10.19	$= +\ 5,767$
	$29.29 \times 3,415 \times 0.01$	$= -\ 1,000$	$10.19 \times 3,415 \times 0.01$	$= +\quad 348$
		$+15,578$		$+\ 6,115$
L.T.	616×29.29	$= +18,042$	616×10.19	$= +\ 6,277$
	$29.29 \times 3,975 \times 0.01$	$= -\ 1,164$	$10.19 \times 3,975 \times 0.01$	$= +\quad 405$
		$+16,878$		$+\ 6,682$

Note: Add 5,000 lb. minimum tension to above figures to obtain tension at any structure.

	Traction Rope Tensions		Down Pressures		Rollers		Track Cable Supports	
	Load. Side	Empty Side	Load. Side	Empty Side	Load. Side	Empty Side	Load. Side	Empty Side
L.T. No. 1	21,878	11,682	4,950	2,550	10	5	—	—
No. 2	20,578	11,115	6,180	3,160	13	7	Stat. curv. saddle	Stat. curv. saddle
No. 3	18,849	10,392	6,050	3,160	12	7	Stat. curv. saddle	Stat. curv. saddle
No. 4	16,654	9,525	6,170	3,330	13	7	Stat. curv. saddle	Stat. curv. saddle
No. 5	11,402	7,479	3,900	2,380	8	5	Stat. curv. saddle	Stat. curv. saddle
No. 6	9,010	6,522	1,510	1,030	3	2	Rocking saddle	Rocking saddle
No. 7	8,269	6,226	2,380	1,720	5	4	Stat. curv. saddle	Stat. curv. saddle
D.T. No. 8	5,000	5,000	1,050 (uplift)	1,060 (uplift)	3	3	—	—

Fig. 28. Approximate traction rope tensions, down pressures, tower rollers, and type of track cable support.

In general, rocking saddles are used for under 10° breakover, and stationary curved saddles for over 10° breakover (see Fig. 27).

Other tension values are given in the table in Fig. 28. Traction rope **down pressure** is computed according to the formula:

$$\text{Traction rope down pressure} = 2 \times \text{T. R. tension} \times \sin\frac{\text{total} \sphericalangle \text{ over struc.}}{2}$$

Sufficient rollers are installed so that the maximum load on each is 500 lb.

OPERATING COST DETERMINATION. In determining the unit cost of operation, it is customary to take the following factors into account:

1. Power required.
2. Track cable replacement.
3. Traction rope replacement.
4. Mechanical equipment replacement.
5. Operating supplies.
6. Operating labor.
7. Maintenance labor.
8. Amortization.
9. Interest charges.
10. Insurance and taxes.

While there is considerable variation in the **life of track cables and traction ropes,** a well-designed tramway should give 1,000,000 to 2,000,000 tons net for locked-coil track cables and 300,000 to 800,000 tons for traction ropes. In general, greater cable tonnage life can be expected of a bicable continuous tramway than of a bicable reversible.

On **mechanical equipment replacement,** it is usually conservative to figure a 60 to 70 percent replacement over 20 years, or a lesser percentage if the anticipated life of the tramway is less.

Costs per Ton-Mile. The average operating costs per ton-mile for bicable aerial tramways, excluding amortization, interest, taxes, and insurance, are shown in Fig. 29, assuming a tramway 1 mile in horizontal length with a drop of 500 ft. The curve reflects average costs prevailing in the 1950's.

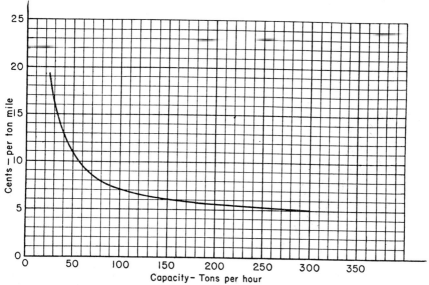

Fig. 29. **Average operation costs of bicable aerial tramway.**

The operating costs per ton-mile decrease when the tramway length increases, although not necessarily in proportion to the **increase** in length.

HAULAGE CONVEYORS

CONTENTS

HAULAGE CONVEYORS

TYPES OF HAULAGE CONVEYORS. Under the general heading of haulage conveyors the main classifications are drag conveyors, flight conveyors, tow conveyors, cable tramways, and car hauls. This Section covers **drag, flight, and tow conveyors.**

The first two divisions—those of drag and flight types of conveyors—involve dragging and pushing of material by means of a chain, or chains, traveling against all sorts of variations in materials and products, making use in some cases of flights and in other cases of the surfaces innate in the chains themselves.

The chain of the third division—tow conveyors—actually tows materials, packaged or otherwise, placed on trucks, dollies, or cars.

Drag Conveyors

EQUIPMENT FOR MOVING MATERIALS ALONG CHANNELS. Drag conveyors consist largely of one or more endless propelling mediums, usually chains or cables, which drag bulk materials in a **trough**, or along a **defined path.**

SINGLE AND MULTIPLE SLIDING-CHAIN CONVEYORS. This type of conveyor consists of **one or more endless chains** sliding in a track or tracks. The materials being carried rest on the chain and are transported along a **defined path.** Fig. 1 shows a multiple-chain drag conveyor operating by this principle.

The chain is usually of the cast pintle combination, barlink, or forged rivetless type. A steel channel most frequently forms the chain track. In some cases this track is equipped with wear bars of steel or other suitable material to provide a good and durable sliding surface.

Applications. Sliding-chain conveyors are used principally for transferring various solid objects in **horizontal or slightly inclined planes.** Objects such as steel billets can be conveyed on a single strand of chain. Four-wheel cars can be moved by placing the two wheels on one side of the car on the chain. Packages are handled on single or multiple sliding chains. Heavy logs in a woodyard are usually transferred on a single moving chain. Large quantities of small logs are carried by multiple strands of parallel chains spaced close together so that they form a sliding bed. Long objects like lumber are placed across multiple strands of parallel chain spaced a few feet apart. All chains move at the same speed and carry the entire load in the direction of travel.

Engineering Characteristics. The designer has a choice of chains in that a variety of simple cast, pintle, combination, barlink, and forged chains is available. The final selection will be based on the analysis of the problem in relation to the operation to be performed, to the shape of the object, and to the capacity of the conveying system. **Double-flex chains** allow a horizontal turn in the conveyor path. For obvious reasons all parts of the channel-shaped chain track or other parts of the conveyor track must be below the top of the chain.

The **chain speeds** should be kept low, around 50 ft. per min., but lightly loaded or high-capacity conveyors may have speeds as high as 200 ft. per min. To improve the operation at higher speeds, water lubrication is provided; for example, on woodyard conveyors in paper mills. Some installations of the same nature use rubber wear bars and water lubrication, with good results.

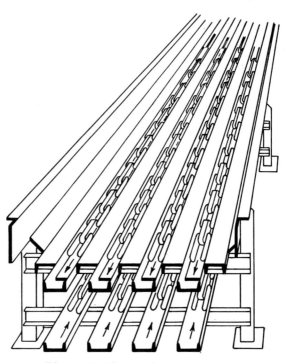

Fig. 1. Multiple-chain drag conveyor.

Because of sliding friction, the **chain pulls** will be rather high, especially where higher tonnages are conveyed, resulting in high power consumption. The installation of conveyors of this type is simple, and if the conveyors are properly designed, they will be trouble-free from a maintenance standpoint. The cost, installed, of this type of conveyor is low. In high-capacity installations the life of the chain is not long—about one to two years on the average. The replacement of chains for this type of conveyor, however, is not costly. The working load of the chain is usually limited to approximately one-sixth to one-fifteenth of the ultimate strength, depending on its wear-resisting characteristics.

Drag-chain conveyors, where the load rests on the chain, are not economical for handling very heavy objects, especially when the weight is concentrated on a small base. A sliding chain should not be used in installations where dust or highly abrasive particles are present, because the excessive wear would greatly shorten the life of the chain. For steep inclines, the plain sliding chain is not suitable. In such cases pusher attachments must be used on the chain.

DRAG-CHAIN CONVEYORS. A wide-chain drag conveyor consists of a single strand of chain with or without integral pusher flights of sufficient width to move a bed of bulk materials effectively along a restricted troughed path, generally on a level plane. The chain is usually made of malleable iron or cast steel, and is equipped with integral wearing shoes and at times pusher flights. The material is usually conveyed on the lower run, the return chain being carried on the upper run by flanged rollers spaced several feet apart or on return tracks (Fig. 2).

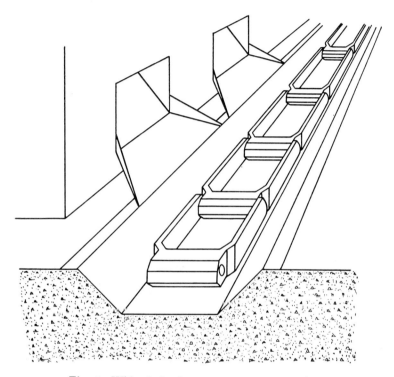

Fig. 2. **Wide-chain drag conveyor construction.**

Applications. This type of conveyor is used extensively for refuse materials such as ashes, clinkers, and sawdust, and also for handling coal, lime, wood chips, and similar bulky materials.

Engineering Characteristics. A wide-chain drag conveyor should be installed when the conditions to be satisfied are low first cost, moderate capacity, and small space requirements.

This type of conveyor is not adaptable to handling extremely free-flowing materials, materials that tend to pack, or materials that are susceptible to damage that will affect salability. The flights will pull through free-flowing materials, such as dry silica sand, and consequently will not effectively move the entire bed of material. Therefore material size is a factor. Materials that tend to pack may build up into undesirable lumps. Damageable objects may become chipped, broken, or scratched during the dragging operation.

The **type of chain** selected for a particular application depends on the nature of the material to be handled. For handling nonabrasive materials a formed steel or light-duty malleable chain is satisfactory. For heavy-duty operation, high temperatures, or abrasive materials, a pearlitic malleable cast-steel or alloy cast-steel chain should be installed.

The cross section of this kind of conveyor is of relatively simple design, and the conveyor is inexpensive. Formed **concrete troughs** are frequently used. For abrasive materials, cast **white-iron troughs** are used. **Mild-steel troughs** are used where the material handled is not excessively abrasive or hot, or where concrete would be impractical.

The **speed** at which this type of conveyor runs depends on the material to be handled and the capacity required. The following are generally the maximum recommendations:

1. Very abrasive materials—Up to 10 ft. per min. and 240 cu. ft. per hr.
2. Mildly abrasive materials—Up to 20 ft. per min. and 660 cu. ft. per hr.
3. Nonabrasive materials—Up to 80 ft. per min. and 1,000 cu. ft. per hr.

Recommended chain pulls for medium-duty conveyors will range up to 6,000 lb., while extra-heavy-duty conveyors will have chain pulls running up to around 20,000 lb.

Maintenance of this type of conveyor is relatively easy because of simple construction of chain and trough. However, since the chain drags either through the material or on the trough which carries the material, no lubrication is feasible except lubricating directly into the grease chamber at the pin articulation points. Consequently, wear of chain flights and trough bed should be frequently checked.

Initial cost is relatively lower than for other types of flight conveyors because the flight, when used, is an integral part of the chain and is not a special bolted attachment. Also, the trough can be of an inexpensive type of construction such as formed concrete.

The limitations to the use of this type of conveyor lie in the adaptability of conveyor to the material to be handled, the quantity to be handled within a given time, and the speed at which the conveyor can be run.

PUSHER-BAR CONVEYORS AND FEEDERS. A pusher-bar conveyor is made up of two strands of endless chain connected by crossbars. The chain rolls or slides on a fixed track and the crossbars move parallel to, but not in contact with, the fixed surface, which is usually a sheet-metal slider bed. Material to be conveyed is pushed along the fixed supporting surface by the crossbars, which are spaced at suitable intervals (Fig. 3).

The chain can be of either the **rolling or sliding type.** The fixed surface can be a slider bed of sheet steel or wood, or—where excessive friction is objectionable—wood or steel rollers. The pusher bar may be a rotatable tube, rollers, or pipe revolving on a rod connecting the two chains, or it may be a fixed member secured between the chains with the necessary attachments.

Pieces being conveyed are loaded at the tail end and discharged over the head end, although the material being conveyed may be dropped out at intermediate points.

Applications. Pusher-bar conveyors are used to convey objects of reasonable solidity which are of such shapes that they can be pushed on one of their own surfaces and slide on another surface.

Rectangular objects, such as cartons and cases, are typical of those most suited for this type of handling, although bags of cement and grain have been successfully transported in this manner. The major industrial groups using this type of conveyor are bottling plants, packing plants, canneries, printing and publishing houses, and the metal industry.

This type of conveyor may be used horizontally, but has its greatest applications when **inclined.** It is highly efficient in elevating or lowering objects from one floor to another while maintaining the desired spacing. It is used extensively as a **booster** to elevate the material from the low end of one section to the high end of the next section in a gravity conveyor system.

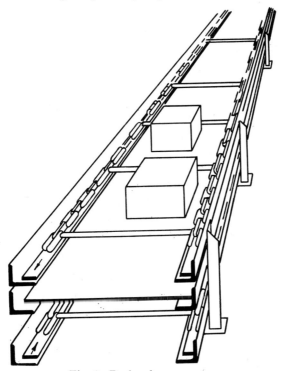

Fig. 3. Pusher-bar conveyor.

When the slider bed is used as the supporting surface, intermediate selective unloading can be accomplished. An opening can be provided in the bed and fitted with a sliding or hinged door which, when opened, will allow a part to drop through.

Pusher-bar conveyors are well suited for use as **scrap-bale conveyors,** since the scrap is usually baled in a pit and the bales must be delivered to a high unloading point, such as the top of a railroad gondola car. They can also be used as feeder conveyors to carry the bales from several balers to a common unloading chute. Orderly discharge can be had at the chute by proper spacing of the pusher bars on the feeders. The handling of bales requires a conveyor of very rugged, thick steel-plate construction, with wear bars for the slider bed and heavy beams for pusher bars.

In cases where the objects being handled can be tumbled about without damage, short pusher-bar feeders can be used to carry the work from any number of locations and unload it at right angles onto one long conveyor.

Engineering Characteristics. The chain can be of either the rolling or sliding type, such as combination, barlink, steel side bar bushed roller, or keystone (rivetless) chain fitted with attachments or extended pins to pick up the crossbars.

Pusher-bar conveyors usually run from 30 to 60 ft. per min. Because of the wide range of applications of this type of conveyor, the chain pull may vary considerably.

Maintenance costs are very low because of the simplicity of design of this type of conveyor. Upkeep is lowest when roller chains and a roller bed are used in the construction. The cost is highest when sliding chains and a slider bed are used. In the latter case it is necessary to replace wearing bars for the chain and to reinforce the slider bed from time to time, depending on the abrasive nature of the material being handled.

ROPE-AND-BUTTON DRAG CONVEYORS. This type of conveyor consists of a single strand of wire rope with buttons or disks affixed at regular spacings over its entire length. It is moved along in a trough constructed of bent steel plate, or concrete, or steel-shod timber. The buttons or disks serve the double purpose of pushing the material handled along the trough and acting as the contact medium with the sprocket which motivates the conveyor.

Applications. Rope-and-button drag conveyors have been used extensively in the pulp industry and for coal handling at mines.

Relative original costs of rope cable conveyors for long centers tend to be somewhat less than the costs of chain-type conveyors for similar service, because of simplicity of construction—a length of cable with flights bolted to it and a simple trough to run in between sprockets. For short centers, chain conveyors usually have a lower original cost. The main use of such conveyors is for handling bulk materials of a kind not harmed by frictional contact with the conveyor trough, such as pulpwood and wood refuse which are found in sawmill or woodworking industries.

Engineering Characteristics. The operation of this kind of conveyor is very simple. The cable runs over adjustable drive sprockets or sheaves which contact the flights or buttons clamped to it. A rope-and-button drag conveyor must have proportionally a longer take-up than chain conveyors to compensate for the stretch of the cable. Early in its life, the cable will stretch substantially. The amount of stretch during the first 2,000 hr. of service is likely to be 80 percent of the cable's total stretch during its service life. After the initial stretch has occurred—and provided the cable is of a size adequate for the pull required—the service life of the cable will probably exceed 5,000 hr.

This kind of cable conveyor is usually operated at 50 to 150 ft. per min. With a 1½-in. diam. cable fitted with 10- to 12-in. diam. flights, a cable conveyor will move up to 100 cords of wood per hr., in 4-ft. lengths. It can carry material on both the top and bottom runs and is particularly adapted for services such as carrying wood pulp to a pile on its top run and later recovering the wood for use on its return run. There are many installations where up to 50,000 cords of wood are handled and stored in this way.

The future possibilities of such a conveyor seem limited because it apparently suffers by comparison with chain and belt types of conveyors which actually carry the load instead of dragging it, thus reducing the breaking of material carried and the maintenance costs of the equipment. Also, the power consumed in overcoming the friction of the material as it is carried along the trough is relatively high.

There do not seem to be any newly developed uses for this type of conveyor that are not prospectively better served by other types of equipment, and new installations are unusual.

The **general life expectancy** of a rope-and-button drag conveyor, as a whole, is high, but maintenance necessary to keep it in operating condition is high also, probably much higher than is the case with competitive chain-type conveyors. Breakdown time is high, mainly because buttons will slip on the cable on account of load shock or heavy pull. When a button gets out of proper space relationship with its neighbor, the cable usually runs off the next sprocket it goes around and can be broken or damaged, adding to the prospect of early failure. Constant vigilance is necessary to keep these flights accurately and securely spaced to avoid breakdown and production delays.

Flight Conveyors

CHARACTERISTICS OF FLIGHT CONVEYORS. A flight conveyor consists of one or more endless propelling mediums, such as chain or other linkage, to which flights are attached to move bulk materials along a defined path.

SINGLE- OR DOUBLE-STRAND FLIGHT CONVEYORS. The single-strand type of conveyor consists of a single endless propelling medium, such as a chain or other linkage, to which various-shaped flights are attached to move

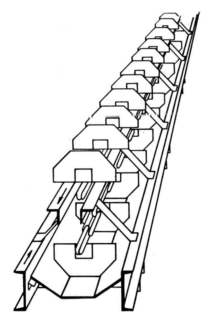

Fig. 4. Construction features of single-strand flight conveyor with scraper flights.

bulk materials along a defined path. The double-strand type uses two endless propelling mediums spaced a fixed distance apart. The flights may be plain or shaped plates which present a pushing face to propel material in a trough. On single-strand types the flights are supported by the trough on the lower, or carrying, run and by a track on the upper, or return, run. Fig. 4 shows a single-strand conveyor of this type. On double-strand types, the flights are more often supported by the chain and the chain by the runways.

Applications. The most frequent application of this type of conveyor is for granular or lumpy (not over 4 in. for the single-strand type, or 8 in. for the double strand) free-flowing, nonabrasive, noncorrosive, or mildly corrosive materials. **Typical materials** of these classes are coal, wood chips, hog fuel, lump lime, crushed ice, foundry sand, sludge, and certain fruits and vegetables.

Engineering Characteristics. This type of conveyor should not be used to convey materials which are sticky, sluggish, or very abrasive or corrosive. Sticky and sluggish materials do not discharge cleanly and tend to build up on the flights. Because the material is scraped along the trough, abrasive materials cause rapid wear on trough and flights. Degradable material which suffers from breakage or lumps is not ordinarily conveyed by this medium. Steel turnings become entangled with flights and chain and so are not to be conveyed by scraper conveyors.

The **path** may be horizontal or inclined but is not usually a combination of the two, although it may be in the case of double strands. Inclines may be as much as 45°, and in come cases more. **Capacities** are reduced when the path is inclined. When the path is a combination of horizontal and inclined travel, the capacity of the conveyor is limited to the capacity of the inclined portion.

Single-chain scraper-flight conveyors are used mostly for low-tonnage and short-center jobs, the double-strand for moderate-tonnage, medium center applications. Detachable, or pintle, bar link, or rivetless chains are all suitable for this service. These chains may run dry—an advantage when the material will come in contact with the chain, although some lubrication should always be provided when feasible. Roller chains are more suitable where hold-down bars are required for vertical curves.

The cross section of the trough is determined by the capacity required and the size of the lumps. **Flight spacing** should be not less than three times the largest lump size. The large lumps should not exceed 10 percent of the total material. Depending on conditions, speeds should not exceed 100 ft. per min.

SINGLE- OR DOUBLE-STRAND FLIGHT CONVEYORS WITH SHOE-SUSPENDED FLIGHTS.

This type of conveyor is similar in construction to the scraper-flight conveyor, previously described, with the exception that the flights are suspended on both carrying and return runs by means of shoes fastened to the flights. On the carrying run the flights do not contact the trough, a small clearance being maintained between the flights and the trough. Because the wear is distributed across the face of the shoes, the life of both trough and flights is extended. The double-strand conveyor has two parallel endless propelling chains.

Applications. Conveyors of this kind are used for the same classes of material as those handled by the single-strand scraper-flight conveyor. They have the additional advantage of prolonging the life of the flights and trough by distributing the wear over the shoes and wear bars. This feature is particularly important when handling even slightly abrasive materials.

Engineering Characteristics. The **path** of a shoe-suspended flight conveyor may be horizontal, inclined, or a combination of both. It is necessary that the radius of vertical curves be as large as possible so as to keep the pressure on the wearing shoes at a minimum.

The same design and engineering considerations apply to shoe-suspended flight conveyors as to scraper-flight conveyors. Similar chains are used and capacity and chain pull are determined in the same manner. **Speed** should not exceed 100 ft. per min.

Single-strand flight conveyors with shoe-suspended flights are suitable for short-center jobs with low tonnage and low chain pull.

Maintenance work on conveyors of this type is somewhat lower in cost than on scraper-flight conveyors. The flights and troughs do not have to be replaced so often, and the shoes and wear bars are not expensive to renew.

SINGLE- OR DOUBLE-STRAND FLIGHT CONVEYORS WITH ROLLER-SUSPENDED FLIGHTS.

Similar in construction to the single-strand scraper-flight conveyor previously described, this kind of conveyor has some additional advantages. The flights of the single-strand type are attached to the chain and to axles on which the outboard or supporting rollers turn. These

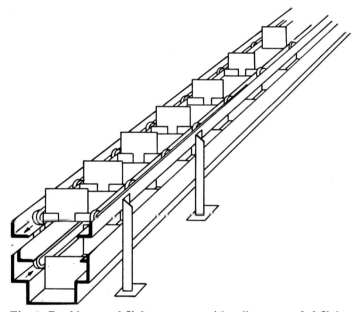

Fig. 5. Double-strand flight conveyor with roller-suspended flights.

rollers, usually flanged to guide the flight, support and carry the flight and the chain. In the double-strand type, engineering chains are used, and the flights are fastened to the side bars of the chain. The power requirements are reduced by substituting **rolling friction** for the sliding friction of the scraper and shoe-suspended flights. Trough, flight, and rollers are designed to provide clearance between the flight and trough. The principle is illustrated by the double-strand conveyor in Fig. 5.

Applications. This conveyor is most frequently used to **transport granular or lumpy, free-flowing, nonabrasive materials**—the same classes that are usually conveyed by the previously mentioned types of scraper conveyors (Figs. 4 and 5). Somewhat larger lumps may be handled, possibly of 5-in. size in the single-strand type where the large lumps do not exceed 10 percent of the total volume. Lumpy materials up to 16 in. in size can be handled in the double-strand type. Sticky, sluggish, abrasive, or corrosive materials are not recommended for this type of equipment for the reasons previously discussed. The double-strand type is best for heavy-tonnage and long-center jobs.

Engineering Characteristics. Flight conveyors with roller-suspended flights are capable of following horizontal, inclined, or combined horizontal and inclined paths. Inclined conveyors should, however, be limited to a maximum angle of inclination of 45°. The roller-suspended flights can negotiate vertical curves better than can the scraper or shoe-suspended flights. Chain pull caused by friction on vertical curves is much less with roller-suspended flights. The capacity of combined horizontal and inclined conveyors is limited by the capacity of the inclined portion.

Pintle chain with MF attachments (M signifying malleable and F being a classification symbol) is most often used for the single-strand type of flight conveyor. Detachable combination, barlink, and rivetless chains can also be used. Suitable attachments are available for these chains. The sprockets used with the MF attachments and pintle chain must be gapped to clear the through-rod which supports the rollers. Rollers are most often cast iron, chilled rim, and bushed if abrasive conditions exist.

Choice of trough section depends upon lump size and total volume to be conveyed. Flight spacing is usually at least three times the largest lump size. A **maximum speed** of 100 ft. per min. is recommended for this kind of conveyor. It should also be noted that in the case of the double-strand type, the most usual cross section shows two channels with the toes turned out. These channels are connected at the lower flange by a plate which forms the bottom of the trough. The largest flight ordinarily used is 18 in. wide by 6 in. high, for the single-strand type, and 36 in. by 12 in. for the double-strand. Beyond this size it is usually more economical to use other types of conveyors.

All types of flight conveyors can be loaded anywhere along the run. They may be discharged at the head end or at intermediate points through openings in the bottom of troughs, which are opened and closed by sliding plates or other means.

The **first cost** of roller-suspended flights is somewhat greater than for either scraper flights or shoe-suspended flights. This added first cost may well be offset by longer life, lower power consumption, and lower maintenance expense.

Tow Conveyors

NATURE OF TOW CONVEYORS. A tow conveyor consists of an endless chain supported by trolleys from an overhead track, or running in a track above, flush with, or under the floor, with means for towing trucks, dollies, or cars.

OVERHEAD TOW CONVEYORS. The overhead tow conveyor is commonly used for towing or pulling trucks, dollies, or cars over a defined path by means of an endless chain, with tow hitches, and strung from trolleys running in, or on, a track located above the floor at sufficient elevation to give headroom for cross traffic (Fig. 6).

Generally the **path** of the conveyor is level and is at a uniform distance from the floor of about 8 or 9 ft. This distance allows sufficient headroom for manual movement of materials by means of hand trucks and gas or electric trucks.

Occasionally, however, the conveyor is installed with slight vertical curves in order to follow floor layouts requiring ramps or other changes of elevation.

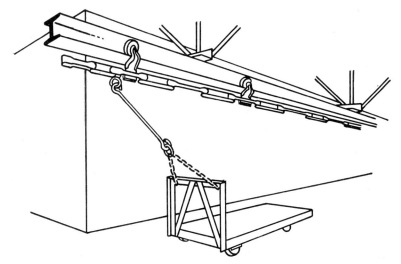

Fig. 6. Typical overhead tow conveyor.

This plan is often objectionable if the slopes exceed rolling friction and require truck guides or other holdback means at the decline points.

Applications. The overhead tow conveyor, where tonnage warrants the initial cost, is probably the most economical way in which to transport material in freight terminals and transfer stations, warehouses, parts depots, and the like. It is particularly efficient where outgoing orders of miscellaneous packaged articles must be made up from stock piles located at widely spaced points. Incoming material may be easily delivered to the stocking areas, or directly transferred or dispatched to outgoing stations.

Engineering Characteristics. The function of the overhead tow is almost identical with that of the underfloor type. The cost of the former is generally less than the underfloor (or infloor) type, and the equipment is more readily installed in existing buildings because no floor excavation is required. In both cases the floor remains clear for normal travel.

The overhead tow conveyor lends itself readily to alteration or extension of path without excessive cost or plant rearrangement.

This kind of conveyor is widely used in railway and express terminals, highway trucking terminals, grocery warehouses, military parts depots, automotive parts shipping stations, and in any location where sufficient tonnage is handled or fluid storage and dispatch are necessary.

The use of this type of conveyor as part of a dispatching system saves greatly on handling costs and reduces the number of articles lost or misdirected, as often occurs when freight handlers act in the capacity of dispatch clerks. Damage to merchandise is less because manual handling is reduced.

Cost per ton on this type of conveyor is probably second only to the fast-moving, bulk-handling belt conveyor.

The **variety of material** handled is great and is limited in size and weight only by the capacity of the carrying trucks. Trucks average 3 ft. wide by 5 ft. long. However, here again sizes vary widely. Capacities of trucks range from less than 500 lb. to over 2 tons. **Tonnage capacity** of the system depends on the load per truck, number of loaded trucks on the line at any one time, and speed of conveyor.

The **path of the conveyor** must be such that it traverses all load, storage, and unload points in the system. Rail, chain, and tow loops on the chain are at an elevation so as to give ample headroom, yet not be too high for easy hitching and unhitching of truck tow chains or hitches. A height of 8 to 9 ft. to the top of the I-beam is generally considered satisfactory. In addition to aisle space required for the conveyor, room should be provided for other trucking.

Speed of the conveyor should be great enough to handle not only the loaded trucks but the empty returns as well, and still have plenty of unoccupied spaces available throughout its entire length so as not to delay loading at any point. The lowest speed that will accomplish the above objectives should be chosen, because loading and unloading difficulties increase with higher speed. A speed of 60 to 80 ft. per min. provides for easy operation, but in most cases a higher speed is necessary to deliver the required tonnage and still maintain the proper percentage of available empty spaces.

Speed in excess of 130 ft. per min. should be avoided. Beyond that speed, loading and unloading trucks from the line become more difficult. Also, trucks traveling at that speed are inclined to drop loose parcels at the turns and at the time of attaching the truck to the moving conveyor.

The most common overhead tow conveyor is made up of a rail of standard 4-in. I-beam section hung or supported from the building roof members. Floor supports are not only expensive but also constitute objectionable floor interferences. The pulling medium is a 4-in.-pitch drop-forged X458 chain strung from ball-bearing trolleys riding on the lower flange of the 4-in. rail. Trolleys are spaced along the chain at 32- or 40-in. intervals, the shorter centers being preferred where short-radius horizontal curves are found. The 40-in. spacing of trolleys is used only to reduce initial cost.

Chain pins forged into special loops are set in the chain at fairly close intervals (say 64 in.) to make them available at as many points as possible for quick loading.

Horizontal roller turns are used at each change of direction in the horizontal path of the conveyor. These turns range from 24 in. in radius up to as great as 12 ft. in radius. High speed ranges and high chain pulls require the larger radii. The trucks negotiate the larger turns with less likelihood of any part of the load falling off. Here again, initial cost often limits the size of the turns. For overhead tow conveyors of this type and speed, the minimum radius should be 36 in.

Permissible length generally covers customer requirements and ranges from less than 500 to over 4,000 ft.

The X458 chain has a working-capacity tension of over 3,000 lb. before stretch becomes troublesome. Drives of this capacity are also available. When loading and length of conveyor cause greater stress in the chain, **multiple drives** involving balancing and synchronizing mechanisms become necessary. The type of drive most often used is that called the **caterpillar drive.** Unlike the sprocket drive, which must be placed only at a horizontal turn, the caterpillar drive may be located anywhere on a straight rail section. The caterpillar drive usually is driven by a smaller auxiliary sprocket and chain with dogs engaging the X458 conveyor chain. Some means for **reducing starting torque** from the electric motor should be used. Multistage electric starters, fluid couplings, or centrifugal-force clutches are all used on high-inertia jobs. See Section 4, Trolley Conveyors, for engineering details.

From time to time a check should be made for **drawbar pull** on all trucks. If the draw pull exceeds 1½ percent to 2 percent—that is, 30 to 40 lb. per ton—the wheel bearings should be checked. Only trucks with antifriction bearings can give this low pull. Plain bearings are not nearly so desirable as a good-quality antifriction wheel.

Trolley wheels should be lubricated at regular intervals, the period to be determined by proper inspection. Check should always be made at such intervals for frozen or tight wheels. They greatly increase drive pull and wear on the rail.

Good **maintenance** is the only way to prolong life of equipment, save on repairs, and prevent costly shutdowns. In the long run, money is saved by proper maintenance. The anticipated life of an overhead tow conveyor, well maintained, should be from 15 to 20 years.

Certain parts, such as the caterpillar drive chain, V belts, roller chain, and roller turn rolls, should be stocked for ready repair replacements.

FLOOR-FLUSH TOW CONVEYORS. The floor-flush tow conveyor is used to move all kinds of loads that have their own carrying mediums, such as wheels, casters, or slides running in guides. The connecting medium between conveyor and load is usually a removable link like a chain with hooks, a rigid drawbar, or a removable dog to push one or more loads (Fig. 7).

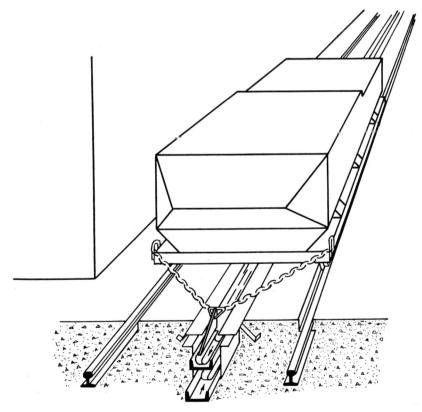

Fig. 7. Floor-flush tow conveyor (sliding type).

Applications. The loads being pulled may be automobiles on auxiliary assembly lines, cars on continuous car-wash lines, dollies on casters that may carry various kinds of unit loads, and other continuous-operation types of work.

Another common use for this type of conveyor is to tow dollies equipped with casters but without any coupling medium between chain and dollies. The dolly is pushed directly on the chain so that the casters on one side of the dolly rest on the chain and the other casters roll on the floor as the chain moves.

This kind of conveyor, called a **floor conveyor,** is used primarily for pulling heavy loads and should not be used when precise sequencing and spacing of loads is required.

Engineering Characteristics. The chains most adaptable for floor-flush tow conveyors are the various combination chains, barlink, steel side-bar bushed, or forged-steel rivetless types without attachments. The pulling medium is hooked into the chain link. These chains are standard and are available from numerous suppliers.

The chain-track cross section consists in most cases of two channels, one above the other, tied together with clip angles. This assembly is set in the floor so that the top of the cross section is flush with the floor, thus allowing trucking over the conveyor. It is advisable to line the channel track with wear bars, preferably of carbon steel. The trench that will have to be cut in the floor is small, approximately 5 to 8 in. wide and 4 to 6 in. deep, except at drive and tail ends. Short-pitch chain, 3 to 6 in., should be installed so that sprocket diameters may be kept as small as possible.

The **speed** of this type of conveyor may be from 2 to 50 ft. per min. Speeds around 10 ft. per min. are the most common.

The **capacity** of floor-flush tow conveyors is limited by the strength of the chain being used. Proper attention must be given to the coefficient of friction of the load-carrying medium when figuring the drawbar pull. **Allowable chain pull** should not exceed one-sixth to one-fifteenth of the ultimate breaking strength of the chain used.

Very little **maintenance** work, except periodic lubrication of the chain, is required to keep the conveyor in proper operating condition. The lubricant can be applied by wick-feed near the drive before the chain enters the return track.

The **cost** of a conveyor of this kind is extremely low because of its simplicity and the fact that all parts are standard stock items and are readily available.

With reasonable maintenance, the life of a conveyor of this kind is long. However, the chain, being of a sliding type, and the track will wear considerably unless they are kept well lubricated. Maintenance should include periodic checking of wear on chain pins to prevent a breakdown. Chain links and pins can be replaced in a very short time with ordinary tools.

This type of conveyor is limited to normal conditions. Any abrasive substance that collects on chain or chain track will wear these parts out in a relatively short time, even if they are well lubricated.

UNDERFLOOR TOW CONVEYORS. The underfloor tow conveyor consists of an endless chain supported by trolleys, wheels, or rollers running in a suitable track below the floor level. The conveyor chain may also slide in a channel or angle track, in which case a replaceable wear bar is usually installed to prevent wear and costly replacement of the main supporting track itself. Usually there is a narrow slot in the floor through which a retractable pin is dropped to connect the truck to the chain below (Fig. 8).

Applications. Underfloor tow conveyors are used for towing a wide variety of products—army tanks, airplanes, automobiles, trucks, wash racks, and so on—on assembly lines in manufacturing plants. They are more commonly used in grocery warehouses, air-base terminals, wholesale paper and stationery warehouses, and freight-handling terminals. In warehouses, when orders are to be made up for shipment, order-filling clerks will attach trucks to the towline. An order-filling process may be used in which each truck carries an order-filling form from section to section of the warehouse, gradually picking up the entire load.

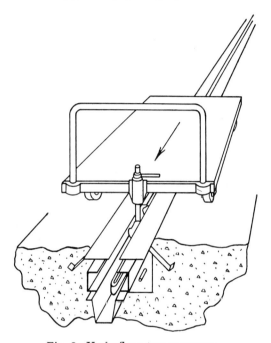

Fig. 8. Underfloor tow conveyor.

In freight warehouses the trucks are usually removed from the conveyor for loading from freight cars or highway trucks and returned to the conveyor for delivery to the area of the terminal where local delivery trucks are being loaded for over-the-road transportation, or vice versa.

Investigation of a particular underfloor installation revealed that:

1. Labor costs were reduced 15%.
2. Freight handled per month was increased by 20%.
3. Shift time was cut from 11 hr. to 9 hr.
4. Number of men on day shift, using conventional methods of handling, was reduced from 60 to 42.
5. Number of men on night shift, using conventional methods of handling, was reduced from 40 to 28 men.
6. Cost of installation was only a little over 50% of the cost of any alternate handling system.

While underfloor tow conveyors may be designed for exceptionally heavy loads, such as towing army tanks under assembly, they are more commonly used in warehouses for the transfer or handling of packages and merchandise. **Speeds** in such cases vary from a few feet per minute to a maximum of about 160 ft. per min., depending on the operation being performed, the production schedule, and allowance for curves to prevent material from sliding off the truck.

Engineering Characteristics. On long conveyors, several synchronized drives may be used to keep the chain pull within the limits of the allowable unit stress of the chain in use. For conventional types, maximum pull equals 4,000 lb., using 458 rivetless chain.

The underfloor tow conveyor is operated by a **drive** usually located in a pit and covered by floor plates that are reinforced to carry any reasonably heavy traffic that may pass over them. In some installations the drive may be hung from the ceiling below, or placed on the operating floor in such a position to be clear of traffic.

Spring, counterweighted, or screw-type **take-ups** or other means are required to keep the chain taut and to prevent accumulation of slack chain resulting from wear, or expansion and contraction from temperature changes.

Various forms of trucks, cars, or dollies are towed by means of short lengths of chain that hook into the main conveyor chain, or by means of various types of pusher dogs or attachments on the main chain that contact pins or pusher bars on the trucks.

The conventional underfloor tow conveyor is equipped with opposing collapsible dogs spaced to suit the trucks and the convenience of the operators. The trucks are each equipped with a sliding pin that can be lowered into a slot in the floor, thus allowing the operator to connect the truck to, or disconnect it from, the conveyor, at will.

The **vertical incline** of such a tow conveyor is limited to 15 degrees to prevent packages from sliding from the trucks.

The chain-on-flat type of conveyor is confined to straight-line travel in plane, the sprockets operating in a vertical plane. However, only changes in elevation are possible, because the chain is able to flex in one direction only.

The chain-on-edge type of conveyor is confined to horizontal changes in direction of travel, the sprockets operating in a horizontal position. Changes of direction are usually accomplished by means of a series of rollers (roller turns) around which the chain travels.

Some chains are flexible in both directions, in which case changes in direction are possible, using radii within the range of chain flexibility.

The most commonly used chains are those of the rivetless type 348, 458, 658, 678, and so on, and the combination type C188 and C131. Other types of chain for specially designed systems are also used.

PUSHER-CHAIN CONVEYORS. The pusher-chain conveyor consists of a single endless chain operated either **on edge or on flat.** To distinguish one kind from the other, the one type is sometimes called the "chain-on-edge" floor conveyor, and the other type is designated as the "chain-on-flat" floor conveyor (Figs. 9 and 10).

The chain-on-edge type has some advantages over the chain-on-flat type in that the conveyor can be made to go around horizontal curves, thus permitting carriers to return to their original starting point. The chain-on-flat type can move its carriers in only one direction.

The drop-forged rivetless chain is the type that makes it perhaps the most economical and the one most generally used on pusher-chain conveyors, because it weighs less per unit of strength and has fewer component parts than most other

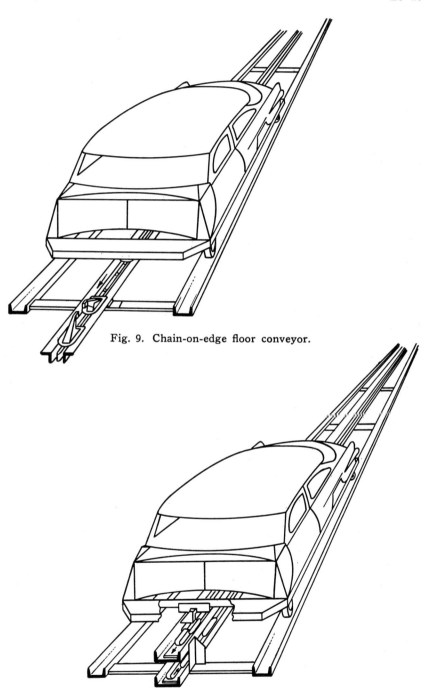

Fig. 9. Chain-on-edge floor conveyor.

Fig. 10. Chain-on-flat floor conveyor.

types of conveyor chains. It is also flexible for traversing vertical or horizontal curves. This chain can be assembled, or sections can be replaced, without the use of tools, and the sections cannot become disconnected while in operation.

Applications. These conveyors usually operate in conjunction with cars or dollies which transport the product during processing, fabrication, or assembly. Many installations of this type of conveyor are found in automobile-body assembly plants.

Another range of applications includes kiln cars carrying refractories, lumber, or cement blocks to be dried, and other materials to be kiln-treated. The conveyor is usually located at the entrance end of the kiln, where there is room for a number of cars which will be pushed, one by one, into the kiln. A removable pusher dog is used which engages a chain link and pushes the last car, thereby moving all cars ahead at one time. In operation, the conveyor will run far enough to push one car into the kiln at the entrance end at the same time that a car is pushed out at the exit end, since the cars operate bumper to bumper. The pusher dog is then moved back and another car is added at the beginning point of the line.

Engineering Characteristics. Different designs of pusher and holdback dogs are attached to the chain and project above the floor to engage the underside of the cars. To provide clearances between the cars when they are traveling around turns, these dogs are usually set in pairs and spaced on the chain to suit the length of the cars. The holdback dog prevents the cars from running ahead when the conveyor is stopping or going down slopes.

The **chain-on-edge conveyor** also has bars called "riders," which are wider than the chain, and are spaced at intervals of 4 to 6 pitches. These bars allow the chain and dogs to slide along the top of the chain track, which is anchored to the floor.

The **chain-on-flat conveyor,** with dogs attached, travels in a channel track, and the return run of chain is also guided in a channel track immediately underneath. The upper and lower channel tracks are anchored together to the floor. The cars or dollies usually have swivel casters running in inverted channels, or V wheels running on the heel of an angle, or the standard flange wheels running on rails; the last type is used for carrying the heavier loads.

The pusher-chain conveyor is serving many industries where a 4-wheel car is needed, as in the assembly of automobiles, trucks, tanks, planes, welding fixtures, and so forth. The **speed** of these conveyors may vary from a few inches per minute to 100 ft. or more per min., using from 1- to 50-hp. motors. The speeds may also be constant, intermittent, or variable to meet any conditions. The chain pull may be up to 10,000 lb. for the chain-on-edge type and up to 60,000 lb. or more for the chain-on-flat type, depending on the rating of the chain used.

The **drive** for the chain-on-edge conveyor may be of either the sprocket or caterpillar type, while the drive for the chain-on-flat conveyor is usually chain- or gear-driven.

Various types of **overload protective devices** are used on all pusher-conveyor drives to guard against overloading the conveyor.

Pusher-chain conveyors are electrically operated by push buttons or limit switches and are sometimes interlocked with other conveyors.

VIBRATING AND OSCILLATING CONVEYORS

CONTENTS

VIBRATING AND OSCILLATING CONVEYORS

CLASSIFICATION. There is considerable overlap in the use of the terms "oscillating" and "vibrating" as designations of the motions of the conveyors described in this section. It has been suggested that classification on the basis of frequency and amplitude should be adopted as a rough rule of thumb when considering a specific conveyor, until such time as research comes forth with a designation generally acceptable throughout the entire industry. The recommended designating terms are used in this section.

VIBRATING FEEDERS AND CONVEYORS. The subject of electrical and mechanical or oscillating vibrating feeders and conveyors needs careful explantation and definition. To make this subject usable and reliable for the engineer, both electric and mechanical **feeders** are defined in contrast to electrical and mechanical **conveyors.**

A **vibrating feeder** may be a trough or tube flexibly supported and vibrated to convey bulk material or objects. Vibration may be induced electrically with a balanced electric power unit, or mechanically through the centrifugal force generated by rotating unbalanced weights. The feeder trough is designed so that it is only long enough to stop the material, at its natural angle of repose, from running off the end of the deck when the feeder is standing idle. A feeder is further defined as a machine whose capacity can be varied over a wide range without changing the bin opening or making mechanical adjustments.

In contrast to the above definition for a feeder, the **vibrating conveyor** may be a trough or tube flexibly supported, and vibration may be induced electrically or mechanically. The vibrating conveyor may be of any length desired, and hence the angle of repose of the material is not the determining factor. Usually, the vibrating conveyor is designed to handle a fixed rate of flow of material. When the rate of flow must be carefully controlled the electric type of feeder may be preferred.

Before any detailed explanations of the many types of vibrators are given, it is necessary to specify the types of materials usually handled.

KINDS OF MATERIALS HANDLED. Any **granular material** which is not sticky or tacky can be successfully conveyed. Vibrators in operation in a wide field of industries are handling over 400 different materials ranging in weight (density) from 5 lb. per cu. ft. to 400 lb. per cu. ft., and ranging in unit size from 5-ft. cubes to powder. For practical purposes, all capacities given are based upon dry, granular, free-flowing material weighing 100 lb. per cu. ft. For materials weighing more or less than 100 lb. per cu. ft., capacity is expressed in direct proportion to 100-lb.-per-cu-ft. material.

Vibrators handle either **hot** (800° F.) **or cold** (−30° F.) **materials,** and many **wet materials** which are free of sticky talc or clay. Vibrators handle these materials with open or enclosed conveying surfaces, and may be furnished gas-tight if required. Special conveyors handling material up to 1,200° F. are in use.

Vibrating Feeders

CHOICE OF VIBRATOR. The choice of a vibrating feeder or conveyor must be carefully made after the following facts are ascertained:

1. What distance must material be moved?
2. Is variable or remote control of rate of feed required?
3. Will material convey and respond to vibration?
4. Is space available for the vibrating type of conveyor?
5. Will the conveyor be carried on ground supports, or must the unit be self-contained and impart no vibration to the superstructure?
6. Will the electric or the mechanical vibrator be more economical?

After the user has studied his problem in the light of the six basic factors given above, he will then be in a position to evaluate and select the correct type of vibrator to use for the particular installation. It is obvious that neither the electric nor mechanical vibrator competes with an elevating or an apron conveyor, if the material must be raised any great distance. Likewise, these conveyors cannot compete with a belt conveyor in first cost or operating costs when the material must be transported over long distances. Vibrators do, however, furnish the engineer with an efficient type of conveyor which, when properly selected and applied, is best and most economical for its purposes.

ELECTRIC VIBRATORS. The widest use of vibrators is in controlled volumetric feeding. The most common uses are as follows:

1. Feeding from stock piles or silos to belt conveyors.
2. Feeding from dump hopper to apron, belt or elevating conveyors.
3. Feeding to primary and secondary crushers, impactors or hammermills.
4. Feeding to scales, sacking machines, trucks, furnaces or charge cars.
5. Spreading feed to driers, screens, packing or sorting tables.
6. Feeding from foundry shakeouts to belts and apron conveyors.

In the services listed above, the electric vibrating feeder finds its most extensive applications. The principle of operation of the electric vibrator may be explained as follows:

A balanced electrical vibrator operates from any standard alternating or pulsating direct current. Either of these currents, when passed through the stator, creates a series of interrupted magnetic pulls on the armature. The four principal parts of the vibrator are:

1. The main frame—a heavy casting or steel member which acts as a reactionary weight in the vibrator and, essentially, as its foundation.
2. The vibrator bars, which are fastened rigidly at both ends to the main frame, but are free to flex at the center.
3. The center clamp, which is mounted within the main frame, rigidly attached to the vibrator bars at their center, but free to oscillate without touching the main frame. The center clamp is the means for directly connecting the power-unit to the deck.
4. The vibrating motor, which consists of a stationary stator mounted on the main frame, and an oscillating armature fastened to the center of the vibrator bar by means of the center clamp. An air-gap separates the armature from the stator at all times so that no physical contact takes place.

OPERATION OF ELECTRIC VIBRATORS. Alternating current, or pulsating direct current, is employed for the operation of electric vibrators. Either of these currents, when passed through the stator, creates a series of interrupted magnetic pulls on the armature. One-half of each vibrating stroke is powered by one of these magnetic pulls. During this half of the stroke the vibrator bars are bent toward the magnet as indicated by the line *ABA* in Fig. 1.

Fig. 1. Movement of vibrator bars.

A **restoring force** is thus built up in the bars, and when the magnetic pull is interrupted this force supplies the power for the second half of the vibrating stroke. The bars return to their former position, and by their own momentum onto a position *ACA*, at which point, in a properly tuned vibrator, another magnetic pull begins. Thus the **bars complete one full vibration**—from *ACA* to *ABA* and back to *ACA*—with each electrical impulse.

The **length of the stroke** is adjustable, in any given machine, from the maximum downward. The maximum allowable depends upon the size and design of the particular vibrator, and may be either $\frac{1}{32}$ in., $\frac{1}{16}$ in., or $\frac{1}{8}$ in., as the case may be.

The **power unit** is attached to the feeder or conveyor deck at a slight angle, usually 20°. In operation, as the deck moves forward, it also moves upward at this angle, and as it moves backward, it descends at the same angle. Hence, material on the deck is lifted forward and upward.

The **movement of the material** is shown in Fig. 2. It is important to note that the material, being free to move, does not return with the backward movement of the deck, but falls under the slower force of gravity until it is intercepted by

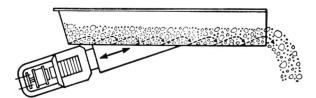

Fig. 2. Particle movement of material on vibrating conveyor.

the next forward and upward stroke. Thus, while in appearance the movement of the material is that of a uniform flowing stream, it is, in reality, a continuous series of rapid, short forward hops which are imperceptible to the eye. This hopping action keeps the material in suspension so that there is no sliding action on the deck surface. Abrasive wear on the deck is therefore negligible, and on large tonnages material can be handled most economically because deck wear is not a serious problem.

Speed of Travel of Material. The speed of travel of any material over the deck of the vibrator depends upon the length of the stroke, i.e., the amplitude of vibration. This stroke is usually controlled manually by means of a rheostat, and capacity may be instantly changed from minimum to maximum while the feeder is running, by merely turning the handle of the rheostat.

Electric vibrating feeders or conveyors may also be automatically controlled by scales, automatic vibration controllers, or ampere-demand meters. The response of an electric vibrator is instantaneous, because there are no mechanical parts which require time for changing position.

The electric vibrating feeder or conveyor may be either supported by shock absorbers or suspended from shock absorbers. When the conveyor is properly installed, no vibration is transmitted to the superstructure, hence the application of the unit, in so far as steelwork is concerned, is simply a matter of designing the steelwork to carry the load of the vibrator plus the material load.

To obtain the **maximum efficiency** from any given vibrating feeder, it should be installed as illustrated in Fig. 3, so that the deck is removed from the bin load, and so that the deck is long enough to prevent the material from running off at its natural angle of repose.

Vibrators are furnished in widths from 1 in. up to 72 in., and in various lengths. Fig. 4 illustrates the capacity in tons per hr. (TPH) of vibrators 12 in. wide and 24 in. wide, and also gives the required horsepower.

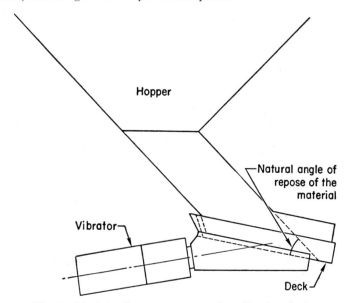

Fig. 3. Ideal loading arrangement for vibrating feeder.

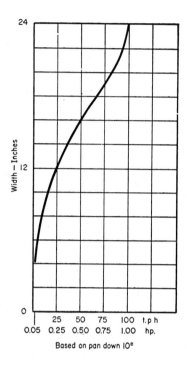

Jeffrey Mfg. Co.

Fig. 4. Capacity chart for electric vibrating feeders, 12 in. to 24 in.

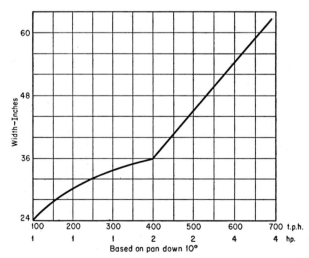

Jeffrey Mfg. Co.

Fig. 5. Capacity chart for electric vibrating feeders, 24 in. to 60 in.

Fig. 5 gives the capacities in tons per hr. (TPH) for 36-in.-, 48-in.-, and 60-in.-wide feeders, along with the required horsepower. Both of these charts are based upon granular, dry, free-flowing, 100-lb.-per-cu.-ft. material.

Electric Vibrating Conveyors

OPERATION OF THE ELECTRIC VIBRATING CONVEYOR. The electric vibrating conveyor may be defined as a multi-power-unit vibrator, the length of which is dictated by the distance over which it is desired to convey the material. The deck may be tubular or pan-type, of any width, diameter, or length, powered by a multiplicity of power units, the number and size of which depend upon the deck size and the particular operation for which the conveyor is to be used. The power units may be located either below or above the deck. The entire conveyor may be either supported or suspended on vibration absorbers, so that no objectionable vibration is transmitted to the superstructure. The **material movement** on the conveyor is the same as that shown in Fig. 2, hence there is very little wear when abrasive material is handled. Electric vibrating conveyors are furnished in tubular sizes from 4 in. to 26 in. in diameter and in pan sizes from 5 in. up to 60 in.

In figuring the **capacity of an electric vibrating conveyor,** when operated level and handling dry, granular, 100-lb.-per-cu.-ft. material, one can figure from 30 to 45 ft. per min. travel for either the tube or pan type. On the pan type, however, depths can be figured at 6 in. to 9 in., and the tubes are to be figured

Jeffrey Mfg. Co.

Fig. 6. Electric vibrating conveyor with 50-ft. tube 14 in. in diameter.

one-half full. When either type is operated down a 10° slope, capacity is materially increased.

Electric vibrating conveyors are ideally suited for **handling hot, gaseous, or abrasive materials** or for **toxic materials** such as iron sinter, lead sinter, and zinc sinter which must be confined within the conveyor. They are also used for handling materials where the decks must be self-cleaning. These units are heavy-duty equipment, designed for continuous 24-hr. service with very little maintenance. They are in no way competitive with belts, screws, or aprons, and should be used where problems involve strict control of a hazardous material or temperatures so high that the normal conveyor cannot handle them.

These units are frequently used for handling the discharge from sintering machines, where the average temperature of the material will be 600° F. Where higher temperatures must be handled, the tubes or decks may be water-jacketed and materials up to 1,800° F. handled with safety. Naturally, these conveyors, in accord with their weight and size, are not cheap. This fact has led to the development of a mechanically operated vibrating conveyor which will be subsequently described.

Fig. 6 is a typical application of a 14-in.-diam. tube having two discharge points and handling a hot, gaseous, toxic sinter.

Mechanical Vibrating and Oscillating Conveyors

USE OF THE MECHANICAL VIBRATING FEEDER. The principal use of this machine is for installations where little or no control of the feed rate is required. For granular, free-flowing, 100-lb.-per-cu.-ft. material, the speed of travel along the deck is figured at 30 ft. per min. when the feeder is operated level. When the same feeder is turned down 10°, the speed of travel is 45 ft. per

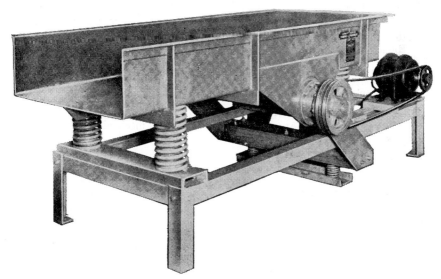

Hewitt-Robins, Inc.

Fig. 7. Heavy-duty mechanical vibrating feeder complete with vibrator mechanism and supports.

min. and the depth of material which can be conveyed is 6 to 9 in. The maximum depth of material that can be moved or fed may be assumed to be equal to two-thirds of pan width, depending on the physical nature of the material.

The mechanical vibrating feeder consists of a free-floating, four-bearing eccentric shaft which is directly connected to a suspended trough on one side and an offset counterweighted arm on the other. By changing the weight and direction or angle of the counterweighted arm, the amplitude of the stroke may be varied from 0 to $\frac{1}{2}$ in., and hence some control of capacity may be obtained. The unit usually operates at from 800 to 1,000 r.p.m. and at an amplitude of $\frac{3}{16}$ to $\frac{3}{8}$ in. This machine may be equipped with a **variable-speed drive** which, in turn, controls the capacity and feed variation.

Fig. 7 is an illustration of a mechanical vibrating feeder complete with its supporting frame and spring supports for the deck and its counterweights.

APPLICATIONS OF MECHANICAL VIBRATING AND OSCILLATING CONVEYORS. Mechanical vibrating and oscillating conveyors were designed to transport or convey materials having the same characteristics as those given above, over greater distances but at lower costs than those for electric vibrating conveyors.

A unit of this kind offers advantages in that it is self-cleaning; conveys abrasive, friable materials which must be handled gently; and safely transports hot and gaseous materials. Since the conveyor operates on the same principles as the electric conveyor, the wear surfaces last for long periods, because the material is being lifted or ratcheted forward. Where it is desirable, the conveyor decks may be lined with wear-resisting steel or rubber.

The engineer contemplating an installation of this kind of conveyor should be careful in applying it for the desired purpose because of vibration problems which may arise in connection with the use of the conveyor.

There are two principal types of this conveyor:

1. The **unbalanced type,** which may impart vibration to the building structure.
2. The **balanced (or counterbalanced) type,** which minimizes vibration in the building structure.

Manufacturers of these conveyors should be consulted when installations over long unsupported spans are being contemplated, especially in the case of the unbalanced type of conveyor.

CLASSES OF MECHANICAL VIBRATING AND OSCILLATING CONVEYORS. There are three major classes of mechanical vibrating and oscillating conveyors:

1. Low-capacity mechanical vibrating conveyors.
2. Medium-capacity mechanical vibrating or oscillating conveyors.
3. High-capacity mechanical vibrating or oscillating conveyors.

The applications and special features of these classes of conveyors are covered in the following discussion.

Low-Capacity Mechanical Vibrating Conveyors. Conveyors in this class carry materials at a rate ranging from a few pounds per hr. up to 30 tons per hr. Normally these conveyors are of the unbalanced type requiring firm foundations. When they are to be installed off the floor, or in ceiling structures, the manufacturer should be consulted. There are counterbalanced units available, but the cost is increased.

These small, compact, light-duty conveyors are finding wide acceptance in industry for **transporting materials over long distances.** One of the basic reasons for the popularity of these conveyors is the fact they are pre-engineered and stocked for quick delivery. They are also simple and dependable. Essentially, the conveyor consists of four parts:

1. The deck or conveying trough (standard widths: 5 in., 8 in., 12 in., 18 in., 24 in.)
2. The vibrator bars or coil springs which provide direction of conveying and also restoring force.
3. The base, usually a channel, which is bolted to the building or concrete foundation, and is the member upon which the deck or trough is supported by the vibrating bars or springs.
4. The drive, usually a simple eccentric directly connected to the deck. These drives may be obtained open or totally enclosed and are designed to shake a given weight or number of feet of deck. When the distance is greater than one is designed to handle, another drive is added.

These low-capacity vibrating conveyors operate at, or near, their natural frequency. The horsepower required is small. Speeds of travel of material along the conveyor vary, depending upon moisture, fineness, and temperature. For granular, free-flowing materials, 20 to 40 ft. per min. is normal. Likewise, the depth of material that will be conveyed is affected by the above factors. Usually, 3 in. is considered a maximum. These small-capacity conveyors must not be overloaded, and where the problem is one which involves peak loads, a wider conveyor must be installed. Otherwise, damage to the conveyor and spillage on the floor or pit will result.

Normally these units are installed level. The manufacturer should be consulted if an upgrade is required, or if the temperature of the material is over 250° F. Fig. 8 supplies a general chart on horsepower requirements, and capacity in tons per hr. (TPH). The chart in Fig. 8 omits deck widths. The tonnage handled and the distance over which it is conveyed are the two factors which determine the horsepower required.

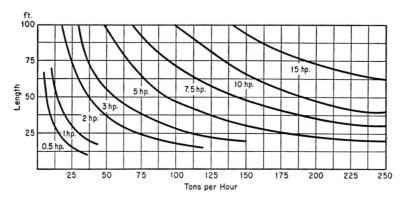

Fig. 8. Horsepower chart for mechanical vibrating conveyors.

Medium-Capacity Mechanical Vibrating or Oscillating Conveyors. Conveyors in this group may be classified on a tonnage basis as having to convey from 20 tons up to 50 tons per hr.

Normally, these stocked or pre-engineered conveyors are of the unbalanced type which require firm foundations. Where such conveyors must be installed above floors, or in roof structures, counterbalanced conveyors are available.

The **four principal parts of the unbalanced conveyor** are as follows:

1. Deck or conveying trough (standard widths: 12 in., 18 in., 24 in.)
2. Vibrator bars, torsion bars, or coil springs—or combinations of these parts: provide direction of conveying and restoring force to the vibration.
3. Base: usually a channel or angle-irons bolted directly to building supports or concrete foundations. This member serves to support and align vibrator bars and conveying trough.
4. Drive: usually a simple eccentric directly connected to the deck. Drives are available, open or totally enclosed, and are designed to shake a given weight or number of feet of deck. Where the weight of the deck or the distance encountered is too great, another drive is added.

Where a **counterbalanced unit** is furnished, somewhat greater cost is involved, sufficient headroom is required, and the location where the conveyor is to be placed in the building must be decided upon. All these factors influence the choice of conveyor to be installed.

Normally, these conveyors operate at, or near, their **material-feed frequency,** and the horsepower required to run them is small. For granular, free-flowing material, a flow of 20 to 30 ft. per min. and a 4- to 8-in. depth are usually the maxima. If peak loads are to be encountered, a deck of sufficient width should be provided, so that there will be no spillage and no damage to the conveyor. Usually these units operate on a level plane.

The manufacturer should be consulted if an upgrade is required. Likewise, if materials over 250° F. are to be handled, the manufacturer should be so informed in order that heat-expansion decks may be furnished. Fig. 9 illustrates one design used where the deck is carried on springs to allow for expansion and contraction caused by heat. These conveyors may be furnished for scalping, cooling, and drying applications.

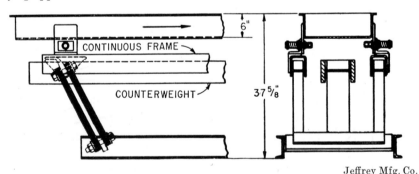

Jeffrey Mfg. Co.

Fig. 9. **Heat-expansion mounting for vibrating conveyor.**

High-Capacity Mechanical Vibrating or Oscillating Conveyors. These conveyors may be classified on a tonnage basis as having to convey from 50 to 500 tons per hr. Problems where tonnages of this magnitude are to be handled usually require special design and fabrication, and it becomes especially important to choose the correct design. The location and service will determine whether the unit should be unbalanced or counterbalanced. A conveyor handling 250 tons per hr. may entail serious vibration problems unless all factors are known and taken into account in the design of the installation.

Mechanical vibrating and oscillating conveyors are available which are **completely counterbalanced and spring-mounted** like the electric vibrating conveyors. They may be installed above floor levels or across silos. **Counterbalancing** may be accomplished in a number of different ways; as shown in the following tabulation:

1. Use of a counterweight independently supported on its own cantilever bars, as shown in Fig. 10.
2. Use of a dynamic balancer to absorb shock.
3. Splitting the conveyor into two equally weighted sections with the drive located in the center and arranged so that, as the eccentrics operate, the two sections oppose one another.
4. Use of dual troughs, mounted one above the other, with the eccentric located between the two decks.

These **heavy-duty conveyors** are widely used for handling hot castings, abrasives, and gaseous materials. Units are available for handling materials from 400° F. to 1,500° F., and where necessary may be water-jacketed. Such heavy-duty units are ideally suited for eliminating dust and spillage, and provide continuous service with very little maintenance.

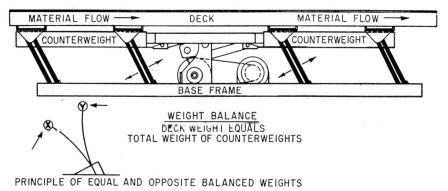

PRINCIPLE OF EQUAL AND OPPOSITE BALANCED WEIGHTS

Jeffrey Mfg. Co.

Fig. 10. Counterbalanced vibrating conveyor.

Fig. 8 gives data determining horsepower requirements. For figuring capacities, a normal speed of 40 ft. per min. is assumed, with a depth of 4 to 6 in. of material, depending upon the kind of material to be conveyed. Units made to fit into the space limitations of individual plants may vary from 24 to 42 in. in height, depending upon width of pan and service required. They are designed to travel as slowly as 15 ft. per min. and as fast as 100 ft. per min.

OSCILLATING (SHAKING) CONVEYORS. The oscillating (often called "shaking") conveyor has long been employed underground for conveying coal and minerals. In recent times it has been used for handling hot castings and sand, and hot abrasive sinters, above ground.

The drive-unit must be securely mounted on firm foundations. The drive—by means of gearing, bearings and linkage—changes the angular motion of an electric motor into an oscillating motion that is transmitted to the pan or trough of the conveyor. This motion is in the form of a forward-and-quick-return stroke, which causes the material to slide along the pan.

The decks are sectionalized and are furnished in widths of 12 to 36 in. and in lengths of 6 to 16 ft., with pan depths of 6 to 18 in. The conveying trough is mounted on rollers which are spaced along the underside of the conveyor. Conveyors may be furnished in sizes up to 500 ft. in length, and in capacities up to 100 tons hourly. Manufacturers have developed proper dimensions for width of pan and type of drive.

PNEUMATIC CONVEYORS

CONTENTS

CONTENTS *(Continued)*

PNEUMATIC CONVEYORS

Pneumatic Pipeline Conveyors

PRESSURE PNEUMATIC CONVEYING. This term generally identifies a pneumatic pipeline conveyor, into which dry, pulverized materials are fed mechanically, and their transportation to the destination by the expanding energy of compressed air. The basic units of such a system are:

1. A positive air-lock feeder.
2. The piping system.
3. A product receiver.
4. The air supply, either a positive-pressure blower or an air compressor.
5. A dust filter (optional).

Generally, this type of conveying is further characterized by its relatively dense **mixture of solids and air,** and movement of the solid particles is brought about by **comparatively low-velocity fluid streams,** in which the material remains suspended until discharged into a receiver. Thus, materials having widely diversfied particle size may be conveyed. (Pneumatic package conveyors are discussed in the section on Package Conveyors.)

Classification of Pressure-Type Systems. Pressure-type pneumatic pipe conveying systems may be divided into three classifications, namely, applications which normally use: (1) the rotary air lock feeder, (2) the solids pump, and (3) the blow tank. Each classification differs slightly in design and method of operation, but certain inherent advantages are offered by all of them:

1. Materials can be conveyed literally anywhere that a pipeline can be placed.
2. Since the necessity of straight-line conveying is eliminated, new-plant design can be simplified, with emphasis on convenience in storing and handling.
3. Existing rail and highway facilities can be utilized.
4. Old-plant modernization and additions of new equipment can be accomplished easily without limiting conveying system design.
5. Materials can be delivered rapidly to remote areas within a plant, for distances far beyond the practical distances of mechanical conveyors.
6. In many instances, several materials can be successfully conveyed with the same equipment, without contamination.
7. Dust nuisances, dust hazards, and mechanical hazards are eliminated.
8. The number of delivery points to which a single system can deliver material is almost limitless, and a system can usually be operated by one man from a single remote-control panel.
9. Maintenance costs are reasonable as compared to other methods of conveying.
10. The self-cleaning and sanitary features of this method of conveying are in many cases of great importance.

Factors in Selecting the System. In selecting any type of pneumatic conveying system some of the many **variables** which must be considered are:

1. Desired capacity of the system.
2. Required conveying distance (horizontal and vertical).

3. Particle size (shape and specific gravity).
4. Air requirements (pressure, volume, density and velocity).
5. Piping system (diameter, material and configuration).

It is also most important that the **physical characteristics of the material** being conveyed be carefully considered, for it is frequently the case that friability, abrasiveness, corrosiveness, and temperature must be major design considerations. Thus, it can be seen that proper selection and application are made difficult by the multiple variables encountered. Engineering and application experience, however, usually indicates to the specialist the type of system which can best accomplish the desired results.

For **short conveying distances** and elevations, equipment and installation costs favor mechanical conveyors in most instances. As the conveying distance and/or elevation increases, or when there are several changes in direction and/or multiple delivery points to be served, the economic advantages of pneumatic conveying increase tremendously. The reasons for these cost relationships will be obvious if it is realized that in any pneumatic conveyor the **basic items are common to all systems,** and that long or complex systems simply involve more piping and valves, with increased motor and compressor sizes.

It is difficult to make a general statement as to relative **power consumption** by comparison with mechanical conveyors. For instance, the solids pump compares favorably with mechanical conveyors in respect to power, regardless of distance. Other types compare unfavorably for short-distance conveying, but show progressively greater power savings for medium- and long-distance conveying. The question of power consumption, within the last decade, has in fact become increasingly less important in comparison to labor-saving methods in the over-all evaluation of economic values. Pneumatic conveying, in a great many instances, affords the user many of these economic values, plus such intangibles as its ability to self-clean, improved plant appearance, reduced housekeeping costs, and improved labor relations.

Since it has been established that pressure pneumatic systems embody similar basic equipment, it is important that equipment application be explored with respect to each classification.

ROTARY POSITIVE-AIR-LOCK FEEDER. Generally, the application which employs the rotary positive-air-lock feeder will require that material be fed into the transport piping system from a bin or container, and that it be transported through the piping system to some designated storage or process-use point. The feeder must therefore perform a dual function: (1) It must feed the material into the piping system; (2) it must maintain a positive air seal between the incoming material and the system's transport air. Thus, the ability of the feeder to maintain a positive air lock against the air pressure required for material conveying generally indicates the application area for this type of equipment. Normally, this class of equipment is used when air pressure requirements do not exceed 10 lb. per sq. in. gage.

Air in appropriate quantities must, of course, be available at the point of material introduction for all types of pneumatic conveying systems, and **air volume requirements** will vary from 0.9 cu. ft. to 15.0 cu. ft. for each pound of material being conveyed. The volume requirements between these approximate limits depends on the type and characteristics of the material and on the length and complexity of the piping system.

Applications of Rotary Positive-Air-Lock Systems. Fig. 1 shows how a typical **in-plant pressure pneumatic pipeline conveying system** can be applied.

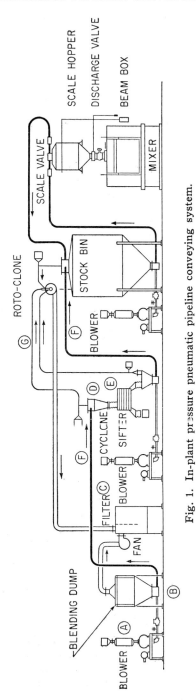

Fig. 1. In-plant pressure pneumatic pipeline conveying system.

The system is designed so that material can be dumped into the blending dump hopper, located, for instance, at or near the receiving area. The necessary system air, at the required pressure and volume, is furnished by blower *A*, connected to the primary piping system *C*, which terminates at cyclone *D*, located above process sifter *E*. The rotary positive-air-lock feeder *B* feeds the material from the blending dump hopper into the conveying line *C* for transportation to the process operation. This operation could very well be located several floors above and several hundred feet away from the hopper. The transport air, after being separated from the material in cyclone *D* is normally piped into a general dust-collecting system in which entrained product is filter-recovered. The secondary and tertiary systems *G*, indicated in the flow diagram, illustrate how the material can be conveyed to additional process-use points. Further flexibility is obtained with automatic operation from a central control panel.

Another typical application is shown in Fig. 2. In this case, material which can be shipped in bulk is unloaded directly from trucks and transported to storage silos at a remote location. This type of application eliminates several handling and container costs, which, when considered alone, amount to approximately $4 per ton. These savings translated into two 50-ton cars per week indicate annual savings of $20,000.

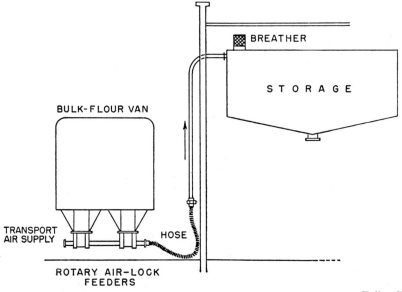

Fuller Co.

Fig. 2. Installation for direct transfer of bulk material from van to storage silo.

Fig. 3 illustrates the application of a **combination "vacuum" and pressure system.** In this combination, the reduced-pressure or vacuum section of the system is used to unload bulk material from special bulk cars and/or box cars, as well as material received in bags or special containers. The pressure section of the system then transports the material to remote storage facilities. Generally, with automatic control, this operation can be considered a one-man operation. The "entoleter" centrifugal machine shown in Fig. 3 is a device for destroying all insect

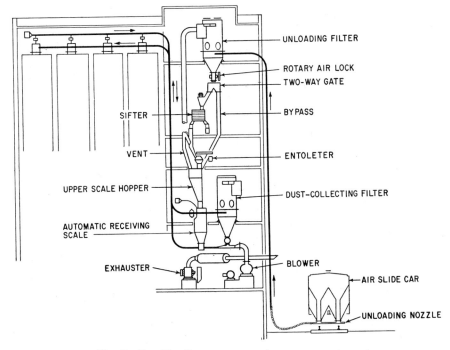

Fig. 3. Combination vacuum and pressure system.

life in flour, meal, mixes, cereals, powdered soups, and similar free-flowing dry materials. It also accomplishes mixing and blending.

THE SOLIDS PUMP. Since the component parts of a pressure pneumatic pipe conveying system are fundamentally the same, and adequate air seal and air pressures are the functional limits of the mechanical feeder, it follows that if increased air pressures are needed, the mechanical feeder employed must be capable of functioning properly against greater air pressure. This would be a feeder of the solids-pump type.

The solids pump is restricted to the transport of relatively fine, dry materials and employs a comparatively low air-to-solids conveying ratio, the movement of the aerated solids being induced by a pressure differential between the feed and discharge ends of the system.

In normal applications, the material to be conveyed enters a hopper by gravity and is advanced through the pump body by an impeller screw. Fig. 4 shows the details of construction and operation of a Fuller-Kinyon stationary pump. As the material advances through the pump body, it is compacted by the decreasing pitch of the impeller screw flights, and is further increased in density at the "seal" between the terminal flight of the impeller screw and the face of the check valve. The exact density required for a complete seal, against line pressure is closely controlled by adjusting the seal length. The material then enters the mixing chamber, where it is made fluent by compressed air, introduced through a series of air jets. From this chamber, the material enters the transport line, in which the energy of the expanding compressed air and the impulse imparted by

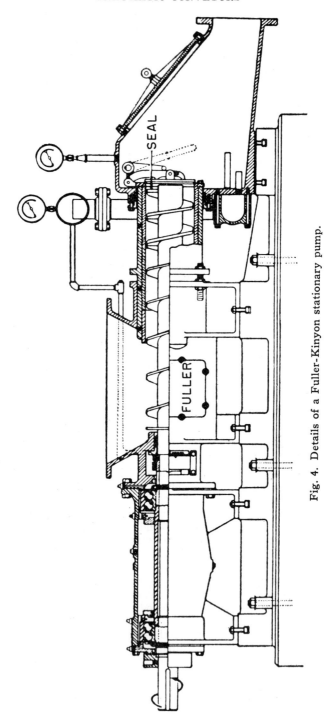

Fig. 4. Details of a Fuller-Kinyon stationary pump.

the impeller screw force the column of fluidized material through the piping system to its destination.

Applications of the Solids Pump. Because of the comparatively extreme distances and higher air pressures involved, the **solids pump** has become practically the standard type of feeder for pressure pneumatic pipe conveying in the cement industry. It is used advantageously in conveying systems handling finished cement, dry raw materials for cement, and pulverized coal. It is also widely used in systems handling fine ores, such as **iron and zinc,** such mineral products as **limestone, dolomite, phosphate, feldspar, bauxite, barite, silica, clay, talc, and fly ash,** and a variety of chemicals, including **refining catalyst, hydrated lime, soda ash, starch, and certain phosphate salts.** In general, system capacities range from 2 to 200 tons per hr., at pressures normally ranging from 15 to 30 lb. per sq. in.

Fig. 5. The pneumatic unit of the portable unloader is powered for self-propulsion by push-button control.

Recently, several special applications of the solids pump in the chemical industry have permitted the feeding of a pulverized solid from atmosphere to a higher-pressure reaction vessel, without loss of pressure, provided the differential did not exceed 45 lb. per sq. in. Investigation has also found the solids pump to be effective in achieving a controlled oxidation of coal to coke. The indicated results were achieved by pumping the material through a coil, located in a controlled-temperature furnace. Increasing use has also been made of a special form of the solids pump for rock dusting in mining practice.

In most instances, however, the maximum application advantages are obtained when **pressure pneumatic pipeline conveying systems,** using the **solids pump,** are used to move dry, pulverized material over long distances. In one case, material was conveyed 1,000 ft. through comparatively small-diameter pipe and distributed into multiple silos under the control of automatic diverting valves. In another case, the delivery of material to a ship was accomplished through a 3,600-ft. piping system. Material was fed into a solids pump located directly below the storage silo. This application is an excellent example of the ability to convey materials "literally anywhere that a pipeline can be placed."

A modification of the stationary hopper-fed solids pump is a **portable unloader** designed particularly for unloading and conveying bulk materials from boxcars, barges, ships, and warehouse storage. A typical situation to which this unit could be applied is shown in Fig. 5. The unit is powered for self-propulsion, which permits extreme flexibility and safety of operation by remote control.

THE BLOW TANK. In general, the "blow-tank" type of line-charger is best when capacity, distance, or pressure, or a combination of the three, require that extremely high air pressures be used. Blow tanks are usually selected when air-pressure requirements are within the 50–125-lb.-per-sq.-in. range. Modifications of the basic principle, however, permit practical applications within the comparatively low pressure range, which in some cases is 15 lb. per sq. in.

The feeder comprises a pressure vessel to which material is admitted by gravity under the control of a cone valve (see Fig. 6). When the material reaches the level of an indicator, it is made fluent by the admission of compressed air, the pressure being raised to a point sufficient to overcome the static resistance of the pipeline system. At this point, a valve opens, and the material discharges into the conveying line until a predetermined minimum pressure has been reached.

The blow tank is excellent for extreme-distance conveying because the vessel forms a dead-end seal against the backward flow of air at high pressure, as distinguished from the material seal of the solids pump, and the comparatively low-pressure air seal of the rotary air-lock feeder.

Material flow from a single vessel is, of course, intermittent. **Continuous flow** is achieved by the use of two vessels, with automatic controls to alternate the feeding and discharge cycle. In some cases, however, with modification of control valves and air activation mechanism, continuous flow is achieved with a single vessel, but only within the comparatively low pressure range (1–10 lb. per sq. in.). Such system application allows increased flexibility and extends the area of use considerably, specifically when applied for in-process conveying within the food and chemical industries. Here, however, it is highly important, particularly in the case of food products, that the system be entirely **free from oil and contamination,** which will require that the air-compressor be most carefully selected.

Blow-Tank Applications. In some cases the blow tank can be applied advantageously because of its ability to assimilate variable feed rates. An example of this would be a packer-spill recovery system. In an application such as this, the amount of material which will be fed into the recovery system may vary considerably within any given period, and the tank in such cases affords the required surge capacity for smooth operation.

The blow tank requires considerable headroom and sufficiently large air receivers so that an adequate volume of compressed air may be available for the blowing period. Also, because of the high instantaneous rate of air release at the system termination, dust-control equipment must be sized carefully.

Power consumption, generally, is somewhat higher per ton of material conveyed than with other pressure pneumatic pipe conveyors, except for extreme-

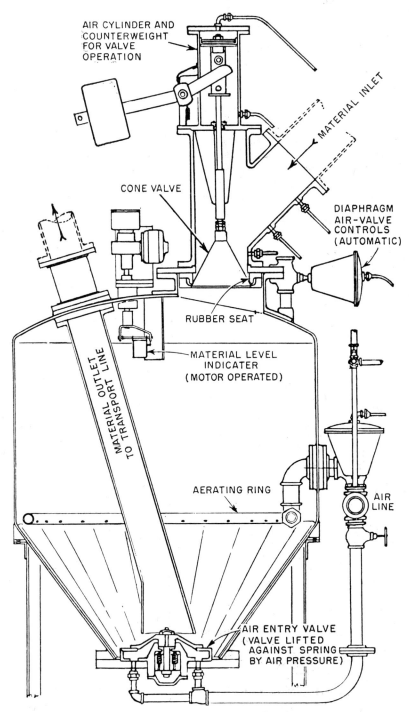

AIR CYLINDER AND COUNTERWEIGHT FOR VALVE OPERATION

MATERIAL INLET

CONE VALVE

DIAPHRAGM AIR-VALVE CONTROLS (AUTOMATIC)

RUBBER SEAT

MATERIAL OUTLET TO TRANSPORT LINE

MATERIAL LEVEL INDICATER (MOTOR OPERATED)

AERATING RING

AIR LINE

AIR ENTRY VALVE (VALVE LIFTED AGAINST SPRING BY AIR PRESSURE)

Fig. 6. Blow tank for providing extremely high air pressures.

30·9

distance conveying, in which case this particular type of system offers advantages not available in any other type. A blow-tank system was used in the construction of Grand Coulee Dam, and was capable of transporting 200 tons of cement per hr. through a system 7,600 ft. long with a rise of several hundred feet.

The blow tank is used in some instances as a primary shipping container, particularly in the transportation of bulk cement into one of the large metropolitan areas, where barge or lighter movement is involved. For this service, five or six tanks, complete with normal operating mechanism, are generally mounted on a special railroad flatcar. Each tank, with a nominal capacity of 10 tons, is filled by gravity, sealed, and then transported on usual rail facilities to an unloading point. It is then connected to a permanent pipe conveying system, and to some source of high-pressure compressed air. The tank is then made to function normally as a pressure vessel, or line-charger, until the container is empty.

GENERAL FACTORS. The capacity and application range into which the pressure pneumatic pipeline conveyor can be applied is wide and varied. Some of the materials which can be successfully conveyed, in addition to materials already indicated, are: **cellulose acetate, corn, flour, soap chips, sugar, vinyl resins, cracked grains, rubber pellets, copra, and iron oxide.** Some of the manufacturing processes in which these materials are required or produced are those connected with the following industries: chemicals, rubber, paper, milling, textiles, soap, baking, distilling, building materials, drugs, steel, water treatment, foundry materials, brewing, and shipping.

VACUUM PIPELINE CONVEYING. Published data dealing with specific problems present in any pneumatic conveying system, are, in most cases, inadequate, and it is most difficult for an individual not familiar with their theoretical and engineering aspects to evaluate and apply generalized data properly. The principal reasons for the lack of reliable published data are the **multiplicity of variables** encountered and the lack of sufficiently exhaustive research to permit a complete correlation and mathematical treatment of variables. In the face of such complex conditions, manufacturers of pneumatic conveying systems have found it impractical to publish information even when data have been acquired by long experience. Furthermore, such items of data are to a large extent, **empirical** in nature.

Air, as a conveying medium, has been given increased attention by industry within recent years, and its utility within the materials handling field is being constantly extended. In fact, depending on the material to be conveyed, pneumatic pipe conveying is usually considered and evaluated for all bulk conveying problems, along with screw conveyors, bucket elevators, belt conveyors, and other types of mechanical conveyors.

Pneumatic conveying piping systems in which air flow is produced by applying reduced pressure or partial vacuum at the discharge end, are commonly referred to as **vacuum** or **suction conveying systems.** This method of pneumatically conveying material through a piping system is by far the most widely employed, and is the one with which industry in general is most familiar. Vacuum conveying systems are manufactured by several well-known companies, both here and abroad, and have been extensively described.

Components of Vacuum Systems. In general, this type of pneumatic conveying system, in its simplest form, comprises (1) a positive pressure exhauster, (2) a piping system, and (3) a collector or separator, in which the material is separated from the conveying air.

Conveying velocities range from 3,000 to 7,500 ft. per min., with **air volume requirements** ranging from 3 to 30 cu. ft. per lb. of material being conveyed. **Pressure requirements,** depending on materials, capacity, and conveying distance, very seldom exceed 5 lb. per sq. in. below atmosphere. **Power requirements** are influenced by so many variables that it is impractical to make any generalized statement with regard to them.

When applying the above fundamentals, with regard to basic equipment and general design data, it is also highly important that **variables**—such as capacities, material characteristics, suitability of equipment and conveying distances—be given serious consideration and proper integration. It can be seen, therefore, that it is highly undesirable to rely on simplified formulas for air volumes, velocities, and power requirements, and that assistance from competent pneumatic-conveying specialists should be sought when considering any type of pneumatic-conveying problem.

Applications of Vacuum Conveying. The vacuum or suction type of pneumatic pipeline conveying system is perhaps most successfully applied in **unloading material from bulk carriers** such as boxcars, ships, barges, and special types of rail or motor-truck carriers. Fig. 7 shows this method applied in its simplest form. Material flows from the car into a portable twin nozzle (1) underneath the hopper bottom car; is pneumatically conveyed through pipe (2) to the filter separator (3); and is then discharged through rotary air-

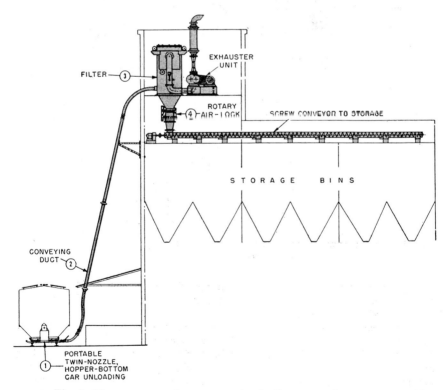

Fig. 7. Vacuum or suction pneumatic pipeline conveying system.

lock feeders (4) for delivery to a distribution system over the storage bins. It should be noted that the filter separator gives 100-percent visible dust retention, thus eliminating material loss and dust nuisance.

Simple unloading systems can, of course, be added to or subtracted from, depending upon unloading requirements. For example, Fig. 8 illustrates how basic equipment can be expanded to a typical ship- or barge-unloading system.

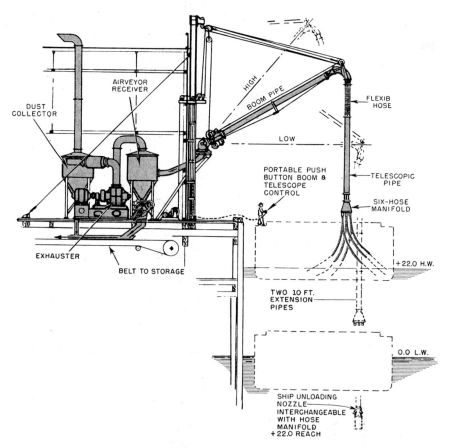

Fig. 8. Basic vacuum pneumatic conveying equipment expanded to typical ship- or barge-unloading system.

Depending on materials and piping characteristics, systems can be developed in which materials such as those listed in Fig. 9 can be transported in tonnages from 5 to 300 tons per hr.

A large segment of modern industry is represented in this list, either by products produced or by raw materials required. For example, many kinds of raw materials are used in the pulp and paper industries. Paper-making requires large amounts of materials such as coating clays, starch, and gypsum; while pulp manufacture requires correspondingly large quantities of pebble lime, salt cake, sodium sulfite, and soda ash. A typical diagrammatic layout of pneumatic materials

Alum
Alumina (calcined)
Ammonium sulfate
Arsenic (trioxide)
Asbestos dust

Barley
Bauxite
Beef cracklings
Bentonite
Blood (dried)
Bone char
Borax
Bran

Calcium carbonate
Catalysts
Cellulose acetate
Clay (dried)
Clay (air-floated)
Coffee beans (green)
Copra
Corn
Corn flakes (brewers')
Cottonseed hull bran
Cyanamid (pulverized)

Dolomite (crushed)

Feldspar (pulverized)
Ferrous sulfate
Flax seed
Flour
Fly ash
Fuller's earth

Grains (dry-spent)
Grain dust
Grits (corn)
Gypsum (raw pulverized)
Gypsum (calcined)

Iron oxide

Lime (hydrated)
Lime (pebble)
Limestone (pulverized)

Magnesium chloride
Magnesium oxide
Malt
Meat scraps (dried)
Middlings

Oats

Resin (synthetic)

Rice
Rubber pellets
Rye

Salt
Salt cake
Sawdust
Silex
Soap chips
Soap flakes
Soda ash
Sodium sulfite
Sodium tetra phosphate
Soy bean meal
Starch
Stucco (hydrocol)
Sugar

Titanium dioxide

Vinylite
Volcanic ash (pulverized)

Wheat
Wood chips
Wood flour

Zinc sulfide

Fig. 9. Materials handled pneumatically at 5 to 300 tons per hour.

handling equipment in a paper mill is shown in Fig. 10. This system is arranged to unload clay from railroad cars for delivery to bulk storage, and to reclaim the clay from bulk storage for delivery to mixers.

Applications in Flour Mills. Vacuum or suction pneumatic pipeline conveying is particularly adaptable to the transport of mill streams in the reduction systems of flour mills, for it is usually required that the in-process streams be elevated at least fifty times. While it is true that the individual streams are comparatively small, the tonnage of material "in process" in any one hour amounts to many tons, even in a moderate-sized mill. For example, a mill capable of producing only 17,000 lb. of flour per hr. will require approximately 100,000 lb. of material "in process" per hr.

These elevations are usually accomplished, particularly in North American flour mills, by **bucket elevators.** While this method of stock elevation is inexpensive and efficient, to the extent that "load surges" are easily handled, other inherent deficiencies have directed attention to the so-called "pneumatic mill."

A **pneumatic mill,** in its simplest form, requires only the basic equipment of a reduced-pressure pneumatic pipeline conveying system. Depending on design conditions, pressure and air volume requirements are generally within the application range of the centrifugal fan exhauster. Normally, the product produced in the mill reduction system is fed into the pneumatic piping system by gravity, and then pneumatically conveyed to a cyclone separator, located above sifting apparatus. The product is then fed out of the cyclone, through a rotary air-lock feeder, into the sifter. The system air is piped from the cyclone to a filter, in

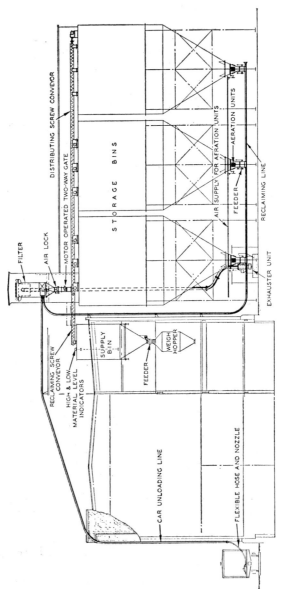

Fig. 10. Pneumatic equipment for unloading, storing, and reclaiming clay.

which entrained stock is recovered, and fed back into the reduction system, thus eliminating any product loss. **Multiple conveying lines,** operating simultaneously and combined into a single system, present a most difficult application and design problem. Successful application requires not only highly specialized pneumatic conveying experience but an equally sound knowledge of milling practices.

In addition to the mill reduction system's required elevations of the product, pneumatic conveying can be successfully applied to the collection and conveying of **finished flour.** Normally, the finished flour product is fed into screw conveyors, located below the sifters, which are as long as the mill building. The location and length of these conveyors present a continuing sanitation and maintenance problem. The self-cleaning feature of pneumatic pipeline conveying, combined with its ability to convey material from, or to, any point where a pipe can be placed, offers a solution to this problem.

Flour mills, including grain elevators, cleaning houses, and flour packing facilities, have presented to manufacturers of the pneumatic conveying equipment a tremendous challenge, which they have met. Complete pneumatic pipeline conveying systems are now available which will take care of all required materials transport. For example, incoming grain can be pneumatically conveyed from cars to bulk bins; from bulk bins to cleaning; through the cleaning process; from cleaning to conditioning; from conditioning to the mill reduction system; through the mill reduction system; from sifters to bulk storage; from bulk storage to packer bins or bulk railroad cars. Practical and economic factors, of course, must be considered in applications such as this, but the component parts are today operating, and, in the future, such applications could conceivably become standard flour-milling practice.

Advantages and Disadvantages of Pneumatic Handling of Flour. Specific **advantages of this type of materials handling** in flour processes are:

1. Improved sanitation.
2. Reduced mill building costs.
3. Improved product,
4. Improved mill operation and greater flexibility.
5. Reasonable power costs, dustless operations, and improved labor relations.

Some specific **disadvantages** are:

1. Indicated higher costs and complexity of applying in existing mill buildings.
2. Increased initial equipment and installation costs as compared to conventional equipment (as applied in existing buildings).
3. Indicated increased power costs as compared to conventional equipment.
4. Lack of comparative operating costs as compared to conventional equipment.
5. Capacity limitations.

It is not here intended to imply that pneumatic pipe conveying systems are unique or unconventional as compared to other methods. Instead the aim has been to illustrate the **practicability of this method of conveying dry, granular materials,** particularly with regard to conveying applications for which a piping system appears to be the more advantageous method. The pneumatic piping system diagrammed in Fig. 11 is a comprehensive example of this type of application. The economics of this application required that the systems be designed for:

1. Extreme flexibility.
2. Strict sanitation.

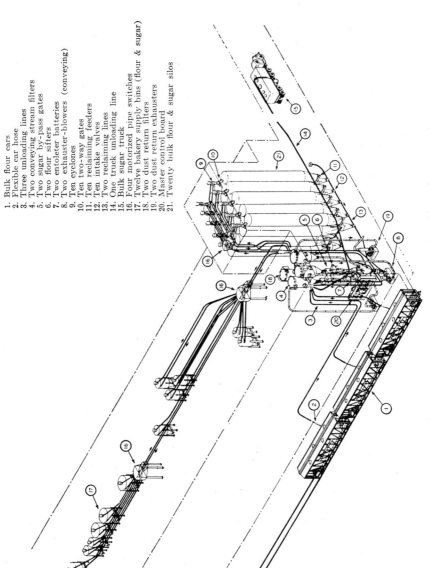

1. Bulk flour cars
2. Flexible car hose
3. Three unloading lines
4. Two conveying stream filters
5. Two sugar by-pass gates
6. Two flour sifters
7. Two entoleter batteries
8. Two exhauster-blowers (conveying)
9. Ten cyclones
10. Ten two-way gates
11. Ten reclaiming feeders
12. Ten intake valves
13. Two reclaiming lines
14. One truck unloading line
15. Bulk sugar truck
16. Four motorized pipe switches
17. Twelve bakery supply bins (flour & sugar)
18. Two dust return filters
19. Two dust return exhausters
20. Master control board
21. Twenty bulk flour & sugar silos

Fig. 11. Comprehensive diagram illustrating practicability of pneumatic conveying of dry granular materials.

3. Dustless operation.
4. Minimum manpower.
5. Maximum good appearance.

In actual operation, the system meets all the above specifications successfully, and is, moreover, operated by remote control.

High-Pressure Pneumatic Pipeline Conveyors

APPLICATION TO CHIP-HANDLING. The application of modern high-pressure pneumatic pipeline conveying methods for heavy materials (75–250 lb. per cu. ft.) to the problem of handling chips and borings in metal-working plants is of relatively recent development. The use of carbide cutting tools in the metal-working industries has led to tremendous production increases and has greatly increased the tonnage of chips, borings, and turnings produced in the average machine shop. Attending this increased chip-handling load, the cost of labor has also risen considerably in the same period, making it necessary in many plants to mechanize chip-handling operations completely.

The high-pressure pneumatic conveying system with its inherent flexibility and low maintenance cost has been widely applied as the standard means of handling this product in large metalworking plants. These systems are also used to transfer small metal parts between manufacturing processes and for conveying punch press skeleton scrap.

The standard forms of pneumatic conveying are maintained in the pneumatic handling of metal chips and borings and metal parts. The basic systems are the pressure-type system, the vacuum-type system, and the combination vacuum-pressure-type system. The last named is used either because of an extremely long length of line or because of considerations of physical layout. It is often necessary to collect materials from multiple points and deliver them to multiple points. In this case a vacuum system with gated branches is used to collect the material from the various feed points, deliver it to interceptor equipment, and discharge it therefrom to a pressure-type system designed to deliver the material to multiple points.

Another case demanding this combination type of system is that of an extremely long conveying line which may utilize a vacuum system to deliver material for half the distance, then discharge it into a pressure-type system from the vacuum system for delivery through the remainder of the distance. In this kind of layout, the blower equipment, air locks, etc., are all located at a common point.

ANALYSIS OF BORINGS AND TURNINGS. Many kinds of chips and borings are pneumatically handled, and effective means of processing are required to permit these materials to be handled efficiently. This processing greatly increases the scrap value of the materials, and the money invested in equipment for efficient low-cost scrap handling is quickly amortized.

Cast-Iron Borings. Cast-iron borings are generally produced in a granular form. They weigh approximately 100 to 200 lb. per cu. ft. When cut, dry, they are easily handled and stored, and seldom require any processing other than screening to remove shop waste. Cast iron, however, is naturally friable, and some of the smaller particles break down to a fine dust, which must be considered when handling this material pneumatically. When cast iron is cut wet, it is the usual practice to remove the moisture from the borings before they are fed to the pneumatic conveyor system. This is generally accomplished by the use of either a centrifugal batch type or a continuous-type extractor.

Steel Turnings. Steel turnings can be classified as to size into two groups. The first group consists of small chips, not too difficult to handle, having a particle size of 3/4 in. or under. These turnings will weigh approximately 70–125 lb. per cu. ft., and, if uniform in size, require no special processing. The second group will consist of long turnings, which tend to snarl, are bulky, and vary in density from 10 to 20 lb. per cu. ft. Such turnings usually take the form of curls and spirals, and range from a few inches to several feet in length. This material cannot be handled in a pneumatic conveyor and cannot be stored in bins. It must be reduced in size by crushing equipment. This operation, by increasing the density of the chips, permits them to be stored in bins arranged for gravity unloading, and handled efficiently in truck and rail transportation.

Aluminum Turnings. Aluminum turnings produced at the machines weigh approximately 5–10 lb. per cu. ft. To reduce this material to a size suitable for storing, it is necessary to pass it through a crusher, which results in a uniform-sized chip capable of passing through a 3/4-in. screen, thus increasing the density to 25–50 lb. per cu. ft. Prior to remelting aluminum chips, it is necessary to remove all of the cutting fluids which adhere to the chips before they are fed to the furnace. This is accomplished by either feeding the aluminum chips through a rotary dryer or through centrifugal extracting equipment of the batch or continuous type before they are fed to the pneumatic conveyor system. Some aluminum alloys in chip form tend to oxidize when exposed to air and moisture. These are often shipped in boxcars, and a pressure-type pneumatic system is employed to blow the chips into the extremities of the car (see Fig. 20).

Brass and Copper Turnings. Brass turnings can be handled in a manner similar to the methods described for steel or aluminum. Crushed brass and copper turnings may weigh 50–120 lb. per cu. ft. Due to the relatively high value of copper and copper alloy chips, they are usually shipped in locked boxcars to prevent pilferage at lay-over points. Therefore, the pneumatic loading of boxcars, as illustrated in Fig. 20, is frequently employed.

Metal Parts. High-pressure pneumatic conveyors are used to transport small metal parts between various processes of manufacture. Pieces up to 4 in. in diameter and 2 in. long can be very quickly conveyed in pipe lines, which are flexible, self cleaning, and require only a small space.

Punch Press Scrap. Punch press skeleton scrap, 16 gage thick, and with a maximum flat dimension of 5 in., is quickly conveyed from presses to railroad gondola cars with high-pressure pneumatic conveyors.

COMPONENTS OF HIGH-PRESSURE PNEUMATIC CHIP CONVEYORS.

The components of a pneumatic conveying system used in chip-handling have the same general characteristics as those for other pneumatic conveying systems described above. Some modifications are necessary, however, because of the abrasive nature of the material handled.

Blowers. The pneumatic conveying of material requires a measured flow of air through a duct of the proper size to move the material in the desired quantities. Rotary positive-pressure blowers are commonly used to produce this flow of air. These are **constant-displacement machines,** compressing a standard amount of air for each revolution of the impellers. Thus, when the unit is connected to a duct, a constant volume of air will flow through the system regardless of the pressure or vacuum losses occasioned by the friction of the material on the duct and the friction of material conveyed.

Air Locks and Ejectors. In the conventional pneumatic chip-handling system, a rotary air lock or ejector-type feed nozzle is used to introduce materials into the conveyor without loss of air. In the **vacuum-type system**, since the air is admitted with the chips at the feed end, there is no need to provide air-lock equipment at this point. However, material must be discharged from the interceptor equipment before the air flow is directed to the vacuum-producing exhauster unit. Rotary or multiple-door airlocks are used for this service to prevent air loss as material is discharged from the interceptor.

In Fig. 12 a typical **ejector-type feed nozzle** is shown. The air supplied by the blower is directed through the nozzle, and the air velocity is increased to a point where the velocity pressure of the air stream overbalances the static pres-

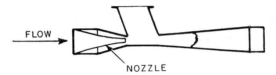

Fig. 12. Ejector-type feed nozzle.

sure to induce air through the feed opening. Material can then be fed into the air stream without the loss of conveying air. It should be pointed out that velocity pressures through the nozzle must be sufficiently high to overcome the entire static head of the remainder of the piping from the point where material is introduced to the discharge point. Therefore, this type of system is necessarily limited to short lengths, seldom exceeding 50 to 60 ft., and to runs with a minimum of bends.

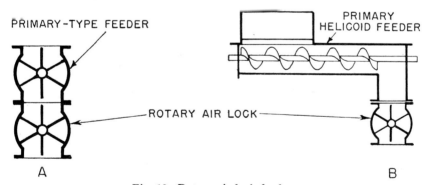

Fig. 13. Rotary air-lock feeders.

Rotary air locks of the types shown in Fig. 13 are perhaps the most widely used equipment for introducing material to the conveying air stream and have been described above. In chip-handling, the characteristics of the material handled require flexing of the rotor blade tips to prevent jamming, and these blades are usually constructed of neoprene rubber, which is resistant to the cutting oils usually found on the chips. Blades are normally set up for approximately 1/32-in. interference with the rotor housing, to provide a tight seal and to give the blades an initial flex which permits them to pass over chips without damage. An air lock of this type, while commonly called a rotary "feeder" in the trade, should not be used to meter the flow of chips to the pipe line. When a head of material is obtained in the hopper over the air lock, the blade pockets rotate completely full of material, and the blades must shear off the load as the blade goes into the sealed area. Common practice utilizes a primary-type feeder operated at about one-third to one-half of the rotary feeder speed. This feeder may be of the rotary type shown in Fig. 14, which is equipped with steel plate blades that operate with considerable clearance to deliver material in fixed quantity to the rotary air lock. An ideal situation exists when the rotor blade pockets rotate one-third to one-half full, which usually results in the least wear on the blades.

Other means of feeding air locks are in wide use, among them being screw-type feeders, vibrating feeders, and, in some cases, apron feeders.

A diagram of **the multiple-door air lock** and its usual operating sequence is shown in Fig. 14. Normally, these units are used under receiver interceptors at the discharge of a vacuum-type pneumatic chip-handling system. Since the chip load is metered at the feed end of the system and the material flow is constant through the duct, there is no need to provide a primary feed to this unit. The

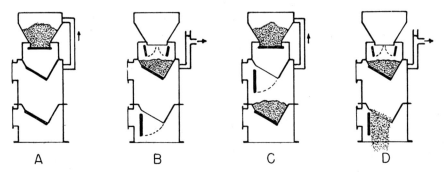

Fig. 14. Operation of multiple-door air lock.

top door is used exclusively as a cutoff device to hold the material that is being received, while the intermediate compartment is discharging into the lower compartment. These units are airtight, the doors being held closed either by compressed-air-actuated cylinders or by a mechanical cam-type motor drive. In addition, the full vacuum of the system is applied to the door, which holds it tight against its seat. This type of unit is excellent from the standpoint of maintenance, since the only wearing parts are the mechanical links and the door plates over which the material slides on being discharged from compartment to compartment.

Ducts and Fittings. In considering ducts and fittings for pneumatic pipeline systems, attention must be given to the material to be handled. In a chip-handling system all elbows, Y-fittings, etc., must be of the long-radius type and provided with handhole plugs of a quick-removable design to allow for inspection. Whenever a change in direction occurs, the elbow initiating the directional change should be cast of a special hard-alloy metal. A Brinell hardness of approximately 500 has been found most suitable for fittings in this type of service. **Elbow backs** should be thickened to provide greater wearing surfaces where the abrasion is heaviest. A **hard-alloy cast wear section** must be used on the downstream side of each elbow to withstand the scouring action caused by the turbulence of the air flow around the bends. These wear sections should be cast of the same material as the elbows, and should be no less than 2 ft. long.

The **intake tee** installed immediately under a rotary air lock where material is admitted to the conveyor line is a source of severe wear in the usual installation. Cast intake tees of venturi design are used for this purpose, and the design should be such that smooth flow lines are created in all directions to allow the material to be rapidly accelerated to the velocity of the air stream, thus minimizing turbulence and wear. These intake tees should also be cast of a special hard iron.

The **duct proper** in a pneumatic chip-handling system is normally constructed of standard black steel pipe, with welding flanges attached at each end. Companion flanges with threaded ends should not be used, since the pipe wall is materially reduced in thickness at the threaded joints, which may cause accelerated wear at these points. In cases of heavy tonnage, it is often prudent to utilize extra-heavy pipe for the straight runs of conveyor duct; and where continuous production with heavy tonnages must be handled through a system, it is good practice to construct the entire duct of hard cast-iron-alloy pipe.

Selector Valve. Where **multiple discharge points** are required from a common conveyor duct, it is necessary to apply valves to divert the flow of material from the main run to the branch being utilized. A diverting valve of this type, commonly known as a selector valve, is shown in Fig. 15. This unit is cast of a machinable hard iron, and is equipped with special wear-resistant cast-iron-alloy liners.

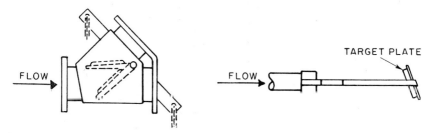

Fig. 15. Selector valve.   Fig. 16. Target plate and bracket.

These selector valves are operated manually or through a compressed-air-actuated cylinder. In the **manually operated unit,** an over-center spring device is used to hold the diverting plate tightly in the intended position to prevent its floating in the air stream. In **air-cylinder-operated gates,** the securing air cylinder holds the plate in place. By using air-cylinder-operated selector valves with solenoid compressed-air valves controlling the air cylinders, and with push-button and relay systems with indicating lamps, effective interlocking arrangements can be obtained when segregating various alloys of materials. These interlocks are mandatory when the value of the alloy is high and contamination with other alloys would considerably reduce its value.

Intercepting Equipment. At the terminus of a pneumatic conveyor line handling metal chips, it is necessary to reduce the velocity of the chip particles so that they can separate from the air stream and be collected in some form of container. The simplest type of intercepting equipment is the **target plate** and bracket shown in Fig. 16, which is used where a pneumatic line discharges into a storage bin. One of the **inherent advantages** of the pressure-type pneumatic conveyor for chips is that a bin may be blown level-full and that it is not necessary to completely decelerate the chips as they flow into the bin. This type of target plate takes the initial impingement of the chips and allows them to bounce off at a velocity considerably lower than the initial velocity. Therefore, the chips scatter in the bin in the fashion of a snowfall and allow for excellent efficiency in loading the bin level-full. The target plate, moreover, reduces the initial velocity to a point where wear is eliminated from the bin walls.

The **storage bin**, of course, should be freely vented to the atmosphere, and the design of the vent should be such that the discharge velocity is sufficiently low to prevent loss of chips with the exhausted air.

In **loading open vehicles** such as railroad gondola cars, motor trucks, etc., the discharge head with target plate is in common use. A unit of this type is shown in Fig. 17. Material is directed against the target plate in the manner described above, and the velocity is reduced, allowing a free gravity fall into the vehicle. Special design considerations are necessary in the fabrication of this discharge head to make sure that the chips can be patterned to discharge into the vehicle and not scatter about.

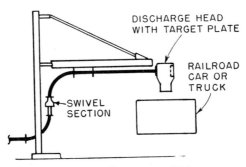

Fig. 17. Loading open vehicles.

Dust-allaying Equipment. In handling cast-iron borings in the dry, dusty state in a pneumatic pressure-type system, it is often necessary to provide **dust-allaying equipment** at the discharge point. **Cyclone-type centrifugal receivers** are used for this purpose(Fig. 18).

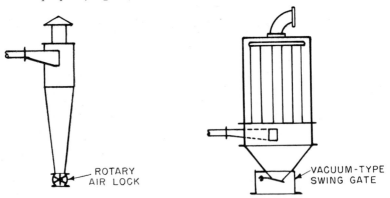

Fig. 18. Cyclone-type centrifugal receiver.   Fig. 19. Cloth-type filter for vacuum systems.

The typical centrifugal action separates the air from the material and allows the air to spiral out through the tail pipe while the material is discharged, or stored in the receiver cone for discharge at a later time. Where continuous discharge is required, it is normal procedure to utilize a rotary air lock or a multiple air lock to avoid short-circuiting the air through the discharge.

In **vacuum-type systems**, it may be necessary to provide **cloth-type filtering** to collect any dust entrained in the air before it is released to the atmosphere. A typical unit of this type is shown in Fig. 19. In this unit, the material is initially intercepted in a centrifugal receiver unit equipped with a multiple-door air lock. The efficiency of this unit is very high, and only the fine dust is carried over. This fine dust and the exhaust air are directed to a centrifugal receiver unit with a bag-filter compartment. Further centrifugal separation, plus the filtering action of the cloth filter bags, removes the final dust particles and allows clean air to be discharged through the blower.

Because of the high efficiency of the primary receiver, it is not usually necessary to provide a continuous-type air lock under the bag filter, and a **simple vacuum-type swing gate**, which is held closed by the vacuum in the system, provides the air seal at this point. The quantity of material collected is small, and a timer can be installed in the electrical control circuit to function through interlocks to vent the receiver unit periodically and allow the fine dust collected to be discharged.

Installations without Interceptors. In some cases, the relatively high carrying velocity of pneumatic chip-handling systems is utilized without interceptor equipment to provide for loading an area not capable of being economically loaded by mechanical methods. Aluminum chips, copper chips, and brass chips are usually shipped in railroad boxcars to the smelter, and as these materials are not dusty, they can be blown directly into the boxcars. The boxcars are bulk-

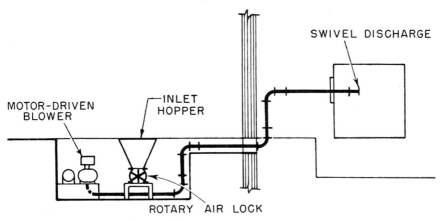

Fig. 20. System for loading boxcars.

headed, and special discharge nozzles, as shown in Fig. 20 are used to direct the chips into the car. With this system, a car can be completely loaded with chips, thus greatly reducing the unit freight cost and the number of cars handled per unit of time. A large producer of aluminum chips found it possible—by constructting a bin approximately 60 ft. square, and by using a rotating motor-driven elbow at the discharge of the pneumatic conveyor duct—to fill the entire bin effectively from the conveyor duct.

Controls and Interlocks. The starting of the pneumatic chip-handling system should be carefully planned so that the various items of equipment are put in operation in sequence and the air flow is established before material is fed to the system. For example, the rotary air lock should never be allowed to start delivering material to the system until the blower is in operation and is producing air flow. A well-engineered control system will provide these safeguards. In the pressure system, a **differential-type pressure** switch should be installed in the air line at the blower, so that if an excessively high air pressure is indicated in the line (with the possibility of plugging), the differential pressure switch will actuate the feed-mechanism interlocks to stop feeding to the system. This provision allows the air stream to clear the line without additional material being fed into the system, which could cause blocking. With this kind of switch the differential pressure is set so that the system is clear before material is again fed to the system.

In conveying to storage bins or other closed containers which can become filled and back up material in the pipe line, some kind of **high-level indicator** must be installed to cut off the feed mechanism and sound an alarm before the bin is overloaded and the pipe line is plugged.

In **handling alloys which must be segregated,** automatic controls are often applied to segregating selector valves to insure that the proper valve is opened to direct the alloy into the proper bin compartment.

Steam-pneumatic Ash Conveyors

STEAM-PNEUMATIC ASH SYSTEMS. A steam-pneumatic ash-conveyor system consists of a closed pipeline through which a high-velocity air flow produced by a steam-exhauster unit transports dry ash and fly ash in both horizontal and vertical directions from points of accumulation in the boiler and thence to storage, for removal from the plant by trucks or railroad cars. The **capacities** of steam-pneumatic ash-conveyor systems range from 4 to 20 tons of dry ash per hr.

The steam-pneumatic system is widely used for ash handling because of its low cost and simple construction, dustless operation, flexibility of design and layout, ease of control and automatic operation, quietness, and operating and maintenance economy. It is the most widely used type of ash-removal equipment for industrial coal-burning power plants.

Steam-pneumatic systems are used to convey ash discharged from all kinds of stokers and pulverized-coal-burning equipment. These systems will collect soot from the stack; fly ash from the rear-pass hoppers, breechings, and dust collectors; and stoker siftings from siftings hoppers. The **ash** is delivered to ash intakes in the system by manual raking from ashpits or by combination of raking and gravity flow from ashpit hoppers. **Fly ash** is delivered to the system through manually or automatically operated feed valves or by motor-driven rotary feeders. The highly aerated fly ash stored in dust-collector hoppers is extremely fluid, and its flow through the conveyor system should be controlled by the conveying cycle of the system. The conveying cycle is controlled by cams on a master timer.

TYPES OF SYSTEMS. Steam-pneumatic ash-conveyor systems are specified by the **capacity** of the system, the **location** of the steam-exhauster unit, the **type of equipment** used to separate ash from air, and the **diameter of the conveyor ducts.** Systems are generally installed with 6-in- or 8-in.-diam. conveyor ducts. Other sizes are available but are not frequently used. The action of the steam exhauster during the period of ash removal may be either continuous or intermittent. In a continuous system, the ash is conveyed during the full period in which the system is in operation. In an **intermittent system**, the ash is conveyed for a controlled period of time and then the exhauster is automatically stopped to discharge the ash. A typical 90-sec. cycle may provide for 80 sec. of conveying time. With a continuous system, the ash-storage silo may be under vacuum or not, depending upon whether the steam exhauster is placed before or after the storage tank in the system. Where the storage tank is under the vacuum, the tank must be airtight. Leakage of air into the system at points after the material pickup reduces the efficiency of the system. In an **intermittent system** the ash-storage silo is always vented to atmosphere. When the steam exhauster is operating, the storage tank is closed off from the system by the swing gates. At the completion of the conveying cycle, the swing gates open and the material accumulated in the receiver and secondary separator units is discharged into the storage tank.

STORAGE FACILITIES. The ash may be discharged to the ash-storage tank mentioned above, or it may be deposited directly into a railroad gondola car or conveyed to the ash dump for fill purposes. Storage tanks are constructed of steel, of vitrified glazed tile, or of concrete. Tile is the most commonly used because of its resistance to the corrosive action of the ash. The storage tank may be designed for discharge to trucks or railroad cars, with either bottom or side discharge chutes.

OPERATION. The ash is conveyed in the system by the action of the air drawn by the steam exhauster. The flow of this air reaches sufficient velocity to produce the movement of material in the system. For purposes of analysis, the material conveyed in the system is considered a **fluid combination of air and ash.** The air is drawn into the system at air intakes located beyond the ash and fly-ash feed units, and it picks up the material to be conveyed at the intake tees. The ash feed units must be designed so that the flow of air is not blocked or the ash will choke the system. This blocking is avoided by making the inlet areas of all intake tees smaller than the area of the conveyor pipe, and by providing for side feeding of ash into the tee. The velocity of flow through the system must be controlled because the rate of duct-wall erosion increases rapidly as the velocity increases.

EXHAUST. The economical method in both construction and operation is to discharge the exhaust steam and air from the steam-exhauster unit into the stack at a point near the breeching inlet. However, in many cases where the stack is located away from the ash-storage tank, or in the case of a continuous semi-vacuum system, the use of an **air-washer** is recommended to clean the exhaust steam and air before discharge to the atmosphere. In the air-washer, the exhaust steam and air are passed through a fine water spray which condenses the steam and traps the dust particles in the air. These particles are carried with the water to a screen located at the bottom of the air-washer. This screen retains large pieces of ash that would otherwise clog the drain line from the air-washer to the air-washer sump. The sludge dam in the air-washer sump settles out dust particles in the water before the water is discharged to the sewer.

POWER REQUIREMENTS. For efficient operation, the steam pressure at the nozzle of the steam-exhauster unit should be 80 lb. per sq. in. or higher. The steam requirements vary, depending upon the conveyor-duct diameter, overall length of system, type of system, steam pressure, characteristics of ash and fly ash—including size of any clinkers or slag—and methods of feeding the system. A typical 6-in. system with a capacity of 6 to 14 tons per hr. will require approximately 230 lb. of steam per ton of ash conveyed.

ADDITIONAL EQUIPMENT. Other details of the system include steam lines, which supply steam from the boiler to the steam-exhauster unit; water supply and drain lines for air-washers; ash-conditioner units and hinged discharge chutes; electrical wiring for control equipment; and compressed air for the automatic operation of gates and valves. Air-washers require 30–50 gal. per min. of water, water-spray discharge chutes for ash-tank gates require 20–30 gal. per min., and ash-conditioners require 40–50 gal. per min.; all at a minimum operating nozzle pressure of 20 lb. per sq. in. gage. Each air-operated steam valve or gate requires ½ cu. ft. per min. at 60 lb. per sq. in. minimum air pressure.

TYPICAL SYSTEMS. The following diagrams illustrate typical standardized steam-pneumatic ash-conveyor systems. Each system demonstrates some of the equipment discussed above and indicates the wide variety of system designs that are in service.

Continuous Semivacuum System. Fig. 21 illustrates a semivacuum system servicing ashpit and boiler rear-pass hoppers, with continuous flow and discharge of ash to the ash-storage tank. The tank is vented to the atmosphere. This system is designed to service underfeed-stoker or traveling-grate-stoker installations for conveying ashes having a low dust content. The ash is fed to the system by removing a plug from the ash-intake tee adjacent to the ashpit to be cleaned, and raking the ashes from the pit to the intake tee (Fig. 24). The **steam exhauster** is placed immediately before the ash-storage tank in the system, and the ash is moist when deposited in the tank. To assure free flow in cold weather, a **steam jacket** is provided on the discharge chute. The air-washer vent installed on the roof of the ash-storage tank completes the removal of any dust entrained in the exhaust before it is released to the atmosphere. The ash-storage silo can be designed for side discharge or bottom discharge to either railroad gondola cars or trucks. The same system may be discharged directly to a fill or to railroad gondola cars by mounting the steam-exhauster unit and deflector box, without the

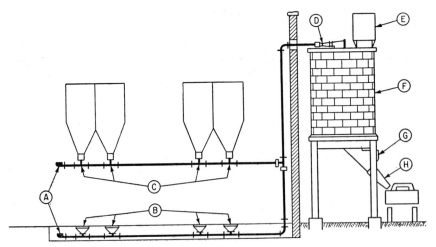

Fig. 21. Continuous semivacuum system (see text for legend).

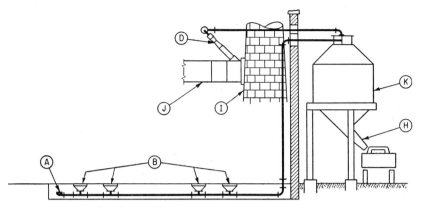

Fig. 22. Continuous full-vacuum system (see text for legend).

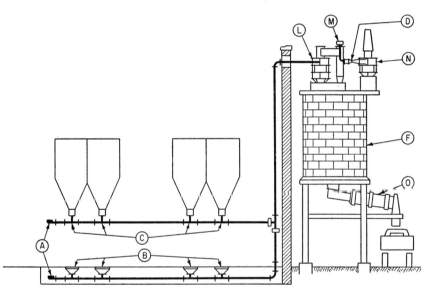

Fig. 23. Intermittent semivacuum system (see text for legend).

storage tank, over the fill area or over the railroad tracks. Elements of the systems shown in Figs. 21, 22, and 23 are:

A.	Air intake	F.	Tile ash-storage tank	K.	Steel storage tank
B.	Ash intake	G.	Gate	L.	Receiver separator
C.	Fly-ash intake	H.	Hinged chute	M.	Secondary separator
D.	Steam-exhauster unit	I.	Stack	N.	Air-washer
E.	Air-washer vent	J.	Breeching	O.	Ash-conditioner

Continuous Full-Vacuum System. This system (Fig. 22) is used for ash-removal in small plants with pulverized-coal or spreader-fired boilers, or other coal-burning equipment where the ash and fly ash to be handled have a high dust content. The operation is similar to that of Fig. 21, except that the storage tank is placed under vacuum during the conveying cycle, and the steam exhauster is placed after the storage tank in the system, so that steam does not come into contact with the ash. This type of system is economical for plants having less than 5 tons of ash and fly ash to be conveyed daily.

Intermittent Semivacuum System. In this system (Fig. 23) ash is transported from accumulation points at the main ashpit hopper, stack, stoker-siftings hopper, rear-pass hopper, and dust collector, and separated centrifugally in the receiver-separator unit. Exhaust air from this receiver is directed through a secondary separator unit for high-efficiency separation. Exhaust air from the secondary separator is directed to the centrifugal air-washer unit, which is provided with a water spray that effectively washes, condenses, and silences the steam. This type of system may also be designed to exhaust to the stack, eliminating the air-washer unit. The air flow for the operation of this system is produced by the **multijet steam-exhauster unit** located in the piping connection between the secondary separator and the air-washer. The ash discharge from the receiver and separator units is stored in the tile silo, supported by a structural-steel frame at a sufficient height for backing trucks under the discharge chute of the rotary ash-conditioner unit. By adding sufficient moisture to the ash, the rotary ash-conditioner eliminates the dust nuisance encountered when unloading ash having a high dust content.

The **system operates intermittently,** conveying for approximately 80 sec. and dumping for approximately 10 sec. During the conveying period, steam is delivered to the exhauster unit through an automatically operated steam valve creating a vacuum and closing the swing doors on the receiver and the secondary separator. This action provides the air seal for the operation of the system, allows the air to flow through the conveyor duct, and causes the conveying of ash. At the end of this conveying period, the steam flow to the exhauster unit is interrupted and the vacuum in the system dissipated. The swing gates of the receiver and secondary separator open and discharge the material accumulated in these units during the conveying cycle. This cycle repeats continuously and is controlled by a motor-operated cam timer unit.

Additional equipment which may be operated by this timer includes the air cylinders or motors operating the feeder valves controlling the flow from rear-pass hoppers, and the air cylinders operating branch-line cutoff gates. For remote control, central-station panel boards may be furnished with push buttons, indicating lamps, and manometers to assure full load-carrying capacity at all times.

LAYOUT OF CONVEYOR SYSTEM. The design and layout of an ash-conveyor system involve the coordination of a number of factors and require a knowledge of steam-plant design and operation. The principal considerations which influence the design of any ash-conveyor system are:

1. Type of ash and fly ash.
2. Size of boiler and amount of ash to be conveyed.
3. Type of plant (central station, industrial plant, hospital, public housing, etc.).
4. Points of ash and fly-ash accumulations (main ashpits, rear-boiler passes, air-heater hoppers, dust-collector hoppers, breeching, stack, siftings hoppers).
5. Disposal of ashes (discharge to fill, storage in bins, removal from plant by truck or railroad cars).
6. Air-pollution-control requirements.
7. Building-code rulings and safety regulations.
8. Services available (steam, water, electricity, and compressed air).

CHARACTERISTICS OF ASH. The quantity of ash to be conveyed is determined by the amount of coal burned, the boiler combustion characteristics, the efficiency of the coal-burning equipment, and the ash content of the coal.

Composition of the ash is affected by the type and amount of soot and fly ash produced in the boiler. The **average size** of the ash particles must be known, as well as the **density.** The characteristics of the ash and fly ash to be handled depend upon the kind of coal burned. For example, ash from anthracite coal is more **abrasive** than ash from bituminous coal. Lignite ash, when subjected to moisture, becomes **plastic** and tends to coat and build up inside the steam-exhauster unit. Therefore, when handling lignite ash, the steam-exhauster unit should be fitted with a steam jacket.

The coal-burning equipment and the boiler temperature determine whether the ash contains a great deal of slag, large clinkers, or medium clinkers, or is fine and granular; also the **ratio of fly ash to bottom ash.** For example, in some pulverized-fuel-burning installations, only 20 percent of the ash contained in the coal is collected in the ashpits, and 80 percent in the form of fly ash, is collected in various boiler hoppers and in dust-collecting equipment. The fineness of the fly ash is determined by the type of dust-collector equipment installed. Chain-grate stokers burning bituminous coal produce a coarse ash with large clinkers; chain-grate stokers burning anthracite coal produce a fine but very abrasive ash. Spreader stokers produce a fine, granular type of ash which has a high dust content. Pulverized-fuel units produce a large percentage of fly ash and a bottom ash with some large clinkers which normally are soft and easily crumbled. To design an ash-conveyor system properly, the engineer must know what type of ash and fly ash is to be handled.

CAPACITY OF ASH-CONVEYOR SYSTEMS. It is good practice to install a system with sufficient capacity to remove in less than 4 to 5 hr. of operation time the ash accumulated in 24-hr. operation of the plant. The amount of ash produced is determined by the rated capacity and the load factor of the boiler. If future expansion of the boiler capacity is anticipated, provision for conveying the additional ash should be made when specifying the capacity of the steam-pneumatic ash-conveyor system.

Ash-conveyor systems are generally furnished with **ducts** of either 6-in. or 8-in. diam. The 6-in. system will convey ash at the rate of 6 to 14 tons per hr. The 8-in. system will convey ash at the rate of 10 to 20 tons per hr. Good operating procedure and effective system design will keep the system operating at full capacity in excess of 65–75 percent of the time during the period of ash removal. The factor which prevents full utilization of the system is the **time required by the operator** to perform the following:

1. Start the system.
2. Travel between ash intakes and to fly-ash intakes, which are sometimes located at different floor levels.
3. Open and close branch-line gates.
4. Remove and replace intake plugs and grids.
5. Open and close ash-hopper doors.
6. Break clinkers.
7. Open and close steam and water lines.
8. Shut down the system.

This **conveying-time loss can be reduced** by designing the system to:

1. Utilize centrally operated automatic controls for fly-ash hoppers and branch-line gates.
2. Maximize gravity flow of ash into intakes by proper selection of slope angles for ash hoppers.
3. Reduce need to break clinkers by using a larger-diameter system.

A 6-in. system will handle ash sized through a 3-in.-square grid, and an 8-in. system will handle material sized through a 4-in.-square grid. If the ash-handling equipment is to service coal-burning equipment that produces large clinkers, the governing factor for the diameter of the conveyor will be the size of the clinkers rather than the rated hourly capacity of the system.

The flow of ash through the system produces a **loss of vacuum** because of friction. This loss is greater per ft. for 6-in. pipe than for 8-in. pipe. The vacuum losses in long systems may be sufficient to justify the installation of an 8-in. rather than a 6-in. conveyor pipe.

LAYOUT OF CONVEYOR LINES. The conveyor line must conform to building conditions and extend from the boiler ashpit hopper and various fly-ash and dust-collector hoppers to a **storage tank.** Storage tanks should be located as close to the boiler room as possible and must be provided with truck or railroad access. The **straight-line layout** with a minimum number of elbows is the best. In laying out the routing of conveyor pipe, consideration should be given to erection difficulties. The use of existing structures for pipe supports eliminates the need of special pipe supports. Horizontal runs of conveyor pipe on ash basement floors, the lowest floor level, may be installed above the floor. When installed on boiler-room floors, however, the conveyor duct may obstruct access passageway. In this case, pipe should be located in dry, well-drained trenches covered with floor plates. All horizontal runs of conveyor pipe should be supported with **adjustable roller supports,** spaced at not less than 8-ft. centers. Roller supports provide accurate height adjustments, reducing deviations in the duct layout and minimizing turbulence. **Cutoff gates** located in heated areas are easily controlled for either manual or automatic operation. **Vertical risers** located inside the building eliminate cutting of holes in the building walls for branch-line connections. For riser lines located outside the building, a tight cover must be provided over the pit at the base of the riser, with provision for proper draining. Adjustable pipe supports provided at the base of vertical risers permit replacement of elbow or wear sections without disturbing the riser line. Vertical sections of conveyor pipe above cutoff gates should be independently supported to reduce the load on the gate. Fixed lateral supports should be installed to maintain the vertical position of the riser line.

All parts of the system which may require servicing should be located for convenient **access and inspection.** This provision is particularly important for wear sections and elbow wearbacks. A wear section approximately 2 ft. long should be installed beyond each elbow. To permit the installation of equipment without special hoisting facilities, the conveyor pipe lengths should not exceed 6 ft. in length and fittings should not weigh more than 450 lb. Expansion joints in riser lines and branch lines to boiler outlets, and in long runs of conveyor pipe, allow for any movement of the pipe. Branch lines should not be less than one size smaller than the main conveyor duct. An 8-in. main line should have 6-in. branch lines, and a 6-in. main line should have 4-in. branch lines. Each air inlet to the system should be provided with an automatic check valve to close the air inlets during the idle period of the conveyor system.

Conveyor pipe and fittings should be cast of an abrasive-resistant alloy metal. The pipe walls should be not less than ¾ in. thick for 6-in.- and $^{15}/_{16}$-in. thick for 8-in.-diam. conveyor duct. All elbows should be provided with handholes and easily removable wearbacks not less than 2 in. thick. Pipe and fittings are provided with integral cast flanges or loose malleable-iron flange clamps. Each joint should be properly bolted to maintain alignment and should be provided with a wire-reinforced composition gasket.

Steam lines should always be generous in size to minimize pressure drop to the exhauster. The size of the steam line does not determine the amount of steam necessary to operate the conveyor. The quantity of steam consumed is determined by the size of openings of the nozzles in the exhauster unit. The steam lines should be short, with minimum bends, and provided with a line-pressure gage. Pressure contactor controls in the water lines to the air-washer will prevent operation of the system without adequate water supply. Well-pitched water drain lines with drainage fittings and cleanout plugs are necessary. Steam lines and exterior water lines subject to cold should be insulated.

Compressed-air lines subject to weather must be protected from the freezing of condensation present in the compressed air. This protection is best accomplished by passing the air through an alcohol reservoir. Compressed-air lines should be provided with filters.

Ash Hoppers. Ashpit hoppers store the ash discharged from stokers. There should be storage capacity in the ash and fly-ash hopper for at least an 8-hr. accumulation of ash at top boiler rating, so that the frequency of ash-conveyor operation is cut down. Greater storage capacity permits flexible ash-removal schedules.

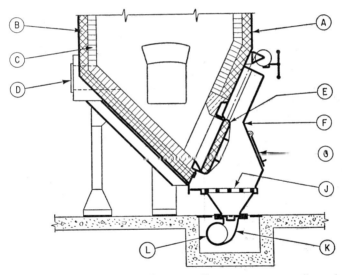

Fig. 24. **Ash hopper with gravity discharge direct to conveyor (lateral section)** (see text for legend).

The design of ashpit hoppers should be planned for the convenience of the operator. A well-designed hopper is illustrated in Fig. 24. It permits the gravity discharge of ash direct to the conveyor duct. The operator controls the flow of ash by adjusting the opening in the vertical-lifting ashpit door. An access door is provided in the dust enclosure for breaking up any oversized clinkers that will not pass through the sizing grid of the ash-conveyor intake tee. Ash hopper components shown in Figs. 24, 25, and 26 are:

A. Ashpit hopper	E. Vertical lifting door	I. Skirt plates
B. Insulating brick	F. Dusttight shield	J. Grid
C. Firebrick	G. Access door	K. Ash intake
D. Inspection door	H. Hinged door	L. Conveyor duct

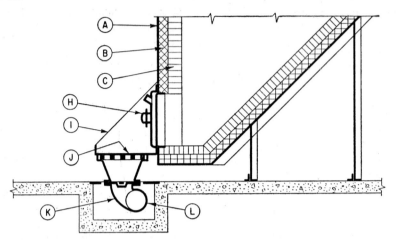

Fig. 25. Ash hopper designed for manual discharge to conveyor (lateral section) (see text for legend).

Another type of ash hopper is illustrated in Fig. 25. This hopper is so designed that the ash does not come in contact with the hinged access door. After opening the door, the operator rakes the ashes to the sizing grid of the conveyor system. Steel skirt plates located on each side of the ashpit door prevent ashes from falling to the floor. The rear inside walls of this kind of hopper are sloped so that the ash flows by gravity to the front of the hopper.

The ash-intake arrangement shown in Fig. 26 is designed to be adapted to existing ashpits where the operator must rake the ash from the ashpit into the ash intake.

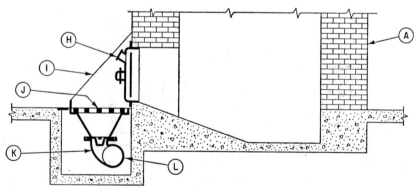

Fig. 26. Ash intake adapted to existing ashpit (lateral section) (see text for legend).

Ashpit hoppers of all-steel construction are generally used. However, concrete or cast-iron hoppers are occasionally substituted for the steel hoppers. In all cases, the hoppers should be refractory-lined. With high-temperature furnaces, it is good practice to use ashpit doors with water-cooled frames. Water-cooled ashpit hoppers eliminate the use of thick firebrick linings and increase the capacity of the hoppers, as well as reducing installation and maintenance costs.

However, water flow through the hoppers must be continuous, and if the plant has a limited supply of water, or the available water contains minerals, it may not be possible to use this type of equipment. Any downward expansion of the boiler, specified by the boiler manufacturer, must be considered in the design of suitable seals for the ashpit hoppers.

Fly-ash and dust hoppers are designed to be self-feeding by gravity. It is good practice to locate fly-ash intakes as close as possible to the discharge flange of the hopper. Where this arrangement is not feasible, the discharge chute from the hopper should increase in cross section as the fly ash approaches the ash intake. Slide gates installed above rotary feeders and totally-enclosed valves facilitate inspection and repair of these units. Aerating nozzles, supplied with compressed air and installed in fly-ash and dust hoppers, aerate the material and prevent arching.

Ash Storage. The disposal of ash may be to storage tanks, directly to railroad gondola cars, or to undeveloped land as fill. In some locations it is permissible to discharge ashes into rivers or the sea. This, of course, is generally true in the case of coal-burning vessels. Ashes are sometimes stored on the ground. However, this practice is not recommended because of the dust nuisance and the high cost of rehandling the ashes from the pile to truck or railroad car for disposal.

Ashes are best stored in **cylindrical storage tanks.** The cylindrical shape produces maximum utilization of structural material, reduces arching and dead storage space, and produces a stronger structure. The capacity of the storage tank must exceed the capacity of the truck (5 to 10 tons) or of the railroad gondola car (40 to 50 tons) into which the ashes are to be loaded, if the loading operation is to be done swiftly from storage. In plants operating 24 hr. a day and over week ends, with ashes removed only during the daytime working hours, sufficient storage capacity must be provided for 3 to 4 days' accumulation of ash

Inside Diameter	Inside Height	Gross Capacity		Live Discharge Capacity*	
		Cu. ft	Tons	Cu. ft.	Tons
8'	12'6"	628	14.1	432	9.6
8'	16'8"	838	18.9	641	14.4
9'	16'8"	1,060	23.8	770	17.3
9'	19'2"	1,215	27.3	882	19.8
10'	20'0"	1,571	35.4	1,164	26.2
12'	19'2"	2,167	48.9	1,426	32.1
12'	20'10"	2,355	53.0	1,613	36.3
12'	23'4"	2,655	59.7	1,898	42.6
12'	25'0"	2,826	63.6	2,088	47.0
14'	23'4"	3,590	80.8	2,532	56.9
14'	25'0"	3,847	86.5	2,789	62.7
14'	27'6"	4,231	95.2	3,173	71.3
16'	25'0"	5,025	113.1	3,382	76.5
16'	27'6"	5,528	124.4	3,884	87.4
16'	29'2"	5,863	131.9	4,218	94.9
16'	31'8"	6,364	143.2	4,721	106.2

* Capacity in tons is based on ash weighing 45 lb. per cu. ft.; 1 ton equals 2,000 lb. (short ton).

Fig. 27. **Sizes and capacities of typical standard ash-storage silos.**

and fly-ash. It is common practice to install high-level indicators inside ash-storage bins to warn the operators when the bin is filled. The sizes and capacities of typical standard ash-storage silos are given in Fig. 27. A statement of typical specifications for ash-storage silos is given in Fig. 28.

Where indicated on the plans, the Contractor shall furnish and install an ash-storage tank on concrete footings extending 1 ft. above grade, which will be furnished by others.

The ash-storage tank shall be cylindrical in shape and shall be approximately ———— inside diameter × ———— inside height. The wall shall be constructed of 12-in. × 12-in. × 6-in. or 10-in. × 12-in. × 6-in. vitrified glazed tile. Each course shall be reinforced with a steel band set in channels provided in the tile for that purpose and embedded in the mortar joints. The floor and roof shall be constructed of 12 × 12 × 4-in. or 10 × 12 × 4-in. vitrified glazed tile, supported on the lower flanges of I-beams spaced 13 in. on centers, covered with concrete to a point 3 in. above the top of the I-beams.

The tank shall be supported on a structural-steel framework, properly braced and designed for live load, dead load, and wind load.

Furnish and install a steel ladder with safety cage from the grade to roof.

Around the top of the storage tank furnish and install a guard rail constructed of 2-in. angle-iron posts, 2-in. angle-iron top rail, 1½-in. angle-iron intermediate rail and 10-gage, 6-in.-high kick plate.

In the roof of the ash tank, furnish and install a cast-iron safety-type manhole frame and cover, and a bag-filter-type vent.

Fig. 28. Typical specifications for ash-storage silo.

To provide a short, straight-line run of conveyor duct, the ash-storage tank should be located as near as possible to the ash intakes in the boiler room. There must be **convenient truck or railroad-siding access to the ash-storage tank,** with provision for adequate clearances. Clearance requirements must satisfy state safety regulations and insurance company standards, and should be checked with the railroad serving the plant. Ash-storage tanks are designed with supporting columns that provide for center–drive-through loading, or for side-discharge loading.

Ash-storage tanks are generally constructed of vitrified glazed tile. Occasionally reinforced concrete or steel is used. While steel is light and strong, the steel interior is subject to severe corrosion from the action of wet ash. Vitified glazed-tile construction resists this corrosion and requires less maintenance against atmospheric conditions, and the smooth, glazed interior surface promotes free flowing of ash to the discharge gate.

Discharge gates furnished for ash-storage tanks should be sufficiently large to permit the rapid discharge of ash. Segmental-type manually operated gates with large discharge areas are generally used to control the discharge of ash from the silo. The gate should draw away from the material as it opens to overcome the tendency of ash to arch. Gates are usually furnished with hinged discharge chutes so that they can be raised to prevent obstruction when not in use. Chutes are designed with water sprays and mixing steps so that the water is well mixed with the ash to eliminate the dust nuisance when unloading the ash. In plants fired with pulverized-coal or spreader stokers, or when a fine dusty ash or fly ash is to be handled, the **rotary ash-conditioner** is used. During the operation of the ash-conditioner unit, the ash enters at a controlled rate and is fed through a rotating drum. Water is sprayed on the ash and fly ash in the drum, and the dustless mixture of ash and water is discharged to trucks or railroad cars.

Hospitals, housing projects, and industrial plants requiring absolute cleanliness of air for sanitary residential reasons, as well as chemical manufacturing and process plants, paper mills, food processes, etc., which must maintain clear atmosphere, should install ash-conditioner units. The installation of the ash-conditioner unit will require special supports, access platforms, and additional structure height above that which is required for the segmental gate and the discharge chute. If there is any question in the designer's mind as to such an installation, it is always wise to provide sufficient height and strength in the building structure so as to be able to install a proper and adequate ash-conditioner unit at a future date.

When an ash-conditioner is installed, it is good practice to install an **emergency unloading gate.** A stairway from grade to the ash-conditioner platform provides easier access than a ladder to this piece of equipment, which is operated at least once every two days. Ladders, however, are perfectly satisfactory for access to the roof of the storage bin, because it is not often necessary for the operator to inspect the equipment on the roof. A steel support with monorail and trolley, installed over the receiver, separator, and air-washer units on the roof of the ash-storage tank, provides an easy method for installation of equipment and facilitates servicing of this equipment.

Shut-off Gates. The flow of ashes through branch lines in the conveyor system is controlled by means of gates. These gates must be leakproof, and may be controlled either manually or by automatic control equipment. Leakproof design with a minimum disturbance of air flow is essential in the design of these gates. Gates are always easy to operate when they are in a horizontal or vertical position, rather than at a slope or an angle. If it is necessary to install a gate at an angle, the gate is best located within hand reach of the operator.

OPERATION AND MAINTENANCE OF EQUIPMENT. The simplicity of the components of the steam-pneumatic ash conveyor and of its operation reduce operating and maintenance problems to a minimum. Operation of typical systems involves releasing steam to the exhauster, control of water supply and drains, feeding of ash and fly ash to the system, and the occasional checking of line suction. Suction-drops in the system indicate air leaks or plugging of the conveyor duct, which will reduce the operating efficiency of the equipment. It is advisable to make certain that all joints in the conveyor system are tight, because air leaks will reduce the capacity of the system, and many leaks may stop the movement of ash and cause plugging of the conveyor duct. The ash should never be wet as it is fed to the system, because wet ash will clog the conveyor pipe, receiver, and ash tank. Operating the ash-conveyor system at off-peak hours reduces the total steam demand. Occasional checks of the steam-consumption rate are necessary to control performance. Water flow at the air-washers and other dust-inhibiting equipment should be checked regularly.

Maintenance inspection is primarily concerned with detecting signs of wear in the conveyor pipe and receiver units. Wear occurs at points where flow turbulence or changes in direction occur. Elbow and fitting wearbacks, wear sections, and receiver wear sections should be inspected at least twice a year. Some plants rotate horizontal runs of pipe to equalize wear, which is concentrated at the lower portion of the pipe cross section. **Steam nozzles** require occasional inspection for wear caused by the pitting action of the steam flow. Proper maintenance, inspection, and lubrication of all equipment will prolong the life of the conveyor and keep its operation at high efficiency.

General Considerations. The simplicity and flexibility of the steam-pneumatic ash conveyor does not reduce the need for careful selection of equipment and for meticulous attention to line layout. The wide range of ash characteristics and of plant installations makes experience extremely important in designing and installing ash-handling systems. The experienced designer, consulted early in the planning of the plant, is able to design the most suitable kind of installation and bring about substantial savings when given relative freedom in the selection and layout of conveyor units. Equipment manufacturers maintain staffs of competent engineers to provide valuable assistance and information to those concerned in this specialized field of steam-pneumatic ash-conveyor systems.

Air-activated Gravity Conveyors

TYPES OF CONVEYORS. Conveyors of this kind are used for many kinds of pneumatic handling. They are divided into three major classes: air-activated gravity conveyors, open type; air-activated gravity conveyors, closed type; and fluidized materials feeders.

AIR-ACTIVATED GRAVITY CONVEYORS—OPEN TYPE. The materials handling method by which dry, pulverized material is conveyed on an inclined porous medium without the use of moving parts is generally referred to as **"fluidized" conveying.** Normally, the method comprises an **inclined porous medium,** either ceramic tile or fabric, which supports a stream of material, fluidized by air to the extent that gravitational force causes the material to flow in the manner of a liquid.

Each dry, pulverized material, when not aerated or packed, has a determinable **angle of repose.** If the material is mixed with air in such a way as to break down the cohesion between the individual particles, the mass becomes air-activated or fluid, and is said to have a fluidized angle of repose. In some cases this angle may be as low as 2°. Then, with the supporting surface inclined to an angle greater than the fluidized angle of repose, gravity pulls the material down to the lower angle, thus creating flow. The surface on which flow occurs is also the **path or conduit on which the material is conveyed.** The creation, support, and direction of flow is, in essence, the function which the open-type chute or conveyor performs when applied as a means to convey material from a bin or silo.

For example, consider the application of this type of inclined porous medium under a head of dry, pulverized material. Then cause the material to be air-activated, or fluidized, for a certain distance above the surface. Assuming that the surface has been inclined to an angle greater than the known fluid angle of repose, movement along the surface is established by the force or pull of gravity to the lower angle. Thus, when the forces which tend to resist the movement of the mass are eliminated, movement is the result, and the basic principle functions. In a typical hoppered-bin application in a cement plant, the conveyor is attached to the hopper opening and comprises a shallow rectangular plenum-type chamber of which the top side is a porous medium, of low air-permeability. Air for the operation is furnished by a small positive pressure blower.

Fluidizing the Material. Assuming that the bin is completely filled with dry, pulverized material, there are numerous forces present within the mass which tend to resist the flow of material out of the bin. Further assuming that the material is thoroughly packed and all pressure forces within the mass are stable, it is obvious that satisfactory flow could not be induced even if the lower end of the conveyor were opened. To produce flow and thus empty the bin, the forces or **pressures within the material mass must be dispersed.** Referring back to the basic principle of the method, air must be introduced into the mass through the porous medium, and the mass above made fluid. The distance above the porous surface to which the fluidity of the mass must reach involves several factors, such as material characteristics, degree of packing, configuration of hopper, bin surfaces, and total static head. With the material fluid for a sufficient distance above the conveyor, the pressures which tend to retard flow are dispersed, and the mass involved moves, under gravitational influence, down to the lower angle.

As the initial mass moves out from under the head of material, pressures within this mass tend to be disrupted and a **downward movement of the mass occurs.** If the pressures within the mass continue to resist movement and **bridging** occurs, it becomes obvious that the fluidity of the primary material mass did not reach high enough into the static mass to disperse all pressures. In the case of some materials and/or hopper configurations, it is necessary that the "fluid line" be extended above the spring line of the hopper.

It is not intended herein to imply that all applications of this method of materials handling conform to the theoretical aspects outlined. In certain applications there are qualifying factors which could seriously disrupt some of the basic principles involved, thereby nullifying the results expected. In such cases, it is highly desirable to **design adequate flow characteristics into the silo or hopper** under consideration, rather than to rely entirely upon the theory embodied in the open-type air-activated conveyor.

When this type of open conveyor is applied under a head of material in which adequate fluidization is obtainable, and the bins and/or hoppers are of reasonably standard design, the maximum advantages inherent in the method are usually obtained. If, however, the basic principles of the method and/or good bin and hopper design are radically violated, this method of materials handling will not work. It is advisable to rely upon the experience and design data of reputable manufacturers when contemplating the installation of equipment of this kind.

Feasibility Factors. Factors which must be taken into account when considering the application of the open conveyor are:

1. The physical characteristics of the material under consideration, namely, temperature, moisture, particle size, gradation, shape, and weight per cu. ft.
2. General over-all configuration and surface conditions of silo and/or hopper.
3. The angle at which the conveyor must be installed to produce adequate flow conditions.
4. The air volume and pressure needed to fluidize the material mass to the extent that continuous flow is accomplished.
5. Provision of adequate control features, such as openings and valves, whereby flow from the conveyor can be controlled and regulated to conform with conveying facilities provided beyond the open conveyor.

Each of these factors has a definite influence on the degree of success with which this method of materials handling functions. It is important, therefore, that each application be carefully analyzed with regard to **feasibility,** as well as to the manner in which it utilizes and conforms to the basic principles involved.

Applications of Open-type Conveyors. The open-type conveyor has been applied in a **ship's hold.** The entire hold bottom consists of multiple open-type conveyors, all of which are inclined at a certain angle toward openings in the vertical bulkhead at the center of the ship. In this particular instance the vessel was designed for the transportation of bulk cement. To unload the cement from the hold, successive sections of the cement mass are air-activated, or fluidized, and the cement flows to and then through the openings, into a collecting screw conveyor, which runs longitudinally amidships. This kind of application has been most successful.

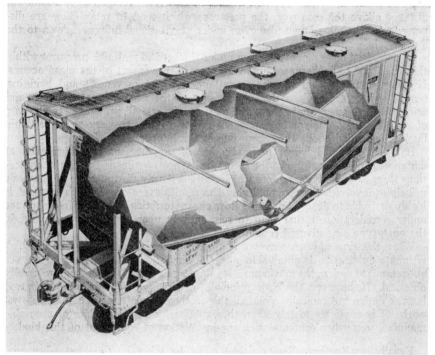

Fuller Co. and Huron Portland Cement Co.

Fig. 29. Open-type conveyor in railroad car.

Another equally successful application is shown in Fig. 29. In this case the inclined open-type conveyor is applied in a **bulk railroad car,** in which many kinds of pulverized materials are transported and unloaded with comparative ease. In fact, it has been found that materials heretofore designated as difficult to unload are readily fluidized and flow freely to the outlets, at the lower end of each converging conveyor.

The open-type conveyor has been applied in a similar manner to **flour trucks,** making it possible to deliver flour in bulk to bakeries and other users whose plants are not located adjacent to rail facilities. The truck likewise can be used to transport other dry, pulverulent bulk materials, such as soda ash, certain resins, fine granulated sugar, etc.

AIR-ACTIVATED GRAVITY CONVEYORS—ENCLOSED TYPE.

The enclosed air-activated gravity conveyor employs the same "fluidized" conveying principle as the open type, but, in addition, the material is contained within the conveyor by means of a **continuous cover.** It then becomes a materials handling method whereby certain dry pulverized materials can be transported from one point to another without the use of moving parts.

Specifically, it comprises (Fig. 30), a shallow rectangular plenum-type chamber or air duct, an upper housing or cover, and a porous medium of low permeability secured between the lower and upper housings. The conveyor is installed at a predetermined operating angle below horizontal, and the material, when sufficiently fluid, flows by gravity.

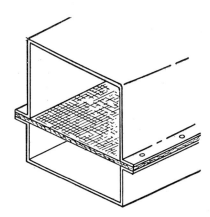

Fig. 30. Use of porous medium of low permeability.

Normally, this type of conveyor is manufactured in standard straight 10-ft. lengths, 4–16 in. in width, of light-gage steel with bent flanges bolted and gasketed. Standard curved sections are available in increments of $7\frac{1}{2}°$ up to 45°, with a 6-ft. radius on the center line. There is **no limit to the length** of any such conveyor, provided proper slope is available.

Air inlets are usually placed on the sides or ends of the conveyors, one inlet being sufficient for lengths up to 150 ft. Generally, when an installation comprises a combination of open- and enclosed-type conveyors, each type should be served by separate air lines so that the air and pressure requirements for each type are under individual valve control.

Operating Characteristics. The closed type conveyor is not usually subjected to a head of material, and the normal depth of the material stream being conveyed seldom exceeds 4 in. Also, in normal operation, air pressures and volumes available from low-pressure centrifugal fans are adequate. Factors such as temperature, moisture, gradation, particle size and shape, and the weight per cu. ft. of material enter into the air requirements for this method of materials handling. No specific **air requirements** can therefore be assumed; but in general, the volumes required are considerably less than for other methods in which air is employed as a conveying medium. **Power requirements** also vary with different materials, but as compared to those for screw conveyors of equal capacity, they are comparatively low.

Flow of material within the individual enclosed-type conveyor is usually under the control of an air-line valve, operated either manually or automatically. The starting and stopping of flow is practically instantaneous when the valve is opened or closed. Bare spots on the porous surface do not affect conveying, for should feed to the conveyor be interrupted, flow is resumed immediately when the material makes contact with the surface. When feed to the conveyor is completely shut off, the residue of material which remains is negligible, and generally the method can be considered self-cleaning.

Capacities vary with different materials, but, in general, the capacity range is from a few cu. ft. per min. to 8,000 cu. ft. per hr. Materials at temperatures up to 275° F. can, in most cases, be conveyed on the fabric type of porous medium. For higher temperatures, up to 800° F., **special porous plates** are used.

Principal Applications of Closed-Type Conveyors. Until a few years ago, the principal applications of this type of conveyor were in the cement industry, where they were used for conveying such materials as cement raw materials and finished cement. At present, however, its utility within the materials handling field is being continually extended to the conveying of many other materials, such as gypsum, soda ash, fly ash, flour, hydrated lime, ground ores, alumina, silica flour, phosphates, talc, resins, detergents, and soap powders.

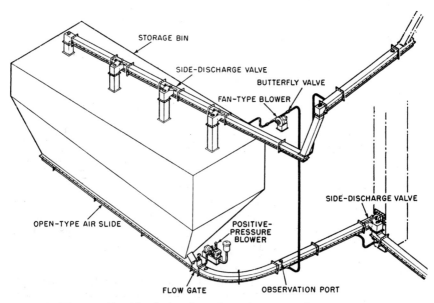

Fig. 31. Combined closed- and open-type gravity conveyor.

A typical installation is illustrated in Fig. 31. The installation is a combination closed- and open-type air-activated gravity conveyor. An enclosed conveyor is used for transporting material from an elevator to multiple storage bins, with the additional feature of side-discharge valves, which may be set for stream diversion in any desired combination. The open-type conveyor is applied to the bottom of the bin hopper, and feeds into another enclosed conveyor.

FLUIDIZED MATERIALS FEEDERS. The feeding of dry, pulverized materials from hoppered bins into some kind of receptacle or conveyor can be accomplished by fluidized materials feeders such as the F-H Airfeeder illustrated in Fig. 32. Its principal parts are:

1. The porous medium through which its fluidizing air flows.
2. The adjustable slide gate.
3. The weir plate.

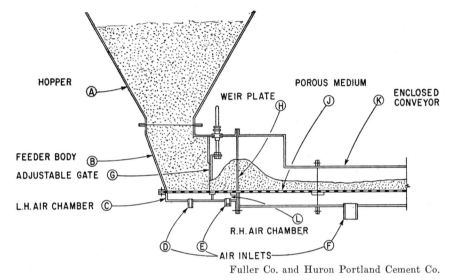

Fuller Co. and Huron Portland Cement Co.

Fig. 32. F-H Airfeeder.

The air chamber under the feeder is divided into two sections. The section on the left (c) is designed so that air passing through the porous medium fluidizes the material mass above to the extent that it flows under the adjustable gate. Air which is supplied to the right side (L) promotes continuing fluidity and flow of material on the surface between the slide gate and weir plate. Fluidizing characteristics of different materials require **variations in air pressure and in the medium's permeability.**

The slide gate is normally opened a certain distance and then set for some desired rate of flow, which rate can be rather closely controlled by the action of the fluidized material mass combined with the retarding effect of the weir.

In a typical application the Airfeeder was applied to the hopper of a 400-bbl. cement storage bin. In this case twin feeders were applied to a single-hopper outlet. Attached to each feeder was an enclosed-type air-activated gravity conveyor in which cement was conveyed to mixers, some distance within the plant.

The **aeration** provided by the F-H Airfeeder prevents arching in the bin, and the draw-off rate can be rather closely controlled without the use of moving parts such as are employed in feeders of the "star-wheel" or screw type.

PACKAGE CONVEYORS

CONTENTS

PACKAGE CONVEYORS

Belt Package Conveyors

CLASSIFICATION OF BELT CONVEYORS. There are two general classifications of belt conveyors for conveying packages or objects. The difference is in the **type of bed** over which the belt travels. One class utilizes a bed made of rollers and is known as **roller-belt conveyors** (Fig. 1), while in the second class, the bed is made of metal or wood and the belt slides across this surface; this second class is known as **slider-belt conveyors** (Fig. 2).

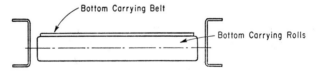

Fig. 1. Roller-belt conveyor, two-way service.

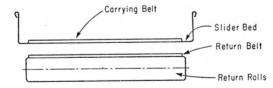

Fig. 2. Slider-belt conveyor, one-way service.

The belt conveyor is the most commonly used power conveyor because of its low first cost, its low operating cost, and its versatility. It can convey with equal facility packages or objects of the smallest size, weighing ounces, and large items weighing hundreds of pounds. Fragile loads can also be conveyed successfully.

The conveyors can negotiate **inclines or declines** with ease. Special treatments on the carrying surfaces of the belting prevent the packages from slipping and sliding. Such special belts will take inclines of 35° with safety when conveying some packages. Under certain conditions, greater angles of incline and decline are practical, but it has been found from experience that the centers of gravity of many loads do not permit greater angles. Often, the center of gravity of the package, rather than the friction between the belt surface and the package, governs the maximum angle.

When great angles of incline and decline are required, it may be necessary to assemble **cleats** on the belting to keep the package from toppling. If other operating conditions permit, the use of cleats is entirely practical. When cleats are used, special treatments on the carrying surface of the belting are usually not required. If cleats are used, however, special means must be provided to support the return belt, because the cleats usually preclude the possibility of using return rollers. If the conveyor is very short (one-floor height or less), the return belt with cleats can hang freely in many cases.

Decline-belt conveyors are frequently used in place of gravity roller, wheel spirals, or spiral chutes when fragile loads are to be lowered or when it is necessary to control the speed of descending loads.

The **rollers** on roller-belt conveyors need be spaced only close enough to keep the belting from sagging unduly between the idler or carrying rolls. For heavy unit loads it is always advisable to have at least one roll under a load on horizontal or level conveyors, while on incline conveyors it is advisable to have two rolls under the load to prevent "bobbing" and a consequent tendency to slip back on inclines or ahead on declines. When light loads are conveyed, the rolls can be spaced on greater centers, sometimes as much as 3-ft. centers. (Loads usually encountered in department stores and mail order houses are examples of "light" loads.)

The **slider-belt conveyor** is ideally suited to small, lightweight packages. Packages having unit weights of over 50 lb. per sq. ft. should not be conveyed on slider-belt conveyors. Heavy loads cause the belting to "seize" on the slider bed, and the friction created results in excessive belt wear and excessive motor load.

BELT-CONVEYOR SPEEDS. Package belt conveyors used in manufacturing can be operated at almost any speed. On assembly lines, a belt speed as low as 6 in. per min. can be used; when used for transportation only, belt conveyors can operate at 200 to 300 ft. per min.

The **diameter of the drive pulley** and the **amount of belt contact** with the pulley are two very important items to be considered in designing a belt conveyor. An oversize pulley will result in otherwise unnecessary gear reduction between the motor and the drive shaft. An undersize pulley will cause excessive wear on the belting and require excessive initial tension in the belt to prevent slip around the pulley.

The amount of **effective pull** required to operate the conveyor will determine the size of the belt. It therefore is an important factor in determining the proper diameter of the drive pulley. The speed and length of the conveyor also play important parts in determining the drive pulley diameter. The table in Fig. 3 shows recommended minimum diameter pulleys for package conveyors. The sizes given are based on many years of operating experience. The effective pull is the difference between the tight side tension (T_1) and the slack side tension (T_2) on the pulley (Fig. 4). The relation of T_1 and T_2 to effective pull for various degrees of contact are shown in Fig. 5.

All belts are rated at **safe working loads** per inch of width per ply; this value is known as "strength per inch per ply." When the effective pull and the degree of contact with the drive pulley are known, the value of T_1 can be calculated. This is the **maximum tension** to which the belting will be subjected and will determine the number of inch plies required in the belting.

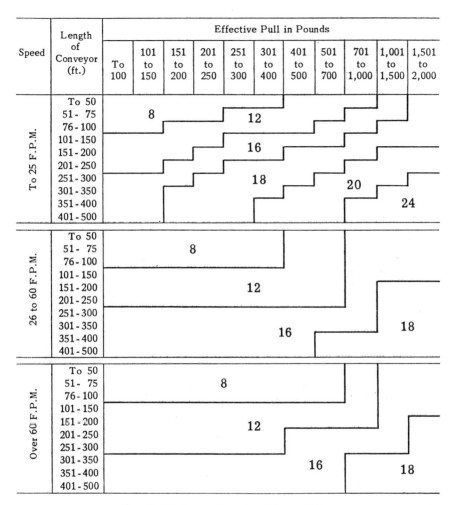

Fig. 3. Minimum-diameter drive pulleys.

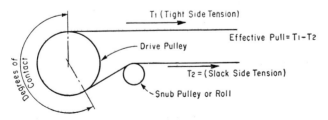

Fig. 4. Effective belt pull.

Degrees of Belt Contact with Drive Pulley	Lagged Pulley		Bare Pulley	
	T_1	T_2	T_1	T_2
180	1.50 EP	0.50 EP	1.85 EP	0.85 EP
200	1.42 EP	0.42 EP	1.72 EP	0.72 EP
210	1.40 EP	0.40 EP	1.67 EP	0.67 EP
215	1.36 EP	0.36 EP	1.64 EP	0.64 EP
220	1.35 EP	0.35 EP	1.62 EP	0.62 EP
240	1.30 EP	0.30 EP	1.54 EP	0.54 EP

EP = Effective pull

Fig. 5. Relation of T_1 and T_2 to effective pull.

It is advisable to utilize the **full strength** of belting where possible, but because of the physical arrangement of conveyors, this is not always practical. The **width of the conveyor**—determined by the width of the packages to be conveyed—is sometimes excessive in comparison to the weight of the load. If the full strength of the belt is utilized, a 1- or 2-ply belt might satisfy loading conditions, but nothing less than a 3-ply belt should be used. Even the 3-ply belt should be confined to widths of 24 in. or less. When wider belts are required, the minimum recommended is 4-ply. Wide, thin belts lack "body" and may undergo excessive stretching. They should be used only when all other conditions are favorable. Many successful installations have been made with 3-ply belts 30-in. and 36-in. wide, but belts of such construction should be used only after careful consideration of all operating conditions.

Calculation for Selecting Ply of Belting. The following example will illustrate how in many cases it is not practical to take full advantage of the strength of the belt.

Assume that the effective pull of a conveyor is 800 lb. A 24-in. belt is required and will have a 210° contact on the lagged-drive pulley. The T_1 tension will be 800 × 1.40, or 1,120 lb. (Fig. 5). Assume that the belt is rated at 25 lb. per in. per ply. Dividing 1,120 by 25 gives 44.8, which means that a belt with 44.8 "inch-plies" is required. As the belt is 24 in. wide, only a 1.8-ply belt, or say 2-ply belt would be required. A 3-ply belt should be used, however, because this is the minimum number of plies recommended for conveyor work.

Determining Minimum Diameter of Drive Pulley. The **speed of the conveyor** is an important factor in determining the minimum diameter of the drive pulley. The faster the conveyor operates, the less is the tendency for the belt to slip on the pulley. Therefore smaller pulleys can be used on high-speed conveyors, as indicated in Fig. 3, because they have decreased slippage losses.

The **length of the conveyor** also plays a part in determining the diameter of the drive pulley, but this factor is not as important as the amount of **effective pull** and the speed of the conveyor. However, all belting will stretch and/or shrink to some extent, and therefore the amount of **initial tension** in the belt will be affected to a greater extent on long conveyors and can be maintained by manual screw take-ups. Because the initial tension must be maintained reasonably close to the theoretical figure, it is important that stretching and/or shrinking be kept to a minimum. The table in Fig. 3 takes into consideration the length of the conveyor, and while this relatively unimportant factor permits certain liberties, the lengths given in the table should not be exceeded greatly unless automatic take-ups are provided. If automatic take-ups are provided, the length of the conveyor is not an important factor in determining the minimum diameter of the drive pulley.

BELTING FOR PACKAGE CONVEYORS. Various kinds of belting are used on package conveyors. The most common kinds are **solid woven cotton, stitched canvas, and rubber-impregnated and rubber-covered belts.** Cotton and canvas belts can be treated with various compounds to minimize stretching and shrinking. Rubber-impregnated belts and rubber-covered belts resist atmospheric conditions and therefore stretch and shrink very little. The amount of take-up required to compensate for stretching and shrinking varies with the kind of belting used. The amount of take-up travel, in percent of conveyor centers, should be at least 1 percent (if possible, 2 percent) for rubber belts, and at least $1\frac{1}{2}$ percent (if possible, 3 percent) for treated canvas and cotton belts. If automatic take-ups are used, the amount of tension maintained in the take-up should be equal to $2 \times T_2$ for nonreversing conveyors and $2 \times T_1$ for reversing conveyors. The tension in the automatic take-up is usually maintained by weights (gravity actuated) but can be maintained by pneumatic means.

The table in Fig. 6 gives **recommended lengths of conveyors** for various actual inch-ply tensions in the belt and different operating conditions, based on 2 lengths of screw-type take-ups.

All types of belting will operate successfully on **roller-belt conveyors.** On **slider-belt conveyors** all types of cotton and canvas belts will operate properly as long as the treatment in the belt is not of a tacky nature. Rubber-covered

		12" Screw Take-up						18" Screw Take-up					
	Type of Belting	Actual Max. Tension per Inch per Ply						Actual Max. Tension per Inch per Ply					
		10#	15#	20#	25#	30#	35#	10#	15#	20#	25#	30#	35#
Indoors – Heated	Inner-stitched canvas	100'	80'	70'	60'	50'	50'	150'	120'	100'	90'	75'	75'
	37½-oz. canvas	100'	75'	60'	50'	40'		150'	110'	90'	75'	60'	
	32-oz. canvas	70'	50'	40'	30'			100'	75'	60'	50'		
	Interwoven cotton	100'	75'	60'	50'	40'		150'	110'	90'	75'	60'	
	Plain-woven cotton	50'	40'	30'				80'	60'	50'			
	32-oz. rubber	150'	140'	125'	100'	100'		200'	150'	150'	150'	150'	
	28-oz. rubber	150'	140'	125'	100'			200'	150'	150'	150'		
Outdoors or Unheated Buildings	Inner-stitched canvas	70'	60'	50'	40'	30'	30'	100'	90'	75'	60'	50'	50'
	37½-oz. canvas	50'	40'	30'				80'	60'	50'	40'	40'	
	32-oz. canvas	40'	30'					60'	50'	40'	40'		
	Interwoven cotton	50'	40'	30'				80'	60'	50'	40'	40'	
	Plain-woven cotton	30'						50'	40'	30'			
	32-oz. rubber	100'	75'	60'	50'	50'		150'	110'	100'	80'	75'	
	28-oz. rubber	75'	70'	60'	50'			110'	100'	90'	75'		

Fig. 6. Lengths of conveyors with screw takeups.

belts with a rubber backing should never be used on slider-belt conveyors, but rubber-impregnated belts will operate properly as long as rubber sealing tape, used on some constructions, is kept from contact with the slider surface.

DEFLECTORS. Packages may be deflected from the normal path of travel on belt conveyors by means of **deflectors** or **plows**, or by **trippers**. These deflectors may be fixed or movable, and can be arranged to deflect certain loads automatically while other loads are permitted to continue along the normal path of the conveyor. When deflectors are used, the belting should be of a type that will permit packages to be moved freely across its surface. Typical belts suitable for deflection are cotton or canvas belts with nontacky treatments and rubber-impregnated belts not equipped with covers or rubber sealing strips.

Formulas for Effective Pull of Belt Conveyors. Any formula for determining the effective pull of belt conveyors should include items for the following factors:

1. Turning effort for any rollers in the bed of conveyor—determined by **weight of such rollers** multiplied by friction of bearings.
2. Pulling effort for moving the belting and live load on the bed of conveyor—determined by the **weight of the belting and live load** multiplied by friction of rollers or friction of belting on slider bed.
3. Resultant of weight of belting and live load on the **angle of incline or decline:** That portion of the weight which acts against the bed of the conveyor must be multiplied by the friction of the bed (rollers or slider), and the other portion of the load that acts parallel to the angle must be added in the case of incline conveyors, and can be deducted in the case of decline conveyors.
4. Proper allowance must also be made for **friction at the pulley ends.** In addition to the weight of pulleys and shafts, there is the loading on the shafts due to the reaction from belt tension. This addition is proportionately greater on short conveyors.
5. If the conveyor is partly inclined or declined, and partly horizontal, **each unit should be calculated separately** as though it were a complete conveyor, and the sum of the effective pulls for each unit will give the total effective pull for the entire conveyor.

The following formulas have been simplified and are based on certain **standardized features.** They assume that rollers (in roller-type conveyors) will not be larger than $2\frac{1}{2}$-in. diam., with free-running bearings and tubing not over 14 gage, that belting will be either 3 ply or 4 ply, and that all pulley shafts will be equipped with antifriction bearings.

Horizontal conveyors.

$$\text{Slider-bed conveyor: } EP = L \, (v + Wf_1)$$
$$\text{Roller-bed conveyor: } EP = L \, (v + Wf)$$

Incline conveyors.

$$\text{Slider-bed conveyor: } EP = L \, ([v + Wf_1] + [0.017WA])$$
$$\text{Roller-bed conveyor: } EP = L \, ([v + Wf] + [0.017WA])$$

On all roller-bed types, and all slider-bed types with over 10° incline, the conveyor will tend to coast backward when the current to the motor is off, while any part of the live load remains on the conveyor. To prevent this **backward travel,** self-locking drives may be provided (self-locking worm gears are one means), antibackup devices may be provided, or solenoid brakes may be provided on the motor.

Decline conveyors.

Slider-bed conveyor: $EP = L ([v + Wf_1] - [0.017WA])$
Roller-bed conveyor: $EP = L ([v + Wf] - [0.017WA])$

where EP = effective pull
L = length of conveyor, in feet
W = live load per foot, in pounds
f = coefficient of friction of rollers, from Fig. 7
f_1 = coefficient of friction of slider, from Fig. 8
A = angle of incline or decline, in degrees
v = "no load" factor, from Fig. 9

Size of Roll or Idler	Free-running Bearings	Grease-packed Bearings
1½ to 2" diameter	4%	10%
2½" diameter	4%	11%
2⁹⁄₁₆ to 3" diameter	6%	12%

Fig. 7. Coefficients of roller friction.

Type of Slider Bed	Type of Belting	
	Cotton or Canvas Untreated Belt	Rubber Impregnated Belt
Steel	21%	21%
Wood	30%	35%

Fig. 8. Slider friction.

Type of Conveyor	Nominal Width								
	To 8"	10" 12"	14" 16"	18" 20"	24"	30"	36"	42"	48"
Slider belt conveyor	0.19	0.27	0.35	0.44	0.52	0.65	0.79	0.91	1.04
Roller belt conveyor (rolls 12" centers or greater)	0.16	0.21	0.27	0.34	0.41	0.49	0.59	0.68	0.76
Roller belt conveyor (rolls less than 12" centers)	0.25	0.33	0.42	0.52	0.62	0.74	0.89	1.02	1.14

Fig. 9. "No load" factor, v.

If the difference $(v + Wf_1) - (0.017WA)$ or $(v + Wf) - (0.017WA)$ is a minus quantity, it must be treated the same as a plus quantity in calculating the effective pull. A minus quantity indicates that the motor holds back the conveyor (controls the speed), and, if electric current is shut off, the conveyor will coast until the live load is discharged. The motor should be equipped with a solenoid brake if such coasting is objectionable.

The formulas given above will be found suitable for ideal operating conditions in normal heated areas. If surrounding conditions are dusty or the conveyor is subjected to great fluctuations in atmospheric conditions, then to the effective pull found by the formulas there must be added the percentages shown in the table in Fig. 10.

Length of Conveyor (ft.)	Degree of Slope							
	Level	To 5°	6° 10°	11° 15°	16° 20°	21° 25°	26° 30°	31° 35°
20	60%	45%	30%	20%	15%	10%	8%	5%
30	45%	35%	20%	15%	10%	8%	5%	4%
50	25%	20%	12%	10%	7%	5%	4%	3%
75	20%	15%	8%	8%	5%	4%	3%	3%
100	15%	12%	7%	6%	4%	4%	3%	2%
150	12%	8%	5%	5%	3%	3%	2%	
200	10%	7%	4%	4%	3%	3%	2%	
250	7%	5%	3%	3%	2%	2%		
300	7%	5%	3%	3%	2%	2%		
400	6%	4%	3%	3%				
500	4%	3%	2%	2%				

Fig. 10. **Percentage additions to calculated effective pull.**

TYPES OF BELTING. Various types of belting are available for belt conveyors and live-roll conveyors. All types are available with special treatments to meet special operating conditions. There are **heat-resisting belts, sanitary belts, oil-resisting belts,** etc. The belting manufacturer is ready to give expert advice on the type of belt best suited to meet any special condition, and the conveyor manufacturer can design the conveyor to insure maximum life of such special belts. The belt is usually the most expensive single item of cost on a belt conveyor, and to preserve its life nothing smaller than the minimum diameter pulley recommended should be used.

The following listing gives the **most commonly used belts,** together with their normal operating strength and recommendations as to use:

1. Treated solid-woven cotton belting. The maximum operating tension is 20 lb. per in. per ply.
2. Interwoven treated solid-woven cotton belting. This belt is interwoven to increase its strength and its resistance to wear. The maximum operating tension is 30 lb. per in. per ply.
3. 32-oz. treated canvas belt. The maximum operating tension is 25 lb. per in. per ply.
4. 37½-oz. treated canvas belting. The maximum operating tension is 30 lb. per in. per ply.
5. Inner-stitched treated canvas belt. This belt is 37½-oz. stitched canvas reinforced with inner stitching to increase its strength and its resistance to wear. The maximum operating tension is 35 lb. per in. per ply.

The above **cotton and canvas belts** are normally used on horizontal conveyors but can be used on inclines up to 10° for most packages. Untreated belts are sometimes used where the treatment would have some damaging effect on the product being conveyed. Untreated cotton or canvas belts are not recommended where great variation in atmospheric conditions prevails. Their use should be confined to installations where the temperature and relative humidity are fairly constant.

The interwoven cotton and the inner-stitched canvas belts also resist abrasive wear and can be used successfully on installations where sharp-edged objects or loads are being conveyed.

Completing the list of commonly used belting are the following two types of **rubberized belting**:

    6. 28-oz. rubber-impregnated belting. The maximum operating tension is 25 lb. per in. per ply.

    7. 32-oz. rubber-impregnated belting. The maximum operating tension is 30 lb. per in. per ply.

The above rubber belts are normally used on horizontal conveyors but can be used on inclines up to 10° for most packages. The rubber belts can readily be supplied with special covers to permit their use on steeper inclines up to 35° in many cases. **Rubber covers** can readily be applied to rubber belts to permit better protection against damage when conveying abrasive loads.

METHODS FOR PASSING TRAFFIC THROUGH BELT-CONVEYOR LINES. Wherever possible, conveyors used only for transportation are installed above headroom, thereby keeping valuable floor space free for productive work. Where conveyors are installed near the floor, because of operating conditions, care must be taken to provide for cross traffic and aisles with as little interruption to conveyor flow as possible.

The conveyor should be elevated at the aisle, if possible, to permit foot traffic as well as trucking. Where it is not practical to elevate a conveyor, it is advisable to provide **stairs and bridges** over the conveyors for foot traffic. For truck traffic it is necessary to interrupt the work flow. **Hinged or gate sections** can be installed on roller and wheel conveyors for this purpose. If it is necessary for trucks to cross through a power conveyor, a separate section of power conveyor can be provided at the aisle. This section is then hinged or raised bodily, when necessary, to allow trucks to go through.

Requirements for Safety. There is now available a comprehensive engineering **safety code for conveyors**. It is designated as "Conveyors, Cableways and Related Equipment, B-20," and is available from the American Standards Association, New York, N. Y. It is advisable to consult this code and design conveyor systems to meet the safety requirements outlined in it. In this way the system installed will satisfy safety engineers in states where the code has been adopted by action of the legislature. Since all states probably will eventually adopt the code, it should be adhered to even if it has not been put into effect in the particular state where an installation of equipment is being made. Where installations are hazardous, there is usually some legal recourse to compel installations to be modified in the interests of the welfare of workers.

Chain Package Conveyors

CONVEYORS OF CHAIN TYPE. Under the general classification of chain conveyors are included here all such conveyors used for conveying packages or objects, except the vertical type of conveyor and trolley conveyors, these being covered in separate sections. The types of conveyors included here under the heading "Chain Conveyors" are the car-type conveyor, pallet-type conveyor, cross-bar conveyor, pusher-bar conveyor, drag-chain conveyor, rolling-chain conveyor, sliding chain conveyor, slat conveyor, and roller-type slat conveyor.

The car-type conveyor consists of a series of cars equipped with wheels and attached to and propelled by an endless chain, while the pallet-type conveyor consists of a series of pallets (wheelless cars) attached to and propelled by an endless chain. In both types the object being conveyed rests on or is fastened to the car or pallet and is conveyed in a defined path. Sometimes the conveyor path forms a closed circuit and may take a circular shape, in which case the conveyor may be known as a carrousel conveyor. In the car type the wheels operate in or on tracks, while in the pallet type the pallets slide on tracks.

CHAINS. The conveying chains in package conveyors generally can be classed as pintle and combination chains, light-roller and heavy engineering roller chains, drag chains, and rivetless chain. The detachable-link-type chain is also used to some extent.

Pintle and combination chains are used mostly on vertical conveyors where there is little need for rollers in the chain. Roller-type chains are sometimes used on vertical conveyors where certain kinds of attachments are themselves equipped with rollers. Ordinarily, **roller-type chains** are used on slat conveyors, pusher-bar conveyors, cross-bar conveyors, etc. Flanged rollers are frequently used on heavier duty conveyors. **Drag-type chains** are used almost exclusively on drag conveyors. **Rivetless chains** are used chiefly on overhead trolley conveyors, car-type conveyors, pallet-type conveyors, etc. Pintle and combination chains are sometimes used on car- and pallet-type conveyors.

TYPICAL INSTALLATIONS. Typical installations where either car-type or pallet-type conveyors are ideally suited are: conveying molds in a foundry to pouring, cooling, and knockout operations; assembly operations where, frequently, assembly jigs are fastened to the car or pallets; stuffing operations in magazine publishing or in bookbinders' plants; and similar mass-production operations.

Cross-bar conveyors, Fig. 11, consist of endless chains supporting spaced, removable, or attached sticks or cross-members from which materials are hung or festooned while being processed. **Pusher-bar conveyors** consist of endless chains cross-connected at intervals by bars or rotatable pushers which move packages or objects along, up, or down stationary wood, metal, or roller-conveyor beds, or troughs. The pusher-bar conveyor, when installed at a decline, is also employed to retard packages or objects.

The **drag-chain conveyor** usually consists of a wide chain operating in a trough and dragging small objects along the path of the trough. The **rolling-chain con-**

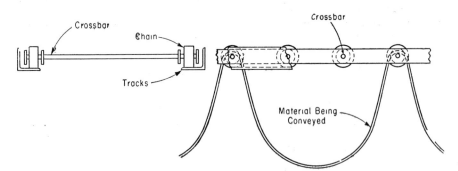

Fig. 11. Cross-bar conveyor.

veyor (Fig. 12) consists of endless chains rolling on tracks with the packages or objects resting and being conveyed on the chains. Similarly, the **sliding-chain conveyor** slides on tracks with the packages or objects resting and being conveyed on the chains.

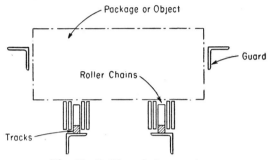

Fig. 12. Rolling-chain conveyor.

Slat conveyors consist of chains to which nonoverlapping, noninterlocking, spaced metal or wood slats are attached to form a moving bed or support for the packages or objects. The **roller-type slat conveyor** (Fig. 13) sometimes known as the **roller flight conveyor,** consists of chains with free-turning rollers, instead of actual slats, forming a moving bed or support for the packages or objects. This

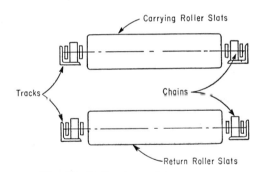

Fig. 13. Roller-type slat conveyor.

type of conveyor is ideally adaptable for storage of blocked loads. The loads or packages can be blocked at will without effect on the driving medium, because the free-turning rolls can readily revolve under the blocked load. In this type of conveyor there is no appreciable pressure exerted against the block or dam holding back the loads, and the conveyor can be used successfully with fragile loads.

FORMULAS FOR CHAIN PULLS. The following formulas for determining the chain pulls in various types of chain conveyors are designed to cover all elements affecting chain pull. If designs can be standardized so that types of chains, bars, pushers, slats, etc., remain constant, then fixed factors covering all dead loads can be established and simplified formulas can be devised. It then will be necessary to add only for the pull required to move the live load.

The formulas are based on car-type and pallet-type conveyors installed in a closed loop or closed circuit. All other chain conveyor formulas are based on a live load on the upper or conveying strand with no load on the lower or return strand. The pull in the chain of the car-type conveyor or the pallet-type conveyor can be calculated from the following formulas:

Level conveyor or level portion of conveyor:

$$\text{Chain pull} = (W + w)f$$

Inclined portion of conveyor at angle θ:

$$\text{Chain pull} = ([W + w]\cos\theta)f + (W + w)\sin\theta$$

Declined portion of conveyor at angle θ:

$$\text{Chain pull} = ([W + w]\cos\theta)f - (W + w)\sin\theta$$

where W = total live load, in pounds
w = total weight of cars and chain, in pounds
f = friction, from Fig. 14

Sliding Chain	Diameter of Rollers in Roller Chain			
	$1\frac{1}{2}''$	$2''$	$2\frac{1}{2}''$	$3''$
35%	20%	20%	15%	12%

Fig. 14. Friction of conveying chains.

The pull in the chains of the cross-bar conveyor can be calculated from the following formulas:

Level conveyor or level portion of conveyor:

$$\text{Chain pull} = (W + w + w_1)f$$

Inclined conveyor or inclined portion of conveyor at angle θ:

$$\text{Chain pull} = ([W + w]\cos\theta)f + (W + w)\sin\theta + (w_1\cos\theta)f - w_1\sin\theta$$

Declined conveyor or declined portion of conveyor at angle θ:

$$\text{Chain pull} = ([W + w]\cos\theta)f + (w_1\cos\theta)f + w_1\sin\theta - (W + w)\sin\theta$$

where W = total live load, in pounds
w = weight, in pounds, of bars and chain in upper strand
w_1 = weight, in pounds, of bars and chain in lower strand
f = friction, from Fig. 14.

Note that any vertical portion of conveyor must be calculated separately with proper allowance being added for the "up" side and credit allowed for the "down" side. Friction in the vertical guides is nil for roller chain and about 10 percent if the chain slides in vertical guides.

The pull in the chain(s) of the pusher-bar conveyor or the drag conveyor can be calculated from the following formulas:

Level conveyor or level portion of conveyor:

$$\text{Chain pull} = WF + (w + w_1)f$$

Inclined conveyor or inclined portion of conveyor at angle θ:

$$\text{Chain pull} = (W\cos\theta)F + (w\cos\theta)f + (W + w)\sin\theta + (w_1\cos\theta)f - w_1\sin\theta$$

Declined conveyor or declined portion of conveyor at angle θ:

$$\text{Chain pull} = (W \cos \theta)F + (w \cos \theta)f + (w_1 \cos \theta)f + w_1 \sin \theta - (W + w) \sin \theta$$

where W = total live load, in pounds
w = weight, in pounds, of chain and bars in upper strand
w_1 = weight, in pounds, of chain and bars in lower strand
F = friction, from Fig. 15
f = friction, from Fig. 14

Note that any vertical portion of pusher-bar conveyor must be calculated separately, with proper allowance being added for the "up" side and credit allowed for the "down" side. Friction in the vertical guides for the chain is nil for roller chain and about 10 percent if the chain slides in vertical guides. However, friction of the live load against vertical guides must be calculated. In both the pusher-bar and drag conveyors the transition from horizontal, or level, portions to inclined or declined portions is usually made with curved tracks or guides. If the radius of such curves is 4 ft. or greater, the curved portions can be considered as part of the incline or decline.

The pull in the chains of rolling-chain conveyors, sliding-chain conveyors, and slat conveyors can be calculated from the following formulas:

Level conveyor or level portion of conveyor:

$$\text{Chain pull} = (W + w + w_1)f$$

Inclined conveyor or inclined portion of conveyor at angle θ:

$$\text{Chain pull} = ([W + w] \cos \theta)f + (W + w) \sin \theta + (w_1 \cos \theta)f - w_1 \sin \theta$$

Declined conveyor or declined portion of conveyor at angle θ:

$$\text{Chain pull} = ([W + w] \cos \theta)f + (w_1 \cos \theta)f + w_1 \sin \theta - (W + w) \sin \theta$$

where W = total live load, in pounds
w = weight, in pounds, of chain and slats in upper strand
w_1 = weight, in pounds, of chain and slats in lower strand
f = friction, from Fig. 14.

Type of Bed	Kind of Package		
	Carton	Wood Box	Steel Box
Steel	35%	30%	20%
Wood	40%		
Rollers with free-running bearings	6%	4%	4%
Rollers with grease-packed bearings	12%	10%	10%

Fig. 15. Friction on bed of pusher-bar conveyor.

Chain conveyors are sometimes used when operating conditions or the load being conveyed would make the use of the more economical belt conveyor impractical.

Gravity Package Conveyors

TYPES OF GRAVITY CONVEYORS. Roller conveyors, wheel conveyors, and slides or chutes are the types of conveyors that can be grouped under the general classification of "gravity conveyors." Packages or objects can be moved manually or by gravity on these conveyors.

GRAVITY ROLLER CONVEYORS. Conveyors usually consist of two light angles or channels designed for a maximum deflection of 0.33 in. in a 10-ft. span and braced to form a frame. Between the sides are mounted a series of cylindrical rollers constructed of tubing (Fig. 16 and 17) and revolving on ball or other free-running bearings. Grease-packed bearings are frequently used when

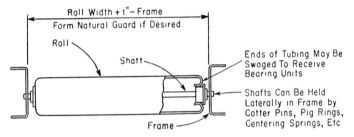

Fig. 16. Section through roller conveyor.

Roll Diameter (in.)	Load Capacity of Roll (lb.)	Wall Thickness
1 to 2	50 to 200	18 gage to 12 gage
2⅛ to 2⁹⁄₁₆	150 to 1,000	16 gage to 7 gage
2¾ to 4	500 to 5,000	10 gage to ½ in.
Over 4	To 8,000	10 gage to ⅞ in.

Fig. 17. Sizes and capacities of rollers.

a conveyor is operated under wet, dirty, or acid conditions. The shafts of the rollers are locked in the side frames, and the inner races of the bearings are, in turn, locked on the shaft to prevent the races from rotating on the shafts and the shafts from rotating in the frames. The gage of the roller tubing (see Fig. 17) is determined by the impact load and is always sufficient to make the rollers as strong as the bearings and shaft. The capacity of the roller is not materially decreased as the length (width) of the roller increases.

The spacing of the rollers is determined by the weight and length of the package or object to be conveyed, the maximum spacing being ⅓ of the minimum package length, so that there are always three rollers under the load.

Loads must have a rigid riding surface. When loads exceed 100 lb. in weight, investigations are necessary to determine if the construction of the package and its contents will permit travel by gravity. There is no way of controlling the speed of these heavy loads and at the same time insuring that they will start from rest if they should be arrested in their travel. It naturally follows that if either the package or its contents are fragile, damage may result if heavy loads are allowed to travel by gravity; likewise, rugged heavy loads may gain too much momentum as a result jump off the conveyor, especially at curves. Loads up to 40,000 lb. have been carried on roller conveyors, but such loads are manually or mechanically pushed on the conveyor. As the average roller conveyor has a bearing friction of only 2 to 3 percent, it is ideally adaptable for advancing heavy loads between operations with comparatively little effort.

Grades. When loads are permitted to travel by gravity, the grades required depend largely upon the weight of object or package, nature of the riding surface, and the number of rolls in contact with the riding surface. Experience indicates that heavy steel drums will move satisfactorily on a slope of $\frac{1}{4}$ in. per ft.; steel tote boxes or hardwood boxes of 15- to 75-lb. weight, on $\frac{3}{8}$ in. per ft.; heavy cartons $\frac{1}{2}$ in. per ft.; while light cartons may require grades of $1\frac{1}{2}$ in. or more per ft. On hard-bottom loads, the grade can be reduced as the weight increases. But on soft-bottom loads (such as soft carton stock) increased weight may cause the load to "drape" over the rolls, and increased grades may be required as the weight increases.

Curves. When curved sections are used, the width of the conveyor should be increased to provide clearance for the package or object. The distance required between guards can be approximated from the table in Fig. 21. Curves are regularly made in units of 45° and 90°, flat or banked, and either right- or left-hand turns. The rolls in curves are either straight rolls, differential rolls, or tapered rolls. In flat curves there is a decided difference in the action of the three different types of rolls. **Straight rolls** will always try to advance the load at right angles to the axes of the rolls, and therefore guard rails are required to assist in keeping the load on the conveyor while negotiating the curve. **Differential rolls** compensate, to some extent, the tendency of the load to travel off the conveyor. While guard rails are still advisable, the pressure against the guards is less, and the load can more readily negotiate the curve. **Tapered rollers,** provided the radius of the curve is properly proportioned to the taper of the roll, will guide loads around the curve perfectly, and guard rails are not required. The straight roll is the most economical, and in the majority of installations it gives satisfactory operation. This type of curve is therefore used most often, and the differential and tapered roll curves are seldom required.

When curves are **banked** or **pitched,** there is practically no difference in the action of hard-bottom, heavy loads negotiating the curve, regardless of the type of roll used. The loads are rigid, and there are only two points of the load in contact with the rolls, because it is physically impossible for the entire flat bottom of the load to contact all the rolls. This condition automatically results in a differential action on the curve, and straight rolls will be just as effective as other types. As the pitch or drop in the curve is reduced, thereby approaching a flat curve, and/or a soft-bottom load is conveyed, more bottom surface is in contact with the rolls, and then the advantage of differential and tapered rolls is realized.

Various **accessories,** such as frog sections, spur sections, switch sections, hinged sections, gate sections, ball-caster sections, and turntables, are available, and all help to increase the versatility of a roller-conveyor installation.

WHEEL CONVEYORS. These conveyors usually consist of two light channels designed for maximum versatility and portability. The channels are braced to form a frame, and between the sides are mounted a series of wheels on rigid through shafts (Fig. 18). Another type of wheel conveyor illustrated in Fig. 19 is suitable for reasonably uniform-width loads and for special loads that may have projections extending below the normal bottom of the load.

The load must have a rigid riding surface and generally should not exceed 100 lb. in weight. This type of conveyor is ideally adapted to extremely light loads, because the light-weight wheels permit grades about half those required for roller conveyor.

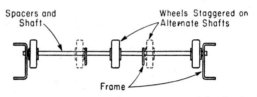

Fig. 18. Section through wheel conveyor—standard wheels.

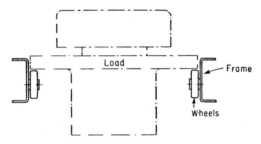

Fig. 19. Special wheel conveyor.

When curved sections are used with guardrails the width of the conveyor may not be affected, but the distance between guards must allow clearance for the package or object. The distance required between guards can be approximated from the table in Fig. 21. Curves are regularly made in 45° and 90° turns, and, as the construction of the conveyor gives a perfect differential action to the curves, the loads negotiate turns in almost perfect alignment. Outside guardrails are provided on turns, partly because of their utility but mainly as a safety precaution.

Since the sections of a wheel conveyor are so much lighter than comparable sections of roller conveyors, they are used extensively where portability is required and where it is necessary to change frequently the setup of conveyor lines. Slight changes in direction of travel can be obtained without the use of curved sections by offsetting straight sections. The differential construction will guide the loads satisfactorily. Various accessories similar to those available for roller conveyors are available for wheel conveyors also.

SLIDES AND CHUTES. Slides and chutes are usually constructed of steel and are used to guide packages or objects down from one level to a lower level. Since **gravity** is used to move the load, here again there is no control over speed, and fragile loads should not be conveyed.

The action of loads in chutes varies with the types of loads and the atmospheric conditions in the surrounding area. The **grade or angle of decline,** when adjusted so that it will be satisfactory for the lightest package, will probably prove to be very fast for heavier packages. Similarly, if adjusted on a dry day, it may prove to be too slow on a humid day. Chutes, therefore, should be used only when the loads will permit comparatively rough handling and where impact of one load striking another load will not be detrimental to the package or to its contents. Chutes, while limited in application, are ideally adapted for lowering many loads between floors. When used in conjunction with roller- or wheel-conveyor systems, the bottoms of the chutes can be equipped with curved sections (Fig. 20) so that the loads do not cut into the rolls or wheels at the lower level.

It is desirable to have a straight section of roller or wheel conveyor leading into the top of the chute. In no case should a curved section deliver directly into the chute. Neither should the bottom of the chute deliver directly into a curve. At least 10 ft. of straight roller or wheel conveyor should always be installed at the bottom of the chute so that the loads can be retarded if necessary, before they negotiate the curve. Also, loads should not be allowed to accumulate on the lower conveyor back to the discharge of the chute, because loads coming down the chute may be damaged when striking against the accumulated loads.

SPIRALS. Roller spirals, wheel spirals, and spiral chutes are formed of continuous curved sections, on which packages and objects are lowered in a substantially **helical path.** In the case of roller and wheel spirals, a continuous series

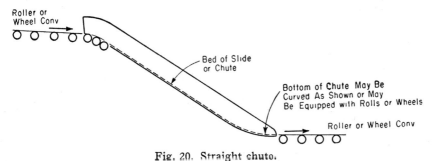

Fig. 20. Straight chute.

of 90° curved sections is used with the grade, at the center line of the curve section, being from $1\frac{1}{2}$ to 2 times the grade required on straight sections. When high packages require steep pitches, to provide clearance, the centerline diameter must be increased to maintain the recommended grade, thus preventing too great speed, which results in damage to the contents of the package. These spirals offer an economical means of lowering loads and may be used for temporary storage, since packages start or come to rest easily and evenly on the roller or wheel runway. It is not advisable, however, to permit storage in these spirals if loads vary greatly in weight or size, because the heavy loads may crush the light loads, and large loads may "jam" smaller loads.

Spiral chutes should be designed so that the **grade** at the outer edge of the spiral is about the same as the grade used on straight chutes. Spiral chutes offer more control over speed of various-weight packages than do straight chutes, because friction against the outer guardrail is greater on the heavier package on account of the increased centrifugal action. Spiral chutes should never be used for storage, and loads should not be allowed to accumulate at the discharge point, because damage to packages will occur and loads will jam.

The width of the runway or the distance between guards of roller and wheel spirals can be approximated from the table in Fig. 21. The width of the runway for spiral chutes can be approximated by reference to the chart in Fig. 22.

Width of Package (in.)	Length of Package															
	4"	6"	8"	10"	12"	14"	16"	18"	20"	22"	24"	26"	30"	36"	42"	48"
4	6	6	6	7	7	7	7	8								
5	7	7	8	8	8	8	8	8								
6	8	8	9	9	9	9	9	9	10	10	10					
7		9	10	10	10	10	10	10	11	11	11					
8		10	11	11	11	11	11	11	12	12	12					
9		11	12	12	12	12	12	12	13	13	13					
10			13	13	13	13	13	13	14	14	14	14	15			
11			14	14	14	14	14	14	15	15	15	15	16			
12			15	15	15	15	15	15	16	16	16	16	17			
13				16	16	16	16	16	17	17	17	17	18			
14					17	17	17	17	17	18	18	18	19	20		
15					18	18	18	18	19	19	19	19	20	21		
16						19	19	19	19	20	20	20	21	22		
17						20	20	20	20	21	21	21	22	23	24	
18							21	21	21	21	22	22	23	24	25	
20							23	23	23	24	24	24	25	26	27	28
22								25	25	26	26	26	27	28	29	30
24								27	27	28	28	28	29	29	31	32
26									29	30	30	30	30	31	32	33

Fig. 21. Distance between guardrails—roller or wheel curves.

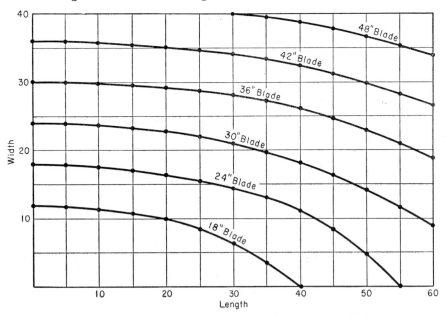

Fig. 22. Chart for determining width of spiral chute blade.

Live-Roll Package Conveyors

POWER-DRIVEN ROLLER CONVEYORS. Various means are used for powering the rolls of power-driven roller conveyors, the most common being the use of a flat belt (see Fig. 23). Another method is with round belts or V-belts (see Fig. 24), and a third method is with chain drive using sprockets on the roll tubing or sprockets on the roll shaft (see Fig. 25). In all cases the roll spacing and size of the roll are determined in the same manner as for roller gravity conveyors.

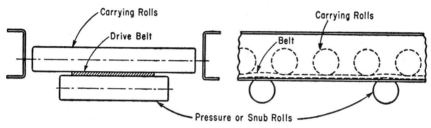

Fig. 23. Live-roll conveyor—flat-belt drive.

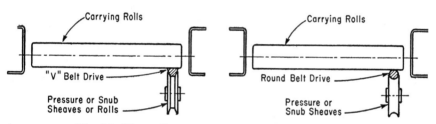

Fig. 24. Live-roll conveyors—V- or round-belt drive.

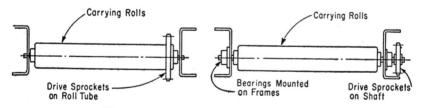

Fig. 25. Live-roll conveyor—chain drive.

Any formulas for determining the effective pull in the belting of the belt-driven horizontal live-roll conveyor should include items for:

1. Turning effort for rollers—determined by the weight of rollers multiplied by the friction coefficient of the bearings.
2. Pulling effort for moving the belting through the snubbing action under the carrying rolls—determined by the weight of the belting multiplied by varying percentages which depend on thickness (plies of belt) and whether surrounding area is heated or not.
3. Pulling effort required to move the live load—determined by the weight of the live load multiplied by the friction coefficient of the bearings (see Fig. 4).

The following formula has been simplified and is based on certain standardized features. It assumes that the rollers will not be larger than 2½ in. in diameter and have tubing not over No. 14 gage. It also assumes that belting will not be over 5 ply in thickness and that antifriction bearings will be used on all pulleys.

$$EP = L(v + Wn)$$

where EP = effective pull, in pounds
L = length of conveyor, in feet
W = live load per foot of conveyor, in pounds
v = no load factor, from Fig. 26 and 27
n = 0.07 to 0.10, depending on type of bearing in rollers.

In Figs. 26 and 27 reference is made to **"heated"** and **"unheated" areas.** "Heated areas" refers to all normal indoor installations where temperatures are approximately 70° F. the year round. "Unheated areas" refers to buildings, sheds, or docks subject to atmospheric changes but with minimum temperatures of 35° F. Belt-driven live-roll conveyors should not be installed where freezing temperatures are likely to occur.

The live-roll conveyor can be installed at **very slight inclines or declines.** In either case allowances may be made to compensate for the additional power required on the incline conveyor. In the case of the decline conveyor, deduction can be made for the negative resultant of the live load on the decline. However, the angles are so slight that these factors may be ignored.

The belt is held against the bottom of the carrying rolls by **snub rolls.** The pressure of the driving belts against the bottom of the rolls must be very light—just enough to propel the load. If the pressure or snubbing action is too great, undue power will be required to drive the belting when the loads on the conveyors are blocked, as is often required in the operation of this type of conveyor.

Belt Ply and Carrying Roll Centers		No Load Factor V								
		Nominal Conveyor Width								
		To 8"	10" 12"	14" 16"	18" 20"	24"	30"	36"	42"	48"
3 ply	Centers 3"	1.22	1.60	2.04	2.42	2.76	3.35	4.05	4.65	5.14
	4"	0.91	1.20	1.54	1.81	2.06	2.51	3.04	3.49	3.87
	6"	0.63	0.84	1.07	1.24	1.45	1.77	2.14	2.46	2.73
	8"	0.50	0.66	0.84	1.00	1.15	1.39	1.69	1.94	2.15
4 ply	Centers 3"	1.36	1.78	2.26	2.69	3.06	3.73	4.50	5.17	5.72
	4"	1.01	1.33	1.69	2.02	2.30	2.79	3.38	3.88	4.30
	6"	0.71	0.93	1.19	1.42	1.65	1.97	2.38	2.73	3.04
	8"	0.55	0.73	0.93	1.11	1.27	1.55	1.88	2.16	2.40
5 ply	Centers 3"	1.56	2.03	2.61	3.10	3.52	4.30	5.18	5.95	6.58
	4"	1.14	1.53	1.95	2.32	2.64	3.20	3.88	4.47	4.95
	6"	0.81	1.07	1.36	1.63	1.86	2.27	2.74	3.14	3.49
	8"	0.63	0.84	1.07	1.28	1.47	1.79	2.16	2.48	2.76

Fig. 26. Factor v for heated areas.

Belt Ply and Carrying Roll Centers		No Load Factor V								
		Nominal Conveyor Width								
		To 8"	10" 12"	14" 16"	18" 20"	24"	30"	36"	42"	48"
3 ply	Centers 3"	2.72	3.56	4.52	5.38	6.12	7.46	9.00	10.34	11.44
	4"	2.02	2.66	3.38	4.04	4.60	5.58	6.76	7.76	8.60
	6"	1.42	1.86	2.38	2.84	3.30	3.94	4.76	5.46	6.08
	8"	1.10	1.46	1.86	2.22	2.54	3.10	3.76	4.32	4.80
4 ply	Centers 3"	3.12	4.10	5.20	6.19	7.05	8.58	10.40	11.90	13.20
	4"	2.32	3.06	3.90	4.64	5.28	6.43	7.76	8.92	9.90
	6"	1.62	2.14	2.73	3.26	3.72	4.54	4.98	6.29	6.99
	8"	1.27	1.68	2.14	2.56	2.93	3.56	4.32	4.95	5.52
5 ply	Centers 3"	3.80	4.99	6.34	7.54	8.57	10.45	12.60	14.45	16.00
	4"	2.83	3.73	4.74	5.65	6.44	7.82	9.45	10.85	12.00
	6"	1.97	2.61	3.32	3.96	4.53	5.52	6.66	7.65	8.50
	8"	1.54	2.04	2.61	3.12	3.57	4.35	5.25	6.04	6.71

Fig. 27. Factor v for unheated areas.

In the case of the commonly used **flat-belt drive**, it is advisable to use as narrow a belt as practical. On the other hand, the belting should not be too thick. Usually 3-ply or 4-ply belting is best. The full strength value of the belt should be used, to keep the width and thickness to a minimum. The round and V-belt types of drive are used on light-duty and, usually, special installations requiring that the conveyor negotiate turns.

The **chain driven type** of live-roll conveyor is usually used for heavy-duty installations or where operating conditions would prohibit the use of flat belts. The chain drive may consist of a continuous chain with only tangential contact at each sprocket. It may also consist of individual chain drives from roller to roller (this construction requires two sprockets per roller). The sprockets may be fastened to the roll tubing, permitting the use of regular gravity rollers having stationary shafts and bearing mounted in the ends of the rollers. As a third method, the chain drive may consist of sprockets mounted on the shaft, in which case the roll tubing and the shafting are integral, with bearings mounted on the conveyor frame.

In the types of chain-driven live-roll conveyors described, the **pull in the chain** drive can be calculated by the following formula:

$$\text{Chain pull in pounds} = \frac{\text{Total load} \times f \times \text{roll diam. in inches}}{\text{Pitch diam. of sprockets in inches}}$$

where $f = 0.12$ for antifriction bearing rolls
$f = 0.30$ for sleeve bearing rolls

The chain-driven type of live-roll conveyor should be used for transportation only and never where loads are to be blocked. All types of live-roll conveyors, when installed outdoors, where they are subjected to the elements, should be used for transportation only and never where loads are to be blocked. Live-roll conveyors are frequently used for transportation conveyors where the nature of the load would prohibit the use of the more economical belt conveyor. Typical of such loads are heavy rough-wood crates with sharp steel reinforcing bands, protruding nailheads, etc., that would cut the belting of the belt conveyor but have riding surfaces that permit conveying on a live-roll conveyor.

Heavy-duty live-roll conveyors are used in steel mills, nonferrous metal mills, etc. These conveyors use the chain type of drives, and frequently the rolls are individually driven, each roll having an independent drive. Such conveyors are used in rolling mills, for conveying slabs or sheets. Live rolls are also used to convey large coils of metal during the manufacturing process.

Vertical Package Conveyors

CONVEYORS OF ELEVATING TYPE. Under the general classification of vertical conveyors are included all package conveyors that convey loads vertically only—either up or down or both. This group includes the arm conveyor, reciprocating conveyor, suspended-tray conveyor, and the opposed-shelf-type vertical conveyor. Bucket elevators are sometimes used for conveying packages or objects, but because these conveyors are primarily used for conveying bulk materials they are discussed in another section.

Arm Conveyors. The arm conveyor (see Fig. 28) consists of an endless belt or one or more chains or other linkage, to which are attached projecting arms or cars for handling packages or objects. This type of conveyor is also frequently installed at an incline to elevate loads and when so installed, is usually used to

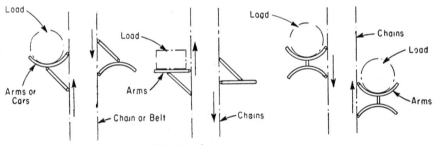

Fig. 28. Arm conveyors.

elevate round objects such as barrels, kegs, drums, etc. The arm conveyor can be manually or automatically loaded and can raise or lower the load to another level, where the load is manually or automatically discharged. The conveyor can convey almost any type of package or object—from the smallest and lightest to loads weighing hundreds of pounds.

Reciprocating Conveyors. The reciprocating conveyor (see Fig. 29) is a power- or gravity-actuated carrier which receives packages or objects and discharges them to another or other elevations. This type of conveyor can be manually or automatically loaded at one level and will raise or lower the load to another level, where the load is discharged manually or automatically. Or the conveyor can be manually or automatically loaded at one level and then it can raise or lower the load to either of several other levels, where it manually or automatically discharges its load. In this latter case the level to which the carrier travels to discharge its load can be manually or automatically selected by signals on the load or by connection with automatic selection on other conveyors feeding the reciprocating conveyor. When gravity-operated, the reciprocating conveyor is used only to lower loads, and the weight of the load combined with the weight of the carrier overcomes the magnitude of the counterweight. It is the counterweight which, after the load has been discharged, returns the carrier to the loading position, ready to receive the next load.

The reciprocating conveyor-carrier or car can be arranged to receive any type of package or object—from the lightest and smallest package; to cartons of canned goods or bottled goods, tote boxes, pans or baskets, barrels, kegs, drums, special jigs or fixtures, etc.; to heavy loads—such as rolls of paper, and skids or pallets containing or supporting loads weighing thousands of pounds.

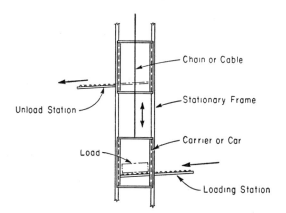

Fig. 29. Reciprocating vertical conveyor.

The reciprocating conveyor is not to be confused with a freight elevator The reciprocating conveyor carrier is designed to receive normally a single package or object—no operator "rides" on the carrier, and the carrier cannot be "called" manually. The carrier can be "dispatched" manually only and can be called automatically only—by the load at the receiving station acting on electrical controls in conjunction with another load at the discharge station. Thus movement of the carrier to a station is automatic only after it has safely discharged its duties at another station.

Suspended-Tray Elevators. Suspended-tray conveyors take several forms. The conveyor consists of one or more endless chains with pendent trays or carriers which receive and deliver packages or objects at one or more locations. Normally, loads are picked up automatically at a loading station or loading stations on the up-traveling side, conveyed over the top sprockets, and discharged to an unloading station or unloading stations on the down-traveling side.

The carriers of suspended-tray conveyors may be constructed of fingers or arms that pass through alternate fingers or arms at the loading and unloading stations, so that packages or objects can be picked up or discharged automatically. In other cases the objects or boxes are fed to the elevating (or lowering) conveyor from a belt conveyor automatically synchronized with the vertical conveyor, so as to remove the packages as they come from the horizontal conveyor. The fingers or arms of the carrier are usually constructed of structural or cast members. The horizontal conveyor, across which the packages or objects roll, may be of the **belt, roller, or wheel type** or may consist of **individual power conveyors** for moving the packages or objects into or out of the vertical path of the carrier.

One type of suspended-tray conveyor employs two endless chains, with the tray or carrier suspended centrally between them. This type is known as the **center-suspension type** and is generally used for loads having low centers of gravity or loads of uniform size so that there will be little danger of unbalanced tray or carrier loading. Sometimes the fingers or arms of the conveyor are curved or V form instead of flat as shown in the illustration and are so designed to convey round objects, such as rolls of paper, rolls of metal, barrels, and drums, more efficiently. The trays or carriers are attached to the chains at the top of the hangers, and the bottoms of the hangers are designed to engage in guiding members throughout the vertical travel of the tray or carrier. The trays are free to swing, as they negotiate the top and bottom sprockets, but the low center of gravity and the uniformity of the object on the tray tend to keep the tray reasonably level. If absolute control must be maintained around the sprockets, the conveyor may be equipped with a mechanical leveling device. Such devices may take the form of escapement wheels engaging nubs or pins on the trays or may be a sun gear on the sprocket shaft engaging planetary gears on each tray.

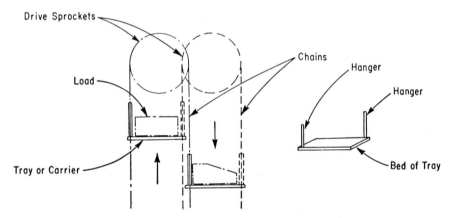

Fig. 30. Suspended-tray conveyor, corner-suspension type.

Another type of suspended-tray conveyor employs two endless chains, with the tray suspended from them on hangers at diagonal corners of the tray, as shown in Fig. 30. This type is known as the **corner-suspension type.** With this construction the trays remain level as they negotiate the sprockets at the top and bottom, even though loads are unbalanced. If the magnitude of the unbalanced load is great, the depth of the hangers must be increased and the tray rigidly constructed to prevent twisting. The corner-suspension type is used, even though balanced loads are to be conveyed, when it is necessary to load and unload the conveyor from the same side. Thus the decision to use center suspension or corner suspension may be guided by physical conditions in the building rather than by the type of load being conveyed.

Both the center-suspension and corner-suspension types can be used for conveying great varieties of loads—from the smallest and lightest to large and heavy loads weighing thousands of pounds.

Still another type of suspended-tray conveyor uses a single strand of endless chain, with the tray suspended from the chain at the top of the hanger and the bottom of the tray or car sliding or rolling against vertical tracks. This conveyor is known as the **uni-strand type.** The loading and unloading stations are of the same general construction as on the other types previously described. The uni-strand type of construction is generally confined to light loads and is used extensively in hospitals for conveying records, films, mail, and pharmaceutical supplies in trays; in office buildings and insurance companies for all vertical handling of mail and files; and in industrial plants for special light-duty applications.

The **opposed-shelf-type vertical conveyor** consists of two strands of chain, with shelves or cars attached at intervals to each strand of chain but with no physical connection between the two shelves or cars that cooperate to convey the load (see Fig. 31). The conveyor actually consists of two or more conveyors synchronized so that opposing cars or shelves are always paired to convey a load.

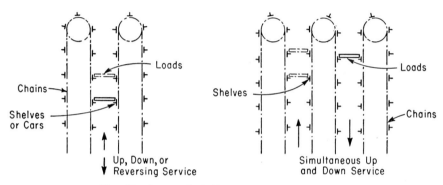

Fig. 31. Opposed-shelf-type vertical conveyor.

The opposed-shelf type of conveyor can be used for up, down, or reversing service or can be arranged to convey loads up or down simultaneously. The loads may be manually or automatically loaded and unloaded from the vertical path of the conveyor. This conveyor is used extensively for conveying trays of food, dishes, and silverware in hospitals, restaurants, hotels, etc. It is used for conveying trays or tote boxes in both commercial establishments and industrial plants. Also, the conveyor can be arranged to convey jigs, fixtures, and other odd-shaped packages or objects. The shelves or cars may be solid members, roller or wheel conveyors, or individual power conveyors.

CALCULATION OF EFFECTIVE PULLS. The effective pull for arm conveyors can be calculated in the following manner:

1. Add the weight of both driving sprockets plus the weight of the shafting, drive gear, all chains, and all arms (cars or carriages) plus all live-load weight. This total equals the **load to be turned** and when multiplied by 0.02 (antifriction bearings) or by 0.04 (sleeve bearings) will give the **turning effective pull.**
2. Now calculate the total **unbalanced live load** (maximum live load that can occur on one side of the conveyor) and add the friction of the chain in the vertical guides in accordance with the applicable formula in Fig. 32. This total will then give the **lifting effective pull.**
3. The total effective pull = the turning effective pull + the lifting effective pull. (The effective pull in lbs., when multiplied by conveyor speed in feet per minute and divided by 33,000 ft.-lb. will give the horsepower at the drive shaft. This calculation applies to all types of conveyors.)

The loading on the drive shaft is equal to the **load to be turned.** The maximum loading in the chain is equal to one-half the weight of chains on one side only plus one-half the weight of arms on one side only plus one-half the live load on the heaviest side. (In these calculations the reference to "one side of conveyor" means the up-traveling side or the down-traveling side.)

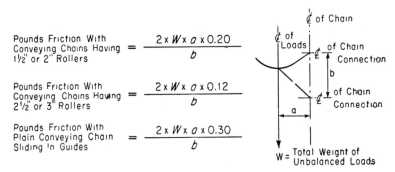

$$\text{Pounds Friction With Conveying Chains Having } 1\frac{1}{2}'' \text{ or } 2'' \text{ Rollers} = \frac{2 \times W \times a \times 0.20}{b}$$

$$\text{Pounds Friction With Conveying Chains Having } 2\frac{1}{2}'' \text{ or } 3'' \text{ Rollers} = \frac{2 \times W \times a \times 0.12}{b}$$

$$\text{Pounds Friction With Plain Conveying Chain Sliding In Guides} = \frac{2 \times W \times a \times 0.30}{b}$$

W = Total Weight of Unbalanced Loads

Fig. 32. Friction formulas—arm conveyors.

CONSTRUCTION OF RECIPROCATING CONVEYORS. Reciprocating conveyors are built two ways: one method is with a counterweight to balance the carriage weight plus part of the live load; the second method is without a counterweight, in which case the cable or chain is wound around a drum.

Effective Pull—Counterweighted Type. The effective pull on the counterweighted type can be calculated as follows:

1. Add the weight of the sprocket or sheave plus the weight of the shafting, gear, carriage, chains or cables, live load, and counterweight. This total equals the load to be turned and when multiplied by 0.02 or by 0.04 will give the turning effective pull.
2. Now add the weight of the carriage and the live load, to which total add 10 percent for friction in the vertical guides. From this total deduct the counterweight, and the balance is the lifting effective pull.
3. The total effective pull = the turning effective pull + the lifting effective pull.

The load on the drive shaft is equal to the load to be turned. The loading in the chain or cable is equal to the weight of the carriage and the live load multiplied by 1.10. The amount of counterweight that should be used is equal to one-half the live load plus the weight of the carriage.

Effective Pull—Noncounterweighted Type. The effective pull on the type of reciprocating vertical conveyor without a counterweight can be calculated as follows:

1. Add the weight of the drum plus the weight of the shafting, gear, carriage, and the live load. This total equals the load to be turned and when multiplied by 0.02 or by 0.04 will give the turning effective pull.
2. Now add the weight of the carriage and the live load, to which total add 10 percent for friction in the vertical guides. The total is the lifting effective pull.
3. The total effective pull = the turning effective pull + the lifting effective pull.

The load on the drive shaft is equal to the load to be turned. The loading in the cable or chain is equal to the lifting effective pull.

Effective Pull—Center- or Corner-Suspension Types. The effective pull on either the center-suspension or corner-suspension types of suspended-tray conveyors can be calculated in the following manner:

1. Add the weight of both driving sprockets plus the weight of the shafting, gears, all chains, and all trays (cars or carriages) plus all live-load weight. This total equals the load to be turned and when multiplied by 0.02 or by 0.04 will give the turning effective pull.
2. Now calculate the total unbalanced live load plus impact (weight of one or more loads that may be picked up by trays simultaneously) and add 10 percent for vertical tray friction in guides. To this total add the weight of one tray (if an odd number of trays are used in the conveyor). This calculation gives the total lifting effective pull.
3. The total effective pull = the turning effective pull + the lifting effective pull.

The loading on the drive shaft for the through-shaft construction is equal to the load to be turned, and for stub-shaft construction the load in each shaft will be equal to one-half the load to be turned. The maximum loading in the chain is equal to one-half the weight of the chains on one side only plus one-half the weight of the trays on one side only, plus one-half the live load on the heaviest side.

Effective Pull—Uni-strand Type of Suspension. The effective pull on the uni-strand type of suspended-tray conveyor can be calculated in the following manner:

1. Add the weight of the driving sprocket plus the weight of the gear, shafting, all chains, all trays plus all the live load. This total equals the load to be turned and when multiplied by 0.02 or by 0.04 will give the turning effective pull.
2. Now calculate the total unbalanced live load plus impact (weight of one or more loads that may be picked up by trays simultaneously) and add friction of the cars in, or on, the vertical guides in accordance with the applicable formula in Fig. 33. To this total add the weight of one tray (if an odd number of trays are used in the conveyor). This calculation gives the total lifting effective pull.
3. The total effective pull = the turning effective pull + the lifting effective pull.

The loading on the drive shaft is equal to the load to be turned. The maximum load on the chain is equal to the weight of the chain on one side plus the weight of all trays on one side plus the live load on one side.

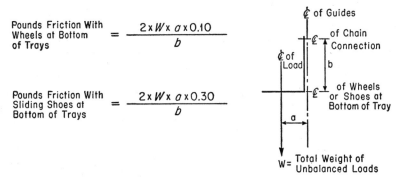

$$\text{Pounds Friction With Wheels at Bottom of Trays} = \frac{2 \times W \times a \times 0.10}{b}$$

$$\text{Pounds Friction With Sliding Shoes at Bottom of Trays} = \frac{2 \times W \times a \times 0.30}{b}$$

W = Total Weight of Unbalanced Loads

Fig. 33. Friction formulas—uni-strand vertical conveyors.

Effective Pull—Opposed-Shelf Type of Vertical Conveyor. The effective pull for the opposed-shelf type of vertical conveyor can be calculated as follows:

1. For each unit (can be two or more) add the weight of the driving sprockets plus the weight of the shafting, gears, all chains, all shelves (cars or carriages), moving siding on chain, if any, plus its proper proportion of live load. This total equals the load to be turned for that unit and when multiplied by 0.02 or by 0.04 will give the turning effective pull for that unit. This amount must be multiplied by 2, 3, or more (depending on number of units) to determine the total turning effective pull for the conveyor.
2. Now calculate the total unbalanced live load and then add 10 percent for vertical friction. This will give the lifting effective pull.
3. The total effective pull = the total turning effective pull + the lifting effective pull.

The loading on any individual drive shaft is equal to the load to be turned for that unit. The maximum loading in a chain is equal to one-half the weight of chains on one side only of a unit plus one-half the weight of shelves on one side only of the unit plus one-half the live load applicable to that unit.

Normally, the opposed-shelf type of conveyor is used for light loads and the shelves are very narrow, so the load is applied close to the center of the chain. The **usual maximum loading** for this type of conveyor is not over 30 lb. per shelf. Any reaction from this slight offset load can normally be ignored. However, if this type of conveyor is modified for **conveying heavy loads** and/or **requiring wide shelves** to accommodate the load, then such overhung load must be taken into account and proper allowances made in calculating effective pull and loading in the chains.

Pneumatic Tube Package Conveyors

PNEUMATIC CONVEYING. The pneumatic conveyors under consideration here are those using carriers or receptacles to convey the objects or materials. The most commonly used conveyors have round, oval, or rectangular tubes. Carriers are propelled through the tube by vacuum and/or pressure, varying from as little as half-pound vacuum to several pounds of pressure per square inch. Centrifugal-type exhausters or blowers are usually used for the lower vacuums or pressures (up to 3 lb.), while reciprocating screw- or vane-type compressors are used for the higher pressures. On occasion, a combination of vacuum and pressure is used on a long line. On shorter lines, where reversing service is desired, vacuum is used in one direction and pressure in the reverse direction when only one power plant is required.

Carriers. The **carrier bodies** are made of various materials, such as leather, plastics, rubber, and metals of different kinds. The bodies of the carriers must be appreciably smaller than the inside of the conveying tube, so that bends can readily be negotiated. To prevent excessive air slip past the carrier, the body is equipped with flexible **accelerator discs** and/or flexible **skirts** which conform to the inside of the tubing and bring about maximum efficiency. The carriers vary in length and construction to accommodate the loads to be conveyed. Carriers range from the simple type, designed to carry papers, to special types to convey such items as hot test pieces, tools, fixtures, jigs, explosives, dictaphone records, bottles of liquids, and a considerable range of other equipment and supplies.

Tubing and Terminals. Various materials are used in making the tubing: aluminum, brass, plastics, and steel—with the latter in most common use. Different methods are used for joining the tube lengths. The kinds of joints most frequently installed are:

1. Lapped joints, where one end of the tube is enlarged to receive the straight end of the next tube, these joints being cemented or welded.
2. Butt joints, where the ends of two lengths are butted and held in place by a sleeve piece, which may be cemented to the two lengths or welded in place.
3. Flanged joints, where the ends of the tubes are flanged or equipped with separate flanged fittings, the flanges being welded or bolted together.

Terminals are designed to permit introduction of carriers into the system and to permit carriers to be exhausted from the system, with minimum interruption to movement of other carriers in the line.

PNEUMATIC SYSTEMS. The simplest pneumatic system consists of **service between two points.** The equipment may consist of two tubes, with service one way in one of the tubes and in the opposite direction in the other tube. If frequency of transmission is lower than average, a single tube may be used with alternating direction of service.

In more **complicated systems,** serving a number of stations, there are two methods of arranging the tube lines. In the **first method** each station is connected to a **central desk,** where the carriers are redispatched to the designated receiving station. In this way, complete intercommunication is provided without the necessity of connecting each station with every other station. The carriers are provided with indicating rings so that the sender can designate to which station the carrier is to be dispatched. Each carrier is also provided with an **identifying number** so that it can be returned to its proper "home" station when empty.

Central-desk systems are used in department store service work, where each selling station must be connected with the cashier, credit department, reference desk, etc. Examples of services other than transmission of messages are those in **office buildings,** to connect the stations with the filing department, mail room, etc.; **hospitals,** where the stations are connected with the pharmacy, patient record-file, etc.; **industrial plants,** where the various manufacturing departments are connected with the factory cost, stockroom, and order departments; **steel mills, railroad yards,** in fact, any operation where the out-stations are responsible to a central control department.

The **second method** of arranging tubes to connect numerous stations is the **switch system.** In this arrangement several stations are connected with a single loop of tube line—usually 10 stations to a loop. The several loops then connect with one another at **selector stations.** When dispatching a carrier the sender designates the station to which the carrier is to go by means of a push button, by dialing, or by setting the rings on the carrier. An automatic arrangement (usually electrically operated) then permits the carrier to pass through any number of station areas until it arrives at the designated station, where it is automatically switched out of the line. If the carrier is destined for a station in another loop, it stops at the **selector station** and is automatically deflected into the loop containing the designated station.

The size and kind of load to be conveyed dictates the size of tube system to be used. For economic reasons the round tube is most often used. The diameters of round tubes most frequently used are the 2¼-, 3-, 4-, and 5½-in. sizes.

TUBES. The most common special-size tubes are the 4-in. × 7-in. **oval** and the 3-in. × 12-in. **rectangular** tubes. The 4-in. × 7-in. pneumatic tube is fre-

Size of Tube (in.)	Inside Dimension of Carrier (in.)
$2\frac{1}{4}$	$1\frac{3}{8}$
3	$1\frac{15}{16}$
4	$2\frac{11}{16}$
$5\frac{1}{2}$	$4\frac{3}{8}$
4×7	$2\frac{9}{16} \times 5\frac{9}{16}$
3×12	$2\frac{11}{16} \times 10\frac{11}{16}$

Fig. 34. Carrier clearance dimensions.

Size of Tube (in.)	Length of Line (ft.)	Vacuum Loss in Ounces and Volume (C.F.M.) of Air Required per Line at Different Carrier Speeds							
		25 F.P.S.		30 F.P.S.		35 F.P.S.		40 F.P.S.	
		Vacuum	Volume	Vacuum	Volume	Vacuum	Volume	Vacuum	Volume
$2\frac{1}{4}$	Less than 300	8		8		8		11	
	300	8	62	11	70	13	80	16	90
	Each 100 over 300	2		3		$4\frac{1}{2}$		5	
3	Less than 400	5		7		10			
	400	6	100	9	120	13	130		
	Each 100 over 400	2		2		3			
4	Less than 500	6		7		9			
	500	7	173	9	213	11	255		
	Each 100 over 500	1		$1\frac{1}{2}$		2			
$5\frac{1}{2}$	Less than 600	5		7					
	600	6	330	8	400				
	Each 100 over 600	1		$1\frac{1}{2}$					
4×7	Less than 600	5		6					
	600	6	350	8	420				
	Each 100 over 600	1		$1\frac{1}{4}$					
3×12	Less than 600	5		5					
	600	5	570	6	680				
	Each 100 over 600	1		1					

Fig. 35. Vacuum loss and volume.

31·30

quently used when the load to be conveyed cannot be rolled to fit into a 4-in. or 5½-in. carrier and for special loads, such as may be encountered in industrial plants, office buildings, hospitals, etc. The 3-in. × 12-in. pneumatic tube is used when complete correspondence files, legal-size files, blueprints, etc., are to be conveyed.

The inside clearance of carriers varies with the length of the carrier desired for the load. Clearances in tube bends and terminals are the determining factors. The inside dimensions given in Fig. 34 will act as a general guide. As only smooth-wall tubing is used for pneumatic conveyors, the friction loss in tube runs is not great. Also, as tube bends are used, the loss around bends is kept to a minimum. The figures given in Fig. 35 have been calculated for pneumatic-tube lines with an average number of bends and can be used to determine the friction loss in lines.

In laying out any system having a number of tube lines, it is first necessary to measure the length of the longest line, including any length required to connect the conveying line to the power unit, or the drum supplying air to the system.

POWER UNITS. If there are only a few long lines in a large system, with a majority of the lines considerably shorter, it may be more economical to use a separate power unit for the few long lines and another unit for the balance of the system. The table in Fig. 35 also gives the cubic footage of air recommended for each line in the system. From these data the total cubic footage of air and the pressure or vacuum required of the power plant for the air circuits can readily be determined. Vacuum loss can be read directly from the table. If it is necessary to convert to pressure, the following formula may be used:

$$\text{Pressure in pounds} = \frac{P \times P}{P - V} - P$$

where P = pressure of free air, in pounds
V = vacuum, in pounds

Pressure of free air at various altitudes is shown in the table in Fig. 36.

Altitude (ft.)	Pressure of Air (lb. per sq. in.)	Altitude (ft.)	Pressure of Air (lb. per sq. in.)
Sea level	14.72	8,000	10.85
1,000	14.17	9,000	10.45
2,000	13.64	10,000	10.06
3,000	13.13	11,000	9.69
4,000	12.64	12,000	9.33
5,000	12.17	13,000	8.98
6,000	11.71	14,000	8.64
7,000	11.27	15,000	8.32

Fig. 36. Air pressures.

In addition to the vacuum required for the air circuit, as above determined, it is necessary to find the **vacuum required to move carriers** and the vacuum required to overcome the loss in air piping to and from the power plant. The vacuum required to move carriers is very small if the frequency of service requires only one carrier in the line at any one time, and assuming that the carrier is of normal light weight. If service is frequent enough to require several carriers in the line at one time, and/or there are unusually long risers in the line, and/or carriers are unusually heavy, then the vacuum required per carrier can be calculated from the following formula:

$$\text{For risers: } V = \frac{16 \times W}{A}$$

$$\text{For horizontal runs: } V = \frac{6.4 \times W}{A}$$

where V = vacuum required, in ounces
W = total weight of carrier and load, in pounds
A = 3.73 for 2¼-in. tube
 = 6.70 for 3-in. tube
 = 11.76 for 4-in. tube
 = 23.00 for 4 × 7-in. tube
 = 37.00 for 3 × 12-in. tube

The **vacuum required to overcome the air friction** in the air drum, if a drum is used, and/or the piping to and from the power unit should be determined from the table in Fig. 37. Each elbow or tee should be figured as equivalent to a pipe

Air Pipe or Drum Diameter (in.)	Vacuum Loss in Ounces per 100 Ft. at Different Air Velocities					
	3,600 F.P.M.		3,000 F.P.M.		2,400 F.P.M.	
	C.F.M.	Loss	C.F.M.	Loss	C.F.M.	Loss
Tube Sizes						
2¼	90	6.5	75	5.0	60	3.8
3	160	4.7	140	3.4	110	2.2
4	350	3.4	300	2.5	230	1.7
Air-Pipe Sizes						
4	300	3.3	250	2.4	200	1.5
5	490	2.4	400	1.8	320	1.1
6	700	2.0	580	1.4	470	1.0
7	960	1.7	800	1.2	640 ·	0.8
8	1,250	1.4	1,040	1.0	840	0.7
10	1,960	1.0	1,630	0.8	1,300	0.5
12	2,820	0.9	2,360	0.7	1,890	0.4
14	3,860	0.7	3,200	0.6	2,560	0.4
15	4,410	0.7	3,690	0.5	2,940	0.3
16	5,030	0.6	4,200	0.5	3,350	0.3
18	6,370	0.6	5,300	0.4	4,240	0.3
20	7,850	0.5	6,540	0.4	5,230	0.3
22	9,540	0.5	7,940	0.3	6,350	0.2
24	11,300	0.4	9,420	0.3	7,530	0.2
26	13,470	0.4	11,200	0.3	9,000	0.2
28	15,350	0.3	12,750	0.3	10,210	0.15
30	17,610	0.3	14,700	0.2	11,750	0.15
36	25,500	0.3	21,200	0.2	17,100	0.15
42	34,600	0.2	28,800	0.15	23,100	0.10
48	45,000	0.2	37,500	0.15	30,000	0.10
54	57,200	0.15	47,700	0.10	38,100	0.10
60	70,500	0.15	58,600	0.10	47,000	0.10

Fig. 37. Vacuum loss in air pipes.

length of 10 diameters. The higher velocity of 3,600 ft. per min. should be used wherever possible, for economic reasons. However, the higher velocity results in greater noise of operation. Therefore if it is essential to have a quiet operating system, it is best to use one of the lower velocities.

The final size of the power unit can then be determined. The total cubic footage of air required per minute is found by multiplying the recommended cubic footage per minute per line, from the table in Fig. 35, by the number of conveyor lines. The total vacuum required is found by adding the vacuum required in the longest air circuit, the vacuum required to move carriers in a riser, the vacuum required to move carriers in the horizontal runs, and the vacuum required to overcome loss in air piping and/or drum.

PORTABLE CONVEYORS

CONTENTS

PORTABLE CONVEYORS

DEFINITION. Since the various definitions of portable conveyors can be confusing, it is important to explain that its moveability does not necessarily place a conveyor in the category of portable conveyors as considered by the conveyor industry. For example, a 10-ft. section of the gravity wheel or roller type of conveyor can often be easily lifted and transported or moved by one man. Portable conveyors, however, are usually made mobile by means of **wheels** or **casters** mounted on the conveyor frame or on supporting members. Within certain limitations almost any kind of conveyor can be made into a portable conveyor by being kept within certain size limitations and with the addition of mobile supports.

When first introduced, about 1916, portable conveyors were used mostly for handling bulk materials such as coal, sand, gravel, etc.; but in more recent years the portable-package, or unit-handling, type of conveyor has come into extensive service. Many new uses have been found for these conveyors. The farm conveyor, while of light construction, is basically of the same general principle as those described in this section. Portable screw conveyors for handling feed have more recently been developed. The trends are shifting generally toward lighter construction and more maneuverability.

The United States Government is by far the largest single purchaser of portable conveyors. These conveyors are widely used for handling military supplies of varying kinds, for the handling of mail and parcel post, and for the stockpiling of bulk materials.

TYPES OF PORTABLE CONVEYORS. Portable conveyors are produced in a large variety of standardized types, widths, and lengths, with a wide range of wheel or caster mountings. They are also frequently used in permanent or semipermanent installations on fixed supports.

There are three general types of portable conveyors (not power-propelled) produced for handling bulk material such as coal, sand, gravel, crushed stone, and the like. They are the **trough-belt conveyor,** the **flat-belt conveyor,** and the **flight (or drag) conveyor.** Capacities range up to 420 tons per hr.; widths from 8 to 30 in. are standard; single unit lengths up to 75 ft. are made with an elevating truck to deliver to a height of 40 ft. Any horizontal distance can be covered by using a number of portable units in series.

For handling packaged materials such as bags, boxes, and cartons, there are the portable belt-type, slat-type, bar-type, and roller and wheel conveyors.

USE IN BULK MATERIALS HANDLING. In developing practical portable conveyor units for handling bulk materials, it has been necessary to break many so-called engineering rules. To facilitate feeding, for instance, tail pulleys are generally made smaller than ordinary rules prescribe. Head pulleys are also usually smaller than on other types of conveyors, in order to:

1. Lessen the drop of friable materials from point of discharge to the chute or screen or other receiving point.

2. Reduce weight and cost.
3. Simplify drives.

In the interest of weight and cost reduction, liberties are also frequently taken in selecting drives. Single-unit troughers are used on some models to reduce the weight and cost of a conveyor unit for handling a comparatively small tonnage. Belt-supporting rollers are eliminated entirely in some models to reduce leakage, maintenance troubles, weight, and cost.

Selecting the Type and Size of Conveyor Needed. The usual procedure followed in selecting a portable conveyor for a given requirement is to:

1. Select the type most adaptable for the job, depending on:
   a. The material to be handled.
   b. The angle of elevation needed.
2. Select the width, depending on the capacity required.
3. Select the length, depending on the height or distance to be covered.
4. Select the mounting which will fill the requirements most practically at the lowest cost.

Representative types of portable bulk materials handling conveyors are shown in this section with typical cross sections. General data are given on each type; that is, the materials for which each type are primarily recommended, and the comparative advantages and disadvantages of each type are stated. More detailed data covering standard widths and lengths, capacities, ranges of elevation, and various mountings are given under the respective headings which classify the respective types of portable conveyors.

Trough-Belt Conveyors

PORTABLE TROUGH-BELT CONVEYORS. Portable trough-belt conveyors are recommended primarily for handling fine, sharp, and abrasive or wet materials, such as sand, gravel, crushed stone, fine coal, sulfur, cement, limestone, and concrete. They are also suitable for small bags and small rolls of cloth, wire screening, etc. Fig. 1 illustrates the cross section of a portable trough-belt conveyor for this kind of service.

From an engineering standpoint the trough-type belt conveyor—with ball or roller bearing, three-unit troughers, cleatless belt, large terminal pulleys, and feed hopper—is among the best available kinds of units for handling all kinds of bulk materials.

The **advantages** of such a unit are no leakage, minimum power requirements, maximum belt life, quiet operation, and minimum upkeep costs. The **disadvantages,** as compared with some other kinds of conveyors of equal elevating ability and capacity, are that the three-unit trough belt conveyor, with plain belt, must be about 50 percent longer, wider, and heavier, as well as 50 percent higher in original cost.

These requirements are the considerations which led to the development of the other types of portable conveyors. The use of **cleats** on the belt was a step to increase the steepness of elevation to permit loading of materials onto a truck or delivery of them to a given height with a shorter conveyor. **Two-unit troughers** were devised to reduce weight and original cost, with some sacrifice in belt life. The **single-unit trougher** was a further step to reduce weight and original cost and increase the carrying capacity of a belt of given width, at a further sacrifice of belt life and power needed. To reduce weight and cost still further for a

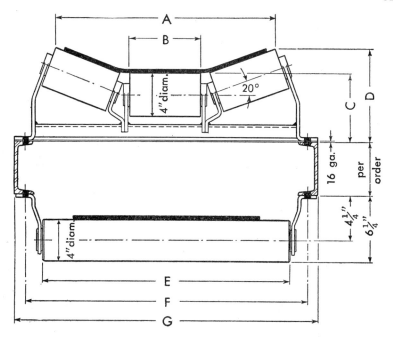

The Oliver Corp., A. B. Farquhar Div.

Fig. 1. Cross section of a portable trough-belt conveyor.

BELT WIDTH	A	B	C	D	E	F	G
18″	21⅛″	6¾″	6⅜″	8¹¹⁄₁₆″	23½″	27″	29¼″
24″	27⅛″	8¹³⁄₁₆″	6⅜″	9⅜″	29½″	33″	35¼″
30″	33⅛″	10⅞″	6⅜″	10⅛″	35½″	39″	41¼″

portable conveyor of given capacity and elevating ability, the **flat-belt conveyor,** with closely spaced full-width cleats, was developed.

MEDIUM-DUTY PORTABLE TROUGH-BELT CONVEYOR. The medium-duty portable trough-belt type of conveyor is most commonly used for handling fines and abrasive materials, such as sand, gravel, crushed stone, lime, sulfur, and earth. It is mounted on a simple V-type truck with steel wheels or on a mast-type truck with or without swivel wheels. On requirements which call for frequent moving of the conveyor over long distances, rubber-tired wheels are used. A tow-plate or bar is attached at the feed end. Shock absorbers are also furnished. Typical specifications are given below:

FRAME. May be constructed of angles and flats, channel sections, or Warren trusses.

TRUCK. May be mast type or V-type, with steel or pneumatic tire wheels; wheels 30 to 54 in. in diameter.

TROUGHERS. Three-pulley, two-pulley, single-unit bell-type or single-unit flat-roller with bell edges supported on slider skirts.

HEAD PULLEY. Rubber-lagged or crowned, 6 to 10 in. in diameter.

TAIL PULLEY. Diameters of 3 to 4 in.

DRIVES. Roller-chain pitch of ⅝ or ¾ or V-belt and shaft through gear reducer.

BELTING. Rubber-covered, 3- or 4-ply, 28-oz. duck with ⅛ × 1½ × 1½ in. angle-iron or other carrying cleats.

HOIST. Worm gears or gear and pinion.

TROUGH-BELT CONVEYORS FOR HEAVY-DUTY SERVICE.

Trough-belt conveyors for heavy-duty service are capable of handling almost any kind of bulk material. Typical of this equipment is the 24 × 60-ft. coal handling conveyor on a mast-type, elevating wheel truck, shown in Fig. 2. The wheels swivel to permit moving the conveyor sideways or in a circle, with the feed end serving as a pivot point. The conveyor shown has an adjustable feed hopper with a sliding gate to control the flow to the belt.

Iowa Mfg. Co.

Fig. 2. A heavy-duty portable trough-belt conveyor with swivel wheels (details in Fig. 3).

The usual practice is to build the boom of this type of conveyor in standard sections, thus providing complete flexibility in operation. The length of the boom can be readily increased or decreased. It can be mounted on an elevating wheel truck or in a variety of horizontal mountings, or it can be laid on supports. It can be easily disassembled for transportation from one job to another and reassembled in its original form, or in some other way to meet changed requirements.

A few typical construction details are shown in Fig. 3.

MEDIUM-DUTY SECTIONAL TROUGH-BELT CONVEYORS.

This type of conveyor, illustrated in Fig. 4, is furnished for the handling of all kinds of bulk materials, or for **package handling.** Units up to 30 or 40 ft. in length may be supported on wheel or caster mountings, or sections may be joined together for permanent or semipermanent installations covering up to 100 ft. or more in a single unit. Wheels may be swiveled to permit sideways as well as backward and forward movement.

Frame construction varies widely, depending on the services demanded. The angle-iron construction illustrated in Fig. 5 or an alternate Warren truss-type of tubular construction is used where units are to be mobile, to be hung on a

Iowa Mfg. Co.

Fig. 3. Structural detail of conveyor in Fig. 2.

The Oliver Corp., A. B. Farquhar Div.

Fig. 4. Medium-duty sectional trough-belt conveyor.

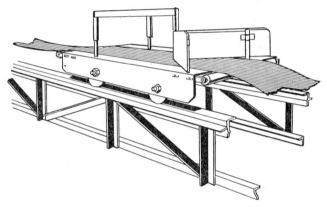

The Oliver Corp., A. B. Farquhar Div.

Fig. 5. Belt scraper.

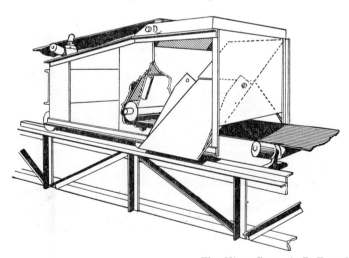

The Oliver Corp., A. B. Farquhar Div.

Fig. 6. Discharge tripper.

block and tackle, or to bridge spans of over 10 ft. This design is that of the lowest cost of construction for permanent or semipermanent installations.

Standard belt widths for this type of conveyor are 18, 24, and 30 in. Capacities range up to 400 tons per hr. Belt-supporting rollers may be of the three-unit, ball-bearing type or of the single-unit, oilless-bearing type.

SCRAPERS AND TRIPPERS. Belt scrapers, as illustrated in Fig. 5, are used to discharge material to either or both sides of a conveyor at any point along its length.

Fig. 6 represents the tripper method of discharging material at any point along a conveyor. Trippers or belt scrapers are available which will discharge the material on either or both sides of the conveyor.

Where incoming material can be delivered to the central point of a storage space or series of bins, the simplest and most economical installation is a shuttle-type mounting, which permits discharge of the material at any point to the right or left of the receiving point for any distance up to the length of the shuttle unit.

Flat-Belt Conveyors

BULK HANDLING APPLICATIONS. The flat-belt conveyor is the most widely used portable type of conveyor for handling coal and coke. Belt speeds can be varied to deliver from 1 to 2 tons of material per min. The low receiving end and the full-width cleats make it easy to feed from piles. Hopper-bottom cars can be unloaded directly without digging a pit or providing a track hopper.

Widths of 14 in. to 18 in. are the usual standards for **flat-belt conveyors.** Lengths of 20 to 30 ft. are the usual standards for loaders.

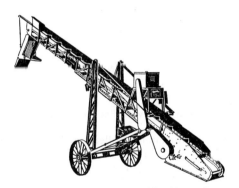

The Oliver Corp., A. B. Farquhar Div.

Fig. 7. Stacker with mast truck and swivel wheels.

Lengths over 30 ft. are usually mounted on mast-type trucks with swivel wheels and are known as **stackers** (Fig. 7). They are used for storing the material in high piles to save storage space and to make reloading easier. On this kind of conveyor it is essential to have a scraper plate under the carrying belt at the feed end to prevent material from accumulating on the feed-end pulley. Material getting onto the return belt is thus automatically carried to the cleanout by the underside of the carrying belt.

Small-diameter, lagged-head pulleys are usually used to reduce to a minimum the "drop" of material from the carrying belt to the screen or pile.

Heavy-duty models are available in 24 and 30-in. widths; 17, 22, 27, and 32-ft. lengths. Standard models include the elevating wheel type, the elevating and horizontal caster type, and the floor-to-floor or hatch type. Figs. 8 and 15 illustrate additional flat-belt conveyors.

Conveyors in this class are recommended primarily for handling coal, coke, ashes, cinders, etc. If large quantities of fines are to be handled, a trough conveyor is preferable, since it eliminates spillage. If large quantities of large-lump coal are to be handled, a drag-type conveyor is recommended, to provide a steeper effective-carrying angle.

Conveyor Specialty Co.

Fig. 8. Flat-belt conveyor with flat steel bed for load support.

From an engineering standpoint the **rollerless flat-belt conveyor,** with full-width cleats and small terminal pulleys, is a decided departure from accepted practices. This type of conveyor, however, has the advantages of maximum capacity for a given belt width, maximum elevating ability for a belt-type conveyor, maximum portability for a conveyor capable of doing the jobs within its range, and lowest production costs, while still keeping operating and upkeep costs within reasonable bounds.

The comparative belt loads of a **cleatless trough conveyor** as compared with a flat-belt conveyor are shown in Fig. 9. In addition, the cleated flat-belt conveyor can carry the materials for which it is designed at a much steeper elevation than is possible with a cleatless trough conveyor.

Flat-belt conveyors were originally designed with rollers supporting the belt. It was found in practice, however, that, because of the constant exposure to weather and fine dust, the rollers froze to their shafts—a condition which created more friction and wear than occurred with the simpler and much-lower-cost steel slides for the belt.

The **disadvantages** of the flat-belt type of conveyor, as compared with other types available, are its tendencies to leak somewhat when handling fines (such as buckwheat coal) and to "gum up" when handling wet or sticky materials. Also, when handling large-lump coal, the flat-belt provides a carrying angle lower than that of a drag-type conveyor.

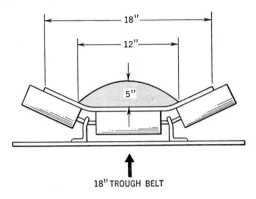

18" TROUGH BELT

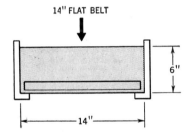

Fig. 9. Comparative loads of trough- and flat-belt conveyors.

Drag and Flight Conveyors

PORTABLE FLIGHT AND RELATED CONVEYORS. Portable flight conveyors of the type shown in Fig. 10 are produced in a wide range of styles and sizes and with various mountings, as shown elsewhere in this section. Booms of standardized portable drag conveyors are often made permanent installations for elevating materials up a steep incline.

The **light-duty type** includes those conveyors having troughs less than 20 in. wide and flights less than 3½ in. high. The boom construction of this kind of conveyor is usually as light as is possible for light-duty use. The boom is seldom made more than 30 ft. long and is usually mounted on a simple V-type wheel truck. The **standard type,** which is the one in most general use, includes the loaders and stackers, which have troughs 20 to 22 in. wide and flights of 4 or 4½ in.

Lengths of 25 ft. or under are usually used only as truck loaders and are, therefore, mounted on simple V-type trucks or light-mast trucks with fixed wheels. Lengths of 30 ft. or over are usually mounted on mast-type trucks with swivel wheels. Since lengths of 30 ft. or over are usually used for storing material in high piles, every effort is made to provide a maximum overhang of the delivery end to permit building the highest pile possible without having the material foul the wheels on which the stacker is mounted. To this end the weight of all the drives and the power unit is concentrated as near the feed end as possible.

Drag-type loaders are also furnished with a curved boom with a built-in bar screen to increase screening efficiency and reduce coal breakage to a minimum.

Heavy-duty drag conveyors are made only for handling extremely large lumps. They are similar in form to the standard machines but have wider and deeper troughs, higher and heavier flights, and heavier plate at the feed end.

The Oliver Corp., A. B. Farquhar Div.

Fig. 10. Heavy-duty drag conveyor.

USE OF PORTABLE FLIGHT OR DRAG CONVEYORS. Portable flight or drag conveyors are recommended primarily for handling coal, particularly of large lump size, and for installation where a steep elevation is encountered. The **advantages** of this type of conveyor lie in its ability to handle large lumps and also smaller sizes at maximum elevation, its ruggedness, and its comparatively low upkeep costs. Its **disadvantages** lie in its greater weight—with the resultant lesser portability in a conveyor which must be moved by manpower—its higher original cost for a conveyor of equal capacity, and its tendency to break coal during the handling operation. The portability disadvantage of this kind of conveyor is overcome by mounting it on a power-driven truck of the wheel or crawler types.

Loaders, Trimmers, and Unloaders

LOADERS. Loaders are available from extremely small-capacity light-duty conveyors of belt widths from 8 to 12 in. and from 12 to 20 ft. in length, to extremely heavy-duty crawler-mounted loaders such as shown in Fig. 11; the lightweight units generally being constructed of formed angles and flats to heavy structural members on the heavy-duty units. Belt speeds will vary generally from 100 to 200 ft. per min.

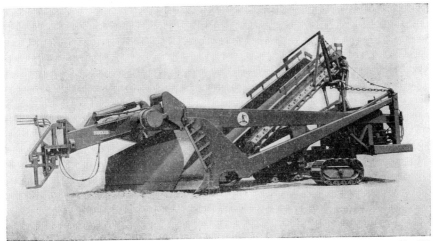

Euclid

Fig. 11. Heavy-duty loader.

TRIMMERS. Trimmers of the lightweight variety are designed, as the name implies, to trim material on piles, in storage bins, etc., to use every available cubic foot. They can be designed for one-man portability or for carrying on delivery trucks for delivery of coal, for example, to bins in houses, apartments, and industrial buildings. They have the following specifications in general:

DRIVE. At the feed end.
POWER. 1 hp. electric or 2 hp. gas engine.
BELT. Usually 2-ply rubber-covered, with or without cleats.
WEIGHT. Approximately 300 lb.
MOUNTED. Steel or rubber-tired wheels.

Fig. 12 shows a typical trimmer.

TYPICAL BELT-TYPE CAR UNLOADER. Car unloaders save wear and tear on the loaders or stackers with which they operate. They speed up the unloading, save the labor of shoveling over from the far hopper, and reduce the work of cleaning up after the car is unloaded. A typical belt-type car unloader is shown in Fig. 13.

Car unloaders may be used at any point along a track. The receiving section is sufficiently thin to fit between the tops of the rails and the bottom of the car hopper. Where this advantage is not necessary the unloader should be placed in a shallow pit beneath the tracks so that it need not be moved after each car has been unloaded.

The **drag-type car unloader** is primarily for coal but will handle coke and cinders. The **belt type** will handle all kinds of bulk materials.

Baughman Mfg. Co., Inc.

Fig. 12. Portable trimmer conveyor.

Atlas Conveyor Co.

Fig. 13. Portable heavy-duty car unloader.

RADIAL STORAGE. A car unloader, installed in a shallow pit under the tracks and delivering to a drag or belt-type stacker mounted on swivel wheels is the most economical and efficient equipment for building stockpiles of all kinds of bulk materials. A car can be unloaded in less than an hour with just one man in attendance. The discharge end of the stacker can be quickly raised or lowered to deliver the material to the pile with a minimum of power and "drop." Bin-type partitions can be constructed to keep materials of different types, qualities, or sizes separated, if required. Speedy reloading to trucks is assured by the height of the pile and consequent ease of feeding. Trucks can be loaded directly from cars by leaving an open space at each end of the semicircular pile.

Package Handling Conveyors

TYPES OF PACKAGE HANDLING CONVEYORS. Conveyors for package handling are designed in a wide variety of types, sizes, and capacities, with a choice of wheel or caster mountings for horizontal conveying or for elevating and stacking. Some examples are given in Figs. 8, 15, 16, and 17. The weights and strengths of the conveyors are increased as required by the size and weight of the packages to be handled. **Light-weight conveyors** handle packages weighing less than 100 lb.; **medium-weight conveyors** handle packages from 200 to 300 lb.; heavy-duty conveyors handle packages up to 500 lb. **Special-duty conveyors** are designed to handle pieces of still greater weight.

The Oliver Corp., A. B. Farquhar Div.

Fig. 14. Light-weight heavy-duty portable package conveyor.

Recent developments by a number of conveyor manufacturers have brought about a class of extremely light-weight conveyors, capable of capacities heretofore thought only possible with heavy-duty equipment. Typical of such developments is the conveyor pictured in Fig. 14, which in a 20-ft. length weighs only 235 lb. Equipped with a ⅓ hp. motor, it will handle gross loads of 125 lb. at a 30-deg. incline, with ample safety factor. Such conveyors are inexpensive to purchase and have a very low maintenance cost. Their versatility and portability make them suitable for many industries, wholesale establishments, and farm use.

Most of the regular-duty work is done with **flat-belt conveyors** (plain, ruff top, or cleated belt). Heavy-duty handling, or handling which would damage a belt, is done with **slat or steel-bar conveyors.**

The standardized portable-conveyor frames are frequently installed permanently at a considerable saving in cost as compared with a specially engineered installation.

Descriptions of typical conveyors in the various weight and type classes follow.

Fig. 15. Flat-belt conveyor mounted on mobile power unit for handling air cargo.

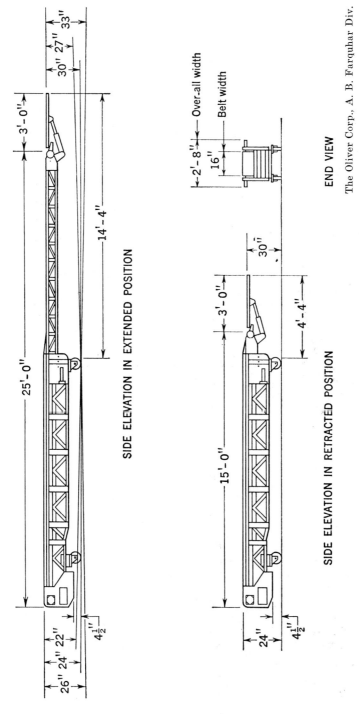

Fig. 16. Expandable flat-belt conveyor.

SPECIFICATIONS FOR PACKAGE HANDLING CONVEYORS.
The following factors give information concerning the data and equipment connected with package handling equipment:

CAPACITY. The 16-in. machine will handle packages weighing up to 300 lb. each. Maximum unit load is two 300-lb. pieces. The 24-in. machine will handle pieces weighing up to 500 lb. each at the rate of 8 per min.

ANGLE OF INCLINE. No set "standards" can be adopted, because of the wide variety in the nature of the package sizes, shapes, and coverings. An experienced conveyor field engineer should be consulted.

BOOM. Angles and flats of $\frac{3}{16}$ in.

PULLEY. Diameter of 8 in., lagged.

SHAFTS. Cold-rolled steel $1\frac{5}{16}$ in. thick.

DRIVES. Usually gear-head motor with $\frac{3}{4}$-in. pitch roller chain to pulley shaft.

BELT SUPPORTS. Slider-bed of wood or steel for light packages.

BEARINGS. Ball-bearing rollers for heavier packages or long units.

BELT GUIDES. Belt should be fitted with guide lugs to assure central belt travel in both directions.

POWER. One horsepower for 16 in. $\times$ 14 ft. to 20 ft.; 2 hp. for 16 in. $\times$ 23 ft. to 32 ft., or for 24 in. up to 20 ft.; 3 hp. for 24 in. $\times$ 23 ft. to 32 ft.

Handling Heavy-Duty Units. Heavier-type conveyor units have been designed to handle packages which weigh over 300 lb. each or which are more bulky than can be handled safely on the medium-duty machine. Construction is such that any one of a large variety of carrying cleats can be attached to the belt to accommodate bulky or oddly shaped packages. Central belt travel is assured by guide lugs attached to the under side of the belt and running in grooves at each side of the frame.

SECTIONAL PACKAGE HANDLING CONVEYORS.
Conveyors of the sectional package handling type are usually engineered to meet specific requirements but are made up of standard gravity-conveyor sections with belting and a driving unit added. They can be constructed in any width from 8 to 30 in. and any length from 10 to 300 ft.

Expandable Conveyors. The conveyor shown in Fig. 16 has been developed for loading and unloading trucks where it is desirable to move the conveyor into and out of a truck without disturbing the conveyor line into the truck. It is available with a 16-in. belt and in two lengths: an 11-ft. size, which is extendible to 18 ft., and a 15-ft. size, extendible to 25 ft. The 3-ft. gravity section is optional for one or both ends and can be lifted to a vertical position when not in use. The extended section is secured in the various positions by means of two spring-loaded pins.

OTHER PORTABLE PACKAGE HANDLING CONVEYORS.
For many kinds of handling and shipping operations there are numerous types of package handling conveyors available. (See Section 31.) In many instances the conveyors incorporate automatic closing and sealing equipment to eliminate hand operations and to speed up the work. These operations are frequently followed by automatic loading and sealing of the shipping containers.

Slat Conveyors. Conveyors of this kind are used in place of belt types when the packages to be handled are rough and abrasive, such as bundles of steel turnings. The slats may be of wood or metal. They are attached to chains driven by sprockets.

ROLLER-BAR-TYPE CONVEYORS. An alternate for the belt type of conveyor is that of the roller-bar type, which is used only when conditions are such that a belt-type conveyor would not meet requirements because of extremes of temperature or moisture. Fig. 17 shows highly flexible portable equipment of this type.

Food Machinery and Chemical Corp.

Fig. 17. Accordion roller conveyor.

Hatch-Type Conveyors. This is a belt conveyor with collapsible canvas pockets which permits carrying in a direction that is almost vertical and has enough depth of frame to prevent fouling of the cleats on the return.

Other Kinds of Conveyors. Certain conveyors may have fingerlike carriers attached to the belt; others may have hinged delivery or feed ends or may be arched. The only limits to what can be done with portable conveyors are those bounded by the imagination of the individual engineer.

FIXED CRANES, DERRICKS, AND CABLEWAYS

CONTENTS

SECTION **33**

FIXED CRANES, DERRICKS, AND CABLEWAYS

Jib, Revolving, and Bridge Cranes

IMPORTANCE OF FIXED CRANES. Among the almost numberless kinds of materials handling equipment used throughout the range of manufacturing and transportation activities, fixed loading and unloading cranes and towers render a most important economic service. If it were not for such equipment, the vast amount of manpower needed to load and unload cargo would raise the cost of such operations to an almost prohibitive level, placing a most burdensome toll on all industry and transportation.

This section presents widely applicable technical information on the many kinds and ranges of industrial loading equipment, available and in use, in the nature of cranes, towers, etc., installed and employed practically universally throughout all pants, terminals, docks, and on rail, water, truck, and air transportation media.

REVOLVING PILLAR JIB CRANES. Revolving pillar jib cranes, **base-mounted** for 360° complete rotation, consist of three essential parts: the jib, the column with a welded base, and the head. The jib is constructed of a standard I-beam section, high-carbon, hydraulically straightened, from which the

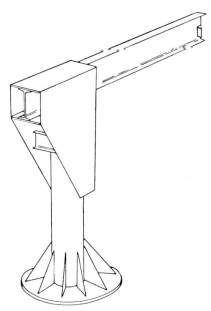

Chicago Tramrail Corp.

Fig. 1. Revolving pillar jib crane—base-mounted.

33·1

trolley and hoist are suspended. Rail stops are mounted on each end of the boom to prevent overtravel of the hoist and trolley. This type of crane is shown in Fig. 1.

The column consists of **structural pipe** varying in diameter from 8 to 24 in. and in weight from 25 to 186 lb. per ft., depending on the capacity, the span, and the distance under the jib. On the top of the column is mounted a thrust bearing of sufficient capacity for the loads handled. The base plate is a steel plate mounted on the bottom of the column, and may vary in diameter from $2\frac{1}{2}$ ft. to $5\frac{1}{2}$ ft., depending on the capacity and span of the crane. The plate normally is welded to the column, along with a number of gusset plates which are welded to the base and sides of the column. The base plate is then bolted to the foundation by a number of anchor bolts.

The revolving pillar jib crane **foundation mounting** is, in general, the same as the base mounting described above except for the omission of the base plate. The column of this kind of jib crane extends 3 to 4 ft. below the floorline, for mounting in a concrete foundation.

SWINGING PILLAR JIB CRANES. The swinging pillar jib crane, **base-mounted,** consists of a column of structural pipe ranging in diameter from 8 to 24 in. and in weight from 18 to 186 lb. per ft. (Fig. 2). The fitting supports are welded to the column. The tie rod and boom fittings are then fastened to the fitting supports. The boom is a structural I-beam section and has end stops at both ends to prevent overtravel of the trolley. Double tie rods are attached to the bottom and top fittings to allow accurate leveling of the boom in relation to

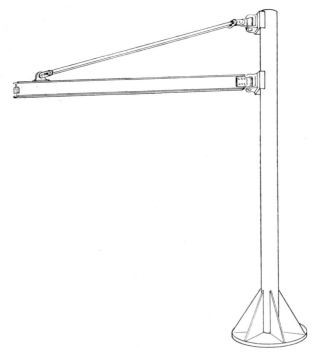

Chicago Tramrail Corp.

Fig. 2. Swinging pillar jib crane—base-mounted. **No. 2 base.**

the column. The fittings carry bronze bearings mounted in steel castings with alemite fittings for proper lubrication. The base consists of steel plate which may vary in diameter from 30 to 60 in. It is welded to the column and is supported by gusset plates which are also welded to the column and base. The base is then bolted to the foundation by means of anchor bolts. Two types of base plates are available.

The swinging pillar jib crane with **foundation mounting** is the same as the base-mounted type described above except for the omission of the base plate, and the extension of the column or pipe 3 to 4 ft. below the floor line for mounting in a concrete foundation.

REVOLVING MAST-TYPE JIB CRANES. The mast-type revolving jib crane is supported at the top and the bottom normally by the following types of bearings: The top bearing may be of bronze or it may be a high-capacity roller-type bearing; the bottom bearing is a tapered precision roller bearing. Both the top and bottom bearings are supported in steel castings. The castings may or may not be equipped with slotted holes to allow for easy alignment. The jib is bolted or welded to the column, which is a structural H-beam section. The jib is supported by either double tie rods or structural shapes. If double tie rods are used, fittings are installed on the end of the jib and on the side of the column to connect the tie rods to the jib and column (Fig. 3).

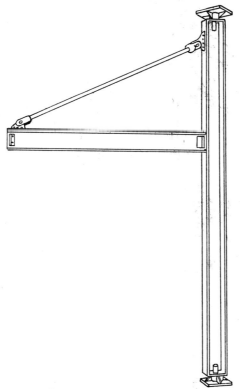

Chicago Tramrail Corp.

Fig. 3. Revolving mast-type supported jib crane.

SWINGING BRACKET-SUPPORTED JIB CRANES. The swinging bracket jib crane is generally known as the wall-bracket type of jib crane with 180° rotation. The jib consists of a structural I-beam section, which may be channel-capped for longer spans and higher capacities to prevent its twisting. The fittings used in conjunction with the boom are bronze bearings mounted in steel castings, with machined surfaces to assure accurate alignment and ease of rotation (Fig. 4).

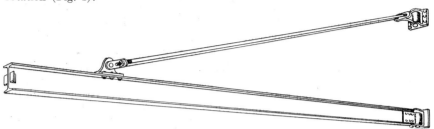

Chicago Tramrail Corp.

Fig. 4. Swinging bracket-supported jib crane.

FIXED-TOWER REVOLVING HAMMERHEAD JIB CRANES. This type of crane is built in capacities of from about 6 net tons up to 350 gross tons. The descriptive name "Hammerhead" is derived from the similarity of the revolving superstructure—the jib—to the head of a hammer.

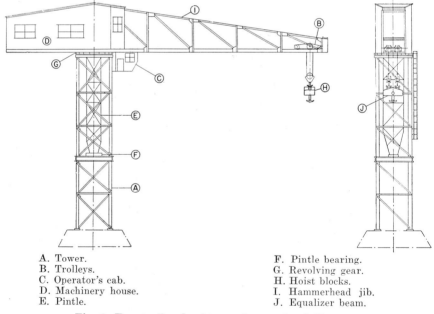

A. Tower.
B. Trolleys.
C. Operator's cab.
D. Machinery house.
E. Pintle.

F. Pintle bearing.
G. Revolving gear.
H. Hoist blocks.
I. Hammerhead jib.
J. Equalizer beam.

Fig. 5. Two-trolley fixed-tower hammerhead jib crane.

The crane consists of a **fixed tower,** supporting at its top a revolving jib whose front portion supports rails upon which one, two, or three rope-type trolleys travel; while the rear portion houses the machinery for the hoisting, trolley-travel, and revolving units, as well as the necessary counterweight. Each of the units is driven by an electric motor, the power being supplied from an outside source. If necessary, a **gasoline- or diesel-engine-driven electric generator set** can be mounted on the crane. A hoist block is suspended from each of the trolleys. The operator's cab is located on the jib in a position to give full visibility of the loads being handled.

When two trolleys are used, as in Fig. 5, they are arranged to be operated (1) individually, or (2) simultaneously. Simultaneous operation is accomplished by the clutching together of their respective hoisting and trolley-traveling units and the use of an equalizing beam between the hoist blocks, each of which has half the rated capacity of the crane. This equalizing beam carries at its center a hook of the rated capacity of the crane.

When a third, or auxiliary, trolley of lesser capacity than either of the two main trolleys is used, it is arranged to be operated independently of them. A crane of this kind has three separate hoisting units and three separate trolley-travel units.

Large cranes of this kind are sometimes provided with a traveling crane arranged to travel on rails supported on the upper chords of the hammerhead jib. This traveling crane is used for repair purposes and also for handling loads of up to about 15 tons (Fig. 6).

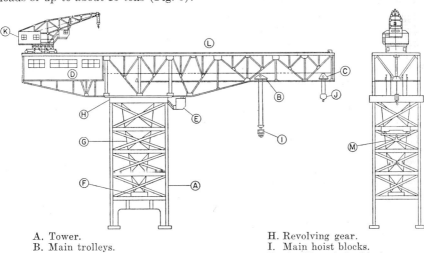

A. Tower.
B. Main trolleys.
C. Auxiliary trolley.
D. Machinery house.
E. Operator's cab.
F. Pintle bearing.
G. Pintle.

H. Revolving gear.
I. Main hoist blocks.
J. Auxiliary hoist block.
K. Traveling crane.
L. Hammerhead jib.
M. Equalizer beam.

Fig. 6. Fixed-tower hammerhead jib crane mounting a traveling revolving crane.

FIXED-TOWER REVOLVING CANTILEVER JIB CRANES. This type of crane is similar to, and used for the same purposes as, the fixed-tower single-trolley revolving hammerhead jib cranes. Its construction differs from that of hammerhead-type cranes in the following features:

1. The revolving jib operates on a turntable on the upper surface of the tower, the pintle and pintle bearing being replaced by a bearing at the center of the turntable. This bearing centers the jib on the tower, vertical loads being taken by the turntable rollers.
2. The machinery house and operator's cab are combined into one, which is located centrally on the tower and directly over the turntable.

The crane consists of a **revolving cantilever truss or jib** mounted on a turntable installed on the top of a fixed tower. The forward cantilevered end of the jib is provided with a traveling rope-type trolley which carries the hoist block. All machinery is enclosed in a house which also serves as the operator's cab. The machinery house is at the center of the jib, directly over the turntable. The counterweight is located at the rear end of the jib.

Cranes of this kind are used in shipbuilding service and also for some industrial uses, such as handling lumber or logs. They have an effective radius of from 75 to 100 ft. and have towers up to 100 ft. in height. The lifting capacity at the maximum radius varies from 5 to 15 tons, with greater capacities at shorter radii.

FIXED REVOLVING DOUBLE-CANTILEVER JIB CRANES.

Cranes in this class consist of a double-cantilevered truss or jib rigidly mounted on a revolving portal frame, which permits passage of the trolley and load from either cantilevered end of the jib to the other. The portal frame is carried on a turntable which may be either at ground level or on the upper surface of the fixed tower, depending upon the height of the crane.

The crane is provided with a traveling rope trolley which carries a hoist block. All machinery, except the revolving mechanism, is enclosed in a house located at the center of the jib and above the trolley runway. The revolving mechanism is located on the turntable. The operator's cab is located at one side of and below the jib, so as to give the operator the best possible view of the load throughout its entire travel. Usually, no counterweight is required. When one is necessary, it is located at the center of rotation; or it may be of the traveling type, operating on a separate runway and connected to the trolley by ropes, but moving in the opposite direction.

Cranes of this kind are used for the same purposes as fixed-tower revolving single-cantilever jib cranes and have the same effective radii, heights, and capacities. Illustrations of cantilever cranes and rope-luffed strut and truss boom cranes are shown in the section on Traveling Cranes and Towers.

FIXED REVOLVING CRANES.

Cranes of this kind are mounted on a system of live rollers or trucks, or on a pintle bearing, with a full 360° swing. Swinging is done by rack and pinion, with the rack mounted on the stationary portion and the pinion mounted on the revolving portion. The swinging unit may have a power take-off from the main power source or may be separately powered. Luffing and hoisting units may be driven from a single power source, or may be separately powered. Power drive may be by electric motor, by steam, diesel, or gasoline engine, diesel- or gas-electric, or hydraulic unit. These cranes may be used for hook or sling work, and have speeds of the various motions commensurate with the loads to be handled, and the duty cycle requirements.

Fixed Revolving Cranes—Rope-Luffed Strut Boom. Cranes of this kind have a strut-type boom with the luffing lines connected at, or near, the boom tip. They are the most widely used types of live-boom revolving cranes in America, and can be found in almost every kind of lifting service for cranes. Capacities range from the smallest loads to loads as large as 250 tons.

Fixed Revolving Cranes—Rope-Luffed Truss Boom. This crane has a truss-type boom, with the luffing lines connected at some point back from the tip, usually to the rear of the mid-point, and carries its load in the manner of a cantilever truss. This construction shortens, and consequently minimizes the stretch in the luffing ropes, although it results in a much heavier boom than that for the strut type. It is usually used for handling heavy loads and also where careful handling is required.

Fixed Revolving Crane—Level Luffing Type. This kind of crane, Fig. 7, runs at extremely high luffing speeds at a small power expenditure because the load is made to travel in a horizontal path for all boom positions. Compensation for raising the dead weight of the boom is brought about by the use of a movable-type boom counterweight. Level luffing may be done through the arrangement of the reeving, by a mechanical linkage, or by means of special arrangement and design of hoists. The boom may be luffed by means of wire ropes, screws, or gearing and linkage.

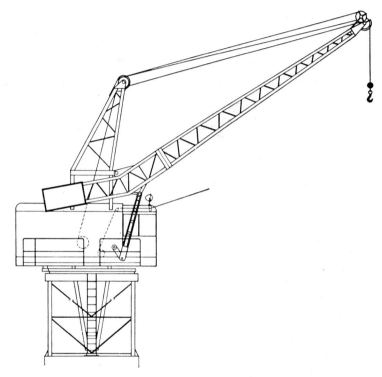

Fig. 7. Fixed revolving crane—level luffing type.

In this crane the load line is reeved as a three-part line between boom-end and mast-top for level travel of the load, and the boom counterweight is mounted on a properly positioned rearward extension of the boom. The boom is moved in and out by means of a crank which rotates through 360°. Cranes of this type are usually used for cargo and materials handling in moderate capacities.

Fixed Revolving Crane—Screw Luffing Type. One or more heavy power screws are used for luffing the boom of this crane, which is of the truss type. In some cases, the steel screw is provided with a single bronze nut which is turned while the screw itself does not rotate, and in other cases, the steel screw is turned and is provided with one or two bronze nuts. The nonrotating member is connected to the boom by heavy links and the axial travel of the nonrotating member raises and lowers the boom. This crane is used in shipyards and other locations where loads are to be accurately spotted and placed. Certain cranes of this class are rack-luffed.

FIXED GANTRY CRANES. Cranes of this kind are the same as traveling gantry bridge cranes, except that the supporting A-frames are anchored to fixed foundations instead of being mounted on wheels and traveling on runways (see section on Traveling Cranes and Towers). Either one or both ends of the bridge girders may be cantilevered beyond its supporting A-frame. These cranes are used only where the working area to be served is directly under the crane and hoisting and trolley travel operations are all that is required, as in a railroad freight yard. Here they are used for loading or unloading heavy or bulky freight, and for transferring it from a car to a truck or from one car to another for reshipment.

Either one or both ends of the cantilevered bridge girder extensions may be hinged, which is desirable when the crane is located on a pier or dock and is used for loading or unloading ships. These cranes are equipped with the same type of trolleys as overhead traveling bridge cranes and traveling gantry bridge cranes.

A hand-operated gantry crane is useful when only occasional light loads are to be handled. It is usually constructed of light structural steel, and consists of a single I-beam girder carried on two A-frames. A hand-operated chain trolley and hoist are generally used on this kind of crane. The cranes are usually constructed in capacities up to about 25 tons and have a span of 25 to 30 ft. (Fig. 8).

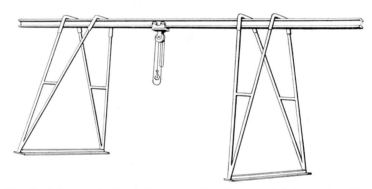

Fig. 8. A-frame single-girder crane—hand-operated hoist and trolley.

Electrically operated bridge cranes range in span upwards to about 200 ft., and to 75 tons in capacity. They may be equipped with a hook for general lifting purposes, with a magnet for handling ferrous metals, or with a bucket to handle coal or other loose materials. Operation is controlled from a cab mounted on either the bridge or the trolley.

Fixed Loading and Unloading Cranes and Towers

CHARACTERISTICS AND USES. Fixed towers are used for loading and unloading bulk materials from ships and barges. Materials such as sand, gravel, aggregates, coal, ore, bauxite, sulfur, sugar and many chemicals are rapidly handled in this manner. Similar equipment is in some cases used for the handling of steel, pipe, lumber, packaged goods, containers, and the like, although these latter cargoes are more often handled by loading and unloading cranes.

Towers and cranes are very similar in characteristics, and the distinction between them is largely one of appearance and performance. The **tower** is in most cases a high structure on a relatively small base, and is usually associated with high-speed handling of bulk materials by grab buckets. In contrast, the **crane** usually has a broader base in comparison with its height, and is employed for handling unit cargo or containers by hook at relatively lower speed. Cranes also are often equipped with grab buckets for handling bulk materials, but usually operating speeds are lower than for towers.

Loading towers and cranes load out by belt conveyor, fixed chute, grab bucket, or hook. For unloading, they are equipped with grab bucket, hook, or some form of marine leg. **Hook- or bucket-type towers and cranes** may be equipped with either rope-operated trolley or man-trolley.

Loaders and unloaders are usually operated by **electric power,** either a.c. or d.c. The rope-trolley type are more commonly a.c., many being located at power stations, while the man-trolley type are more commonly d.c., many being used at steel mills. Adjustable-voltage d.c. is being used for some recent installations. A few unloaders, constructed years ago, are still operated by steam.

Fixed loaders and unloaders require that the barge or ship to be loaded or unloaded be moved along the dock by means of barge-pulling winches during operations.

Capacities vary greatly with the type of material handled, required lift, required trolley-travel distance, type of vessel being unloaded, and disposition of cargo.

CANTILEVER FIXED LOADING AND UNLOADING CRANES. A cantilever-type crane consists of a fixed structure supporting a trolley runway cantilevered beyond the face of a dock over the water, and extending back through the structure, in some cases to the rear of the structure. Cranes may be equipped with one or more trolleys supporting individual hooks arranged to operate separately, or in parallel supporting a lift beam. Trolleys may be rope-operated, with machinery and operator in a fixed location. They may also be electrically operated, with the operator in a fixed location, or may carry an operator as well as the operating machinery. The fixed structure is often provided with an open portal spanning one or more tracks, for railroad cars delivering and receiving cargo.

HINGED-JIB FIXED LOADING AND UNLOADING CRANES. Cranes in this class are similar to cantilever fixed loading and unloading cranes, except that the water cantilever is replaced by a hinged jib which can be raised to clear the rigging of a vessel being berthed or moved along the face of a dock. Cranes of this kind are usually of the single-hook type and of moderate capacity and speed, but many are of large capacity, or are arranged with multiple hooks to hoist and travel special lifting cradles (Fig. 9).

One form of the hinged-jib loading and unloading crane is that employed by Seatrain Lines, Inc., for placing loaded freight cars aboard ship at their point of origin and removing them at their destination. A lifting cradle is provided, which nests into a recess in the incoming railway track. The loaded car is shunted onto and blocked on the cradle, which is then hoisted, traveled, and lowered to a selected track recess within the ship hull, after which the still-loaded freight car is rolled off onto a track on the ship's decks. At the destination, the reverse operation takes place.

Many cranes function as both **loaders and unloaders,** transporting cargo in and out over the same cantilever runway or hinged jib. Occasionally cranes are used on a finger pier, unloading on one side and loading out on the other.

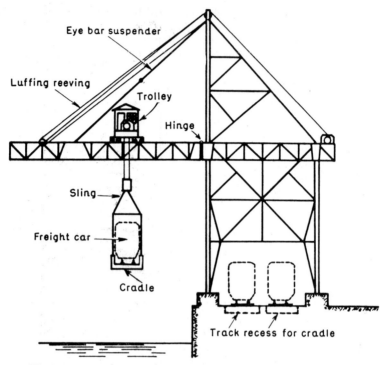

Fig. 9. Hinged-jib fixed loading and unloading crane (as used by Seatrain Lines, Inc.)

CANTILEVER BELT-CONVEYOR FIXED LOADING TOWERS.

Installations of this kind consist of a fixed loading tower supporting a cantilever which projects over the vessel. They are equipped with a conveyor on the cantilever, which receives a continuous supply of ore, coal, grain, fertilizer, sugar, chemicals, or other bulk commodity from related equipment and discharges this material over the end, or to a trimmer suspended from the outer end of the cantilever. The trimmer is essentially a vertical chute with controllable gates at its lower end which is arranged to direct, as desired, the material delivered to the vessel. The chute is arranged to rotate about a vertical axis, and may be equipped with a flinger or thrower at the lower end below the gates to cast the material under the decks in the desired direction.

Fixed cantilever loading towers are usually used for **loading barges or similar vessels** with low rigging, and the trimmer chute may be capable of telescoping to accommodate the growing height of the pile. Capacities of loading towers vary greatly according to the product being loaded. Where trimmers and flingers are used, capacities may be as high as 1,500 tons per hr. Where trimmers are not used and heavy bulk materials are discharged directly from the end of the conveyor, capacities may be as high as 6,000 tons per hr., or greater, for heavy material such as iron ores.

HINGED-JIB BELT-CONVEYOR FIXED LOADING TOWERS.

The hinged-jib loading tower is similar to the cantilever belt-conveyor fixed loading tower, except that the fixed cantilever is replaced by a jib hinged to move in a vertical plane (Fig. 10). The jib is raised to the high position to clear the rigging of a ship being brought in or moved along the dock. It is then lowered to a near-horizontal position for operation. The hinged jib provides latitude for the handling of ships of various sizes, and permits carrying on operations at varying tides or water stages.

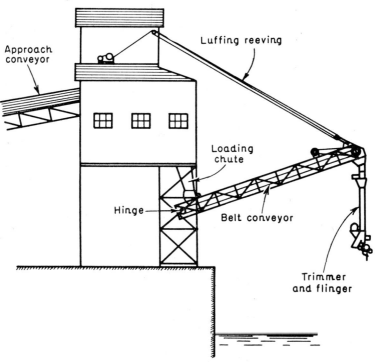

Fig. 10. Hinged-jib belt-conveyor fixed loading tower.

CANTILEVER FIXED LOADING AND UNLOADING TOWERS.
Such equipment consists of a fixed tower structure supporting a cantilever runway, outboard of the tower structure and over the water and vessel to be loaded or unloaded. The runway extends back through the tower—in some instances beyond, to the rear of the unloader—and supports a traveling trolley from which is suspended a grab bucket (Fig. 11). The unloading tower generally handles bulk materials which may be dumped directly into cars, into a hopper for loading into cars, into a hopper for loading onto a conveyor belt, or to a storage-pile or trough for rehandling by other equipment.

Unloading towers are of two kinds, the rope-operated-trolley type and the man-trolley type. In general, the rope-operated towers are of smaller capacity, having small buckets and operating at high speeds. Buckets vary from 2 tons to 12 tons in capacity, with free-digging capacities up to 1,400 tons per hr. depending on the lift and trolley travel required. The man-trolley towers use large buckets and operate at lower speeds—the buckets ranging from 5 tons to 20 tons in capacity—and provide free-digging capacities up to 1,800 tons per hr.

Net average unloading rates with this equipment may be as high as 70 percent of free digging capacity under the most favorable conditions—as when unloading from open barges with easily dug materials—and may be less than 30 percent under unfavorable conditions—as when unloading from tramp ships with small hatches in which materials are stored under decks or alongside shaft tunnels, and are generally inaccessible to direct reach of the bucket. Man-trolleys are sometimes provided with a turntable or twister by means of which the bucket may be revolved in a horizontal plane about a vertical axis, to facilitate removal of material from ships.

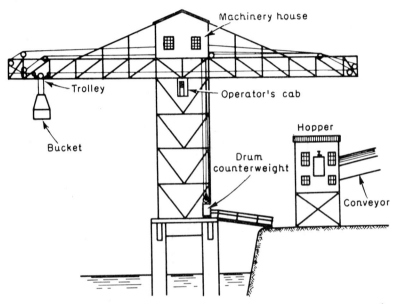

Fig. 11. Cantilever fixed unloading tower (rope-operated-trolley type).

Equipment of this kind is used largely for unloading and only very occasionally for loading. Where large quantities are to be loaded, the grab bucket is relatively inefficient as a loader, as compared with the belt conveyor loading tower.

HINGED-JIB FIXED LOADING AND UNLOADING TOWERS. This tower is a loading and unloading tower similar in all respects to the cantilever fixed loading and unloading tower, except that the fixed cantilever is replaced by a hinged jib permitting the tower to operate with vessels having high superstructure or rigging.

MARINE-LEG FIXED-TOWER UNLOADERS. This class of bulk or unit materials handling equipment utilizes a marine leg in combination with a fixed tower. A marine leg, Fig. 12, consists of a belt-and-bucket, bar-type, or two-strand bucket elevator. For handling bulk materials, the conveyor or elevator is enclosed in a steel casing and reeved around an upper and a lower sprocket. The drive is at the upper sprocket and the discharge is over the upper sprocket to a spout or chute which delivers the material into a bin or onto a belt conveyor. The lower end carries a boot at the bottom arranged so as to be self-feeding. For effective coverage of the ship hold, the marine leg is arranged to sweep the entire hatch area, and to be raised and lowered as necessary.

Marine legs are used for handling the **lighter-weight bulk materials** such as coal, sugar, grain, ashes, seeds, fertilizer, and chemicals. Probably the best-known use is that of handling grain, the maximum capacity in this service being about 600 tons per hr., or 25,000 bushels of wheat per hr. For handling unit cargo, such as bunched bananas, bagged coffee, case goods, or similar produce, the elevating means consists of chains on which are mounted bars, pans, or special trays for the particular product involved. The construction is open, and the trays must be loaded and unloaded by hand. Another form of marine-leg unloader is the pneumatic type, which utilizes the velocity of moving air to lift the lighter bulk materials such as grain.

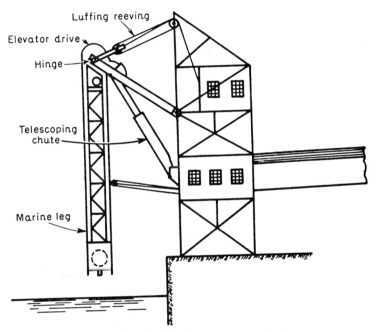

Fig. 12. Marine-leg fixed-tower unloader.

Derricks

GUYED DERRICKS. The guyed derrick, Fig. 13, consists of a rotating mast and boom, the mast being vertical and supported at its upper end by a number of fixed guy wires. It is supported at its lower end by a ball-and-socket or antifriction-bearing fitting. The boom is rope-supported at its outer end, and pinned to the lower portion of the mast at its inner end. A bull wheel is attached to the lower end of the mast, with sway rods running to each side of the boom, for swinging the derrick. Ropes are led to an operating winch through sheaves at the base of the derrick. The bull-wheel ropes are led through guide sheaves to an independent swinger, or a swinger attached to the winch.

The mast height and the angle of the guy wires are arranged so that the boom, while rotating, can pass under the guy wires at any radius. An exception exists in the case of the steel erector's guy derrick, where it is necessary to boom in against the mast before rotating, because of the steep angle of the guys. This derrick is used where 360° rotation is required, and where there is no problem in anchorage of the guys. It is employed principally for hook work, because the guy-wire support is not ideal for the impacts of duty-cycle work. Capacities of this kind of derrick have ranged up to 250 tons, with boom lengths up to 200 ft. For extremely high lifts, the derrick can be mounted on a guyed tower.

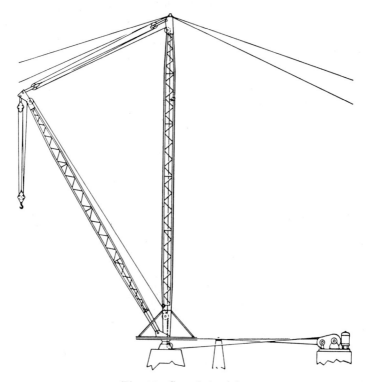

Fig. 13. Guyed derrick.

STIFFLEG DERRICKS. A derrick of this kind consists of a rotating mast and boom, the mast being vertical and supported at its upper end by two stifflegs which have a horizontal angle between them of 60 to 90°. The mast is supported at its lower end by a ball-and-socket fitting. The boom is rope-supported at its outer end and pinned to the lower portion of the mast at its inner end. A bull wheel is attached to the lower end of the mast, with sway rods running to each side of the boom, for the purpose of swinging the derrick. Horizontal sills, running from the lower end of the stifflegs to the structural support under the mast, are used to eliminate horizontal and eccentric forces from the derrick foundations. Ropes are led to an operating winch through sheaves at the base of the derrick, or through sheaves above the top of the mast. The bull-wheel ropes are led through guide sheaves to an independent swinger, or a swinger attached to the winch.

This kind of derrick is used where less than 360° rotation is sufficient, and where support of the mast must be kept within a limited area. Capacities of such derricks have ranged up to 200 tons and boom lengths up to 185 ft.

SELF-SWINGING STIFFLEG CRANE DERRICKS. This crane derrick consists of a rotating mast, a machinery house and an end-luffing boom. The mast is supported at its upper end by two stifflegs and at the lower end by a ball-and-socket fitting. The bull gear is mounted on the mast foundation with the machinery house directly above it, to permit self-swinging by an independent or clutch-type swinger. Capacities and reaches are comparable to those of the conventional stiffleg derrick (Fig. 14).

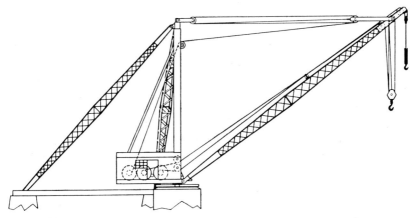

Fig. 14. Self-swinging stiffleg crane derrick—double hook.

A-FRAME DERRICKS—SHEAR LEG. This derrick has an A-frame for supporting the load to be lifted, and can be inclined forward by means of a multi-part line attached to its upper end and anchored to the rear. Upper and lower load blocks are attached to the upper end of the A-frame. This arrangement is a simple one for handling heavy loads in a single plane over a short distance.

TRIPOD DERRICKS. A tripod derrick consists of a fixed tripod with load blocks suspended from the upper end of the members. Usually only light loads are handled with a derrick of this kind, because of the fairly short members.

GUYED GIN POLES. The guyed gin pole, Fig. 15, consists of a single guyed pole with a load block at its upper end and a universal-joint type of support at its lower end. The pole is arranged for working in a vertical or slightly inclined position. Such equipment has been constructed in capacities up to 150 tons, and lengths up to 180 ft. have been used. Basically, the gin pole is a special-purpose device of limited application. It is being supplanted by the guy derrick, which can handle the heavy loads at short radius, and lighter loads over a large area.

SELF-SWINGING GUYED SINGLE-JIB CRANE DERRICKS. This derrick consists of a rotating mast, single jib, and machinery house as shown in Fig. 16. The mast is supported at its upper end by guy wires and at the lower end by a ball-and-socket or antifriction-bearing fitting. The bull gear is mounted on the mast foundation with the machinery house directly above it to permit self-swinging by an independent or clutch-type swinger. The trolley is of fleet through-type for use with grapple, bucket, or spreader bar. This type of derrick has been used for moderate radii, and capacities. Power may be electric, or supplied by steam or internal combustion engine.

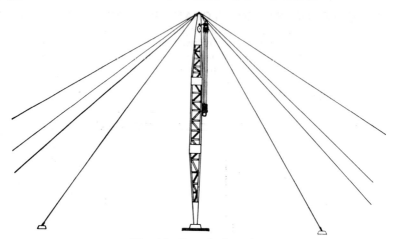

Fig. 15. Guyed gin pole.

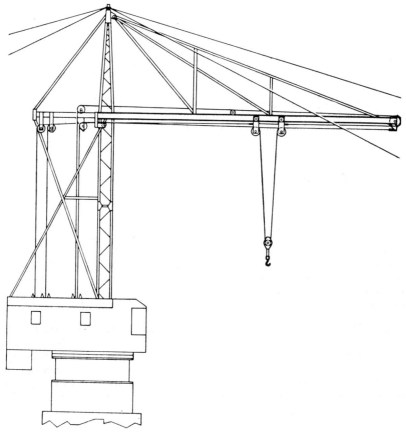

Fig. 16. Self-swinging guyed single-jib crane derrick.

TOWER BOOMS. This equipment is a boom which can be mounted on the side of a tower, tank, or building. It has a fitting at the boom heel which permits manual swinging in a horizontal plane. The outer end of the boom is supported by either a fixed or operating multi-part line. Load blocks are hung from the boom's outer end. Tower booms have been used for moderately heavy capacities and moderate lengths.

Cableways, Drag Scrapers, and Cable Shifters

TAUTLINE CABLEWAYS. The cableway is a hoisting and conveying device which operates over a clear span. It differs from a tramway, which is used primarily for conveying materials and not for raising and lowering loads. The fact that the cableway **hoists as well as conveys** makes it particularly well adapted for the handling of materials, for excavating, for placing of concrete in dam construction, and for use in the erection of bridges and other structures. The carriage traveling on a track-cable, suspended between two towers, supports the loads, which can be lifted from any point, conveyed in either direction, and lowered or dumped wherever desired along the span of the cableway.

Cableways are built to meet different requirements. Both towers may be fixed, one tower may be fixed with the other traveling radially, or both towers may travel on parallel tracks. Spans of over 3,000 ft. have been used, and under favorable conditions longer spans are feasible. One limitation is the length of track that cable manufacturers can produce in one length. Net loads handled on cableways for construction work vary up to 25 tons. At Hoover Dam, the United States Government installed a cableway rated at 150-ton capacity for use in handling heavy unit loads consisting of penstock sections, machinery, loaded railroad cars, and the like.

The cableway is primarily a high-speed device, because it is intermittent in operation, and so must be operated at high speeds to secure a large output. The conveying speed on a conventional cableway is usually 1,200 ft. to 1,500 ft. per min., with hoisting speeds of 300 to 400 ft. per min. Lowering speed is usually 400 ft. per min.

The essential elements of a cableway are:

1. Towers.
2. Hoist.
3. Carriage.
4. Cable Trackway.
5. Operating Ropes.

Towers and Masts. In the stationary, or radial, cableway, fixed structures are utilized. The **mast** is mounted on a hinge-pin or ball-and-socket arrangement, and is held in position by guys and the track cable. The **self-supporting fixed tower** is mounted rigidly on its foundation, but in most cases is guyed to take the heavy load imposed on the structure by the tension in the track cable. In the case of a **radial cableway**, the stationary structure is fitted with swivel connections, permitting the track cable to move freely and assume a position in line with the span. The height of towers and masts varies considerably, depending on the site condition, the profile of the ground, and the length of the span. Ball-and-socket masts up to 250 ft. in height have been successfully used. Stationary structures can be designed to function as either head- or tail-towers.

Traveling towers for both radial and parallel cableway systems are constructed of steel and run on tracks. They are counterweighted to provide stability. The front leg of the tower is battered to coincide with the resultant of the dead-weight forces of the tower and the pull of the cables and ropes. The batter is usually about one horizontally to two vertically. The front tracks are usually inclined so as to be perpendicular to the leg of the tower. The back tracks are level.

The towers are most commonly moved laterally by **individual electrical drives** located on the trucks. Various arrangements of drives have been used: Sometimes the drives are located on one set of trucks only, at other times on combinations of any two sets of trucks, and in certain cases on each set of trucks. Wire-rope drives have also been employed. Heavy-duty steel wheels are used on the trucks. Traversing speed ranges from about 50 to 125 ft. per min. Traveling towers up to 200 ft. in height have been used, and towers of a greater height are entirely practical.

Hoists and Controls. Modern cableways are designed to operate various hoisting and conveying devices from the point of greatest vantage, through the use of remote control. The simplest form of cableway hoist has manually operated friction clutches and brakes, but later developments use compressed-air friction clutches and brakes, operated by magnet valves or graduated air valves, these operating valves being located at the hoist, or in an elevated position at one of the towers, or at a distance. Systems of control are used whereby cableways may be completely controlled in regard to hoisting and conveying from a point 1,000 ft. or more away from the hoist. The conventional cableway hoist is of the double-tandem friction-drum arrangement. Both drums have welded steel barrels and flanges, with inside stiffening rings. Gearing is usually all of the herringbone type.

Carriages. Carriages are of rigid construction and the wheels are articulated to provide uniform distribution of the load on the track cable. A sufficient number of wheels are designed for each carriage to keep the load per wheel within a reasonable figure. This load, to a large degree, is determined from experience. It has been the practice to use 16-wheel carriages on the heavy-duty, 25-ton cableways. Fatigue in track cable wires increases as the ratio of the load to the tension in the track cable increases. It is advantageous to keep the ratio of G/t as small as possible in the interest of longer track-cable life. As the ratio increases, the degree of bend caused by the load becomes greater, thus increasing the rate of fatigue. This relation is one of the most important factors in the service of a track cable. The G/t ratio can be minimized by keeping the track cable up to recommended tension and by increasing the number of wheels in the carriage. Track cables are usually of the anchored-span type on cableways, with the G/t ratio increasing as the load approaches either the head or tail towers. The nature of operations on cableways is such that a definite load pick-up point is usually established. Minimum distance of pick-up point from tower should be 10 percent of span, to obtain good track-cable life.

Cable Trackway and Operating Ropes. Locked-coil track cable is constructed to present a smooth continuous surface contact between the wheels and cable, resulting in a maximum cable area of contact and a low unit bearing pressure on the cable, when compared with other kinds of cable being manufactured. It has proved most economical on a cost-per-ton-handled basis. Round wire track strands are sometimes used when the life or size of a job will not justify the use of locked-coil construction. (See section on Cable Conveyors.)

Track cables are operated under high tension, resulting in a minimum deflection, with consequent lowering in the heights of towers and masts so as to obtain necessary clearance, a substantial saving in power costs, and a smoother operation when dumping loads, due to reduced change in deflection between loaded and empty conditions.

Operating ropes are usually 6 x 19 in either Seale Patent (1-9-9), Type 'M' (1-5-5-10), or Type 'N' (1-6-6-12) construction, depending on the particular installation, and to some degree on personal preference. The method of reeving cables for such installations is shown in Fig. 17.

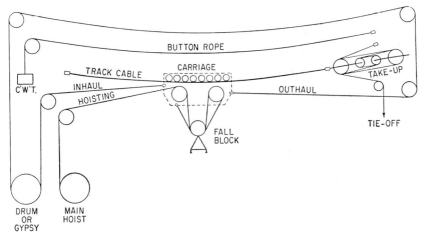

Columbia-Geneva Steel Division, U. S. Steel Corp.

Fig. 17. **Reeving diagram for cableway.**

APPROXIMATE HANDLING CAPACITIES OF CABLEWAYS. Fig. 18 indicates approximate hourly capacities that can be handled by a cableway when operating at a conveying speed of 1,200 ft. per min., a hoisting and lowering speed of 300 ft. per min., and an average lift height of 100 ft. An allowance of $1\frac{1}{2}$ to 2 min. per cycle has been made to couple and uncouple the carrier and discharge the load.

Gross Hook Load	Net Work Load (assumed)	Average Length of Travel in Each Direction (ft.)		
		500	1,000	1,500
5	3.4	61	49	41
10	6.7	120	97	80
15	10.0	180	144	120
20	13.4	224	182	153
25	16.7	280	215	182

Fig. 18. **Net tons per hour handled by cableway.**

SLACKLINE CABLEWAYS. Slackline cableways, Fig. 19, are used primarily to excavate, convey, and raise materials. This kind of unit is adaptable to digging material from rivers, pits, and otherwise inaccessible points, and conveying and raising it to the desired point at a higher elevation.

These cableways are simple in operation. The digging bucket is suspended from a carriage which travels on an inclined track cable. The track cable is slackened to lower the bucket into the pit, and tightened to raise the bucket in the air for conveying it to the discharge point. A double-drum hoist is used, one drum governing the slackening and tightening of the track cable, and the other, the inhaul or load cable. When the bucket is loaded, the track cable is tightened or raised so that the bucket will clear unexcavated material. The load is conveyed to the discharge point and the bucket dumped automatically, its position being predetermined by a stop-button on the track cable. After the bucket is dumped, it returns to the point of excavation by gravity.

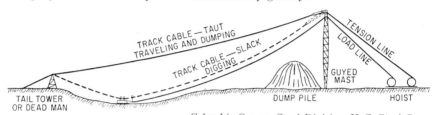

Columbia-Geneva Steel Division, U. S. Steel Corp.

Fig. 19. Slackline cableway.

Slackline cableway systems usually use buckets of 2 cu. yd. capacity or less, although satisfactory installations of twice this capacity have been made. Spans of 1,000 ft. and more have been used. It is necessary to maintain the proper relationship between the length of operating span and the height of the headmast, since the bucket returns to the point of excavation by gravity. The cost of operating a slackline cableway on a unit cost basis is usually low, since normally only one man is required to run it.

DRAG SCRAPERS. Drag scrapers are used to move bulk material on the ground from one location to another. The simplest design consists of a double-drum hoist with an inhaul rope on one drum and an outhaul rope on the other. These two ropes attach to the front and rear, respectively, of a bottomless bucket by means of bridle chains. At the head end of the installation the two ropes pass through blocks attached to a mast. At the rear of the installation the outhaul passes through a movable tail block and its position is adjusted manually. This tail block may also be moved by a third drum on the hoist. Installations using buckets up to 4 cu. yd. capacity have been made. Fig. 20 shows a typical drag scraper installation.

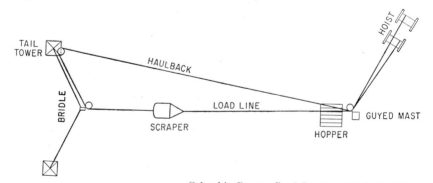

Columbia-Geneva Steel Division, U. S. Steel Corp.

Fig. 20. Diagram of drag scraper system.

WIRE ROPE HAULAGES. Wire rope haulage systems have been satisfactorily and economically used in many instances. Several haulage systems have been developed to meet the individual conditions of the varying problems to be solved. The basic systems are:

1. Endless haulages.
2. Main-and-tail haulages.
3. Inclined-plane or direct haulages.
4. Self-acting inclines.

Endless Haulages. The endless haulage consists of a wire rope spliced endless, properly guided and supported along a desired route, to which are attached cars for transporting men or materials on a surface roadbed. An adequate drive and tensioning device is provided. The rope operates continuously in one direction. This system is particularly adaptable to **mining operations** where it is necessary to transport large tonnages of materials continuously, and space for storage of material and rolling stock is at a minimum.

The drives commonly used are the "Gypsy" type and the single or twin parallel sheaves. Wire ropes for endless systems are usually fabricated from comparatively coarse wires to withstand abrasion, crushing, and abuse. Hence, it is necessary that the drive sheaves be correspondingly large. Tensioning devices are installed to compensate for stretch in the rope. Lang lay ropes are most commonly used.

The speeds vary considerably, ranging from about 1 mi. per hr.—where cars are constantly attached and detached—to as high as 10 or more mi. per hr. on passenger systems, or where trains of cars are moved between two points.

In this kind of system it is advantageous to keep the rope off the surface being hauled over, whenever possible. With a large number of cars equally spaced on the line along an undulated trackway, it is common practice to support most of the rope by the cars, by what is known as over-rope haulage. It is possible to eliminate some of the support rollers between the tracks by using this system. Lashing chains are commonly used for attaching the cars to the rope.

When there is no difficulty in keeping the rope on, or near, surface level, the rope is usually located between the bottom of the cars and the surface. Lashing chains, or some kind of clip couplings, are ordinarily used for attaching the cars. When surface traffic is encountered, it is necessary to locate the haulage rope beneath the surface, and to use a split type of rail-tie so that the grip lever may extend from the car to the rope without interference.

Main-and-Tail Haulages. The main-and-tail haulage system uses two drums, one being driven to haul the incoming rope, and the other idling to let out the returning rope. On double-track roadways, a tail rope is attached to the back end of the full and empty cars, this tail rope passing around a return sheave at the far end of the track. In the case of a single track, the tail rope is attached to the back of the car, around the return sheave, and back to the drive. These haulages operate very satisfactorily at speeds up to 15 mi. per hr. or more, regardless of gradient.

Direct Haulages. In the direct-haulage system, the drive is normally located at the top of the incline. It operates with a **hauling rope** connected directly with the car. Since no tail rope is used, the gradient of the incline must be steep enough for the minimum resultant gravitational forces to pull out the rope and overcome the frictional forces, so that the cars may return to the bottom of the incline. Most installations operate with a **single drum and single track.** However, when conditions warrant, sometimes **double drums and two sets of tracks** are employed. In this case, the power developed by the loads traveling downward may be utilized in assisting the upward-traveling loads. The skips handle loads of as much as 15 to 20 tons.

Self-Acting Inclines. With self-acting inclines, the loaded cars haul up the empties. Since there is power developed by the system, the speed is controlled by various methods, such as brakes only, regenerative electric motors, air compressors, etc.

CABLE SHIFTERS. Cable shifters are hand- or power-operated towing devices having a horizontal rope-winding drum or drums, rotated through gears, or a series of gears, and shafting contained by a suitable supporting frame. Cable shifters are produced in various capacities in which the line-pull rating is the starting line-pull, or, when powered electrically, is the line-pull reached when the maximum torque of the electric motor is used. Gasoline or diesel power can also be employed. The no-load or light-line speed is slow, possibly ranging down to less than 20 ft. per min. for barge and ship-moving applications, and up to over 50 ft. per min. for car moving.

Ship and Barge Shifters with Opposing Winches. Two single-drum winches opposing each other are used in shifting ships or barges along a dock or wharf. While one winch is making the tow, the opposing winch is offering a slight resistance to prevent the rope from unspooling off the drum faster than required, which would result in the loose rope's becoming tangled and spooling unevenly on the drum. This slight line pull resistance by the opposing winch is accomplished either by electric countertorque or by a drag brake on the drum. This opposed system is limited in distance of operation by the amount of rope that can be wound on the drum (see section on Winches).

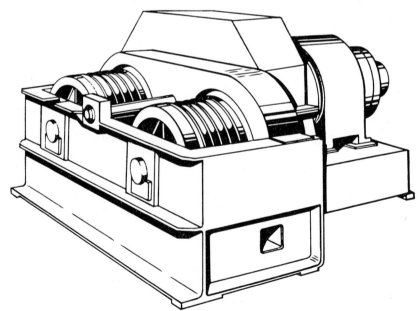

Fig. 21. Electric barge-shifting winch.

Barge and Car Shifters with Reversing Continuous Cable Loop. In a continuous-cable barge- or car-shifter system, power is applied through a series of gear reductions and shafting to a double-drum rope friction drive, such as that shown in Fig. 21. Slip rings, grooved to fit the running cable, are mounted on two drums assembled in a single frame. A continuous cable is reeved from one drum to the other and over several slip rings on each drum, and then run out through the shifter system. It is necessary to have a counterweight provided in the bight of the running cable on each side of the shifter, to provide a force to drive the running cable by friction in either direction. A sling is fastened to the running cable for hooking to a car or barge.

Car Shifters with Single Cable. This is a single-drum unit similar to the single-drum units of the opposed system mentioned above, except that towing is required in only one direction. The cable is pulled out by hand after disengaging the drum by means of a jaw clutch to allow the drum to turn freely. Towing in the opposite direction can be done by the use of conveniently located sheave blocks. The cable is then run off the drum out to the sheave block and back toward the shifter to connect to the car or barge. Car shifters are somewhat related to capstans, and should be considered when installations are being planned.

TRAVELING CRANES AND TOWERS

CONTENTS

CONTENTS *(Continued)*

CONTENTS *(Continued)*

TRAVELING CRANES AND TOWERS

Overhead Traveling Bridge Cranes

TYPES OF TRAVELING OVERHEAD BRIDGE CRANES. Traveling overhead bridge cranes are made in a number of different types which include cranes with **underrunning bridges** where the end trucks are supported by overhead tramrails attached to the building structure. This underrunning type of bridge crane may have either single or double crane girders. With all underrunning bridge cranes, the trolleys are always underrunning also. These types of cranes are shown in Figs. 1, 2 and 3.

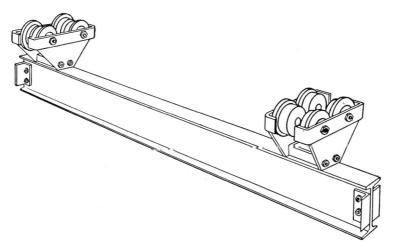

Fig. 1. Underrunning single-girder push crane with swiveling end trucks.

For many applications of overhead bridge cranes, the **top-running type** crane is preferred. Figs. 4 and 5 show various types of top running cranes, some with single and some with double-crane girders. The single-girder crane will have an underrunning trolley, and the double girder crane may have either a top running or underrunning trolley.

The underrunning **single-girder push crane** shown in Fig. 1 has swiveling end trucks. This is a very versatile underunnning crane which is usually light in capacity and manually moved. With swivel end trucks, this crane can be supported by two parallel tramrails, or if the tramrails are brought together by means of curves and a switch into a single track, this crane can operate on a single tramrail and in effect becomes a long wheel base monorail carrier.

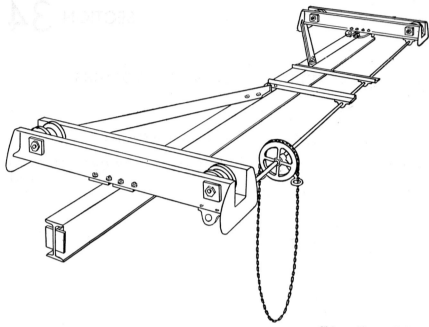

Chicago Tramrail Corp.

Fig. 2. **Hand-geared underrunning single-girder crane.**

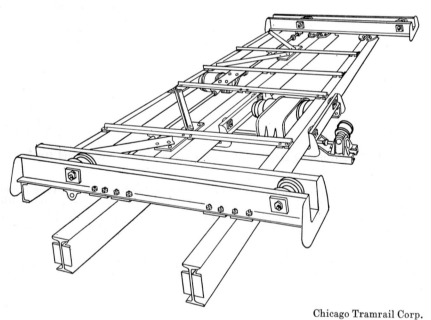

Chicago Tramrail Corp.

Fig. 3. **Motor-driven underrunning double-girder crane with underrunning trolley.**

The **capacity and duty** of overhead bridge cranes range from the small hand push crane to the very large top running double girder crane of tremendous capacity. The small cranes that are used infrequently are often of the push type where the bridge and trolley are both moved by hand. With somewhat heavier cranes and ones having more continuous operation, a hand geared bridge or trolley is used or an electric drive provided. Although many small cranes are in use in small shops, the best known and most widely used type of crane is the electric traveling top-running double-girder crane seen in most manufacturing plants and used in most factory building and yard installations.

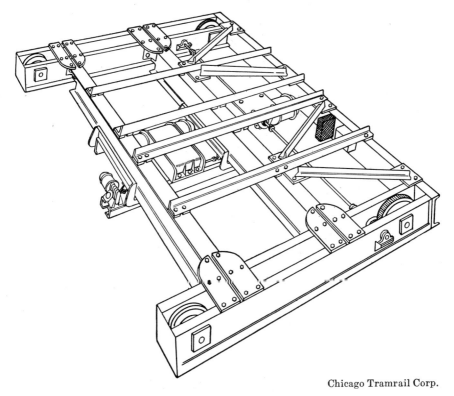

Chicago Tramrail Corp.

Fig. 4. Top-running double-girder electric crane with underrunning trolley.

The single- or double-girder underrunning bridge crane has wide use as a **transfer bridge** in overhead tramway systems. For light duty, a single girder crane can be the transfer link between various monorail tracks of a tramrail system. For heavier duty use, the double girder transfer bridge can be used with a double track tramway system. Used as a transfer bridge, these underrunning cranes are equipped with automatic safety stops and interlocking latches.

With the large overhead electric cranes, it is frequently desirable to have a man on the floor to hook up loads. A **system of signals** between the crane operator in the cab and the man on the floor has been developed which has become standard practice; Fig. 6 illustrates the standard hand signals for use with overhead bridge cranes.

OVERHEAD ELECTRIC TRAVELING BRIDGE CRANE SELEC-TION. If every overhead traveling crane installation were to be made on the basis of the exact loadings and travel required, the final selection of the proper-size crane and auxiliary equipment would become a fairly simple engineering matter. Unfortunately, except for bulk-handling plants and production-line layouts, most installations are capable of only very general limitations of loading and material movements. Therefore, the selection of the **right crane for economic**

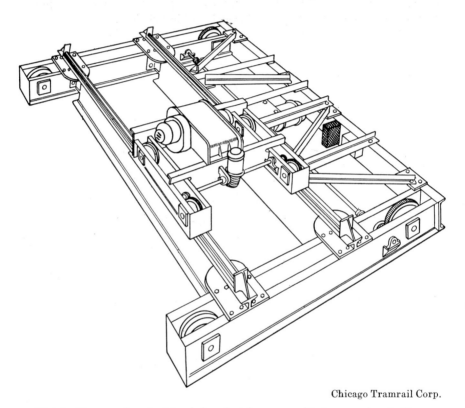

Chicago Tramrail Corp.

Fig. 5. Top-running double-girder electric crane with top-running trolley.

investment and subsequent **low-cost maintenance** depends considerably upon the individual interpretations that the different crane manufacturers give to service requirements in offering their equipment for the job in question. This selection is not normally based on the foot-ton service requirements or the foot-ton service capacity of the equipment offered but rather on **experienced judgment based on similar installations.** Hook-type cranes have, as a general rule, been classified as to service into the following classes:

Class 1 cranes are used for stand-by duty such as in powerhouses and motor rooms. This type of crane usually is designed for slow speeds because its use in such service is only occasional. The service life of the equipment is equal to the minimum operating standards and the maximum demand of full load lifts per hour is about 2 to 5.

Class 2 cranes are for light-duty service such as in machine shops and warehouses. In this instance the moderate speeds and infrequent lifts call for a service life comparable to the service expectancy. Maximum demand of full load lifts per hour is between 5 and 10.

Hoist—Forearm vertical, make small horizontal circle with the hand.

Lower—Arm extended. Hand below hip. Wave forearm downward.

Stop—Arm extended, hand level with the hip, hold position rigidly.

Rack—Arm extended, hand at hip level, fingers closed, thumb extended horizontally. Jerk hand in direction of racking.

Travel—Forearm vertical, hand open, wave forearm in direction of travel.

Emergency stop—Arm extended, hand level with the hip, wave hand quickly to right and left.

Fig. 6. Standard hand signals for overhead bridge cranes.

Class 3 cranes are for moderate duty such as light foundry work and service in storage yards (Fig. 7). With the average speeds and intermittent lifts encountered in this service, the service life of the parts and equipment should be equal to normal requirements. Maximum demand of full load lifts per hour is about 10 to 20.

Class 4 cranes are for constant heavy-duty service encountered in heavy foundry work and production-line service. With fast, constant operation the service life of the parts and equipment must be equal to the sustained service requirements. Maximum demand of full load lifts per hour is between 20 and 40.

Class 5 cranes are for very severe duty such as magnet operation, grab buckets and service in stockyards (Fig. 8). Here the fast and extra fast speeds, together with steady use, call for rugged construction to withstand maximum operating conditions. Maximum demand of full load lifts per hour is between 40 and 80.

Harnischfeger Corp.

Fig. 7. Multiple, moderate-duty cranes in a heavy-machine shop (Class 3).

Harnischfeger Corp.

Fig. 8. Severe-duty cranes for heavy yard handling (Class 5).

Load Ratings. The above five classifications of overhead traveling cranes, based upon the duties they are to perform, can best be illustrated and translated into load ratings of the crane manufacturer's trolley and bridge drives. For instance, the typical loading on the 20-ton trolley frame for service classifications would be as follows:

Class 1, Stand-by duty
  150 percent of nominal load rating .... 30 ton
Class 2, Light duty
  125 percent of nominal load rating .... 25 ton
Class 3, Moderate duty
  Nominal load rating .... 20 ton
Class 4, Constant duty
  75 percent of nominal load rating .... 15 ton
Class 5, Severe duty
  50 percent of nominal load rating .... 10 ton

Thus with a 20-ton pattern trolley, the crane builder can build a 10-, 15-, 20-, 25-, or 30-ton crane, depending upon the service for which the crane is desired. Therefore, by proper selection of these capacity frames, he will provide engineering designs for the entire field of crane capacities and will cover service requirements adequately without having special or overlapping patterns or leaving service demand gaps. Such nominal ratings in frame sizes cover 5-, 10-, 20-, 30-, 50-, 75-, and 125-ton sizes. In the selection of trolley patterns by the crane manufacturer, his nominal load rating for that particular trolley size—or for Class 3 cranes, the basic drum diameter for the cable used at that particular rating—provides him with a safety factor of 5 on the cables, and a drum diameter that is equivalent to at least 30 rope diameters. This example illustrates one of the basic principles of crane design.

Bridge Design. For the bridge drive, the **maximum wheel load** on the crane, and the **speed,** determine the **size of bridge wheels** to be used. The physical proportions of the wheels will keep the loadings well within the permissible limits. The ratings on the individual wheels and bearings used on wheel axles do not vary greatly among the various manufacturers. However, the bearing sizes used for these wheel loads provide certain **life hours.** For the bridge and trolley drives of antifriction-bearing cranes, it is based upon certain load factors so as to obtain these bearing life hours. The following bearing life hours are used for various crane classifications:

Class 1:   3,000 hr. minimum—load factor 1.25
Class 2:   5,000 hr. minimum—load factor 1.00
Class 3: 15,000 hr. minimum—load factor 0.75
Class 4: 30,000 hr. minimum—load factor 0.60
Class 5: 50,000 hr. minimum—load factor 0.50

The **basic bridge-wheel diameters,** in inches, are as follows: 13, 15, 18, 21, 24, 27, and 30. Therefore each of these wheel diameters has a bridge drive unit designed for it to provide a certain life expectancy under certain imposed wheel-load conditions and bridge speeds. The diameter of the cross shaft and the diameter of the axles are proportionately designed to this wheel diameter and horsepower requirements and, most important of all, the bridge bearing life of the truck axle bearings is determined on the basis of the size of bearing which it is possible to install on the truck wheel shaft.

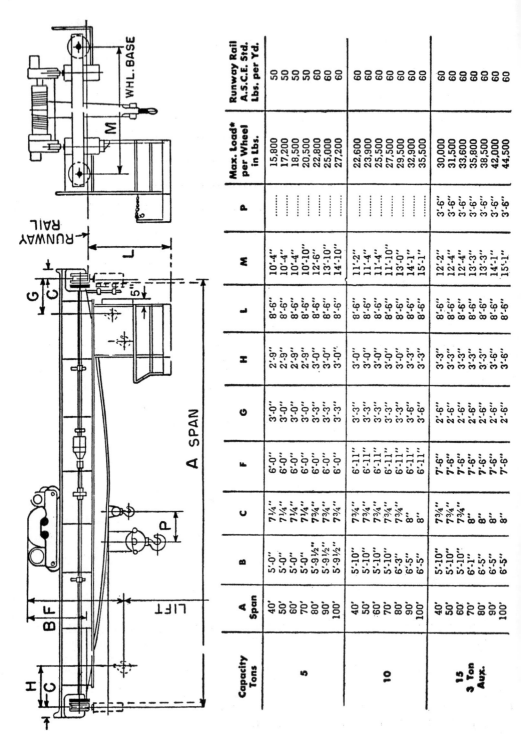

Capacity Tons	A Span	B	C	F	G	H	L	M	P	Max. Load* per Wheel in Lbs.	Runway Rail A.S.C.E. Std. Lbs. per Yd.
5	40'	5'-0"	7¼"	6'-0"	3'-0"	2'-9"	8'-6"	10'-4"	......	15,800	50
	50'	5'-0"	7¼"	6'-0"	3'-0"	2'-9"	8'-6"	10'-4"	......	17,200	50
	60'	5'-0"	7¼"	6'-0"	3'-0"	2'-9"	8'-6"	10'-4"	......	18,500	50
	70'	5'-0"	7¼"	6'-0"	3'-0"	2'-9"	8'-6"	10'-10"	......	20,500	50
	80'	5'-9½"	7¾"	6'-0"	3'-3"	3'-0"	8'-6"	12'-6"	......	22,800	60
	90'	5'-9½"	7¾"	6'-0"	3'-3"	3'-0"	8'-6"	13'-10"	......	25,000	60
	100'	5'-9½"	7¾"	6'-0"	3'-3"	3'-0"	8'-6"	14'-10"	......	27,200	60
10	40'	5'-10"	7¾"	6'-11"	3'-3"	3'-0"	8'-6"	11'-2"	......	22,600	60
	50'	5'-10"	7¾"	6'-11"	3'-3"	3'-0"	8'-6"	11'-4"	......	23,900	60
	60'	5'-10"	7¾"	6'-11"	3'-3"	3'-0"	8'-6"	11'-4"	......	25,500	60
	70'	5'-10"	7¾"	6'-11"	3'-3"	3'-0"	8'-6"	11'-10"	......	27,500	60
	80'	6'-3"	7¾"	6'-11"	3'-3"	3'-0"	8'-6"	13'-0"	......	29,500	60
	90'	6'-5"	8"	6'-11"	3'-6"	3'-3"	8'-6"	14'-1"	......	32,900	60
	100'	6'-5"	8"	6'-11"	3'-6"	3'-3"	8'-6"	15'-1"	......	35,500	60
15 3 Ton Aux.	40'	5'-10"	7¾"	7'-6"	2'-6"	3'-3"	8'-6"	12'-2"	3'-6"	30,000	60
	50'	5'-10"	7¾"	7'-6"	2'-6"	3'-3"	8'-6"	12'-4"	3'-6"	31,500	60
	60'	5'-10"	7¾"	7'-6"	2'-6"	3'-3"	8'-6"	12'-4"	3'-6"	33,600	60
	70'	6'-1"	8"	7'-6"	2'-6"	3'-3"	8'-6"	13'-3"	3'-6"	35,800	60
	80'	6'-5"	8"	7'-6"	2'-6"	3'-3"	8'-6"	13'-3"	3'-6"	38,500	60
	90'	6'-5"	8"	7'-6"	2'-6"	3'-6"	8'-6"	14'-1"	3'-6"	42,000	60
	100'	6'-5"	8"	7'-6"	2'-6"	3'-6"	8'-6"	15'-1"	3'-6"	44,500	60

Capacity (Ton)	Aux. (Ton)	Span									Wheel Load* (lb)	
20	3 or 5	40'	6'-4"	8"	8'-2"	2'-6"	3'-3"	8'-6"	12'-5"	4'-0"	36,000	60
		50'	6'-4"	8"	8'-2"	2'-6"	3'-3"	8'-6"	12'-7"	4'-0"	39,500	60
		60'	6'-4"	8"	8'-2"	2'-6"	3'-3"	8'-6"	12'-7"	4'-0"	41,800	60
		70'	6'-11"	8½"	8'-2"	2'-6"	3'-3"	8'-6"	13'-3"	4'-0"	44,500	70
		80'	6'-11"	8½"	8'-2"	2'-6"	3'-6"	8'-6"	13'-3"	4'-0"	47,500	70
		90'	6'-11"	8½"	8'-2"	2'-6"	3'-6"	8'-6"	14'-2"	4'-0"	50,500	70
		100'	6'-11"	8½"	8'-2"	2'-6"	3'-6"	8'-6"	15'-2"	4'-0"	54,500	70
25	3 or 5	40'	6'-4"	8"	8'-8"	2'-6"	3'-3"	8'-6"	12'-11"	4'-0"	45,000	60
		50'	6'-9"	8½"	8'-8"	2'-6"	3'-3"	8'-6"	12'-2"	4'-0"	47,500	70
		60'	6'-9"	8½"	8'-8"	2'-6"	3'-3"	8'-6"	12'-2"	4'-0"	49,000	70
		70'	7'-1"	8½"	8'-8"	2'-9"	3'-6"	8'-6"	12'-2"	4'-0"	52,500	70
		80'	7'-1"	9"	8'-8"	2'-9"	3'-6"	8'-6"	13'-6"	4'-0"	56,500	80
		90'	7'-1"	9"	8'-8"	2'-9"	3'-6"	8'-6"	14'-4"	4'-0"	62,000	80
		100'	7'-1"	9"	8'-8"	2'-9"	3'-6"	8'-6"	14'-10"	4'-0"	65,000	80
30	5 or 10	40'	7'-4"	8½"	9'-6"	3'-0"	3'-6"	8'-6"	12'-2"	4'-7"	50,500	70
		50'	7'-4"	8½"	9'-6"	3'-0"	3'-6"	8'-6"	12'-2"	4'-7"	54,000	70
		60'	7'-8"	9"	9'-6"	3'-0"	3'-6"	8'-6"	12'-10"	4'-7"	57,000	70
		70'	7'-8"	9"	9'-6"	3'-0"	3'-6"	8'-6"	12'-10"	4'-7"	60,000	80
		80'	8'-0"	9"	9'-6"	3'-0"	3'-9"	8'-6"	13'-4"	4'-7"	65,000	80
		90'	8'-0"	9¼"	9'-6"	3'-0"	3'-9"	8'-6"	14'-4"	4'-7"	68,000	80
		100'	8'-0"	9¼"	9'-6"	3'-0"	3'-9"	8'-6"	14'-11"	4'-7"	75,000	100
40	10 or 15	40'	7'-7"	9¼"	10'-9"	3'-3"	4'-0"	8'-6"	13'-10"	4'-7"	62,000	80
		50'	7'-7"	9¼"	10'-9"	3'-3"	4'-0"	8'-6"	13'-10"	4'-7"	66,500	80
		60'	8'-0"	10"	10'-9"	3'-3"	4'-0"	8'-6"	14'-1"	4'-7"	69,000	100
		70'	8'-0"	10"	10'-9"	3'-3"	4'-0"	8'-6"	14'-3"	4'-7"	73,000	100
		80'	8'-3"	10"	10'-9"	3'-3"	4'-0"	8'-6"	14'-11"	4'-7"	79,000	100
		90'	8'-3"	10"	10'-9"	3'-3"	4'-0"	8'-6"	14'-11"	4'-7"	84,000	135
		100'	8'-3"	10"	10'-9"	3'-3"	4'-0"	8'-6"	15'-4"	4'-7"	88,000	135

Harnischfeger Corp.

Fig. 9. Clearance dimensions for Class 3 and 4 cranes—box girder cranes.

* Wheel loads are without impact, based on 300-ft.-per-min. bridge speed and standard features such as open cab, drum control, wood flooring on platform, and a 30-ft. lift.

Based upon static stresses, the mechanical details of the basic design of Class 3 cranes would carry a **factor of safety** of 5, based upon the ultimate strength. Structural details can be worked out upon the same basis. They should be modified, however, when deflections exceed the limits of stability as required in girders. **I-beam-type girders** are entirely adequate for the shorter spans of Class 1, 2, and 3 cranes, while **welded box-section girders** offer maximum service performance in the longer spans, especially for Class 4 and 5 service. Bridge drive design of the stationary-pin type is satisfactory for Class 1 and 2, but the conventional master carbuilders axle construction should be incorporated for Class 3, 4, and 5 with heat-treated wheel treads. **Double-bridge drive** should be used on all 4-wheel cranes where bridge speeds are over 500 ft. per min. Surface hardening of gear teeth and similar wearing parts will provide necessary service life on designs for Class 4 and 5 cranes.

Clearance Dimensions. Clearance dimensions for Class 3 and 4 cranes are given in Fig. 9. The dimensions given cover standard cranes of moderate operating speeds and manual drum control and are to be used for estimating purposes only. Dimensional data for cranes requiring fast or extra-fast speeds may vary from these lists. Before any actual construction is started by prospective crane users, **certified clearance prints** should be obtained from the crane manufacturer to show exact dimensions of the crane recommended for the capacity, speeds, and degree of service.

The type of crane to be used and any special features should depend upon the exact conditions under which it will operate and the specific functions to be undertaken. In this regard, it cannot be too strongly emphasized that the recommendations of crane engineers, based on their knowledge and experience, should be given careful consideration and, circumstances permitting, the policy of adhering to the use of builders' standard equipment should govern. Therefore, it is very important that **liberal clearances** based on standard cranes be used in new building construction so that the crane user may benefit by these advantages. Liberal space permits the selection of the best equipment that any builder can economically and quickly provide.

THE IMPORTANCE OF ELECTRICAL EQUIPMENT. Since electrical equipment is the heart of the crane, and its performance will definitely determine the ability of the crane to operate without interruption, the electrical equipment requires most of the maintenance time and therefore should receive the crane user's greatest share of attention. The functions of each piece of electrical apparatus and specific recommendations for the electrical apparatus for each classification of crane are outlined in the following data.

MOTORS. All direct-current motors should possess certain inherent characteristics, as well as defined mechanical features, in line with modern practices. All motors should be totally enclosed and provided with antifriction bearings and a shaft of a large diameter, preferably tapered on the end on which the brake wheel is mounted. Motors should be series wound and provided with a full number of interpoles to insure perfect commutation over all load conditions. They should likewise be so designed as to provide ease of inspection of the commutator and brushes, together with accessibility to the terminals, in case of motor failure. Due consideration should be given to the selection of a motor that will provide the least amount of down time of the crane for making any armature change or complete motor change. For this purpose, split-frame construction is desirable.

For the alternating-current-operated cranes, the slip-ring or wound-rotor type of motor is best. Squirrel-cage motors do not provide good speed regulation, which is essential on overhead traveling cranes in handling all loads.

The **wound-rotor motor** should be sturdily built, preferably to National Electrical Manufacturers' Association (NEMA) standardized dimensions, with a tapered shaft extension on the brake end of the motor for easy removal of the brake wheel. It should be of the antifriction-bearing type, grease lubricated, with a capsule-mounted bearing. The stator of the motor should be constructed so that laminations are well anchored and cannot work loose in the reversal service to which the motor is subjected. Well-braced motor windings able to withstand plugging, and well insulated, provide long, uninterrupted performance under service conditions. The rotor of this motor should be well balanced and of low WR^2. The slip rings should be made of high-quality bronze. Brushes and rings selected should be of the type that resist pitting under plugging service. Openings should also be provided for convenience in inspecting the brushes.

Wound-rotor **induction motors,** as usually applied to overhead traveling cranes, are built in the open type (rated 30-min., 50° rise), the enclosed type (rated 30-min., 55° rise), and the totally enclosed, externally fan-cooled type (rated 1-hr., 55° rise). From the standpoint of price, the open motor is cheaper than the totally enclosed type. From a standardization point of view, however, as well as from the service angle, the totally enclosed motor will pay for itself over a comparatively short period of time. Exclusion of dust and dirt from the motor windings and the internal parts of the motor reduces maintenance work and prolongs service life.

Motors may be selected for the various classes of cranes as follows:

Hoist Motor—Class 1 Cranes. Determine the horsepower of the motor from the foot-tons and speed required. Select a motor of standard rating on the basis of at least a 15-min.-rated frame size, using the horsepower calculated or a slightly higher horsepower. The length of lift to which the crane is subjected must be given consideration when selecting a 15-min.-rated motor. When the lift is excessive, a 30-min.-rated motor must be used. From a commercial standpoint, it has been found advisable to use nothing but 30-min.-rated motors for this classification.

Bridge and Trolley Motors—Class 1 Cranes. Bridge and trolley motors are selected on the basis of the running horsepower required. For a full-roller-bearing crane, select the required horsepower by using the ratio shown in Fig. 10 as a multiplier.

This ratio will give sufficient motor power for the acceleration of the crane. For a sleeve-bearing crane, this ratio should be increased by the difference between antifriction and sleeve-bearing friction values. The selection of too large a motor for these drives will definitely sacrifice speed regulation and cause the crane to start very abruptly. The equation to be used is as follows:

$$\text{Motor hp.} = \text{running hp.} \times \text{acceleration ratio}$$

Speed regulation for a Class 1 crane, especially one for powerhouse duty, is essential, and the proper selection of motors is as important as the proper selection of control.

Class 2 Cranes. Selection of motors for light-duty cranes is made in the manner described above except that no consideration is given for the 15-min. rating, as all motors are rated on the basis of 30-min., 55° rise.

DRIVE	SPEED IN F.P.M.	CLOSE SPEED CONTROL		STANDARD CRANE CONTROL			
		CLASS 1 & 2	CLASS 3	CLASS 3	CLASS 4 & 5	CLASS 4 & 5	
		30-Min.-Rated Crane Motors		30-Min.-Rated Crane Motors	1-Hr.-Rated Crane Motors	30-Min.-Rated Mill Motors	
Trolley	75	1.3	1.4	...	...	...	
Trolley	150	1.4	1.5	...	...	...	
Trolley	225	...	1.6	1.7	1.7	2.0	
Trolley	300	...	...	1.8	1.8	2.1	
Trolley	375	...	...	1.9	1.9	2.2	
Trolley	450	...	...	2.0	2.0	2.3	
Bridge	150	1.8	1.9	2.0	...	...	
Bridge	300	2.0	2.1	2.2	2.2	2.5	
Bridge	450	...	2.3	2.4	2.4	2.7	
Bridge	600	...	...	2.6	2.6	2.9	
Bridge	750	...	...	2.8	2.8	3.1	
Bridge	900	...	...	3.0	3.0	3.3	

Fig. 10. Ratio of rated to running horsepower for trolley and bridge motors, allowing for rolling and flange friction, track condition, and acceleration.

Class 3 Cranes. The method employed for selection of motors is the same as for Class 2 cranes, and motors are rated on the basis of 30-min. 55° rise with normal frame construction.

Class 4 Cranes. For constant-duty cranes, the same method as described above is employed, and motors are selected on the basis of 30-min., 55° rise. However, the heating effect of the motor should be checked by the root-mean-square method for frame size, and motor size should be corrected accordingly. Ambient temperatures as well as altitudes must also be considered.

Class 5 Cranes—Severe Duty. In this classification, particularly where magnet and grab-bucket cranes are involved, and where they are operated by direct current, the hoist motors should be carefully selected.

Motor Selection. Usually, on **magnet and grab-bucket cranes,** a definite duty cycle can be determined, and in most cases the amount of material to be handled per hour is known. On this basis, the root-mean-square method can be used to determine the heating of the motor. For the majority of such applications, if one does not utilize more than 60 percent of the rated horsepower of a 30-min.-rated motor, the thermal capacity of the motor will be sufficient. A direct-current-operated motor does not have the ability to radiate heat as readily as the alternating-current motor, since the internal heat of the motor must first pass through air before it is radiated from the motor frame.

In this classification, particularly on grab-bucket cranes, the space factor for two adjacent motors may be such that proper consideration must be given to Class B insulation. On **hot-metal cranes,** and on other cranes intended for constant-use service, Class B motors should definitely be used. Bridge and trolley motors for roller-bearing cranes should be selected on the basis of running horsepower multipled by the ratios shown in Fig. 10. Bridge- and trolley-drive motors for sleeve-bearing cranes should be selected on the basis outlined under Class 1 cranes.

Selection of alternating-current wound-rotor motors on the basis of crane classifications as in **Classes, 1, 2, 3, and 4** can be made in a manner similar to that described above for direct-current-operated cranes. For **Class 5,** severe-duty cranes, the root-mean-square method is again employed, but serious consideration must be given to Class B insulation, as well as to the totally enclosed, externally fan-cooled motor, particularly on magnet and grab-bucket cranes, where space is at a premium. Large motors on overhead traveling cranes necessitate greater end approaches and therefore diminish the actual floor coverage of the crane. The use of alternating current on magnet or grab-bucket cranes is common.

For the **Class 5** cranes that do not have a definite duty cycle, the hoist motors may be determined, first, by finding the horsepower required under the foot-ton method, and then by selecting, for the hoist motion, a motor with an actual running horsepower that does not exceed 80 percent of the rated horsepower of the motor. On a.c. cranes, 80 percent has been selected, whereas on d.c. cranes, 60 percent has been the determining factor. The reason for the difference is that the winding on a.c. motors is imbedded in the steel stator core, and this core is directly connected through its entire circumference to the outside frame of the motor. Therefore, radiation of heat from an a.c. motor is far more rapid than from a corresponding d.c. type.

Bridge- and trolley-travel motors are selected in a manner similar to that described above for d.c. motors for both the roller- and sleeve-bearing-equipped cranes. Hoist, trolley, and bridge traverse speeds for standard-type cranes are given in Fig. 11 together with horsepower requirements.

CRANE BRAKES. Various types of brakes are used on overhead traveling cranes, such as a.c. and d.c. electric-magnet brakes, rectifier-operated brakes, hydraulically or mechanically operated foot brakes, constant-drag brakes, and combination electric-hydraulic brakes.

SELECTION OF CRANE BRAKES. The selection of brakes on an overhead traveling crane is dependent upon the classification of the crane, the horsepower of the motor, and the type of control used in the crane. In general, however, all brakes must possess one inherent characteristic: within the rated capacity of the crane, they must be able to **stop the motion of the crane** under all service and weather conditions. They should be equipped with a lining material that provides a constant coefficient of friction, does not wear rapidly, and does not score the brake wheel but rather gives a polish to the wheel. This lining should be of sufficient thickness to provide long service life. The brake mechanism should likewise be positive, designed for long life and operation with a minimum of adjustments, and so constructed that these adjustments need not be disturbed if replacement of the armature becomes necessary. The action of the brake should be positive.

D.C.-operated brakes equipped with series-wound coils should release at 40 percent of the rated current of the hoist motor, and **a.c. brakes** should release at a minimum of 80 percent of rated voltage. **Hydraulically operated brakes** should be so designed that the pedal pressure and stroke should not be fatiguing to the operator, preferably with a pedal pressure of 30 lb. or under.

Selection of proper brakes cannot be overly stressed. The brake selected must retard, stop, and hold whatever load the motive power of the crane can handle, besides overcoming the inertia of all the moving parts that have been set in motion. Overbraking a crane, however, can be just as detrimental as underbraking. Too much braking torque on the hoist motion will cause sudden stops and thereby create excessive strain and wear on keyways, splines, gear teeth, bearings, etc. Too large a brake on the bridge motion of a crane will allow skidding

Capacity	SLOW					MODERATE					FAST†				
	Hoist		Trolley*		Bridge*	Hoist		Trolley*		Bridge*	Hoist		Trolley*		Bridge*
	Speed	Req'd H.P.	Speed	Req'd H.P.	Speed	Speed	Req'd H.P.	Speed	Req'd H.P.	Speed	Speed	Req'd H.P.	Speed	Req'd H.P.	Speed
5	25	10	125	2	250	40	15	175	3	350	65	25	200	5	450
7½	25	15	125	2	250	35	20	175	3	350	45	25	200	5	450
10	25	20	125	3	250	33	25	175	5	350	45	35	200	5	450
15	20	25	125	3	250	30	35	175	5	350	42	50	200	7½	450
20	15	25	125	5	250	22	35	175	7½	350	32	50	200	10	450
25	14	30	125	5	250	20	40	175	7½	350	25	50	200	10	450
30	12	30	125	7½	250	20	50	175	10	350	25	60	200	15	450
35	12	40	100	7½	200	17	50	150	10	300	20	60	175	15	400
40	11	40	100	7½	200	17	60	150	10	300	20	75	175	15	400
45	10	40	100	7½	200	16	60	150	10	300	20	75	175	15	400
50	10	45	100	10	150	14	60	150	15	250	20	85	175	15	300
60	10	50	100	10	150	15	75	150	15	250	20	100	175	15	300
75	9	60	75	15	150	13	85	100	20	250	16	100	125	20	300
85	8	60	75	15	150	13	100	100	20	……	…	……	……	……	……
100	8	75	75	15	150	11	100	100	20	……	…	……	……	……	……
125	6	75	75	20	100	8	100	100	30	……	…	……	……	……	……
°150	5	75	50	20	100	7	100	75	30	……	…	……	……	……	……
°175	4	75	50	20	100	6	100	75	30	……	…	……	……	……	……
°‡200	4	2-35	35	2-15	100	6	2-60	50	2-20	……	…	……	……	……	……
°‡250	3	2-35	35	2-15	100	5	2-60	50	2-20	……	…	……	……	……	……
°‡300	3	2-50	35	2-20	100	4	2-60	50	2-25	……	…	……	……	……	……

Fig. 11. Hoist, trolley, and bridge traverse speeds of standard-type cranes.

Operating speeds in ft. per min. for roller-bearing, hook type, industrial, and powerhouse electric traveling cranes.

* H.P. of bridge-drive motor depends upon span of crane.
° Based on sleeve-bearing design.
‡ Double-trolley crane.

† Extra fast speeds can be had when duty cycle operation demands.
* Trolley speeds depend on span of crane. Faster speeds should be used for longer spans.

of the wheels, resulting in troublesome flat spots as well as undue wear on bridge drive parts. Too large a brake for the trolley motion may cause undue swinging of the load and excessive wear on the driving parts.

Selection of **brakes for the hoist motion** of cranes under Classes 1, 2, 3, and 4 should be made on the basis of 150 percent torque of the name-plate rating of the hoist motor, when used in conjunction with d.c. dynamic lowering control, as well as a.c.-operated cranes equipped with mechanical load brakes. Proper consideration, however, should be given in the selection of brakes, particularly on a.c. installations, to the type and use of the particular classification of the crane. Here the **control** situation must also be considered. For a large-capacity powerhouse crane under Class 1, where exact inching of the loads is necessary, a brake with quick response in setting as well as releasing is required. This requirement precludes from selection certain types of slower operating mechanisms on the a.c. brakes.

Selection of hoist-motor brakes for Class 5 severe-duty cranes again depends upon the **service** in which the crane is operating and the **type of control apparatus** used in conjunction with it. For instance, on a magnet crane, for a.c. operation and used in conjunction with a regenerative type of control, the brake should have a torque rating of at least 200 percent of the name-plate rating of the motor. The same requirement holds true for grab-bucket cranes equipped with a regenerative type of control. For these two types of cranes equipped with a dynamic lowering or countertorque type of control, a brake of 150 percent torque rating would be considered sufficient. In this case, the control provides a definite electrical slowdown before the brake sets, whereas in the regenerative type of control, all stopping of the load must be done by the electric brake.

Class 5 Cranes. In cranes with a.c.- or d.c.-operated brakes, two electric brakes are usually employed, each possessing 100 percent torque rating of the motor, one of the brakes being mounted on the motor extension shaft and the other on the motor-coupling extension shaft. This arrangement again allows the use of two similar brakes. It was common practice a number of years ago to provide a so-called second-shaft brake. This brake was necessarily very large, because of the higher torque ratings that were obtained on the second reduction shaft, making it a very expensive brake and one requiring considerable space as well as many different parts for spare equipment. In many cases, the torque rating of the second shaft was such that it was greater than any available commercial brake. It was necessary, therefore, to reduce the factor of safety on torque requirements. Fortunately, this method is no longer the accepted practice.

In the selection of a.c.-operated brakes for any of the five classifications of cranes, the most rugged brake is the **d.c.-operated magnet brake** used in conjunction with the dry-type rectifier unit. This combination provides for the durability and ruggedness of a d.c.-operated brake, together with the time-proved dry-type rectifier. The rectifier has no moving parts and can withstand the vibrations encountered on overhead traveling cranes. This brake, used in conjunction with a low-voltage d.c. shunt-wound coil, gives the same characteristics as a series-wound coil. It is made up of large-diameter wire and few turns and gives ruggedness as well as the speed of operation that closely parallels the d.c. magnet-brake operation. The selection of this brake can be made on the basis outlined. This type of brake is particularly recommended for Classes 4 and 5 so as to allow constant service on the crane with the absolute minimum of maintenance.

Brakes for Bridge Drive. The choice of a proper brake for the bridge drive can be made on the basis of a brake unit that provides at least **150 percent re-**

tarding torque, based upon the rated torque of the motor. This selection holds good for Classes 1, 2, 3, 4, and 5, as too large a bridge brake would be detrimental to the operation of the crane, just as would be too small a brake. Modern practice dictates the use of a **hydraulically operated brake** rather than a mechanically operated one. The hydraulic brake is more readily installed, and it can be easily synchronized on double-bridge drives to operate two brakes from a single foot pedal. The mechanically operated brake, with its long linkage and drag-link connections, requires constant attention for both lubrication and maintenance. Wear in the holes and on the pins causes much lost motion and eventually requires additional pedal strokes to obtain the same retarding force.

Trolley Brakes. Trolley motion for roller-bearing cranes can be equipped with a 50 percent torque brake. The free movement of the roller-bearing trolley necessitates the use of a brake, either of the electrical type or of the constant-drag type. Experience has shown that a 50 percent torque brake of either of the other types will provide a gradual stopping action of the trolley under average load conditions, within the rated capacity of the crane, without undue swinging of the load. Under constant maximum capacity loads, the selection of a 75 percent or even 100 percent brake may be necessary.

Abrupt stopping of light loads by too large a trolley brake is a most dangerous practice. Providing a large-torque-rated brake on either trolley or hoist motion and adjusting the torque spring to provide less than the rated amount of retarding torque is assuredly not recommended. The working of the solenoid or magnet against the torque spring is essential so as to reduce the hammer action. This is particularly true of the a.c. solenoid with a laminated structure. A long stroke and unrestricted action cause deterioration of the solenoid.

Installation in Bridge-mounted Cabs. On all outdoor operating cranes, where the cab is attached to the bridge, an **electric-hydraulic brake** should be installed on the bridge motion. This brake combines a spring set and electric release as well as a hydraulic closing. The selection of this brake should be made on the same basis as the hydraulically or mechanically operated foot brake mentioned above. For d.c. installation, the electric operating mechanism should consist of a shunt-wound coil directly connected to the load side of the main-line disconnect switch on the crane protective panel. For a.c. operation, the brake may be of the a.c. solenoid type or of the d.c. magnet type used in conjunction with a rectifying unit but connected in the same manner as the d.c.-operated brake just mentioned.

The hydraulically operated mechanism is **independently actuated.** It performs the same function as the independently operated hydraulic brake, the stopping of the crane being at the control of the operator actuating the foot pedal in the crane cab. This type of brake has a distinct advantage on all roller-bearing cranes, as it provides an **absolute stop** in case of power failure and provides a **parking brake** when the crane is not in operation. It can readily be seen that if a crane parked overnight does not have such a combination brake, a high wind might roll the crane down the runway and cause serious damage. Even this type of brake, of course, is not adequate for winds of hurricane velocity. In vicinities where cranes may be subjected to such conditions, a positive means of **chaining them to the runway,** or other proved locking means, gives the only real assurance against such storm hazards.

Installation in Trolley-mounted Cabs. Installation of brakes as above described covers the majority of applications for cranes operated in the conventional manner of having a cab attached to the bridge. In some instances, however, where the cab is attached to the trolley, the trolley motor drive is equipped with a hydraulically or mechanically operated foot brake. The bridge drive must then be actuated by some other means, since it is not practical to operate it by hydraulic or mechanical means. In these cases, the use of a **shunt- or series-wound brake for d.c. operation, or a solenoid- or thruster-operated brake for a.c. operation,** is used. Usually in these instances the control is provided with a drift point, thereby allowing the crane to coast before the brake is applied and diminishing the abruptness of the retarding action. Where this occurs, a brake of 100 percent rated torque should be used, since too abrupt a brake would cause serious swinging of the loads. For a.c. operation, a thruster brake has some distinct advantages. The thruster can be equipped with a time-delay action in setting the brake, which allows the gradual application of the braking torque. This action is similar to that of a foot-operated hydraulic brake.

Eddy-Current Brake. Another successful method is to operate the control of the bridge in conjunction with an eddy-current brake. This arrangement definitely provides a slowdown when decelerating from the full-on toward the off position. Consequently, with the bridge speed reduced by such means when the off position is reached, an electric brake can be used on the bridge drive, thereby preventing the sudden stop and the swinging of the load.

Other Considerations. Floor-controlled cranes naturally cannot be readily equipped with hydraulic brakes for the bridge or trolley motion and are therefore usually equipped with **electrically operated brakes** of 100 percent retarding torque.

Hydraulically operated bridge brakes should be designed to stop the fully loaded crane within a distance equal to 10 percent of the distance traveled in one minute at full load speed of the bridge.

LIMIT-SWITCH SELECTION. Selection of a proper limit switch for the hoist motion of the crane must be given due consideration, with an understanding that the limit switch is only a safety feature and is not to be used as a constant stopping device for the upper travel. Selection of a limit switch is determined by the classification of the crane as well as by the hoisting speed, the length of lift, and the obstructions on the floor over which the crane must operate. The last factor is of great importance, since the crane must be constructed so that it will not be necessary to trip the limit switch on high lifts to move over these floor obstructions. The correct solution is to design the building so that the crane runway is high enough to avoid such operation, thereby insuring the safety of the limit switch.

The **prime requisites of a good limit switch** are that it must be positive in action, its contact must be of such design that the switch will not freeze, and it must automatically reset itself upon the lowering of the hook block.

TYPES OF LIMIT SWITCHES. Fundamentally, there are two types of limit switches that can be used for either a.c. or d.c. operation. The first classification is known as the **control-circuit type** of limit switch, which is connected in series with the operating coil of a limit-switch contactor. The breaking of the limit-switch circuit opens the circuit to the contactor coil, which in turn opens the power circuit to the motor. These control-limit switches are built in two types, namely, the **weight-operated type,** which is actuated by the load block, and the **screw type,** which is geared or directly connected to the hoist-drum shaft. The weight-operated unit is almost universally used, inasmuch as it possesses the singular feature of maintaining constant hoisting height. This height does not alter, regardless of cable replacement or cable stretch. The screw-type limit switch must be adjusted upon the installation of a new cable and periodically checked to allow for the normal stretch in the cable.

The screw-type limit switch does, however, have a feature that provides a limit in the lowering direction of travel. This feature is most desirable in cranes under Class 1 service, especially in powerhouses, and prevents the possibility that the cable may be wound up in the lowering direction, thereby raising the hook block. The use of the control-circuit type of limit switch of the weight-operated unit is recommended for cranes under Classes 1, 2, and 3.

Another type of limit switch recommended for use on Class 4 and 5 applications is the **motor-circuit type,** which is weight-operated and mounted on the crane trolley. This unit has a quick make-and-break mechanism which opens up the limit-switch contacts. These contacts are directly connected to the power supply of the hoisting motor. On d.c.-operating cranes, this quick-break mechanism closes another set of contacts which connects the hoist motor, together with a suitable resistance, into a dynamic braking circuit. This circuit allows a very quick stop of the hoist motor, since it provides both an electrical slowdown and the stopping effects of the electric magnet brake. For a.c. installations, this same type of safety motor-circuit limit switch can be used. It may be connected either in a circuit whereby the power leads to the motor are disconnected, allowing the electric brake to bring the motor to a full stop, or by providing the second set of contacts with a suitable resistance and connecting the motor into a plugging or reversed connection, again allowing the motor to come to a very quick stop by means of both the electrical connection and the aid of the electric brake.

Limit Switches on Bridge or Trolley. Switches for limiting the trolley travel or bridge motion are applied in some unusual operating conditions, but as a general rule they are not used on the majority of cranes, because they tend to **restrict the floor coverage** of the crane. For instance, when applying limit switches to the bridge travel of a crane, the limit switch must break the circuit to the bridge motor, allowing the crane to stop within a distance equivalent to 10 percent of the distance traveled in one minute at the full load speed of the bridge. Therefore, the application of such limit switches would restrict the floor coverage. If bypass switches were installed to allow the crane to operate within these restricted areas, the feasibility of such safety devices would be debatable.

SELECTING CONTROLS. The selection of the proper controls for an overhead traveling crane probably requires more judgment on the basis of experience than the selection of any other piece of crane apparatus. No mathematical formula can be utilized to determine the correct type of control. The experience of the crane builder and the buying habits of the customer are the usual factors involved in the decision. Since the control governs the movements of the crane, it naturally must possess good speed-regulating properties. It should provide a minimum of five steps of control, be designed in accordance with NEMA standards, and be readily accessible for maintenance and replacement of parts. In addition, it should be compact, well-insulated, amply protected against shorts and grounds, easy to operate, and mounted to provide clear vision for the operator.

TYPES OF CONTROLS. Fundamentally, there are three different types of control for both a.c. and d.c. operations, namely, **manual, semimagnetic, and full magnetic.** Crane users appear to favor magnetic control, which involves a higher initial cost but has the distinct advantages of ease of operation and lower maintenance cost. Some crane buyers, however, prefer to view installations in terms of initial investment. For this reason the manual type of control must always be considered.

Manual Type. The **manual type of control**, of the drum type, is generally used on all cranes of Classes 1, 2, and 3, provided the horsepower requirement for this control falls within the limiting factors. Limiting factors for the manual control are as follows:

1. For d.c. dynamic lowering hoist controllers, maximum 15 hp. at 230 volts.
2. For reversing service, such as is used on bridge and trolley drives, 40 hp. at 230 volts d.c.
3. For a.c. reversing service for hoist, bridge, and trolley motions, the hoist motion used in conjunction with a mechanical load brake, 49 hp. at 220 volts.

Semimagnetic Type. For Class 3 moderate-duty service, a semimagnetic type of control is recommended; this type is likewise recommended for either Class 1 or 2 if the horsepower requirements are beyond the limitations outlined above. The limiting factors for the semimagnetic control are as follows:

1. For dynamic lowering hoist service, 25 hp. at 230 volts d.c.
2. For reversing service for bridge and trolley travel, 50 hp. at 230 volts d.c.
3. For a.c. reversing service for either hoist, bridge or trolley motion, up to 75 hp. at 220 or 440 volts.

Full Magnetic Type. For Classes 4 and 5, the **full magnetic type of control** is recommended for both a.c. and d.c. applications. For Class 5, severe-duty cranes, variations of the full magnetic control are applicable, particularly on the a.c.-operated units. Magnet and grab-bucket cranes are not equipped with mechanical load brakes in the hoisting motion. Because of the severity of service, the use of a mechanical load brake becomes a decided maintenance problem. In such cases, the countertorque or a regenerative type of control is recommended. Regenerative control provides a constant speed in the lowering direction when the control handle is operated from the full on lowering toward the off position by the use of secondary short-circuit contactors and is recommended up to 15-hp. operation. Above that horsepower, the countertorque type of control, which provides an electrical slowdown operated from the full-on lowering toward the off position, with an overhauling load on the hook, is recommended.

Care must be exercised in the selection of a.c. control, particularly for hoist motions, used without a mechanical load brake, to determine definitely that such type of control does not cause **undue heating** of the motor windings in the lowering direction. This precaution is particularly necessary in regard to some of the so-called single-phasing circuits that have recently been developed. While these units have a definite field, it is recommended that they not be used in cases where it is necessary to lower on a control step for any length of time, because this operation will cause undue heating of the motor windings.

Hoist Control. The popularity of a.c. cranes has increased during the past few years, particularly because of the improved **a.c. hoist control** that has been developed. This hoist control consists of an eddy-current brake coupled into the drive of the hoisting motor and provides speed regulation without the use of a mechanical load brake and without undue heating of the motor windings. This control—known in some trade sources as **Magnetorque** control—provides speed regulation in the hoisting motion of the crane equal to that of d.c. dynamic lowering, and in the hoisting side even surpassing it. By virtue of this control, the vast majority of a.c. cranes are now being built without the use of a mechanical load brake, and this eddy-current-brake or electric-load-brake type of control is used in its stead.

Bridge and Trolley Control. As stated above, the control for the bridge and trolley travel, in manual, semimagnetic, or full magnetic, must be capable of reversing service. Since it is not readily possible to provide a plugging contactor or plugging protection for the manual and semimagnetic controls, the full magnetic control must possess such a plugging relay on the magnetic board.

Variations from Standard. Variations from the above standards are numerous. For instance, under Class 1, stand-by-duty crane service, for a powerhouse installation necessitating a very long lift, and with slow hoisting speeds, consideration must be given to the adequacy of the mechanical load brake as well as to proper selection of both motor and control equipment. It is also possible that a crane in this classification might be equipped with pendent-rope or selective push-button control for floor operation (Fig. 12). Floor-controlled cranes fall

Fig. 12. Selective push-button control for floor operation.

into either Class 1 or 2 and very seldom fall into Classes 3, 4, or 5. The frequency of operation of equipment in the latter classifications makes it economical to have a crane operator in the cab at all times, whereas cranes of Classes 1 and 2, because of their infrequent service, might readily be operated from the floor.

Pendent-rope control, in conjunction with manual control, has been used for many years but is being rapidly replaced by selective push-button control. The latter control is of the magnetic type, and the push-button element is so designed that the proper sequence of contactors are energized upon the pressing of the push buttons. Speed can be thus controlled at the discretion of the operator, but such control should not be confused with the automatic-acceleration type.

In some cases, d.c. cranes of Classes 3, 4, and 5 might require the use of an **electrical slowdown** for the bridge or trolley motion. This slowdown is customarily brought about by providing an armature shunt point at the first step of the controller, or it can be accomplished by providing a dynamic braking point on the controller.

Choice of Resistors. In conjunction with the proper selection of control for an overhead traveling crane, choice of the proper resistors to operate with this control is of equal importance. Fundamentally, resistors can be classified in two different classes—**the cast-grid and the ribbon-wound types.** The latter unit has its advantages; yet it possesses the disadvantage of not having the thermal capacity of the cast grid. Resistors should be selected, of course, in accordance with **NEMA standards.** The classifications that are ordinarily used for crane duty are the 130, 140, 150, 160, 170, and 90.

For overhead traveling cranes in Class 1, where the lift is not too great and the cranes are equipped for pendent floor operation, NEMA Class 130 or 140 resistors can be used. On long-lift cranes in this classification, it is recommended that Class 150 or 160 be used, with further thought being given to the fact that if loads must be lowered at reduced speeds with resistance in the circuit for a considerable length of time, heavy intermittent, or continuous duty, Class 170 or 90 resistors should be used.

For Class 2, light-duty cranes that are pendent-rope operated, NEMA Class 130 or 140 resistors can be used, but if these cranes are cab-controlled, NEMA Class 150 should be employed. For cranes in Classes 3, 4, and 5, normally the resistor classification of 160 should be used. An exception to this rule, however, may be made, depending upon the specific requirement of the crane. For all roller-bearing cranes, the resistor should be selected to provide 50 percent torque on the first control step. The proper selection of resistors cannot be arrived at by a definite, set rule but must be based upon long experience.

MOTOR-PROTECTIVE DEVICES. All a.c.- and d.c.-operated cranes are provided with a motor-protective device of some sort. It is recommended that this device consist of overload relays set to approximately 150 percent current of the motor that they protect.

D.c.-operated cranes should have one **overload relay of the inverse time relay type** inserted in each of the lines to the motor circuit which they control and an

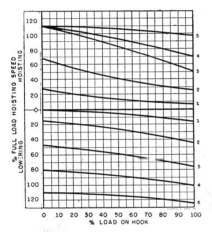

A. Curve for a.c. Magnetorque hoist control.

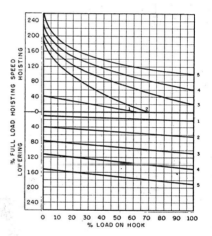

B. Curve for d.c. dynamic lowering hoist controller.

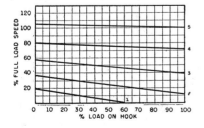

C. Curve for a.c. magnetic controller with bridge or trolley motions.

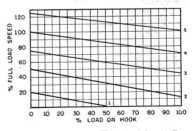

Harnischfeger Corp.

D. Curve for d.c. magnetic controller with bridge or trolley motions.

Fig. 13. Speed-load curves.

instantaneous trip overload relay connected in the common line. These relays provide short-circuit protection. In the case of a.c.-operated cranes, **overload relays of the dual-coil type,** or single-coil relays in each of two of the three power leads to the motor circuits are recommended.

Such protection can be provided either in a separate crane-protective panel or on the full magnetic-control panel if the crane is so equipped.

SELECTION OF CRANE PROTECTIVE PANEL. The selection of the crane-protective panel, which is customarily mounted in the crane cab at the rear of the operator, is dependent upon the total horsepower load of the crane. The panel, however, should be provided with a main-line disconnect switch that can be readily locked in the open position. This main-line disconnect switch should be provided with a safety door latch that makes it impossible to open the doors to the front of the crane-protective panel unless the knife switch is in the open position. This same interlock prevents the main-line knife switch from being accidentally closed while the cabinet doors are open. Such protection and safety are essential in modern crane practice.

SPEED-LOAD CURVES. The development of speed-load curves may be helpful in the analysis and understanding of the performance of crane control mechanisms. Typical examples of this type of curve are shown in Fig. 13.

Grab-Bucket Overhead Bridge Cranes

HANDLING OF BULK MATERIALS. Overhead grab-bucket cranes are widely used for handling materials such as coal, coke, cinders, ashes, sand, gravel, crushed stone, slag, mill scale, cement clinkers, cement ores, chemicals, fleshings,

Fig. 14. Overhead grab-bucket crane handling cement clinkers.

garbage, refuse, bones, shells, and wood chips (Fig. 14). These materials are bulky and generally are handled in considerable tonnage. High operating speeds are therefore quite essential. Hoisting speeds vary, depending upon the service of the crane, from about 150 ft. per min. to 450 ft. per min. Grab-bucket crane service is ordinarily the hardest of all crane work because the crane is called upon to operate continuously under full load over long periods of time. As distinguished from the standard hook crane for handling occasional loads, the grab-bucket crane is a production tool of the highest importance.

BUCKET CRANE COMPONENTS. A high-speed crane with a small bucket capacity is preferred to a slow-speed crane with a large bucket capacity. The saving is not only in the crane equipment itself but also in the runway supporting structure.

Buckets. Bucket selection is governed by the physical characteristics of the material to be handled, such as weight, moisture content, temperatures, and tendency to pack, and also by the type of container from which the material is unloaded and stored or into which it is reloaded for shipment. The most economical size of a suitable bucket depends on a variety of conditions, such as daily tonnage, average lift, and horizontal travel distance. These factors react directly on the rated capacity of the crane and the strength of the structure upon which it operates. A rational solution of these various problems can be based only on wide experience in this particular field of materials handling.

Trolley. The trolley for a grab-bucket crane consists of a hoisting mechanism using two independently operated units (Fig. 15) mounted on a common trolley frame, one for the holding line and one for the closing line, each unit consisting of a standard hoist gear train with motor, controller, and a braking medium.

Hoisting Mechanism. The hoist with the holding line is attached to the bucket proper by a crosshead or load bar, while the closing line is reeved directly to the bucket-operating mechanism for either the power-wheel or lever-operated type of bucket. In hoisting or lowering an open bucket, the holding unit carries all the load, the closing unit paying out or taking in slack cable. In

Fig. 15. Trolley mechanism for a grab-bucket crane.

hoisting or lowering loaded or closed bucket, the load is automatically distributed between the two, because the motors parallel themselves under load.

Since the bulk of material handled by bucket cranes is usually of a dusty nature, crane equipment is furnished with totally enclosed, preferably **fan-cooled motors** on these heavy-duty installations, providing more liberal motor ratings

Bridges. The design of bucket-crane bridges is determined by the total weight superimposed upon them. This weight is made up of the trolley, grab bucket, and the net load in the bucket. The latter two constitute the live load by which the crane is rated. As explained above, crane trolleys consist of two hoisting units generally arranged for carrying the live load suspended directly from the hoisting drums. Such trolleys, therefore, weigh about twice as much as a standard trolley for hook service. This fact explains why a 5-ton grab-bucket crane may require a 10-ton girder section. If it becomes necessary to suspend the operator's cab from the trolley in such a way that it overhangs the rear girder, the latter carries about two-thirds of the combined load, which further increases the girder section and weight.

The **general design of crane bridges** for grab-bucket cranes follows closely that of standard overhead traveling cranes. Due allowance is made for impact and the fact that on every trip the bucket crane is carrying the full load at a much higher speed and much more often than is the case with a standard industrial crane. The girder sections depend upon capacity and span. For smaller capacities and for the shorter spans, the rolled-section I-beams are most suitable, whereas the larger and heavier cranes are built with box-section girders.

End trucks and bridge-drive machinery are of the same type as those on hook-type cranes. On cranes of long span with high speeds, where a certain amount of vibration is unavoidable, bar conductors are preferable to span wires and are usually specified.

GRAB-BUCKET CRANE CAPACITY DETERMINATION. To determine how many tons of material a typical grab-bucket crane can handle in an 8-hr. day, a **typical duty cycle** for a typical crane will be reviewed. Assume that this crane has hoisting speeds of 180 ft. per min., a trolley speed of 210 ft. per min., and a bridge speed of 300 ft. per min. The bucket that was selected will handle a pay load of 4,000 lb. with each bite of the bucket. In the cycle in which this crane is to operate, the crane must hoist a distance of 60 in., the trolley must travel 35 ft., and the bridge 150 ft. Thirty feet of line is required to close the bucket. The bridge and trolley acceleration is calculated at 1.5 ft. per sec. per sec. Assume the bucket crane must handle 450 tons of material in an 8-hr. day.

HOIST CYCLE

Operation	Time	Distance
1. Accel. (hoist)	3 sec.	–
2. Close	10 sec.	30 ft.
3. Hoist	20 sec.	60 ft.
4. Dec.	3 sec.	–
5. Accel. (dump)	3 sec.	–
6. Dump	10 sec.	30 ft.
7. Dec.	3 sec.	–
8. Accel. (lower)	3 sec.	–
9. Lower	20 sec.	60 ft.
10. Dec.	3 sec.	–
	78 sec.	

Trolley Cycle

Operation	Time	Distance
Accel.	2.3 sec.	4 ft.*
Run (out)	7.7 sec.	27 ft.
Dec.	2.3 sec.	4 ft.
	12.3	35 ft.
Return	× 2	
	24.6 sec.	

Bridge Cycle

Operation	Time	Distance
Accel.	3.3 sec.	8 ft.*
Run (out)	26.8 sec.	134 ft.
Dec.	3.3 sec.	8 ft.
	33.4	150 ft.
Return	× 2	
	66.8 sec.	

* Average velocity is half the full speed, since initial velocity is zero; therefore, distance traveled = $\dfrac{\text{time} \times \text{speed in feet per second}}{2}$

The time to complete one cycle without overlap of any motions would be 78 + 24.6 + 66.8 = 169.4 sec. However, it is no problem to overlap the trolley cycle during the bridge cycle, and with efficient operation it is possible to perform hoist cycles 3, 4, 8, and 9 during the bridge cycle. Based on the above assumptions, the hoist-cycle time when the bridge is idle would be 32 sec. (78 sec. − 46 sec.), which, added to the time to complete a full bridge cycle, equals 98.8 sec. (32 + 66.8). This is the total time required to complete one full cycle of operation based on 100 percent efficiency. To allow for the human factor, it is advisable to add 25 percent; therefore, the total time is 124 sec., or 2.06 min. The crane is capable of completing 233 cycles in an 8-hr. shift (480 ÷ 2.06 = 233).

Since the bucket will have an average payload of 4,000 lb. with each bite, the crane will handle 932,000 lb., or 466 tons, of material in an 8-hr. day (233 × 4,000 ÷ 2,000 = 466).

PRECAUTIONS FOR A GRAB-BUCKET CRANE INSTALLATION.

If bins or hoppers are placed too close to the end of the runway or too close to the side of the building, the trolley or the bridge must hit the end stops when depositing material at these spots. This abrupt stop slows down the operation and may damage the crane and building structure. A typical clearance diagram with specifications is shown in Fig. 16.

In designing an incinerator, it is well to make the crane runway longer than the pit. This provision makes it unnecessary to swing or cast the bucket in order to clean up the ends of the pit, thereby preventing damage to the bucket as well as to the crane trolley itself.

It is necessary to provide **sufficient height to the building** to allow debris to hang from the lower lips of the bucket when depositing it into furnaces or hoppers. At least 3 ft. of clearance between the bucket and the top of the hopper is desirable.

Capacity (cu. yd.)	A Span	B	C	F	G	H	L	M	Maximum Load per Wheel	A.S.C.E. Rail (lb. per yd.)
1	40'	5'-6"	8¼"	12'-7"	4'-6"	3'-6"	9'	13'-8½"	19,000	60
	50'	5'-7"	8¼"	12'-7"	4'-6"	3'-6"	9'	13'-8½"	20,500	60
	60'	5'-10"	8¼"	12'-7"	4'-6"	3'-6"	9'	14'-9½"	22,000	60
	70'	5'-10"	8¼"	12'-7"	4'-6"	3'-6"	9'	14'-11½"	24,000	60
	80'	5'-10"	8¼"	12'-7"	4'-6"	3'-6"	9'	14'-11½"	26,000	60
1½	40'	5'-6"	8¼"	13'-1"	4'-6"	3'-6"	9'	13'-8½"	20,000	60
	50'	5'-7"	8¼"	13'-1"	4'-6"	3'-6"	9'	13'-8½"	21,500	60
	60'	5'-10"	8¼"	13'-1"	4'-6"	3'-6"	9'	14'-9½"	23,000	60
	70'	5'-10"	8¼"	13'-1"	4'-6"	3'-6"	9'	14'-11½"	25,000	60
	80'	5'-10"	8¼"	13'-1"	4'-6"	3'-6"	9'	14'-11½"	27,000	60
2	40'	6'-0"	8¼"	14'-3"	5'-0"	4'-0"	9'	13'-8½"	23,000	60
	50'	6'-1"	8¼"	14'-3"	5'-0"	4'-0"	9'	13'-8½"	25,000	60
	60'	6'-4"	8¼"	14'-3"	5'-0"	4'-0"	9'	14'-9½"	27,000	60
	70'	6'-4"	8¼"	14'-3"	5'-0"	4'-0"	9'	14'-11½"	29,000	60
	80'	6'-4"	8¼"	14'-3"	5'-0"	4'-0"	9'	14'-11½"	31,000	60
2½	40'	6'-0"	8¼"	14'-10"	5'-0"	4'-0"	9'	13'-8½"	24,000	60
	50'	6'-1"	8¼"	14'-10"	5'-0"	4'-0"	9'	13'-8½"	26,000	60
	60'	6'-4"	8¼"	14'-10"	5'-0"	4'-0"	9'	14'-9½"	28,000	60
	70'	6'-4"	8¼"	14'-10"	5'-0"	4'-0"	9'	14'-11½"	30,000	60
	80'	6'-5"	8½"	14'-10"	5'-0"	4'-0"	9'	15'-2"	32,000	60
3	40'	6'-0"	8¼"	15'-7"	5'-0"	4'-0"	9'	13'-8½"	26,000	60
	50'	6'-1"	8¼"	15'-7"	5'-0"	4'-0"	9'	13'-8½"	28,000	60
	60'	6'-4"	8¼"	15'-7"	5'-0"	4'-0"	9'	14'-9½"	30,000	60
	70'	6'-5"	8½"	15'-7"	5'-0"	4'-0"	9'	15'-2"	32,500	60
	80'	6'-5"	8½"	15'-7"	5'-0"	4'-0"	9'	15'-2"	35,000	60

Fig. 16a. Clearance specifications for grab-bucket cranes for material weighing 50 lb. per cu. ft.

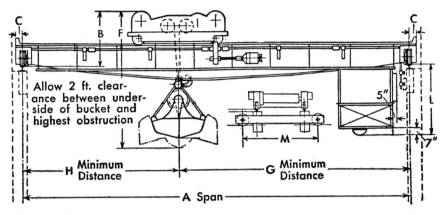

Fig. 16b. Clearance diagram for grab-bucket cranes for material weighing 50 lb. per cu. ft.

When designing the crane runway for a bucket installation, it is necessary that a **higher impact value** be calculated into the runway design. A production tool such as a grab-bucket crane is no better than the runway that supports it.

Crane Bids

EVALUATING CRANE BIDS. Overhead traveling electric cranes are not purchased on the same basis as small tools or automobiles, which have a life expectancy of only a few years. For cranes used in production, such as magnet cranes, bucket cranes, or cranes having a definite duty cycle to perform each day, the average **life expectancy is from 25 to 30 yr.** In some cases cranes have been in use for 40 to 60 yr.

Tabulation of bids and buying on a price per pound basis is no longer an acceptable way to negotiate the purchase of an overhead traveling crane. The modern crane—with welded instead of riveted girders, welded end trucks instead of cast and riveted end-truck construction, welded trolley sides instead of cast trolley sides, and welded drums instead of cast drums—has been designed to produce a crane having a **lower dead weight** than its predecessors. As an example, a 20-ton, 65-ft.-span crane built in the late 1920's weighed 73,000 lb. A duplicate of that crane, with the same lifting capacity, the same factor of safety, the same speeds—different only to the extent of such modern improvements as welded design—at the present time weighs only 61,400 lb. Yet this crane, which has to lift a 20-ton live load, itself weighs only about 30 tons. The trend has been to reduce the dead weight of the crane.

ANALYSIS PROCEDURES. Assume that there is under consideration the purchase of a 20-ton crane with a 5-ton auxiliary, 90-ft. span with a 35-ft. lift, to be used for machine-shop service, a standard industrial crane (Fig. 17). Assume also that the current supply available is 230 volts d.c. Hoist speeds for bidders A and B are identical. The horsepower on the hoist motors and the rating of the hoist motors are also identical. The computed horsepower required is identical for both bidders on the main and auxiliary. Some variation among manufacturers exists in the computing of hoist motors, particularly in the assumed efficiency of

	BIDDER A		BIDDER B	
GENERAL:				
1. Capacity	2% ton		2% ton	
2. Span	90'		90'	
3. Lift	35'		35'	
4. Total Net Weight	88,000 lb.		77,000 lb.	
HOISTS:	Main Hoist	Aux. Hoist	Main Hoist	Aux. Hoist
1. Hoist speed	25 F.P.M.	54 F.P.M.	25 F.P.M.	54 F.P.M.
2. Horsepower of hoist motor and rating	40 hp. 30 M.-55° C.	20 hp.	40 hp.	20 hp.
3. Computed horsepower required	39	19.7	39	19.7
4. Number and parts of rope	8 parts $5/8$"	4, $1/2$"	8, $9/16$"	4, $3/8$"
5. Type of wire rope	$6/19$ improved plow steel	$6/19$ improved plow steel	$6/19$ improved plow steel	$6/19$ improved plow steel
6. Diameter of hoist drum	20"	15"	15"	10"
7. Material in drum	Welded steel	Cast iron	Cast iron	Cast iron
8. Type of bearing	Hyatt roller	Hyatt roller	Hyatt roller	Hyatt roller
9. Make and type of gears and pinions	Spur gears, welded steel; forged-steel pinions	Spur gears, welded steel; forged-steel pinions	Spur gears, welded steel; forged-steel pinions	Spur gears, welded steel; forged-steel pinions
10. Material of gears and pinions	Gears SAE 8630, pinions SAE 8742; heat-treated, hardened	Gears SAE 8630, pinions SAE 8742; heat-treated, hardened	Gears SAE 1040, pinions SAE 1045	Gears SAE 1040, pinions SAE 1045
TROLLEY:				
1. Trolley speed	200 F.P.M.		125 F.P.M.	
2. Horsepower of trolley motor and rating	7.5 hp.		3 hp.	
3. Computed running horsepower required	3.5		1.96	
4. Service factor used	2.14 hp.		1.53 hp.	
5. Diameter of trolley wheels	$13\frac{1}{2}$"		12"	
6. Spread of trolley	8'		7'	
7. Type of bearings	Hyatt 5214		Hyatt 5212	
8. Make and type of gears and pinions	Welded spur gears, forged-steel pinions		Welded spur gears, forged-steel pinions	
9. Material of gears and pinions	Gears SAE 8630, pinions SAE 8742; heat-treated, hardened		Gears SAE 1040, Pinions SAE 1045	
10. Weight of trolley complete	18,400 lb.		13,000 lb.	
BRIDGE:				
1. Bridge speed	300 F.P.M.		300 F.P.M.	
2. Horsepower of bridge motor and rating	25 hp.		20 hp.	
3. Computed running horsepower required	8.85		8.75	
4. Service factor used	2.83 hp.		2.29 hp.	
5. Girder section at center of span	Top, $28 \times 3/4$"; Bottom, $28 \times 1/2$"; webs, $60 \times 1/4$"		Top, $28 \times 5/8$"; Bottom, $28 \times 3/8$"; webs, $54 \times 5/16$"	
6. Number and diameter of bridge wheels	4, 24"		4, 21"	
7. Maximum wheel load	50,600 lb.		44,000 lb.	
8. Wheel base	13'8"		12'3"	
ELECTRICAL:				
Control—				
1. Make and type of hoist control	Semimagnetic drum		Drum control	
2. Make and type of auxiliary hoist control	Semimagnetic drum		Drum control	
3. Make and type of hoist limit switches	Motor circuit		Control circuit	
4. Make and type of trolley control	Drum		Drum	
5. Make and type of bridge control	Drum		Drum	
6. Make and type of overload protection	Overload relays		Fuses	

Fig. 17. Bid analysis comparison sheet.

the gear train and the efficiency of the ropes and sheaves. No great variation should exist, but in some cases it may fall within the difference between one motor rating and another. In all cases it is advisable to overmotor the crane in the hoist motion rather than to undermotor it.

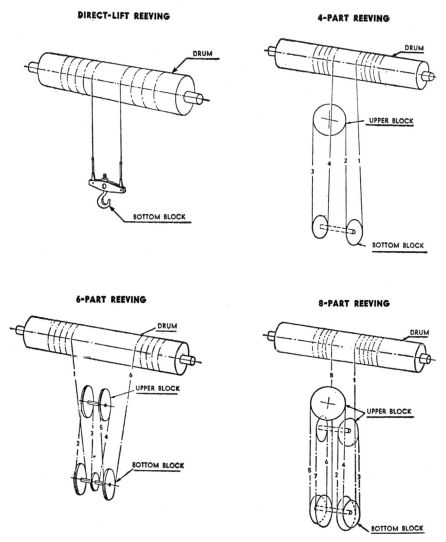

DIRECT-LIFT REEVING

4-PART REEVING

6-PART REEVING

8-PART REEVING

Fig. 18. Typical cable reeving diagrams for overhead traveling cranes.

Cable. On the next item, number and parts of rope, bidder A on his **main hoist** has provided 8 parts of ⅝-in. rope (See Fig. 18). The ⅝-in. cable is rated by the cable manufacturers as being sufficient to hold 16.6 tons. This weight multiplied by 8 parts of rope and divided by a safety factor of 5, equals 26.6 tons allowed weight. This is sufficient, since the rated capacity required is only 20 tons. Bidder B is using 8 parts of $\%_{16}$-in. rope. This rope is rated at 13.5 tons, which, multiplied by 8 parts of rope and divided by a safety factor of 5, gives an allowed tonnage of 21.6, which is just within the safety factor of 5. Checking back, then, it is found that on the main hoist, bidder A has actually a factor of safety of 6 on the ropes, in comparison with a factor of 5 for bidder B. On the **auxiliary hoist,** bidder A has specified that he is using 4 parts of $\frac{1}{2}$-in. rope. This rope is good for 10.8 tons. Multiplying by 4 parts of rope and dividing by 5 gives a tonnage on this particular reeving of 8.64. Bidder B has used $\frac{3}{8}$-in. rope, which has a tonnage of 6.3 per rope. Multiplying by 4 parts of rope and dividing by 5 gives a tonnage of 5.04. Therefore, it is clear that bidder A has a safety factor of better than 8 on the auxiliary hoist ropes, whereas bidder B has a factor of only 5. Both bidders have specified $\%_{19}$ improved plow steel rope.

Hoisting Drums. Item 6 is a vital point in the analysis. Hoisting drums should be equal in diameter to at least 30 rope diameters. The $\frac{5}{8}$-in. rope specified for the main hoist by bidder A means that a minimum drum diameter of $18\frac{3}{4}$ in. is required; therefore, the 20-in. drum that is specified exceeds the 30 minimum rope requirement. Bidder B has specified a 15-in. drum and a $\%_{16}$-in. rope. However, multiplying 30 by $\%_{16}$ shows that the minimum drum diameter should be 16.87 in. Therefore, the 15-in. drum which bidder B has specified is less than 27 times the rope diameter. Moreover, on the main hoist, it clearly indicates that bidder A, from a standpoint of rope size and safety factor, is providing more crane than bidder B.

On the auxiliary hoist, bidder A has provided $\frac{1}{2}$-in. rope, which requires a 15-in. diameter drum, and he has specified it; therefore, the requirement to provide 30 rope diameters has been met. Bidder B has specified $\frac{3}{8}$-in. rope, which means that a minimum diameter of 11.25 in. is required for 30 rope diameters, and the 10-in. drum which he has specified is less than 27 times the rope diameter.

In Item 7, **hoist drum material,** we find that bidder A has specified a welded-steel drum for the main hoist and a cast-iron drum for the auxiliary hoist. Bidder B has indicated that a cast-iron drum is supplied for both the main and auxiliary hoists. The welded-steel drum that bidder A has specified is clearly a better mechanical unit than the cast-iron drum specified by bidder B. This is because of the solid steel plate material under the rope grooves, requiring less material under these grooves than is normally required on a cast-iron drum, providing a lighter-weight and certainly a stronger drum.

On Item 8, both bidders have specified **roller bearings** on the hoist gear train. On Item 9, both bidders have specified welded-steel spur gears and forged-steel pinions. However, under Item 10, the material of the **gears** and **pinions** provided by bidder A is SAE-8630 for the gears and SAE-8742 for the pinions. This is a nickel-alloy steel, and with the heat treatment specified, it provides a tough, hard-wearing surface and a long-wearing gear. Bidder B has stated that he uses SAE-1040 for the gears and SAE-1045 for the pinions. This is a high-carbon steel and is a good gear but does not compare in quality with the nickel-alloy steel gear provided by bidder A.

Trolley. For the **trolley speed,** bidder A has specified 200 ft. per min. This is more in line for a 90-ft. span crane than the 125 ft. per min. specified by bidder B. Bidder A's trolley would travel across the bridge in approximately 27 sec., whereas bidder B's would require approximately 43 sec. to travel the full 90 ft.

From an analysis of Items 2, 3, and 4 together, it is found that bidder A has a $7\frac{1}{2}$-hp. motor, naturally larger because of the higher trolley speed. The computed running horsepower is 3.5 and the service factor is 2.14, compared with the 3-hp. motor for bidder B, requiring 1.96 running horsepower and providing a factor of only 1.52, which is entirely inadequate for satisfactory acceleration of the trolley motor.

Under Item 5, diameter of the **trolley wheels**, bidder A has provided trolley wheels 13½ in. in diameter in comparison with bidder B's 12-in. wheels. This again indicates that bidder B has figured on a smaller trolley than bidder A. The size of the trolley wheel with its bearings is determined in a manner similar to that given for bridge truck wheels.

Under Item 6, the **spread of the trolley** for bidder A is 8 ft. and for bidder B it is 7 ft. This spread is determined principally by the lift required and the amount of cable that has to be piled on the drum. Therefore, 8 parts of ⅝-in. cable will take more space or winding capacity on the drum than 8 parts of ⁹⁄₁₆-in. cable.

On Items 7 and 8 both bidders have specified essentially comparable items. On Item 9, material of gears and pinions, bidder A has specified the same type of gearing that is in the hoist gear train, namely, nickel-alloy steel SAE-8630 and SAE-8742, as against the high-carbon steel SAE-1040 and SAE-1045 specified by bidder B.

Bidder A has a heavier complete trolley. A summation of the features of the trolley shows that bidder A has provided a larger trolley pattern based upon 30 rope diameters for the hoisting drum and has a larger factor of safety in the hoisting cables than bidder B. He has also provided a higher trolley speed, and therefore the crane will be relatively faster in handling material.

Bridge. Under the bridge specifications the **bridge speed** for both bidders is 300 ft. per min. In considering the horsepower of the **bridge motor**, Items 2, 3, and 4 should be taken together. Bidder A has provided a 25-hp. motor and computed the running horsepower at 8.85, providing a service factor of 2.83. Bidder B, with a 20-hp. motor, has a computed running horsepower of 8.75 and has a service factor of only 2.28. The higher bridge motor factor used by bidder A is definitely an advantage.

Under Item 5, the **girder section** at the center of span, bidder A has provided ¼-in. web plates 60 in. in depth and has cover plates 28 in. by ¾ in. for the top and 28 in. by ½ in. for the bottom. Bidder B has provided web plates 54 in. deep and ⁵⁄₁₆ in. thick. The cover plates are 28 in. by ⅝ in. and 28 in. by ⅜ in. The thicker cover plates of bidder A give his unit a definite advantage in that respect. The **minimum depth of web plates** at the center of span should not be less than ⅛ of the width of the span. By this rule, the span involved would require web plates with a minimum depth of 60 in. Therefore, bidder A, although he has thinner web plates, has provided sufficient depth to the girder. Although bidder B may have just as strong a girder, because of the ⁵⁄₁₆ in. thickness of web plates, he has provided more dead weight in the girder than is necessary. This dead weight does not add any strength. His depth at the center of span is less than the one-eighteenth rule-of-thumb requirement.

Under Item 6, bidder A has provided four 24-in. **truck wheels**, against bidder B's four 21-in. truck wheels. A 24-in. truck wheel will have more service life and greater **bearing life hours** built into its corresponding drive parts than the 21-in. wheels and drive parts of bidder B. However, the crane builder should submit the bearing life hours, either in average life hours or in the B-10 rating which is now being widely adopted. This would give definite proof of the life expectancy of the bridge truck bearing.

Item **7** is a very important factor in the bearing life hours of truck wheels. Bidder A has shown a **maximum wheel load** of 50,600 lb., against bidder B's 44,000 lb. Maximum wheel load means that the crane trolley will be at its closest approach toward the crane runway and have a 20-ton load suspended from its hook. Under normal conditions, the cage corner or the corner of the crane where the cage is suspended will have the maximum wheel load. On this corner is concentrated the weight of the cage with its control apparatus in addition to the weight of the trolley and its load.

If the crane has full magnetic control mounted on the platform, this also must be included in the wheel reaction at the cage corner, since the concentrated weight of full magnetic control mounted on the platform will materially affect the maximum wheel load. Since wheel loads and their methods of calculation differ among various crane builders, it is well for a buyer to use the heaviest wheel load specified in order to be on the safe side. A crane is no better than the **runway** that supports it, and if the runway is designed too lightly on the basis of a low wheel load, it will not remain in good alignment. A runway that does not keep in good alignment will require constant maintenance to the crane itself.

Under Item 8 of the bridge, the **wheelbase** specified by bidder A is 13 ft. 8 in., and that specified by bidder B is 12 ft. 3 in. The rule-of-thumb ratio of wheelbase to span should be a minimum of 1 to **7**. According to this ratio, a 90-ft. span would require an approximate minimum wheelbase of 12 ft. 9 in. $(90 \div 7)$, and therefore bidder A has exceeded this minimum requirement, while bidder B is somewhat under it. The reason for this rule of thumb is to provide squaring action for the crane itself. If the wheelbase is too short for the span, the squaring action of the crane and its ability to run straight down the runway will be greatly impaired.

Bidder A has met or exceeded minimum requirements. Bidder B has not met these minimum standards. Therefore the bridge as supplied by bidder A is superior to that supplied by bidder B.

Electrical Equipment. In regard to electrical equipment, bidder A indicates that the type of main **hoist control** is of the semimagnetic drum type, while bidder B specifies drum control. Bidder A therefore indicates that the power circuit to the motor is made and broken by a magnetic contactor rather than by the drum controller itself. This would definitely require less maintenance and would certainly justify a greater initial cost. The auxiliary hoist control is indicated to be the same as the main hoist. The same reasoning would favor the semimagnetic control over the plain drum control of bidder B. The **hoist-limit switch** specified by bidder A is of the motor-circuit type, while bidder B specifies the control-circuit type. This would indicate that bidder A has provided a limit switch which is direct acting by the bottom block and opens the motor circuits by such action, whereas bidder B has a control-circuit limit switch which is direct acting by the bottom block and opens the limit-switch contactor coil circuit, which in turn will open the main motor circuit. Bidder A's motor-circuit limit switch would definitely be more reliable.

The **trolley control** is specified as drum type by both bidders, as is the type of bridge control. The type of overload protection specified by bidder A has overload relays, as against the fuses specified by bidder B. Definitely, bidder A has provided more and better material than bidder B. **Overload relays** are positive in action and do not require replacement of fuse links or fuses themselves. From the safety angle, the advantages of overload relays over fuses for a crane-protective panel are obvious. If an overload occurs, one should definitely trace the cause of it rather than replace the fuse with one of larger capacity. The **crane-overload protection panel** is provided for the protection of the crane operator and the crane owner.

Summary. The highlights of the tabulation are (1) for the hoist, compare the rope diameter with the safety factor and the rope diameter to the drum diameter; (2) for the bridge, the size of bridge wheels determines to a great extent the bearing life hours of the truck axle. The depth of girder section at the center should not be less than ⅟₁₈ of the span, and the ratio of the wheelbase to the span should be a minimum of 1 to 7.

Design and Installation of Overhead Bridge Cranes

FORMULAS FOR CHECKING CRANE DESIGN. The following formulas and data are helpful in checking crane design.

Hoist Motor Hp.

$$\text{Hp.} = \frac{\text{Load in lb.} \times \text{speed in ft. per min.}}{\text{Efficiency} \times 33{,}000}$$

Efficiency Roller Bearing Crane Between Motor Pinion and Load

86 percent for direct lift	76 percent for 10 parts cable reeving
83 percent for 4 parts cable reeving	74 percent for 12 parts cable reeving
81 percent for 6 parts cable reeving	71 percent for 14 parts cable reeving
78 percent for 8 parts cable reeving	69 percent for 16 parts cable reeving

Bridge or Trolley Motor

$$\text{Travel resistance} = \frac{d \times GF \times BF \times (W \times L)}{D}$$

$$\text{Running hp.} = \frac{\text{Tr.} \times \text{Speed in ft. per min.}}{33{,}000}$$

Motor hp $=$ Running hp. $\times$ Acceleration ratio

d = Pitch diam. of rollers in truck
GF = Gear friction = 1.05 for each reduction
BF = Bearing friction = 0.030 for roller bearing
W = Total weight of trolley or crane
L = Live load or capacity of crane
D = Tread diam. of truck wheel
Acceleration ratio, see Fig. 13

$$\text{Full load motor torque} = \frac{\text{Hp. of motor} \times 5{,}250}{\text{R.P.M. of motor}}$$

Girder checks: Depth of girder should be not less than ⅟₁₈ of span.
Span in inches: Distance between web plates in inches—not to exceed 55.
Ratio of wheelbase to span: Not to exceed 1:7.

CRANE RUNWAYS. A properly constructed runway must be provided and maintained. The runway **rails** must be of satisfactory size for the wheel loads and not less than the size recommended by the crane builder. The rails should be of the correct **span**, center to center, throughout their entire length, with both rails level and of even elevation. A correct span should not vary by more than ⅛ in., plus or minus, in the center-to-center measurements or be out of a straight line in the runway length. The runway must be of sufficient **strength** to avoid undue vertical deflection between columns and should be supported sideways to withstand the starting and stopping of the trolley with load. A poorly constructed runway is a continual source of trouble and the cause of excessive wear on truck wheels.

RUNWAY DESIGN. So that a runway may be designed satisfactorily for the crane which it supports, impact and lateral and longitudinal loads on crane runways should be computed according to the following instructions.

To calculate **impact values** for the runway of a standard hook crane it is assumed that the trolley is in position to produce maximum bridge-wheel loads. The **impact load** on the bridge will be considered as 0.5 percent of the maximum hook load for each foot per minute of the full-load hoist speed. This load will be distributed on the runway according to the position of the hook in relation to the runway rails.

For example, 20-ton crane: span 55 ft.; speed of hook, 60 ft. per min.; position of hook, 2 ft. 6 in. from runway rail; max. static wheel load, 38,000 lb.

$$0.5 \times 60 \text{ f.p.m.} = 30 \text{ percent * impact}$$

$$\text{Hook load of 40,000 lb.} \times 30 \text{ percent} = 12,000 \text{ lb. impact on bridge}$$

$$\frac{12,000 \times 52 \text{ ft. 5 in.}}{55 \text{ ft.}} = 11,450 \text{ lb. total impact on runway}$$

$$\frac{11,450}{2} = 5,725 \text{ lb. impact per wheel (for a 4-wheel crane)}$$

$$\begin{array}{r} 5,725\text{-lb. impact} \\ 38,000\text{-lb. static wheel load} \\ \hline 43,725\text{-lb. total wheel load} \end{array}$$

$\dfrac{43,725}{38,000} = 1.15$ percent = Increase in bridge-wheel load for impact on runway. (This value not to be less than 1.10 percent of the maximum bridge-wheel load.)

* Impact load of 0.5 percent for each foot per minute of the full load hoist speed, but not to exceed 50 percent or to be less than 20 percent of the main hook load.

For bucket and magnet cranes the amount of impact on the bridge shall be 50 percent of the live load (trolley considered dead load). This impact load is distributed on the runway according to the position of the bucket or magnet in relation to the runway rails.

Lateral load on runway due to trolley movement = 10 percent of the weight of the trolley with full load (75 percent of this lateral load on one runway). This load is resisted by the top flange of the runway.

Longitudinal load on runway due to bridge movement = 10 percent of the maximum bridge-wheel load on one runway.

CONDUCTORS. Fig. 19 gives the recommended current capacities of figure-8 copper wire when used on crane runways.

METHOD OF DETERMINING SIZE OF MOTOR GENERATOR SET REQUIRED. Fig. 20 lists the generator rating necessary in kilowatts expressed in terms of the horsepower of the crane motor, according to the number of cranes in operating service.

The motor-generator rating is expressed in kw. and is a certain percentage of the total hp. capacity of all motors. For example, an installation of five cranes of 200-hp. total motor equipment would require a motor-generator set of $200 \times 0.40 = 80$-kw. capacity.

The rating of the generator should be based on a temperature rise of 50° C. under continuous operation under full load. The set should be capable of sustaining overloads of 100 percent for 1 min. without exceeding the maximum torque of the motor and without undue sparking at the generator.

AMPERE CAPACITY AT 220 VOLTS

For 440 Volts Use Current in Column Under One-half the Length of Runway

Kind of Power	Size of Wire	LENGTH OF RUNWAY IN FEET*																
		50	75	100	125	150	175	200	225	250	300	350	400	450	500	550	600	700
AMPS. D.C.	0	325	315	300	270	220	190	170	150	130	110	95	85	75	65	60	55	46
	00	413	400	380	330	280	240	210	188	170	150	120	105	95	85	78	70	64
	000	534	526	520	416	348	320	267	238	214	178	155	133	120	108	98	89	75
	0000	674	664	650	520	440	380	337	300	270	225	192	168	150	135	120	110	95
AMPS. A.C. 60 CYCLE	0	255	248	236	210	173	150	134	112	102	87	75	67	59	51	47	43	37
	00	288	277	264	229	194	166	145	129	118	104	84	73	65	59	54	48	44
	000	295	292	288	250	210	193	161	143	130	107	93	80	72	65	59	53	46
	0000	347	332	325	275	230	200	177	158	142	120	100	89	79	71	63	58	50
AMPS. A.C. 25 CYCLE	0'	325	315	305	285	230	200	190	159	137	115	100	90	79	68	63	58	48
	00	413	400	380	330	280	240	210	188	170	150	120	105	95	85	78	70	64
	000	510	505	500	400	330	305	258	230	205	170	149	128	115	104	95	86	72
	0000	555	545	535	430	360	310	277	246	222	185	157	138	123	110	100	90	78

* Length of runway refers to the distance from feeders to end of line.

A

AMPERES PER H p.		
Current	Volts	Amps.
D. C.	115	8
	230	4
Three Phase	220	3
	440	1.5
	550	1.2
Two Phase	220	2.6
	440	1.3
	550	1.1

Cranes Per Runway	Multiplying Factor
1	1
2	0.95
3	0.91
4	0.87
5	0.84

B

C

To find the proper size of conductor: The sum of all the hoist hp. + ½ the sum of all the bridge hp. will be the estimated maximum hp. demand.

Max hp. × amps. per hp. (from Fig. 19b) = max. ampere demand.

Max. amps. × multiplying factor (from Fig. 19c) = max. load on wire. Using this value, determine the size of wire by means of Fig. 19a. Example: Max. amps. are 200, to find the wire size for 175-ft. runway, feed at center, 220 volts a.c., 60 cyc. Center feed makes the effective length 88 ft. In the 100-ft. column—60-cyc. section, the value next in size above 200 is 236. The wire to be used for these conditions is No. 0.

Fig. 19. Recommended capacities of figure-8 copper wire when used on crane runways.

Number of Cranes	Generator Rating Expressed in Kw. in Percentage of the Crane Motor Hp.
1	120 percent of largest motor
2	60 percent of all motors
3	48 percent of all motors
4	42 percent of all motors
5	40 percent of all motors
6	38 percent of all motors
8	35 percent of all motors
10	33 percent of all motors
12	32 percent of all motors
15	31 percent of all motors
20	30 percent of all motors
30	28 percent of all motors

Fig. 20. Required size of motor generator set.

CRANE RAIL END CHOCKS. Since most cranes today are of the anti-friction-bearing type in bridge truck axles, provision must be made for the elimination of shock loads on the bearings so as to provide maximum bearing life. The use of crane-runway rail chocks for roller bearings of a type that contacts the structural frame of the end truck rather than the wheel is therefore recommended. The illustrations in Fig. 21 suggest designs, but variations in runway

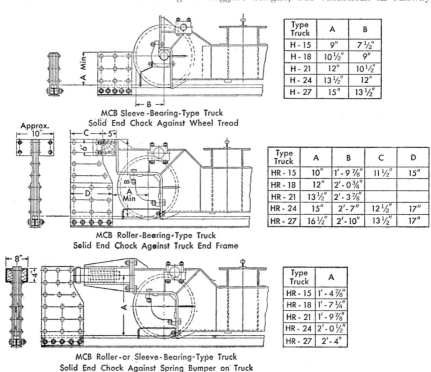

MCB Sleeve-Bearing-Type Truck
Solid End Chock Against Wheel Tread

Type Truck	A	B
H-15	9"	7½"
H-18	10½"	9"
H-21	12"	10½"
H-24	13½"	12"
H-27	15"	13½"

MCB Roller-Bearing-Type Truck
Solid End Chock Against Truck End Frame

Type Truck	A	B	C	D
HR-15	10"	1'-9⅞"	11½"	15"
HR-18	12"	2'-0¾"		
HR-21	13½"	2'-3⅞"		
HR-24	15"	2'-7"	12½"	17"
HR-27	16½"	2'-10"	13½"	17"

MCB Roller-or Sleeve-Bearing-Type Truck
Solid End Chock Against Spring Bumper on Truck

Type Truck	A
HR-15	1'-4⅞"
HR-18	1'-7¼"
HR-21	1'-9⅞"
HR-24	2'-0½"
HR-27	2'-4"

Fig. 21. Runway rail chocks for overhead traveling cranes.

construction, different types of end-truck construction, crane bridge clearances, and bridge speeds may necessitate extreme variations in the actual details in connection with a specific application. It is impractical to design end chocks that will not shear off when struck with the full speed of the crane bridge with the full load on the crane hook. Therefore, it is customary to design these end chocks to withstand half load on the crane hook and half speed for the bridge drive.

For sleeve-bearing bridge truck-wheel axles, a **solid-type chock**, rigidly connected to the runway girder and contacting the truck wheel tread, is adequate and simple to apply. For roller-bearing cranes, a solid chock rigidly attached to the crane runway girder and contacting a solid block on the end truck, or a spring bumper so mounted, is desirable. A **spring-type chock** attached to the crane runway girder contacting the end-truck frame is also one of the approved methods.

On account of the variations mentioned above which must be considered in each installation, it is recommended that detailed dimensional data be obtained for the specific crane so as to avoid error in application.

The same general recommendations apply to the use of **bumpers** between cranes. However, on account of the speed and motion of the crane bridges, spring bumpers afford the best protection, and the additional cost is slight compared with the added protection obtained.

TAPER-TREAD CRANE WHEELS. The use of taper treads on the drive wheels of a crane bridge eliminates flange wear and breakage by automatically positioning the crane on the runway to avoid wheel flange contact with the rail.

General practice prescribes a taper of $\frac{3}{4}$ in. per ft., with the large diameter of each drive wheel assembled on the inside of the runway rail. The difference in tread diameter for $\frac{1}{8}$-in. side movement of contact is then approximately 0.05 in. When the span dimension is held, the above dimension applies to both drives, giving a resultant 0.1-in. variation in wheel-tread circumferences. It is obvious that if one wheel tread is operating at a large diameter, that side of the crane will travel ahead of the other in proportion to the above dimensions and will tend to skew the crane on the runway. An appreciable movement of the crane as it skews will cause the wheel of the large diameter to travel laterally away from the rail and toward a decreased diameter. Meanwhile, on the driven wheel at the other truck, the opposite motion has taken place and the contact has moved from a small to a larger diameter.

Thus the ultimate action of the taper-tread wheel is to run at a **common speed at both ends of the crane** and at a contact of common diameter. If the width of the wheel tread has sufficient clearance over the railhead width to take up all span variations, the wheel flanges will never come in contact with the railhead. It is, therefore, absolutely necessary when using taper-tread wheels, to allow as much as practical for span variations, generally from 1 in. up to 50 percent more than the railhead width. The above allowance results in a wider truck build-up, and, as the crane operates within the above figures for span variation, the crane end clearance must also be increased for these two variations.

To accomplish the desired results, the taper tread feature must be maintained for the duration of the crane's working life. This may be done by the use of long-service-type wheels on the original installation, or by refinishing the wearing wheels to maintain alignment. Truck wheels with hardened treads are recommended for their greater wearing qualities.

The taper-tread action exerts practically a continuous thrust on the inside truck-axle bearing. The taper gives a thrust loading of approximately 6.25 percent of the wheel load; hence the necessary bearing area and a suitable means for wheel lubrication must be provided. This thrust reaction, of course, is transmitted through the rail. Rail wear is localized on the inside surface of the railhead. The rail wear and rail load reaction are two factors necessitating straight treads on the idler wheels. The idler wheels have no influence in maintaining the taper-tread action.

Other Factors in Taper-Tread Wheel Design. Other factors must be considered in the design of the runway and the bridge truck. The size of the runway rail and the diameter of the truck wheels should be selected with regard to crane speed and wheel load. Modern high-speed (above 500 ft. per min.) antifriction-bearing cranes should have the permissible wheel loading reduced to allow for slippage and skidding of the wheels under rapid starting and stopping conditions. The **wheel loads** should be held at 25 to 50 percent of the permissible maximum loading conditions. Crane capacity should be obtained by using a larger number

Location _____ Crane No. _____ Date _____

What Condition found using Key.

KEY: OK, Good, Fair, Worn Badly, Attention, Change, Loose, Tight, Dirty, Clean, Adjust, Tension, Burned, Bent

Motor Parts	Amature	Commutator	Field	Brushes	B. Holders	Bearing	Grease Oil	Rotor	Stator	Gears Pinions
Bridge Motor										
Hoist Motor										
Aux. Hoist Motor										
Rack Motor										

Controller Parts	Brushes	B. Holders	Finger	Contacts	Levers	Resistance	Bolts	Wiring
Bridge Controller								
Hoist Controller								
Aux. Hoist Controller								
Rack Controller								

Knife Switches	Bridge Track Wheels	End Tracks
Limit Switches	Trolley Track Wheels	Gear Guards
Safety Switches	Bridge Axle Bushing	Cage
Fuse Clips	Trolley Axle Bushing	Bolts and Rivets
Relays	Traverse Bushing	Railings
Electric Brake	Bearing (not motor)	Walks
Mech. Brake	Drums	Sanders
Foot Brake	Drum Gear	Bumpers
Main Collector Shoes	Drum Pinion	Windows
Trolley Collector Shoes	Bridge Gear	Ladders
Conductor Rails	Trolley Travel Gear	Gen. Wiring
Trolley Wires	Intermediate Gear	Stairways
Cables	Traverse Shaft	Grease Cups
Bottom Blocks	Main Hoist Shaft	Crane Alignment
Top Blocks	Aux. Hoist Shaft	

For Additional Remarks, Use Reverse Side

Remarks:

_____

_____

_____

_____

_____

_____

_____

_____

_____

_____

_____

_____

_____

_____

_____

Inspected by _____

Harnischfeger Corp.

Fig. 22. Crane inspection report.

CRANE MAINTENANCE RECORD

INVENTORY NO. _____ MFG. SERIAL NO. _____ PURCHASE DATE _____ LOCATION _____ NEXT WORK PERIOD

JAN.	FEB.	MAR.	APR.	MAY	JUNE	JULY	AUG.	SEP.	OCT.	NOV.	DEC.

CRANE SPECIFICATIONS

MAKE _____ CAPACITY _____ MAIN HOIST _____ AUX. HOIST SPAN _____ LIFT _____ VOLTAGE _____ CLEARANCE SK. _____

	WHEEL DIAM. & TYPE	RUNWAY LENGTH	WEIGHT OF GIRDERS	WEIGHT END TRUCKS		SPEEDS			WHEEL DIAM. & TYPE	CABLE SIZE-LENGTH & TYPE		WEIGHT OF TROLLEY	WEIGHT OF CAB
SPEED						MAIN HOIST	AUX. HOIST	TROLLEY		MAIN HOIST	AUX. HOIST		
BRIDGE				TROLLEY									

ELECTRICAL DATA

MOTORS

MOTION	Type	Hp. & Speed	Mfg. Ser. No.	Mfg. Cat. No.
MAIN HOIST				
AUX. HOIST				
TROLLEY				
BRIDGE				

BRAKES

Size	Mfg. Ser. No.	Mfg. Cat. No.

CONTROL

Type	Mfg. Ser. No.	Mfg. Cat. No.	Wiring Diag.

RESISTOR

Type	Mfg. Ser. No.	Mfg. Cat. No.	Conn. Diag.

REMARKS:

MAINTENANCE COST RECORD

DATE	MECHANICAL				DATE	ELECTRICAL			
	DESCRIPTION OF WORK DONE	MATERIAL	LABOR	TOTAL		DESCRIPTION OF WORK DONE	MATERIAL	LABOR	TOTAL

Fig. 23. Crane maintenance record.

of truck wheels to obtain the required service loading and not by highly loaded, large-diameter wheels and heavy-section runway rails.

In using taper-tread wheels on crane bridge drives, a **runway conductor system** should be installed that will operate under the increased lateral movement of the bridge end truck without causing interference or excessive wear. This precaution is especially important in applying the taper-tread wheels to existing installations. Also, methods must be provided to keep the runway rails straight and in span with the tread clearance allowed.

The taper-tread wheel is not a cure-all, but it tends to reduce flange wear under both normal and misaligned runway conditions. Maintaining the proper runway conditions and keeping crane wheels of proper diameter on straight-tread design will still offer the best operating buildup for ordinary service installations.

When taper-tread wheels are specified for industrial-type cranes, they are furnished with a taper of 1 in. in 20 in. as standard. This taper provides adequate squaring action on the runway and allows a larger contact area between wheel and rail, with a decrease in the eccentricity of the load on the rail. The taper slightly reduces the pressure on the thrust washer and is especially desirable on stationary-pin-type trucks. On mill-type cranes, wheels with a taper of 1 in. in 16 in. are furnished, unless otherwise requested by the customer.

ERECTION OF AN OVERHEAD TRAVELING CRANE. All cranes, after receiving a light-load running test in the crane manufacturer's shop, are dismantled for shipment. Parts that can be shipped in one piece within the permissible shipping limits of the rail carrier are not dismantled. All parts of the crane are usually **matchmarked to facilitate handling in erection** with the least amount of time and expense. Most crane manufacturers provide the crane purchaser with a matchmarking diagram to facilitate the identification of the crane assembly and the proper field connections. The electrical connections are also broken and dismantled from the crane proper, to be replaced when the crane is erected at its final location.

CRANE MAINTENANCE. The care and operation of electric overhead-traveling cranes should be carried on in the same manner in which one would take care of a machine tool. **Preventive maintenance** cannot be overly stressed. The performance of an overhead traveling crane will be no better than the maintenance provided for it. Proper lubrication and systematic inspection of the electrical equipment, motors, brakes, and control are of major importance.

Many crane users have **systematic crane inspections,** and some require reports by the crane operator at the end of each operator's shift. A typical crane inspection report is given in Fig. 22. It is also well to keep a record of **crane-maintenance costs.** On this crane-maintenance cost-record card should be pertinent data concerning each and every crane, for ready reference and for ease in ordering repair parts. Good housekeeping demands that records be kept of crane maintenance (Fig. 23) in order that the user may detect troublesome items so that these can be quickly corrected.

Traveling Gantry Cranes

TYPES OF TRAVELING GANTRY CRANES. This type of crane is somewhat similar to the overhead traveling bridge crane, except that either one or both ends of the bridge girders are supported by an A-frame, which operates on a runway, usually flush with the ground (Figs. 24 and 25). When only one

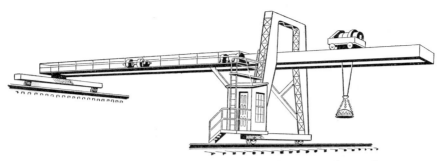

Fig. 24. Double-girder semigantry crane with toprunning trolley.

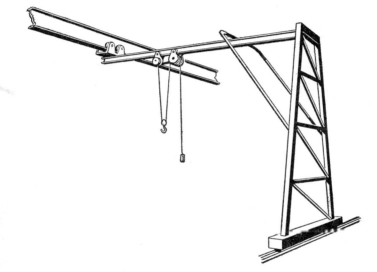

Fig. 25. Single-girder semigantry push crane with underrunning trolley and motorized hoist.

end of the bridge girders is supported by an A-frame, the crane is classified as semigantry. In addition, either one or both ends of the bridge girders may be cantilevered beyond the supporting A-frame (as shown in Fig. 26), a feature not possible in overhead traveling bridge cranes. Either one or both of the cantilevered bridge girder extensions may be hinged, which is desirable when the crane operates on a pier or dock and is used for loading or unloading ships.

The construction of these cranes is similar to that of overhead trolley bridge cranes, and they are equipped with the same type of trolleys. The bridge travel speed, however, is usually under 100 ft. per min.; otherwise the spans, capacities, and speeds are the same.

The most widely used kind of gantry crane is the **cantilever type.** This crane receives its name from its cantilevered extensions, which are at either or both ends of the bridge, extending out over the loading and unloading zone at such distances as are consistent with the crane ability to balance full loads when the trolley is in the extreme end positions. These cranes are necessarily built in

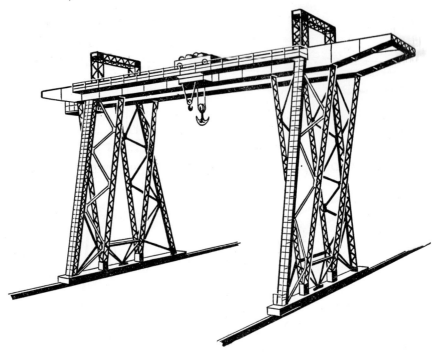

Fig. 26. Double-girder, motor-driven, cantilever-type gantry crane.

accordance with the requirements of each particular installation. They combine the advantages of the three motions of an overhead traveling bridge crane, plus the ability to run the trolley beyond the part of the runway which is between the vertical supports.

A **hand-operated gantry** crane is useful when light loads are to be handled only occasionally. It usually is constructed of light structural steel and consists of a single I-beam girder carried on two A-frames which are mounted on two wheels that operate on bearings of the bushed-pin-and-keeper type. The push-type gantry is mounted on rails and is pushed along the track by hand. A hand-operated chain trolley and hoist are generally used on this kind of crane. The cranes are usually built in capacities up to about 10 tons and have a span of 25 to 30 ft. **Electrically operated gantry cranes** range in span up to about 200 ft. and in capacity up to 75 tons. They may be equipped with a hook for general lifting purposes, with a magnet for handling ferrous metals, or with a bucket to handle coal, ore, or other loose materials. Operation is controlled from a cab mounted either on the bridge or on the trolley.

TRAVELING PORTAL GANTRY CRANES. These cranes are of two types, in one of which the crane portion is fixed with relation to the gantry, while in the other the crane portion revolves. The **revolving-type crane** is mounted on a system of live rollers or trucks, or on a pintle bearing, with a full 360° swing. Swinging is accomplished by rack and pinion, with the rack mounted on the stationary portion and the pinion mounted on the revolving portion. The swing unit may have power take-off from the main power source or may be separately powered.

Luffing, hoisting, and racking units may be driven from a single power source or may be separately powered. Power may be supplied by an electric motor, a steam engine, diesel engine, or gasoline engine or by a diesel-electric, gas-electric, or hydraulic unit.

The gantry is of the height required by vertical hook travel or clearance under the machinery cab or jib. An open portal, or semiportal, which provides clearance for railroad cars, trucks, conveyors, or hoppers, or spans other obstructions, is included. The gantry travels on single or double rails, with single- or multiwheel trucks at each corner of the gantry. Some, or all, of these wheels may be driven from power units at the corners of the gantry, from single power units mounted in the gantry, or from power equipment located in the machinery cab. These cranes may be used for hook work or materials handling, with speeds of the various motions commensurate with the loads to be handled and the duty-cycle requirements.

Traveling Portal Gantry Crane—Cantilever-Jib Type. The fixed cantilever jib projects from one side of the gantry and has a rope-moved load trolley of the fleet-through type mounted on it. A jib extension on the opposite side of the gantry may be provided for a fixed counterweight. For handling bulk materials, a receiving hopper may be built into the gantry structure. This crane is used where it is necessary to handle loads to one side of the gantry only. It is usually of only moderate capacity and reach.

Traveling Portal Gantry Crane—Double-Cantilever-Jib Type. The fixed double-cantilever jib is centered on the gantry and has a rope-moved load trolley

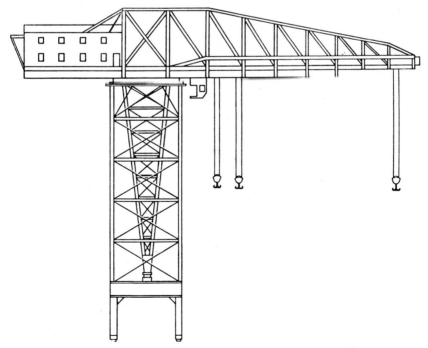

Fig. 27. Traveling revolving portal gantry crane—hammerhead type.

of the fleet-through type and a counterweight trolley mounted on it. The trolleys are arranged to travel in opposite directions so that the overturning forces on the crane are kept to a minimum. This crane has been used extensively for concrete placing in dam and powerhouse construction, with independently powered hoisting and racking units with elaborate electrical control. For this service, spans up to 330 ft. have been used, with loads up to 13 tons.

Traveling Revolving Portal Gantry Crane—Hammerhead Type. The revolving cantilever jib, Fig. 27, projects from the center of rotation with one or more rope-moved load trolleys of the fleet-through type mounted on it. An opposite extension of the jib supports the machinery house and crane counterweight. This kind of crane is used in the larger sizes for hookwork with electric power and in the smaller size for grapple or bucket work with internal-combustion-engine or electric power.

Traveling Revolving Portal Gantry Crane—Rope-luffed Strut Boom. This crane, Fig. 28, has a strut-type boom with the luffing lines connected at or near

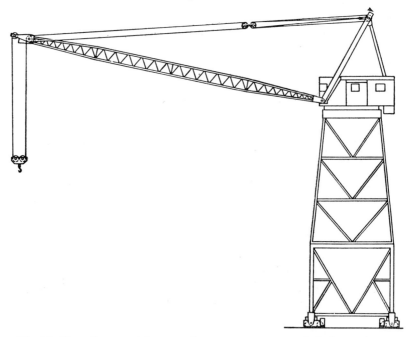

Fig. 28. Traveling revolving portal gantry crane—rope-luffed strut boom.

the boom tip. It is the most widely used kind of live-boom revolving crane and is found in almost every type of lifting service for cranes. Capacities range to as high as 250 tons.

Traveling Revolving Portal Gantry Crane—Rope-luffed Trussed Boom. This kind of crane has a truss-type boom, shown in Fig. 29, with the luffing lines connected at some point back from the tip, usually to the rear of the midpoint, and carries its load as a cantilever truss. This construction shortens and consequently minimizes stretch in the luffing ropes, although it results in the use of a much heavier boom than the strut type. It is usually used for handling heavy loads and where careful handling is required.

Traveling Revolving Portal Gantry Crane—Level-luffing Type. This crane attains extremely high luffing speeds with small power expenditure by causing the load to travel in a horizontal path for all boom positions and by compensating for raising the dead weight of the boom through the use of a movable boom counterweight. Level luffing may be accomplished by the arrangement of the reeving, by mechanical linkage, or by means of special arrangement and design of hoists. The boom may be luffed by means of wire ropes, by screws, or by gearing and linkage.

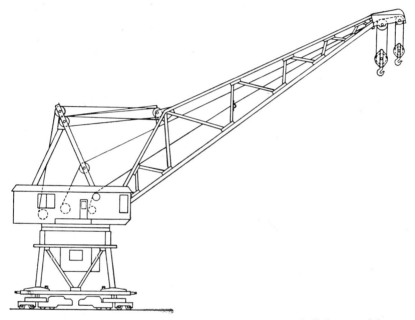

Fig. 29. Traveling revolving portal gantry crane—rope-luffed trussed boom.

One rope-luffing type has a two-piece boom in which the outer end folds down as the boom is luffed in, so that the end sheaves, and consequently the suspended load, move along a horizontal path. The movement of the outer boom section is controlled by a pair of curved channels of special form for proper positioning of the outer section at all radii. This arrangement has the special advantage of keeping the length of free rope between the load and the boom end to a minimum at all radii, and also provides a gooseneck type of boom with extra clearance under it as compared to a straight boom. This crane is usually used for cargo and materials handling in moderate capacities. A fixed version of another rope-luffing type is illustrated in the section on Fixed Cranes, Derricks, and Cableways.

Traveling Revolving Portal Gantry Crane—Screw- or Rack-luffing Type. This crane, Fig. 30, uses one or more heavy power screws for luffing the boom, which is of the truss type. In some cases, the steel screw is provided with a single bronze nut, which is turned while the screw itself does not rotate. In other cases, the steel screw is turned and is provided with one or two bronze nuts. The non-rotating member is connected to the boom by heavy links, and the axial travel of the nonrotating member raises and lowers the boom. This crane is used in shipyards and other locations where loads are to be accurately spotted and placed.

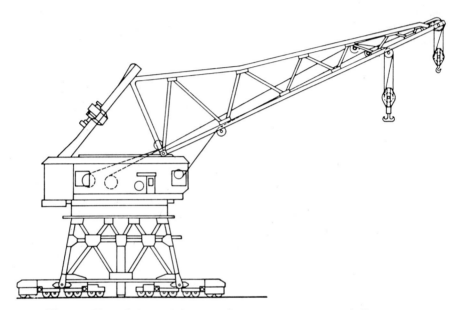

Fig. 30. Traveling revolving portal gantry crane—screw-luffing type.

TRAVELING GANTRY STORING AND RECLAIMING BRIDGES.

These cranes are a special type of double-girder traveling gantry cranes and are called "bridges" because of the resemblance of their built-up truss girders to those of railway or highway bridges. They are of the gantry type, with the conventional A-frame legs for spans of 100 ft. or less. For greater spans, special supporting legs are used which permit relative movement in the horizontal plane between the supporting legs and the bridge girders, so as to avoid excessive stress in both the girders and supporting legs, which is caused by skewing, that is, the difference in travel between one leg and the other caused by slipping of the driving wheels on the rail runways. These stresses can be allowed for in the design of a short-span bridge, but for bridge spans of 400 ft. and upward it is impractical to design for such high stresses. The supporting legs are called "pier leg" or "tower" at one end of the bridge and "shear leg" at the opposite end. The pier leg is designed to stabilize the bridge in directions both parallel to and at right angles to its rail runway. The shear leg stabilizes only in a direction parallel to its rail runway but leans from the perpendicular at right angles to its rail runway, thus compensating for the increased distance between the two rail runways measured parallel to the bridge center line when in a skewed position. There are various designs of both pier and shear legs, but all the designs accomplish the result described above.

Usually this kind of bridge has **cantilevered extensions of the girders** at one or both ends, as shown in Fig. 31. When such a bridge is used for unloading ships, a folding boom may be used to permit clearance of the masts and rigging of ships.

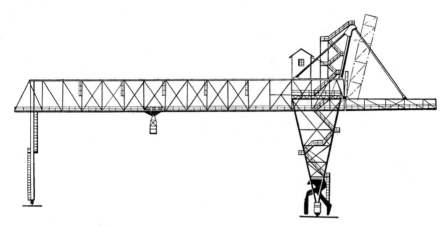

Fig. 31. Traveling storage bridge with folding jib—rope-operated trolley.

Cranes of up to about 10 tons capacity are provided with a "rope trolley." The electric-motor-driven hoist and trolley-travel units are enclosed in a machinery house located on the girders and above the pier leg. The operator's cab is located on the pier leg. Cranes of from 10 to 22 tons capacity are provided with a "man-trolley," which carries the electric-motor-driven hoist and trolley-travel units as well as the operator's cab, so that the operator has the best possible view of the work being done.

The bridge drive is usually of the shaft-drive type for narrow spans and of the direct axle-driven type for the wider spans. The range in operating speeds of these bridges is as follows:

Hoisting	200 to 400 ft. per min.
Trolley travel	600 to 1,200 ft. per min.
Bridge travel	50 to 100 ft. per min.

The rope trolley or the man trolley, when used on these cranes, usually is equipped with an automatic bucket and is used to unload ore, coal, sand, gravel, and other bulk materials from cars or ships into storage and to reclaim these materials from storage for delivery to the blast furnace or to cars for reshipment.

The above bridges are those in the most general use, but in addition there are several special designs constructed for particular purposes.

Traveling Storage Bridges with Retractable Jibs. Bridges of this kind incorporate a retractable jib carried on rollers in the bridge girders and moved in and out by electric-motor drive. This arrangement serves the same purpose as

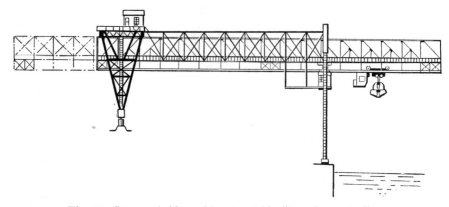

Fig. 32. Storage bridge with retractable jib and man-trolley.

the folding boom in clearing ships' masts, etc. (Fig. 32). A rope-trolley or a man-trolley is used on the retractable jib in the conventional manner.

Traveling Storage Bridges with Traveling Revolving Jib Unloader and Belt Conveyor. These bridges have rail runways on the upper chords of their girders, upon which a traveling revolving jib unloader operates (Fig. 33). Two

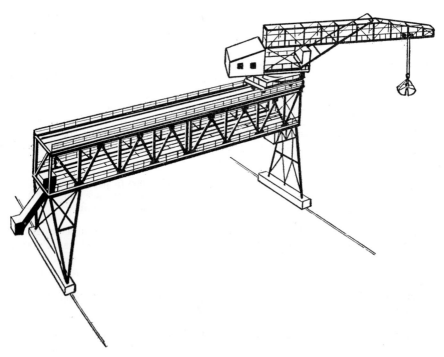

Fig. 33. Storage bridge with traveling revolving jib unloader and belt conveyors.

belt conveyors with feeders are also provided, one between the upper chords and the other between the lower chords of the girders. The unloader feeds the lower conveyor when unloading into storage and feeds the upper conveyor when reclaiming from storage.

Traveling Rope-operated Storage Bridges with Belt Conveyors. These are conventional bridges with the addition of a belt conveyor which is used for storage only, being fed from a conveyor parallel to the rail runways. The bucket is used for reclaiming only (Fig. 34).

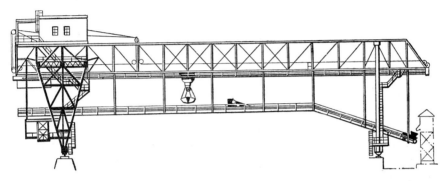

Fig. 34. Rope-operated storage bridge with belt conveyors and traveling tripper.

Traveling Storage Bridges with Belt Conveyors. Bridges in this class do not have the usual bucket handling equipment but instead only a belt conveyor which is used for storage, being fed from a conveyor parallel to the rail runways. Materials are reclaimed through gates and conveyors in tunnels underneath the storage area (Fig. 35).

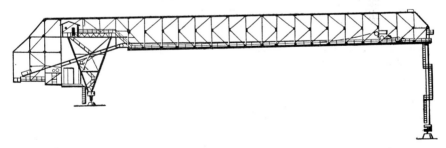

Fig. 35. Storage bridge with belt conveyor and tripper.

TRAVELING GANTRY BULK-MATERIAL LOADING AND UN-LOADING TOWERS. Traveling equipment for the loading and unloading of bulk cargo is very similar to the fixed loading and unloading cranes and towers described in the section on Fixed Cranes and Towers, except that the supporting structure is equipped with wheeled trucks which operate on rail runways supported by suitable foundations. Thus equipped, unloading towers are able to serve a greater area than can be covered by a stationary crane, and the unloading equipment often may be more readily moved than the vessel which is being loaded or unloaded. Where several unloaders operate to unload a single vessel, it is necessary that they have the means for traveling, because they must move independently from hatch to hatch while the ship remains stationary.

Formerly, the truck wheels were driven from a single motor through line shafting and bevel gearing, but the modern practice is to install several motors direct-connected to the driving wheels, and usually all wheels are driven. Traveling equipment is often protected against damage from high winds by means of rail clamps which automatically clamp the structure to the runway rails.

Capacities of traveling towers are similar to those for comparable fixed units. Additional forms of traveling loading and unloading towers not usually used as fixed towers include revolving-jib traveling gantry loading and unloading towers, retractable-jib traveling gantry loading and unloading towers, and hulett unloaders, all of which are discussed below.

Cantilever Belt-Conveyor Traveling Gantry Loading Towers. This equipment consists of a loading tower with fixed cantilever boom, boom conveyor, and trimmer and is similar to the cantilever belt-conveyor fixed loading towers discussed in the section on fixed cranes and towers, except that it is arranged to travel. The traveling feature increases flexibility of operation of the loader but requires special arrangements to insure a supply of material to the loader boom-conveyor. Where approach conveyors are used, a traveling tripper may serve this purpose.

Trimmers and fingers are used when necessary to assure proper distribution while loading bulk cargo in the hold. They may be used to load cargo in spaces under the decks and to balance and trim the loading, to protect some types of cargo from weather and wind, or to prevent degradation of certain materials. As loader flexibility increases through mobility—with ships designed with wide-open hatches and fully exposed holds, and with materials where degradation is not important—trimmers may be eliminated, the materials being dumped directly from the boom conveyor into the vessel. This practice may also be followed with iron ores. Capacities for iron ore dumped direct into the vessel may reach as high as —and even in excess of—6,000 tons per hr. from a single boom belt.

Hinged-Boom Belt-Conveyor Traveling Gantry Loading Tower. This equipment, illustrated in Fig. 36, consists of a loading tower similar to the cantilever belt-conveyor traveling gantry loading tower except that a hinged boom is used in lieu of a fixed cantilever. The hinged-boom traveling loader has fullest flexibility of operation of all the bulk-material loaders because of its ability to vary the boom angle and to travel at will.

A variety of conveyor arrangements exists in which the boom is made extensible to accommodate a wide range of tidal conditions and ship sizes. Two conveyors are required on the boom, one on the main section and a second on the extension, with material transferable from one to the other regardless of the position of the extension.

Cantilever Traveling Gantry Unloading Tower. Equipment of this kind consists of an unloading tower similar to the cantilever fixed loading and unloading towers but mounted on a wide-gage traveling gantry. Unloading towers of this kind may be rope-operated, or they may be equipped with a man-trolley.

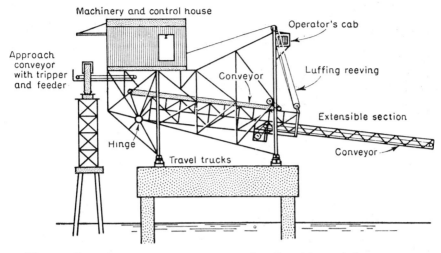

Fig. 36. Traveling gantry loading tower with hinged-boom belt conveyor.

Hinged-Jib Traveling Gantry Unloading Tower. This type of traveling tower (Fig. 37) is similar to the above cantilever traveling gantry unloading towers except that it is provided with a hinged jib in place of a fixed cantilever.

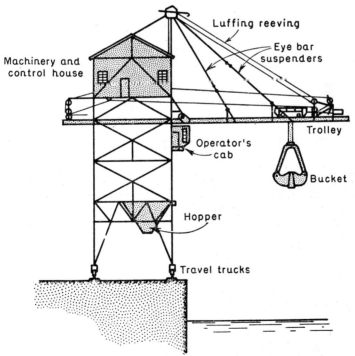

Fig. 37. Hinged-jib traveling gantry unloading tower—rope-reeved-trolley type.

Revolving-Jib Traveling Gantry Loading and Unloading Tower. This equipment, shown in Fig. 38, consists of a traveling tower with upper structure and hinged jib arranged to swing together. Usually it constitutes a multiple-purpose machine provided with a hook block for unit-load handling. For the handling of hook loads both luffing and swinging are desirable. When used as a bulk-material unloader, the jib is lowered to the horizontal and a rope-operated trolley is carried on the underside of the jib. This equipment has the flexibility of an all-purpose full-revolving crane and in addition the ability to discharge bulk cargo at relatively higher speeds.

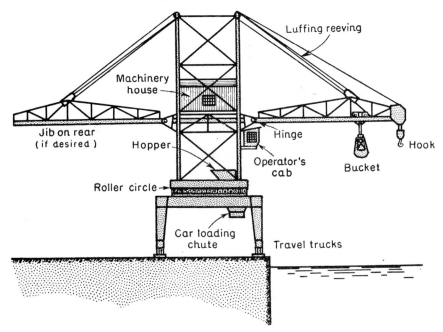

Fig. 38. Revolving-jib traveling gantry unloading tower.

Retractable-Jib Traveling Gantry Loading and Unloading Towers. This type of traveling tower (Fig. 39) is similar to the hinged-jib traveling gantry loading and unloading tower, except that the movable jib, instead of being hinged to the tower, is made retractable in a horizontal direction and thus will clear ships' rigging and superstructures. Retractable-jib towers may be of either the rope-trolley or the man-trolley type, and the travel of the jib may be either concurrent with or independent from the trolley travel. Two distinct types of retractable jib arrangements are in use, the positioned-jib or ram type and the shuttling-jib type. The jib is arranged to travel on a runway in the tower structure, and the trolley travels on a runway on the underside of the jib.

The **positioned-jib- or ram-type tower** is provided with separate travel drives for the jib and trolley. The jib may be positioned as desired for work to be performed, and usually may project beyond either face of the tower. The trolley works over the desired operating range along the jib, with the jib remaining stationary. If desired, jib and trolley may be operated simultaneously, yet independently of one another. The positioned-jib tower is commonly used where the handling capacity is large and a man trolley is needed.

The **shuttling jib** is provided with a single travel drive which operates both the jib and trolley in such relationship that when jib is fully extended in one direction the trolley is at the extended end of the jib. As the shuttling jib travels back, the trolley travels back along the jib so as to arrive at the rear end of the jib when the jib is fully extended to the rear. The shuttling-jib type of tower is usually used for very light loads and small capacities, and is usually rope-reeved for both racking and hoisting. In this type of equipment the jib is always in motion if the trolley is moving, and vice versa.

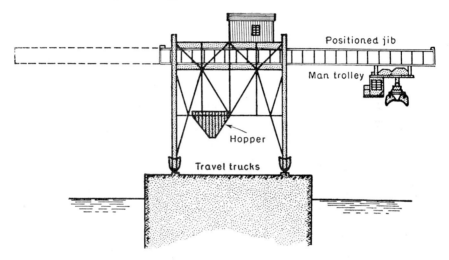

Fig. 39. Retractable-jib traveling gantry loading and unloading tower positioned-jib or ram type.

HULETT UNLOADERS. These unloaders (Fig. 40) are sometimes designated stiffleg unloaders but are more popularly called Hulett unloaders after their inventor. This type of unloader consists of a self-propelled gantry which is arranged to travel along a dock and on which is mounted a trolley traveling at right angles to the ship. At the top of a frame at the forward end of the trolley, a walking-beam is pivoted. From the water end of the walking-beam is suspended a bucket-leg, and to the other end a balancing counterweight is applied. A further leg-brace connects the bucket-leg and the trolley in such a manner that, during hoisting and lowering, the bucket-leg is kept in a vertical position by the parallelogram formed. The bottom of the bucket-leg carries a pair of **bucket scoops** which close to form a clamshell bucket. The leg and bucket are arranged to rotate to permit digging in any direction, and the operator rides with the leg.

The Hulett unloader is equipped with buckets having capacities of from 10 to 20 tons, and for handling heavy free-digging iron ores has free-digging capacities up to 1,800 tons per hr. Buckets have been made with up to 20 cu. yd. capacity for handling trash and garbage. In unloading iron ore, the Hulett unloader generally discharges the ore into a hopper at the front of the gantry, whence it is fed to a conveyor for delivery to a trough or initial ore pile at the rear of the machine. It is rehandled from this point by other equipment.

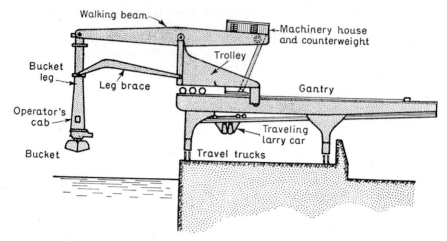

Fig. 40. Hulett unloader.

TRAVELING MARINE-LEG GANTRY UNLOADERS. Equipment of this kind constitutes a classification of bulk- or package-handling equipment similar to marine-leg fixed-tower unloaders, and utilizing the various forms of marine leg in combination with a traveling gantry. Where gantries are not employed, marine legs are often mounted on the dock face on hinged booms, handled as separate units by ship's rigging or by other cranes, or mounted on hulls to form floating grain elevators. In a few instances marine legs have been used to load out bulk materials. Mounted on a traveling gantry, they elevate and discharge the material to a chute leading to the ship's hold.

Traveling Low-Carriage and Wall Cranes

TRAVELING LOW-CARRIAGE REVOLVING CRANES ON BROAD-GAGE TRACKS. These cranes are of the revolving type described under the discussion of traveling portal gantry cranes, except that the supporting members under the revolving portion of the crane are mounted directly on the travel trucks, thus eliminating the open portal.

Cranes of the traveling revolving portal gantry type may be mounted in this manner.

TRAVELING BRACKET JIB WALL CRANES. Traveling bracket or wall jib cranes are generally used as auxiliaries to overhead traveling bridge cranes, but are sometimes used as separate cranes. They are employed to a great extent in foundries and machine shops and—within the limits of the jib and travel—serve the same purpose as overhead traveling bridge cranes. They are usually placed under an overhead crane to handle lighter loads, or may be installed in a group along a shop wall to handle loads too heavy for workers to lift (Fig. 41).

The general construction consists of a single- or double-girder jib supported by a wall frame or vertical truck, provided with a top and bottom set of wheels, traveling in a runway secured to the side wall of the building. The jib is either top- or bottom-braced and is fixed rigidly to the wall frame. A crane trolley is mounted on the jib.

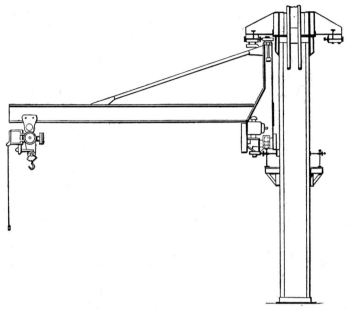

Fig. 41. Wall jib crane.

The **crane travel** may be hand-powered, and a chain hoist, an air hoist, or an electric hoist may be used for lifting purposes, but generally the crane is entirely electrically operated, controlled either from a cab on the crane or by pendent push-button or pull cords accessible from the floor. The jibs may be up to 30 ft. long, and the crane capacities range up to a maximum of 10 tons.

Stiffleg Trolleys for Furnace Chargers

SPECIAL TROLLEYS ON TRAVELING BRIDGE CRANES. Special trolleys are used on the girders of overhead or gantry traveling double-girder bridge cranes for charging furnaces, both open-hearth and reheating. They are similar to standard trolleys, with the addition of a **vertical hanger or stiffleg,** which may be either fixed rigidly to the trolley frame or arranged to revolve about a vertical axis. The lower end of the stiffleg is provided with bearings in which a horizontal charging-ram is pivoted, which gives the ram an up-and-down motion at the end. This **charging ram** may also be arranged to rotate about its horizontal axis. At the end of the ram there is a head, or a peel, or tongs, according to the nature of the material being handled. All operations of the trolley, as well as of the bridge, are controlled from an operator's cab attached to the lower end of the stiffleg. An individual electric-motor drive is provided for each of the required motions. Capacities of these trolleys range from 3 to 15 tons.

When the trolley is used to charge open-hearth melting furnaces, the end of the ram is provided with a head to engage the charging boxes. A locking device is also provided to secure the box to the ram head. This device is usually operated by hand, but may also be power-actuated, either by hydraulic or air pressure or by direct motor drive. The charging ram rotates about a horizontal axis to discharge the contents of the box into the furnace. Open-hearth practice in the United

States is to bring the boxes on cars to a point in front of the furnaces, which permits the vertical stiffleg to be fixed rigidly to the trolley frame. European practice, however, requires that the stiffleg revolve about its vertical axis to reach the charging boxes.

When it is used to charge copper cathodes into a melting furnace, the end of the ram is provided with a peel together with a **pusher-head** to push the charge into the furnace. The pusher-head is usually actuated by either hydraulic or air pressure, but may be provided with a direct motor drive. The construction of the copper-melting furnaces requires that the stiffleg revolve about its vertical axis in order to deposit the cathodes in the proper location. The ram, however, does not rotate about its horizontal axis.

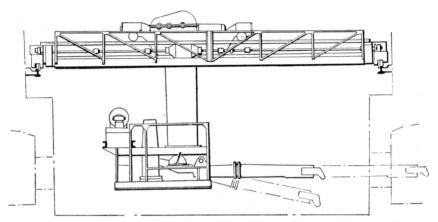

Fig. 42. **Double-girder bridge crane with stiffleg trolley and furnace charger.**

When it is used to charge and discharge ingots, billets, slabs, or plates into and out of reheating furnaces, the end of the ram is provided with **tongs** (Fig. 42). These tongs may be either side-grip or end-grip, and are usually operated by hydraulic pressure, although some older machines used a motor-driven screw-and-nut device to operate the tongs. Both the vertical stiffleg and the horizontal ram may be rigidly fixed or may be arranged to revolve about their axes, depending upon the requirements of each individual installation.

Crane-Trolley Built-in Hoists

CRANE-TROLLEY HOISTS. Hoists of this kind are mounted on trolleys which also carry the trolley-travel units, both of which have electric motor drives whose control panels, resistors, and master switches are mounted externally of the trolley. Both the hoist and the trolley-drive units may be driven by means of either spur-gear or worm-gear reductions. The trolley is carried on four or more wheels, depending upon the capacity of the hoists, which varies from 3 tons to 200 tons or more. Hoists of this kind are generally used on the following classes of cranes:

    1. Fixed gantry bridge cranes.
    2. Overhead traveling bridge cranes.
    3. Traveling gantry bridge cranes.
    4. Traveling wall cranes.

There are several types of these built-in hoists which are available; they are as follows:

Single-Hook Trolley Hoists. Such hoist units consist of one drum on which are wound the ropes for a single-hook hoist block. The axis of the drum is at right angles to the direction of the trolley travel.

Twin-Hook Trolley Hoists. These units have two hoist blocks operated simultaneously and in unison by a single electric-motor drive. Usually, there is only one long drum, which may have its axis either parallel to or at right angles to the direction of trolley travel. Occasionally, however, there are two short drums keyed to one drum shaft. Twin-hook trolley hoists are used for handling long lengths of materials, such as pipe and structural steel sections.

Main-and-Auxiliary and Bucket-handling Trolley Hoists. Main-and-auxiliary trolley hoists consist of two hoist units, the drum of one winding the ropes for the main hoist block, and the drum of the other winding the ropes for the auxiliary hoist block. The axes of both drums are at right angles to the direction of trolley travel. Bucket-handling hoists are similar, except that the two hoist units are essentially duplicate, the drum of one winding the "holding" ropes and the drum of the other winding the "closing" ropes of an automatic bucket. The bucket capacity is 22 tons or less, making a total maximum lifted load of about 50 tons, depending upon the weight of the bucket used. This load is divided between the two hoist units.

Man-Trolley Hoists. These hoists are similar to the crane-trolley built-in hoists but also have a control house and operator's cab containing the control panels, resistors, and master switches. There are several kinds of these trolleys:

1. Single-hook man-trolley hoists.
2. Twin-hook man-trolley hoists.
3. Main-and-auxiliary trolley hoists, and bucket-handling man-trolley hoists.
4. Bucket-handling man-trolley hoists with revolving turntable.

The last-mentioned type is distinguished by having the hoist units mounted on a motor-driven revolving turntable which enables the bucket to be turned about its vertical axis. This feature is useful when the same crane or bridge is used to unload both ships and railroad cars.

Bucket-handling Man-Trolley Hoists with Revolving Rope-Anchors. These hoists are variants of the bucket-handling man-trolley hoists, the hoisting ropes being reeved through the bucket and anchored to a motor-driven revolving ring on the trolley, which permits the bucket to be turned in the same manner, and for the same purpose, as on the bucket-handling man-trolley hoists with revolving turntable.

Monorail or Tramrail Systems

OVERHEAD MATERIALS HANDLING EQUIPMENT. Overhead materials handling equipment of the kind generally known as monorail or tramrail systems is capable of fulfilling practically all the basic requirements of overhead materials handling. A hoist or carrier of great capacity can be used when it is necessary to handle a large unit of production. The carrier with a chain hoist or electric hoist attached to it is capable of picking up the load at one point and transporting it to its destination on the overhead trackage system without rehandling. If the item to be manufactured can be suspended on a carrier on the overhead track system during assembly, a proper working height can be established, since flexibility in height at different operations is possible through the use of manually or electrically operated hoists. When materials are handled overhead, the floor can be kept clear for manufacturing, size of working areas can be reduced, and aisle widths can be held to a minimum.

RAIL DESIGN. Prior to the development of specialized overhead rail systems, the only overhead track available was the conventional **I-beam.** The I-beam shape, however, was never intended for use as an overhead track; its main original purpose was to serve as a structural section for a building. Being rolled of soft steel and having tapered flanges, the I-beam did not lend itself readily to use as a track for a movable carrier or trolley. Because of the **rolling action of the carrier wheels** on one surface of the flange, peening occurred, which eventually caused the flange to turn down. Such a section, used as a track, has a relatively short life when subjected to medium or heavy service.

Reduction of Peening Action. Peening causes the metal on a surface to flow, and thus distorts the shape of the member affected. It can be reduced to some extent by using a section of steel of high ultimate strength, and the specialized rail manufacturers of monorail or tramrail systems now have rail sections rolled by the steel mills with a carbon content of 45 to 65 percent, or an ultimate

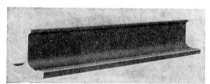

Cleveland Tramrail

Fig. 44. Track section with raised wearing strip rolled into the flange.

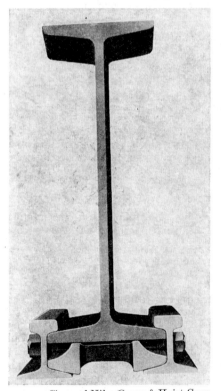

Shepard Niles Crane & Hoist Corp.

Fig. 43. I-beam track with T-rail sections.

Louden

Fig. 45. Single T-rail of high-tensile steel with flat flanges.

strength of 100,000 to 125,000 lb. However, wherever such section is subjected to hard service, peening eventually occurs, and replacement of the rail section is necessary. Some manufacturers offer a section consisting of mild-steel I-beams with two **T-rail sections** clamped to the lower flange (see Fig. 43). Such design is applicable on heavy systems—above 10 tons capacity—and larger-radius curves.

The **simplest rail design** which will resist peening is one having a raised **wearing strip** rolled into the flange (see Fig. 44). Such design provides a relatively narrow width of rail, and, because of the raised wearing strip, it is possible to roll such a section with a perfectly flat surface on the running flange, thereby providing a horizontal surface for the wheels of a carrier or trolley to ride upon.

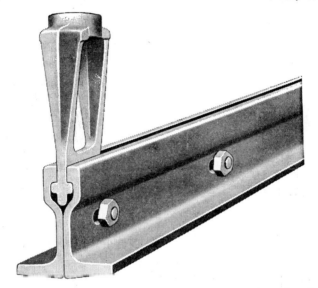

American Monorail

Fig. 46. Flat-flanged track of high-tensile steel, twin-section construction.

The rolling action of carrier wheels will cause the metal in the wearing strip to compact or flow, just as it would in a section without a wearing strip. But because this metal can flow freely, no stretching of the main section of the track will occur, and as long as the wearing strip remains on the rail no peening stresses are imposed in the flange itself. When the wearing strip is worn off by service, such a rail will of course have a tendency to peen.

Some manufacturers have designed shapes having rail sections with relatively flat flanges, rolled with high tensile steel. Such sections give satisfactory service when properly applied (see Figs. 45 and 46). Attempts have been made from time to time to weld or rivet **strips of high-carbon steel** on structural I-beams. These experiments have not proved satisfactory because of the tendency for the metal to flow in the strip, causing it to stretch between the points of attachment and eventually resulting in the destruction of the wearing strip.

Choice of Rail Section. In determining the choice of a rail section for a monorail or tramrail system, consideration should be given to the **load imposed** on the rail itself. The weakest points of all overhead materials handling systems lie in the same places—at the switch points, and, where transfer cranes are used, at the point where the end of a transfer crane interlocks with the spur section of rail. Some clearance must be provided at these points, resulting in a gap and causing wheel impacts on the section ends. This factor is not a problem on continuous lengths of a system, because it is possible—with proper application of couplings—to join the ends of the rail sections together solidly, or, by welding the joint, to make use of the full capacity of the rail. Since most monorail or tramrail systems include switches or transfer bridges, the loads must be limited to the weight capacity at these points.

Factors in computing the **capacity** of a rail section must be considered so as to obtain the longest life possible with the most economical design of a track section. Fig. 47 illustrates some dimensions of available specialized rails, and the computation of the stresses imposed on each rail for steels of various ultimate strengths, based on straight or angular rail cuts. A **safety factor** of 5, based on the ultimate strength of the steel used, should be used in designing a rail to assure long life and minimum maintenance cost.

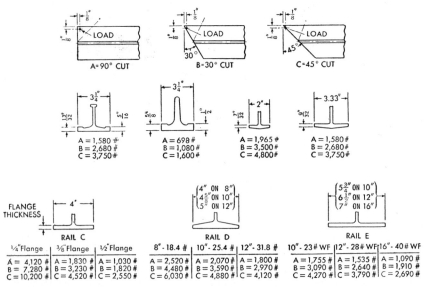

Values for A, B, and C are stress in flange on Line X produced by 100-lb. load at point indicated. To get actual stress in flange, multiply A, B, or C values by actual carrier wheel load and divide by 100.........................$fs = \dfrac{A, B \text{ or } C \times WL}{100}$

To get maximum allowable wheel load, take safe allowable working stress in section selected, and divide by above values for A, B, or C and multiple that by 100.

$WL = \dfrac{fs \times 100}{A, B, \text{ or } C}$

Standard Mild Steel I beams should not be stressed over 12,000 lb. per sq. in.
40 carbon sections or I beams should not be stressed over 16,000 lb. per sq. in.
60 carbon sections or I beams should not be stressed over 25,000 lb. per sq. in.

Monorail Manufacturers Assoc.

Fig. 47. Computation of stresses for raised and flat flanged rails.

The values shown for the various sections indicate only the actual load imposed on the full flange-thickness of a rail, except for the rail section with the raised tread, this tread not being included in the calculations. If a system is to be subjected to medium or hard service, allowance should be made for **wear**; therefore the thickness of a section without a raised tread should be increased to provide long life. The capacity of the rail with T-rail clamped on (Fig. 43) or with the wearing strip rolled in remains the same until the tread or attached rail is worn down. The capacity of a rail without the wearing strip will decrease in service. Therefore, it is important that rails should be designed with sufficient thickness not only to carry the load but also to provide for wear. Under all conditions, peening or flowing of the metal will occur, but where an extra thickness of the rail is provided, this wear will be unimportant for a period of time.

Track sections are available in various capacities and depths for application in buildings of different **truss spacings.** Some sections are made of a single rolling of steel, others are compound sections with the wear-resisting rail welded to an upper member of mild steel. This latter design has advantages over the single-piece section in that it is possible to design different combinations of section depths and flange widths to meet different truss spacings.

In all instances it is desirable that **deflection in the rail** be limited to $\frac{1}{450}$ of the span between suspension points on a single track or in a crane system. When the layout involves a transfer crane or interlocking crane, the deflection in the runway trackage should be limited so that the vertical deflection will not exceed $\frac{1}{16}$ in. when the end of a transfer crane lines up with a discharge point, or with an adjacent interlocking transfer crane on the adjacent runway. This arrangement prevents stubbing of the carrier wheels when they pass over open ends. Manufacturers of monorail or tramrail systems have various means of limiting this deflection to the specified minimum.

SUSPENSION OF MONORAIL OR TRAMRAIL SYSTEMS. The most satisfactory suspension for a monorail or tramrail system consists of a hanger rod assembly, with some movement incorporated in this assembly so that the carrier wheels or trolley wheels always contact the rail on each side. This contact

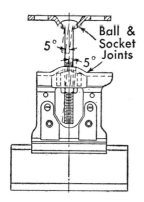
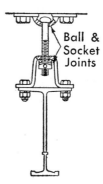

Cleveland Tramrail

Fig. 48. Ball-and-socket suspension.

can be accomplished by a **ball-and-socket suspension** (see Fig. 48). Some manufacturers use a **T-type suspension** which assumes adequate longitudinal bracing and gives maximum lateral flexibility at the point of the load (see Fig. 49). This provision is quite satisfactory on single-track systems, but since the track used in monorail or tramrail systems is also used as a runway for underrunning cranes, some type of suspension must be provided in the runway tracks to compensate for any misalignment when a crane travels down the runway. It is therefore evident that if the suspension incorporating some movement in the hanger rod is used in the suspension of a **single track,** the same suspension is also desirable in a **runway track.**

Louden

Fig. 49. T-head hanger suspension.

CARRIER OR TROLLEY DESIGN. The early carrier designs used on the conventional I-beams generally consisted of rigid side plates with four wheels —two wheels mounted on each side, with a relatively short wheelbase. It was found that such construction was not satisfactory because too much effort was required to move a load along the track. Modern design, as offered by the specialized rail manufacturers, incorporates two **swiveling yokes or heads,** each of which contains a pair of wheels, permitting the carrier wheels to align themselves with the rail. With the advantages of a flat—or near-flat—flange section, considerably less effort is required to move a load along the track. This element is important when determining whether a carrier should be hand- or electrically propelled.

If loads are occasionally to be manually propelled, it obviously becomes important to select a carrier that will permit moving a load with minimum effort. The same condition applies if a hand-propelled crane will fit the needs in solving a materials handling problem. Manufacturers of specialized rail systems now offer a carrier that will move a 1-ton load with a **starting effort** of about 20 lb., and continue movement of such load with an effort of 12 to 15 lb. Assuming that an operator is able to exert an effort in a horizontal direction equivalent to one-half his weight, an operator weighing 150 lb. can exert an effort of 75 lb., and can thus move approximately 3½ tons of material via this carrier without unduly exerting himself.

Fig. 50 illustrates two types of carriers made by the specialized rail manufacturers. A longer-wheelbase carrier will operate more smoothly than a short-wheelbase carrier in handling a given load. The longer **wheelbase** makes less effort necessary to move a carrier around a curved section of track, eliminates binding, and—because of the swiveling motion incorporated in such carriers—considerably shortens the radii of the curves used. A 4-ft.-minimum-radius track-curve is the one most satisfactory.

Louden

American Monorail

Fig. 50. Typical carriers.

SWITCH SYSTEMS. Considerable flexibility is possible with an overhead monorail or tramrail system, because curved sections can be incorporated in the layout. Main-line tracks can be connected to switches, thus permitting movement of a carrier to a spur track. The possibilities for extension of a system are made unlimited by the addition of a transfer crane interlocking with stationary spur tracks, or connecting with jib cranes which may be necessary to span a railroad track, or with raise or drop sections. Switch systems are available with the necessary safety devices incorporated, such as auxiliary guards, spring bumpers, and safety stops, to prevent carriers from running off an open end of a system. Combinations of the various pieces of equipment are limitless and reduce manual handling to a minimum. Figs. 51 and 52 show representative examples.

Louden

Fig. 51. Tongue-type switch.

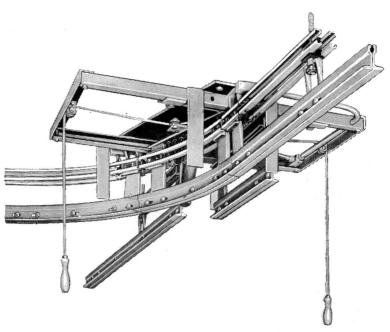

American Monorail

Fig. 52. Electrified sliding switch.

CRANES AND TRANSFER BRIDGES. Underrunning cranes or transfer bridges of up to 10 tons capacity are available, operating on two or more runways, and offering greater flexibility in handling materials than is possible with a conventional **top-running bridge crane.** With the proper suspension of the runway trackage for such a crane, the crane or transfer crane can be of considerably less weight than the conventional top-running crane. Design of the end trucks of an underrunning crane with a proper suspension permits movement of such a crane down a runway without a skewing or binding effect. It is important to avoid skewing or binding because a steel structure has a tendency to some movement which may cause misalignment of a rigid runway. The proper suspension of an **underhung runway,** with means for adjustment in the hanger rod suspension, permits maintenance of alignment even after a building has settled.

Underrunning cranes or transfer cranes have been installed which operate at speeds up to 600 ft. per min. The weight of such cranes, depending on building width, can be as little as one-half or less of the weight of a top-running deepgirder crane. While on a long-span crane more than two runways are necessary, the saving in headroom or height of the building, or in steel required in the building, many times offsets the higher cost of an underrunning crane with the additional runway. More important, a long-span crane can readily be converted into a transfer crane, permitting transfer of loads from one bay to another. Where a wide bay is necessary for manufacturing operations, two or more cranes can be interlocked so that practically the entire area of a manufacturing bay can be served most efficiently.

An important example of such an application is provided in the aircraft industry, where buildings up to 250 ft. wide have been designed to assemble large transport planes. **Multirunway, underrunning transfer cranes** of half the building width have been installed with provision for interlocking them when necessary to transfer plane assemblies from one area to another in the same bay. Such transfer cranes can be interlocked and controlled by one operator, thereby traveling down an area as one unit. Such combinations present limitless possibilities. Similar installations have been made in tube plants, warehouses, and other industries.

TURNTABLE SWITCHES. Turntable switches are sometimes installed in an overhead system. It is desirable to limit the use of such switches, because they may run to large sizes and the length of the track in the turntable must be based on the length of the carrier. When a loaded carrier is positioned in the turntable, considerable effort is required to rotate the moving member. If the carrier is

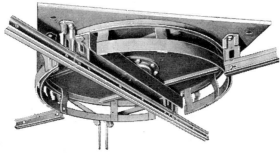

American Monorail

Fig. 53. Turntable switch.

American Monorail

Fig. 54. Special trolley racks move fruit from cars to ripening rooms via automatic lift to lower level.

Louden

Fig. 55. Track lift dunks load in a degreasing operation.

long, the operation of the turntable is very slow, and quite frequently a motor drive is required. When such a switch is rotated, the weight of the rotating member, the weight of the carrier, and the weight of the live load equal the total weight. This total weight offsets the few advantages that might be obtained over a sliding or transfer-type switch. A typical example of this kind of unit is shown in Fig. 53.

DROP AND RAISE SECTIONS. Drop and raise sections can be incorporated in a monorail or tramrail layout to permit movement of a loaded carrier from a fixed track elevation to a lower or higher track elevation. Units of this kind are very desirable in applications involving painting, dipping, cleaning, or transferring a load from one elevation of track to a higher or lower track elevation. Drop and raise sections can be provided with all the necessary safety devices which prevent accidental running off of a carrier when the sections are not in alignment, and can be operated automatically by controlling the movement of the sections as a carrier passes over a certain area of the stationary track. Typical designs and installations are shown in Figs. 54 and 55.

HOIST CARRIERS. Carrier designs are available which will permit the attachment or suspension of a **hand-operated chain hoist** to a carrier. The installation of such a hoist is justified where intermittent handling is necessary. Under the high cost of labor, installation of even the most efficient hand-operated hoist is never justified unless the operations are very infrequent.

The **electric hoist** is the most efficient piece of equipment for raising or lowering a load, and manufacturers of electric hoists have developed designs which can meet almost any requirements for hoisting operations. Electric hoists for light-duty service are available in capacities of 500 lb. to 2 tons. They are either motor-operated chain hoists or cable-type hoists of light weight, and when properly applied, they render highly satisfactory and efficient service. Where a handling system is subjected to hard service, it is highly advisable to select an electric hoist on the basis of its fitness for such rigorous service, rather than on the basis of first cost.

BASIC DESIGN OF HOIST. Such elements as the gearing, motor, bearings, drum, cable, and load block must be of proportions commensurate with long life and minimum maintenance expense. Control equipment must be of such design as to function without too frequent replacement of contacts; and where push-button control is used for controlling the hoist motion, reversing contactors and push-button design must be such that constant inching will not occur and cause the contacts to burn.

The hoist should be designed so that minimum "drift" occurs when the push button is actuated; therefore it must have a mechanical and electric **holding brake** of generous proportions. This requirement is not so important when boxes and barrels or raw materials are handled as it is in the movement of pieces into and out of a machine tool or in assembly or foundry mold handling operations.

Hoists operating on direct current and with variable speed control were formerly standard, but electric hoists operating on **alternating current** and with push-button control are now widely employed. Most manufacturing plants have dispensed with direct current wherever possible, and the alternating-current electric hoist now fulfills requirements for practically every application.

Variable speed control (usually five to seven control steps), being designed to handle the maximum capacity load of the hoist, is not adapted to the slow speeds desirable for handling light loads. In addition, with push-button control, the bulk of the button panel itself precluded easy manipulation. The tendency today is toward the use of a two-speed hoist. With d.c. variable speed control, the degree of control varies with the load. With the a.c. two-speed motor, a creeping speed is obtainable, regardless of the load on the hook, within the capacity of the hoist. Generally **hoist speeds** are determined on the basis of three to one, that is, a 30-ft.-per-min. top speed and a 10-ft.-per-min. slow speed. This proportion is satisfactory for almost all handling operations.

Possibly the most delicate handling operation is that for closing molds in a foundry. Installations have been made with two-speed units which, in comparison with variable-speed direct-current hoists, have proved more satisfactory because of the fixed speed that is obtainable in either the high or the low position. Such hoists require only a simple squirrel-cage rotor and a double-winding stator, and while an additional contactor is required to obtain the two speeds in addition to the reversing contactors, resistors are eliminated, thereby reducing cost and maintenance to a minimum.

Where a handling cycle involves raising or lowering a load a considerable distance, particularly when the hoist handles a load in the lowering direction, consideration must be given to the **capacity of the hoist,** not so much from the standpoint of the actual load lifted as from that of the handling cycle. A mechanical brake, being part of an electric hoist, is subjected to wear and tear (in the lowering direction only). If the various brake members of a hoist are not generously proportioned, these brake members will wear out under hard service. In many instances it is desirable to consider purchasing a hoist of higher capacity for such applications to obtain the extra life available in the mechanical brake, so that maintenance is reduced to a minimum. Fig. 56 shows a typical electric hoist carrier.

MOTOR-DRIVEN CARRIERS. The specialized monorail and tramrail manufacturers have developed ingenious designs of motor-propelled carriers for operation on their respective tracks. These range from the floor-controlled model shown in Fig. 56 to the man-trolley crane shown in Fig. 57. As in the selection of an electric hoist mounted on such a carrier, it is important to investigate thoroughly the various designs of motor-propelled carriers.

The load-carrying wheels should be of proper design, and either produced from drop-forge heat-treated steel or have cast-iron chilled treads. Bearings should be of a kind to give at least 15,000 hr. of normal operating life under full load conditions. Wheels should be so designed that they will not wear the sides of the rail. Possibility of such wear can be overcome by flangeless wheels and guide rollers contacting the side of the rail. This protection is important when a carrier is to travel around curves in an extensive system.

The **design of the carriers** should incorporate a pair of wheels mounted on a swiveling yoke, as in a hand-propelled carrier. This arrangement permits easy propulsion of the carrier along the rail or on a girder of a crane or transfer crane, and the carrier wheels can align themselves with the rail without binding. If the driving wheels are driven by a train of gears and a motor, traction is dependent on the wheel loads imposed on the driving wheels. The tractive effort obtainable is usually calculated as being equivalent to 4 percent of the wheel load.

Some kinds of drives are available where a fixed pressure is exerted on a combination of wheels or rollers contacting the underside of the rail. Such wheels are provided either with rubber treads or hardened steel faces. Where a rubber wheel or contact roller is used, particularly on a crane or transfer crane drive, adjustment must be possible to maintain the same pressure on the drives because the resiliency of the rubber may allow reduction in diameter of the rubber drive, resulting in excessive wear of the rubber wheels.

Cranes or transfer cranes are supplied with a similar arrangement of drives on the **end trucks.** Some manufacturers provide a separate drive on each end truck, others use a squaring shaft driven by one motor, the shaft connecting with the underdrive of the driving wheels at each truck. With a squaring-shaft drive it is important that the shaft be of ample proportions to resist undue torsion, and care must be taken in aligning the bearings supporting the shaft to prevent undue deflection. The manufacturers who supply individual drives for each end truck are not confronted with this problem. Choice of either drive is dependent upon consideration of the detail design of either drive.

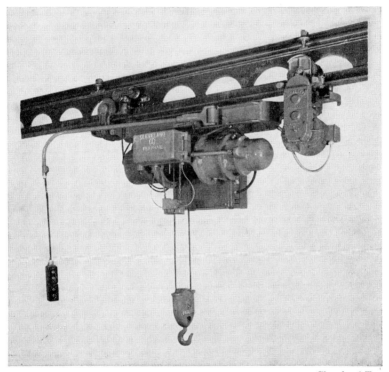

Cleveland Tramrail

Fig. 56. Motor-driven carrier with electric hoist, push-button-operated, floor-controlled.

Manufacturers of heavy-duty, top-running-type cranes, particularly those used in steel mill operations, are to some extent eliminating the squaring-shaft drive and supplying a separate drive on each truck. This may be an indication of a new trend in crane design. Gantry cranes of the double- or single-leg type are now being built with **separate drives on each truck,** and no connecting squaring-shaft and bevel-gear combination. It would appear that application of separate motor drives to heavier conventional cranes indicates that a separate motor-drive on an end truck of an underhung crane has some advantages over a squaring-shaft drive for an underhung crane.

Cleveland Tramrail

Fig. 57. Motor-driven carrier with underslung operator's cab.

Motor Drive Carrier Control. A wide **choice of control equipment** is available for a motor drive for either a motor-propelled carrier or a crane. At relatively slow speeds, a fixed step of resistance can be inserted in the power circuit which cushions the start of a unit. This provision is satisfactory at speeds of 75 ft. per min. and less. At higher speeds, some means of reducing the inrush of current is desirable, and this reduction can be accomplished by accelerating control of 3 to 5 steps on d.c. or a.c. current. Also, on a.c. current a saturable reactor provides a smooth starting effort and accelerates to full speed of the motor with the simplest arrangement of control equipment. Where variable speed is required, it can be provided by means of **variable-speed controllers** for a slip ring motor on alternating current or for a series motor on direct current. But since the tendency is towards alternating current, multispeed squirrel-cage motors, such as are used on alternating current electric hoists, can be supplied.

Some designs of drives recently developed incorporate a **fluid clutch.** There has been a difference of opinion on the relative merits of such drive. When used on a carrier propelled along a single-track system, a fluid drive or clutch presents no problem, inasmuch as it acts only as a cushion between the motor and the final drive of a carrier. But no control of speed is possible, and therefore, to obtain variable speed, some form of variable-speed controller must also be used with the motor. Thus, the advantages of such drive apparently are not as great as they might at first appear.

When a fluid clutch is used on a multi-motor-driven crane, based on the wheel load imposed on each of the trucks, one motor may reach its maximum speed faster than the motors on adjacent trucks. Consequently there may be some unevenness in the starting of a load, resulting in strains in the crane girders. Since no variable speed is obtainable, here again the advantages of a fluid clutch are not important. A properly proportioned control for a straight fluid clutch are not important. A properly proportioned control for a straight gear drive on a crane, or carrier drive, will provide the same advantages that are claimed for the fluid drive. Moreover, where it is necessary to provide some means of **braking**, this braking must be provided between the fluid clutch and the gear train. This arrangement can present some complications in the design of the driving unit.

ELECTRIFICATION OF A MONORAIL OR TRAMRAIL SYSTEM.

The manufacturers of specialized rail systems have each designed their own means of providing the proper conductor-bar electrification for supplying power to motor-driven equipment operating on the system. The conductor bars are usually mounted on suitable insulators supported at proper centers to prevent undue vertical deflection when pressure is exerted by the contact means in the form of a collector wheel or shoe. The collectors can be mounted either on one side of the rail or in a symmetrical arrangement for direct current obtainable by mounting a conductor bar on each side of the rail.

It is also possible to **use the rail as one-conductor and two-conductor bars,** when a three-phase a.c. power source is used for operating a track system through the secondary of an insulating transformer. Through the use of such a transformer, the voltage in the conductor bars can be reduced to 220 v., which is desirable from the standpoint of safety; and by using the rail as one phase of a three-phase power source, simplification of track layout and a saving in the amount of conductor bar required is possible.

Insulating transformers are available in combinations of 550 v. to 220 v., 440 v. to 220 v., or 220 v. to 220 v. This arrangement of connections has been approved under the National Electric Code and is described in Article 610 of the National Code. Whenever it is practical to use this arrangement of connections, there are other savings in the cost of an installation. It costs more to supply a switch, or transfer crane, or discharge point with three conductors than with two conductors. Where automatically dispatched carriers are part of a system, occasionally an extra conductor must be used to perform some of the control functions; and with a three-phase, three-wire system, if a fourth conductor must be used, it would be impractical—without special designs—to provide the fourth conductor along the rail. This problem also arises in connection with remote control or pulpit control of a motor-driven carrier or crane.

Enclosed vs. Open Conductor Bar Systems. The manufacturers specializing in monorail or tramrail equipment have made available conductor-bar systems of the open type, but for safety reasons, demands have been made on the industry to develop an **enclosed conductor-bar system.** These systems are now available, and it is expected that within possibly the next few years the National Code will be amended making enclosed conductors mandatory for all overhead track systems or crane or transfer bridge installations.

There are also independent manufacturers of enclosed conductor-bar systems which can be applied on some makes of specialized rail systems, but since each rail manufacturer has his own design, with clearances different from those of other manufacturers, it is difficult to adapt independently manufactured enclosed systems to a rail system.

Considerable research has been done to determine the best design of a **contacting means on the conductor bar** for supplying power to a motor-driven carrier or crane. Some manufacturers provide a collector-wheel contacting means of the single- or double-wheel type. Others have developed sliding contact shoes. It appears from the research done so far that, as a contacting means, a sliding contact shoe will provide longer life than either a revolving roller or a collector wheel.

TRAVEL SPEEDS OF MOTOR-DRIVEN EQUIPMENT.

When determining the speed at which a piece of overhead equipment should travel, consideration must be given to the kind of load handled. If a carrier is required to handle a long load, the speed of travel must be determined primarily by safety in handling the load down the aisle of a manufacturing plant. The recommended speed generally is not over 150 ft. per min. if the carrier is controlled by an operator walking with the load. The same requirement applies on a crane or transfer-crane layout. For miscellaneous handling of less bulky items, speeds up to 250 ft. per min. are practical.

If the carrier, crane or transfer crane is operated from a cab the load can be transported at a higher elevation, and the speed then depends on how fast the handling cycle must be performed to keep up with production. Generally, the recommended speed is 250 to 350 ft. per min., and while higher speeds up to 600 ft. per min. are possible, the acceleration to the top speed of travel is possible only with increased horsepower in the motor drives. This additional horsepower involves additional cost in control equipment. Maintenance becomes more costly, and it has been determined by experience that better acceleration is obtained at slower speeds, so that the handling cycle can be performed in practically the same time as would be possible with higher-speed equipment.

Where carrier units are dispatched automatically and must come to rest at the end of travel, the speed must permit the carrier to stop within a limited distance at each end of travel. Even with brakes on the carrier units, there will be a tendency to drift and run into end stops; therefore, a safe maximum recommended speed is about 125 ft. per min., unless a slow-speed step is inserted in the control circuit. If the load is bulky, this speed may have to be reduced because of the tendency of the load to pendulum when the carrier reaches the limit of travel.

HAND-PROPELLED CRANES OR TRANSFER CRANES.

Hand-propelled cranes or transfer cranes are available in designs requiring that comparatively little effort be exerted to move a loaded unit down the runway. Where the handling application justifies consideration only of a hand-propelled system, cranes or transfer cranes are available which require a starting effort of only 20 lb. per ton of total weight moved. However, the height of a hand-propelled crane installation should not exceed 12 to 14 ft. because, when such a unit is moved down a runway with no load on the hoist hook, a downward pull is exerted in moving the unit, and this would appear to require considerable effort. When a load is suspended on the hoist hook, an effort exerted in the horizontal direction on the load will start and continue moving the crane with as little effort as would be required to move a carrier on a single track.

Some manufacturers can supply hand-operated chain drives on the end trucks of transfer cranes, but the effort required to move such cranes is greater, and the unit cannot be moved down the runway as fast as an operator can walk. There is a further disadvantage in using a crane of this kind, in that the hand-operated chain drive can be located only at one point. Therefore it is necessary for the operator to raise his load onto the carrier, then walk over to the chain drive to move the unit down the runway. In a completely hand-propelled unit, an effort exerted on the load will move the unit at a speed at which the operator wishes to walk.

LAYOUT OF PRODUCTION LINE. An underrunning multirunway crane system requires less headroom than a conventional, top-running crane. In addition, after a plant is in production, there is always the possibility of extending the usefulness of an underrunning type of crane by providing discharge points which permit the transfer of the carrier onto a similar crane in the adjacent bay or bays.

With multirunway underrunning cranes, greater spans are possible for buildings with complete coverage by such cranes, than for the conventional top-running type of crane, at a considerable saving in the steel required for such buildings. Other forms of materials handling equipment, particularly those operating on the floor, require aisle widths anywhere from 6 to 12 ft. If a proper analysis is made of the handling operations, much of this space may be saved by using overhead monorail or tramrail systems.

When designing a new building, provision should be made for extra capacity in the building trusses in addition to that required to carry the roofing and the snow load. Building costs for providing this extra capacity are low. If such provisions are not made and extra space is needed later, reinforcing existing building trusses may become a very expensive undertaking.

PORTABLE CRANES

CONTENTS

CONTENTS *(Continued)*

PORTABLE CRANES

Railroad Cranes

RAILROAD CRANES (RAILROAD GAUGES ONLY). A railroad crane is generally described as a single-flange-wheel, rail-mounted traveling crane. The **wheel gauge** may vary from narrow to wide. The **locomotive crane** is self-propelled, provided with trucks, brakes, automatic couplers or hooks, fittings, and clearances which will permit railroad hauling. Modern locomotive cranes are of the rotating-deck type, consisting of a hinged boom attached to the machinery deck, which is turntable-mounted and operated by a rotating mechanism. The boom is operated by powered topping line with a hoisting mechanism to raise and lower loads. Power is usually deck-mounted with the deck completely housed.

The crane may be powered by steam, internal-combustion engine, electric motor, or the combination of the internal-combustion engine, electric generator, and motor. The internal-combustion engine has very rapidly outdated the older steam-driven crane, with further progress producing the combination of the internal-combustion engine, generator, and electric motor. The car body and machinery deck usually are ballasted, thereby adding stability to the crane when it is rotated under load.

Railroad cranes range in **lifting capacities** upward to 100 tons (excluding wrecking cranes). Many locomotive cranes are so designed that power-shovel, pile-driver, hook, bucket, or magnet attachments may be installed, and the crane used in such service. They are used most extensively in railroad work, and steel mills, and are in rapidly increasing demand in the industrial plants. Usually, locomotive cranes have sufficient propelling power not only for the machine itself, but also for switching service and hauling cars.

Several types of compressed air traction **brake equipment** may be provided. The first and simplest type permits applying the crane brakes only from the crane cab by means of air supplied by the crane. With this type, a through air line is provided, which permits brakes on cars attached with the crane in a train to be applied by means of air supplied by the locomotive hauling the train. A second type of brake, known as "AB"-type freight-car brakes, may be used. This type permits applying the crane brakes either from the crane cab or from the locomotive hauling the crane in a train. A third type, known as straight-and-automatic, permits operation similar to the "AB" type described above, but in addition permits applying brakes on attached cars from the crane cab when the crane is used as a locomotive.

Four-Wheel, Full-Swing-Turntable Railroad Crane. The 4-wheel crane is manufactured in a medium capacity, light weight, and reduced over-all dimension size. Axles are nonswiveling, with conventional railroad journal size and shorter car body than the 8-wheel type (Fig. 1). Full swing provides 360° rotation of the upper deck. Some such cranes are **steam-powered,** with a boiler on the crane deck or steam from an outside source, and some are powered

35·1

by an internal-combustion engine. Other cranes of this type are powered by the combination of **internal-combustion engine,** generator, and electric motor. The engine may drive only the generator which, in turn, drives all crane motions; or it may drive some of the crane motions by mechanical connection while the others are driven electrically by the generator.

Four-Wheel, Part-Swing-Boom Railroad Crane. The part-swing-boom crane consists of an inclined boom attached to a rotating member supported by a frame or pillar, guyed or stiffleg-supported. It is mounted on the car body, forming a single unit with only the boom swinging in a part-circle. Single-flanged wheels, axles, and journals form the car-body support. The crane can be provided with power for travel, hoist, swing, and booming.

Power may be supplied by steam, internal-combustion engine, electric motor, or the combination of internal-combustion engine, generator, an electric motor. **Capacities** normally range upward to 10 tons, but many railroad cranes have much higher capacities. The majority of these railroad cranes are used almost exclusively for materials handling. In a steam-powered 4-wheel, part-swing-boom railroad crane, the steam supply may be on the machinery deck or other source. When the crane is powered by an internal-combustion engine combined with electric generator and motor, the drive may be partly mechanical and partly electric, or electric to all crane motions.

Eight-Wheel, Full-Swing-Turntable Railroad Crane. The crane is generally mounted on two 4-wheel swiveling trucks with brakes, axles, journals, fittings, clearance, and truck capacity to meet railroad requirements (Fig. 1). General description and uses are the same as those already described for railroad cranes in general. Rotation is over a full 360° swing.

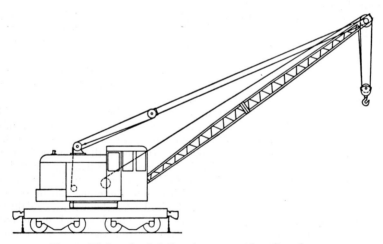

Fig. 1. Eight-wheel, full-swing-turntable railroad crane.

Twelve-Wheel, Full-Swing-Turntable Railroad Crane. The 12-wheel crane is commonly mounted on two 3-axle equalizing trucks. Brakes may be on all or only on some of the wheels. The crane may be pulled or self-propelled, with a selected number of driving axles. Another combination is two 4-wheel swiveling trucks with pedestals between the trucks supporting four wheels. The crane may be powered by steam, internal-combustion engine, electric motor, or the combination of internal-combustion engine, generator, and electric motor. The full-swing-turntable railroad wrecking crane is built with a short boom of gooseneck design with a large capacity and short reach (see Fig. 2). The machinery deck is of typical locomotive-crane design.

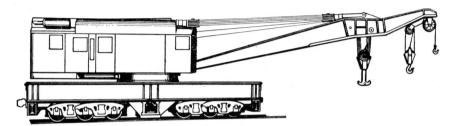

Fig. 2. Twelve-wheel railroad wrecking crane.

Twelve-Wheel, Part-Swing-Boom, Double-End Railroad Wrecking Crane. The trucks for this type of crane are like those for the full-swing-turntable railroad crane. The part-swing-boom double-end railroad wrecking crane has a stationary machinery deck combined with the car body, an independently-operated boom on each end which swings only part way, and either fixed or movable reach. The boom is commonly of the gooseneck design, with multiple-part mainload reeving, auxiliary hoist line, and relatively short reach. The hoist line may be payed beyond the end of the boom and used to drag an object within lifting range. Lifting capacities range upward to 250 tons or more. The crane may be self-propelled or nonpropelled. Power may be supplied by steam, internal-combustion engine, electric motor, or the combination of internal-combustion engine, generator, and electric motor. This type of crane is used predominantly for railroad wrecking, and is adaptable for heavy-material lifts.

Full-Swing-Boom Cranes Mounted on Railroad Flatcars (Not Self-propelled). The full-swing boom pedestal-, or pillar-type, crane has a self-supporting pillar on which the boom and mast top is supported. The boom is normally movable to vary the reach and is winch-controlled. Either a double drum or two independently geared drums are used to vary the radius and hoist a load. Winches and swinger may be hand- or power-operated. This type of crane is **relatively light-duty** and is used for materials handling.

The full-swing-boom Whirley revolving crane mounted on a railroad flatcar is of typical locomotive crane design, minus the trucks and travel mechanism. The turntable body is mounted directly on the flatcar. Although this crane is not self-propelling and cannot be used as a locomotive, its capacities and uses are otherwise equal to those of the locomotive crane.

A small, full-swing, 4-wheel railroad crane can be mounted on a railroad flatcar and functions like a locomotive crane. The major deviation is the shorter body with smaller flanged wheels mounted on rails attached to the flatcar to provide for fore and aft travel. Uses are the same as for a locomotive crane except the car is not self-propelled.

DERRICKS ON RAILROAD FLATCARS. The **stiffleg derrick** mounted on a railroad flatcar is constructed as described under Stiffleg Derricks in the section on Fixed Cranes and Towers except that it is flatcar-mounted and has limited capacities. Maximum lifting capacities are governed by flatcar stability. The circular range of this type of derrick is restricted by the limited location of the stifflegs.

A-Frame Derrick Mounted on Railroad Flatcars. The derrick is as described in the section on Fixed Cranes and Towers and is flatcar-mounted. As with the stiffleg derrick, capacities are limited to car stability. The circular range is greater than that of the stiffleg type.

Gin Poles Mounted on Railroad Flatcars. This gin-pole derrick is as described in the section on Fixed Cranes and Towers and is flatcar-mounted. Circular range and capacities are restricted by flatcar size. Uses of the gin pole, flatcar-mounted, are those of the conventional gin pole except for the limitations imposed by flatcar size and location.

Crawler Cranes

GENERAL SPECIFICATIONS. Crawler cranes are mounted on pairs of endless-tread belts consisting of pin-hinged links or shoes forming continuous belts which fit around the crawler side-frames. The propelling mechanism permits driving either or both tread belts forward or backward for traveling and steering. The length and width of the tread belts provides a large ground bearing area which permits operation on soft and uneven ground and the handling of heavy loads. The usual crawler has one pair of tread belts. Very large crawlers may have a pair of treads at each corner of the base.

Crawler mounting is used where travel distances are nominal and where relatively **slow travel speeds** are acceptable. Crawler maintenance becomes excessive with frequent travel over long distances. Crawler-crane **capacities** vary from approximately 1 ton to over 100 tons. Basic crane rating is the maximum allowable lift with the shortest boom at its minimum operating radius. Rated capacities are generally 75 percent of the load required to tip the crane. Crawler cranes, in general, are adaptable for use as shovels, backhoes, draglines, etc., and may be used with auxiliary equipment.

Full-Swing-Turntable Crawler Crane with Revolving Controls. This is the usual commercial crawler crane. Basic crane ratings vary from approximately 4 to 100 tons. The crane consists of three major components: the revolving turntable, the crawler mounting, and the boom. The revolving **turntable** consists of a bedplate which supports the power plant; the mechanism for hoisting, swinging, propelling, and boom luffing; and the controls for all functions. The bedplate also includes an A-frame structure for supporting the boom luffing cables and sheaves, as well as hinge seats at the forward end for boom foot support.

Power may be supplied from an internal combustion engine, electric motors driven by an outside power supply, a bedplate-mounted combination of engine, generators and motors, or combinations using hydraulic drive. Steam power became obsolete about 1930. Internal combustion engines require a disconnect clutch to permit engine-starting and machinery maintenance, and frequently incorporate variable-speed-gear transmissions, hydraulic couplings, or torque converters. Variable-output speeds are sometimes essential to meet specific lifting requirements. The converter provides increasing torque output with decreasing output speed. It provides a cushion between power and machinery and load, and permits close speed control from zero to maximum. Throttling back the engine permits limited load-lowering.

The **hoisting mechanism** provides for lifting and lowering loads generally by means of one or more drums spooling the hoisting cables. Drums on the usual crawler crane are independently controlled by friction clutches and brakes; those on large cranes may be direct-driven by separate motors. The **swing mechanism** provides rotation of the turntable through 360° in either direction, by means of a pair of friction clutches or by means of an independent reversible motor. The **propelling mechanism** provides travel forward and backward, and steering, by means of a pair of friction clutches or by means of an independent electric motor or motors. Propelling motors may be placed in the crawler mounting. The same pair of friction clutches may provide both swing and propel power, jaw clutches being used to select the proper function. The **luffing mechanism** permits raising and lowering the boom through an arc pivoting about the hinge seats on the bed-plate. Crane service requires accurate, rapid, and reliable luffing for close spotting of loads. The luffing mechanism usually rotates one or more drums for spooling the cables between the supporting A-frame and the boom point (Fig. 3).

Control may be mechanical, air, hydraulic, vacuum, or electrical (independent operation). Controls for all functions are grouped and located for best operator visibility, usually on bedplate level but higher, where required.

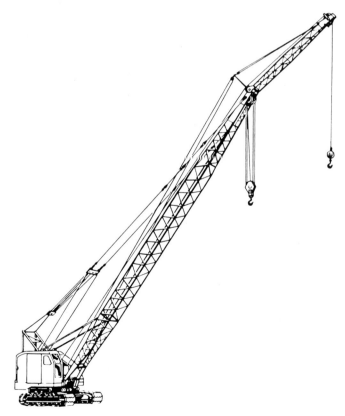

Fig. 3. **Full-swing-turntable crawler crane with revolving controls, powered by internal-combustion engine.**

The **revolving turntable** is carried on the crawler mounting by means of a system of circular tracks and rollers or balls, providing alignment of the turntable and crawler and 360° swing. Swing is actuated by rack and pinion, with the rack mounted on the crawler unit.

The **boom** for small cranes may be of one-piece construction. Larger cranes use a basic boom constructed in two parts with pin, flange, or splice-plate connections. Two-piece booms may be lengthened by intermediate center sections in multiples to obtain lengths up to the maximum recommended by the manufacturer. The use of long booms sometimes requires the use of a high A-frame boom support. Where boom lengths must be greater than recommended, or where an offset tip is required, tip extensions may be installed above the boom head. Such tips have adjustable offset, and are for light service with single or two-part hoisting cables. Fixed gooseneck booms are used for load clearance at minimum operating radius, for clearance of obstructions, and for maximum crane capacities. Boom tip extensions are provided with a single head sheave. Main and gooseneck booms are provided with one or more head sheaves as required for lifting capacity. Special booms are available for special service. The heel-type log-loading boom is an example.

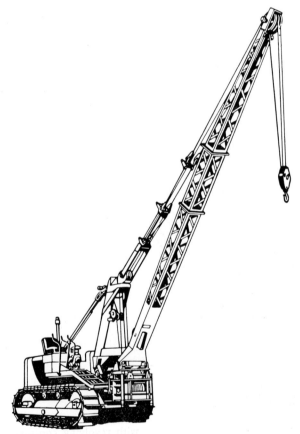

Fig. 4. Part-swing-boom crawler crane with fixed controls.

A full-swing-turntable I.C.E. crawler crane with revolving controls may be **powered** by an internal combustion engine fueled with gasoline, diesel oil, or lique-fied petroleum gas, or, as in the case of the full-swing-turntable I.C.E. hydraulic crawler crane with revolving controls (Fig. 3), may be powered by an internal combustion engine or electric motor(s) driving a hydraulic pump. The pump (or pumps) in turn drive hydraulic motors or rams to perform the various operating functions. Another crane is powered by an internal-combustion-engine generator set and an electric motor or motors. Electric power may also be supplied from an outside source through trailing cable or contact shoes.

Full-Swing-Boom Crawler Crane with Fixed Controls. This type of crane is generally built as an attachment for a crawler tractor. Swing is through an arc of 360°. Capacities are light—approximately 2 tons—and reaches are short. The boom's operating radius may be variable or fixed. The controls do not rotate with the boom. There are three varieties of the **internal-combustion-engine type** of crawler crane with full-swing boom:

1. The full-swing-boom crawler crane with fixed controls, which is powered by an internal-combustion engine, either the tractor engine or a separate engine.
2. The crawler crane with fixed controls, powered by an internal combustion engine driving a hydraulic pump or pumps, which, in turn, drive hydraulic motors or rams.
3. The electric crawler crane with fixed controls, powered by an internal com-bustion-engine generator set which provides power for the operating motor or motors.

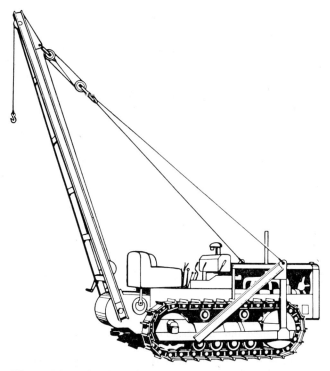

Fig. 5. Nonswing-boom crawler crane with fixed controls.

Part-Swing-Boom Crawler Crane with Fixed Controls. Cranes of this kind are generally built as an attachment for a crawler tractor. Swing is through an arc of approximately 270°. Capacity varies up to approximately 7 tons. Booms are available in lengths up to approximately 50 ft. The boom's operating radius is variable. The controls do not rotate with the boom. The three varieties of the internal-combustion-engine, part-swing-boom crane are:

1. The type powered by an internal-combustion engine, either the tractor engine or a separate engine, such as shown in Fig. 4.
2. The type powered by an internal-combustion engine driving a hydraulic pump or pumps, which, in turn, drive hydraulic motors or rams.
3. The electric crawler-crane type powered by an internal-combustion-engine generator set which provides power for the operating motor or motors.

Nonswing-Boom Crawler Crane with Fixed Controls. Cranes of this type are generally built as crawler tractor attachments. Boom swing is accomplished by steering the tractor. **Maximum capacity** is approximately 10 tons, and maximum boom length is approximately 30 ft. **Operating radius** may be fixed or variable. The controls are fixed (Fig. 5).

Truck and Wagon Cranes

GENERAL DESCRIPTION. Wheeled cranes are mounted on solid or pneumatic rubber tires, or on steel-rim wheels. Steel-rim wheels are obsolete except for light, simple cranes. Capacities vary from a fraction of a ton to approximately 50 tons. Basic crane rating is the maximum allowable lift with the shortest boom at its minimum operating radius. Rated capacities are generally 85 percent of tipping loads. Many wheeled cranes are adaptable for use as shovels, backhoes, and draglines for handling bulk materials.

FULL-SWING-TURNTABLE TRUCK CRANE WITH REVOLVING CONTROLS. This class covers the usual commercial types of truck crane. The crane consists of **three major components**—the revolving turntable, the carrier mounting, and the boom. The revolving turntable consists of a bedplate which supports the turntable power plant on 2-engine machines; the mechanism for hoisting, swing, and boom-luffing; and the controls. The bedplate also includes an A-frame or similar structure for boom outer-end support, and hinge pins for boom inner-end support (Fig. 6).

Truck cranes may have **power** only in the carrier, or they may have two power plants—one in the carrier and one on the turntable. Power may be supplied by an internal-combustion engine, electric motors driven from storage batteries, an outside source, or from an engine-generator set, or an internal-combustion engine driving hydraulic power equipment. Variable output is frequently essential for specific lifting or traction requirements. Variable-speed gear or hydraulic transmissions, hydraulic couplings, or hydraulic torque converters are used. The converter provides control from zero speed to maximum, torque output increasing with decreasing output speed. Throttling back the engine permits limited load lowering.

The **hoisting mechanism** provides for lifting and lowering loads by means of clutched drums for spooling the cables, or by means of hydraulic rams operating directly or through cable and sheaves. The **swing mechanism** provides rotation of the turntable through 360° in either direction by means of a pair of friction clutches or by independent motors or hydraulic rams. The **luffing mechanism** permits raising and lowering the boom through an arc pivoting about the hinge

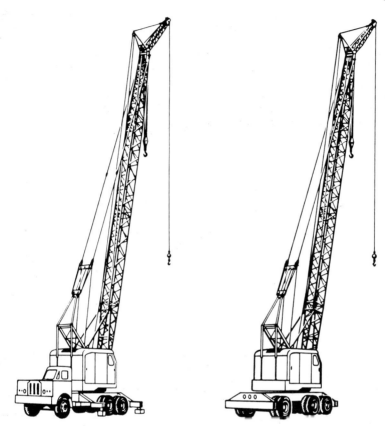

Fig. 6. Six-wheel, two-engine, full-
swing-turntable truck crane.

Fig. 7. Six-wheel, full-swing-turntable
wagon crane.

seats on the bedplate. Crane service requires accurate, rapid, and reliable luffing
for close load-spotting.

Controls for the turntable machinery are mounted on the turntable. Controls
for the carrier may be mounted on either the carrier or on the turntable. The
carrier mounting supports the turntable on a system of circular tracks and
rollers or balls providing alignment of the turntable and carrier and 360° swing.
Swing is generally by rack and pinion. Carriers consist of a frame supported on
two, three, or four axles. The usual arrangement provides equalized support over
the rear axle or axles with spring support over the front axle or axles. Drive from
the carrier engine may be either to the rear axles only or to all axles. Carriers are
designated as 4 × 2 (two axles with rear only driven), 4 × 4 (two axles with both
driven), 6 × 4 (three axles with two rear driven), etc., with dual tires counting
as one wheel. Propel speeds vary to a maximum of approximately 30 mi. per hr.

Booms for small cranes may be of **one-piece** construction, or telescoping for
variable length. Larger cranes use a basic boom in two parts with pin, flange,
or splice plate connections. **Two-piece booms** may be lengthened by intermediate
center sections in multiples to obtain lengths up to the maximum recommended
by the manufacturer. The use of long booms sometimes requires the use of a

high A-frame or boom support. Where boom lengths must be greater than recommended, or where an offset tip is required, **tip extensions** may be installed above the boom head. Such tips have adjustable offset, and are for light service with single or two-part hoisting cables. **Fixed gooseneck booms** are used for load clearance at minimum operating radius, for clearance of obstructions, and for maximum crane capacities. Boom tip extensions are provided with a single head sheave. Main and gooseneck booms are provided with one or more head sheaves as required for lifting capacity. Special booms are available for special service. The heel-type log-loading boom is an example.

There are several types of internal-combustion-engine, full-swing-turntable truck cranes with revolving controls:

1. A 4-wheel, 2-engine crane with 2 axles either 4 × 2 or 4 × 4, powered by one internal-combustion engine in the carrier for propelling; and a second internal-combustion engine on the turntable for hoisting, swinging, and luffing. Propelling controls may be mounted on the carrier, or on the turntable, or both locations.
2. A 4-wheel crane with two axles, either 4 × 2 or 4 × 4, powered by an internal-combustion engine mounted on the carrier.
3. A 4-wheel crane with two axles, either 4 × 2 or 4 × 4, powered by an internal-combustion engine with hydraulic transmission of power for part or all of the functions. The internal-combustion engine is mounted on the carrier.
4. A 4-wheel crane with two axles, either 4 × 2 or 4 × 4, powered by an internal-combustion engine prime mover with electric transmission of power for part, or all, of the functions. The internal-combustion engine is mounted on the carrier.
5. A 6- or 8-wheel crane with 2 engines and three or four axles. Drive for the 3-axle crane in Fig. 6 may be 6 × 4 or 6 × 6; for the 4-axle crane it may be 8 × 4, 8 × 6 or 8 × 8. The crane is powered by an internal-combustion engine in the carrier, for propelling, and a second such engine on the turntable for hoisting, swinging, and luffing. Propelling controls may be mounted in the carrier, or on the turntable, or in both locations. (Fig. 6.)
6. A 6- or 8-wheel crane with three or four axles, powered by an internal-combustion engine mounted in the carrier. Drive for the 3-axle crane may be 6 × 4 or 6 × 6; for the 4-axle, 8 × 4, 8 × 6, or 8 × 8.
7. A 6- or 8-wheel crane with three or four axles, powered by an internal-combustion-engine prime mover, with hydraulic transmission of power for part or all of the functions. The internal-combustion engine is mounted on the carrier. Drive for the 3-axle crane may be 6 × 4, or 6 × 6; for the 4-axle crane it may be 8 × 4, 8 × 6, or 8 × 8.
8. A 6- or 8-wheel crane with three or four axles, powered by an internal-combustion prime mover, with electric transmission of power for part or all of the functions. The internal-combustion engine is mounted on the carrier. Drive for the 3-axle crane may be 6 × 4 or 6 × 6; for the 4-axle crane it may be 8 × 4, 8 × 6, or 8 × 8.

FULL-SWING-TURNTABLE WAGON CRANE WITH REVOLVING CONTROLS. Cranes coming under this classification are similar to those described above (Full-Swing Turntable Truck Cranes) except that the power plant is on the revolving turntable, all the controls are located on the turntable, and the propelling speeds vary up to a maximum of 8 mi. per hr. Carrier propelling power is transmitted from the turntable to the carrier by a vertical shaft at the center of swing. There are eight types of wagon cranes in this classification:

1. A 4-wheel internal-combustion-engine wagon crane with 2 axles, either 4 × 2 or 4 × 4 drive.

2. A 4-wheel crane with two axles, either 4 × 2 or 4 × 4, powered by an internal-combustion-engine prime mover, with hydraulic transmission of power to part or all of the functions.

3. A 4-wheel crane with two axles, either 4 × 2 or 4 × 4, powered by an internal-combustion-engine prime mover, with electric transmission of power for part or all of the functions.

4. A 4-wheel crane with two axles, either 4 × 2 or 4 × 4, powered by an electric motor or motors. Power may be supplied either by storage batteries or from an outside source.

5. A 6- or 8-wheel crane with three or four axles, powered by an internal-combustion engine (Fig. 7). Drive for the 3-axle type may be 6 × 4 or 6 × 6; for the 4-axle type it may be 8 × 4, 8 × 6, or 8 × 8.

6. A 6- or 8-wheel hydraulic crane with three or four axles, powered by an internal-combustion-engine prime mover, with hydraulic transmission to part or all of the functions. Drive for the 3-axle crane may be 6 × 4 or 6 × 6; for the 4-axle crane it may be 8 × 4, 8 × 6, or 8 × 8.

7. A 6- or 8-wheel electric full-swing-turntable wagon crane with three or four axles, powered by an internal-combustion-engine prime mover, with electric transmission to part or all of the functions. Drive for the 3-axle crane may be 6 × 4 or 6 × 6. For the 4-axle crane it may be 8 × 4, 8 × 6, or 8 × 8.

8. A 6- or 8-wheel electric full-swing-turntable wagon crane, with three or four axles, powered by an electric motor or motors. Power may be supplied either by storage batteries, or from an outside source. Drive for the 3-axle crane may be 6 × 4 or 6 × 6; for the 4-axle crane it may be 8 × 4, 8 × 6, or 8 × 8.

Another wagon crane is the English turntable crane, which is shown in Fig. 8. This crane is now widely used in the United States.

Coles Cranes, Inc.

Fig. 8. Turntable electric wagon crane with gas-electric power.

Industrial Mobile Cranes

DEFINITION AND USE. Included in this group are a variety of hoisting mechanisms mounted on **self-propelled** automotive vehicles. These mobile cranes can be used to lift and transport materials in, into, and out of plants, in yards and to and from transportation vehicles and terminals. The basic components of such cranes are shown in Fig. 9. These versatile cranes can readily be adapted to the handling of many objects, but there are certain well-defined conditions where their application is especially indicated:

1. Where the load must be reached for, obstructions being so placed that the handling equipment must remain at a distance.
2. For the unloading, from ground level, of gondola cars, boxcars, trucks and trailers.
3. For handling irregularly shaped objects not readily palletized.
4. For handling loose bulk material in containers or with bucket or magnet.

Although the several classifications of wheeled cranes are widely different in appearance, design, and construction, they all have one characteristic in common: the load is handled on a hook. The load is usually attached to the hook by the use of any one of a wide variety of slings made of chain or cable, or, if the loads are reasonably similar, by means of automatic grabs (see section on Auxiliary Crane Equipment). In addition, there are many kinds of buckets, grapples, and

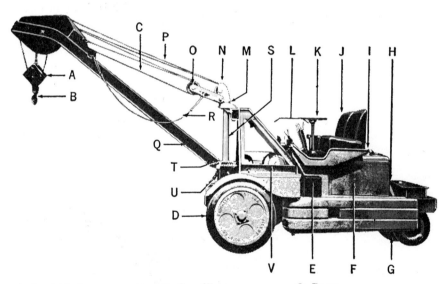

A. Load block.	I. Gas filler.	Q. Boom.
B. Load block swivel hook.	J. Seats.	R. Boom support cable.
C. Boom-topping cable.	K. Steering hand wheel.	S. Masts.
D. Traction wheels.	L. Control levers.	T. Boom-swinger gear sector.
E. Battery.	M. Mast upper bearing.	U. Mast lower bearing.
F. Hood assembly.	N. Mast top sheaves.	V. Frame side channel.
G. Steering wheels.	O. Boom bar sheaves.	
H. Rear steering assembly.	P. Load hoist cable.	

Silent Hoist & Crane Co.

Fig. 9. Components of mobile cranes.

electric magnets that can be used when the material handled calls for some special handling device.

BASIC TYPES. The mobile crane is designed for one-man operation. The simplest type of crane is the one which has a **nonswinging boom** and is used in stevedoring. It will lift loads within its rated capacity without the use of jacks or outriggers and will transport them to the desired destinations. Although capable of high lifting capacity, these units are very compact in their over-all dimensions, and are readily maneuvered. Possibly the most important of the industrial mobile cranes are those adapted to handling their load with a **powered swinging boom.** The operator can not only raise, lower, and transport the load, but also, when required, can readily swing it to right or left without time-consuming maneuvering of the truck. This feature is especially desirable when operating space is at a minimum, making it difficult to turn the entire truck chassis. Like their counterparts in industrial fork trucks, these units can be adapted to gasoline, diesel, or electric-battery operation, and are available on solid or pneumatic tires.

Designed for Industry. Self-propelled cranes used in industrial materials handling are properly designated as industrial mobile cranes, as distinguished from truck and wagon cranes. They are popularly known in the steel industry as **tractor cranes,** and are also known as **crane trucks,** the emphasis being on the vehicle for the reason that many early installations were attachments on motor vehicle trucks.

The industrial mobile crane is an original type and owes little to the older types of turntable cranes used in the construction industry. Industrial mobile cranes of various kinds on the market today are available with power from prime movers —gasoline and diesel—as well as in storage-battery-driven and gas-electric types. All these types are available with swing booms turning generally through a half circle. Some are available that will swing in larger arcs, up to a full circle. **Unit booms** and sectional **telescopic booms** of various kinds and shapes are also available.

The industrial mobile crane is used in every industry where heavy or bulky loads must be lifted and moved: for loading and unloading operations, erection work, combined lifting and transporting operations, placing work in machines, plant maintenance, and many other plant and outside-of-plant materials handling operations.

Origin of Tractor Crane. The earliest kind of tractor crane was developed because of the need for a mobile crane for cargo-handling on the waterfront. As the designation implies, the towing tractor, already a feature on the wharf, was called into this service. The installation of a fixed boom on the forward end and a winch at the rear completed the metamorphosis. Including a few refinements, the description will apply generally to stevedoring cranes in use today.

MODERN STEVEDORING CRANE. The modern stevedoring crane developed from the above type, and is generally of nonswing-boom construction, but with a great many improvements (see Figs. 10 and 11). It is still the preferred type of crane for use on the waterfront. The **lower first cost** of this kind of crane is a factor in its preference. Where ample space is available on the wharf or in the plant for the crane to turn in—avoiding the need for slewing the boom—this kind of crane is usually faster to operate and simpler to handle.

In the modern crane the load is usually carried on the **traction wheels** and the steering is at the rear, so that the transportation of a load does not adversely

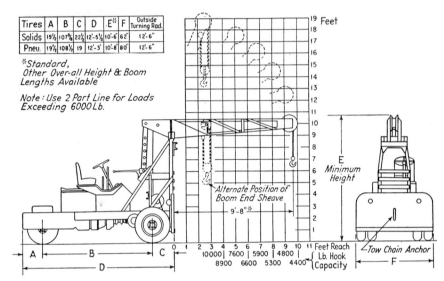

Tires	A	B	C	D	E*	F	Outside Turning Rad.
Solids	19½	107⅝	22½	12'-5½	10'-6"	62"	12'-6"
Pneu.	19½	108½	19	12'-3	10'-8"	80"	12'-6"

*Standard,
Other Over-all Height & Boom
Lengths Available

Note: Use 2 Part Line for Loads
Exceeding 6000 Lb.

Feet Reach | 1 | 2 | 3 | 4 | 5 | 6 | 7 | 8 | 9 | 10 | 11
Lb. Hook Capacity: 10000 | 7600 | 5900 | 4800 | 8900 | 6600 | 5300 | 4400

Fig. 10. Capacity table and tire chart for nonswing-boom stevedoring crane.

affect the traction or the steering of the vehicle. The large driving wheels in front are suited to carry the concentration of tractor and working load, thus providing a maximum of tractive effort for traveling, light or loaded. This type of crane is generally of 5-ton capacity and has a **boom**, hinged on top of the frame, providing the maximum of reach with a minimum of required headroom. The boom is generally of balanced cantilever girder design, power-operated, and can be raised and lowered by power from the driver's seat. It can also be adjusted—without a load on the hook—to any of a number of positions of reach and height of hook, depending on the character of the load and the overhead conditions in the operating area. Often the crane has a hydraulic ram that can raise and lower the boom even when a full-capacity load is suspended from the hook.

SWING-BOOM MOBILE CRANE. Cranes of the type shown in Fig. 12 have, in addition to a load line hoist, facilities of a mechanical or hydraulic design for topping the boom, and a swinger mechanism for slewing the boom in varying degrees, usually up to a half circle or full circle. In the usually compact design of industrial cranes, as distinguished from turntable cranes, the **crane and travel controls** of swing-boom cranes are centralized and the operator is stationary in an open or closed cab. This design is practically universal. A disadvantage that must generally be accepted in cranes of this kind having a boom swing of more than 180° is that the tail swing of the boom—usually counterweighted and swinging over the operator's head—is beyond the normal dimensions of the crane. It is fortunate, therefore, that the vast majority of the requirements of industry and transportation do not entail the slewing of the boom beyond a half circle, or 90° to each side of the crane.

For operations requiring more than 180° of swing, several cranes are available. One variety, developed for military service (Fig. 12) will lift and transport its rated capacity of 8,000 lb. It has a telescopic boom which can be raised from horizontal to approximately a 40° angle, and is rotatable through 360°. The

Silent Hoist & Crane Co.

Fig. 11. Hydraulically operated, nonswinging-boom crane.

angle of the boom can be changed during operation under load. Another type provides a swing through 320°. Swing-boom mobile cranes are available in lift capacities from 2,500 lb. to 20,000 lb.

Power Supply. Mobile cranes for industrial applications are available with electric, gas-electric, gasoline, and diesel-engine drives. The **storage-battery-powered machines** are generally designed for indoor service and are preferred for use in warehouses, and in plants where flammable materials are stored, or where exhaust gases are a problem. Cranes on storage-battery-operated industrial trucks have reached a high degree of development. They operate most successfully in-plant on good pavement. Cranes are available in capacities ranging from 1 to 5 tons. A gas-electric unit (Fig. 13) sometimes replaces the battery. **Gasoline-engine-driven cranes** are generally preferred for outside-plant operations for their greater power, speed, and capacity for uninterrupted work.

FEATURES OF SWING-BOOM MOBILE CRANES. The **design of a crane** is influenced by the duty, capacity required, ground conditions, frequency of the operation, nature of the product to be handled, and other factors.

Austin-Western Co.

Fig. 12. Heavy-duty, swing-boom, hydraulic mobile crane.

The industrial mobile crane has certain characteristic features. It is provided with large **traction wheels** suitable for indoor as well as outdoor service. Some cranes are designed mainly for outdoor service and generally have **pneumatic tires.** Cranes for both indoor and outdoor service are usually equipped with **solid-type cushion tires** since they enable the designer to keep the cranes much narrower. Mobile cranes may be equipped with ample low-pressure tires to negotiate the most adverse ground conditions, mud, snow, sand, etc.

Automatic Transportation Co.

Fig. 13. Swing-boom, gas-electric powered mobile crane with telescopic boom.

The modern swing-boom crane has a drive to the front traction wheels and is steered from the rear wheels. It provides good vision to front, rear, and both sides. It is designed for relatively **low headroom** to enable it to go indoors and under overhead obstructions. It has a relatively short turning radius and, above all, stability in handling loads from the front and either side without the use of jacks or outriggers. Careful balancing with properly placed **counterweights** provides nearly equal stability and capacity from the front and both sides. It provides a travel-speed range of not less than three speeds in forward and reverse. The operator should be able to pick up and swing safely to either side any load within the capacity of the crane. The **range of speeds** is required for the conditions in which a choice of speeds is very necessary for efficient operation. In many operations in the plant, and especially in narrow aisles, the operator is required to back his machine up as frequently as he drives forward. It is necessary for him therefore to have a good range of speeds in reverse.

Fluid Drive Crane. Cranes are now available with hydraulic fluid-coupling drive, sturdy enough for heavy-duty industrial service. The fluid drive provides a hydraulic cushion, smooth starting, and smooth acceleration, and eliminates overload shocks to driving gears. Better performance and over-all daily efficiency is obtained, as well as longer clutch life and reduction of maintenance expense.

CRANE CONTROLS. The modern mobile crane will have conveniently located centralized controls for all of the operations and travel of the crane. It

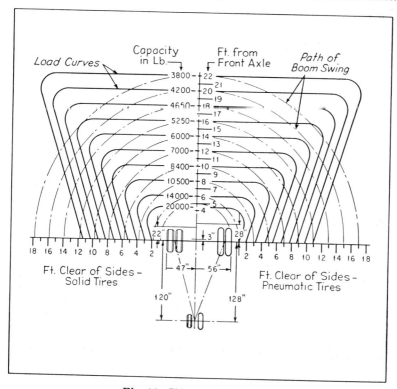

Fig. 14. Side-capacity chart.

will in all cases provide positive hoisting and lowering of the load without dependence on brakes. It has a **boom winch** that will enable the operator to top the boom with a full load or light load under any conditions, and independent of the other functions of the crane. It will be provided with a hydraulic or mechanical **slewing mechanism** for swinging the boom to the right or to the left, without danger of overswinging. Fig. 14 is a side-capacity chart. Loads picked up at the front of the crane can be swung around to the side, either right or left, and transported safely within the ranges indicated on the chart.

The mobile crane is generally used for hook-line work, which requires of it an ability for deliberate, accurate lowering and hoisting of fragile as well as heavy loads. The hook-clearance chart in Fig. 15 gives the reach and capacity of the truck for various boom lengths. Positive **hoisting and lowering** must be available through gearing which will automatically hold when the power fails or the winch is disconnected; **braking** should be completely automatic; and provision should be made for automatic disengagement of the power when the upper limit of the boom is reached. Likewise, the boom-hoisting winch should provide positive power for raising and lowering of the boom and disengage automatically when the upper limit of the boom is reached.

Mobile cranes may occasionally be used for the handling of loose materials with a clamshell or orange-peel bucket, or other grab (see section on Crane Equipment). They are definitely neither designed nor suitable for continuous

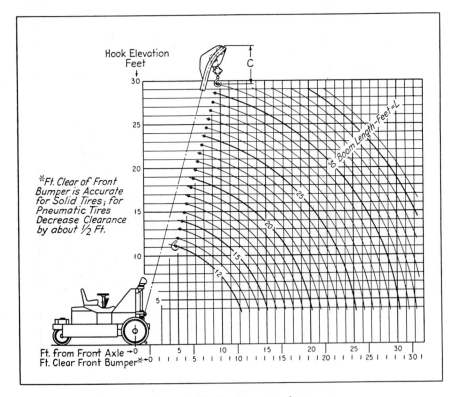

Fig. 15. Hook-clearance chart.

operation in this type of use. On such applications, additional auxiliary equipment is required, and such machines may be equipped with friction clutches, to permit a gravity drop of the bucket.

Cranes are now available in which many functions of the crane here discussed are accomplished through hydraulic rams or hydraulic motors, which replace mechanical gearing as intermediate drives. Such a crane is shown in Fig. 11. For some kinds of machines this hydraulic equipment has simplified the design and operation of the equipment. There are definite limitations to the uses of these types of power transmission devices, however, and these limitations must be considered. **Hydraulic controls** have come into considerable use and offer a simplicity of operation and in many instances a degree of safety and convenience not available with mechanical controls.

DESIGN MODIFICATIONS. One of the more recent developments is a **small crane** 51 in. wide, having an 11-ft. turning radius. It will maneuver in and out of boxcars, and will handle loads easily in cramped, congested areas. This small crane swings its boom by power through an arc of 250°, and provides four geared speeds in 4 to 25 sec. It is equipped with a heavy-duty tractor-type engine developing approximately 45 hp., and can be supplied with the usual accessories and attachments for any kind of crane service within its capacity.

A **dual-function machine** combining the capacities of a crane and a lift truck is shown in Fig. 16. This development should not be confused with auxiliary attachments which are covered elsewhere. The crane referred to is as efficient a

Automatic Transportation Co.

Fig. 16. Mobile crane with hammerhead boom on electric, low-lift platform truck equipped with outriggers.

lift truck as it is a crane, and was developed primarily for stevedoring service. It is used in industries that require the services of a crane and a fork truck at different times, but do not need specialized machines of both kinds.

Fig 17 shows a special development of the **pneumatic-tired mobile crane.** It is designed to operate on soft ground and on the beach, is equipped with dual-traction tires and a wide steering axle, and has a weight capacity of 20,000 lb. The forward wheels are equipped with 10- × 24-in., 12-ply pneumatic tires. The crane will easily carry rated loads on ground conditions that would otherwise require a track-laying vehicle.

Silent Hoist & Crane Co.

Fig. 17. Industrial truck crane with oversized pneumatic tires for operations on beach or soft terrain.

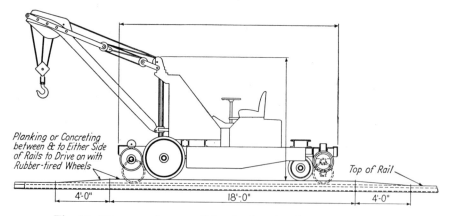

Planking or Concreting
between & to Either Side
of Rails to Drive on with
Rubber-tired Wheels

Top of Rail

4'-0"   18'-0"   4'-0"

Fig. 18. Diagram of convertible-wheel, swing-boom mobile crane.

Another development of the mobile industrial crane is a machine, shown in Fig. 18, that may be used alternately on railroad tracks, in the storage yard, or on the highway. The **auxiliary flanged wheels** are retractable, and a technique has been developed to permit the crane to leave the tracks rapidly and operate on the highway or yard area on pneumatic rubber tires. This technique, reversed, returns the vehicle onto the rails with the flanged steel wheels.

Portable Floor Cranes

USE OF PORTABLE FLOOR CRANES. Non-self-propelled portable floor cranes are in general use in machine shops, plant assembly departments, outdoor yard service, and warehouses, at transportation terminals, and in garages. They are frequently employed in shipping and receiving departments for unloading incoming raw materials, large and heavy cases, lumber, etc., and loading outgoing shipments. They are likewise employed to supplement overhead traveling cranes and other power-operated equipment. In many small manufacturing plants, they are—aside from hoists and other local service equipment—the only kinds of materials handling equipment in use.

Selecting a Portable Floor Crane. In selecting a portable floor crane, it is frequently necessary to give first consideration to the height of ceiling and doorways in the location where the crane is to be used. The over-all height of crane and the distance it will lift from floor level should then be considered, in addition to the crane's lifting capacity.

PORTABLE GANTRY FLOOR CRANE. Portable gantry cranes are generally available in one- and two-ton capacities. The gantry crane is comprised of two A-frames, fabricated of structural steel or pipe, connected by a beam providing a track for a trolley (Fig. 19). The frames are usually of welded construction for permanent shop-floor use and can be equipped with wheels. Such cranes

Fig. 19. Portable gantry crane.

Fig. 20. Gooseneck shop crane with U-base.

Revolvator Co.

Fig. 21. Portable cantilever floor crane with revolving base and hinged upright.

are also made in bolted sections so that they may be knocked down and conveniently transported. For this purpose the units are made of tubular sections so designed as to be easily taken apart for carrying or for compact storage.

JIB AND GOOSENECK CRANES. The cantilever-jib or gooseneck type of crane is the commonest and most convenient type of portable floor crane, and is used in many shops to supplement an overhead monorail system or a traveling crane in reaching locations that cannot be served by the regular overhead equipment. It is also used in railroad freight houses and terminals where overhead systems are not available. Gooseneck cranes have been made with cast, forged, or fabricated steel frames. In modern design for economy and light weight, they are generally of welded construction of rolled steel sections. These cranes are made in many varieties, sizes, and capacities (Fig. 20).

Worm-geared and spur-geared **winches** of the safety type are usually installed on the cranes. On a frequently used type, the hoist-handle controls movement of the crane automatically, the wheels becoming locked when the handle is raised to the completely vertical position. Wheels and casters for several different types of mounting are available, and are usually of ball- and roller-bearing types.

Spur-geared winches are provided with ratchet and pawl which hold the load suspended at any point. Another kind of floor crane is provided with a friction **load-brake** which automatically provides safe suspension of the load at any

Stratton Equipment Co.

Fig. 22. Portable hand hydraulic-boom floor crane.

point, and permits the load to be lowered by reversing the crank. It provides accuracy of control and is to be preferred for many applications. Portable shop cranes are very handy tools in garages, assembly departments, and machine shops, for moving motors, engines, castings, etc., into and out of machine tools, or dies into and out of punch presses, and for loading and unloading trucks and moving heavy articles in and around the shop.

SPECIAL FEATURES. A useful feature found on some portable cranes is the adjustable boom which slides in and out to any working position. Another feature which increases the usefulness of the crane is a revolving base that may be safely locked in any of several positions. Still another valuable feature available on many cranes permits the vertical frame, which is hinged, to be folded down to allow the crane to pass through ordinary doorways (Fig. 21). Other special designs include the hydraulic boom crane shown in Fig. 22 and a jib crane mounted on a telescopic mast. The mast for the latter is raised and lowered by a hydraulic pump or by a cable and pulley system actuated by a hand or electric winch. The unit is mounted on a wheeled base for portability.

Floating Cranes and Derricks

DEFINITION AND USE. Floating cranes and derricks consist of hulls or pontoons on which are mounted some form of unit-load- or bulk-material-handling equipment similar in function, arrangement, and detail to that used on land. In some cases, the installations are very elaborate and have no similarity to land equipment. They furnish a means for handling material on, around, and from the water which cannot otherwise be reached, and they can be moved on the water to locations inaccessible to other equipment. In the field of heavy lifting equipment they furnish a mobility not readily available in any other class of portable cranes. Floating cranes and derricks are used for salvage work, harbor-clearing, dredging, excavating, pipe-laying, alongshore and offshore construction, ship-servicing, and ship repair, and for package- and bulk-cargo loading or discharging. They may be equipped with hooks, buckets, grabs, pile-leads, or any device needed for special operations. Capacities vary from the smallest to as large as 800 tons.

The hull may be a single pontoon of wood or steel, or may consist of a number of smaller pontoons of such a size as will permit disassembly of the floating

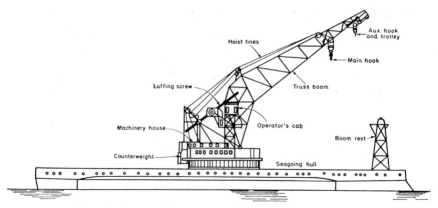

Fig. 23. Crane ship *Kearsarge*—capacity, 250 gross tons.

crane for shipment by rail to land-locked waters (see Fig. 24). This disassembly feature is usually confined to floating cranes of smaller capacity, up to perhaps 50 tons maximum. Hulls may be arranged for towing, or may be self-propelled and equipped with rudders. **Self-propelled** cranes, except for crane ships, are usually of slow speed, primarily for maneuvering. Hulls may be suitable for still-water service only, or specially designed for service in rougher or less protected waters. Fig. 23 depicts the seagoing crane ship "Kearsarge," of 250 gross tons capacity.

The **crane** or **derrick** may be a fixed structure with no motion of hook except hoisting, in which case further maneuvering of the hook load is accomplished by the motion of the floating crane in the water. The hook may be mounted on a trolley so that the load may be moved in or out. Swinging, or luffing, or both, may be incorporated in the operations. Swinging, when provided for, may be partial or full. Luffing may be by rope, rack and pinion, or link. Level luffing may be employed as described later in connection with the operation of floating revolving cranes.

Floating cranes and derricks may be **powered by steam, diesel engine, or diesel-electric equipment.** Gasoline is sometimes used for small units, and hydraulic applications are sometimes made in the case of large special equipment.

During operation, floating equipment may be held in position by **tie-lines** or lashing from appropriate deck-fittings to docks, other floating equipment, or to stationary shore objects such as trees; or held stationary by means of several **anchors,** with anchor lines to deck windlasses or capstans, thus affording maneuverability; or by spuds extending through spud wells in the pontoon and into the material below. Limited travel of **nonpropelled** floating equipment is sometimes accomplished by means of a casting weight where the crane or derrick is of a type which can cast the weight ahead.

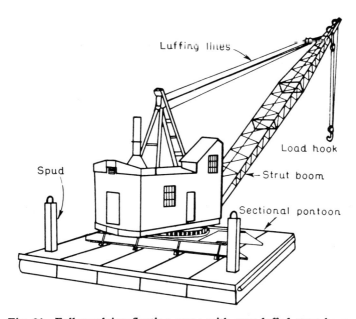

Fig. 24. **Full-revolving floating crane with rope-luffed strut boom.**

FLOATING REVOLVING CRANES. An important general class of floating cranes is that in which the crane portion swings freely on a system of **live rollers** or **trucks,** or on a **pintle-bearing,** with swing unlimited in any direction. Floating revolving cranes, such as those shown in Figs. 24 and 25, are constructed in a wide range of types, capacities, and speeds, with a maximum capacity of 350 gross tons. **Rope speeds** vary from 150 to 350 ft. per min., and, when ropes are reeved single-part for light loads or light buckets, hoisting speeds will

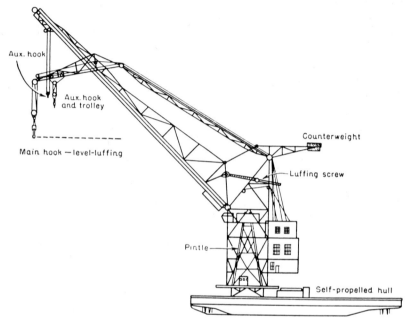

Fig. 25. 350-ton, full-revolving floating crane with level luffing.

be the same. For heavy loads, the hoisting speed is reduced by the reeving, usually chosen with service requirements in mind. Typically, a 100-ton hook-load may travel from 15 to 20 ft. per min. Larger loads are handled at still slower speeds. Hoisting speeds are usually higher for bucket work than for hook work. Similarly, swing speeds may vary from 3 r.p.m. for light cranes up to several minutes for one revolution on heavy cranes.

Engines for floating revolving cranes may be multiple-drum friction engines, or separate direct-connected engines may be installed for each motion. Friction engines are more often used for normal-capacity equipment up to 100 tons. Individual engines are used for larger cranes and for some smaller cranes. **Swinging** is accomplished by rack-and-pinion gear, with the rack mounted on the stationary portion and the pinion mounted on the revolving portion. The swing-engine may be operated through a power take-off from the main engine, or it may be separately powered.

Floating revolving cranes may be **self-propelled, or nonself-propelled** and moved by towing. A crane ship is a revolving crane, usually of large capacity, mounted on a self-propelled hull of ship shape, fully equipped for relatively long seagoing operations and moving at a moderately high speed. Most often, floating revolving cranes are nonself-propelled, but in some instances they are provided with limited propulsion for local maneuvering.

Luffing of revolving cranes is most frequently accomplished by **wire-rope reeving. Strut-type booms** are usually used with the reeving mechanism attached at, or near, the boom tip. This arrangement is used on cranes wherein a conventional "Whirley," "Whirler," "Revolver," or other similar crane is mounted on a single large pontoon or multiple smaller pontoons. The strut-type boom carries its load as a latticed column or strut. Wire-rope luffing is also used with **truss-type booms,** where the boom carries its load largely as a cantilever truss; the luffing reeving is attached at a position usually back of the midpoint. Truss-type booms are often used where the boom foot-pin is elevated to provide substantial vertical clearance below the boom at the side of the crane hull, to permit work close to the side of a ship, cofferdam, or other structure.

Special luffing arrangements provide **level luffing,** as in the floating crane in Fig. 25, wherein the raising and lowering of the boom cause the hook load to move in and out on a level path without change in elevation. For level-luffing cranes, the boom may be luffed by means of wire rope, screws, rack-and-pinion gearing and linkage, or other mechanical arrangements, and level luffing may be accomplished by the arrangement of the hoist reeving, by movable-boom-tip sections mechanically- or rope-operated, by specially designed hoisting engines, or by other means. Level luffing is used only infrequently for floating cranes, and is more commonly practiced in Europe than in the United States. It is most commonly used for high-speed cargo cranes. Extremely fast luffing is possible when the boom weight is balanced by a boom counterweight. Occasionally, level luffing is used for very large cranes. For the larger floating revolving cranes, truss-type booms are most commonly used and screw or rack-and-pinion luffing is often employed.

FLOATING DERRICKS—PARTIAL SWING. Floating derricks constitute a general classification in which the many forms of derricks are mounted on hulls or pontoons. Floating derricks of the partial-swing type are usually limited to an arc of from 180 to 270°. The boom and load are swung by rope-operated **bull wheel,** by **vang lines** attached to the boom, and in some instances by **rack and pinion** (self-swinging). Many arrangements of derricks are used. Steam, direct diesel, or diesel-electric power equipment can be used for moving the derricks. Engines are usually of the multiple-drum friction type and are mounted on the deck to the rear of the derrick, particularly in the case of the smaller sizes. They may be mounted on the mast or A-frame in the case of self-swinging derricks.

Floating derricks are mainly of small **capacity,** but may range up to 250 tons in capacity. They are used primarily for marine projects such as construction of docks, jetties, breakwaters, bridge piers, underwater pipe-laying, pile-driving, and similar work, and, when equipped with clamshell buckets, may be used for cofferdam and underwater excavation and dredging. In some instances they are used for offshore cargo handling.

Floating derricks may be equipped with a **standard stiffleg derrick** as in Fig. 26, or a **special marine derrick.** A marine derrick differs from the land variety only in that lay legs are omitted, the hull deck serving to fulfill the support function. The limiting size of hulls together with the necessity for keeping the various hull structures clear for operations results in many different arrangements of guys and stifflegs. Derricks have been constructed with a mast and two stifflegs, a mast and three stifflegs, or a mast and four stifflegs. They are also

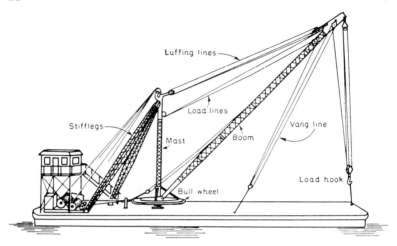

Fig. 26. Floating stiffleg derrick with mast and two stifflegs.

constructed with a mast and one rear stiffleg, using guys for lateral support. Another arrangement consists of a mast with stifflegs for lateral support, and supports consisting of fixed guys extending generally to the rear. In some cases masts are omitted where more than two stifflegs are used, and the boom is independently supported on the deck.

A **bull wheel** operating from an independent swinger engine is used for swinging derrick booms in the case of the smaller higher-speed derricks, but **vanging lines** are used for the heavier-capacity derricks usually operated at slower speeds. A special form of derrick is the **self-swinging type** wherein the hoisting machinery is mounted on a platform framed to the mast in such a way that the platform, hoisting machinery, and mast swing as a unit (see Fig. 27). This arrangement permits self-swinging by rack and pinion, and also permits the addition of a counterweight at the rear of the hoist-engine's supporting platform, which reduces hull list when a load is lifted from the side.

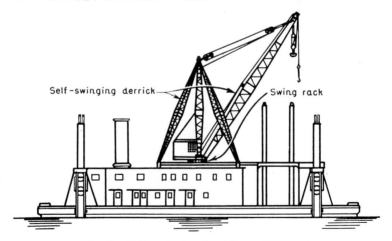

Fig. 27. Self-swinging derrick on drill boat.

Derricks are usually constructed of steel in the form of **latticed struts** and ties, although steel pipe construction is often used. **Timber** is still employed for derricks of small capacity.

FLOATING CRANES AND DERRICKS—NONSWINGING. This is a general class of heavy floating cranes, specially designed for specific service where limited motion of the load is sufficient. The main function of such cranes and derricks is to raise loads, and in some cases to move these loads along a fixed runway. Such cranes have been constructed with auxiliary crane equipment mounted thereon to serve a secondary purpose quite apart from the handling of the main load.

Nonswinging floating cranes and derricks take a variety of widely differing forms and arrangements. Among these are the **floating guyed A-frame (shear legs) derrick,** and the **floating luffing A-frame (shear legs) derrick.** These derricks comprise a shear legs, usually a braced framework in the form of the letter "A," mounted near the front end of the hull, canted forward for stability, and

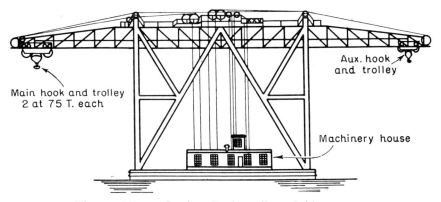

Fig. 28. 150-ton, floating, fixed cantilever bridge crane.

carrying the load block at the apex or top of the frame. The **guying arrangement** includes fixed rearward guys, and the motion of the load is limited to hoisting and lowering. The **luffing arrangement** includes rearward guys consisting of multiple-part reeving which may be extended or taken up, thus permitting not only hoisting and lowering but a limited horizontal movement. Derricks of this type are used largely for salvage work or on special types of construction.

A **nonswinging crane** providing somewhat more flexibility of operation results when a **fixed cantilever bridge crane** such as that shown in Fig. 28 is mounted on a hull. Cranes of this type may be provided with one or two extended cantilevers and one or more trolleys and are capable of lifting and transferring loads from one side of the crane hull to the other or from one side of the crane hull to the crane deck. Such cranes are used for miscellaneous cargo handling where they may lie between a ship and lighter and transfer cargo either way. They are also used for marine repair work under the same conditions and can be used effectively on some types of marine construction such as the building of jetties or breakwaters.

A **fixed cantilever crane**—one type of which is shown in Fig. 29—may be mounted on a hull with load hook suspended at the outer end of the cantilever. Hoisting machinery is located at deck level. The hoisting machinery provides only a means for hoisting and lowering. Floating fixed cantilever cranes are sometimes provided with a truss structure, level along the top, on which is mounted a small- or moderate-capacity low-carriage-type full-revolving traveling crane.

Floating cranes constructed for **special purposes** and operations are often known by names which describe their use or application. Typically, a "Gate Lifter," is a floating crane designed particularly to lift heavy lock gates for repair and replacement and may have a capacity up to 500 tons. Such a special crane may require a hull with curved rear to decrease turning radius and permit maneuvering between lock walls.

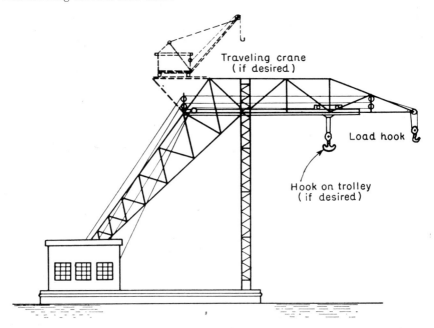

Fig. 29. Floating fixed cantilever crane.

GRAB-BUCKET OR DRAGLINE DREDGE. Equipment of this kind makes up a general classification of floating cranes or derricks equipped with clamshell or dragline buckets, or arranged to operate with either. Properly, the term dredge applies to equipment specifically designed for underwater excavation, but dredging is performed by many floating cranes. **Capacities** vary up to 10 cu. yd. for clamshell buckets and somewhat higher for dragline buckets. Dredges may be equipped with special buckets or grapples for particular operations. Grab-bucket and dragline dredges are of two main types—the full-revolving crane type and the stiffleg-derrick or partial-swinging type, which is shown in Fig. 30.

Full-revolving grab-bucket dredges are usually all-purpose, full-revolving cranes mounted on a suitable hull with engines and reeving arranged to operate the grab bucket. Grab-bucket operation requires two hoist drums of equal diameter and speed and boom-point sheaves arranged in tandem or in parallel to suit bucket reeving.

Full-revolving dragline dredges are usually full-revolving cranes mounted on a suitable hull, with engines and reeving arranged to handle the dragline bucket; or they may be constructed by utilizing land dragline machines. Dragline dredges require a fair-lead for the drag rope at the front of the rotating structure and a single sheave at boom tip. Usually the drag drum of the engine operates at slower speed and provides a greater line pull than does a hoist drum. While such machines are mostly of the full-revolving type, this feature is not always required, because dredging is usually performed from the front of the dredge, the excavated material being deposited in a scow alongside.

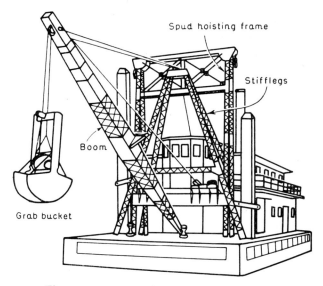

Fig. 30. Stiffleg-derrick, grab-bucket dredge.

The most usual form of grab-bucket dredge is of the **stiffleg-derrick type,** consisting of a derrick with four stifflegs, with or without mast, mounted on a hull, and usually complete with living and maintenance facilities. It is of very rugged construction for heavy duty. The boom is usually of moderate length to reach over the front of the hull for digging and over the side of the hull for dumping into barges or scows. Swing of the boom is usually limited to slightly under 180°. Swinging may be by bull wheel, vang line, or by the use of the bucket-hoist lines reeved so as to produce a side force on the boom. Capacities vary with digging depth, material being handled, and size of dredge.

Auxiliary Cranes on Vehicles

DEFINITION. All kinds of cranes have been mounted on motor trucks, wheeled and crawler tractors, and railroad cars. The choice of type is determined by the **nature of the operation and its specific requirements.** The cranes covered here are those mounted on motor truck chassis that are primarily transport vehicles, the cranes being auxiliary units to aid in the loading and unloading of trucks as well as in the handling of the material within reach of the truck. By this definition these types of installations are distinguished from the several other kinds of cranes covered elsewhere in this handbook, in which the vehicle is primarily a carrier for the crane and does not serve to transport a useful load for any considerable distance.

SWINGING BOOM PEDESTAL CRANES ON MOTOR VEHICLES.

Cranes in this category are available in capacities of from 1 to 20 tons and are illustrated by the typical installation in Fig. 31. A unit having a capacity of 2,000 lb. will occupy only about 20 in. of space behind the driver's cab, and might be used by a public utility to collect portable tool carts and materials from the streets and deliver them to various destinations. A crane which occupies about 40 in. of space behind the cab is capable of loading a 10-ton transformer onto the truck, delivering it to the site, and lowering it into the street vault. Whether used by a public utility in operations similar to those described, or in industry, or by a trucker or rigger, these cranes make the transport vehicle independent of outside materials handling equipment at terminals, this latter equipment in many instances being ineffective for the handling work, or not available at all.

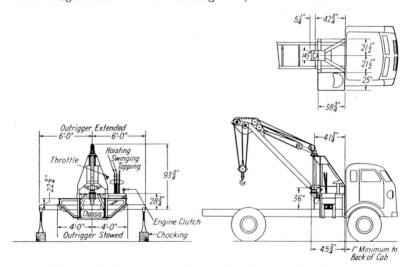

Fig. 31. Auxiliary powered, swinging boom, pedestal crane.

Cranes of this type are generally characterized by the sturdy fabricated steel A-frame at the back of the cab which houses the winches and swinger gear and provides support for the mast. A hinged boom of either the single-piece or the telescopic type is attached at about 4 ft. above the base of the mast, this height providing an adequate clearance under the boom for loading the truck.

The characteristic and inexorable limiting factor in the **lifting capacity** of crane installations on motor trucks is the stability of the truck. Unlike the standard truck crane, which is self-stabilized by counterweighting, the motor truck cannot practically be encumbered with counterweights. Fortunately, the truck is seldom called upon to transport a load on the end of the hook.

Motor truck auxiliary crane installations are often provided with a **telescopic outrigger** for each side of the chassis. For heavy-duty installations, two such outriggers may be necessary. At the end of each outrigger a jack, often hydraulic, is lowered to the ground. By this arrangement, the truck's springs and tires are relieved of the load, and the turning base of the crane is greatly extended.

The **maximum rated capacity** of a truck auxiliary crane installation is usually at a 6-ft. radius, which, on the usual truck body platform, provides approximately a 2-ft. clearance from the sides. The size of the chassis for a crane installation is determined by the capacity of the crane, as well as by the nature of the operation for which it is to be used. The size of the motor is seldom a factor, since the power requirement of the crane is relatively light. A 10-ton load lifted at 20 ft. per min., will only require about 20 hp. Therefore the selection of the proper size of chassis will be decided more by the loads that the truck will be called upon to transport and the stability of the unit than by the loads the crane will be called upon to lift. As stated, the **power and power transmission** of even the average 1½-ton truck is adequate for a 5-ton crane installation. The chassis frame will of course have to be reinforced, even on a 5-ton chassis. It is imperative on every crane installation, on truck or tractor, to check with the vehicle's manufacturers regarding the carrying capacity of the frame, transmission housing, or any other point that will sustain added stress.

Motor truck auxiliary cranes derive their power from the truck engine through an auxiliary gear box called a **power take-off,** attached to the truck's transmission (Fig. 32). Thus the engine that provides power for the motor truck

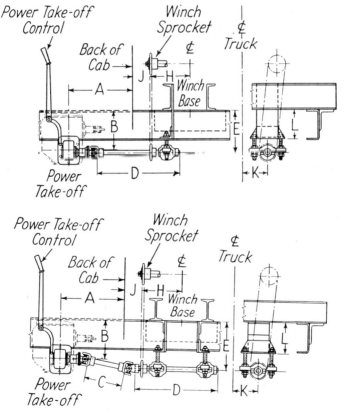

Fig. 32. Power take-offs for auxiliary cranes, available for all makes and models of motor trucks.

also serves as the power unit for the crane that is mounted on the truck. The controls for shifting the power take-off into gear and the various controls for the crane are usually grouped and located at the crane side behind the cab.

Fig. 33 illustrates the smaller cranes of 1-, 2-, and 3-ton capacity, where the hook is raised and lowered by power, and swinging of the boom and topping of the boom is ordinarily accomplished manually. The **larger cranes are completely power-operated.** The worm-geared winches are power-reversing for raising and lowering the hook, for swinging the boom from right to left, and for topping the boom. The completely power-operated cranes, of course, are faster, more versatile, safer, and easier to operate. They are usually preferred for these features by public utilities, industry, and professional riggers. Because of the manifold uses that truck auxiliary cranes are called upon to serve, they are occasionally furnished with special attachments such as an orange-peel bucket for cleaning sewer basins or for handling bulk material.

Silent Hoist & Crane Co.

Fig. 33. Manually operated, swinging boom crane.

SWINGING JIB CRANES. Thus far, the illustrations have been devoted to swinging boom pedestal cranes, wherein the boom is raised and lowered to adjust the hook for reach and height. Other types of cranes, classed as swinging jib cranes, wherein the boom is horizontal, swings, and is outfitted with a trolley for the hook (see Fig. 34). This kind of crane is generally used for picking up commodities that are loaded uniformly over the entire truck body. A typical application of this crane is in the transportation of test weights for the testing of public scales. The truck is loaded with calibrated weights, usually of 1,000 lb. and 2,000 lb., and the function of the crane is to lift these weights from the truck body onto the scale, and then return them from the scale back onto the truck body.

Silent Hoist & Crane Co.

Fig. 34. Auxiliary swinging jib crane.

SWINGING BOOM HYDRAULIC CRANE. A light demountable swinging hydraulic crane mounted in a socket in the rear of a truck bed and operated by a hand hydraulic pump is used for swinging a load from the ground into the truck body. The boom and hydraulic mechanism are similar to that shown in Fig. 22.

FIXED-BEAM CRANES. A modification of the jib crane is a crane outfitted with a horizontal trolley beam permanently fixed over the truck body and extending a few feet beyond the rear edge of the body (Fig. 35). This overhead

Silent Hoist & Crane Co.

Fig. 35. Fixed-trolley-beam crane.

horizontal beam is outfitted with a trolley for the hook. Such a crane can lift loads only at the rear of the truck. This truck-mounted fixed trolley beam crane is used for testing scales, and in industry generally it is used for the lifting and transporting of motors, engines, and other heavy equipment. This fixed beam crane is also used in wrecker service for picking up disabled automobiles and trucks and towing them back to the service station. A common modification of this crane can be made by eliminating the trolley and having the hoisting hook located at the rear of the truck only.

Silent Hoist & Crane Co.

Fig. 36. Truck-mounted tripod derrick,

TRIPOD AND A-FRAME DERRICKS. Another truck-mounted crane consisting of a tripod derrick and a worm-geared winch also is used for towing and wrecking service. The larger tripod cranes with longer legs are used extensively by public utilities for setting power-line and telephone poles (Fig. 36). These tripod derricks, of course, are demountable and, because of their telescoping legs, are conveniently stored in the truck's utility body when not in use.

Other forms of truck-mounted cranes consist of special structural A-frames with a power or manual winch which generally fulfills the same function as the tripod derrick, their chief function being to lift something at the rear of the truck, such as a disabled motor truck, automobile, or a heavy piece of machinery which is to be lifted and transported from one location to another.

AUXILIARY CRANES MOUNTED ON INDUSTRIAL TRACTORS. Cranes of various kinds are mounted on industrial tractors and should be considered as attachments to such tractors. These tractors are either wheeled and fitted with rubber tires or of the crawler-tread type (Fig. 37). In the early days of development, many manufacturers who now produce a unit-built mobile crane, or a mobile front-end scoop loader, mounted such attachments on existing industrial commercial tractors that were available. As the need for mobile cranes increased, it became economically possible to build special vehicles designed to serve as truck cranes, wagon cranes, or crawler cranes. There are still, however, a large number of auxiliary crane attachments available for existing industrial tractors.

Industrial tractor cranes are available in 1-ton to 10-ton capacities. Here again, the crane gets its source of power through a power take-off which is attached

Silent Hoist & Crane Co.

Fig. 37. Swinging boom crane mounted on crawler tractor.

Caterpillar Tractor Co.

Fig. 38. Tractor with pipe-layer side booms.

to an outlet on the tractor transmission. Thus the engine that provides propulsion for the tractor provides power for the crane. Usually the controls for a crane installed on a commercial industrial tractor are grouped so that the operator, from the normal driving seat, may operate the tractor or operate the crane. For the wheeled or crawler tractor, as on motor trucks, several types of cranes have been developed. The simplest type consists of a fixed boom located at the front, or at the side of the tractor as in the case of the pipe-layer in Fig. 38.

Silent Hoist & Crane Co.

Fig. 39. Heavy-duty swinging jib crane mounted on railroad service car.

AUXILIARY CRANES MOUNTED ON RAILROAD CARS. Railroad cars, whether self-propelled or not, were among the earliest vehicles upon which cranes were mounted. All kinds of cranes and hoisting machinery have been mounted on railroad cars and many such cranes are now in use. An interesting development is illustrated in Fig. 39, which shows a completely powered swinging jib crane for handling railroad ties, rails, frogs, etc., in use by railroad stores departments, and for maintenance-of-way. Such cranes are used in the subway system by the City of New York. These cranes have the jib boom fitted with a power trolley for movement of the hook fore and aft, and the jib can telescope by power. This feature was necessary to permit the crane to maneuver with precision in limited headroom through the congested caverns of the subway system.

ELEVATORS

CONTENTS

CONTENTS *(Continued)*

ELEVATORS

Freight Elevators

IMPORTANCE OF FREIGHT ELEVATORS IN INDUSTRY. Directly and indirectly, modern freight elevators contribute to efficient materials handling and thereby speed up operations throughout an entire factory, warehouse, or multi-story terminal. A properly planned freight elevator installation results in the handling of a greater volume of materials, in lower operating costs, and in higher net earnings. In new buildings, freight elevators make possible **compact layouts** that fully utilize available space and **minimize handling distances,** both internal and external. With modern elevator equipment, every floor of a multi-story building can have almost the same accessibility as the first floor. Savings in land and in construction costs reduce overhead as well as operating expenses.

In **old buildings,** outmoded equipment can be replaced by up-to-date freight elevators to speed the flow of materials and permit substantial increases in production. With adequate elevator service, waste space in building basements or upper floors can often be put to useful purposes. Automatic operation of modern elevators conserves labor and cuts operating costs.

Freight Elevator Applications in Handling Materials. Freight elevators can be integrated with almost every method of horizontal materials handling—manual or mechanized—to speed the vertical flow of raw materials and in-process or finished goods. A short vertical movement of a hand truck by elevator may save hundreds of feet of time-consuming, costly horizontal hauling. Initial movement of a commodity may be by elevator to an upper level, to take advantage of gravity flow through subsequent processing. Power-driven towing units are often used to move trucks of materials onto and off elevators. Where palletized loads are handled, fork trucks may stack such loads on elevators for removal by a fork truck on another floor.

In **retail stores,** freight elevators are used to carry incoming shipments from the receiving platform to stock floors, merchandise from stock rooms to selling floors, and "send" orders to the shipping-room level. They are also used to carry store personnel, to distribute supplies, and to remove trash from upper floors.

Handling Industrial Equipment. The elevator used to transport materials can also carry parts, tools, and entire machines, within a minimum of time and without rehandling. Properly engineered freight elevators not only simplify maintenance operations, but also expedite relocating and replacing machinery to keep facilities abreast of changes in demand and improvements in technique.

Transporting Personnel. Where necessary, a freight elevator can carry people as well as materials. If passenger traffic does not warrant a separate elevator, controls and door operation of the freight elevator can be modified to comply with building-code provisions and permit carrying passengers.

CRITERIA OF FREIGHT-ELEVATOR EFFICIENCY. A freight elevator, to be a worthwhile investment, must perform its task efficiently. It must be **dependable,** for even temporary failure of a freight elevator may stop an entire production line. It must operate at as **low a cost** as possible compared to its work-load. Major cost items are labor—the service of an attendant, if necessary—power consumption, and maintenance. **Maintenance** operations should be simple and low in cost. **Long life** built into an elevator means smaller annual charges for depreciation and a lower final over-all cost. For a particular installation, a freight elevator must have a **capacity adequate** to handle all loads that may be imposed on it. In many cases it must carry not only materials but also many kinds of lift trucks, some of which may weigh, loaded, three or four tons.

Meeting Service Requirements. Whether the service load on an elevator is light or heavy, concentrated or distributed, depends primarily on the layout of the building and the kind of activities the building houses. Service loads on freight elevators vary greatly from building to building, making necessary a correspondingly wide range of elevator capacities.

The total rise or travel of the elevator has an important influence on the type of equipment to be used. Floor-to-floor heights and the number of stops determine, in part, desirable speeds and other operating characteristics.

During any given period—a working day, for example—**effective capacity** depends on the maximum load an elevator can carry on each trip and the number of round trips it can make. Load-per-trip depends, in turn, on the elevator's size and lifting power, trips-per-day on its speed. Load-per-trip multiplied by trips-per-day, multiplied again by the number of freight elevators, roughly indicates the **total handling capacity** of a freight elevator installation. It should include ample margin for traffic peaks and for future expansion of the company's operations. Providing extra capacity in the beginning is often less expensive than making alterations later on. But capacity far in excess of probable loads and extent of service may be the wasteful result of a poorly engineered installation.

Speed. While passenger elevators may travel as fast as 1,400 ft. per min., speeds of more than 150 ft. per min. are seldom required of freight elevators. Since freight-elevator "rises" are usually much lower than those for passenger elevators, **time to load and unload** the elevator may be a more important factor than time in transit in determining the handling speeds of plant operations. Freight-elevator speeds are usually in keeping with the **building height.** However, a fast-paced production line might call for a higher elevator speed than would otherwise be economical.

Size, Shape, and Lifting Capacity. The largest and heaviest unit load likely to be carried determines the size and shape of the car and the lifting capacity of the elevator. The elevator must be able to accommodate not only the load itself, but also the container, truck, or other equipment in, on, or by which the load is moved.

In stores, warehouses, and other installations where the elevator will carry a number of separate loads at the same time, a **wide, shallow car** is often preferred. That shape facilitates loading and unloading each piece of merchandise without disturbing the other freight on the elevator.

Floor strength of the building often determines the lifting capacity to be required of the elevator. If, for example, the upper floors of a plant or warehouse cannot support a loaded power truck, unit elevator capacity beyond maximum permissible unit floor loading would be unwarranted. In that case, a practical solution might be to break loads down into smaller units and use two small elevators with a total handling capacity equal to that of one large elevator.

Effective Capacity. Speed and lifting capacity largely, but not entirely, determine a freight elevator's effective handling capacity. Two elevators may travel at the same speed, but one may make more **round trips per hour** because it is equipped with automatic controls and self-opening doors that reduce actual floor-to-floor time. Such factors as the method by which an elevator is loaded and the available space at loading platforms and other levels also make a difference. In a low building, loading, unloading, and door operation account for a great part of the elevator's round-trip time. Speed of travel is a more significant factor in a taller structure.

Analysis of Capacity. How much work an elevator can do depends on its speed, its capacity, and how it is loaded. The following analysis of round-trip times for two elevators in refrigerated warehouses in Newark, N. J., shows how elevator efficiency may be tested. Each of the two elevators in the test carried two loaded pallets. The data in the table, Fig. 1, include time required on the

Travel	Elevator A—200 F.P.M.		Elevator B—100 F.P.M.	
	One Pallet per Trip	Two Pallets per Trip	One Pallet per Trip	Two Pallets per Trip
Main floor to:				
1st floor	93 sec.	213 sec.	95 sec.	215 sec.
2d floor	98 sec.	218 sec.	107 sec.	227 sec.
3d floor	103 sec.	223 sec.	119 sec.	239 sec.
4th floor	108 sec.	228 sec.	131 sec.	251 sec.
5th floor	112 sec.	232 sec.	143 sec.	263 sec.
6th floor	117 sec.	237 sec.	155 sec.	275 sec.
7th floor	122 sec.	242 sec.	No 7th or 8th floors in	
8th floor	127 sec.	247 sec.	this building	

Fig. 1. Analysis of elevator handling capacities under two methods of elevator operation.

main floor for the fork truck to carry the pallet, or pallets, 30 ft. from checker to elevator, and on the upper floor for the high-lift truck to move the load 50 ft. to the storage space. Doubling the times for a single-pallet trip indicates that it is faster for the 200-ft.-per-min. elevator A to carry one pallet at a time to all floors below the seventh, while for the 100-ft.-per-min. elevator B, the third floor is the highest for efficient single-load movement. Automatic operation and power-operated doors would further reduce round-trip times.

INTEGRATING ELEVATORS WITH THE BUILDING PLAN.
Location and arrangement of the elevators must be planned in accordance with the plant or building as a whole and with the anticipated flow of materials. If most vertical movement will be concentrated in one area, **grouping all elevators** there may provide the fastest and most continuous service. Single elevators may be "spotted" at locations where vertical flow is heavy.

Accessibility is enhanced when an elevator is located at the head, or alongside, of an aisle. One elevator with doors at both ends may serve two aisles. There should be enough room around the elevator entrances for easy maneuvering of lift trucks, hand trucks, and other equipment. More maneuvering space outside the elevator was the reason that a retail store which moved incoming merchandise on flat industrial trucks found that it could handle more material by changing over from a two-truck to a smaller one-truck elevator. Under the former arrangement, packages had to be unloaded directly from motor truck or trailer onto the flats on the waiting elevator. Substituting a smaller elevator let the store enlarge the receiving platform, on which a number of flat trucks could be loaded, ready to be rolled onto the elevator as soon as it arrived at street level. Effective handling capacity of the elevator installation was thus increased by an improved building layout that enabled the store to keep the smaller elevator busy almost continuously.

Surveying the handling of merchandise in a larger store, elevator engineers found, on the other hand, that an elevator accommodating two flat trucks would substantially speed the unloading of incoming shipments. This store had stockrooms on two floors. With the larger elevator, merchandise could be unloaded directly onto the flat trucks destined for each floor, both flats could be rolled onto the elevator together, and each flat rolled off at its respective floor. Again, this arrangement kept elevator **waiting time** at a minimum, useful **handling capacity** at a maximum.

Elevators as Part of the Handling System. Years ago, freight elevators were usually loaded and unloaded manually or by hand trucks. In modern installations, special provisions often make the elevator an integral part of the plant's materials handling system. Elevator loading is mechanized, usually by one of the following methods:

1. Fork truck or platform lift truck.
2. Tow truck and trailers.
3. Roller-track conveyor.
4. Overhead monorail conveyor.

ELEVATOR HOISTING MECHANISMS. The building imposes certain limitations on the elevator, which, in turn, places stresses on the building structure. This two-way relationship must be considered in planning an installation that will perform efficiently under the conditions that prevail in a particular case.

Drum-Type Elevators. Light-duty freight elevators may be of the drum type (Fig. 2). Essentially, the drum elevator is a winch: it consists of a cylinder or drum to which a rope is firmly attached. The other end of the rope is fastened to the elevator car. An electric motor turns the drum through reduction gearing, usually a worm and gear. When the drum turns, it winds up the rope and raises the elevator. A counterweight, usually equal to the weight of the empty car plus one-third of the duty load, increases the load that can be lifted by a motor of given horsepower.

Flexibility is the chief advantage of the drum-type elevator: the hoisting machine can be located above, below, or to one side of the hoistway. But for high rises, the size of the drum becomes unwieldy. There is also the danger that, if the motor fails to stop in time, the elevator car may be pulled into the structure at the top of the hoistway.

Traction-Type Elevators. To overcome the limitations of drum-type elevators, the traction type (Fig. 3) was developed. Essentially, a traction-type freight elevator consists of a car connected to a counterweight by cables or "ropes" running over a driving sheave, as diagrammed in Fig. 3. The car is attached to

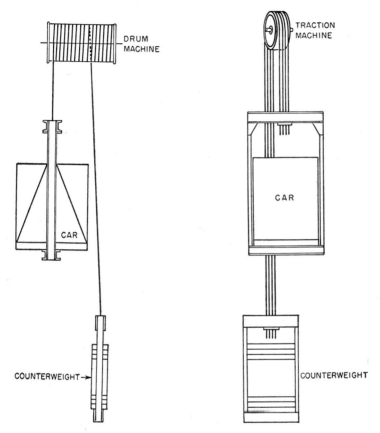

Fig. 2. Elements of a drum-type freight elevator.

Fig. 3. Elements of a traction-type freight elevator.

one end of the set of ropes and the counterweight to the other end. Traction between ropes and sheave raises and lowers the elevator. Car and counterweight each move on their own sets of guide rails. The motor that drives the sheave, the equipment that controls this motor, and several safety devices complete the elevator's basic components. All are installed in a hoistway in the building.

Height of rise is not limited by the size of the sheave. Should the motor continue to run and permit either car or counterweight to strike bottom, traction would be lost, preventing either car or counterweight from being driven into the overhead structure.

Beneath both the car and the counterweight are **buffers** to absorb the impact in case the car or counterweight overtravels the lower terminal. Over the hoistway are the hoisting machine and machine beams, if the machine is located above, or the overhead sheave beams if the machine is located below. Also located at the top of the hoistway is the **governor** which slows down the driving motor if the elevator overspeeds and finally, if this is not effective, sets the car safety mechanism to bring the car to a halt. Located with the machine in the machine room are the controller, selector, and motor-generator set.

Fig. 4. General-purpose plunger elevator and shaftway.

Since the **ability to lift heavy loads** is usually more important for a freight elevator than extremely high running speeds, most freight-elevator motors are linked to the sheave through reduction gearing. Two-to-one roping accomplishes the same effect as reduction gearing—it gains power by sacrificing speed. Heavy-duty freight elevators may use both reduction gearing and two-to-one roping. Combinations of the available systems of roping and gearing make it possible for the standard hoisting machines to handle a wide range of loads.

Plunger Electric Elevators. For low-rise applications where first cost is a prime consideration, a plunger electric elevator (Fig. 4), may be used. Its car frame is mounted on a steel column moving in a vertical cylinder sunk into the earth as deep as the rise of the elevator is high. To raise the elevator, an electric-motor-driven pump forces oil or water into the cylinder. In modern installations the pump motor is controlled from the elevator car, usually automatically by push buttons. Push buttons also control the operation of the valve which releases fluid from the cylinder to lower the elevator.

Factors in Selecting Equipment

TYPES OF FREIGHT ELEVATORS. Many cases arise where elevators are needed for particular purposes. The following two cases are instances in which elevators have performed transportation services at considerable savings to the user companies.

An eastern manufacturer of wire cloth for household and industrial screens, upon moving into a new single-story plant, discovered that he could keep production at a more stable level by storing supplies of wire in otherwise-wasted basement space under a machine area. To operate under this plan he needed an economical means of getting wire reels from the basement up to the main floor, and found the solution in an economical **light-duty freight elevator,** installed without substantial alterations to the building structure, and operated without a special attendant.

Load	Platform Size
2,500 # (Sidewalk)	5'6½" x 4'10"
1,500 #	5'4" x 6'0"
2,000 #	6'4" x 7'0"
2,500; 3,000 #	5'4" x 7'0"
2,500; 3,000; 3,500; 4,000 #	6'4" x 8'0"
4,000; 5,000; 6,000; 8,000 #	8'4" x 10'0"
5,000; 6,000; 8,000; 10,000 #	8'4" x 12'0"
10,000; 12,000; 16,000 #	10'4" x 14'0"
18,000 #	10'4" x 16'0"
20,000 #	12'0" x 20'0"

Fig. 5. Standard freight-elevator capacities and sizes.

An automobile plant faced a vertical materials-handling problem in which heavy loads were involved. Gasoline fork-trucks transporting palletized body parts had to get up to the second floor for assembling and finishing, and the assembled bodies had to be returned to the first floor to be mounted on chassis. Both jobs are now being done by one **heavy-duty industrial-truck freight elevator,** which can carry more than 7 tons and can withstand the impacts of industrial-truck operation. This large elevator is equipped with power-operated doors having simple automatic controls that any workman in the plant can operate.

Between the light-duty freight elevator—often called a "self-supporting" elevator because it imposes only negligible stress on the building structure—and the powerful industrial-truck elevator is the inclusive category of **general-purpose freight elevators.** They are available in a wide range of capacities (Fig. 5) and duties to meet varied materials-handling needs.

Choice of a freight elevator depends on the traffic to be handled and the structural features of the building. There are a number of basic types of freight elevators, each available in a range of sizes, capacities, and speeds, and with a choice of control systems. These standard components can be combined in a complete installation matched to specific individual requirements.

"SELF-SUPPORTING" LIGHT-DUTY ELEVATORS. For small plants, warehouses, and other buildings of limited height where elevator loads are light, an economical freight elevator known as the self-supporting type has been developed. It has a self-supporting framework that transfers most of the vertical load to the bottom of the hoistway and permits installation in new and in most existing hoistways without reinforcing the building, adding overhead supports, or constructing a penthouse.

Three **standard sizes** having rated lifting capacities of 1,500, 2,000, and 2,500 lb. are in general use. They are available for rises up to 35 ft.—usually two or three stories—for which a speed of 25 ft. per min. is usually adequate.

Construction of Self-Supporting Elevators. Made up of three extra-heavy vertical T-rails, cross-member channels, and a load-distributing steel channel base, the **guide-rail structure** carries the hoist ropes and sheaves, the elevator car, and the full freight load. It transfers heavy vertical loads to the bottom of the pit. If the hoistway has a load-carrying rear or side wall, the third structural steel T-rail can be eliminated, further reducing the cost of the installation. The structure is steadied by attaching a **steadying member** to the building at each floor level and at the top of the hoistway. A steadying member is also employed to carry the governor and dead-end hitch. The light horizontal thrust and vertical loads thus imposed are easily carried on the rear hoistway wall.

To reduce overhead clearance, the drum-type **hoisting machine** is mounted as a complete unit on a concrete foundation near the bottom of the hoistway. The a.c. electric motor is equipped with ball-and-roller antifriction bearings. Two stages of speed reduction are used between the motor and the drum. The first stage consists of a worm-and-gear unit comprising a bronze gear hobbed to a close tolerance and a steel worm that is hardened and ground to a perfect fit. The second stage of speed reduction is accomplished by an external pinion and gear with helical cut teeth for smoother power transmission. The **controller panel** is supplied complete, with automatic magnetic switches.

Two steel **hoisting ropes** travel up from the drum of the hoisting machine to an overhead sheave, then down under the car, and finally up to the top of the hoistway where they are secured to a dead-end hitch, giving a two-to-one lifting ratio. This method of roping doubles the lifting capacity of the machine and reduces the tension in the individual ropes by half.

Car frame and platform are of structural steel, with flooring of tongue-and-groove maple over a layer of spruce. Nonskid steel flooring may also be used. The car enclosure is made of sheet-steel panels, interlocked so that all joints are flush. There are no vertical moldings to come loose or get knocked off. The control panel is flush-mounted in a recessed box inside the car, and the car light is also recessed in the ceiling to protect it from damage by moving freight.

Horizontally folding **gates** reduce hoistway headroom requirements above the top landing to 10 ft. 9 in. Where extra headroom permits, a vertical-lifting metal gate may be used to leave the full door width clear for loading. An additional gate can be provided at the rear of the car if the building layout or the elevator loading plan calls for hoistway entrances on opposite sides of the hoistway.

Usual **operation** is by constant-pressure push buttons. Automatic push-button operation can be provided in place of the manual constant-pressure buttons. Elevators should be equipped with standard safety devices.

GENERAL-PURPOSE FREIGHT ELEVATORS. Industrial, commercial, and institutional buildings often need heavier-duty freight elevators than the self-supporting elevator, without requiring the special features of the industrial-truck elevator. This wide range of "in-between" needs is served by general-purpose freight elevators, which are available with capacities as low as 2,500 lb. or as high as 10,000 lb., speeds from 25 to 600 ft. per min., and rises as high as 214 ft. Designed for a variety of freight-handling needs, general-purpose freight elevators are available with variable-voltage speed regulation, self-leveling, and a choice of control systems for efficient self-service or attendant operation. Traction drive is usual. Elevators are frequently equipped with **oil buffers,** to slow down the descent of elevators—in case the car should overtravel the lower landing—and bring the car to a smooth stop. Power-operated, vertical bi-parting, all-steel hoistway doors are recommended, as are power-operated car gates. In addition to their more usual applications in commercial and industrial buildings, general-purpose freight elevators also serve as automobile elevators, marine elevators, mine elevators, etc.

INDUSTRIAL-TRUCK ELEVATORS. A common hand truck usually weighs about 500 lb. when loaded. Its relatively small payloads are pulled into the elevator and located by hand. Full car loading is gradual, and the extra weight of the hand truck is unimportant. This type of traffic is easily handled by a self-supporting or general-purpose freight elevator.

Increasing use of skids and pallets, and of power trucks to handle them, imposed new and severe loads on freight elevators. Industrial trucks, in their first stages of use, were of such varying design, and truck applications were so different, that each elevator installation for handling trucks had to be treated as a special case, and the entire elevator had to be engineered from start to finish. But industrial trucks have now been standardized to an extent where the **load distribution** and **wheel-load concentration** are standard for many different sizes of trucks, and therefore a single standardized design of industrial-truck elevator can be provided.

Forces Caused by Eccentric Loading. The design for a standardized industrial-truck freight elevator must make provision for possible **load concentration** at one edge and one side of the platform. The effect of such an eccentricity of loading on the car is to produce moments which tend to rotate the platform about its two principal horizontal axes. To resist these couples and prevent the car from skewing, the platform, side braces, and car frame must be strong and rigid.

The car itself, moreover, is a freely floating body, restrained vertically by the ropes, and laterally by the pressure of the guide shoes on the rails. Since the ropes are flexible, they will oppose none of the **rotational forces** acting on the car, so the entire rotational effect of the eccentric car loading must eventually be transmitted to the rails and thence to the rail brackets and the building structure.

Because of the way the industrial truck balances the load with the weight of its own engine, the entire pay load of the truck, plus most of the weight of the truck itself, may be concentrated on the front axle of the truck. Hence, in the extreme case of the fork truck, the live load plus the weight of the truck may all be concentrated at the outer edge of the elevator platform. This simultaneous increase in load and eccentricity produces reactions that are from 2 to 2.5 times greater than when the elevator is manually loaded.

Forces Caused by Impact. Additional forces caused by industrial trucks but not present with hand loading are the horizontal and vertical forces resulting from impact. **Vertical impact** forces occur when the platform is lower than the landing and the wheels of the truck drop from the landing onto the platform. With even a small drop the impact forces may be very great, and since these forces increase with the load and with the distance of fall, automatic leveling should be a "must" on all industrial-truck elevators.

The **horizontal impact** forces on the platform result from changes in the momentum of the truck with its load, and tend to force the elevator car toward the rear of the hoistway and also to twist the car frame about the axis of the ropes. No one who has ever watched an experienced driver move his loads at high speed, swing around, and stop short, will underestimate the reality or magnitude of these forces.

Extra "Static" Load. An industrial-truck elevator is subject to much more serious overloading than a regular freight elevator. When the elevator is loaded to capacity with four pallet loads—one on each quarter of the platform—most, if not all, of the weight of the fork truck is on the platform when the last load is deposited, and this extra "static" load may amount to 50 percent or more of the full load-carrying capacity of the elevator. The added weight must be supported by the frame, ropes, and sheave shaft, and must be opposed by the brake and—in an emergency—by the car safety, even though the elevator will not be called upon to lift the extra weight (except in releveling).

DESIGN FEATURES OF INDUSTRIAL-TRUCK ELEVATORS.

The platform **frame** of the elevator must be strengthened to support the flooring and the concentrated weight of the truck and its load. For an installation where a handtruck-loaded elevator platform would require 9-in. front and rear channels and four 5-in. channel stringers, a power-truck-loaded elevator platform would require 12-in. front and rear channels and six 7-in. channel stringers. To support the heavily concentrated wheel loads, resist the wear and splintering action of suddenly applied brakes, and withstand heavier impact loads when the platform is lower than the landing, the **flooring**, of selected maple tongue-and-groove with an underlying layer of heavy spruce, is usually made 1 in. thicker than it would be for handtruck loading. Nonskid steel flooring may also be used.

The **car enclosure** is made of rigid steel panels interlocked to obtain maximum strength and provide flush interior surfaces. The car can be equipped with wood **rubbing strips** to protect the side of the car at points where the loading truck or pallets are likely to strike the car walls. Vertical **sliding gates** leave the full elevator width clear for loading. Where minimum loading time and maximum traffic-handling capacity are important, power-operated car gates and hoistway doors are recommended.

To carry the full weight of the car and its full impact loads and static loads, and to resist the severe twisting forces created by off-balance loading and the tendency of the car to tilt alternately forward and backward, the **car frame** is constructed of angle-reinforced channels or extra-heavy ship channels to insure sufficient rigidity and safety. Diagonal bracing likewise is strengthened to take care of the extremely heavy and highly concentrated impact, live, and static loads that would ordinarily tend to tilt the platform first downward and then upward during off-balance loading.

Heavy-duty hoisting machines are used with **variable-voltage speed regulation** for faster acceleration and deceleration, accurate stopping and precise leveling, and reduced power consumption during starting, accelerating, and leveling. This lessens wear and tear by eliminating heavy strains due to jerky acceleration.

Self-leveling keeps the elevator platform level with the landing under all loading conditions. When the concentrated front-wheel load of the power truck pushes the car down, the leveling system brings it back flush with the landing. Self-leveling eliminates the extra horizontal impact when the platform is higher than the landing, and the increased vertical impact when the platform is lower than the landing. It also eliminates the time-wasting "jockeying" needed for leveling by hand operations.

Any of the control methods described later in this section can be used with industrial-truck elevators, although collective and single **automatic controls** are most common. The usual fixtures on landings can be supplemented by pendant-type push-button controls suspended from the ceiling along the traffic approach to the elevator, so that the truck driver can save time by summoning the elevator without leaving his truck.

Structural Requirements. Method of loading, capacity, platform size, and floor heights are all factors which determine the magnitude of forces exerted on the elevator guide rails and subsequently on the **hoistway structure.** These forces, which produce horizontal, vertical, and torsional stresses on the hoistway structure, must be analyzed for each installation.

Existing elevators which are to be converted from conventional hand truck to power-truck loading may require heavier guide rails and fastenings, additional rail support brackets, and strengthened supports. In some cases it may be necessary to provide some type of rail backing—particularly if the floor heights are excessive and rail fastenings between floors are required. New industrial buildings should be designed to provide extra hoistway strength for possible future power-truck loading, even though hand trucks are used initially.

In many cases the hoistway structure will have adequate strength to withstand the forces imposed by an industrial-truck elevator, particularly in installations involving 8,000- or 10,000-lb. elevators. However, the higher-capacity elevators require a more suitable structure for rail fastenings which is economically provided by guide-rail fastenings between floors where the hoistway walls are inadequate to withstand the forces imposed by the elevator installation.

SIDEWALK ELEVATORS. When the only way to get freight into and out of a basement is through the sidewalk, freight handling can be mechanized by the installation of an electric sidewalk elevator. Mechanically and electrically similar to self-supporting elevators, sidewalk elevators have a lifting **capacity** of 2,500 lb. and a maximum **rise** of 30 ft., and travel at 25 ft. per min. between the sidewalk level and one or two basement levels. As the elevator rises through the sidewalk opening, its swing covers are opened by a bow-iron at the top of the car. The bow-iron allows the covers to close as the elevator descends to the basement.

A sidewalk elevator is operated either by "up" and "down" buttons at each basement landing or by "up" and "down" key switches at the sidewalk level. One of the sidewalk-level switches must be closed before the elevator can be moved through the sidewalk—an important safety provision. In a three-stop installation—sidewalk and two basements—the car is equipped with a double-button control, while in a two-stop installation the car is controlled only by the landing buttons or switches. An optional "call bell" will ring when the elevator is about to rise through the sidewalk, or when an open car or hoistway gate or door prevents operation of the elevator by key switch or landing button.

ELECTRIC DUMBWAITERS. To speed handling of supplies, food, packages, or merchandise, electric dumbwaiters are available in capacities up to 500 lb. Cars are sound-deadened, have removable shelves, and may have stainless-steel or gray utility-enamel finish. Entrances are arranged for bi-parting, slide-up, slide-down, or special doors, and may have prime finish, baked-enamel, or stainless-steel finish.

Choice of a completely automatic **control system** depends upon the type of service required. For two-floor service, the dumbwaiter is usually equipped with a "call and send" system. The car can be called to, or sent from, either landing by push buttons located at each landing. For three or more floors, intensity of service determines the type of control: "multibutton" control for intermittent service; "central station dispatching" for intensive dumbwaiter service. With automatic "multibutton" control there are buttons at every landing and the car can be called to any floor, or dispatched from any floor. A signal light in the button panel, hall lanterns, or call buzzers can be provided if desired. Cars can be equipped to return automatically when unloaded, or signals can be installed to indicate where the car has stopped and when it is ready to be returned.

Electric dumbwaiter **speeds** depend upon the height of the installation:

For 2 floors	50 F.P.M.
For 3–5 floors	100 F.P.M.
For 5–12 floors	150 F.P.M.
Over 12 floors	300 F.P.M.

Components of a dumbwaiter installation may be arranged in either of two ways, depending on service requirements, available space, and other factors.

Machine-above Arrangement. With its hoisting machine and automatic controller mounted above the hoistway, this dumbwaiter is like a small freight elevator. Door openings can be at the front, sides, or rear.

A traction or drum-type machine may be used for a rise up to 30 ft. 6 in. and traction for a higher rise. In the traction-type machine-above arrangement, hoist ropes go from the dumbwaiter car, over the traction drive sheave on the machine, and past the deflector sheave to the counterweight. With a drum-type machine, the hoist rope goes from the car to the machine, where it is wound on the drum. No counterweight is used with this type of machine. The length of hoist rope that can be wound on the drum limits these installations to low rises.

Under-Counter Arrangement. Fitting under a counter at the upper floor, this dumbwaiter has a capacity of 300 lb. at 50 ft. per min. and a maximum rise of 30 ft. 6 in. Its hoisting machine, of the drum type, is located at the bottom of the hoistway, while the automatic controller can be placed in any convenient space. The dumbwaiter car is underslung so that the hoist rope travels under the car, over the overhead sheave, and down to the machine.

SELECTING THE CORRECT ELEVATOR. Service demands and the elevator equipment required vary greatly from one installation to another. As each building or plant has its own vertical-handling problems, **each elevator installation has its own unique characteristics** that adapt it specifically to do a specific job. While most freight elevators are engineered from standardized parts, hardly any two complete installations are exactly alike. The problem is to select the kind of elevator whose capacity and speed, method of operation, and special features of equipment will most closely match the requirements. For efficient results, each installation demands an individual study, broad enough in scope to include all the important factors bearing on elevator use and service.

EFFICIENT ELEVATOR OPERATION. A principal criterion of freight-elevator efficiency is the time required to move goods from floor to floor. **Factors in floor-to-floor handling time** are:

1. The elevator's speed of travel.
2. Time for opening and closing doors and gates.
3. Time to load and unload freight at each stop.
4. Time for acceleration, retardation, and leveling.
5. If there is more than one elevator in an area, time taken to assign a call to the nearest elevator.

Elevator speeds, door operation, and methods of loading have already been considered. The fourth factor is determined by the method of operation, and the fifth by group supervision. **Methods of operation** and **supervision** govern the efficiency of an elevator installation. Through determining effective speed, these factors influence both the rate of production elsewhere in the building and the number of elevators required. Both manual and automatic systems of operation are now in use.

Manual Operation. One of the simplest methods of operating a freight elevator, and the least expensive in terms of equipment required, is by means of a **car switch.** The operating lever controls the elevator starting, stopping, speed, and direction of travel. When it is moved to the left, the elevator starts upward; when to the right, downward. Moving the lever to the centered position stops the elevator. The lever automatically returns to the centered "stop" position when released. On higher-speed cars, the attendant has two or more running speeds under his control to slow the car down as it approaches a landing. Contacts in the car switch close circuits for different control magnets, which in turn close contactors on the controller and operate the motor. Car-switch operation requires the services of a **skilled elevator attendant.** The degree of skill required may be reduced by using car-switch operation in conjunction with self-leveling, described below.

Double-Button Operation. A method that is relatively inexpensive to install, yet permits a person without special skill to operate the elevator, is double-button operation, also known as **"constant-pressure."** At each landing and in the elevator car is a pair of buttons, one "up" and the other "down." The elevator will rise as long as any "up" button, in the car or at a landing, is pressed, and will descend while a "down" button is pressed. Releasing the button stops the elevator. An operator keeps the "up" or "down" landing button pressed until the elevator reaches his floor, then presses the proper button in the car to move it in the desired direction. Double-button elevators are usually equipped with **automatic controls** that make the landing buttons ineffective as long as a button in the car is kept pressed. A double-button elevator is seldom self-leveling. But it can be equipped with an "inching" button which permits the car to be brought, at slow speed, level with a landing.

Self-Leveling. An automatic means of bringing an elevator to a stop so that its platform is level with the landing is known as "self-leveling." This feature is especially desirable in freight elevators where vehicles of any kind are wheeled on or off the car. When the car gets within a few inches of the landing, automatic controls take over and gently slow the elevator to a perfect, level stop, regardless of the load in the car. These controls correct automatically for rope stretch and for changes in the load, gradual or sudden. Besides saving the time that would be taken in "jockeying" the elevator to a level stop, self-leveling also reduces electric power consumption and wear and tear on the elevator. Riders getting on and off a self-leveling elevator do not trip, and hand and power trucks do not bump over the threshold, damaging themselves or their loads. For power trucks, many of which have wheels as small as 3 in. in diameter, self-leveling is virtually essential.

Automatic Elevator Operation. A significant recent development has been the application of automatic controls to freight elevators. An automatic elevator can return its cost in self-service operating economies within a few years.

Even when elevators will normally be operated by attendants, engineers often specify automatic operation. Elevators are then ready for service at all times, including occasions when, for any reason, no attendant is available. On the faster freight elevators, automatic controls are almost a necessity for efficient operation. At higher speeds it becomes increasingly difficult for an attendant to make accurate, level stops with an old-style manually operated elevator.

Many of the automatic systems now used on freight elevators can readily be switched from attendant to self-service operation, depending on conditions. For example, a building occupied by several tenants can keep an attendant on the car during busy hours to assure adequate service to all occupants. Even in a plant occupied entirely by a single concern, management sometimes finds an elevator attendant worthwhile because, by helping to load and unload the elevator, he can save time for other workers. In some cases, however, it has been found more economical to dispense with regular attendants and let plant employees operate the automatic elevators.

Automatic Operating Systems. Several systems of automatic operation are used for freight elevators:

1. Signal control.
2. Collective control.
3. Two-stop collective control.
4. Single automatic push-button control.

Each of these systems has been developed for specific service conditions. High-speed, heavy-duty freight elevators are often equipped for signal-control operation. Where traffic is lighter, collective-control equipment may provide the best automatic operation. A feature common to both **signal-** and **collective-control** elevators is their ability to "remember" calls. Going up, a signal- or collective-control elevator will automatically stop as it reaches each floor for which an "up" call has been registered, reverse when it has answered the highest call, and similarly answer all "down" calls in turn on its way down. Such an installation is shown in Fig. 6. The girl shown in the illustration can send the elevator to any floor, by button control, without riding the car herself.

Both signal- and collective-control elevators can be equipped for operation by or without attendants. In either system, momentary pressure on a landing or car button is sufficient to stop the elevator at the proper floor. There is a pair of buttons, one "up" and the other "down," at each intermediate landing, and on the car control panel, a numbered button for each floor served.

Otis Elevator Co.

Fig. 6. Collective-control elevator with control panel at landing and in the car.

An important distinction between the two systems is that signal-control elevators are usually specified for **intensive, continuous service,** while collective-control elevators are for **on-call service.** A collective-control elevator automatically returns to the busiest floor when the last call has been answered (the "home station" feature). Pressing a "nonstop" button lets a loaded car bypass landing calls, which are stored until the button is released. As its name implies, **two-stop collective control,** a simpler and less expensive system than full collective control, applies its principles of operation to an elevator with only upper and lower landing.

If a single load is usually big enough to fill the car, plant and building owners may prefer an economical **single-automatic-push-button elevator** which can answer only one call on each trip. It will not respond to other calls until the first user has released the elevator, nor can it "remember" calls as signal- and collective-control elevators do. Single-automatic-push-button operation is generally found on low-speed elevators—100 ft. per min. or less.

In a "bank" of two or more signal-control or collective-control elevators, a landing call will automatically be answered by the elevator that can do so most efficiently. Simple switches make it easy to detach one elevator from group control so that it may be operated independently for special loads. If traffic is heavy and continuous, signal-control elevators in a group can be automatically dispatched at intervals to provide continuous service.

Construction and Maintenance

ELEVATOR ELEMENTS. The parts of which an elevator is constructed must be of high-quality materials so as to prevent accidents to personnel and equipment. In both fabrication and erection it is highly important to make sure that every precaution is taken to avoid failures of any parts or assemblies.

Otis Elevator Co.

Fig. 7. Gearless traction hoisting machine.

Elevator Ropes. The cables from which the elevator car and counterweight are suspended are known as "ropes." Typical elevator ropes consist of **wire strands,** for tensile strength, around a **hemp core,** for flexibility.

Guide Rails. Both elevator and counterweight run on guide rails in the hoist-way. Guide rails are usually of steel, their weight being specified by local building codes according to the capacity of the elevator. An unevenly loaded elevator car imposes **deflecting forces** on the guide rails. Action of the safety device also imposes forces on the guide rails, tending to spread them apart. Not only the guide rails themselves, but also their supports and the building structure on which they are mounted, must also be able to resist such forces. Forces exerted by each shoe on the guide rail can be reduced by increasing the height of the elevator car.

Power Plants for Freight Elevators. Higher-speed, lighter-duty freight elevators can use a **gearless traction** hoisting machine (Fig. 7). Its advantages are simplicity of construction, long life, and smooth, quiet operation. However, since speed is usually secondary to lifting capacity in freight elevators, most freight-elevator hoisting machines are of the **geared type** (Fig. 8), to minimize

Otis Elevator Co.

Fig. 8. Motor-generator set (left) mounted on same base as geared hoisting motor (center) and sheave and brake (right).

the size of motor required. Worm gearing is an integral part of all geared machines. To increase lifting capacity further, the worm gear is supplemented by an external rack-and-pinion gear. In both types of gearing, helical-cut teeth are advisable to reduce vibration and to provide gradual engagement and continuous contact of the engaging teeth.

Today, a.c. power systems are nearly universal; but whether the driving motor is a.c. or d.c. depends on the type of motor control. Where low first cost is a primary consideration, resistance control is used with a.c. motors. Where performance requirements are more exacting, variable-voltage control is used with d.c. motors.

Regardless of the kind of current, all elevator driving motors should have **good speed regulation,** with the smallest possible difference in speed between ascent with a full load and descent with a full load. The motor must be able to feed power back into the line when the elevator is descending. It should have a high starting torque with low starting current. The motor should be controllable down to a low speed with dynamic braking. It should be quiet and dependable in operation. Since an elevator motor does not run continuously at constant load but is stopping or starting much of the time, it must be able to handle great variations of load without overheating. Alternating-current motors for elevator service are invariably induction motors. They are usually polyphase motors, of squirrel-cage construction, with either one or two speeds. Direct-current motors have round frames of steel with two, four, six, or eight poles, according to size.

Controlling the Elevator Motor. Control equipment is the part of an elevator installation that regulates the operation of the hoisting motor—its starting, stopping, direction, and speed. Two types of control are used on freight elevators: resistance and variable-voltage.

If **service is intermittent and duty relatively light,** a.c. resistance control may be used for speeds up to 100 ft. per min. with automatic operation and 150 ft. per min. with manual operation. Resistance control uses resistances in series with the stator windings. The resistances function in starting only and are thrown in and out of the circuit by magnet switches. For two-speed operation, the motor should have two stator windings. The slow-speed winding is used in retardation and automatic leveling.

Variable-voltage control is preferred for **heavy-duty, intensive-service applications.** Even with a fast, powerful hoisting machine, variable-voltage control can effect the fine speed regulation required for smooth yet rapid stopping and starting and for self-leveling and automatic operation. The heart of the

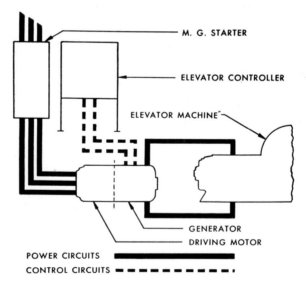

Fig. 9. Basic circuits for variable-voltage control.

variable-voltage system is a motor-generator set. Its a.c. driving motor operates off local power lines, while its d.c. generator supplies controlled power to the hoisting motor. The basic circuits are diagrammed in Fig. 9. The rotor of the driving motor and the armature of the generator are mounted on the same steel shaft and rotate as a unit. In operation, the motor drives the generator at constant speed. The generator responds to changes in its field current, as regulated by the controller, by delivering current at varying voltages to the armature of the driving motor of the elevator hoisting machine. Since the driving motor tends to rotate at a speed directly related to the voltage impressed on its armature, this arrangement provides a means for **regulating the speed of the elevator** with a smoothness and accuracy not obtainable from other systems of elevator speed control.

Advantages of variable-voltage control are many. It is adaptable to either a.c. or d.c. power supply but, regardless of power supply, it employs a d.c. hoisting motor with its inherently desirable operating and control characteristics. The smoothness with which changes in voltage and speed are accomplished reduces peak starting currents and permits maximum acceleration and retardation. Full speed from rest and stopping from full speed are attained in shorter distances, allowing more travel at full speed. Good speed control, because of definite voltage steps not too greatly affected by load, means greater accuracy of stopping on higher-speed elevators.

Because control is accomplished through generator shunt fields, the controlled currents are low, and the magnet switches handling them are small compared to the switches that would be required to handle the armature currents. Handling only field currents, the switch contacts have longer life and require less attention. The absence of control resistance eliminates high resistance losses. The use of direct current for controller magnet coils and brake improves the quietness and reliability of their operation. The accurate speed control obtainable with generator field control, even at low speeds, makes unnecessary a separate leveling machine and permits the use of the main motor for leveling.

Car Frame. The loads and stresses to which it is subject make the car frame of particular importance in freight elevators. It consists of a **crosshead, uprights,** and a **safety plank.** For gross capacities up to 25,000 lb., which includes most elevators, car frames are constructed of **standard sections** of channels for crossheads and planks, and either standard or ship channels for the uprights, connected at the ends by means of gusset plates at the upper corners and connection angles at the lower corners. Occasionally, when it is required for unusual conditions, the uprights are reinforced by angles riveted to the channel flanges. For greater capacities, uprights are of built-up sections, consisting of two channels connected with crossplates at right angles to the webs. The crossheads and planks are in this case either channels or I-beams.

Platform and Enclosure. Freight-elevator cars must withstand years of hard industrial use. If the elevator is loaded by power trucks, its platform and floor may have to support a maximum load of 7,000 lb. per wheel. The platform consists of a **steel frame** with two layers of **wood flooring.** The frame, usually of channel girders, has one or more stringer channels parallel to the side of the frame. The load-bearing floor is the underfloor, which is laid directly on top of and at right angles to the side channels and stringers. The subflooring is fastened to blocks and bolted to channels in the steel frame. The top flooring, which acts as a wearing surface, is laid at right angles to the under floor.

The **freight enclosure,** mounted on the platform, consists of a rigid structural-steel frame, solid sheet-metal side panels, and a metal top which is usually perforated. Vertical side panels are made of sheet steel and are interlocked to give maximum strength and rigidity and to provide flush interior surfaces. The car operating panel is located in a recessed box and does not project into the car interior. Horizontal extension panels and perforated top are also made of sheet steel. The perforated top permits ventilation and provides protection against falling objects. It is equipped with one or two centrally located lighting fixtures, depending on the size of the car, and contains one or two hinged exit panels.

Guide Shoes. Fixed to the car frame are the guide shoes which slide along the guide rails in the hoistway. The part of the shoe that comes in contact with the rail is a removable gib. It is made of cast iron, usually in one piece.

Counterweight. The elevator car is suspended from one end of the hoisting ropes, the counterweight from the other end. It consists of a structural steel frame which carries cast-iron weights. The counterweight runs along its own set of guide rails.

Elevator Entrances. Much of the efficiency and safety of the entire elevator installation depends on the elevator entrances. They determine, in part, the speed with which the elevator can be loaded and unloaded and its economy of operation. Since a large proportion of elevator accidents occur at the entrances, their proper design can be an important contribution to safety. To keep the full width of the

Otis Elevator Co.

Fig. 10. **Vertical bi-parting hoistway door (shaft-side view).**

elevator entrance unobstructed, **hoistway doors** are usually of the vertical bi-parting type, as illustrated in Fig. 10, and **car gates** are of the vertical-lift type. Bi-parting doors are inherently faster in operation and safer than the "guillotine" doors formerly used. Each half of the bi-parting door serves as counterbalance for the other. When closed, these doors shut off the entire hoistway entrance and provide fire protection. The doors operate inside the hoistway and require no landing sill because the top of the lower door section forms an adequate bridge to the elevator car platform, even for heavy trucking. Special modifications of bi-parting doors include **pass-type doors,** which make possible high vertical clearance in a building of relatively low floor height. Weather-strip doors can be installed where entrances are exposed to the elements. **Electric "operators"** mounted on hoistway doors and car gates open and close them in one-third the time required for manual operation. For safety and silence their motion is automatically slowed just before the doors or gates reach the fully opened or closed position.

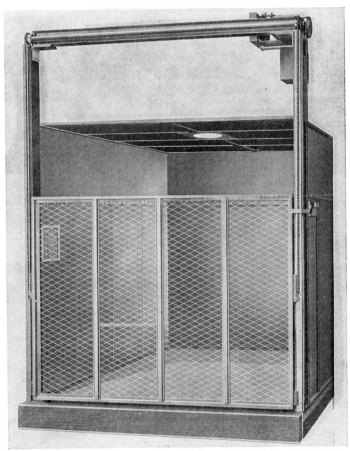

Otis Elevator Co.

Fig. 11. Vertical-lifting car gate.

Hoistway doors have replaced open-slat wooden gates, the first means used to protect elevator entrances. Early doors were of "kalamine" construction—a wood core covered with galvanized sheet steel. Modern hoistway doors are all-steel, with separate panels which can be replaced if damaged. All-steel construction reduces weight and improves fire protection, and the doors operate more quietly than do those of the old kalamine type. Fig. 11 shows a vertical-lifting-type car gate with expanded steel panel framed and braced by aircraft-type steel sections. In opening, the entire gate glides upward on four bronze guide shoes running on cold-rolled steel guides.

Power Doors To Speed Elevator Operation. Demands for faster handling of freight and for closer control of labor costs have intensified interest in the power operation of elevator hoistway doors and car gates. Operated by electric motors, doors and gates open and close "in step" with the stopping and starting of automatic elevators. Doors and gates that open automatically as the elevator levels to a stop not only save time but also permit employment of handicapped or over-age persons as elevator attendants.

An elevator can have an entrance at both ends, one opening, for example, on a loading platform and the other giving access to the interior area of a building. For elevators with entrances at both ends, **three types of door operation** are available:

1. **Selective,** in an installation where there are two entrances at each floor, and the doors will operate only at the side where the button is pressed.
2. **Nonselective,** with two entrances at each floor, both of which will open regardless of which button is pressed.
3. **Semiselective,** where opposite entrances are at different levels, and the doors will operate at any floor only if there is an entrance at that side.

Power doors and gates may be arranged to operate in sequence to comply with safety code provisions for carrying passengers. Control circuits are set so that the hoistway door automatically opens first to eliminate the tripping hazard.

Safety Provisions. Over the years, safety devices have been developed that make the freight elevator one of the safest means of materials handling. Proper maintenance of these devices is as important as their installation in the first place.

Modern freight elevators are equipped with **brakes** controlled by a governor in the machine room, which will stop the car automatically if its descending speed becomes excessive. In such a case, if the brakes are not effective, the governor trips the roll-type, or flexible-guide-clamp **safety** on the car frame. The safety grips the guide rails and slows the elevator to a stop. **Limit switches** cut off power and set brakes if the car overruns the upper or lower terminal. Should the car descend to the bottom of the hoistway, its motion will be stopped by a set of **oil buffers** (Fig. 12). Spring buffers will similarly halt the counterweight.

Interlocks are the safety switches that prevent the starting of an elevator until all car and hoistway doors are closed, and prevent any of them from being opened while the car is moving through the hoistway. Doors or gates can be opened only at a landing where the car is leveling or has halted. Power-operated doors have **safety shoes** that stop the doors from closing if a person or an object gets in the way, and controls are designed so that doors can be closed only by continuous, deliberate pressure on a door-closing button within plain view of the entrance.

Special Features for Special Service. While the complete freight elevator is assembled from standardized parts, most installations are individually planned to incorporate specific components best adapted to the specific requirements. When

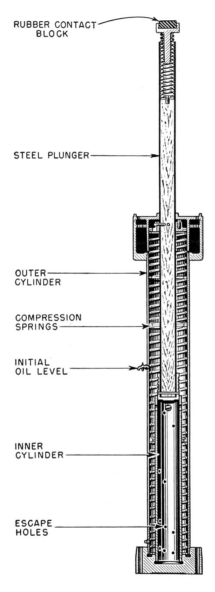

RUBBER CONTACT
BLOCK

STEEL PLUNGER

OUTER
CYLINDER

COMPRESSION
SPRINGS

INITIAL
OIL LEVEL

INNER
CYLINDER

ESCAPE
HOLES

Otis Elevator Co.

Fig. 12. Oil buffer.

necessary, freight elevators can be equipped with such extras as lighting equipment, car bumper strips, moisture- and corrosion-resistant fittings, and explosion-proof equipment.

Every freight elevator has a job to do. Whether it includes special equipment or only standard components, a well-planned freight elevator installation combines them in the way that will do that job most economically, most effectively, and at the lowest possible cost over the longest possible useful life.

IMPORTANCE OF ELEVATOR MAINTENANCE. Proper mainte-
nance can keep a freight elevator operating at peak efficiency for decades. The larger manufacturers of freight elevators offer maintenance service under contract to owners of their equipment. Some users of freight elevators have set up their own systematic maintenance programs. Whether performed by the elevator manufacturer or by the owner, the objective of maintenance is to assure maximum service from freight elevators, minimize shutdowns and production stoppages, and extend the life of elevator equipment.

Preventive Maintenance—Key to Uninterrupted Service. Years of experience in contract maintenance have developed and shaped the preventive **maintenance service** now being offered by elevator manufacturers. Their comprehensive records cover the life expectancy of parts, points of wear, and required frequency of servicing. On the basis of this experience, an elevator manufacturer can plan systematic maintenance activities that will keep equipment functioning as if new at minimum cost.

A manufacturer with an extensive maintenance organization is likely to have a completely equipped and competently staffed **local office** within reasonable traveling distance of most installations of his equipment. Emergency service, usually included in the maintenance contract, is thus facilitated, as is periodic maintenance. Equipped with specialized tools, the maintenance force is organized to provide methodical inspection, adjustment, lubrication, repair, and replacement of parts under systematic supervision. Complete assortments of replacement parts are carried in stock or, when necessary, can be made to order.

A comprehensive **maintenance program** enables the service men to discover and prevent many possible breakdowns. Since parts are repaired or replaced as soon as they show signs of wear, the installation is kept as good as new, with its efficiency unimpaired over the years.

Maintenance Cost Factors. Elevator manufacturers' experience with maintenance service also enables them to calculate closely the cost of such service. The most common arrangement is a **flat monthly charge,** which entitles the elevator owner to complete maintenance service. Thus there are no large, unexpected repair bills, but only the easily budgeted, regular monthly fee. Maintenance rates are usually lowest if the owner takes out a contract when the elevator is new, and this favorable rate differential continues as long as the service is retained. Prompt availability of repair and replacement parts through the maintenance service of the manufacturer relieves an owner of the trouble and expense of keeping his own parts inventory.

Advantages of Comprehensive Maintenance. The following advantages are obtained through a plan of comprehensive maintenance:

1. Higher output, because the elevators are always ready to serve production needs, and materials flow steadily.
2. Faster, more economical deliveries, because merchandise moves without delay, costly truck waiting-time is reduced.
3. Uninterrupted service, because modern elevators are virtually proof against man-failure, and maintenance prevents equipment-failure before it occurs.
4. Operating efficiencies, because well-maintained elevators economize manpower and kilowatt hours.
5. Savings on overhead, because proper maintenance makes it unnecessary to stock repair parts or keep a skilled maintenance crew.
6. Savings in depreciation reserves, because well-maintained elevators have an unusually long useful life.

Owner or Contract Maintenance? A plant or warehouse with a large number of freight elevators may find it economical to organize its own maintenance program, employing the necessary technicians and acquiring tools, parts, lubricants, and other supplies from the available sources. Some large companies, however, have preferred to leave the specialized task of elevator maintenance to the elevator manufacturer. For the owner of but a few elevators, this is usually the more desirable policy, from the standpoint of cost as well as of quality and dependability of service.

Other Elevators and Skip Hoists

CONSTRUCTION ELEVATOR HOISTING MACHINES. Elevator hoists are usually power-operated devices having one or more clutched hoisting drums for purposes of handling one or more material cages, passenger cages, concrete buckets, or elevator booms (more commonly called "Chicago booms"). This type of hoist is generally made light in weight for portability and is powered by gasoline or diesel power units, or by electric motors when electric power is available.

Generally, in the handling of material cages in construction elevators, only the hoisting line pull and line speed need be considered, unless loads are to be lowered other than the empty cage, or when a specific duty cycle is involved. The **drum brakes** of this type of hoist are generally proportioned for intermittent service, or for service where brake heating will not be excessive. This also applies in handling of loads with the "Chicago boom."

In the handling of construction passenger cages or concrete buckets, it is necessary to analyze the frequency or duty cycle for the purpose of applying the proper **size of hoist** to handle the brake load without excessive brake heating.

Some states or cities have very strict laws regarding the use of construction elevator cages for **passenger service.** Where these laws pertain, it is necessary to provide an **automatic controller** for the hoisting drum of the passenger cage. This automatic controller will set the brake for a gradual slow-down stop when overspeeding or overtravel of the limit switches occurs. Installations planned should be checked to see whether they conform to the latest requirements in safety regulations and operating practices.

CONSTRUCTION ELEVATOR WITH INSIDE CAGE. This elevator, shown in Fig. 13, is of single- or double-well type, with a platform for raising or lowering building materials and a bucket for raising concrete. In the double-well type, the platform or buckets may be independently controlled or they may be arranged for opposite direction of travel simultaneously to reduce the load on the operating winch. The concrete bucket can be of the self-dumping type with a discharge hopper attached to the side of the elevator frame. The tower may be of unlimited height, towers of many hundreds of feet having been used.

CONSTRUCTION ELEVATOR WITH CANTILEVERED CAGE. An elevator of this type, Fig. 14, can be towed to the job site on its own trailer wheels, assembled on the ground, and the tower raised to a vertical position by the single-drum operating winch. A platform or a self-dumping concrete bucket can be attached to a rope-moved carriage which travels on one face of the tower. A **boom attachment** can be mounted on the tower top for hook work when the concrete bucket is mounted on the carriage. This attachment requires a second drum on the winch. **Self-erecting tower** heights of 40 to 60 ft. have been used,

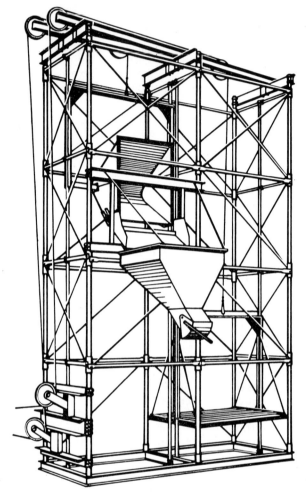

Fig. 13. Construction elevator with inside cage, for raising or lowering building materials.

and heights up to 120 ft. have been used with the tower rigidly braced to a building. A platform capacity of 2,500 lb. and a bucket capacity of one-half yard of concrete have been used on construction jobs.

Suspended Scaffolding. This scaffolding consists of a working platform which is suspended at its ends by **multipart lines.** These lines may be hand- or power-operated from platform level, from ground level, or at suspension level, to raise and lower the scaffolding.

Suspended Bosun's Chair. This chair is similar to the suspended scaffolding but with space for only one workman, and usually only one point of support for a multipart suspension line.

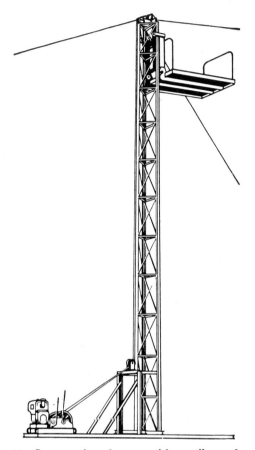

Fig. 14. Construction elevator with cantilevered cage.

MINE ELEVATORS OR HOISTS. A mine hoist consists of the following elements:

1. The hoist or **winding machine,** which is driven either by steam or by electricity. Mine hoists or winding machines are described later in this section.
2. The **head-frame,** which is located at the head of the shaft, and supports the head-sheaves and receiving bins for the material being mined—either coal or metallic ores. Head-frames are triangular in shape and are constructed of either timber or structural-steel members.
3. The **mine-shaft,** which is either vertical or inclined, and in which are the guides or tracks for the cages and skips and, in inclined shafts, for cars for hoisting men or material. Vertical shafts are either circular or rectangular in cross-section, while incline shafts are rectangular. One shaft may consist of one or more compartments.
4. The **cages,** skips, and cars for handling the material or men.
5. The **wire rope,** either round or flat, used to hoist the cages, skips, and cars. It is attached to the winding machine.

Hoisting Operations. Hoisting from great depths may be done in more than one **stage,** usually not in more than three, each stage comprising a separate and complete hoist. Often the same hoist is used for both material and men, but sometimes separate hoists are provided for the two. These hoists may operate in separate shafts, or in several compartments of the same shaft.

Hoists are arranged to operate unbalanced, balanced, or counterweighted. **Unbalanced hoisting** consists of a single-drum winding machine which winds one rope attached to the cage, skip, or car operating in a single compartment or shaft. The winding machine provides the entire force for hoisting. **Balanced hoisting** consists of either a single-drum winding machine which winds two ropes, or a double-drum machine, each drum of which winds one rope. In either case, one rope winds "on" while the other rope winds "off." The ropes are attached to cages, skips, or cars which operate in separate compartments of the shaft. The winding machine provides only the force necessary to nullify the difference in rope pulls between the ascending loaded and descending empty cages, skips, or cars. Tail-ropes are sometimes attached to the underside of the cages or skips, when used in vertical shafts, to reduce still further the difference in rope pulls at the drum or drums. **Counterweighted hoisting** is similar to single-drum balanced hoisting, except that one of the ropes is attached to a counterweight, equal in weight to that of the empty skip plus one-half of the weight of material.

Mine hoists have **capacities** as follows:

> Rope load .... up to 90,000 lb.
> Rope speed
>   For material .... up to 5,000 F.P.M.
>   For men .... 1,200 F.P.M.
> Hoisting distance .... depths to 5,000 ft.

In general, **hoists for shallow mines** have larger load capacities with lower speeds, while those for deep mines have smaller load capacities with higher speeds. In **hoists for deep mines,** the weight of the wire rope is a large proportion of the lifted load, which consists of the cage and/or skip together with their contents, plus the weight of the length of rope from which the cage and/or skip are suspended. This total lifted load is limited by the strength of the wire ropes available, which is the reason that hoists for shallow mines can have greater loads than those for deep mines. To compensate for the reduced lifted loads for deep mine hoists, it is necessary to use **higher rope speeds** to obtain the desired output. The limitation on rope speed is the horsepower of available motors. This limitation applies to hoists for both deep and shallow mines.

Cages. Cages are generally used in vertical shafts for the hoisting of men and of materials other than coal and ore, but in some cases the floor of the cage carries tracks for the mine cars, which, together with their contents of coal or ore, are hoisted to the surface. Often this latter type of cage has the floor arranged to tilt, discharging the loaded cars at the surface and the empty cars at the bottom of the shaft or at intermediate levels. Cages sometimes have two decks.

Skips. Skips are used in both vertical and inclined shafts for the hoisting of coal and ore. They are self-dumping and discharge their contents automatically at the end of the hoisting cycle. Fig. 15 shows a 12-ton self-dumping coal skip fitted with safety catches and spring drawbar, and designed to operate in a shaft fitted with T-rail guides.

Cars. Regular mine cars may be used as hoisting containers, and may be emptied by a revolving car-dumper located in the head frame or may be self-dumping. Monitor cars are provided with seats and are used for handling men and/or material other than coal or ore.

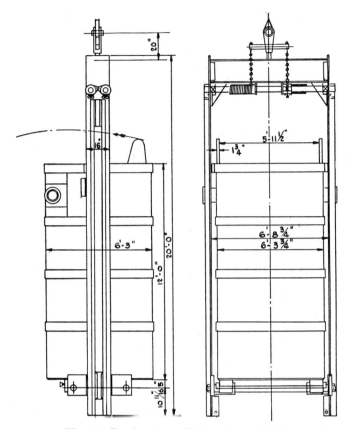

Fig. 15. Twelve-ton self-dumping coal skip.

MINE-ELEVATOR HOISTING MACHINES. Mine hoists or winding machines have either steam or electric drives and are further classified by the type and number of their **drums,** either single or double. A typical mine elevator hoisting machine is shown in Fig. 16. Various kinds of drums are as follows:

1. Cylindrical
2. Conical
3. Reel

4. Cylindro-conical
5. Bi-cylindro-conical

Each hoist drum is provided with a **brake** of either the band or post type, which is either manually applied or applied and released by oil, air, or steam power. Electrically operated magnetic brakes are not usually used.

One drum, and occasionally both drums, of double cylindrical drum and reel hoists are provided with **clutches** of the band, axial plate, or gear type, and are operated either manually or by oil, air, or steam power. Conical, cylindro-conical and bi-cylindro-conical drum hoists are usually not equipped with clutches.

Hoist drives, either steam or electric, are of the following types:

1. First-motion: the drum or drums being mounted directly on the steam engine crankshaft, or on a drum shaft coupled directly to the electric motor armature shaft.

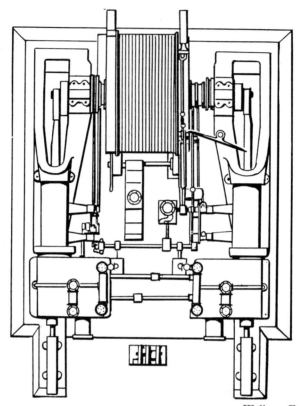

Wellman Engineering Co.

Fig. 16. Mine-elevator hoisting machine.

2. Single-reduction-geared: a single pair of spur or herringbone gears being provided between the steam engine or electric motor and the drum shaft.
3. Double-reduction-geared: two pairs of spur or herringbone gears being provided between the steam engine or electric motor and the drum shaft.

Mine hoists are provided with dial indicators, one for each drum, to show at what level or depth of the mine the cage, skip, or car is at all times. **Safety devices** are also provided to prevent overtravel and overspeed in case of operator's negligence.

Mine hoists are classified as follows:

1. Vertical shaft mine hoists with single cage. These hoists use a single cage suspended from the hoisting rope for either unbalanced or counterweighted hoisting, or a single cage suspended for each rope for balanced hoisting.
2. Vertical-shaft mine hoists with skip (coal or ore). These hoists use skips instead of cages.
3. Vertical-shaft mine hoists with combination cage and skip. Hoists of this kind are similar to those with a skip except that a cage and a skip are suspended from the rope, the cage being attached beneath the skip.
4. Inclined-shaft mine hoists with skip (coal or ore). Hoists equipped with skips are similar to vertical shaft mine hoists with skips, except that they operate in inclined instead of vertical shafts.

5. Inclined-shaft mine hoists with car or cars (coal or ore). Such hoists are similar to inclined-shaft mine hoists with skips, except that one or more coal or ore cars are used instead of skips.
6. Inclined-shaft mine hoists with monitor car. These hoists are similar to inclined-shaft mine hoists with skip except that monitor cars for handling men and/or material other than coal or ore are used instead of skips.

BLAST-FURNACE SKIP HOISTS. Blast-furnace skip hoists are similar to inclined-shaft mine hoists with skips, arranged for balanced operation, except that the skips travel on inclined tracks to the top of the blast furnace instead of in an underground inclined shaft. The length of travel is relatively short—about 250 ft.—and the maximum weight of ore in each skip is 40,000 lb. Hoisting speed is about 400 ft. per min.

The complete installation consists of:

1. The hoist proper, which usually has an electric drive and is described in detail under "Skip Hoisting Machines."
2. The inclined skipway, supporting the tracks on which the skips travel and the sheaves on which the hoisting ropes run.
3. The skips for handling the iron ore, limestone, and coke.
4. The wire rope for hoisting the skips. For double insurance against accident due to rope breakage, two ropes are attached to each skip, each rope of sufficient strength to withstand the load, with the usual factor of safety.

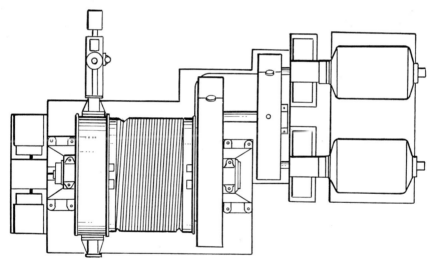

Wellman Engineering Co.

Fig. 17. Skip hoisting machine.

The **operation of these hoists is automatic,** the operator having only to push a button to start the hoist. Acceleration, deceleration, and stopping are controlled by multicontact limit switches, one for each skip. In addition, program-sequence controls are provided which automatically enable the operator to load a predetermined number of skip loads of iron ore, limestone, and coke.

INDUSTRIAL SKIP HOISTS. These hoists are similar to blast furnace skip hoists, but are of lesser capacity and speed, and are used for the handling of bulk industrial materials.

SKIP HOISTING MACHINES. Skip hoisting machines usually have Ward-Leonard electric drives with two generators and two hoist-drive motors, each of which is capable of hoisting the maximum ore load at reduced speed, to insure **continued operation** in case of failure of one generator and/or one motor (Fig. 17). Constant-potential d.c. drives are also used for these hoists. These provide the operating characteristics of the Ward-Leonard drives by means of field-weakening and armature shunt of the driving motors.

These hoists have single cylindrical drums driven by two motors. Some hoists have the two motor-drive pinions driving through one intermediate gear and a single drum pinion and drum gear, while others have the two motor pinions driving through two intermediate gears, and two drum pinions with a single drum gear. All the gears are of the herringbone type and operate in oil-tight housings. All shafts are mounted on self-aligning roller bearings. Both kinds of hoists are equipped with an electric magnetic brake on each motor; but, in addition, the type with only one drum pinion has an emergency post brake on the drum, which is weight-applied and power-released by an air cylinder. **Safety devices** are also provided, to prevent overspeed and overtravel in case of failure of the limit switches which automatically control the acceleration, deceleration and stopping.

WINCHES

CONTENTS

WINCHES

WINCHES DEFINED. As integral parts of cranes and elevators, winches are seldom seen, though their service is quite obvious. Winches, as independent or auxiliary units, also play an important materials handling role. In general, they are a type of **hoisting machinery** that gains mechanical advantage through the medium of spools or drums.

CLASSIFICATION OF WINCHES. The nomenclature has been considerably confused, due largely to the use of this equipment on ships. Winches can be classified as follows: windlasses, capstans, single-drum winches, multiple-drum winches, auxiliary winches.

WINDLASSES. A windlass is a hand- or power-operated device to hoist and lower loads by the use of a wildcat sprocket engaging a chain or chains.

The **wildcat sprocket** (Fig. 1) is a grooved and flanged wheel with grooving formed to fit the required size of chain for the purpose of gripping each chain link as it passes through. The wildcat is generally made of cast steel.

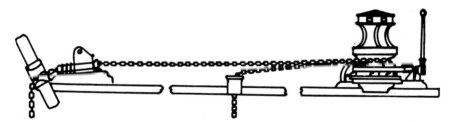

Fig. 1. Hand anchor windlass.

It is most commonly used as a ship's **anchor windlass** to hoist anchors, drop them when desired, and to veer chain as required. It has the secondary function of handling lines and warps when the vessel is docking or undocking, which is done by means of drums or warping heads on extensions of one or more of its shafts. The windlass is also used where it is necessary to handle extremely heavy loads at slow hoisting speed.

Types of Windlasses. There are six kinds of windlasses in regular service. They are:

1. Hand anchor windlass.
2. Steam anchor windlass.
3. Electric anchor windlass.
4. Hydraulic anchor windlass.
5. Electric water gate windlass.
6. Gasoline or diesel water gate windlass.

A **hand anchor windlass** is a hand-powered device to hoist or lower the anchor of small vessels. A wildcat and warping head are located adjacent to each other on a common shaft and may be horizontally or vertically mounted. The wildcat is engaged or disengaged by means of a block key. To operate the warping head separately, the wildcat is disengaged and held with pawl and friction hand brake.

The **power-operated type** of anchor windlass is commonly made to handle two ships' anchors. Power is transmitted through a series of gearing to the horizontally mounted wildcat shaft. The wildcats are jaw-clutched to this shaft and when declutched are each held by a friction hand brake. Warping heads may be mounted on this same wildcat shaft or some intermediate shaft where they may be declutched from the anchor hoisting operation.

The anchor windlass must perform several operations:

1. Drop both anchors together or independently by using the brake.
2. Slack out both anchors together by power.
3. Slack out either anchor by power, at will.
4. Veer chain on either anchor or both anchors.
5. Heave in both anchors together at not less than 30 ft. per min.
6. Heave in either anchor at not less than 30 ft. per min.
7. Warp hawsers with a maximum pull of 75 percent of hawser breaking strength.

Most modern vessels are designed for the **electric-powered windlass.** Steam power is still used on many new oil tank vessels because of the reduced fire hazard.

Another more recent means of powering is by **hydraulic power.** Hydraulic motors can very easily replace an electric motor installation and give exceptionally good performance. A **water gate windlass** is power driven to perform its function of raising and lowering the gates of a water dam to maintain desired water levels. It is generally specially designed to suit each individual application. In some instances, this type of equipment is of enormous proportions and the lifting capacity may run over 700,000 lb. chain-pull at a very slow speed. Generally, this equipment is electric powered; however, gasoline or diesel power may be used.

CAPSTANS. A capstan, frequently called a snubbing drum, is a hand- or power-operated device having a **smooth or whelped drum,** vertically or horizontally mounted, for use with a manila rope or even cable for towing or light hoisting operations. Several turns of a rope or cable are coiled closely around the drum. With a light pull on the loose end of the rope a greater pull is exerted on the load end as power is transmitted by friction from the rotating drum to the several coils of rope.

There are six typical kinds of capstans:

1. Hand vertical capstans.
2. Steam vertical capstans.
3. Gasoline or diesel vertical capstans.
4. Electric vertical capstans.
5. Gasoline or diesel horizontal capstans.
6. Electric horizontal capstans.

Vertical Capstans. The hand-powered bar-type of capstan is a device for handling lines or warping such as in towing or docking and is generally found aboard small vessels but may also be located on the docking wharf. By use of a bar the head is revolved clockwise, and the vertical drum turns at the same speed and in the same direction. When the head is revolved counterclockwise the vertical drum still turns clockwise but at a ratio of 3 to 1 for power. Locking pawls on the lower end of the barrel engage a ratchet in the base.

The **power-operated vertical drum capstan** (Fig. 2) is used principally where heavy line pulls are required as in warping larger ships and barges and in other towing operations. Manila rope is used in most instances, except where extremely heavy line pulls are required, when wire rope is used. Vertical capstans with electric motor drives are frequently used as **car pullers** or as **barge movers.** Where a large number of railroad cars are being shunted into a plant, yard, or siding, the low-cost car puller can be used instead of a costly switching locomotive. Capstans of this type are generally available in capacities from 2,000 lb. to 40,000 lb. line pull. Units most frequently used for car pulling are those of 5 to 10 hp. proving single line pull of 5,000 lb. at an approximate rate of 45 ft. per min.

Fig. 2. Powered vertical capstan.

The type of power to be used depends upon the source of power available or upon preference. **Electric power** may be used if it is readily available. **Steam** may be preferred if other nearby equipment is also steam-powered or it may be used, as on new oil tank vessels, to reduce fire hazard. **Gasoline or diesel** power may be used where the capstan and its power unit are self-contained.

The capstan head is powered through a vertical shaft with a **worm** and **gear drive** at the lower end, and where further speed reduction is required, a **spur** or **helical reduction set** reduces the speed between the motor and worm gear set. The power machinery may be either close coupled to the vertical drum or as in the case aboard ship may be extended below deck or on the deck below.

Horizontal Capstans. The horizontal capstan (sometimes called a **gypsy**) may have either one or two power-operated drums used for heavy lifts or tows. The power is coupled to a worm gear reducer with the horizontal drums mounted on the worm gear shaft extensions. Gasoline or diesel power (Fig. 3) is used where electric power is not available. It is readily adaptable for use on trucks for loading or unloading heavy equipment by connecting to the truck power take-off at the transmission.

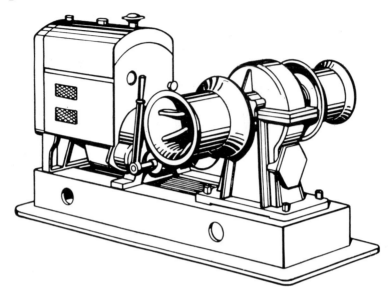

Fig. 3. Horizontal capstan.

DRUM WINCHES. These winches, also called **hoists** and **winding machines,** are hand- or power-operated devices having one or more horizontal rope **winding drums,** which rotate through gears, or a series of gears, and shafting contained by a suitable supporting frame. In operation, the end of the end rope or cable is attached to the drum, where it is coiled and stored as it is wound in. They are universal hoisting tools made in different ways to suit specific applications, with light weight for portability and strength to stand up to rugged use. Three types of power transmission are commonly used. The first of these is the **friction clutch,** utilizing a cone or discs between the driving shaft and the drum. This is the oldest type and is preferred in many applications in which a high degree of slippage and gravity lowering are desired. The **jaw clutch** is often used where the highest degree of control and safety is desired with freedom to disengage power from the drum. Power is transmitted by engaging a sliding jaw or dental clutch on the drive shaft with a mating clutch on the drum. One advantage of a clutch-driven drum is that the drum can be disengaged while an auxiliary horizontal winch head mounted on the end of the shaft remains in operation. The third type is **direct transmission,** whereby the drum is keyed or otherwise permanently secured to the drive shaft.

Single-Drum Winches. There are five types of single-drum winches:

1. Hand winches.
2. Steam single-drum winches.
3. Air single-drum winches.
4. Gasoline or diesel single-drum winches.
5. Electric single-drum winches.

A **hand-powered winch** is usually portable and can be carried by one man. Some units have line-pull ratings exceeding 15 tons. A winch may have two speeds or more, employing spur gears between the crank handle and the horizontal drum, and includes a friction brake and dog for locking (Fig. 4). Its many uses include truck mounted applications for moving heavy machinery or for use as wrecking cars to snake autos out of ditches. It may be used on derricks, gin poles, spotting cars, boathouse and dock operations, land clearing, stump pulling, etc. Single-speed worm-drive hand winches are frequently used as **column winches** for light hoisting work.

Winches in marine service are generally either **steam or electric powered** and are provided with one or two winch heads or warping heads. Their principal purpose is to hoist or lower cargo, but they are frequently used for topping and lowering cargo booms, handling lines, and assisting in warping ships into or out of their berths.

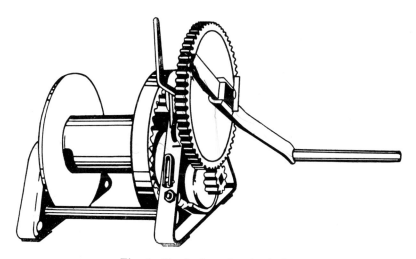

Fig. 4. Single-drum hand winch.

In **construction and general service,** any type of power may be used for the winches, depending upon sources available or upon preference. A typical arrangement has a chain or gear drive from the power unit to a driveshaft which is geared to a drumshaft. The drum is free to rotate on the shaft and is engaged by a friction clutch. The drum has a ratchet ring fastened to it that can be engaged by a pawl for locking the drum. A friction brake is also a part of the drum assembly, and it is used to control the drum in lowering or holding loads.

The electric-powered **car-, barge-, or ship-mover** has a range of sizes in which the line-pull rating is the starting line pull and is reached when using the maximum torque of the electric motor. The no-load or light-line speed is slow, possibly ranging from less than 20 ft. per min. for barge- and ship-moving applications to over 50 ft. per min. for car moving. The drum type of car-mover is directly geared to the electric motor. It has a sliding-jaw clutch to disengage the drum when the line is pulled off the drum. A foot-operated friction brake is used to control the drum speed, preventing rope from becoming loose on the drum. Two-drum-type car-movers can be used in an opposed arrangement. While one car-mover is pulling a car, the other is exerting a small countertorque to keep the line taut on the opposing drum. This system is limited in distance of operation by the amount of rope that can be wound on the drum (see section on Fixed Cranes).

Where compressed air is available, the **air-powered winch** (Fig. 5) may be used. It is a self-contained unit with all gearing enclosed in the drum, and the air motor is an integral part of the winch. The commonest sizes of air winches have less than 4,000 lb. line pull and are of slow line speeds.

The air winch may be used for general hoisting or towing work but is especially adaptable for work underground where space limitations call for a compact hoisting unit.

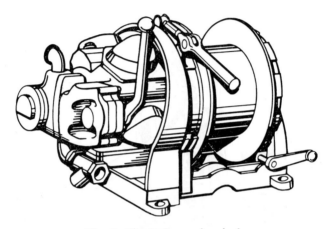

Fig. 5. Single-drum air winch.

Multiple-Drum Winches. Multiple-drum winches are power-operated lifting devices having two or more horizontal drums for use in operating **derricks, cranes,** etc. Power is transmitted through chain- or gear-drives—or a combination of both—to the drumshafts wherein the drums are engaged through friction clutches. Each drum may be controlled independently of the others and allowed to unwind, giving free fall to the load, or it may be controlled by an external contracting-type friction brake which is an integral part of the drum assembly. A ratchet and pawl are generally provided to engage the drum for locking against rotation.

The **means for operating the clutches,** pawls, and brakes may be: by manual controls, which require the greatest effort; by hydraulic controls, which give excellent characteristics of operation; or by air controls, which are equally easy to operate and control as are other means and are most frequently used because of the low cost for powered control.

A hoist is generally thought of as a lifting device, but in many instances it may also have to lower loads great distances and maintain a definite time-cycle in its operation. An engineering problem is encountered in calculating the proper brake size to dissipate heat generated by excessive friction.

Winch heads may be provided for handling auxiliary lines, usually of manila rope. A winch head keyed to the drumshaft is generally provided, but a jaw-clutched type of winch head may be preferred where it is desirable to hold off the load on the winch head while doing other work with the hoisting drum. The winch head is provided with a ratchet for engagement with a pawl for locking.

A **swinger unit** is attached to the front of the hoist, or an independent swinger may be required in derrick work where poker swing is essential. A single drum for reversing operation may be preferred to a double-drum arrangement when the derrick and hoist installation presents some operating problem such as space limitation.

The **number of hoisting drums** in a hoist is determined by the number of independent operations required of a derrick or crane. One drum is required where a derrick boom must be raised or lowered for variable radii of the load. Another drum is required wherein one main load block is to be handled. Another drum is added when the main load block is double-reeved and two drums lift the main load simultaneously. Another drum is added where lighter loads and high speeds are required.

Hoists are used in general construction: to hoist cages in towers; for derrick work in quarries, steel erection, clamshell bucket operations, etc.; and on cranes which are used for handling steel and subassemblies as in shipyards, for concrete bucket work as in oil field service and offshore drilling platform construction, and many similar types of hoisting operation.

Steam Multiple-Drum Winches or Hoists. Steam power is not used as commonly since the advent of the gasoline and diesel engines. There are applications, however, where steam power is still more desirable—for example, for cranes mounted on most floating barge installations where steam is the source of power not only for the operation of the hoisting machinery in the crane but of all deck auxiliaries such as anchor windlasses, anchor hoists, water pumps, and air compressors. Steam power gives smooth operation and precision of control.

Gasoline or Diesel Multiple-Drum Winches or Hoists. Gasoline engine power has the advantage of "first" low cost. It is easily mounted and serviced, and is by far the most popular type of power used on hoisting equipment. It is a self-contained power plant and is, therefore, desirable where hoist portability is required (Fig. 6).

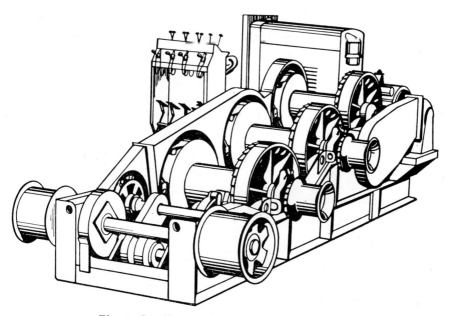

Fig. 6. Gasoline or diesel multiple-drum winch.

Diesel engine power is desirable because of its low fuel cost, low consumption, and its exceptionally good torque characteristics for handling overloads. The initial cost is generally higher than a gasoline power unit and will weigh more per hp.

Electric Multiple-Drum Winches or Hoists. Hoists powered by electric motors give excellent performance with proper controls. Loads can be hoisted or lowered under power. The cost of electrical equipment runs high when increased precision of control and other features are desired. Hoists with electric motors and controls can be used as portable equipment provided that electric power is available at the job site.

Hoist Auxiliary Equipment. In many instances auxiliary equipment has been developed for use in connection with hoisting equipment. Two kinds of mechanisms which are in use in the hoisting field are the torque converter and multiple-speed transmissions. The **torque converter** is a hydraulic coupling that has the desirable characteristics of increasing torque with decreasing speed. It cushions the handling of a hoisted load and gives precision control of the load from zero speed to maximum, and it allows limited lowering of the load when throttling back the engine and thus lets the load torque overcome the output torque at the converter.

Silent Hoist & Crane Co.

Fig. 7. Capstan winch mounted on truck.

The torque converter has been applied to many types of hoisting either where precision of control is necessary, as in steel erection work, or where torque multiplication is desirable without stalling the engine, as in the logging industry.

Multiple-speed transmissions are devices that allow changing speeds for handling various loads. The operator selects the gear speed at which the output torque will handle a given load at maximum speed.

There are various types of transmissions, all of which employ gears for changing speeds. The speed change can be made when the load is in motion if it is of the syncromesh or planetary type. Other jaw-type and sliding gear transmissions require stopping the load and jogging to enter the proper gear speed.

Two-speed planetary type transmissions are being applied after the torque converter to increase the range of operation in hoisting service.

AUXILIARY WINCHES. This class of winches covers **winding machines** that are mounted on various types of primary equipment to assist in or add to the handling functions of the primary unit. In general, these winches fall into the same basic types previously described although they will usually include only units of relatively small capacity. Some are hand-operated while others are powered by self-contained power units or by the power plant of the primary unit through a power take-off device (see section on Portable Cranes). Hall classifies auxiliary winches according to the type of primary equipment on which they are mounted. The classification includes winches mounted on lifters, motor vehicles, tractors, other handling equipment, and column winches.

Silent Hoist & Crane Co.

Fig. 8. Auxiliary winch mounted on mobile crane.

Auxiliary Applications. Fig. 7 shows an **auxiliary vertical capstan** mounted on a truck. Normal commercial sizes, driven from the truck engine, range from 1 ton to 6 tons capacity. This type of installation is used by truckers and riggers for loading and unloading heavy materials as well as for various hoisting and pulling operations.

Fig. 8 shows a **single-drum winch** with auxiliary gypsy head mounted on a mobile swing boom crane. In a typical industrial application the winch is used to drag heavy loads from the interior of a building to a loading platform where it can be handled by the crane. **Single-** and **double-drum winches** are frequently mounted on trucks and tractors and may be driven through chains from a power take-off. When using double-drum winches on trucks or tractors, the most economical arrangement is to have both drums mounted on a single-drum shaft.

AUXILIARY CRANE EQUIPMENT

CONTENTS

AUXILIARY CRANE EQUIPMENT

Crane Grabs

FUNCTIONS AND TYPES OF GRABS. A crane or hoist by itself can serve no purpose until a load is suspended from it. Some kind of device must be employed for actually grasping the object to be lifted. Such devices, known as **grabs or grapples,** are used for many reasons in addition to their basic function as the connecting means between the crane and the load. They perform an important safety function in the handling of hot or gaseous loads. They permit the safe handling of objects into and out of pickling tubs, as in the metal industries, or into and out of hot caustic solutions, as in the veneer industry. In atomic plants they permit remote handling of radioactive material. They make it possible to store materials, parts, subassemblies, assemblies, equipment, etc., in a minimum space, to considerable height, and to keep men away from stored materials that may shift. In addition to safety, their use, especially in the case of those of the more specific types, increases speed of operation in practically all cases, and vastly reduces labor cost.

In general, grabs or grapples may be classified into two groups.

Group 1 (Gravity Type). Grabs that apply pressure equal to the mechanical advantage of the leverage system multiplied by the weight lifted. This group in turn may be further divided into:

1. Those manually applied and removed, and almost universal in application.
2. Those manually applied and removed, but designed for a specific purpose.
3. Those semiautomatic in operation. Such grabs must be manually applied, but can be released and made ready for the next piece without manual assistance merely by placing the load into its final position, by means of a special cam arrangement.
4. Those fully automatic in operation. Such grabs are equipped with cams which enable the grab to grasp and release the load alternately without manual assistance.

Group 2 (Power-operated Type). Grabs wherein the power for grasping is supplied by electrical, pneumatic, or hydraulic sources.

GRAVITY-TYPE GRABS VS. POWER-OPERATED GRABS. Whether to use a gravity-type grab or a power-operated grab is determined by the frequency of use, the ease of application, the access to the object to be lifted, and the safety factor. The actual design of the grab itself is determined not only by the weight of the load but also by the material of which the load is composed, such as paper, steel, wood, etc.; by its form such as cylindrical, rectangular, etc.; by its dimensions; and, very importantly, by the variations in all these factors which must be taken into account.

The grab finally chosen must first, of course, be strong enough to lift the load. Second, the grab must be so designed that the space occupied will be the absolute minimum. Third, the grab must occupy no more than the space available on the gripped sides to allow the grab to enter. Fourth, the weight of the grab should be kept at a minimum so as to permit a given crane to lift a maximum useful load or to permit the use of the lightest possible hoisting equipment for a given load. This requirement may not seem important, but, if neglected, it may at times involve an unnecessarily large expenditure, not only for the hoisting equipment but also for the supporting means. Fifth, the grab must be of a type to be operated in minimum time, though not necessarily less than the minimum time essential for the particular conditions under which it is to be used. Sixth, safety is of paramount importance.

Though not, strictly speaking, a grab, the **sling** is the simplest device and is adopted for industrial application when use is infrequent, and first cost is more important than efficiency. It is flexible in form, and the same sling can frequently be applied to objects of varying dimensions and shapes. It is made of such material as hemp, wire, chain, canvas, and nylon, and in the form of woven wire belting. Examples of simple slings are shown in Fig. 1.

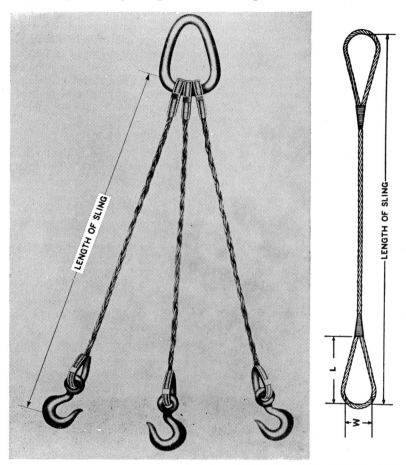

American Steel & Wire Div., U. S. Steel Corp.

Fig. 1. Simple slings.

SEMIAUTOMATIC AND AUTOMATIC GRABS. Early grabs were manually applied and manually released. Later, semiautomatic hold-open devices, such as the one shown in Fig. 2, and fully automatic cams were introduced. Both grabs use the **ice-tongs principle** for gripping. In the semiautomatic unit a notched cross link is added. When the load is set down and the hoist hook is lowered, the grab opens, the notch drops over the pivot pin, and the grab is thus prevented from closing when lifted. It remains open, ready for the next load. To

Mansaver Industries, Inc.

Fig. 2. Semiautomatic grab applied to shell forging.

pick up the load, the hold-open lever must be manually lifted. The semiautomatic grab requires the services of a "hooker-on" to guide the grab and lift the lever so that it will attach itself to the load, but does not require a man at the discharge point. With an automatic grab, no man is needed to position the grab on the object. A special cam mechanism is suspended from the lifting link. This cam arrangement is so designed that the protruding end will alternately permit and prevent the grab from gripping the load, merely by raising and lowering the crane hook.

Disadvantage of Semi- and Fully Automatic Tongs. Although there are advantages in the use of both the semiautomatic and the fully automatic tongs, there is the following disadvantage: Cams are included, and the cam must go through its entire cycle in performing its function. Since the grab, when picking up loads of varying width, must be able to pick up the load of greatest width, the cam is set to keep the grab open after depositing the widest load. Although when the cam is released the grab can pick up narrow as well as wide loads, the grab must always open to its widest extent in order for the locking action of the cam to take effect. Thus the space required for lifting a narrow object is usually the same as that required for a wide object, as shown in Fig. 3. If the object to be lifted is always taken from the end of a pile, that loss of space does not occur, but

Space Requirements with Automatic Grabs

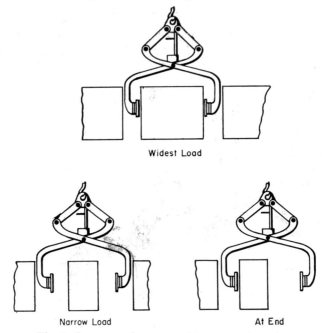

Fig. 3. Space requirements with automatic grabs.

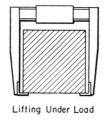

Lifting Under Load

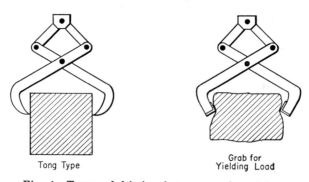

Fig. 4. Types of friction between grab and load.

a hooker-on may be required at the release point to open the grab and permit the cam to catch.

COEFFICIENT OF FRICTION. Grabs, whether manual, semiautomatic, or fully automatic, lift either by getting under the load, as with a sling or sheet-lifter, or by friction (see Fig. 4). When objects are lifted by friction, the pressure that must be applied to the object to be lifted varies directly with the coefficient of friction. The highest coefficient of friction, and therefore the least grip required, exists when either one or both surfaces are such that parts of one surface will catch under parts of the other, thus obtaining almost the equivalent of a fully supported load. Another combination resulting in maximum friction is typified by a pair of single-pointed ice tongs making contact with a smooth box or a cake of ice. Sufficient initial friction must be obtained between the points on the tongs and the load to cause the points to dig further into the load. A similar effect is obtained when tongs with broad lifting surfaces are applied with sufficient pressure to force themselves into a yielding mass, such as, for example, a bale of waste paper, which has sufficient resilience to regain its original shape without damage.

In some instances the material lifted is such that a digging action would be harmful. Then the gripping surface of the grab must be faced with a material having the highest possible coefficient of friction relative to the material to be lifted, and of sufficient strength and wear-resistance so that it has long life. Although rubber is usually the first material considered, grabs have been surfaced with brake-lining, wood, steel, and other materials.

Pressure and Coefficient of Friction. The choice of material with a maximum coefficient of friction is of considerable importance. The ability of a grab to lift is brought about by the total friction, that is, by a combination of the coefficient of friction and the pressure applied. The higher the coefficient of friction, the lower is the pressure requirement. The lower the pressure, the lighter the grab and the more fragile the object handled may be. It is for this reason that the aim of a grab designer is to use a system of leverages which will have the same pressure for a given weight of load regardless of the variation in sizes of loads to be handled. This objective is extremely difficult of attainment. When dimensions of the loads which are handled with the same grab vary, it frequently becomes necessary to make the grab heavier.

Application to Grab Design. Since the gripping pressure in most systems of leverage decreases as the size of the object to be lifted decreases, a grab designed to apply adequate pressure to a smaller object will apply greater than adequate pressure to a larger object. This aim, to obtain the same gripping force for a specific weight regardless of the variations in dimensions of the objects to be lifted, may be attained by adjusting the grab to the various widths to be handled, such adjustment being made either manually or by electric, hydraulic, or pneumatic power. Where such changes have to be made frequently, the power-operated grab is being increasingly used. The power-operated grab can be operated from a remote point, just as the fully automatic grab can. However, in the case of the power-operated grab, the adjustment to load variation as well as the gripping and release of the load are at all times under full control of the hoist or crane operator, whereas the mechanical grab is actuated only by placing the load in position.

In the case of some power-operated grabs, power is used merely to adjust for changes in dimensions, and the necessary friction for lifting is obtained by the same means as in the case of a mechanical grab. In such instances, the pressure applied is in direct proportion to the load lifted. With other power-operated grabs, both gripping power and adjustment are power-actuated so that the force applied—being furnished by an outside source—can be independent of the weight lifted.

With a mechanical leverage system for gripping, sometimes more power is applied than is necessary. For example, if it were desired to pick up both coated and uncoated paper rolls, a grab would have to be designed with sufficient frictional quality to lift the more slippery material. Then, with the less slippery material, more pressure than necessary would be applied. When, however, the pressure is applied by power, only such pressure need be applied as is permitted by the fragility of the object to be lifted and demanded by the friction required. Thus, a power-operated grab can give greater flexibility, not only in sizes of objects lifted, but also in the pressure that has to be applied in lifting the objects of various sizes.

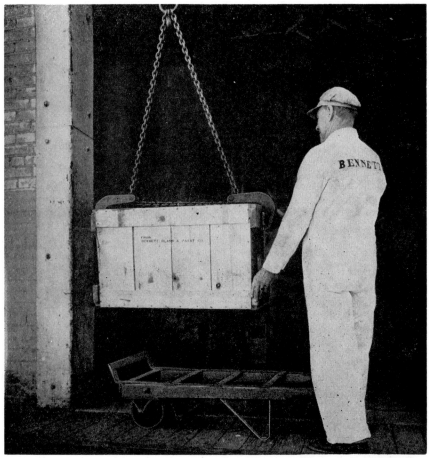

Mansaver Industries, Inc.

Fig. 5. Chain grab for handling crates.

GRAB APPLICATIONS. So far, grabs have been discussed from the stand-point of the designer. However, for the production man who is more interested in performance than design, there are innumerable applications which can be illustrated from a wide range of industrial fields.

Box and Carton Grabs. Grabs adaptable to any industry are those for handling boxes, barrels, and cartons of various shapes. Since even these grabs vary greatly in design, only general applications can be given here. Fig. 5 shows a typical chain-operated grab used with crates in the glass industry. This grab is made adjustable by means of the hook shown attached to the lifting ring. The length of chain can be varied to fit the box length by shortening the chain and hooking it onto any particular link. A grab of similar design may be applied to a **wood frame box.** When boxes have to be handled frequently, they can be handled to advantage by **motor-driven grabs,** one of which is shown in Fig. 6.

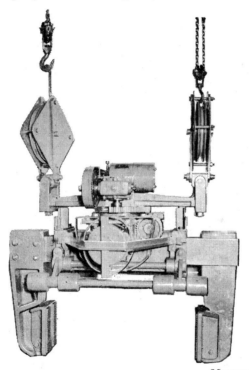

Mansaver Industries, Inc.

Fig. 6. Motor-driven grab and hoist for heavy duty.

Barrel Grabs. Variations in the design of barrel grabs are numerous. Applications illustrated here are limited to typical barrel grabs in general use. Fig. 7 shows a simple grab used for handling a barrel either horizontally or vertically by attaching the hook to the proper ring. Drums can be handled by the rim with automatic or semiautomatic tongs-type grabs. If it is desired to empty a drum of its contents, a grab which grips around the circumference is used. The turning is under the control of the operator, either manually with a lever or, if accurate control is desired, by means of a self-locking worm gear.

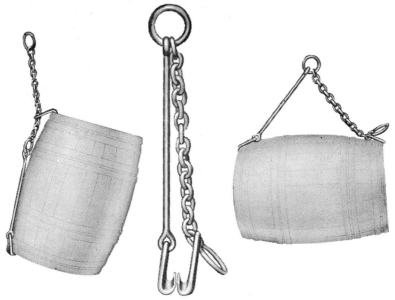

Mansaver Industries, Inc.

Fig. 7. Simple chain grab for carrying barrels vertically or horizontally.

Mansaver Industries, Inc.

Fig. 8. Special ingot-mold tongs, which can also be designed to lift more than one
mold at a time.

Grabs for Lifting Ingots. Grabs are used in the handling of ingots after the molten metal has been poured from the furnace into ingot molds. The metal is allowed to cool, after which the mold is removed by an automatic grab of the type shown in Fig. 8. The ingot proper is handled by a large automatic cam-type grab similar to that described earlier in this section.

Coil Grabs. Rolled metal is often wound in coils and stored vertically or horizontally. When stored vertically, these coils are usually gripped on the rim to eliminate the possibility of deforming the coil. Rim gripping means that every layer is held rigid, and telescoping of the coil is thereby prevented.

Heppenstall Co.

Fig. 9. Extra-heavy tongs for handling rolls of sheet metal.

Fig. 9 shows a rim-gripping grab lifting and storing coils into vertical piles. **Rim-gripping grabs** of this type permit such vertical piling without time-consuming spacers being placed between coils. The coils have a greater resistance to crushing than when stored horizontally. During the various operations of rolling and slitting, the coils must be turned from the horizontal to the vertical and back, and it is usually necessary to place them on a mechanical upender. A chain or a sling can be threaded around the rim of the coil for turning it only one way. Care must be exercised in resting the coil on its edge as it is being turned, to avoid possible damage to the material.

Mansaver Industries, Inc.

Fig. 10. Handling two coils at once. The same grab can be used for handling one coil.

Power-operated grabs are available for eliminating this last difficulty. They also reduce dangerous instability in vertical piling. Small coils can be handled two at a time with the grab shown in Fig. 10. This grab is adjustable and designed for low-headroom operation. Multiple handling of coils in vertical position can also be accomplished by grabs similar to the one shown handling racks in Fig. 21.

Grabs for **horizontal coil-handling** are produced in many forms. Fig. 11 shows a simple grab which has to be manually attached and detached and lifts by means of hooking under the coil rim. When headroom is low the same **hooking principle** is used by a grab consisting of a horizontal spacer bar with hinged tongs at each end. By proper manipulation, the crane operator can remove this

Littell Page

Fig. 11. Hook grab and chain for horizontal coil-handling.

grab without floor assistance. Adjustment for coil width must, however, be made by a "hooker-on." A fully automatic grab of this nature that can be removed and placed in position by the crane operator is shown in Fig. 12. The pendent legs are slid in to meet the coil and are held open, by the automatic cam box shown, to permit picking the next coil.

Other grab designs are used for handling coils horizontally. The first is a type of hairpin hook that enters the core from one side instead of both. Another grips the coil around its circumference with wide curved tongs. To reduce the pressure against the side of the coil and to eliminate the necessity for always open-ing the grab for the widest coil, a **motor-driven grab** may be used. To be certain that the coil is in a position to unwind properly, this grab may be supplied with a motor-driven turntable. The 20-ton grab in Fig. 12 is equipped with motor driven legs and turntable. Controls of both the turning motion and the motions for adjustment are regulated by the crane operator, with considerable saving in labor. Several horizontal coils can be handled at once with the multiple grab shown in the brass mill application in Fig. 13.

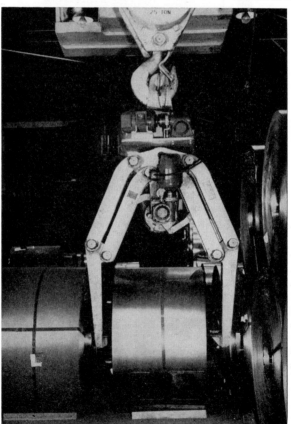

Fig. 12. Automatic grabs for handling variable widths of rolls. (Top) Extension grab; (bottom) grab with motor-regulated legs and turntable.

Fig. 13. Multiple horizontal coil handling grab.

Handling Sheet Stock. Coils of rolled metal are cut into sheets of various lengths and widths. Grabs for handling these sheets are made either hand-operated or motor-operated, with an increasing tendency on the part of mills handling heavy bundles to motorize their equipment. A motorized unit is shown in Figs. 14 and 15. These grabs are arranged so that the crane operator can move the lifting legs in and out, depending on the width of bundle to be handled. In the case shown in Fig. 14, short as well as long sheets are being handled, and motor-driven end-hooks are supplied. These end-hooks also are controlled by the crane operator, who can thus place the bundle in its ultimate location without floor assistance. The function of the end-hooks is both to reduce the sag of the sheets and to increase safety of operation.

Where motor-drives for heavy sheet grabs are not required, a grab with hand-chain operation is indicated. While the gripping principles used in this grab are similar to those of the motor-driven grab described above, it is controlled by a chain wheel or handwheel, the latter being used when load heights are low.

Sheets are usually shipped in bundles. These bundles were, in the past, handled with chains. Because of edge damage and high labor cost, this method of handling is rapidly disappearing. In the small plant, where probably a carload a month or less is handled, a 5-ton grab, probably slow in operation, but economical in use, and one that reduces edge damage as shown in Fig. 15, is used. Where high speed of operation is desired, a grab similar to the one just described but heavier in construction and equipped with handwheel-controlled legs is used. The latter operates with much less effort on the part of the operator and is much faster in operation. The operator adjusts the grab to proper sheet width by turning a handwheel that requires little effort. This type of grab is frequently motorized. With the motor-driven grab, it is not necessary for the hooker-on to travel with the crane, because, as a rule, the crane operator is sufficiently skilled to place the bundle in its ultimate position and remove the motor-driven grab without floor assistance. In many instances, the crane operator can also reclaim the load without floor assistance. As a rule, however, in unloading motor trucks, especially when a single-hook crane is used, a hooker-on will speed up the job. To some extent the principle applied here is similar to that governing the unloading of a ship. The time saved in unloading the ship or the motor truck compensates for

Mansaver Industries, Inc.

Fig. 14. **Motor-driven sheet grab handling steel sheets in widths from 24 in. to 72 in. and lengths from 72 in. to 168 in.**

Cullen-Friestedt

Fig. 15. Eighty-ton motor-operated grab for sheet stock 30 to 144 in. while stacked 8 ft. high. Also 5-ton hand-operated sheet grab.

the added cost of a larger stevedoring crew or the presence of the hooker-on. At the plants of most converters, the hooker-on is some member of the warehouse crew who is temporarily taken from his other duties.

In addition to the above grabs which handle coils and bundled sheets, there are grabs made for handling individual, heavy-gage sheets or plates as well as thinner, light-gage sheets. These grabs are made in simple form for hand application in handling horizontally or vertically, and require some space between loads for the grab application.

Slab-handling Grabs. In the brass industry the ingots, some before and some after being rolled, may be placed on a machine which scalps the top and bottom surfaces. A fully automatic **edge-gripping grab** is used to lift the slab from a pile and place it onto a feeding table leading to a machine which noses the slab so that it may better enter the rolling mill. The gripping surfaces of the grab clamp firmly on the edges of the slab which is carried in a horizontal position. When the slabs have been rolled into longer, lighter-gage sheets of varying widths, they are stacked into unit piles which are handled by the type of sheet grab described above. Sometimes as the slabs leave the mill they have an edge curvature or camber. Safe handling of these cambered slabs would require a grab with a very broad, space-consuming carrying angle. To save space, vertical pivoted legs are used as in Fig. 16. They are L-shaped, with a long member on the bottom

Cullen-Friestedt

Fig. 16. Chain-operated grab mill, handling slabs from 18 in. to 60 in. wide, with rotating supporting legs.

of the L. These L-shaped legs are mounted on a movable carriage which moves in and out, allowing adjustability for width. In view of the fact that a long bottom carrying member is desired, the ability to turn the legs results in the reduction of the space between bundles. By turning the leg, the bottom member can be made of any reasonable length and the space between the loads reduced considerably, determined by the load width rather than by the length of the leg.

Individual slabs of brass can be moved with vacuum lifts or by a manually or automatically applied edge-gripping grab.

Bales. Individual or multiple bales of wood pulp or scrap paper are handled at paper mills by a grab similar to that shown in Fig. 17.

Mansaver Industries, Inc.

Fig. 17. Grabs for handling baled materials.

Rolled-Stock Grabs. Today in the paper industry the small as well as the large plants tend to handle paper in rolls. The paper rolls are handled either with industrial trucks or overhead cranes, the larger plants using the over-head handling method to the greatest extent. As paper in roll form is received, it is handled in the small plant with a type of grab somewhat like that shown in Fig. 18. In applying these grabs, core plugs are removed from the roll and the

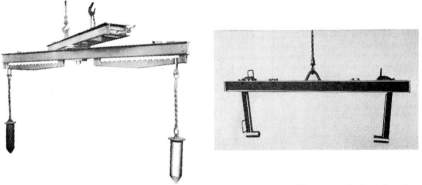

Mansaver Industries, Inc.

Fig. 18. Simple roll grabs.

grab plugs inserted in their place. This necessitates a man climbing over rolls to disengage the grab as well as to attach it. More efficient is a motor-driven grab such as the one shown in Fig. 6. This grab may be supplied with single suspension or with twin-hook suspension and may be operated from a man-trolley. When it is desirable to rotate the roll either 90° to take it through a doorway or 180° so that it may unwind properly, this gram is frequently equipped with a motor-driven turntable. Thus, all of the operations are controlled from the crane cab. The operator can put the material into storage without floor assistance and remove it from storage in the same manner. This particular grab is designed with motor adjustments, but with a mechanical grip in the pad. In some plants grabs are also supplied for vertical storage of rolls. These grabs may be motor-driven, semiautomatic, or fully automatic. In some instances, the grab is equipped with a motor-driven arrangement which will permit rotating the roll from the horizontal position in which it may be received to the vertical position in which it may be stored and then back to the horizontal position in which it is used in the corrugating machine or in the printing press.

The motor-operated grabs mentioned are used to an appreciable extent in plants in which rolls are used in large quantities. There are, of course, many small establishments in which motorized grabs could not be used because of lack of crane capacity or would be impractical because of the relatively small amount of material to be handled. An ice-tong-type grab, either semi- or fully automatic, is frequently used in such cases. A grab similar to that shown in Fig. 19 may also be used. This is similar in principle to the motorized grabs, but instead of gripping the face of the roll, it has a plug on the end which enters into the core of the roll. Where rotation is required in the horizontal plane, hand-operated turntables may

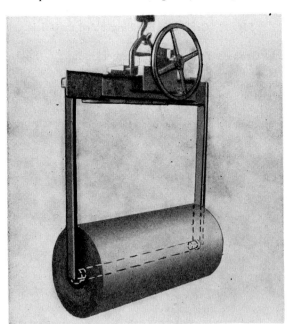

Mansaver Industries, Inc.

Fig. 19. Hand-operated horizontal roll grab.

Cleveland Tramrail

Fig. 20. Roll grab application in the carpeting industry.

be attached. Other types of rolled goods, such as carpeting, may be handled with the grabs illustrated in Fig. 20. In this application, the grab is suspended from an overhead monorail crane.

Grabs for Long Stock. Grabs for handling stock such as bar, rod, pipe, or long extrusions have special features. The conventional method of handling such material without racks is with a spreader bar from which are suspended chain, cable, or rope slings. The spreader or load bar may be of I-beam or truss construction. Although it is not frequently done, the spreader bar may be suspended from a turntable to permit greater flexibility in handling operations. This type of grab is generally used unless space can be allowed around the material to permit the entrance of a mechanical or power-driven grab. Under some circumstances, it is desirable to permit the rods or bars to fall directly into a rack or container. That container can then be lifted by one of many types of grabs, one of which is shown in Fig. 21. (In this particular sketch, the grab is equipped with a motor-driven turntable.) Using this rack or container method, one loaded container can be placed on another and the containers handled in multiple instead of having to be handled one at a time. This container method is often best when the material has to be handled carefully.

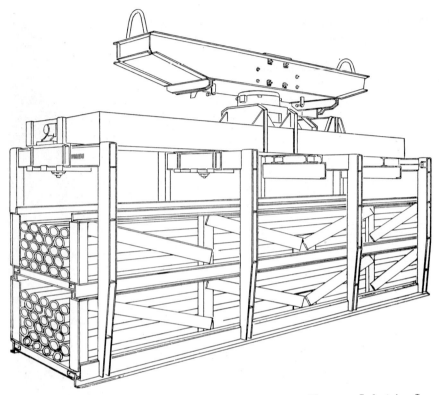

Mansaver Industries, Inc.

Fig. 21. Grab for handling preracked tubing.

When the material is of such a nature that no damage is done if it moves against adjoining material as it is being picked up, a grab of the type shown in Fig. 22, which here shown is fully automatic, can be used without the necessity for any containers. With this type of grab, as with a sling, the rods shift as the bundle is lifted. Where no motion of the material on itself can be permitted, a grab is used that has rotating legs, so formed that they conform to the shape of the receptacle from which the material is removed. This form insures that there is no motion of one tube on the next as the grab goes into action.

Fig. 23 shows a motor-driven grab handling logs in the veneer industry. Here the logs have to be removed from incoming freight cars and from storage and placed into soaking pits, a very dangerous operation. With these tongs, the crane operator from a remote point is in a position to grasp the log, place it in the soaking pit, and remove it, without danger. The grab is designed so that it is motor-adjustable to logs of various length and diameters.

Pallets and Other Unitized Loads. The use of pallets usually suggests fork-truck handling. However, pallets and other containers can also be transported, and sometimes to definite advantage, by overhead cranes with grabs. Fig. 24 shows a typical pallet-grab application. The bottom of the grab is made the same as the fork on the fork truck. The grab itself is so balanced that a crane

Heppenstall Co.

Fig. 22. Tongs for lifting and transporting loose rounds.

operator can without floor assistance cause the forks to enter the pallet just as is done by the lift truck operator. This type of grab may be used for handling and storing in high places.

A large number of crates can also be handled at one time without palletization. Unit loads, one crate wide and several high, are built up between spacers arranged to permit entry of the grab. A grab with rotating legs is lowered over the load and the legs are turned to get under the bottom box. The lifting legs can be so designed that the loaded grab can be placed on the bed of a motor truck, the legs rotated, and the load dropped only a few inches directly onto the truck without the necessity for spacers.

Mansaver Industries, Inc.

Fig. 23. Grab for longitudinal handling of logs.

Mansaver Industries, Inc.

Fig. 24. Pallet-grab application.

Fig. 25 shows one type of container which in this instance is being handled by a manually operated grab, the flanges of which catch under the lips of the container to support it. By this method, the containers can be stored directly against each other, making a very stable pile. Another automatic grab is designed to grasp lugs mounted on the container. With this grab, the operator can reclaim the rack without workmen climbing on the pile, and the material can be stored somewhat higher than with the manually operated grab. For speed of operation, with a single-hook crane, it may be desirable to have a floorman steer the load into position as it is being lifted or set down.

Mansaver Industries, Inc.

Fig. 25. Frame clamp for trough carrier handling bar stock.

An unusual unit load application is illustrated by the grab shown in Fig. 26; this is used for handling aluminum billets previous to their being rolled. This grab consists of two elements, the lower element, which has legs that move in and out to get under the billets, and a motor-driven turntable. The motor-driven turntable makes it possible to alternate the layers of bars as indicated in the illustration and to stack without the use of intermediate spacers. After a complete stack has been built up, it is placed in storage. With this same grab, billets can be placed on furnace cars or handled one layer at a time onto furnace conveyors.

The grabs illustrated and described here should serve to indicate the great variety of designs and applications that are possible. It cannot be emphasized too strongly that the proper grab should be considered at the same time that an overhead crane or hoist is considered, because the use of the proper grab will make a tremendous difference in the efficiency of operation and will, in many instances, considerably reduce the cost of both the crane and the building in which the crane operates.

Mansaver Industries, Inc.

Fig. 26. Handling a unit load of aluminum billets.

Crane Buckets

TYPES OF CRANE BUCKETS. Applications of crane buckets are given in the following tabulation:

1. **Digging clamshell buckets** are used for digging compact materials. This type bucket is generally used on mobile swinging boom-type cranes of the excavator class. These buckets are either of the multiple-rope or lever-arm type, can be equipped with digging teeth and counterweights, and vary in weight according to their size and the type of material to be handled.

2. **Rehandler clamshell buckets** are for the handling of materials previously mined or excavated. The 2-line type have a wide range of sizes and are generally used on mobile swinging boom type cranes. The 3-line type are generally used on overhead-type cranes, and the 4-line type are used on overhead cranes. bridges, and unloaders. The 2- and 3-line type may be either multiple-rope or lever-arm type. The 4-line type is universally multiple-rope reeved.

3. **Cleanup buckets** are, as the name implies, for final cleanup operations in railroad cars, barges, lake vessels, or ocean vessels. They vary in width and open length and may also be of the 2-, 3-, or 4-line type, either multiple-rope or power-arm. Lake-vessel cleanup-type buckets are generally of the 4-line type and may be as much as 12 ft. wide by 24 ft. spread. They are of either the gravity-operating type or are provided with an opening mechanism operated by the two opening lines.

4. **Single-line- or hook-on-type clamshell buckets** are for operation on single-drum cranes. These buckets vary in weight and size to suit the materials to be handled (see Fig. 27).

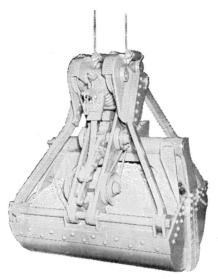

Wellman Engineering Co.

Fig. 27. Three-quarter cubic yard closed-head hook-on single-line clamshell bucket.

5. **Hydraulic clamshell buckets** are used for excavating and require a hydraulic cylinder for the opening and closing forces. Since in general they are rather slow in operation, they are not very efficient.

6. **Orange-peel buckets** are used in excavating, where it is necessary to dig a round hole. They vary in size, according to the size hole that is to be dug, and have three or four blades for digging members, rather than two scoops, which are used on the conventional digging clamshell bucket.

Blaw Knox Co.

Fig. 28. Two-blade grapple.

7. **Hydraulic orange-peel buckets** are similar in construction to the cable-operated orange-peel buckets, but differ in that they have a hydraulic cylinder to supply the opening and closing forces. Here again a hydraulic orange-peel bucket is not so efficient as the cable-operated orange-peel bucket.

8. **Two-blade grapples** operate on the principle of the conventional ice-tongs and are generally used for handling large logs, boulders, pipe, etc. There are other types, which operate on the principle of the conventional clamshell and are used for handling stacked pulpwood (see Fig. 28).

Owen

Fig. 29. Single-cable 4-tine (or orange-peel) grapple handling cordwood.

9. **Three-tine grapples** are designed along the lines of a conventional multiple-rope clamshell bucket, but instead of having scoops the grapples are fitted with two tines on one side and a single tine on the opposite side, for picking up irregularly shaped objects, such as large stones.

10. **Four-tine grapples** are used principally for handling drop-piled pulpwood and are either of the power-wheel or rope-reeved design. In the plan view of the open position, the points of the tines are 90° apart (see Fig. 29).

POSITIONING EQUIPMENT

CONTENTS

POSITIONING EQUIPMENT

———

Work Positioners

IMPORTANCE OF WORK POSITIONING. Positioning as a phase of materials handling requires careful study and analysis. The positioning operation is often a production operation rather than one of materials handling. In some instances the dividing line is very close. In the accompanying example (Fig. 1) the flow of material from receipt to the finished product is broken down into three classifications: transportation and tiering; positioning; and production.

In this example, of the 20 operations, 30 percent involved materials handling; 45 percent involved positioning; only 25 percent of the operations actually involved processing by production machinery.

As a result of this study, **portable hydraulic elevating tables** were installed which greatly simplified eight of nine positioning operations. The opportunity to improve the positioning by such a large margin justified the comparative small cost of the elevating tables which were needed to transport and position the work in process.

Benefits of Proper Work Positioning. A study of better materials handling methods should never be considered complete until full consideration has been given to the handling problems of the **individual worker** and improvements have been introduced into his work. Manual operations are the most expensive operations in industry today. Highly skilled workers should not be expected to take the time to lift, hold, or secure work in machines if that job can be done as well, or better, by one of the many operating mechanisms or special devices that are now available—or can be made available—to production workers. There is much room for improvement in this field of materials handling, and progressive manufacturers are rapidly extending the study of better handling to the many individual hand and machine operations which most products pass through.

The greatest advantage obtainable from better positioning lies in **increased production.** Workers' energies will be conserved to process more units of material when machine operatives do not have to take the time to bend, lift, turn, or hold parts on which they are working. To avoid "down time" or waiting for parts, positioners that hold reserve stock should be installed. Better personnel relations will result, jobs will be made easier, employees will be happier, and the resultant reduction of worker fatigue will bring about higher production. When these steps have been taken, **safety** is usually greatly improved and manual handling is reduced or practically eliminated. Fewer lost-time accidents, lower compensation insurance rates, and reduction of accident hazards are all direct benefits that can accrue when better work positioning is included in plans for plant improvement.

Scientific positioning also results in reduction of spoiled work and better finishing of parts. Whenever a piece can be so placed that the operator can work

Operation No.	Description of Job	Equipment Used
1	Unload 4,000 lb. bundles of sheet from freight car onto trailer transport to storage area and tier.	Power fork truck
2	Take down bundle of tiered stock, transport it to shear, and deposit on floor.	Power fork truck
3	Pick up, hold, and position sheets to bed of shear.	Manual
4	Cut sheets to size.	Shear
5	Place sheared pieces on skid or pallet.	Manual
6	Transport load of sized pieces and deposit in front of punch press.	Hand lift or pallet truck
7	Pick up, hold, and position pieces for punching operation.	Manual
8	Blank sheets.	Punch Press No. 1
9	Place blanked pieces on skid or pallet.	Manual
10	Transport load of blanks to next punch-press operation.	Hand lift or pallet truck
11	Pick up, hold, and position blanks for second punch-press operation.	Manual
12	Feed blanks for punching.	Punch Press No. 2
13	Place punched blanks on skid or pallet.	Manual
14	Transport load blanks to press brake.	Hand lift or pallet truck
15	Pick up, hold, and position pieces to press brake.	Manual
16	Form sheet on four sides.	Press brake
17	Place formed pieces on skid or pallet.	Manual
18	Transport parts to assembly department.	Hand lift or pallet truck
19	Pick up, hold, and position parts for assembly.	Manual
20	Assemble product.	Manual

SUMMARY OF OPERATIONS

Materials handling (transporting and tiering)	6
Production operations	5
Positioning operations	9
Total	20

Fig. 1. Analysis of material flow and handling operations.

on it in a normal position, the end result will almost always be a better product. Expensive losses in the form of rejects and reworking can be held to a minimum.

ADAPTING EQUIPMENT FOR POSITIONING FUNCTIONS. Where many kinds of small parts are being manufactured in a plant, it is often possible to set up a completely integrated materials handling and work-flow positioning system by coordinating the use of industrial trucks, steel boxes, gravity hoppers, stands, racks, wire baskets, trays, and equipment of related kinds. The advantages of such a system are numerous.

1. Small parts and loose material may be made up into unit loads for handling between points of operation.
2. Drop-bottom boxes, open-end baskets, and related equipment allow spot-control dumping.
3. When work stands and gravity hoppers are incorporated into the system, parts under production can be supplied to operators at convenient working heights.
4. Storage space can be saved by group stocking or rack storage at points of production.
5. Floor area can be conserved by placing receptacles to receive scrap and waste materials at points from which they can be readily removed.

In operations where the number of parts being handled is considerable—or where the nature of the parts is such that bulk handling might cause them to be damaged—trays and tote boxes may often be incorporated into the production system.

Positioning Materials by Industrial Trucks. Power-truck and portable-lifter manufacturers have designed and built many ingenious devices for the purpose of positioning materials after they have been transported to work areas. Roll-over and tilting devices are available for emptying drums, positioning rolls of paper, and handling reels and cylinders for easy placement into machines. One kind of attachment is made especially for handling drop-bottom stock boxes, another up-ends crated refrigerators as they are being loaded into freight cars. Side-shifting devices allow accurate positioning for the purpose of die changing and performance of heavy assembly operations. In many operations industrial trucks are equipped with all necessary facilities for the required positioning of the work to be done with them.

Conveyors. An example of the combination of materials handling equipment and its use in positioning can be seen on the assembly line of any automobile plant. Automobile parts move into place on floor and overhead conveyors, reaching the proper work station at a predetermined moment. In the case of engines and body sections, the units arrive on an overhead conveyor system coordinated with the floor conveyor carrying the main frame.

When the unit to be installed reaches its proper work station it can be switched off the moving conveyor and held suspended by an overhead hoist. The assemblers lower the part into place and hold it until the mounting bolts are inserted and fastened. The hoist then elevates the carrier frame, which returns to the moving overhead conveyor for a new load. Except for small parts, manual handling and positioning are practically unknown on an automobile assembly line today.

POSITIONING HOLDING FIXTURES. Many kinds of positioning equipment are now available, ranging from the simplest to the most complex, that make operations possible which otherwise could not be performed. For example, improvements have been made in the common vise which now make it possible not only to hold an object securely but also to turn it horizontally, vertically, or, by use of ball-and-socket joints, to move it in any desired plane, and lock it in almost any position. When the material which is to be worked on is once clamped in the jaws of the positioning device, further manual handling of the piece itself may often be eliminated because all other manipulations for positioning the work involve not the part but the tool.

Welding Positioners. One of the earliest and best known kinds of positioning equipment is the welding positioner. Units of this kind are made for large and small welding jobs and range from simple to highly complex mechanisms. The product or part to be welded is fastened to a work surface, which is usually a circular platen (see Fig. 2). The positioner is so designed that all further move-

Cayuga Machine & Fabricating Co., Inc.

Fig. 2. Welding positioner for holding, tilting, and turning work.

ments of the work can be controlled by the operator. The unit illustrated has a 1,000-lb. capacity and a table rotation speed range of 20–1. On simple positioners, handwheel and screw arrangements allow the operator to raise or lower his work, turn it 360°, or tilt it forward or backward in a 180° arc. The larger and heavier units are raised and lowered by hydraulic rams, and the other movements are power-operated. Headstock and tailstock positioners are designed to hold very large weldments.

Turning-roll positioners are used to position large cylindrical pieces properly during welding and other fabricating operations. The operation can be controlled so that the operator works in a convenient position, and the materials being welded move past the joint of welding contact automatically. The use of welding positioners eliminates all manual handling of work after the work is once clamped in the machine. The positioner holds the piece securely in place and reduces the chance of accidents when heavy parts are being welded. Working in awkward positions is also eliminated, better work is done, and there is a substantial reduction in worker fatigue.

The Buck. Another type of positioning device is the "buck," which is a rigid frame with locating masts and clamps so constructed as to permit the positioning of an automobile body roof, sides, and floor to close tolerances. With all details in correct location, gages are used to check the accuracy of the loading of the fixture and then welding is performed. The completed automobile body is removed from the buck when clamps and gates are opened.

Magnetic Bench Positioner. Another device for holding work firmly in position while permitting the operator free use of both hands is the magnetic bench positioner, shown in Fig. 3. The device consists of three magnets, each adjustable

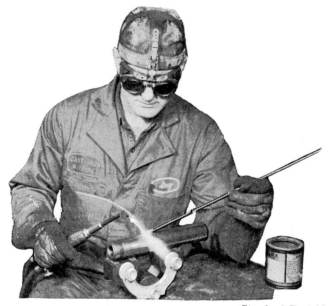

Standard Portable Cord Co.

Fig. 3. Simple bench positioner with three magnets.

through 360°. It is extremely flexible, as it can be set at any desired angle with one magnet gripping the bench top and the others securing the work in the desired position.

Positioning Holding Fixtures of Special Design. Work positioning is especially important in assembly operations, and many important kinds of devices have been designed for this purpose. A large company manufacturing telephone equipment employed women to wire complex switchboard assemblies. For many years the assemblies were placed on a fixed stand, and the operators had to reach up and down to make the many connections as the assembly job progressed. A study of this particular job showed that it could be made much easier of accomplishment if the assemblies could be moved up and down to eliminate the reaching and bending for high and low connections. Special **elevating platforms** were therefore designed to hold the assemblies, and a foot-controlled hydraulic pumping unit was installed which made it possible for each operator to keep the switchboard reading at just the right height so that all connections could be made from a sitting position. As a result of this change, production increased and the workers found their job much easier to perform. The operators now work from a seated position whereas previously they had to stand, reach up, and bend down in doing the work.

One company manufacturing trailer bodies uses **overhead hoists** to position the large trailer sections during a riveting operation. At the start of the body assembly operation, the prefabricated framework moves into position and is picked up by two overhead hoists which are synchronized in their raising and lowering movements. The side panels are placed on the framework when it is elevated. At this time the bottoms of the panels are at the proper working level for the riveters, who are standing on the floor. As the bottom sections of the panels are fastened, the whole assembly is lowered into a narrow pit and stopped when the panel is in the correct position for the next row of rivets. By lowering the side section in steps, the riveters are enabled always to work from one convenient floor-level position.

In **service stations and auto repair shops** specializing on auto radiator repairing, a unique positioner holds the radiator in various positions for soldering and straightening. It also serves to lower the radiator in water for pressure testing.

Manipulators and Chargers

FORGING MANIPULATORS. Forging manipulators are designed to relieve the mechanism of forging shocks; to provide variable-position tongs to accommodate the varying dimensions of a forging billet while being formed under the press or hammer; to rotate and position the forging accurately; to give the

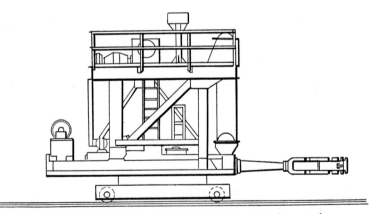

Fig. 4. Traveling forging manipulator with revolving carriage.

operator an unrestricted range of vision over the forging operation and instant control of all motions. They are built in capacities up to 15 tons (see Fig. 4).

The manipulator consists of a four-wheeled undercarriage, with motor and gearing, which supports an upper carriage. The **undercarriage** provides the longitudinal motion toward and away from the forging press or hammer. Its frame incorporates a large-diameter ball bearing upon which the upper carriage rests and may be revolved at will. **Rails** on the floor, in line with the throat of the press or hammer, guide the undercarriage to and from the forging position. The 360° revolving motion enables billets to be handled laterally to the press or hammer and floor-rail axis.

The **upper carriage** with machinery for revolving, hoisting, tong-rotate, and tong-grip has a cast-steel base on which is built up a structural frame for hoist and cab platforms. Its forward end is formed, on both sides, to act as guides for the vertical motion of the tong-spindle frame.

The cast-steel **spindle frame** is pivoted, at the rear, on a vertically and longitudinally guided crosshead which may be elevated, at will, by hydraulic cylinders shock-mounted on the hoist platform above. The frame connection to the crosshead includes a spring shock absorber for the press or hammer shocks transmitted through the tong spindle. Hoist-cable sheave blocks, attached to the forward end of the spindle frame, are spring-mounted at their hangers to carry the billet load reactions without vertical shock. The spindle frame is hollow and includes bearings, front and rear, for the revolving spindle inside.

The **spindle** is hollow for passage of a push-pull rod used to actuate the tongs. This rod is attached to a large rotating-type hydraulic cylinder mounted on the spindle axis, at the rear of the spindle frame. This cylinder is operated by a two-stage **hydraulic pump** with a **dumping valve.** This provides rapid tong opening and closing, maintains gripping pressure, and prevents loss of tong-jaw pressure in event of power failure. The **tongs** are revolved by rotating the spindle. The tong jaws may be arranged for removable inserts for a variety of shapes and sizes of billets.

To allow for **varying dimensions** of the forging while being processed, the hoisting mechanism and its control are designed to provide a wide range of lateral and vertical movement of the tong spindle. To give the widest **range of vision** over the work, the operator's platform is placed forward in the structure and above the spindle frame, where the view is unobstructed. The electrical master switches and hydraulic valves are arranged for convenience of manipulation and unobstructed view. A press or hammer may be placed at either end of the floor rails, provided sufficient space is allowed for revolving the manipulator with a billet.

Variations in Design. Another forge plant arrangement having the throat of the press or hammer at right angles to the floor rails requires the manipulator to move in two directions.

For this arrangement the manipulator above described is mounted on a **bridge** operating on a pair of floor rails. It has two rails along its girders for the manipulator undercarriage. The bridge is also designed for minimum vertical dimensions. The manipulator carriage rails are bracketed from the insides of the main girders so that the carriage actually travels between the girders.

Each girder is laterally braced by a wide horizontal plate with an auxiliary beam on its opposite edge. This structure is reinforced and built up, where required, for mounting motor, brake, gear box, and shaft hangers. It is bolted to two end carriages to provide a rigid frame for the manipulator to run on. Cast-steel end carriages have two wheels each for the floor rails. Generally, two wheels on one side of the bridge are driven by gearing, squaring shaft, gear box, and motor. The bridge is generally operated in a pit to get the proper tong height at the press anvil.

A third type of forging manipulator consists of a **stiffleg revolving trolley** which is carried on an overhead traveling bridge crane.

TONG FURNACE CHARGERS. These chargers may consist of a stiffleg trolley operating on the girders of an overhead or gantry traveling double-girder crane (see section on Traveling Cranes and Towers), or they may be of the floor type, operating in a similar manner and for the same service. The latter, shown in Fig. 5, consists of a crane bridge which travels on rails laid on the floor. An

Fig. 5. Tong furnace charger.

intermediate carriage or trolley of the inner-running type travels on the bridge girders. A revolving upper carriage is mounted on the intermediate carriage. This upper carriage supports the pivoted charging ram as well as the mechanisms for hoisting, tongs gripping, and ram rotating, if the last feature is required. It also supports the operator's platform or cab.

An ingot, billet, or slab is picked up by the tongs with the ram at right angles to the bridge. The upper carriage is then revolved so that the ram is parallel with the bridge, and the intermediate carriage travels on the bridge, thrusting the ram into the furnace and depositing the piece on the hearth. The piece can be withdrawn from the furnace by reversing the above operations.

The advantage of the **floor-type charger** is that an overhead traveling bridge crane can operate above it and be used for other purposes.

Another kind of **overhead charger** operates in a similar manner, but, instead of a pivoted ram, guides are provided in the vertical member of the stiffleg trolley in which the ram is raised or lowered.

Overhead-type chargers are built in capacities from 1 to 15 tons, while the floor type is built in capacities up to 20 tons.

All movements of the charger are powered with individual electric motor drives, and the speeds of the various motions are coordinated to give a production of 30 to 60 pieces per hr., as may be required by the individual installation.

PEEL FURNACE CHARGERS (WITHOUT PEEL ROTATION OR TONGS). This kind of charger is used to charge copper cathodes into melting furnaces and for similar operations. The charger is built in capacities up to 5 tons.

The charger shown in Fig. 6 is of the overhead type and consists of a stiffleg trolley operating on the girders of an overhead or gantry traveling double-girder crane. The vertical hanger or stiffleg revolves about its axis and is provided with guides at its lower end in which a charging ram is raised or lowered by means of wire ropes and a hoisting unit, which gives a vertical motion at the end of the ram. The end of the ram is provided with a peel, together with a pusher head, to push the charge into the furnace. The pusher head is actuated by either hydraulic or air pressure. All operations are controlled from the operator's plat-

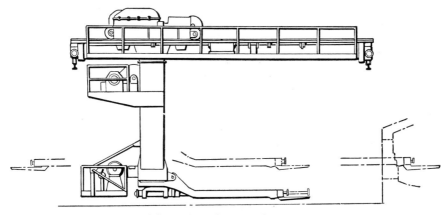

Fig. 6. Peel furnace charger.

form or cab, which is mounted on the lower end of the hanger. Individual electric motor drives are provided for each of the motions.

PUSHER FURNACE CHARGERS. Pushers for slab- and billet-heating furnaces may be divided into two classes, namely, the long-stroke, rack, **pinion and gear-driven pusher** commonly used for moving slabs into and through the furnace, and the **short-stroke lever-and-crank pusher** which is often used on furnaces that heat square billets for rolling into wire and rods.

Long-Stroke Pusher. The long-stroke pusher consists essentially of the main frame, usually of cast steel or a combination of castings and weldments, incorporating the elements of the driving mechanism, and the pusher head to which is attached the guide members and driving racks. The pusher head may be of the disappearing or fixed type, depending on the desired method of operation.

In some instances the pushers are installed immediately adjacent to the furnace, and a crane is used to place the slabs on top of the pusher, one at a time, the slabs being advanced into the furnace individually. In other instances several slabs may be placed edge-to-edge on the pusher, and all are advanced into the furnace. In still other instances the pusher may have a magazine in which a pile of slabs is placed by the crane, and at each stroke of the pusher one slab is moved from the bottom of the pile into the furnace.

Where the plant layout permits, the most desirable arrangement is to have the slabs delivered to the charging end of the furnace by a roller conveyor table. Adjustable stops in the conveyor can properly position the slabs in front of the furnace and, as each slab comes against the stop, the pusher advances the slab into the furnace. In some instances the section of conveyor in front of the furnace is built as an integral part of the pusher, while in other instances the conveyor is a separate structure, and the pusher head moves across the conveyor when advancing slabs into the furnace.

Short-Stroke Pusher. Short-stroke pushers for billet furnaces consist of a heavy shaft extending across the charging end of the furnace. Lever arms are spaced along the shaft and their outer ends are pin-connected to the approximately horizontal pusher bars that contact the billet. The above-mentioned shaft is oscillated by means of a motor-driven crank mechanism, or a hydraulic cylinder, which imparts a reciprocating motion to the pusher bars. This kind of pusher is commonly used for comparatively small square billets, and the stroke seldom exceeds 12 in. and may be as little as 6 in.

The two above types of pushers may be arranged so that all pusher heads or pusher bars move in unison, or they may be equipped with clutches or double-drive mechanisms, so that two rows of slabs or billets may be separately advanced through the furnace. When desired, the double-drive units can be locked together so that one row of longer slabs or billets may be pushed through the furnace.

The **operation** of the pusher on any furnace is controlled by the furnace heater or his helper, from the discharge end of the furnace. Whenever the mill is ready to take a hot slab or billet, the heater or helper operates a switch, push button, or similar device, causing the pusher to advance the steel in the furnace until a slab or billet is discharged, or is in the discharge position.

COKE PUSHERS. Coke pushers are used in connection with by-product coke ovens, their functions being to remove and replace the pusher side oven doors, push the hot coke from the ovens, and level the coal charge. Sometimes the mechanism for handling the doors is omitted, a separate machine—a duplicate of that for handling the coke side doors—being used for this purpose. A machine with all three of the above functions is called a combined coke pusher, coal leveler and door extractor; the other is called a combined coke pusher and coal leveler. The weight of the coke handled from each oven is from 12 to 14 tons, and the speeds of the various motions of the machine are sufficient to maintain a 5-min. cycle, that is, one oven is pushed and the new coal charge leveled every 5 min. Speeds of the motions are as follows:

Main travel	250 ft. per min.
Pusher ram	60 ft. per min.
Leveler bar	80 ft. per min.
Door ram	50 ft. per min.

Coke Pusher Operation. The machine (Fig. 7) travels on rails, at ground level, spaced at about 30-ft. centers, in front of the oven battery which it serves. Usually there is one machine for each battery of 40 to 60 ovens. The main frame

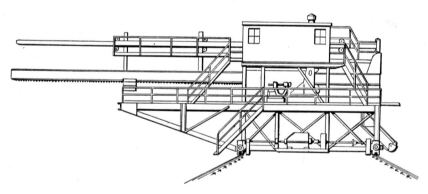

Fig. 7. Coke pusher.

of the machine consists of two end trucks each mounted on two wheels running on the rails, one pair on the rail nearer the ovens and the other pair on the rail farther from the ovens. These end trucks support framing, which in turn supports the main machinery platform, which is at the level of the oven bench—

usually about 10 ft. above the ground level. This platform carries the mechanisms for performing the several functions. All exposed areas are covered with checkered steel floor plate. Stairs give access from the ground to this platform, and also to the control house and all elevated mechanism requiring inspection, lubrication, or repair.

The **pusher ram** consists of a steel girder about 30 in. deep, 13 in. wide, and 70 ft. long, having a cast tooth rack on its lower surface which engages the driving pinion. This pinion is driven by an electric motor through an enclosed gear reducer. The ram travels between rollers mounted in brackets on the machinery floor. A cast-steel pusher head is attached to the forward end of the ram, and pushes the hot coke out the opposite end of the oven.

The **leveller bar** consists of two 10 in. x 1 in. side bars tied together to form a member 9 in. wide and 60 ft. long. This bar travels in rollers supported by a framework at approximately the top of the oven chamber. The bar is traveled into and out of the oven by means of wire ropes attached near the rear end, and running over sheaves to the driving drum, which is driven by an electric motor through an enclosed gear reducer. The leveler bar is used to level, or even off, the upper surface of the coal, which is charged through several openings in the roof of the furnace.

The **door extractor mechanism** consists of a ram, moved to and from the face of the ovens by a rack-and-pinion drive similar to that for the pusher ram. The ram carries an extractor head at its forward end for the removal and replacement of the oven doors.

Tables, Lifts, and Bridges

POSITIONING TABLES. These are essentially tables of adjustable height that are used to hold the work at the level at which it can be manipulated easily, safely, and efficiently.

Elevating Sheet-Feeding Tables. Sheet steel is a difficult item to handle because of its varying ratio of weight to size and gage. A portable lifting table with a compensating lift permits a lift of sheet steel to be positioned at the front side of a press so that the level of the top sheet is kept at the correct working height as the sheets are removed and fed to the press.

Elevating sheet-feeding tables, of the type illustrated in Fig. 8, are made in various sizes and capacities, ranging from small units designed to handle strip material to large models for heavy sheets. These may have compensating springs which raise the work gradually as each successive piece is fed to the machine, until the last unit has been fed in, or, as in the table shown, they may be hydraulically driven and controlled by foot pedal.

While many savings can be made by the proper use of sheet-feeding tables, their greatest value is in the **increased volume of production** that can be put through the heavy expensive equipment they serve. When work is correctly positioned so that each piece moves straight into a press, production may be increased by as much as 50 percent over the rate possible when work is stacked at random height in front of the machine. When several standardized production lines are set up in large stamping plants, a few relatively low-priced elevating sheet-feeding tables may provide an output level that would otherwise require additional presses and more operators.

In small plants, use of a single sheet-feeding table may often result in **large labor savings.** One man and a table can do the work of two men when the

The Raymond Corp.

Fig. 8. Sheet-feeding table truck which permits accurate feeding of shear at bed height.

table is so positioned that it holds one end of the sheet being fed into the machine.

While sheet-feeding tables are not classified as conveying equipment, they do function as trucks in some plants. Strips or sheets are loaded on the portable tables in the stock room and towed by industrial trucks to the press operation. One large company manufacturing business machines has two tables assigned to each punch press so that material handlers can deliver strip material to the work stations with only one handling operation. When unused stock is left at the end of a run, it is moved back into the storage area with the table. Housekeeping in this plant is always neat because no left-over material is ever allowed to accumulate in the work areas. The tables are usually portable, but some heavy models are designed so that they can be moved about by bridge cranes with crane lugs. **Capacities** range from 2,000 lb. to 20,000 lb. in the standard equipment. Heavier units can be built to special order. Heavy bundles of strips and sheets are usually brought to the press and deposited on the table by industrial fork trucks or bridge cranes. Where crane and truck service is too slow to keep stock in constant supply, stand-by tables for reserve stock are used to keep the press line in continuous operation.

Importance of Sheet-Feeding Tables. Safety programs have been receiving much more attention recently than in previous years, because metalworking plants have had high accident histories. Heavy sheets and sharp-edged, light-gage metal are hazards when lifted and held manually in position. The installation of proper supporting equipment, such as sheet-feeding tables, is improving safety records in many plants. Elimination of manual handling has reduced worker fatigue and improved personnel relations between workers and management. In at least one instance the suspicion of a job "speed-up" by the use of powered elevating tables was voiced by union workers, but the objection was withdrawn when it was shown that the use of this equipment would make the job easier for the workers.

When each sheet is so positioned that it can be fed into the press brake or shear evenly and squarely, the resulting work is usually of better quality. Rejections of bad work are held to a minimum, use of the sheet-feeding tables has reduced spoilage, and the quality of the finished product has been greatly improved.

Die-Handling Table. Another kind of table that has wide applications in the metalworking industry is the standard elevating or die-handling table. This equipment is usually of 1-ton capacity and has a square or a rectangular top. Hydraulic lifts are operated by foot pumps or by means of screw mechanisms actuated by hand cranks. Although this equipment was designed primarily to facilitate the handling of dies into and out of presses and the moving of them to storage areas, the adjustable-height feature has made them useful for many other jobs.

Drill-press operations, for example, often involve the handling of long objects which require support for overhanging ends. A table adjustable for height is particularly useful in such cases. It can also be used to hold stock boxes or small parts at convenient working heights, and to serve as an adjustable support for lining up heavy parts for assembly operations. These tables can be modified for sheet- and strip-feeding jobs, and can serve as low-cost welding positioners, especially when provided with tops that can be revolved, or locked in one position. Some manufacturers make tables without tops but with a special mounting plate on which the user can put a holding jig or other special fixture for positioning material undergoing welding, grinding, and other operations. These tables are inexpensive and are ruggedly constructed so that they will give years of low-cost, trouble-free service.

Large dies weighing up to 15 tons have presented special handling problems that have now been greatly simplified by the use of heavy-duty positioning tables which have adjustable bed heights. The tables are portable and are rolled up alongside the press by the die-handling crew. The platform is raised to a level with the height of the bed and the die is moved in or out of the press as the case may be. These tables are often furnished with roller tops and with hand- or power-operated winches for moving the heavier dies. One company is using a table which has fixed columns that extend outward 2 in. above the platform when the platform is in its lowest position. The space left between the lowered table top and the bottom of the die allows **slings from overhead cranes** to be used for moving the dies to and from the storage area.

The **use of proper die-positioning equipment** eliminates the need for shoring timbers and other such makeshift supports. It greatly reduces the hazards of moving heavy dies and speeds up the work and considerably cuts the cost of the die-changing operation. Many die-positioning problems can be solved by the use of high-lift trucks or portable lifters. Construction and maintenance crews find such equipment very useful for many jobs where heavy fixtures have to be accurately positioned before being permanently installed. Portable lifters, when equipped with overhanging booms and chains, are ideal die-handling devices, especially because their wide range of lifts allows them to store dies in racks at considerable heights.

Tray Positioner. A portable positioning device with compensating springs is shown in Fig. 9. This self-leveling device keeps the top tray of work pieces at a constant height while it is being unloaded in the course of machining operations.

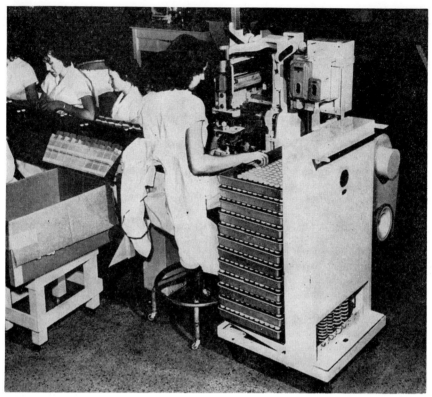

American Machine & Foundry Co.

Fig. 9. Lowerator, self-leveling work positioner.

The platform, shown in the illustration in its extreme position at the base of the device, is depressed by the weight of the material which it carries. As the top tray is emptied and removed, the reduction in weight permits a gradual rise of the movable platform. The stock in the top tray remains at a level within reach of the operator. As successive trays are unloaded, the next tray moves to the top position. When all trays are unloaded, another lot of trays is stacked on the truck.

Other applications of this **constant-level workplace method** are of particular advantage in heavy industries because repeated lifting of material from floor to operating level is eliminated. Since fatigue is practically eliminated, the operator is able to perform more efficiently and at a higher rate of output.

Spring-loaded positioning units similar in principle to the above are now being manufactured for restaurant and hotel use. China and glassware are placed in the positioning device, which lowers as it is loaded and automatically raises as pieces are taken from the top. In addition to providing a continuous supply of chinaware at a convenient level, the use of these positioners keeps the reserve supply of pieces clean, since only the top layer is exposed at one time.

Bale Positioner. In many companies, especially those engaged in continuous manufacturing, it is particularly necessary to **keep the flow of work under close**

control. In a certain plant manufacturing feed bags, heavy bundles of burlap were lifted manually to a table, by stock boys. As material ran out, the women sewing-machine operators often had to wait for a man to lift a new supply to their machines, valuable production time thus being lost. The superintendent of this plant designed a battery of lifting platforms that would lower to the floor and elevate to the height of the sewing-machine tables. Under this new arrangement bales of material were placed on the lowered platform, and a micro-switch on a balanced arm rested on the top layer of the bagged material. As the operators drew the cloth from the bale and across a table to the sewing machine, the micro-switch lowered slightly and actuated a hydraulic solenoid valve which automatically raised the supply of material to table height, at which point the micro-switch cut off. The cycle was repeated until the bale was used up. The platform was then lowered to floor level and the operator put a new bale on, set the micro-switch arm, and resumed work. The stock boy brought a new supply to the work station, no time being lost waiting for the new lot. Production on this operation was stepped up, work was fed evenly to the sewing-machine table, manual lifting was entirely eliminated, and the need for employing several extra stock men was removed.

HYDRAULIC LIFTS. Another common positioning device in use is the **hydraulic lift,** an elevating device controlled by an operator to lift or lower an object to a desired position. Fig. 10 shows a hydraulic lift used to service an industrial fork truck. Here the truck is positioned on the lift and elevated to a convenient height for lubrication and service work.

In operations where sheet steel is fed into a machine, top production rates can be maintained by means of a **hydraulic stock lifter** of similar design. The operator can adjust the lift to position the sheet at the most convenient height for fast, continuous feeding.

A large **department store** uses special elevating platforms in the department where furniture is inspected, touched up, and polished before delivery. These platforms are set into the floor and are flush with the floor in the lowered position. Furniture to be inspected and polished is placed on the platform, which can be revolved. The refinisher raises the work gradually so that every part can be closely checked. When work on the piece is completed, the worker transfers it to a conveyor which moves it directly into the packing department. Another company uses a similar positioner for spray-painting metal office furniture.

In a **food-processing plant** one of the final operations requires that the packed and sealed cans move off a conveyor and be stacked on special racks for transportation to the cookers. A hydraulic elevating positioner is set in a pit in the floor, and lowers as the racks become filled, so that the shelf being loaded is always level with the feeding conveyor. When the rack is completely filled, the positioning platform is raised to floor level, so that a hand lift truck can pick the cooker rack up and move it into the cookers. After being thus processed, the cans are again positioned so that they can move onto a conveyor setup for labeling and final packing into cartons.

DOCKS AND TRANSFER BRIDGES. One of the problems in using fork trucks to unload palletized unit loads from highway trucks is the variance in relative heights of the motor truck floors and the loading docks. By hinging a section of the dock and providing a means for raising and lowering this section, the hinged ramp can be kept on the level with the truck floor. This positioning compensates for varying truck bed heights and truck spring deflections as the

Wayne Pump Co.

Fig. 10. Industrial-truck service lift.

truck is loaded. Faster and safer power-truck operation results from using these **self-leveling dock ramps.** Another solution to this problem is the use of the truck leveler shown in Fig. 11.

Many small shops are located in buildings that are not equipped with truck docks. To load and unload material from highway carriers in such cases, a **portable dock,** as shown in Fig. 12, has been developed. When not in use, the portable dock folds up compactly for storage and may be rolled out of the way. This portable dock not only permits use to be made of mechanical equipment such as pallet trucks, but, in addition, trucks may be loaded or unloaded at any place in the factory yard.

Rotary Lift Co.

Fig. 11. Hydraulic truck leveler.

The Raymond Corp.

Fig. 12. Portable dock.

A portable positioning device, known as a **tail gate elevator,** may be built integral with a highway delivery truck. One type is a hydraulically operated tail gate which permits the truck to load and unload material without hazardous manual lifting. By a system of linkages the platform moves up or down, maintaining a horizontal position. When not in use, the platform folds up into a vertical position to function as a gate at the back of the truck.

A "short cut" is provided by the **transfer bridge.** This hydraulically operated bridge forms a roadway to permit plant traffic to move quickly across railroad tracks in a warehouse. Needless detours are eliminated and handling operations are speeded up. When lowered, the rails on the transfer bridge become a part of the depressed railroad track.

Dumpers

PORTABLE DUMPERS. Flexibility of equipment is required in many modern materials handling applications. To meet this need, portable positioning devices have been designed and built. Fig. 13 shows a portable skip hoist for load-

Essex Conveyors, Inc.

Fig. 13. Portable skip hoist with automatic barrel dump.

ing chemicals into mixing kettles at the plant of a well-known manufacturing chemist. The mechanism is positioned by hand in front of the workplace and a power connection is made by means of a cable to the nearest electrical outlet.

With the movable container, designed specifically for load type, at the floor position, an open bag, barrel, or box is loaded in an upright position. The manual control switch operates the motor of the hoist which lifts the container to the top of the lift where it automatically tilts, dumping the chemicals down a chute into the kettle. The portable feature of this device permits its use at a number of points and removes the hazards of manually lifting bags or barrels up the stairs and dumping the contents into the kettles.

REVOLVING OPEN-CAR SIDE DUMPERS. The revolving open-car side dumper is used to side-dump railroad cars containing coal, coke, ore, bauxite, and other bulk material shipped in open-top cars. The dumpers are built to handle cars loaded with up to 120 tons of material, and at a rate of more than 60 cars per hr., depending on the facilities for getting the cars into and out of the dumper. The ordinary capacity requirement, however, is from 10 to 25 cars per hr. The maximum dimensions of the cars that may be dumped are approximately: height 12 ft. 7 in.; width 11 ft. 0 in.; and length up to 52 ft. Fig. 14 illustrates car dumpers of this type.

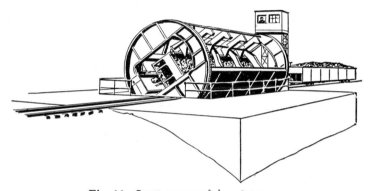

Fig. 14. Open-car revolving dumper.

These dumpers are usually placed at about ground level; they dump into a hopper beneath the dumper, from which the material is carried away by means of conveyors. Before being conveyed away, the material is sometimes crushed and/or screened.

The dumper consists of a **revolving cradle** supporting a platen which carries the car to be dumped. This platen moves sidewise at the start of rotation to permit the car to rest against the dumping side of the cradle. The cradle supports the car clamps and the mechanism which operates the clamps.

The framework of the cradle terminates in end frames of circular contour. Each end ring is bound with a rail which makes contact with rollers mounted in sills which, in turn, rest on the foundation. When the cradle is seated in the upright position, the car rails on the platen are in line with the approach and run-off car tracks. The length of the cradle will depend on the maximum length of cars to be dumped. The usual length, center-to-center of end rings, varies between 50 ft. and 60 ft.

For **rotating the dumper,** a motor, mounted on the foundation midway between the end rings, drives a cross-shaft on each end of which there is keyed a pinion which meshes with a rack gear secured to the end ring. The motor is fitted with a magnetic brake to hold the dumper, should power be interrupted during any part of the dumping cycle. The usual angle of rotation to dump a car is 155°. Occasionally, however, revolving dumpers are made to rotate 180°.

The **clamping arrangement** for holding the car in the cradle as it is being dumped is entirely automatic in action. There are several arrangements in use, but in all cases the clamps are fully elevated to allow the highest car to enter the dumper, and all descend by gravity onto the top of the car to lock it in position. A common form of clamping arrangement involves the use of two, three, or four beams extending across the top of the cars. In other arrangements independently operated hooks engage the top of the car at both sides.

Spotting Cars. Several methods are in use for **moving loaded cars into dumping position** on the dumper. For a maximum capacity of 20 or 25 cars per hr. the usual procedure is to push the leading car of a train of loaded cars into the dumper by means of a locomotive. As the loaded car enters the dumper, the empty car that has just been dumped is bumped out of the dumper and onto the run-off track. The loaded car is then spotted and uncoupled, after which the train is withdrawn. The run-off track has a slight downgrade and the empty car rolls by gravity to the empty-car yard.

For faster operation a **car haulage** is used. In this case the dumper is set at a higher elevation with the approach track on an incline leading to the dumper. The loaded car is uncoupled at the foot of the incline and pulled up the incline and into the dumper by the **barney car** of the haulage. In this case, either a car retarder on the dumper is used to retard and stop the car in proper position to be dumped, or a rider on the car spots the car by using the hand brakes on the car.

Occasionally it is required that the material be weighed in the car. In this case the entire dumper structure is mounted on scales. In the past the scales have been of the beam-track type. More recently the **electronic system of weighing** has been used. The dumper with the loaded car is first weighed, then, after dumping, the dumper with the empty car is weighed. The difference, of course, is the weight of material dumped.

ROLLING OPEN-CAR SIDE DUMPERS. The rolling open-car side dumper is used to side-dump open-top railroad cars loaded with different kinds of bulk materials. The loaded car is placed in a cradle, which has a movable platen and car clamps similar in construction to the cradle of the revolving dumper. Instead of rotating around a fixed axis, however, as does the revolving dumper, the rolling dumper rolls sidewise and up a steep incline. The dump pile is therefore at some distance from the side of the car tracks, and the hopper or trough for receiving the material need not be submerged as is the case with the revolving dumper (see Fig. 15).

As the cradle moves on the incline, it is positively guided and held in alignment by means of a **cog wheel and track** arrangement at each end of the cradle. It is moved on the incline by cables attached to the cradle, and leading off the top of a circular flange on each end ring. These cables pass over sheaves in the top of a tower, which extends above the high end of the incline, and down to a pair of motor-driven **cable-winding drums** at the base of the tower. The load in these cables that roll the dumper on the incline is partially relieved by other cables that wind on the opposite side of the drums, to lead upward and over sheaves at the top of the tower, and then downward to suspend weights that slide in guides on the rear columns of the tower.

Cars are handled through the dumper in a manner similar to the method used with the revolving dumper.

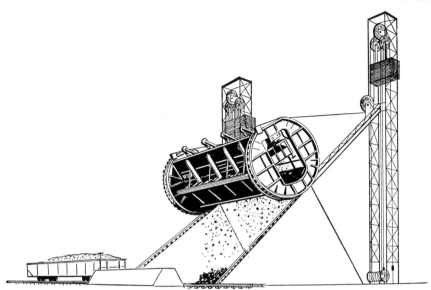

Fig. 15. Open-car rolling dumper.

HIGH-LIFT OPEN-CAR SIDE DUMPERS. The high-lift open-car side dumper is used mainly for loading lake or ocean-going vessels with coal brought to the dumper in open-top railroad cars. The usual run of coal cars having a capacity up to 100 tons or more may be dumped with the modern lifting dumper at a rate of 50 or more cars per hr. (Fig. 16).

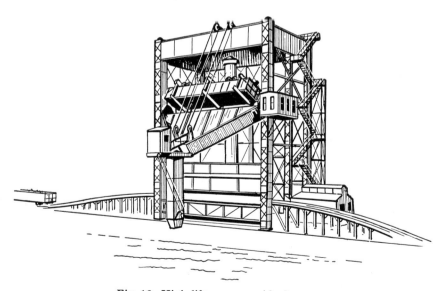

Fig. 16. High-lift open-car side dumper.

The **framework of the dumper** is rectangular in shape, with a heavy girder arranged to slide vertically between the front columns of the frame. This girder, called the **pan girder,** is supported on two vertical screws, one at each end of the girder, which impart a vertical motion to the girder as the screws are rotated.

The inner and wide end of a converging **pan** is pinned to the pan girder. The outer end of the pan projects over the deck of the boat to be loaded, and is supported and moved up or down on cables leading upward and over sheaves at the top of the frame, and then downward to be attached to a motor-driven drum on the foundation. At the outer, and narrow, end, of the converging pan, a **telescopic chute** is pinned so that it may be swung athwart the boat being loaded. In some dumpers the telescopic chute is provided with a fore-and-aft swing also. The machinery for telescoping and swinging the telescopic chute is located on the pan, with control in the operator's house at the outer end of the pan.

The lower end of the telescopic chute is usually provided with a **regulating gate** for controlling the flow of coal into the boat. For loading ocean-going boats the regulating gate is frequently replaced with a belt trimmer, described in the section on Belt Conveyors.

An **L-shaped cradle,** with a movable platen, supports the car to be dumped. At each of the upper ends of the vertical side of the cradle a trunnion and sliding block is provided. The blocks slide in guides on the front posts of the frame. At each of the lower ends of the vertical side of the cradle a roller is provided. These rollers engage the front columns of the frame and stabilize the cradle, as it is being hoisted and lowered. The **drums and driving machinery** for hoisting the cradle are located on the foundation. Cables lead from the drums upward and over sheaves at the top of the frame, and then downward to be attached to the cradle. The car clamps are of the beam type with the holding force applied by counterweights sliding in guides in the rear side of the frame.

Operation. When not in use, the hinged pan and telescopic chute are stored in the high position to clear moving boats at the dock. In operation, the pan and chute are lowered, with the chute extending into the hold of the boat and the pan at a downward slope to cause the coal to flow. The pan girder is adjusted to proper elevation and a loaded car is placed on the cradle. The cradle hoist machinery is started and the cradle with car—now moved sidewise with the platen to engage the side of the cradle—is lifted until the trunnions on the cradle engage hooks on the pan girder. Here the guide rollers at the lower end of the cradle leave their paths and the cradle starts to turn over. At a predetermined point of rotation the clamp beams engage the top of the car to hold it firmly in place. Rotation is continued until the contents of the car are dumped into the pan, then slides down the pan and through the telescopic chute and into the boat. The hoist mechanism is then reversed. The cradle rotates back to its upright position and, with its guide rollers engaging the front columns, is lowered to its seat on the foundations. In the meanwhile, the car clamps are released and the platen is moved sidewise, moving the car clear of the vertical side of the cradle. The empty car is then bumped out of the dumper by the incoming loaded car. To lessen the load on the hoisting mechanism, the dead weight of the cradle is partially balanced by counterweights that move vertically in guides in the rear side of the frame.

In practically all cases a **car-haulage system** is used to move the loaded cars into the dumper. The cars are spotted on the cradle, either with a mechanical car retarder or by a rider who operates the hand brakes on the car.

Two **operators** are required to operate the dumper. One is stationed in a house mounted on the approach end of the frame. This operator has control of the cradle hoist, pan hoist, pan girder hoist, car haulage and the car retarder, if used. The other operator is stationed in a cab at the outer end of the pan. He controls the telescoping of the chute, swinging of the chute, and the gates or trimmer at the bottom of the chutes, as the case may be.

TURNOVER OPEN-CAR SIDE DUMPERS. Turnover open-car side dumpers are employed for discharging coal, coke, iron ore, and other bulk materials from open-top railroad cars by inverting the car sideways and dumping the contents into transfer cars, bins, or storage yards.

Fig. 17. Turnover open-car side dumper.

This type of dumper consists of a rectangular structural framework supporting an **L-shaped cradle**, pivoted at its upper end so that it may be rotated. The cradle supports a laterally moving platen on which the car to be dumped is spotted. During the first part of the dumping operation the platen is released and moved toward the dumping side of the cradle, until the car rests against the car blocking on the cradle. The dumping operation is accomplished by rotating the cradle 155 to 160° around its pivot by means of hoist cables attached to rope-winding drums located on top of the dumper frame. A set of counterweight ropes attached to each end of the cradle supplements the hoisting effort of the cradle-hoist mechanism. Automatically operated **clamps** of the beam-and-counterweight-type clamp the car to the cradle during the dumping cycle (Fig. 17).

Turnover car dumpers handle cars varying in height from 6 ft. 6 in. to 13 ft. and varying in width from 8 ft. 6 in. to 11 ft. Cars of 52 ft. or more in length, and up to 120 tons capacity, can be handled. These dumpers usually dump cars at the rate of 15 to 20 cars per hr.; however, dumping rates of 40 or more cars per hr. can be attained if a car-haulage system is used to move the cars into the dumper. In this case, either a car retarder on the dumper is used to retard and stop the car in the proper position to be dumped, or a rider on the car spots the car by using the hand brakes on the car.

Two types of tilting open-car side dumpers are in use: the stationary type described above, and the movable type. The movable dumper has the entire structure mounted on trucks, and is provided with an approach and run-off trailer to allow cars to enter and leave the dumper. The movable car dumper propels itself along the storage area, rendering unnecessary the use of conveyors or transfer cars.

END-TILT OPEN-CAR DUMPERS. End-tilt open-car dumpers or ram-type tippers are employed to discharge coal, coke, and other bulk materials from small capacity, open-top cars through the end door of the car by raising the opposite end of the car.

The dumper consists of a cradle pivoted at one end, with means for raising the other end after the car has been positioned on the cradle. The raising of the cradle is effected by a tipping ram; this tipping ram is powered either by an electric motor or by hydraulic cylinders. The motor-operated-type ram is driven by either a rack-and-pinion drive or a screw drive.

Cars must enter the dumper with the door end foremost, unless the mechanism is provided to tilt the car in either direction.

The **speed at which cars can be handled** depends on the rate at which they can be fed onto the dumper, but an average rate of 10 to 12 cars per hr. is generally obtained. Cars of 10 to 15 tons capacity are handled with these dumpers.

TILTING AND REVOLVING BOXCAR DUMPERS. Tilting and revolving boxcar dumpers (see Fig. 18) are employed for unloading grain and other free-flowing materials from railroad boxcars by discharging the material through an open side door by the combined effect of first tilting the car sidewise and then endwise in either direction.

This type of dumper consists of a **car-carrying bridge** which is provided with retractable car clamps to hold and position the car on the bridge. The car-carrying bridge is mounted on a semicircular cradle resting on rollers to permit endwise tipping to about 40° from the horizontal in either direction. Sidewise tipping to an angle of approximately 15° in one direction is accomplished either by pivotally mounting the car-carrying bridge or by pivoting the entire cradle structure on knife-edge bearings with a stabilizing arrangement. **End locks** are provided to lock the car-carrying bridge in the horizontal position when a car is not being discharged. The tilting drives of the dumper are powered by electric motors and are equipped with electric brakes to hold the cars in the tilted positions.

The **unloading operation** is as follows: A loaded car is spotted on the car-carrying bridge, with the outer door of the car open on the dumping side. The retractable car clamps of the dumper are brought into contact with the car couplers to center the car on the main cradle. End locks which hold the car-carrying frame in the horizontal position are then released. The door-opening mechanism is brought into contact with the grain door, and the car is tipped sidewise about 15°. Simultaneously, the grain doors are gently lifted away from the grain by the door-opening mechanism. The car is up-ended to an angle of approximately 40° while side tilt is maintained. Second and third end-tilt operations are required to empty the car. After the car has been emptied of its load, the car-supporting platform with its empty car is again brought to its normal horizontal position. The door opener is withdrawn, allowing the grain door to fall to the car floor. The end clamps are retracted, and then the empty car is ready to be moved off the platform and a full car rolled in.

Richardson Scale Co.

Fig. 18. Tilting and revolving boxcar dumper.

The **time required** for the complete unloading cycle is approximately 4½ min., exclusive of time for spotting of car. This type of dumper can handle an average of 10 cars per hr. Dumping rates as high as 13 cars per hr. have been reached.

Pallet Loaders

PALLET-LOADER OPERATION. The pallet loader (see Fig. 19), automatically stacks packages onto a pallet in any predetermined pattern, eliminating entirely any manual operation. A system of **gravity roller** or **wheel conveyors** and **live-roll conveyors** accumulates the packages from one or more packing or sealing lines, until a full pallet load has been accumulated. When any line has accumulated a full complement of packages, and the loader is ready to receive it, the line is automatically released, and the packages proceed to the machine.

The packages enter the loader on a roller conveyor and then feed to a short belt conveyor which deflects all packages into proper alignment and also spaces them for turning, if required, and for counting. The **electrical counting device** also actuates all control mechanisms that govern the functions of the loader. The packages are fed in single file to the package conveyor and when a complete row has been accumulated a ram moves forward, pushing the entire row onto a

Fig. 19. Pallet-loader installation.

stripper plate. (In the row, none or any number of the packages may have been turned at right angles, depending on the pattern requirement.) The ram is then retracted and another row of packages is released to the package conveyor. Subsequent rows are accumulated and rammed in the same manner until a complete pallet layer has been formed on the stripper plate.

When the stripper plate is withdrawn, the entire layer is deposited onto the pallet, which is in position immediately below the stripper plate. A lowerer-governor, resting on top of the packages, controls the lowerer movement, and when the first layer has descended a proper amount the lowerer comes to rest. The stripper plate returns for another layer of packages. This operation continues until the pallet has been loaded with its full complement of packages. When the last layer has been deposited, the lowerer continues downward until it discharges the full pallet load onto a system of chain conveyors for discharge from the loader.

As the full pallet load is being discharged, another empty pallet is automatically fed, by the empty pallet magazine, to the lowerer mechanism. When in position the empty pallet is elevated to a point underneath the stripper plate, where it is ready to receive its load of packages.

Temporary Storage. The full pallet, when it is discharged from the loader, may travel to roller-conveyor storage, from which it is picked up by lift trucks for transportation to storage, delivery trucks, cars, etc. The full pallet may be discharged to a system of conveyors that transfer the load to a right-angle conveyor where full pallet loads are accumulated ahead of lift truck operations. Or the full pallet may discharge to a system of power conveyors for automatic delivery to vertical conveyors (either reciprocating type or suspended-tray type) for dispatch to other floors before the lift trucks pick up the load.

Fig. 19, previously referred to, shows a typical installation of a pallet-loader, palletizing cartons from three sealing machines. The layout of a typical conveyor system for carrying on automatic operations is shown in Fig. 20.

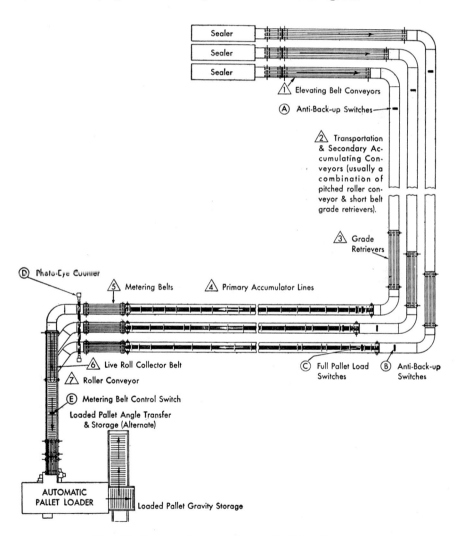

Fig. 20. Layout diagram of a typical installation.

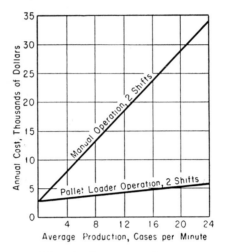

Fig. 21. Cost comparison.

The loader will handle units such as cartons of canned goods and bottled goods, packaged material, cases of beer and soft drinks, rigid bag goods, such as consumer-size "bales" of sugar, etc. One loader will automatically handle the production from several lines, producing different-size packages, different weights, and with each package requiring a different loading pattern.

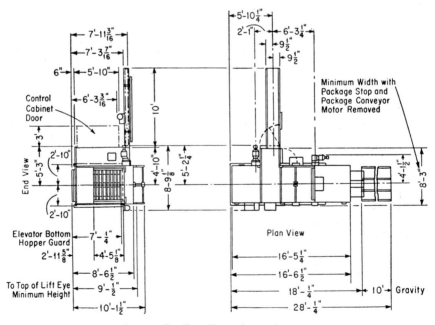

Fig. 22. Outline dimensions of loader.

Capacity and Costs. The capacity of a loader depends on the size of the package, the number of packages in a layer, and the number of layers in a full pallet load. In general, the **capacity of the machine for single-line operation** is 35 packages per min. and up to 30 per min. for **multifeed systems.** The full pallet load should not be in excess of 3,000 lb.

The **average cost of electricity and air** for pallet-loader operations varies from 16 to 18 cents per hr. The annual cost comparison with manual loading for a two-shift operation is shown in the chart in Fig. 21. The line showing pallet-loader operations starts at $2,570 at zero cases and represents the cost of depreciation, etc., on the machine. The outline dimension shown in Fig. 22 may be of assistance in making layout drawings of conveyor systems utilizing the pallet-loader.

The above text refers to a simple type of loader designed to place loads on the normal wood pallet. Other loaders are built for forming loads on paper pallets (expendable pallets) and for forming pallet loads for handling with clamp-type lift trucks. In the latter no form of pallet is used. Some loaders are equipped with gluing devices and other types of accessories.

Some loaders do not employ a stripper plate, and these units transfer layers of loads to a pallet by use of suction heads, clamps, etc.

POWERED INDUSTRIAL TRUCKS

CONTENTS

POWERED INDUSTRIAL TRUCKS

TRUCK SELECTION. Regardless of the class of truck required, several manufacturers will be able to supply models that meet the general specifications. To make a selection based on proper evaluation of facts the specifications of each must be analyzed and compared. The form in Fig. 1 will be helpful in organizing the data to be studied. While the elements listed in this form are for walkie or rider platform lift trucks, the same form listing somewhat different items may be used for any type of truck.

Rider-Type Trucks

FIXED PLATFORM POWERED INDUSTRIAL TRUCKS. These trucks are designed for use in operations where there is no need for elevating or lowering the body of the trucks, as, for example, railroad terminals and highway truck terminals. They have great maneuverability and are light in weight (see Fig. 2).

They are available in **capacities** ranging from 2,000 lb. to 60,000 lb., and may have **frame styles** including straight or drop platform and fixed or dump body.

These trucks are especially adaptable to haulage jobs where the bed of the truck is loaded by hand, hoist, or crane, and are most popular as railway baggage or maintenance department delivery trucks.

The **electric-powered flat-bed truck** often has one-end stand-up control. Levers are used for steering and forward and reverse. Braking is done by means of foot pedal on stand-up platform.

Gasoline-powered trucks, with fixed flat beds, are also available. In one model the engine is located under the driver's seat. Steering is done by means of a lever in front of the driver. The engine and driver's seat are located to one side, leaving clearance for the handling of long items. These trucks are extremely versatile and especially valuable for light delivery jobs and hauls over moderate distances.

Drop platform trucks are designed for handling bulk cargo. One 4,000-lb. model has a travel speed varying from less than 1 m.p.h. to 8 m.p.h. fully loaded, and from 10 to 12 m.p.h. empty. Its front turret section contains the drive wheel and motor as a rigid unit. Direction is changed by turning the turret.

Typical of the **drop center platform truck** is the electric-powered nonelevating baggage truck. It can usually be controlled from either end and is commonly used for handling baggage, express, and mail in railroad and steamship terminals.

Fixed and Dump Body Trucks. Gasoline-powered **fixed body trucks** with wooden stakes for high piling are often used for handling large bulky loads (Fig. 3). Capacities of this type of truck range from 2,000 to 6,000 lb. Overhead crane, hoist, or manual loading and unloading are required. Many body variations can be applied to fixed or dump body trucks of this type just as with 4-wheel hand

Low- and High-Lift Power-Operated Platform Trucks
Walkie and Rider Types—Gasoline and Electric Types

Name of Manufacturer								
Model No.								
Technical Data:								
1. Rated capacity								
2. Lowered height								
3. Maximum lift								
4. Size of platform								
5. Service weight								
6. Over-all length								
7. Over-all width								
8. Underclearance at center								
9. Height of driver's platform								
10. Wheel base								
11. Drive wheel or wheels— type and size								
12. Turning radius—inside								
13. Turning radius—outside								
14. Intersecting aisles								
15. Rt. angle stack—aisle req.								
16. Top speed—forward loaded								
17. Top speed—forward unloaded								
18. Top speed—reverse loaded								
19. Top speed—reverse unloaded								
20. Lift speed—loaded								
21. Lift speed—unloaded								
22. Driver control position								
23. Type of lift								
24. Driver's vision								
25. Type of drive coupling								
26. Hand and/or foot controls								
27. Type of steer								
28. Ampere-hour capacity of battery for 8 hr.								
29. Weight of battery								
30. Price of battery								
31. Position of hand control								
32. Location of raising & lowering buttons or levers								
33. Length of steer handle in fully extended position								
34. Position of regular brakes								
35. Position of dynamic brakes								
36. Degree of grade it will climb with full load								
37. Complete truck price, less battery								
38. Type and capacity of charger recommended								
39. Price of charger								

(Items 31–35 marked "Walkie Only")

Fig. 1. Form for analyzing manufacturers' specifications.

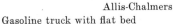

Allis-Chalmers
Gasoline truck with flat bed

Hyster
Drop platform truck

Yale and Towne Mfg. Co.
Drop-center electric baggage truck

Fig. 2. Fixed platform trucks.

trucks. The driver's position may be before or behind the load, depending on the requirements of the jobs for which the truck is designed.

Gasoline- or electric-powered platform trucks with **tilting body** design are often used to position loads directly onto the floor. A tilting platform is mounted in front of the driver. Such trucks range in capacity from 2,000 to 10,000 lb. and may be equipped with pneumatic tires for outdoor use.

Clark Equip. Co.

Fig. 3. Truck with fixed stake body.

Gasoline-powered **dump body trucks** for handling bulk materials of all kinds are useful where speed and distance traveled are factors. The driver faces the dump body in this type of truck.

Special Body Trucks. Gasoline- and electric-powered special body trucks have been made for the performance of particular materials handling operations. New designs are created as the use of the industrial truck becomes more popular.

Fig. 4 illustrates a gas-electric truck with **roller-conveyor platform** and winch used for handling large coils of strip steel up to 20 tons over comparatively long distances between operations and buildings.

Fig. 4. Roller-conveyor platform truck.

INBOARD PLATFORM LIFT TRUCKS. Powered industrial inboard lift trucks are primarily designed for handling skid platforms or pallet loads of material. They range in **capacities** from 1,000 to 20,000 lb., and in special cases have been made for capacities up to 80,000 lb. Their distinctive feature is that in operation the wheels are located either underneath the platform or between the pallet runners. These trucks are the forerunners of the present fork truck and are available in gas, electric, and gas-electric models. Platforms on the low-lift type raise the load 6 to 24 in. from the ground. Their design enables them to carry greater weights in shorter working areas, and they are widely used in many industries.

High-lift platform trucks are used for hauling skid platforms of all types. They differ from the low-lift type in that they have a single or telescopic mast for high stacking. Trucks with lifts of 24 in. or more come under this category. Medium-height lifts up to 60 in. have masts but do not require the telescopic feature. These trucks are also available in gas, electric, and gas-electric models. Fig. 5 shows some typical platform trucks. Note the various arrangements and controls for sitting or standing rider operation and the different wheel patterns.

INBOARD PALLET LIFT TRUCKS. Trucks of this kind are shown in Fig. 6. **Low-lift** pallet trucks are designed with small wheels that enter into double-faced pallets with some boards removed on the bottom decks. This permits the wheels to protrude through pallets when trucks are in raised positions. The standard **width** for the wheel frames is 27 in. over-all, with a 6-in. space usually left between them. Collapsed **height** is 3⅜ in., raised height up to 7⅜ in., capacities up to 6,000 lb. Greater capacities can be had in special trucks.

High-lift pallet trucks are designed to support the load in front of the operator. The load is distributed over two outriggers that go to either the outside of the pallet or skid or under the edges of a wing-type pallet. Their usefulness derives from the high **stackability** made possible by straddling the load, and from their **maneuverability** in very narrow aisles. While stabilizing casters may be added,

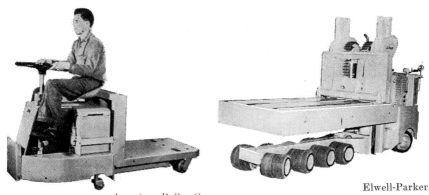

American Pulley Co.

Electric low-lift platform truck with front sit-down or stand-up control. Capacities up to 6,000 lb.

Elwell-Parker

Gas-electric high-lift platform die-handling truck

Automatic Transportation Co.
Electric low-lift platform truck with side standing control.

Fig. 5. Representative platform lift trucks.

they are basically 3-wheel trucks and they derive their ability to turn in short spaces from this fact.

This type of truck also has a **light-weight advantage** that makes it possible to use over low-floor-load-capacity areas and on and off elevators in multistory buildings.

Outriggers are 3 or 4 in. wide and are usually 75 percent of the load length. Distance between straddle-type outriggers is usually taken to be 1½ in. wider than the pallet or skid being handled. With this arrangement pallets to be handled must be stacked some distance apart to permit entry of the outriggers. Where space it at a premium, the wheels may be placed directly under the forks as in the case of low-lift pallet trucks. With this type only single-faced pallets or skid platforms may be used.

The **driver's position** is usually to one side of the drive wheel. Special models can be had with adjustable outriggers or standard lift truck attachments for special applications. Various kinds of wheels are also available for different floor conditions.

This truck is not desirable for running in and out of highway vehicles, especially on inclines, or on bad floors, because of the low underclearance of outriggers and small wheel size. Telescoping, nontelescoping, tilting, and fixed masts are available.

Truckman
Gasoline low-lift pallet truck

Automatic Transp.
Electric high-lift pallet truck with
straddle outriggers

Fig. 6. Typical pallet lift trucks.

SPECIAL INBOARD LIFT TRUCKS. High-lift trucks are available with man-carrying platforms mounted on telescoping masts. These may be designed with straddle-type outriggers and may have tilting masts. They are used for maintenance work and for loading or selecting from high racked stock bins. Elevating and tilting controls are mounted on the platform.

OUTBOARD INDUSTRIAL LIFT TRUCKS. The **fork lift truck**— with electric, gasoline, diesel, or propane gas power—is probably the best-known mobile kind of materials handling equipment. It is built in a range of **capacities** from 1,000 to 80,000 lb., and is well suited for combined horizontal and vertical movement of material. The normal industrial range of capacities is from 1,000 to 10,000 lb. capacity, measured in the form of a 48-in.-cube homogeneous load. The 48-in.-cube homogeneous load is normally used as the rating load for fork trucks.

The lift truck has become a basic tool in most industries. Although basically this truck is equipped with tapered steel **forks** to handle palletized loads, or loads on skids, it is possible to equip these trucks with various kinds of **attachments** for specialized application. Paper roll clamps, carton clamps, cotton, wool, and scrap paper bale clamps, rotators, side shifters, scoops and end dumping devices are representative of the varieties of attachments available.

Approximately 90 percent of the fork trucks in use are within the 6,000-lb. capacity range. The **standard sizes** within this range are 1,000 lb. @ 24 in.; 2,000 lb. @ 24 in.; 4,000 lb. @ 24 in.; and 6,000 lb. @ 24 in. These trucks are

Yale & Towne Mfg. Co.

60,000-lb. nontilting die truck

Lamson-Mobilift Corp.
3,000-lb. gasoline tilting fork truck

Clark Equipment Co.
25,000-lb. tilting-mast gasoline-powered fork truck

Fig. 7. **Single-mast fork trucks.**

also available with pneumatic tires which permit operation over rough-surfaced areas.

TYPES OF INDUSTRIAL OUTBOARD LIFT TRUCKS. These trucks, also known as **counterbalanced trucks,** can be classified according to design features as follows:

> Single-mast tilting powered fork trucks.
> Single-mast nontilting powered fork trucks.
> Telescoping-mast tilting powered fork trucks.
> Telescoping-mast nontilting powered fork trucks.

In trucks with **tilting masts** the load in raised position can be tilted back toward the truck, thus bringing the load center more nearly over the wheels of the truck for better stability. While tall single masts are available, the **telescoping mast** permits high lifts for trucks that must run through areas of limited head room. Figs. 7 and 8 show representative models of these trucks.

Towmotor Corp.   Hyster Co.
4,000-lb. tilting fork truck powered by LPG   15,000-lb. tilting gasoline-powered truck

Fig. 8. Telescoping-mast fork trucks.

TRUCKS WITH RETRACTABLE FORKS. This type of powered industrial truck has both outboard and inboard features. Loads are picked up and placed outboard but are carried inboard for greater stability. They may be designed as end loaders or side loaders and may have telescoping masts for high stacking. The fore and aft decks of the side loader make it particularly suitable for handling long stock with safety.

Mechanisms for extending and retracting the forks are varied. In one type both the fork and mast move inboard or outboard on tracks that are fastened to the chassis of the truck. In another the forks are moved in and out on **pantagraphs.** Typical examples of retractable fork trucks are shown in Fig. 9.

CAPACITY RATINGS OF FORK TRUCKS. See Fig. 10. True capacity = (distance B to C + distance A to B) × rated load weight. For example, if a truck is of a rated capacity of 3,500 lb. at 18-in. load center (B to C), with distance of 14 in. from the center of the front axle to the heel of the forks (A to B), true capacity will equal 14 in. + 18 in. × 3,500 or 112,000 in.-lb.

Lewis-Shepard Products, Inc.

High-lift electric side-loading lift truck with retractable grab

Lewis-Shepard Products, Inc.
2,000-lb. electric lift truck with pantagraph

Moto-Truc Co.
4,000-lb. electric lift truck with
retractable mast

Baker-Rauling Co.
High-lift gasoline side-loading lift truck
with retractable mast and forks

Yale & Towne Mfg. Co.
3,000-lb. electric lift truck with sliding
retractable forks

Fig. 9. Powered industrial trucks with retractable forks.

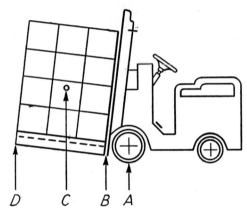

D C B A

A, center of axle. B, heel of forks. C, center of gravity of load. D, end of load.

Fig. 10. Capacity diagram.

The maximum weight that can be placed on a pallet is determined by working backward. The formula is:

$$\text{Maximum weight on a } 48 \times 40 \text{ in. pallet} = \frac{\text{True Capacity}}{\tfrac{1}{2} \text{ pallet length} + (A \text{ to } B)} \text{ or}$$

$$\frac{112{,}000}{\tfrac{1}{2} \text{ of } 48 + 14} \text{ equals 2,947 lb. for the truck in the example above.}$$

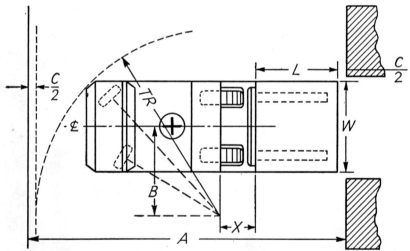

Fig. 11. Aisle width diagram.

AISLE WIDTH REQUIREMENT. To derive the formula for aisle requirements, the following factors, illustrated in Fig. 11, should be used:

    $A =$ Width of aisle
    $B =$ Distance from center line of truck to center line of point about which truck turns when wheels are completely cramped
   $TR =$ Turning radius

W = Width of the load
C = Clearance (set at 6 in.)
X = Distance from center line of drive axle to face of fork

The aisle width formula is:

$$A = TR + X + L + C$$

This simple formula is easily applied by substituting the correct values and adding. It is important that the width W of the load be less than twice the value of B. This relationship of W to B must be observed to allow sufficient aisle width for turning.

For example, if a fork lift truck has a turning radius (TR) of 60 in. and carries a 36-in. load (L), the clearance is 6 in. or 3 in. ($C/2$) on each side of the truck.

Furthermore, if manufacturer's specifications place the distance from the heel of the forks to the center of the front axle (X) as 15 in. and (B) is 25 in., minimum aisle width required would be computed as follows:

1. Determine that the load width is less than twice B, then using the formula solve for A:

$$A = 60 + 15 + 36 + 6$$
$$A = 117 \text{ in. minimum aisle width}$$

2. When the loads to be carried are greater than $2 \times B$, the following formula is used:

$$A = TR + \sqrt{(X + L)^2 + (W/2 - B)^2} + C$$

Thus, if the load width is increased to 60 in.:

$$A = 60 + \sqrt{(15 + 36)^2 + (60/2 - 25)^2} + 6$$
$$A = 117.2 \text{ in. minimum aisle width}$$

It should be repeated that the minimum aisle widths vary from actual functional widths. However, after experience with these formulas, they can be used with fairly good accuracy to foretell approximate minimum aisle widths required.

STRADDLE-CARRIER, POWERED INDUSTRIAL LIFT TRUCKS. The straddle carrier is important for its **maneuverability** and large weight-lifting capacities (Fig. 12). Loading and unloading can be accomplished in 3 sec.

By straddling or coming over the load, it is possible for this vehicle to lift more than twice its own weight. These trucks range in **capacities** from 10,000 to 50,000 lb. They can travel over highways at speeds up to 60 m.p.h.

An extremely versatile truck, its special applications have been unlimited in scope.

FORK LIFT TRUCK ATTACHMENTS. Recent developments have produced attachments capable of handling packages and cartons without the use of pallets or skids. These devices include equipment such as package **grabs** and crate grabs which pick up stacks of containers by gripping them with opposing plates; sheet-holding devices; and grip-fork-type devices, which handle unit loads of cartons, boxes, cement blocks or bricks by gripping pillar rows and supporting the load in the same manner as with a pitch fork. The latter devices are designed to handle full- or half-width "slices" of high capacity trailer loads.

A fork truck equipped with a **side shifter** mechanism enables the operator to make more accurate placements of loads without repeated backing and filling.

Clark Ross
40,000-lb. wide straddle carrier for steel
plates

Clark Ross
Narrow straddle truck with hold-down
attachment

Clark Ross
30,000-lb. unit for high load of lumber

Hyster Co.

18,000-lb. truck with adjustable lifting arms

Fig. 12. **Representative straddle trucks.**

Allis-Chalmers
360° rotating clamps

Yale & Towne Mfg. Co.
Vertical drum-handling attachment

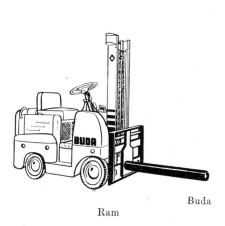

Buda
Ram

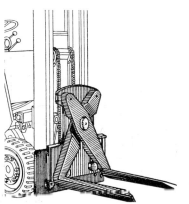

Yale & Towne Mfg. Co.
Scissor-type adjustable forks

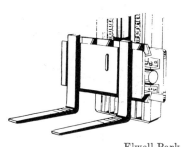

Elwell-Parker
Side shifter

Buda
Brick and block forks

Fig. 13. Fork truck attachments (continued on next page).

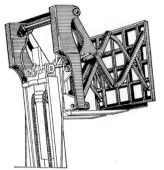

Yale & Towne Mfg. Co.
Pusher-type pallet unloader

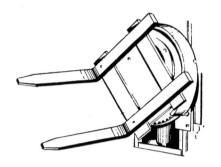

Elwell-Parker
360° revolving forks

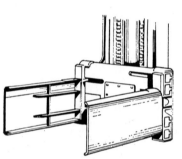

Elwell-Parker
Bale clamp

Elwell-Parker
Tin plate clamp

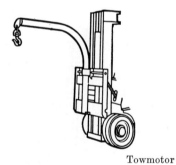

Towmotor
Swinging boom

Towmotor
Scoop

Fig. 13. (Concluded.)

Pushers may be mounted on forks to facilitate unloading. **Rams** permit rapid handling of coils, tires, rolls, and other hollow-center materials. **Boom crane** attachments are available for handling heavy machinery and may be specially designed for specific operations. **Dumping attachments** include hoppers, scoops, and rotating devices on forks and clamps. Fig. 13 illustrates some of the devices available. Overhead guards for operator safety and cab enclosures for operator comfort are also available.

Since most of these attachments are specially adapted from standard models to suit the particular handling operation, it is usually necessary to consult with the manufacturer of the truck to secure the best possible attachment for the particular operation.

Walkie Trucks

MOTORIZED WALKIE TRUCKS. Motorized walkie trucks are similar to the larger rider-operated trucks in their application, but are operated by controls on the handles. Motorized walkie trucks are available in many of the larger powered industrial truck types.

All these trucks are electrically, gas-electric-, or gas-propelled. In some cases the low-lift trucks are provided for manual or foot operation, the power being used only for transportation purposes. The high-lift trucks can be provided with most of the attachments used on standard rider-type industrial trucks.

This type of equipment is usually employed on **light service** for **short hauls** where the travel does not exceed 250 ft. The trucks are used in place of or to supplement the rider types, especially where lower initial cost is a factor. They are generally the simplest type of electrical equipment to operate, and very little instruction and operating skill are required in learning how to operate them.

Most of the trucks are equipped with **dead-man controls** which will stop the truck when the handle reverts to its upright or its lowest positions. These safety features are especially needed where trucks are used on ramps.

When purchasing equipment of this kind, it is especially important to investigate the trucks from a **safety** standpoint, and to check on such items as brakes, position of controls, protection for the driver's hand, and clearance for operator's foot along the understructure. The trucks should also have safety control valves which will allow them to lower their loads at a limited speed in the event of hydraulic hose failure or mechanical breakdown.

Trucks of this kind in the higher-price classes have **time-delay** and **relay controls** which allow for a pause between forward and reverse movements.

FIXED-PLATFORM WALKIE TRUCK. The electric-power-propelled trucks with **nonelevating load platforms** are known as "burden-carrying" or "fixed-platform" power walkie trucks. They are usually powered by battery, gas-electric motor generators, or small gasoline engines. A typical truck is shown in Fig. 14. The operator walks ahead of the truck and controls it by means of switches on the truck handle. He stops the truck by means of built-in brakes. It is loaded and unloaded by manual means or by hoists or cranes. These trucks are constructed in standard models ranging in capacity from 1,000 to 4,000 lb.

Walk-Along Fixed and Dump Body Powered Industrial Trucks. Fig. 15 shows a 3-wheel rubber-tired gasoline-powered truck with fixed platform that carries loads up to 1,000 lb. Power relieves the operator on short hauls, especially where poor floor conditions exist. Note rubber pneumatic tires.

Fig. 14. Burden-carrying electric-powered walkie truck.

Fig. 15. Fixed-body walkie truck.

A gasoline-powered version of the wheelbarrow does all the jobs possible with the normal wheelbarrow faster and with less operator fatigue. It is adaptable to outdoor and indoor work, it can operate up and down ramps, and in close quarters (Fig. 16). Its capacities range up to 1,000 lb., and its load buckets can carry 10 to 18 cu. ft. Buckets can be removed and replaced with platforms for warehouse work.

Fig. 16. Motorized wheelbarrow.

LOW-LIFT PLATFORM WALKIE TRUCK. The low-lift platform walkie truck is the same in principle as its rider-type counterpart. The platform is lifted 3 to 4¼ in., depending on the make. Standard units range from 2,000 to 6,000 lb. **capacity.**

Platform heights, widths, and lengths are available in different sizes depending on the size of skid platform handled.

HIGH-LIFT PLATFORM WALKIE TRUCK. The walkie motorized high-lift platform truck is directed by a walking operator through controls on the handle and mast assembly.

These trucks are constructed in various platform lengths and widths. They are used primarily for handling and stacking materials on skids and for setting dies, stacking boxes, etc. The design allows for maneuverability in crowded quarters. Low- and high-lift walkie platform trucks are shown in Fig. 17.

PALLET LOW-LIFT WALKIE TRUCK. These trucks, controlled by a walking operator, have power and control units similar to those for lift platform walkie trucks. The forks, similar to those used in rider-type pallet trucks, elevate about 4 in., thus allowing the trucks to handle either single- or double-faced pallets. These trucks are available in various fork lengths and widths in capacities up to 6,000 lb. They are especially useful in crowded areas, on elevators, and in buildings with restricted floor loads.

HIGH-LIFT PALLET OUTRIGGER-TYPE WALKIE TRUCK. High-lift outrigger trucks do not require any counterweight, since the load is supported on outriggers located alongside the forks and under the load. The elimination of the counterweight shortens the length and decreases the weight of the truck, thereby making it particularly suitable for use in smaller aisles and low-floor-load areas. These considerations are quite similar to those for rider trucks of this type.

Allowances must be made in the design of pallets, racks, or skids for the clearance of outriggers. The mast design is the same as that for a regular fork truck except that the mast does not tilt forward and backward. As with rider-type high-lift pallet trucks, stabilizing casters are used to support the mast.

FORK LIFT WALKIE TRUCKS. A fork lift walkie truck is an adaptation of the standard fork truck. These trucks carry the loads supported in front of them. Forward, reverse, raising, and lowering power motions are controlled by the walking operator. The truck in Fig. 18 is counterweighted to balance the front supported load, which ranges from 1,000 to 4,000 lb.

The forks can be lowered to rest on the floor, the minimum height then being the thickness of the forks, usually 2 in. Maximum heights vary with capacities. The more generally used trucks have 68-in. mast heights, giving 108-in. lift with a telescoping mast. The relatively light weight of the truck permits it to be used on elevators and in areas where floor-load allowances are low.

Like the rider type, these trucks are made with single or telescoping masts of tilting or nontilting design.

SPECIAL INDUSTRIAL WALKIE TRUCKS. These trucks, controlled by walking operators, are power-propelled, but may, or may not, have power-operated lifting devices.

They can be constructed on many special designs, two of which are illustrated in Fig. 19. The roll truck will pick up rolls from the vertical position and tilt the truck for carrying in a horizontal position over the truck body. The vat dumping truck is used in meat-packing operations.

Moto-Truc

Low-lift platform truck

Lift Trucks, Inc.

Low-lift platform truck

Fig. 17. Motorized lift platform walkie trucks (continued on next page).

High-lift platform truck   Barret Cravens

Fig. 17. (Concluded.)

Fig. 18. High-lift fork walkie truck, counterbalanced type.

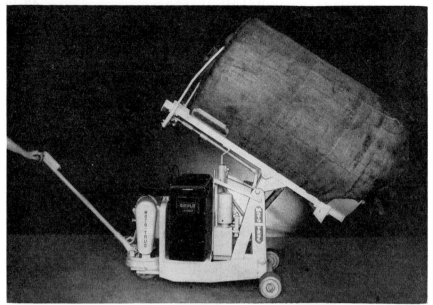

Moto-Truc

Roll truck

Moto-Truc

Outrigger-type walkie lift truck with dumping attachment

Fig. 19. Special industrial walkie trucks.

Powered Industrial Truck Characteristics

TIRES. Gasoline-powered industrial trucks are manufactured in **capacities** from 1,000 to 60,000 lb. and can be equipped with both cushion- and pneumatic-type tires. **Cushion-type tire** trucks are intended for indoor operation over smooth, hard-surfaced floors with ramps up to approximately 20 percent, in low gear up to 30 percent, and over bridge plates for loading freight cars and trailers. **Pneumatic-tired** trucks are intended for rough-surfaced outdoor areas. Special vehicles are available for use in traveling over rough terrain or soft ground. The general **operating speeds** for gasoline-powered trucks with solid (cushioned) tires and pneumatic tires are shown in Fig. 20. Safe operating speed for indoor work is normally not more than 5 m.p.h.

Capacity (lb.)	Running Speed (M.P.H.), Loaded		Hoisting Speed (F.P.M.), Loaded	Lowering Speed (F.P.M.), Unloaded	Tilting Speed (sec.), Loaded — Full Backward to Full Forward
	Forward	Reverse			
			SOLID TIRES		
2,000	7	6	30	27	7
4,000	7	6	30	27	7
6,000	7	6	30	27	7
			PNEUMATIC TIRES		
2,000	7–9	7–9	30	27	6
4,000	8–10	8–10	30	27	6
6,000	10–13	10–13	30	27	6

Fig. 20. Normal operating speeds for gasoline trucks.

UNDERWRITERS' RATINGS. Gasoline-powered trucks carry **Underwriters' Laboratories ratings** type G for general application, and type GS for semi-hazardous locations. The areas of use permitted by the National Fire Prevention Association and Factory Mutual for various types of gasoline-powered trucks are shown in Fig. 21. Gasoline-powered trucks are entirely suitable for **indoor operation** provided that there is adequate ventilation. Oxycatalytic mufflers are available for gasoline-powered trucks which reduce the carbon monoxide concentration to practically zero, thus permitting the use of internal-combustion-engine trucks in closed areas.

Battery-powered electric trucks are available with Underwriters' Laboratories ratings for various kinds of applications. They normally bear the following Underwriters' Laboratories designation:

Type E for general-purpose trucks.
Type EE for dusty and hazardous locations.
Type EX explosion-proof.

The areas of use for industrial trucks as permitted by the National Fire Prevention Association are shown in Fig. 21.

Classification	Type	Usage
Class I, Groups A, B, C	None	Acetylene, hydrogen, ethyl ether vapor
Class I, Division 1 Group D only	EX	Other flammable gases—explosive mixtures (gasoline, petroleum, naphtha, alcohol, acetone, lacquer, natural gas)
Class I, Division 2	EE	Flammable liquids or gases normally confined
Limited usage in Class I, Division 2	GS	Storage of compressed gas or flammable liquid Groups A, B, C and D
Class II, Divisions 1 and 2 Groups E and F	EX (Special)	Only by special permission and investigation by local authority
Class II, Division 1 Group G only	EX	Group G covers grain dusts only
Class II, Division 2	EE GS	Combustible dust not suspended in air, but in some hazardous accumulations (if local authority O.K.'s)
Class III, Division 1	EE	Fibers or flyings suspended in air
Class III, Division 2	EE GS * E	Handling of fibers and flyings such as cotton, rayon, jute, waste excelsior * If local authority says O.K.
Piers and wharves	E G	Unless classified by authority as being in one of above hazardous classes
Piers and wharves—hazardous	As classified	
Outside or inside storage of combustible fibers		Shall be considered as Class III, Division 2
General inside and outside storage		Local authority to determine degree of hazard and place in one of above categories if hazard exists

Fig. 21. Digest of NFPA usage designations for UL specifications.

TRANSMISSIONS. Gasoline-powered trucks are available with four kinds of transmission:

1. Standard manual gear-shift transmission.
2. Automatic transmission.
3. Gas-electric transmission.
4. Hydraulic transmission.

Three types of transmission are available in most sizes of trucks. The dimensions of the truck do not vary according to the various types of transmissions available. The hydraulic transmission is not widely available in all sizes.

Standard Transmission. This is the most commonly used type. Normally it employs the same number of speeds for forward and reverse operation. The average truck is provided with two forward and two reverse speeds in capacities up to 8,000 lb., and three or four speeds forward and reverse in capacities above 8,000 lb. The normal operation of the truck requires that the driver operate the clutch and brake pedals in the conventional manner and select the desired gear, speed, and direction manually, with either a single or double shift lever. Some manufacturers provide a standard transmission with fluid coupling for smoother operation of the vehicle. Shifting is necessary to reverse direction.

Automatic Transmission. This type, offered by several industrial truck manufacturers, normally provides for a simple forward and reverse directional selection and is manufactured in capacities up to 8,000 lb. In capacities above 8,000 lb. a combination of speed-selection and torque-converter operation provides the necessary ratios for comparable speed changes. The automatic transmission is recommended for "high-cycle" operations, where a considerable amount of **direction changing** is involved in the operation of the truck. The purpose of automatic transmission is to reduce operator fatigue and to increase the operating speed of the truck. The **torque converter** provides increased acceleration of the vehicle under load, thus increasing the speed of the operation without necessarily increasing the top speed. Both hydraulically operated and manually operated clutches are available for direction selection, depending on the preferences of the manufacturer. The manufacturer generally provides additional cooling for the hydraulic fluid used in the transmission circuit, usually by means of a heat exchanger built into the radiator or a separate heat exchanger through which the cooling water from the engine passes.

Gas-electric Transmission. This type of transmission involves the use of a gasoline-engine-driven generator, which in turn drives a traction motor. Acceleration of the engine is transmitted electrically to the traction motor. No speed changes are necessary—the operator selecting direction only. This kind of transmission provides smooth and rapid acceleration in either direction.

All-hydraulic Transmission. The all-hydraulic transmission uses an internal combustion engine with a hydraulic pump mounted on it. Oil is pumped to a valving chamber where it is distributed to the truck's drive, lift, and tilt mechanisms as required. One pump supplies pressure for all of these uses. A hydraulic motor is mounted on the steerable drive-wheel trunion. The motor is connected to the drive wheel by a heavy-duty roller chain. Flexible pressure hose is used to link the motor to the pump. Part of the braking action is accomplished through the hydraulic transmission system. As in the case of the gas-electric transmission, speed changes are accomplished by varying engine speed, and it is claimed that this transmission requires a minimum of maintenance.

STEERING. Usually the front wheels of fork lift trucks provide the traction and also carry the greater percentage of the gross load being transported. Steering is done by means of the rear or trailing wheels. These wheels are heavily loaded only when the truck is empty. The great amount of **counterweight** required for the cantilevered type of truck is carried largely on trailing wheels.

To facilitate operation of the vehicle and to reduce **operator fatigue,** power steering is usually required in trucks of over 6,000 lb. capacity. Hydraulic power for the steering is obtained either from the hydraulic pump for lifting and tilting or from a separate pump conveniently mounted on the engine.

DIESEL TRUCKS. The general characteristics of gasoline-powered industrial trucks apply also to diesel industrial trucks. Most manufacturers provide interchangeable gasoline-engine or diesel-power units in sizes of 4,000 lb. and up. There is usually no change in the over-all dimensions of the truck.

Diesel fuel is believed by many users to be **safer** than gasoline, and is recommended for certain operations where gasoline fuel is considered a hazard. Diesel trucks can be equipped with hydraulic or pneumatic starters, thus completely eliminating any requirements for an electrical ignition system. At least one manufacturer provides an "explosion-proof" diesel truck, with certain modifications to the air intake and exhaust system to permit operation of this type of truck in semihazardous locations.

The comment regarding **transmissions** under gasoline-powered industrial trucks applies also to diesel-powered trucks.

LPG FUEL TRUCKS. The use of **liquefied petroleum gas** as a fuel for fork lift trucks has increased rapidly, and the use of this kind of fuel has received Underwriters' Laboratories approval. Certain insurance requirements must be met concerning the refilling of gas cylinders and storage. Use of liquefied petroleum gas brings about improved engine operation and reduces **maintenance and fuel costs.** It is common practice to provide tanks for fuel which are quickly demountable, thus permitting refilling and storage of gas tanks in an area adjacent to the area where the trucks are in operation. One of the advantages claimed for the use of LPG fuel is reduced engine wear with corresponding engine life.

Power Plants and Accessories

POWER PLANTS, TRANSMISSIONS, AND FUELS. O. S. Carliss (Yale and Towne Mfg. Co.) classifies industrial trucks into two basic categories with regard to power plants. **Electric industrial trucks** are normally battery-powered, although gasoline-driven generator-powered units are available as substitutes for batteries. **Internal-combustion-engine-driven industrial trucks** use various kinds of fuels, including gasoline, diesel fuels, and liquefied petroleum gas. The following comments on power plants and transmissions are applicable in general to all industrial trucks. In many cases, however, they also apply to industrial tractors.

BATTERY-POWERED INDUSTRIAL TRUCKS. Battery-powered fork trucks are suitable for warehousing and other operations in confined areas. The use of battery power permits the operation of this type of truck, whereas gases and odors from gasoline-driven types might prove objectionable either to the material being handled or to workers. The **battery voltage** has been largely standardized by the manufacturers. Carliss lists the types of industrial trucks, their capacities and the average voltage employed for their operation as in Fig. 22.

Types of Batteries. Batteries may be of either lead-acid or nickel-alkaline types and of sufficient ampere-hour capacity to insure a full day's operation.

Advantages claimed for the **lead-acid battery** are lower first cost; ability to provide greater kilowatt-hour capacity in a given space; and lower internal resistance, which results in a lesser reduction in voltage during the discharge.

Type of Truck	Truck Capacity (lb.)				
	1,000 to 6,000	7,000 to 10,000	Over 10,000 to 16,000	Over 16,000 to 40,000	Over 40,000
Motorized hand trucks ..	12 v.	—	—	—	—
Fork lift trucks	36 v.	36 v.	—	—	—
Platform trucks	36 v.	36 v.	36 v.	48 v.	72 v.
Ram trucks	—	36 v.	48 v.	72 v.	120 to 144 v.

Yale & Towne Mfg. Co.

Fig. 22. **Average operating battery of various industrial trucks.**

Benefits of the **nickel-iron-alkaline battery** include longer life; superior mechanical strength, as the cells are made almost entirely of steel; noncorrosive electrolyte (KOH) which is not subject to freezing regardless of state of charge; a shorter period of time (7 hr.) required for a normal recharge; and noncritical control of the charging current.

The routine **maintenance** of both types of batteries is very similar in that water must be added at required intervals, and they must be cleaned periodically to minimize the possibility of electrical grounds. The process of adding water can be simplified and speeded up by using the automatic filling devices which are available. Because abnormally high temperatures are detrimental to the well-being of all storage batteries, they should be avoided.

Battery Ratings. It is essential that sufficient battery capacity be provided to insure satisfactory operation of the vehicle during the normal operating period. In the event that the capacity of truck required for the operation is not normally provided with a battery of sufficient capacity for an 8-hr. shift, Carliss points out that it is common practice to change batteries at the 4-hr. period and thus provide adequate battery capacity for the full 8-hr. operation.

Batteries are normally **rated** in ampere-hours for a 6-hr. discharge period. This rating, divided by 6, indicates the ampere draw which, if continued for a period of 6 hr., will cause complete discharge of the battery. The installation of an undersized battery is one of the most frequent causes of poor electric truck operation. The **battery sizes** for trucks of various capacities have been generally established by the manufacturers. Fig. 23 shows the sizes of batteries usually available for various capacities and kinds of trucks. The information in this figure is general; for specific application one should check with the manufacturer. In general, the **average voltage** of a given battery should be approximately equal to the **normal voltage rating** of the motor. For this purpose it may be assumed that the voltage of a lead-acid battery is about 2 volts per cell. Therefore, if a given truck is equipped with a 36-volt motor, the proper lead-acid battery would consist of 18 cells connected in series. Likewise, the Edison nickel-iron-alkaline battery has an average voltage of 1.2 volts per cell; when applied to a truck utilizing a 36-volt motor, the battery would consist of 30 cells connected in

Trucks	Motorized Hand			Fork Lift & Platform			Platform			Ram & Platform		
Voltage	12			36			48			72		
	L	W	H	L	W	H	L	W	H	L	W	H
Lead-acid Batteries	$13\frac{9}{16}$	13	$21\frac{1}{4}$	$38\frac{3}{4}$	$23\frac{1}{8}$	$21\frac{7}{8}$	$36\frac{3}{8}$	$32\frac{7}{8}$	31	$48\frac{1}{4}$	$72\frac{1}{4}$	31
	$18\frac{3}{16}$	13	$21\frac{1}{4}$	$38\frac{3}{4}$	$25\frac{3}{8}$	$21\frac{7}{8}$	$37\frac{7}{8}$	$36\frac{3}{8}$	31	43	54	31
	$20\frac{7}{16}$	13	$21\frac{1}{4}$	$38\frac{3}{4}$	$32\frac{1}{8}$	$21\frac{7}{8}$	$41\frac{1}{8}$	$36\frac{3}{8}$	31	$52\frac{3}{4}$	$72\frac{1}{4}$	31
	$25\frac{1}{8}$	13	$21\frac{1}{4}$	$38\frac{3}{4}$	$34\frac{3}{8}$	$21\frac{7}{8}$	$46\frac{3}{8}$	$36\frac{3}{8}$	31	$53\frac{3}{4}$	$37\frac{1}{2}$	31
	$27\frac{3}{8}$	13	$21\frac{1}{4}$	$38\frac{3}{4}$	$38\frac{1}{8}$	$21\frac{7}{8}$	$50\frac{7}{8}$	$36\frac{3}{8}$	31			
Nickel-alkaline Batteries	$28\frac{7}{8}$	$8\frac{1}{4}$	$23\frac{1}{2}$	$37\frac{5}{8}$	$17\frac{5}{8}$	$25\frac{1}{8}$	$43\frac{1}{4}$	$37\frac{3}{4}$	29	$63\frac{3}{8}$	37	29
	$20\frac{1}{4}$	13	$23\frac{1}{8}$	$37\frac{5}{8}$	$20\frac{1}{2}$	$25\frac{1}{8}$	$46\frac{3}{8}$	45	29	$65\frac{1}{8}$	$55\frac{11}{16}$	29
	$23\frac{3}{8}$	13	$23\frac{1}{8}$	$31\frac{1}{2}$	$31\frac{1}{4}$	$25\frac{1}{8}$	$53\frac{1}{8}$	45	29			
	$26\frac{1}{8}$	13	$23\frac{1}{8}$	$37\frac{1}{4}$	31	$25\frac{1}{8}$						
	$29\frac{3}{8}$	$13\frac{1}{8}$	$23\frac{1}{8}$	$42\frac{3}{4}$	$32\frac{3}{4}$	$25\frac{1}{8}$						

Fig 23. Generally available battery sizes for various industrial trucks.

series. It is, therefore, apparent that total battery voltage, as determined by the number of cells connected in series, controls the speed of the truck operation.

ENERGY CALCULATION. Fig. 24 shows watt-hours of **travel current** required to both accelerate and drive a truck over given distances. Figures may be interpolated for intermediate distances.

Grade Current. Extra current required for going up grade (in addition to that required for level running): Watt-hours (extra) = tons (truck plus load) × feet (length grade) × grade (percent) × 0.013.

Going down grades steeper that 2 percent should require no power, and distance down grade may be subtracted from length of run.

Lifting Current. Watt-hours per lift loaded = tons of load × feet of lift × 2. Watt-hours per lift empty = ⅓ load capacity in tons × feet of lift × 2.

Tilting Current. Kilowatt-hours per tilt loaded = tons of load × 1. Watt-hours per tilt empty = ⅓ load capacity in tons × 1.

CONTROL OF BATTERY POWER. Power to the traction motor of the truck is usually controlled through a **four-speed controller** on rider-type trucks, a **three-speed controller** on rider-stacker trucks, and a **two-speed controller** on motorized hand trucks. The control of battery power through the controller is accomplished either by straight resistance in a series motor circuit or by various kinds of split-field arrangements which result in a lower consumption of battery power in the resistor elements. **Hoisting and tilting** is powered by a separate motor driving a hydraulic pump. This motor is operated only during hoisting and tilting operations. For trucks in excess of 6,000 lb. capacity, it is usually recommended that power steering be considered in order to facilitate operation of the truck and to reduce driver fatigue.

BATTERY CHARGING. In the installation of battery-powered industrial trucks, provision must be made for the adequate **maintenance and recharging of batteries.** Automatic battery-charging equipment which has adequate capacity to charge the batteries should be used. Provision should be made for handling

A. APPROXIMATE WATT HOURS REQUIRED BY FORK TRUCKS
TO TRAVEL ON LEVEL CONCRETE

Weight (Truck Plus Load Pounds)	Length of Run (Feet)											
	50	100	200	300	400	500	600	700	800	900	1000	1100
1,000	1.8	2.5	4	5.5	7	8.5	10.5	12	13.5	15	16.5	18
2,000	3.5	5	8	11	14	17	21	24	27	30	33	36
4,000	7	10	16	22	28	34	42	48	54	60	66	72
6,000	10.5	15	24	33	42	51	63	72	81	90	99	108
8,000	14	20	32	44	56	68	84	96	108	120	132	144
10,000	17.5	25	40	55	70	85	105	120	135	150	165	180
12,000	21	30	48	66	84	102	126	144	162	180	198	216
14,000	24.5	35	56	77	98	119	147	168	189	210	231	252
16,000	28	40	64	88	112	136	168	192	216	240	264	288
18,000	31.5	45	72	99	126	153	189	216	243	270	297	324
20,000	35	50	80	110	140	170	210	240	270	300	330	360

B. APPROXIMATE ADDITIONAL WATT HOURS REQUIRED BY FORK TRUCKS
TO TRAVEL UP EACH 1% OF GRADE

Length of Grade (Feet)	Weight in Pounds (Truck Plus Load)											
	1,000	2,000	3,000	4,000	5,000	6,000	7,000	8,000	9,000	10,000	11,000	12,000
10	.07	.13	.20	.26	.33	.39	.46	.52	.59	.65	.72	.78
15	.10	.20	.29	.39	.49	.59	.68	.78	.88	.98	1.07	1.17
20	.13	.26	.39	.52	.65	.78	.91	1.04	1.17	1.30	1.43	1.56
25	.16	.33	.49	.65	.81	.98	1.14	1.30	1.46	1.63	1.79	1.95
30	.20	.39	.59	.78	.98	1.17	1.37	1.56	1.76	1.95	2.15	2.34
35	.23	.46	.68	.91	1.14	1.37	1.60	1.82	2.05	2.28	2.50	2.73
40	.26	.52	.78	1.04	1.30	1.56	1.82	2.08	2.34	2.60	2.86	3.12
45	.29	.59	.88	1.17	1.46	1.76	2.05	2.34	2.63	2.93	3.22	3.51
50	.33	.65	.98	1.30	1.63	1.95	2.28	2.60	2.93	3.25	3.58	3.90
55	.36	.72	1.07	1.43	1.79	2.15	2.50	2.86	3.22	3.58	3.93	4.29

C. APPROXIMATE WATT HOURS REQUIRED BY FORK TRUCKS FOR LIFTING

Lift (Inches)	Load (Pounds)											
	1,000	2,000	3,000	4,000	5,000	6,000	7,000	8,000	9,000	10,000	11,000	12,000
12	1	2	3	4	5	6	7	8	9	10	11	12
24	2	4	6	8	10	12	14	16	18	20	22	24
36	3	6	9	12	15	18	21	24	27	30	33	36
48	4	8	12	16	20	24	28	32	36	40	44	48
60	5	10	15	20	25	30	35	40	45	50	55	60
72	6	12	18	24	30	36	42	48	54	60	66	72
84	7	14	21	28	35	42	49	56	63	70	77	84

Fig. 24. Watt-hour requirements for lift trucks.

the batteries into and out of the trucks and for addition of distilled water during the charging cycle. Industrial batteries used in fork lift trucks are intended for approximately 300 rechargings per year, or on the average of one per 24-hr. day. It is not recommended that industrial batteries be recharged more frequently than once in 24 hr., or the over-all life of these batteries may be considerably impaired.

The **purpose of battery-charging** equipment is to replace the energy used up in the operation of industrial power-driven trucks in such a manner that the maximum life of these batteries is realized. In general, the time required to charge a truck battery that has delivered its rated capacity is 6 to 8 hr. The best and most economical battery life is obtained when the number of discharge cycles is limited to an average of 300 per year, or approximately one discharge per 24-hr. working day. If trucks are operated in multishifts and require the use of more than one battery during the daily period, provisions should be made for interchange of the batteries.

TYPES OF BATTERY-CHARGING EQUIPMENT. Generally speaking, there are two types of charging equipment in use today: the motor-generator set and the dry-plate rectifier. Each type has its advocates and can be satisfactorily applied to the charging of either lead-acid or nickel-iron-alkaline storage batteries.

Motor-Generator Set. The motor-generator set (Fig. 25) consists of a motor which is built to operate from the plant power supply (generally 220-volt or 440-volt, 3-phase, 60-cycle a.c.) and which drives a d.c. generator of the voltage and ampere capacity required by the number and size of the batteries to be charged. An M-G set may be a **single-circuit** machine which will charge only

Hertner Electric Co.

Fig. 25. Typical motor-generator set with four-circuit panel.

one battery at a time, or it may be a **multiple-circuit** machine which will charge from 2 to 20 batteries simultaneously, depending on the number of circuits required. The individual circuits or panels in a multiple-circuit setup are all connected in parallel, so the **voltage** of the generator remains the same regardless of the number of circuits involved. However, the **ampere capacity** of the generator must be increased in direct proportion to the number of batteries being charged at one time. This, of course, demands a corresponding increase in the horsepower rating of the a.c. motor which is driving the d.c. shunt or compound-wound generator. This method of battery charging is known as the **Modified Constant Potential System,** and it can be made fully automatic. A resistor located in the circuit of each charging panel can be adjusted to provide the proper amount of current in amperes for the battery being charged; once this resistance value is established, no further adjustment is required.

The **automatic features** of a multiple-circuit installation include:

1. Automatic termination of the charge as each battery reaches a fully charged condition.
2. The M-G set will shut down when the last battery in the circuit becomes charged.
3. The charging rate in amperes is automatically and properly controlled during the charging period.
4. Should the line power fail, the M-G set will, of course, shut down, and reverse current breakers will prevent the batteries from discharging through the generator. When the power is again restored, the M-G set will automatically resume operation and proceed to complete the battery charging.

Dry-Plat Rectifier. The dry-plate rectifier, Fig. 26, established itself in battery charging during World War II. The **two general types** most widely used are the copper oxide and the selenium rectifiers. Both types are built only as **single-circuit chargers,** so they are very easy to install. Since the only moving part in a rectifier is a ventilating fan, the charger is simply parked in any convenient, cool, clean spot and plugged in to the plant power supply. A clean location is highly desirable, because the fan pulls air up through the bottom and exhausts it out the back of the unit, after it has passed over the rectifier stacks. Dirt carried by the air flow would lodge between the plates of the rectifier stack, and high temperature and breakdown of the plates would soon follow. Like the

General Electric or Westinghouse

Fig. 26. Copper oxide rectifier.

single-circuit M-G set, the rectifier may be shelf-mounted so that it will be off the floor and out of the way. Likewise, all the **automatic features** obtainable with M-G equipment are also available with rectifiers, and the initial cost per charging circuit is just about the same.

Charging Lead-Acid Storage Batteries. The proper charging of lead-acid storage batteries in an 8-hr. period requires a high initial charging rate (about

25 amp. per 100 amp.-hr. of battery capacity) and a low finishing rate equal to about 20 percent of the initial rate. This can be accomplished automatically by a **motor-generator** set using the Modified Constant Potential System equipment, if the voltage applied at the battery terminals is equal to 2.63 volts per cell. During the charging period the charging rate tapers downward as the battery voltage rises and bucks the charging voltage of the generator.

The inherent characteristics of the **rectifier**, however, are such that the charging rate does not taper sufficiently to meet the requirements of proper lead-acid battery charging. Therefore, a **two-rate system** is employed which utilizes a voltage relay in the charging circuit. When the battery voltage rises to a predetermined value, the relay functions and adds resistance to the circuit so that the charging rate is materially reduced. It then tapers slightly to the proper finishing rate.

Charging Nickel-Alkaline Batteries. The proper charging of nickel-alkaline batteries in a 7-hr. period calls for a charging voltage at the battery terminals equal to 1.85 volts per cell. However, the greater number of cells in the alkaline battery means that the generator voltage is higher than that required to charge a lead-acid battery of the same voltage. Each size of nickel-alkaline cell has a specified normal charging rate in amperes, and the starting rate, when a discharged battery is charged on the Modified Constant Potential System, is about 140 percent of this figure. The amount of taper during the charging period is such that the average charging rate is about equal to the normal charging rate of the cell.

When a **rectifier** is used for the charging of alkaline batteries, the voltage relay and resultant two-rate system are not necessary, since the small amount of taper in the charging rate is perfectly acceptable. Actually, a constant rate of current equal in amperes to the normal charging rate of a given size of cell would be highly suitable for alkaline batteries, were it possible to attain it. It naturally follows, therefore, that a 110-volt d.c. power line or, if available a d.c. welding machine, can be used for charging alkaline batteries by simply inserting the proper amount of resistance in the line. Such a hookup would not be considered very efficient from the standpoint of power cost, unless about 60 cells were charged in series, but no harmful effect would accrue to the alkaline batteries.

Universal Chargers. In recent years the manufacturers of both motor-generator and rectifier charging equipment have introduced what are known as "universal chargers." These units are designed to handle the charging of either lead-acid or nickel-alkaline batteries of comparable voltage and ampere-hour capacity. A very simple and speedily made adjustment is all that is necessary to make the charger suitable for one type of battery or the other.

Control Devices. Before placing an industrial battery on charge, one must be certain that the charging will terminate when the battery reaches a fully charged condition. When charging continues beyond this point, the gassing or decomposition of water proceeds at an accelerated rate, and cell temperatures may build up to the danger point. Various instruments are, therefore, available which protect a battery from this possibility.

One system involves the **T.V.R. voltage relay,** which is most widely used in conjunction with lead-acid batteries, although it has been used very successfully with nickel-alkaline batteries in a few installations. This instrument is located on the panel of each charging circuit and is inoperative until the voltage of the battery on charge rises to a predetermined value which is equal to 2.35 volts per cell for lead-acid batteries or 1.7 volts per cell for alkaline batteries. At this point the relay functions and sets in motion a small a.c. synchronous motor, which in turn runs a time clock for 2 or 3 hr. When the time clock hand works around to zero, a breaker on the panel is tripped and the charge automatically terminated.

Another method involves the **Sangamo ampere-hour meter** which is also installed on the circuit panel. The clock-like dial is calibrated in ampere-hours and a stationary red hand is set at the point which indicates the ampere-hour capacity of the battery normally charged on that circuit.

Before the charge is started, a hydrometer is used to check the **specific gravity of the electrolyte** in a lead-acid battery. The gravity reading indicates the state of charge, and reference to a chart reveals the number of ampere-hours out of the battery. A movable black hand on the dial of the ampere-hour meter is then manually set at this figure and the charge is started. As the charge progresses, the black hand works around toward zero and upon arrival a contactor is tripped which opens the breaker on the panel.

Since the specific gravity of electrolyte in an alkaline cell does not change, for all practical purposes, between a charged and a discharged state, a hydrometer cannot be used as a guide to setting the black hand on the ampere-hour meter. In its place, therefore, a **charge test fork** is used which determines the voltage of a pilot cell while discharging through a shunt resistor on the fork. This reading is then converted by a chart to ampere-hours out of the battery, and the black hand is set accordingly.

Time clocks are also used extensively, particularly on rectifiers, to control the length of charge; they operate very much the same as the black hand on the ampere-hour meter. Hydrometer readings and/or test fork readings are converted to hours and minutes rather than ampere-hours, and the time clock is set accordingly.

BATTERY MAINTENANCE ORGANIZATION. The charging and maintenance of storage-battery equipment can be handled on either a centralized or a decentralized basis. The system is centralized when all charging and maintenance facilities are in one area within a plant and the operation is handled by a small number of individuals who thoroughly understand the few simple rules governing storage-battery operation and maintenance. Since the charging equipment is constantly under competent supervision, it is felt that the centralized

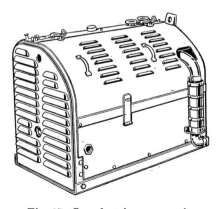

Fig. 27. Gas-electric power unit.

system results in better care of the equipment and lower costs over an extended period of time.

In a **decentralized system,** single-circuit chargers and watering outfits are spotted about the plant, so as to be located near or in the areas where individual trucks are working. The truck driver usually waters the battery and places it on charge, so in effect there are just as many battery maintainers as truck drivers. A wide variation in quality of maintenance is almost certain to show itself in such a setup, and costs will be correspondingly high.

GAS-ELECTRIC UNITS. Electric industrial trucks can be equipped with **gasoline-engine-driven generator units** (Fig. 27). In these units a governor-controlled gasoline engine drives a generator. The generator maintains constant speed under varying loads and provides a continuing flow of electric current for operation of the electric truck. One advantage of these power-pack units is that they provide a greater supply of power within the same volume of space, thus permitting the use of a heavier-duty cycle without increasing the size of the truck to accommodate a larger battery. The maintenance cost of this kind of equipment naturally is increased because of the maintenance of both the gasoline engine and the generator, as well as of the standard traction motor and controls.

SECTION 41

INDUSTRIAL HAND TRUCKS

CONTENTS

CONTENTS *(Continued)*

INDUSTRIAL HAND TRUCKS

HAND TRUCK CLASSIFICATION. Hand trucks, sometimes called floor trucks, are grouped into two major divisions or classifications, **2-wheel hand trucks** and **multiple-wheel hand trucks**—those having more than two wheels. Such trucks are used primarily for horizontal movement. The multiple-wheel units are often employed in trailer-train or towline (tow conveyor) operations, where they are pulled by a power unit driving an overhead or underfloor conveyor chain.

Under each of these two major classifications there are a number of subdivisions, based on the use to which the respective types of trucks are put. Many of the trucks are of **general application** in manufacturing plants, warehouses, terminals, department stores, delivery services, and numerous other industries. Other types of trucks are of a **specialized nature** for handling particular kinds of materials and commodities where certain special requirements exist.

In selecting the specific class or type of truck for a particular use, the following factors should be considered:

1. **Load.** Bulk of the load, weight in relation to floor load, susceptibility to damage in transit, and possible operator abuse.
2. **Floor conditions.** Trucks are cheaper to replace than floors. Therefore truck wheels should be selected to minimize wear of the floor over which the trucks will operate. Use of steel wheels on concrete floors is not recommended. Proper rubber-tired wheels should be used.
3. **Truck wheels.** The type and size of wheel which should be used can best be determined by a consideration of the kind and condition of the floors over which the truck will run, and the weights of trucks and their loads. Generally a roller-bearing wheel is considered best.
4. **Over-all conditions.** After analyzing the above elements of the problem, the prospective truck user should select the correct type of truck for each kind of handling operation. Before ordering trucks he should check the widths of doorways through which the trucks will have to pass. In older plants there may not be sufficient clearance for the wider types of new trucks.

Two-Wheel Hand Trucks

COMMON NOMENCLATURE. There is a common nomenclature applicable to this group which should be known and understood for its importance in explaining the features of the various subdivisions. Fig. 1 will be helpful in making this nomenclature clear.

BASIC TYPES. There are two basic subdivisions of 2-wheel hand trucks:

1. Eastern type
2. Western type

The **eastern type** of truck (Fig. 2) has a tapered frame, wheels located outside the frame, and either curved or flat cross members. It is normally equipped with straight handles, although many makes can also be equipped with curved handles if these are desired. It is furnished in heights from 48 to 60 in. A truck of this kind can be used for handling mixed freight such as boxes, barrels, cartons, bags, and other bulky objects.

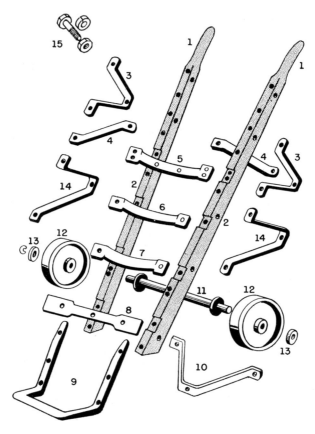

1. Handle	6. 3d crossbar	11. Axle
2. Side rail	7. 2d crossbar	12. Pressed steel wheel
3. Leg	8. 1st crossbar	13. Retaining ring
4. Leg brace	9. Nose	14. Axle bracket
5. Top crossbar	10. Axle brace	15. Nut, bolt, and lock washer

Fig. 1. Parts of a common 2-wheel hand truck.

The **western type** of truck (Fig. 3) has a parallel frame, wheels inside the frame, and either curved or flat cross members. It is normally equipped with curved handles, although many makes can also be supplied with straight handles if these are desired. It is furnished in heights from 48 to 60 in. Types for use in heavy handling around railroad and motor truck terminals have reinforcing, usually in the form of two strengthening members running the length of the truck as extra bracing for the cross members.

Fig. 2. Hand truck, eastern type, with   Fig. 3. Hand truck, western type, with
curved cross members.   flat cross members.

There are certain deviations from these basic designs that warrant individual consideration:

1. Barrel trucks   4. Appliance trucks
2. Bag trucks   5. Utility trucks
3. Beverage trucks   6. Special-purpose trucks

BARREL TRUCKS. This type of truck is designed for handling heavy barrels and drums. It is equipped with short nose prongs and a special hook mechanism, and usually stands in a vertical position at right angles to the floor. Many such units are equipped with floating axle construction. All these features, with variations in wheel equipment, make for easy loading, handling, and unloading (see Figs. 4 and 5).

BAG TRUCKS. Such trucks may be of either eastern or western design, differing only from the basic truck design in length or type of nose, for ease of handling bagged materials (see Fig. 6).

BEVERAGE TRUCKS. In recent years there has evolved a standard pattern of truck design for case and beverage handling that makes use of any one of three handle designs: tipped-top bar handle (Fig. 7), single-grip handle (Fig. 8), and the usual double-grip handle. These trucks have parallel side rails and a plate or open nose, and, when empty, stand upright at right angles to the floor. Some unique features have been developed, one of which is axle interchangeability, so that several sizes of wheels can be interchanged quickly without affecting truck balance. These trucks are of light but rigid construction to withstand shock loads such as those brought on by running over door sills and curbings.

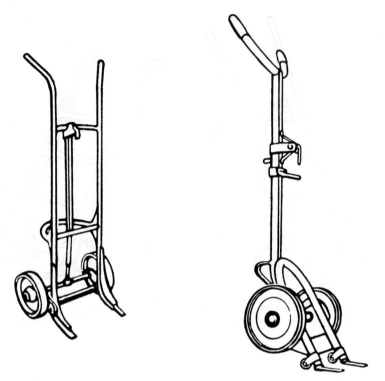

Fig. 4. Drum truck for heavy barrels and drums.

Fig. 5. Drum truck with large and small rubber-tired wheels.

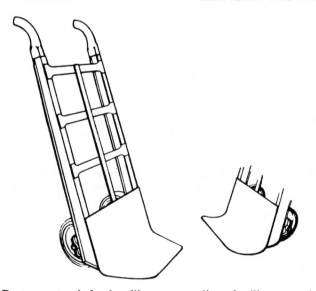

Fig. 6. Bent-nose truck for handling cement, lime, fertilizer, etc., in bags.

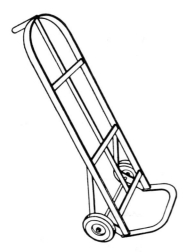

Fig. 7. Tipped-top–bar-handle truck.

Fig. 8. Single-grip-handle truck.

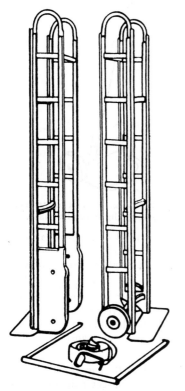

Fig. 9. Trucks for handling large appliances. Model on left has endless belt in place of wheels.

Fig. 10. Universal warehouse truck adjustable for width and height.

APPLIANCE TRUCKS. Trucks in this class are designed for handling refrigerators, stoves, deep-freeze units, and other items of household equipment. Some appliance trucks are equipped with endless-belt mechanisms which enable the trucks to operate on stairs, literally making a ramp of the stairway (Fig. 9). Other trucks are caster-equipped for right-angle movement in restricted areas such as stairwells. Patented locking devices are incorporated on web strapping for fastening units securely to the truck. There are also units that are adjustable in width and height to fit various sizes of appliances and furniture (Fig. 10).

UTILITY TRUCKS. Various types of light, inexpensive, **general-purpose trucks** are used for handling materials of varying bulks, shapes, and weights. Two such trucks are shown in Figs. 11 and 12. These trucks have different kinds of one- and two-handle construction. Frames are also of varied design. No fixed pattern is adopted, the construction usually being determined by the individual decision of the manufacturers, each of whom may produce several different

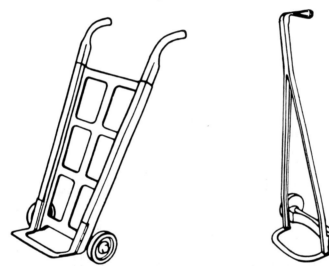

Fig. 11. Heavy-duty truck for heavy cases or boxes.   Fig. 12. Single-grip truck for transporting long, lightweight cases.

models, depending on trade demand. Such utility trucks are used largely on delivery trucks serving beverage distributors, supermarkets, etc., to enable the driver to handle deliveries more readily. Their prime requisites are light weight and sturdiness.

SPECIAL-PURPOSE TRUCKS. In this category are trucks that differ from those of the specific classifications previously covered in that they have certain characteristics adapting them to very specific handling jobs. Only the more common types which serve important industrial and transportation uses can be included here.

Cannery Trucks. This type of truck, shown in Fig. 13, has a fork-type nose and two pairs of handles located on different planes, the larger pair forming long side rails. The nose of the truck is run under a small pallet on which cases are piled. The second set of handles is used to lower the load to easy trucking position.

Grain Trucks. The grain truck is a standard eastern-type truck, except for a longer nose and wheel guards, both to protect the load of grain in burlap bags in handling. Many models are also equipped with hub caps to prevent tearing of bags. This type of truck is also widely used for handling general cargo in many sections of the United States.

Cotton Trucks. Trucks for handling cotton are of conventional basic design except that they are equipped with short, tapered, prong-type noses that are engaged into the bale instead of under it, thus providing better load balance. These trucks can be either eastern (more common, and illustrated in Fig. 14) or western in type.

 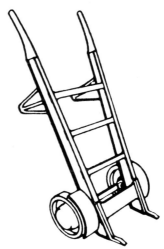

Fig. 13. Cannery or bottling truck for handling goods piled high on pallets.

Fig. 14. Truck for handling baled or bundled material (eastern type).

Cylinder Trucks. Trucks for handling cylinders depart completely from the basic designs previously mentioned. They have large wheels, a right-angle plate nose, and a chain-locking device for holding the cylinders on the trucks. They are also often equipped with a toolbox to contain welding tips, torches, and other small tools. Fig. 15 shows a single-cylinder-handling truck and Fig. 16 shows a multiple-cylinder-handling truck with toolbox.

Pry Trucks. Trucks in this class (Fig. 17) pry up the load on a crowbar nose and roll it away. They are used for loads too heavy or bulky for ordinary 2-wheel trucks, and are well adapted for use in motor trucks, freight cars, warehouses, etc., where space is limited. In many cases they are used in pairs by two men.

OTHER TYPES OF 2-WHEEL TRUCKS. Additional types of special-purpose trucks include those for handling carboys, paper rolls, radiators, furniture, ash cans, fish, etc. Roll and cylinder trucks for heavy and light duty are likewise available for handling paper rolls, etc., of 30 to 54 in. in diameter, and in capacity ranges from 500 to 2,000 lb. Certain **heavy-duty models** will not only transport but will also raise objects to machine height.

There are many special 2-wheel hand trucks designed and built for some single purpose or for a specific customer, and their use to date has been very limited and they are therefore not considered here.

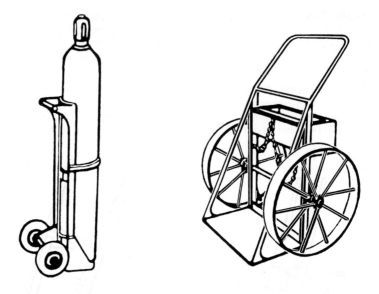

Fig. 15. Single-cylinder acetylene truck.   Fig. 16. Multicylinder acetylene tank truck.

Thomas Truck & Caster Co.

Fig. 17. 5,000-lb.-capacity pry truck.

Multiple-Wheel Floor Trucks

STANDARDS DEFINING RUNNING GEAR. There is no clearly defined nomenclature for multiple-wheel floor trucks, as there is for the 2-wheel types, but certain standards have been developed by the Caster and Floor Truck Manufacturers' Association that define the basic running-gear arrangements. These are summarized in Fig. 18. In determining the specific type of truck required, attention should be given to the factors outlined on page 1 of this section.

DOLLIES. These units are constructed of **wood or metal** and in varying sizes, depending on the load to be handled. They are made in four basic designs: four or six rigid wheels for short, straight movement; three or four swivel casters for short movement, straight, angle, or turning; two rigid and two swivel casters also for straight, angle, or turning movement; and 6-wheel tilt-type, where center wheels are either of larger diameter or center axles are on a different level, for straight, angle, or turning movement (see Fig. 18). Selection is based on loads to be handled and customer preference.

Dolly **frames** may be rectangular, triangular, or circular. They may have solid or open decks or may be specially designed to hold specific loads. Some typical dollies are shown in Figs. 19 and 20. The triangular dolly in Fig. 21 is designed to facilitate its being pushed under barrels and crates which have been tilted. **Rollers** are sometimes used in place of or in combination with wheels. A **stevedoring dolly** has a low profile and has a row of four rollers mounted in its steel frame on either side permitting movement in a straight line. A **timber dolly** has a single large roller mounted across the middle of the frame at right angles to the axis of the load and to the line of movement. Some dollies, Fig. 22, combine rollers and swivel casters to permit a 360° lateral revolution.

PLATFORM TRUCKS. Platform trucks, which are actually a larger edition of the dolly, have two basic chassis constructions: tilt or balance type, and nontilt type. These trucks are produced in many sizes in light-, medium , and heavy-duty construction.

Tilt or Balance Type of Truck. The chassis on the tilt or balance type of truck has rigid load wheels or rigid casters located in the center of the chassis, and one or two swivel casters—usually of smaller diameter—located at or near each end of the platform, permitting maneuverability, with load shift between load wheels and swivel casters at each end by a slight tilting action (see Fig. 23).

Nontilt Type. The chassis on the nontilt type of truck has load wheels at or near one end and swivel casters, usually of smaller diameter, located at the other end, so that the load is distributed at all times and all wheels function at all times. Corner post holders attached to these trucks enable high loads to be braced against spilling. They are also made with steel slat-racks and steel frames.

For very heavy work, trucks of this class have heavier chassis construction. The running gear is also heavier to meet the load requirements. They are made in tilt or balance types with the same maneuverability, but it is not recommended that they be operated on steep ramps. By means of couplers, and with extra reinforcement, such trucks may be used for light-duty trailer service or towline conveyor systems.

WAGON-TYPE TRUCKS. The wagon-type truck differs from the standard nontilt-type platform truck in that the swivel casters are replaced by either a **knuckle-steer arrangement** or a **fifth-wheel assembly** to which a tongue-type

TILTING STYLE

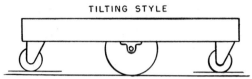

No. 1 Type. Four-wheel tilting style, two main wheels at center, and one swivel caster at each end; for light and medium duty.

No. 2 Type. Six-wheel tilting style, two main wheels at center and two swivel casters at each end; for medium and heavy duty.

SEMILIVE "SKIDS"

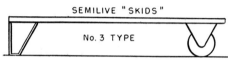

No. 3 Type. Semi-live skid with two main wheels or rigid casters at one end and rigid legs at the other end; to be used with a lift jack.

NONTILTING STYLE

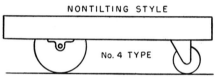

No. 4 Type. Four-wheel nontilting style, two main wheels near one end and two swivel casters at the other end; for medium and heavy duty.

NONTILTING STYLE

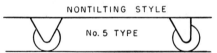

No. 5 Type. Caster type, two rigid casters at one end and two swivel casters at the other end; desirable for low platform requirements; for light and medium duty.

No. 6 Type. Caster type, one swivel caster at each corner; for light and medium duty.

TILTING STYLE

No. 7 Type. Caster type, 6-wheel tilting style with two rigid casters at center and two swivel casters at each end; for regular- and medium-heavy-duty low-platform requirements.

No. 8 Type. Caster type, 4-wheel tilting style with two rigid casters at center and one swivel caster at each end; for light- and medium-duty low-platform requirements.

TILTING STYLE

No. 9 Type. Caster type, 4-wheel tilting style with two rigid casters at center and one rigid caster at each end; for light- and medium-duty low-platform requirements.

Fig. 18. Caster and wheel diagrams of standard running gear arrangements.

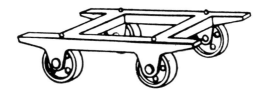

Fig. 19. Four-rigid-wheel, nontilt dolly.

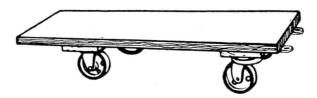

Fig. 20. Nontilt dolly with two rigid, two swivel casters.

Fig. 21. Rubber-tired, 24-in. triangular dolly.

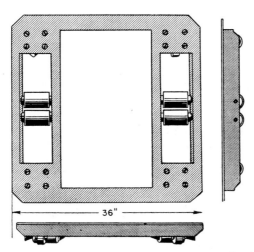

Frank L. Robinson Co.

Fig. 22. Swivel dolly with casters and rollers.

Fig. 23. Platform truck with two removable end racks of pipe.

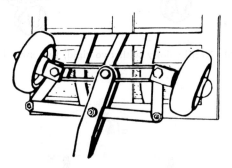

Fig. 24. Knuckle-steer mechanism.

handle is fitted for pulling the truck. These trucks are generally used for handling long, overhanging loads which are difficult to push. Knuckle-steer arrangement (Fig. 24), is preferred for maximum stability because it maintains a wide 4-point wheel support which prevents tipping or spilling of the load.

JOLT-FREE TRUCKS. An aircraft company needed equipment with which to move delicate testing devices over rough ground without jarring. To solve the problem, engineers designed the truck shown in Fig. 25 consisting of a welded steel frame mounted on double-action spring casters, two of which are double-ball-bearing-swivelled and two rigid. Wheels have roller bearings and mount puncture-proof pneumatic tires for additional cushioning.

SUPERSTRUCTURES FOR TRUCKS. Superstructures are many and varied, ranging from four corner stakes to completely enclosed containers. The design in each case is based entirely upon the function to be performed and the requirements of the truck involved (Fig. 26). **Materials** of both platform trucks and their superstructures may be all wood, all metal, or a combination of both. Certain superstructures have also combinations of fiber or canvas with wood or metal or both. **Wheels and casters** vary in size in proportion to unit load ratings and required truck platform heights.

SEMI-LIVE SKID PLATFORMS. Semi-live skid platforms are platforms with two load wheels at one end and two permanent legs at the other. The skid platform is activated by a lift jack consisting of a long handle mounted on a

Douglas Aircraft Co. and Faultless Caster Co.

Fig. 25. Truck for handling delicate testing equipment.

Fig. 26. Various types of rack bodies used on trucks.

pair of wheels, with a hook arrangement over the wheels to engage the coupling on the dead end of the skid and to exert a jacking or prying action. The unit thus formed is equivalent to a three-point suspended-platform truck (see Fig. 27).

Fig. 27. Semi-live skid platform.

Fig. 28 illustrates a self-locking lift jack adaptable for lifting platforms of any reasonable length. The jack will engage with only 12 in. of headroom. The semi-live skid platforms used will handle 3,000 lb. or more. The lift jack will raise such a load with a handle pressure of 76 lb. and will operate with a platform of reasonable length. Tanks, racks, and bins can be readily handled by this type of lift jack and platform.

Clark Equipment Co.

Fig. 28. Self-locking lift jack and skid.

MAINTENANCE OF INDUSTRIAL HAND TRUCKS. It is important from the very first to set up an adequate maintenance program and proper procedures to keep trucks in good operating condition, and to install proper equipment for this purpose. With reasonable care the average truck will give many years of satisfactory service when given **regular inspection,** adequate lubrication and repairs, and careful use. The truck manufacturer in practically all cases has supplied his trucks with suitable lubricating fittings, or at least has provided oil holes leading to the various bearings. **Periodic lubrication** is imperative for satisfactory operating service, and the dates when inspections are made and the required adjustments taken care of should be entered in the repair department's records.

It is likewise advisable to maintain a suitable stock of maintenance parts, especially of the parts that are most likely to need replacement, so that repairs can be promptly made and the trucks restored to service without any costly delays.

Hand Lift Trucks

APPLICABILITY OF HAND LIFT TRUCKS. Hydraulic and mechanically operated hand lift trucks are especially adaptable to handling operations where space is at a premium and it is necessary to operate within narrow aisles. The light weight of this equipment also makes it particularly suitable for use on floors of low capacity and on elevators. Improvements in the mechanical features of such trucks and in the design of wheels and bearings have made it possible for truck operators to handle much larger and heavier loads with less effort than formerly.

The lifting mechanism of a hand lift truck is operated by the actuation of a series of levers. With a hydraulic hand lift truck the lifting action is started mechanically by the operator, and is transmitted through the hydraulic system to levers that raise and lower the loads. For purposes of general grouping, hand lift trucks are usually classified as follows:

1. Trucks: Hand Lift, Hydraulic:
   a. Pallet, low-lift.
   b. Platform, low-lift.
   c. Special.
2. Trucks: Hand Lift, Mechanical:
   a. Pallet, low-lift.
   b. Platform, low-lift.
   c. Special.

ANALYZING TRUCK REQUIREMENTS. The selection of the right truck for particular needs is largely a matter of studying the pertinent factors that enter into a plant's handling operations. The proper combination of truck and skid platform or pallet for specific loads and operating conditions is necessary. Several other basic considerations must be taken into account to determine the type of lift truck best suited to specific requirements. Use Fig. 29 as a guide to the factors to be considered.

Size and Capacity of Truck. The size and capacity of the trucks to be used depend upon the loads to be carried—their length, width, height, weight, and shape. Work-flow conditions and locations of inclines, or ramps, loading docks, elevators, aisles, doorways, etc., also affect truck selection, and the size and

Name of Manufacturer					
		Technical Data			
1.	Rated capacity				
2.	Maximum lift				
3.	Lowered height				
4.	Number of strokes required				
5.	Lb. of effort required to lift load				
6.	Service weight				
7.	Over-all length				
8.	Over-all width				
9.	Size of front wheel or wheels				
10.	Type of wheel				
11.	Underclearance in lowered position				
12.	Type and size of bearings				
13.	Method of lifting				
	a. Handles (type)				
	b. Actuating lever				
	c. Foot pedal				
14.	Turning radius				
15.	Percent of grade				
16.	Wheel base				
17.	Safety features				
18. *(Straddle Trucks)*	a. Distance between outriggers				
	b. Width of outriggers				
	c. Height of outriggers				
	d. Length of outriggers				
	e. Number of wheels in outriggers				
	f. Size of outrigger wheels or casters				
	g. Type of fork or platform				
	h. Length of fork or platform				
	i. Width of fork or platform				
	j. Forks adjustable or fixed				
	k. Outriggers adjustable or fixed				
19. *(Pallet Trucks)*	a. Length of pallet arms				
	b. Width of pallet arms				
	c. Distance between pallet arms				
	d. Underclearance at center in lowered position				
	e. Size of wheel—single or double				
	f. Type of lead edge— (R) Roller or (S) Slide				
	g. Adaptable to platform truck				
20. *(Platform Trucks)*	a. Length of platform				
	b. Width of platform				
	c. Type of wheels				
	d. Size of wheels				
21.	F.O.B. Price				

Fig. 29. General specifications for hand lift trucks, hydraulic and mechanical.

capacity of trucks presently in service must likewise be taken into account when deciding on trucks to be used for a particular job.

Loads to be Handled. Two general factors must be considered in analyzing the loads which must be handled:

1. **Maximum weight of the loads to be moved.** The greatest weight to be handled in any one load will determine the capacity of the truck to be selected.

Sample loads should be actually weighed. Loads should be limited in weight so they are not excessively heavy for the particular trucks to handle. The truck that can handle the heaviest loads likely to be encountered should be selected.

2. **Maximum size of the load.** Load volume or size should be limited so that loaded trucks can be operated easily in aisles, in and out of elevators, through doorways, on loading docks, and elsewhere. For handling a variety of loads, skid-platform sizes should be selected that will accommodate any and all of the pallets in use, with a minimum of waste space.

TRUCK SELECTION. Assume that a truck is to be selected and used for certain handling operations. The following factors must be taken into account.

Truck Capacity. Loads carried by trucks should not exceed 90 percent of their **rated load-carrying capacity.** For easy lifting, a multiple-stroke truck should be used instead of a single-stroke truck. **Single-stroke trucks** are recommended for the lighter loads—3,000 lb. or less—and in cases where single-lift operation is desired for some particular reason. These single-stroke trucks are built with a compound lifting mechanism to provide the easiest possible elevation with one full stroke of the handle. The one-stroke lift is a little faster but is not so easy to operate.

Multiple-stroke trucks are recommended for all loads over 4,000 lb., and for easier lifting of loads under 4,000 lb. The multiple-stroke action, either mechanical or hydraulic, makes it much easier for the operator to elevate the load. Loads are lifted by making several short strokes with the truck handle.

Truck Width Compared to Width of Load. The load to be carried on a truck should not overhang the truck-frame more than 8-in. on each side. The best practice is to select the widest appropriate truck, thereby increasing the stability of the loads and permitting speedier handling. A good rule to follow, to obtain proper truck width, is to select a narrow model of truck for skid platforms up to 34 in. wide and a wide model of truck for skid platforms over 34 in. in width. On extremely wide loads, guide rails can be installed on the underside of the skid platform (Fig. 30) to insure proper centering of the truck.

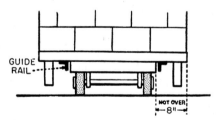

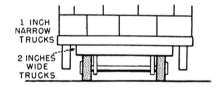

Fig. 30. Guide rails to position wider skid on standard lift truck.   Fig. 31. Side clearance of standard skid platform on standard lift truck.

Clearance between truck frame and skid platform legs should be at least 1 in. on narrow-model trucks and 2 in. or wide-model trucks (see Fig. 31). For load stability and better operation, the truck should be centered under the load.

Truck Length Compared to Length of Load. Through experience, certain relative dimensions have been set for length of loads vs. length of trucks. Where skid platforms are 48 in. or less in length, the truck frame should be 6 in. shorter. Where skid platforms are 54 in. long, or longer, truck frames 12 in. shorter are considered best (Fig. 32). Where extremely long skids are necessary, a greater overhang is permissible. However, when skids overhang the truck excessively, there is danger of the load's "hanging up" where ramp or floor levels change.

Truck frames should not extend beyond the length of the skids to be handled. If the truck frame is too long, skids cannot be spotted close to a wall or close to other loaded skids, and valuable storage space will be wasted. On the other hand, if the **skid overhangs the truck too much,** the load is likely to "lift" at the rear when traveling up or down inclines.

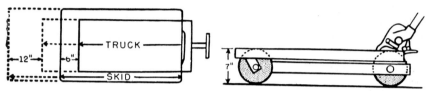

Fig. 32. Normal vs. extreme permissible lengths of loads on standard lift trucks.

Fig. 33. Standard height of lift truck platform.

Heights of Truck Platforms. The heights of truck platforms depend upon the wheel diameter of the trucks. For example, a truck with 7 in. wheels measures 7 in. from top of frame to floor; one with 11 in. wheels, 11 in. to the floor. The United States Department of Commerce recommends 7-in.- and 11-in.-high truck platforms (see Fig. 33).

Wheel Sizes. Trucks for handling heavy loads should have wheels of large diameter. Large wheels make for easier starting and easier rolling than small wheels, under heavy loads. Where floors are rough or uneven, it is especially advisable to use large wheels, so as to reduce the possibility of jarring boxes off pallets.

If power lift trucks are also to be used, the hand lift trucks employed should be of the standard 11-in.-high type. Any further additions to the system should be of the same size and type for the sake of uniformity, convenience in maintenance, and long service.

A clearance of ½ in. between the truck frame and the underside of the skid deck is recommended. On trucks with a higher lift, however, 1 in. clearance between the truck platform and the underside of the skid-deck provides a greater allowance for possible sagging of the skid boards under heavy loads.

Ground Clearance. Special attention must be given to problems that may arise when trucks are to be used on ramps, in and out of freight cars, on motor trucks, or on and off elevators. Trucks may "hang up," as shown in Fig. 34, through lack of proper ground clearance. If ramps, elevator entrances, or loading docks are likely to offer clearance difficulties, trucks with high lift or great ground clearance should be used. Note that while the hydraulic lift truck in

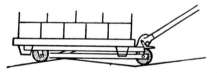

Fig. 34. Effects of insufficient clearance in truck movement over an uneven surface.

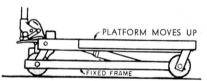

Fig. 35. Fixed-frame truck is hampered in moving over uneven surfaces.

Fig. 35 has a fixed frame and low ground clearance, the entire frame of the truck shown in Fig. 36 will move upward, thus giving better ground clearance.

Skid Platform Leg Clearance. The height of lift of skid-handling trucks is in definite relationship to the clearance between the bottom of the skid legs and the floor, after the skid has been picked up by the lift truck. Thus, a truck with a higher lift gives greater leg clearance, which is often a decided advantage when the truck is operating over rough or uneven floors. Multiple-stroke hand lift trucks provide higher lifts, and thus get skid legs higher above the floor.

Selecting Wheels to Suit Floors. Lift trucks are usually equipped with either semi-steel or forged steel wheels. Floor-protective wheels, however, are also available, including those made of rubber composition and of plastic materials. Rubber-tired wheels are resilient and protect floors from damage. They require more tractive effort per sq. in. of contact area than do metal wheels. They also reduce vibration in moving loads over rough floors. When of suitable size and capacity, rubber tires require a slightly higher starting effort than metal wheels, but roll over rough floors as easily.

CHECKING ON OPERATING CONDITIONS. Certain checks should be made to ascertain whether existing operating conditions are satisfactory. Among these checks are the following:

Check aisles over which trucks must operate. Unless aisles are sufficiently wide, some of the larger trucks and skids may not be usable in certain areas of the plant.

Check the floor and aisle layout. In some areas, narrow passageways or short turns may prevent trucks from traversing certain aisles or departments, as in Fig. 37.

Check door openings. Doorways between departments and entrances to elevators may be so narrow that loaded hand lift trucks cannot pass through.

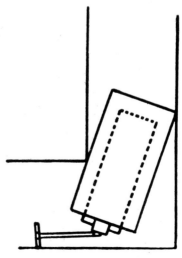

Fig. 36. Entire frame of truck will rise, giving ample ground clearance.　　Fig. 37. Narrow aisles may prevent turns.

The narrowest points on the routes over which the trucks travel determine the widths of the skids that can be used in these areas.

Hydraulic Hand Lift Trucks

LIFT MECHANISM OF HYDRAULIC TRUCKS. Hydraulically operated hand lift trucks have a greater mechanical advantage than ordinary mechanical lift trucks. They operate on the principle of the simple lever, and require less effort to lift the load. The longer the operating arm, the less the

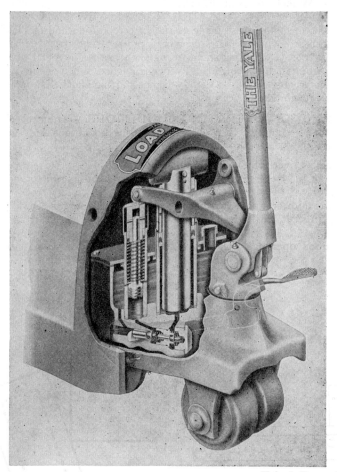

Yale & Towne Mfg. Co.

Fig. 38. Hydraulic mechanism of a hydraulic hand lift truck.

effort required. Such lifts are of two types: the **foot-operated** and the hand-operated. In both, the lifting mechanism is actuated by moving the handle arm up and down like a pump handle for a well. The **hand-operated type** requires less effort because of the greater leverage. With the hydraulic hand lift truck, both the lowering and the lifting are done with the same pump unit. Where unstable loads are being handled, or where a truck is being used in a multistory building with low-capacity floors, the lowering valve should be controllable so that lowering speed can be regulated.

Simplification of mechanism and ease of removing the operating unit are important factors. Handles should be balanced so as to prevent them from falling over, causing injury to the operator. The grip and design of the handle should be such that it is comfortable in the hands. Trucks should have a minimum underclearance of 2 in.; otherwise there is a tendency for the wheels to be raised off the ground while the truck is going up ramps or dock boards. **Steel wheels**

Barrett Cravens Co.

Fig. 39. **Hydraulic hand lift platform truck, showing levers which raise the platform.**

with ball bearings are usually the best. Where light loads are being used, tapered bearings are suitable. These trucks are usually designed in capacities ranging from 1,000 lb. to 20,000 lb. The single-stroke lift truck is used for light loads, and the multiple-stroke truck for heavier loads. Fig. 38 shows the hydraulic mechanism of a hydraulic hand lift truck, showing the oil reservoirs, the pump mechanisms, and the lowering and release valve. Fig. 39 illustrates the lever system for raising the platform.

LOW-LIFT PALLET TRUCKS. Fig. 40 shows a completely hand-operated lift truck, on which the load is raised, and which is pulled, by hand power, the truck frame being arranged so that it can enter between the top and bottom boards of a pallet. The rear wheels are lowered through 8-in.-minimum openings between the boards in the bottom of the pallet for raising the pallet and load from the floor for transportation.

These trucks are constructed with large forward wheels connected to a steering handle attached to the main frame, and connected through a linkage or hydraulic system to the rear wheels, which are generally depressed in the main frame. At the end of the main frame, near the back, additional small wheels or slides are mounted in the frame, which assist the operator in propelling the forks into the pallet. The pallets have openings in the bottom deck, both front and rear, so that the truck can enter from either end. After the truck has been run into the pallet, the lifting mechanism is operated and the small wheels in the rear of the truck are lowered through the pallet openings sufficiently to raise the pallet 2 or 3 in. above the floor, for transportation.

Fig. 40. Hand-operated low-lift pallet truck with hand-operated pump.

Applications of Low-Lift Trucks. The hand pallet truck is used in conjunction with pallets constructed with bottom openings. The objective of the hand pallet truck system is to reduce the number of handlings. By having the materials loaded on pallets, a change of location or handling between operations may be quickly accomplished. The hand pallet truck is for **horizontal movements only** and is not suitable for stacking. It works well in conjunction with power-elevating fork trucks. It can be used where power trucks cannot be operated, such as in packing rooms, at freight terminals, or for the movement of palleted loads in boxcars, onto trailers, etc.; also where aisle space or floor load is limited. The small rear wheels limit its use to short hauls (50 to 75 ft.).

It has been widely accepted throughout industry that standard truck models be 27 in. wide and that the length should be equal to the length of pallet. The trucks are designed for loads up to 60 in. long. Load capacities range from 1,000 lb. to 6,000 lb., with a 4 in. lift to provide greater underclearance.

Pallets designed for use with these trucks should have 8-in.-minimum openings on the bottom side, with 6-in. chamfered end boards and center boards for easy truck entry.

The toggle-booster wheel system shown in Fig. 41 is typical of the arrangements used to facilitate insertion of the truck into the pallet. As the truck is inserted in the pallet, Roll 2 strikes the edge of the end board, causing Roll 1 to engage with the face of the end board. The inertia of the truck causes Roll 1 to raise the truck's rear wheels (4) from the floor as shown in part B of Fig. 41. The helper roll (3) and the rear wheel (4) are now in position to roll through the pallet, placing the truck in lifting position. The pallet should be positioned on the pallet truck so that the edge of the pallet rides against the inside end of the left platform. Forks are inserted immediately underneath the deck with the pallet in elevated position and the rear wheels of the truck dropped through the space between the lower deck boards, contacting the floor surface.

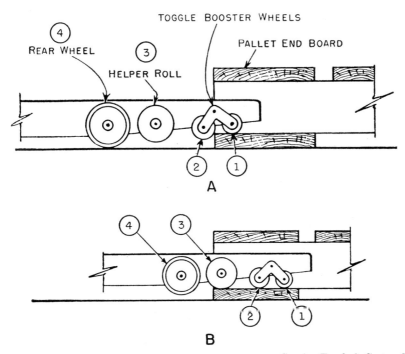

Service Truck & Caster Co.

Fig. 41. Toggle-booster wheel system used on pallet lift trucks.

Hand Low-Lift Platform Trucks. Trucks of this kind are constructed with the forward wheels connected to a steering handle attached to the main frame. The rear wheels are attached to the same frame, which is fastened to the platform or platform frame by means of link arms which are actuated up and down by the hydraulic system. The trucks are generally used with skids. Platforms may be solid, or open as in Fig. 39.

Standard trucks of this kind have **capacities** of from 1,000 to 6,000 lb., widths of 18 to 27 in., lengths of 30 to 72 in. in 6 in. increments, and lift heights of 6 in., 7 in., 9 in., and 11 in. They have either wood or steel platforms, depending on the use to which they will be put. Special trucks are built in capacities up to 20,000 lb. and with platforms wider and longer than standard.

Special Types. In plants where large quantities of specialized shapes are handled, it may be practical to modify the design of the hand lift truck. A unique design for handling reels is shown in Fig. 42.

Yale & Towne Mfg. Co.

Fig. 42. Special hand-operated hydraulic lift truck for handling reels.

Mechanical Hand Lift Trucks

MECHANICAL LIFT MECHANISM. Mechanically operated hand lift trucks are similar in design to hydraulic hand lift trucks, but are operated by a system of **levers** rather than by hydraulic cylinders. The action of this kind of truck is comparable to that of an automobile hand jack. The platform is raised by actuating a handle which, in turn, raises a pawl that falls into a slot or groove. Lowering is accomplished by releasing the pawl. There are many modifications of this mechanism. In a single-stroke, low-lift unit, a latch on the tow handle engages a lifting lever which is coupled to the platform. The platform is secured

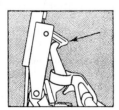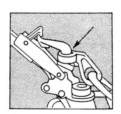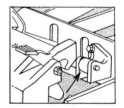

Barrett Cravens Co.

Fig. 43. One-stroke lever-type lift mechanism.

in raised position by another latch which is released for lowering. The tow handle may be equipped with a spring that relieves the operator of the handle weight and which keeps the handle off the floor when the unit is not in use. Fig. 43 shows certain features of this single-stroke lever-type mechanism.

Mechanical hand lift trucks are used where relatively light loads are to be handled, where low initial cost is an important factor, and where frequency of use is not a problem. They do, however, require more effort than the multiple-stroke type truck to operate.

MULTIPLE-STROKE-TYPE TRUCK. Illustrated in Fig. 44 is a 2,000-lb.-capacity multiple-stroke pallet lift truck. It lifts 4 in. and requires five strokes for raising. This truck can be operated with double-faced pallets having a 3⅝-in.

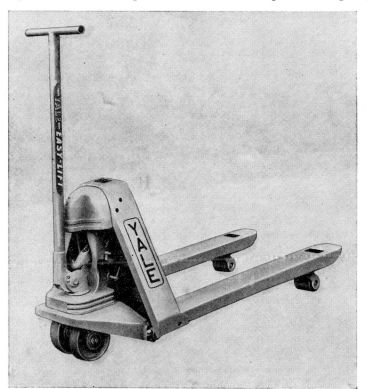

Yale & Towne Mfg. Co.

Fig. 44. Multiple-stroke pallet lift truck, 2,000-lb. capacity, mechanically operated.

minimum opening for truck entry. Rear wheels are 3 in. diameter by 5 in. face and are available in steel, rubber, aluminum, and plastic. These trucks usually weigh in the vicinity of 300 lb. each.

INDUSTRIAL TRACTORS

CONTENTS

INDUSTRIAL TRACTORS

—

General Considerations

DEFINITION. Tractors are divided into several categories, many groups, and many types. However, before going into a detailed discussion of this equipment, the term "tractor" should first be defined in its entirety. The term has been erroneously applied to almost any type of industrial vehicle which runs on wheels or crawlers and has its own source of motive power, be it of the burden-bearing, cantilever, or prime-mover type of equipment. This misnomer is particularly prevalent in certain heavy industries and has caused considerable consternation not only to the equipment manufacturers but to sales and application engineers as well.

The term "tractor" is used in the industrial field today to describe a vehicle with its own source of motive power used as a **prime mover** to supply locomotion to other, or groups of other, vehicles which do not have their own source of motive power, such as **trailers, semitrailers, transfer cars,** etc. This also applies in the earth-moving field to such equipment as scrapers, rakes, and drop-bottom earth-hauling equipment, and other types of vehicles used in this particular industry.

Tractor vs. Locomotive. The term "tractor" should not be confused with the term "locomotive" which, today, applies to equipment used as a prime mover to supply locomotion to railroad cars or any other type of rail cars. A locomotive rolls only on flanged wheels running on tracks or rails. The course or direction of travel of the locomotive can only be controlled by the track on which it runs, or by switches on the track. The tractor has steerable wheels, or crawler tracks, which can, at the driver's discretion, be caused to follow any course of travel; at the same time the tractor can perform most of the locomotive's duties of pushing or pulling railroad cars, transfer cars, or any other vehicle mounted on flanged rail type wheels, provided that the area between the rails is paved and not of open-tie construction. This does not necessitate concrete paving; wood block or macadam will suffice for the average wheel type tractor.

While tractors can be used to move rail cars they cannot successfully perform all the duties of the locomotive. The comparison above is specifically limited to intraplant or interplant operation when in adjacent areas, and it definitely does not apply to points between distant cities or interplant operations where plants are not located on adjoining properties.

TRACTOR APPLICATIONS. The **tractor-trailer** method of materials handling is possibly one of the oldest methods of transportation in history. The ox-drawn cart, the horse-drawn stone boat, the horse- or mule-drawn farm wagon or sleigh were all units of transportation without their own medium of propulsion, using oxen, mules, or horses as prime movers. Less than 30 years ago one of our nationally known manufacturing plants still handled castings from foundry to machine shop on a horse-drawn cart. In the mining industry, the mule-drawn mine cars were recent predecessors of the mine locomotive and mechanized mining equipment.

The **tractor trailer system** does not always involve a trailer train with several trailers for the movement of large quantities of material over long distances. In many instances a tractor and one trailer, or similar vehicle, perform important phases of materials handling, in a given area, not only by pulling but also by pushing the load; an example of this is large die trailers which have capacities ranging up to 80 tons. These are not only pulled to locations but also pushed into position for loading and unloading operations, yet still operate in a relatively confined area.

While the tractor is primarily considered a prime mover, with an attachment added it becomes a very versatile tool. For example, put a **rotary broom** either on the front or the back of it and it will sweep the sidewalks or roadways; with an **angle blade** mounted in front, it is an efficient snowplow; equipped with a **back hoe** attachment, it can be used in excavating or trenching. There are an unlimited number of such devices. Because of its flexibility, the tractor has wide possibilities in materials handling applications.

TRACTOR CATEGORIES. Tractors are generally grouped into five categories, namely: industrial, construction (earth moving and coal stripping), agricultural, highway (over the road hauling), and military.

Industrial Tractors. The industrial tractor is usually of the **wheel type** and is used primarily for the movement of one or more trailers in various capacities in interplant or intraplant transportation systems. There are many instances, however, where **crawler type** tractors are used—mostly in outdoor and yard service where terrain is rough and paved roadways are not always available. In fact, they perform the same duties as the wheel type but usually not on such long hauls or at such high speeds.

Construction Tractors. The construction type tractor is principally used in heavy construction industries for **earth-moving** purposes where a great number of different types of attachments are used with it. To mention a few, there are scrapers, angle blades, dozer plates, rippers, rakes, shovels, back hoes, etc. These tractors are put to many haulage uses including the movement of heavy machinery to and from locations. They are also used as a prime mover for heavy burden-bearing drop-bottom type trailers which transport earth and other building materials in large volumes. At one time the **crawler type** tractor was almost the only type of equipment used in this industry; however, in recent years the **wheel type** tractor has made its appearance in this field, especially since the development of the mammoth size pneumatic tires with traction type treads. Both the crawler and wheel type construction tractors are used very extensively in the lumber industry, mainly in logging operations. Their duties are many but the most important of them are to drag logs out of the woods to shipping locations and to load logs onto the railroad cars. Most tractors used in the logging industry are equipped with **cable winches** which help to make them most versatile pieces of equipment. Another industry in which the construction type tractor is extensively used is strip-mining operations, where it performs practically the same duties as in construction and earth moving and where it gains versatility through the use of many different kinds of attachments.

Agricultural Tractors. The agricultural tractor is possibly one of the oldest types of tractor. Early models had wood-burning steam-power traction engines with the large-diameter herringbone cleated drive wheels. Steam power has been replaced almost completely by internal combustion gasoline engines. One of the early gasoline-powered farm tractors to be manufactured on the production line made its appearance shortly before World War I and was known as the "Fordson" tractor. Today the tractor is used very extensively in the agricultural industry for every possible haulage operation. It is used for plowing, planting, cultivating, and in harvesting and hauling the crops to storage. There are numerous attachments which can be applied to this tractor, such as air compressors, grass- and brush-cutting attachments, winches, rakes, snowplows, etc.

Highway Tractors. The highway tractor is basically a heavy motor truck with body removed and an articulating turntable mounted in its place and it is used in conjunction with semitrailers. (See section on highway motor vehicles.)

Military Tractors. Military tractors are generally found to be both wheel and crawler type or a combination of both known as **half-track.** There is little basic difference between the military and the modern construction and industrial tractors. Military tractors range in size from the small tractor which is used for transportation systems in supply depots to the mammoth crawler which is used for the movement of munition, guns, and other military supplies.

NOMENCLATURE. There are many different features of tractors that distinguish one from another. However, for purposes of identifying the types hereafter mentioned, it is only necessary to describe the following basic characteristics: wheel drive, crawler drive, single-wheel drive, two-wheel drive, four-wheel drive, all-wheel drive, front-wheel steer, rear-wheel steer, four-wheel steer, walkie, sit-down, stand-up, and rider type. These terms refer to the basic characteristics of the equipment. Any proper combination of them will give a thumbnail description of any type of tractor (e.g., rider type, sit-down, four-wheel drive, front-wheel steer).

Tractor Types

CLASSIFICATIONS. Tractors may be classified into the following four classifications: small, medium, large, and extra large. The first three are usually used in agricultural, industrial, and construction service, while the extra large are mostly used in construction and military service only. There are instances, however, where the extra large tractors are used in the industrial field, but only under extreme conditions. The size of a tractor is usually determined by the **draw-bar pull rating:** small tractors range from 200 lb. normal to 1,000 lb. maximum DBP; medium-size tractors range from 500 lb. normal to 3,500 lb. maximum; large tractors range from 3,000 lb. normal to 10,000 lb. maximum; and extra large tractors will range up to 60,000 lb. or 70,000 lb., depending upon their total weight and horsepower.

There is actually no fixed rule whereby any tractor can be classified by physical dimensions, weight, horsepower, and draw-bar pull. These factors do not always have a definite relationship because each factor has its own definite value insofar as total **tractive effort** is concerned. For instance, a heavy tractor with a low horsepower engine cannot achieve tractive effort in direct relation to its weight because it cannot develop sufficient torque even though its weight provides sufficient traction. On the other hand, a lightweight tractor with an abundance of power and large physical dimensions cannot be classified as a large tractor because it cannot develop sufficient tractive effort, due to its light weight and insufficient traction. Therefore, when the proper ratio of horsepower versus weight is put into a tractor, regardless of physical size, then and only then can

Automatic Transportation Co.   Lift-Trucks, Inc.
Single front-wheel drive   Dual front-wheel drive

Fig. 1. Electric walkie tractors.

HORSEPOWER REQUIRED AT 100 PERCENT EFFICIENCY AND 50 LB. PER TON DRAW-BAR PULL
(LEVEL FLOORS—SMOOTH CONCRETE)

Total Load in lb.	1 m.p.h.	2 m.p.h.	2.5 m.p.h.	3 m.p.h.	3.5 m.p.h.	4 m.p.h.
2,000	0.133	0.267	0.333	0.400	0.467	0.533
3,000	0.200	0.400	0.500	0.600	0.700	0.800
4,000	0.267	0.533	0.667	0.800	0.934	1.066
5,000	0.333	0.667	0.833	1.000	1.167	1.333
6,000	0.400	0.800	1.000	1.200	1.400	1.600
7,000	0.467	0.934	1.167	1.400	1.667	1.867
8,000	0.533	1.066	1.333	1.600	1.867	2.133
9,000	0.600	1.200	1.500	1.800	2.100	2.400
10,000	0.667	1.333	1.667	2.000	2.333	2.667
12,000	0.800	1.600	2.000	2.400	2.800	3.200
14,000	0.934	1.867	2.333	2.800	3.266	3.733
16,000	1.066	2.133	2.667	3.200	3.733	4.270

1 hp. = 33,000 ft. lb. per min.
1 m.p.h. = 88 ft. per min.
Hp. (required) = Load (in tons) × m.p.h. × .133
Draw-bar pull = 50 lb. per ton (calculated on total load)
Approximate transmission efficiency at 3 m.p.h. = 80% (rated loading 3 hp.)
Drive wheels 10 in. diameter circle 31 in. or 2.58 ft.
Gear ratio = 20:1

Fig. 2. Horsepower requirement table.

it be properly classified, providing it has been equipped with **running gear** of size and capacity consistent with good engineering practice.

SMALL WALKIE TRACTOR. Fig. 1 illustrates the small walkie type of industrial tractor. These tractors are of the **three point suspension** type and are equipped with solid rubber tires throughout. A tee handle provides the medium

Barrett-Cravens, Inc.

Fig. 3. Remote controlled walkie tractor with trailers.

for steer and includes the push-button control for forward and reverse operation. The **tractive effort** varies and is in direct relation to the gross weight and horsepower of the drive motor. Manufacturers rate them from 200 lb. to 800 lb. DBP in their specifications. These small tractors can be equipped with various types of **couplers,** such as a pintle hook, drop pin, or full automatic self-latching coupler. They are available in single front-wheel and dual front-wheel drive, as illustrated. The **driving mechanism** usually consists of an electric motor transmitting power through a straight spur gear reduction train or a combination of gears and roller chain and sprocket. Another type of drive used in these tractors is a worm and wheel with differential gearing totally enclosed in a gear housing. The **braking system** usually consists of either a manually operated shoe type

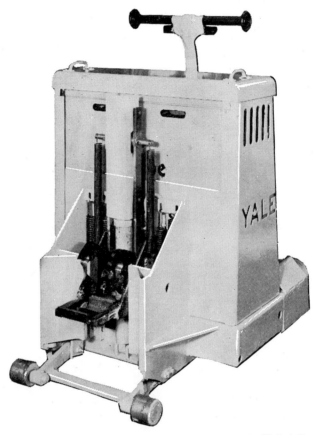

Yale & Towne Mfg. Co.

Fig. 4. Electric grip-tow tractor.

brake or an electrodynamic brake operated by push button from the steering handle. While most of these units are storage battery operated, they are available with gasoline-electric power unit. These small walkie tractors vary in weight depending upon the size of the battery being used, the average being between 1,700 lb. and 2,000 lb. gross. Fig. 2 shows the **horsepower requirements** for certain loads in direct relation to speed desired. These values are based on 100 percent efficiency of motor and transmission. In making calculations they should be corrected to the efficiency factor of the equipment being considered, which in most cases is approximately 80 percent.

Applications of Small Walkie Tractors. Fig. 3 illustrates an order-picking operation in a wholesale grocery warehouse. This tractor is **electronically controlled**. By means of a small **radio transmitter** fastened to his belt, the operator directs the tractor over any course. Guiding rails (either overhead wires or metal strips embedded in the floor) are not essential as long as the operator can maintain control through proper judgment.

Fig. 4 illustrates a tractor with a special towing attachment which will elevate 4 to 5 in. These are usually used in conjunction with **semilive skids**. The towing attachment engages a pin or in this case a bracket on the skid and lifts the skid legs from the floor, after which it is free to travel or maneuver into any position. The lifting mechanism is usually actuated by a hydraulic system. These tractors vary little from the standard walkies described in connection with Fig. 1, except that they usually have smaller trail wheels to provide clearance for low skids. Because of the exceptionally small diameter of these trail wheels they are usually made of plastic or steel to provide sufficient load-carrying capacity.

COMBINATION WALKIE RIDER TRACTORS. Fig. 5 illustrates the small stand-up rider-type walkie. These tractors differ from the walkie only in

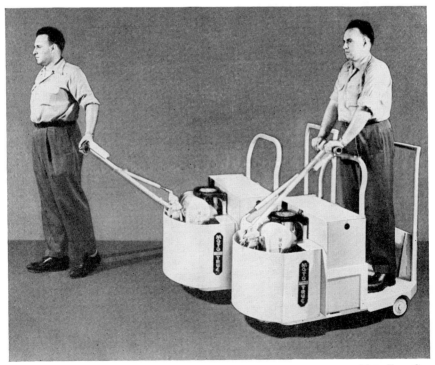

Moto-Truc Co.

Fig. 5. Walkie tractor with walk or ride control.

that an operator station has been added together with a back rest for safety and comfort. This type of small tractor is useful in operations where moderately long hauls are necessary.

SMALL RIDER-TYPE TRACTOR. Representative models of this class of tractor are shown in Fig. 6. Both sit-down and stand-up types are available. They may be equipped with the usual hook-on couplings, automatic couplings, or with special couplings for handling semilive skids as shown on the electric **stand-up model.**

The other stand-up tractor shown is powered by an air-cooled gasoline engine. It drives and steers by the front wheel which is built into the **turret type engine housing.** Steering is done by turning the turret, which rotates 360°.

Hyster Co.
Stand-up control gasoline tractor with turret

American Pulley Co.
Electric tractor with sit-down control—750 lb.

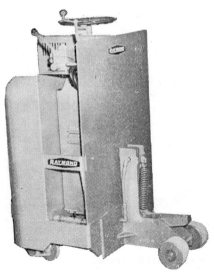

The Raymond Corp.
Electric stand-up tractor with coupling for semilive skid platforms—200 lb.

Automatic Transportation Co.
Three-wheel electric tractor with sit-down control

Fig. 6. Small rider-type tractors.

International Harvester Co.
Diesel farm tractor with hydraulically controlled draw bar

Clark Equipment Co.
Rear-control gasoline tractor—4,600 lb.

Elwell-Parker Electric Co.
Rear-control electric tractor

Towmotor Transportation Co.
Front-control gasoline tractor

Mercury Mfg. Co.
Front-control electric tractor—DBP
2,500 lb.

Fig. 7. Medium sit-down control tractors.

The turret principle, integrating the engine with the drive and steer wheel, is also used in connection with a steering wheel mounted vertically on a fixed bracket. One such tractor with sit-down rider control is rated with DBP up to 500 lb. Both **sit-down** rider tractors shown in Fig. 6 are electric storage battery driven. Both are rear-wheel drive and front-wheel steer. Steering control is accomplished through a horizontal lever in one case and a hand wheel in the other. These tractors also are of somewhat heavier construction and naturally will handle heavier loads.

Medium Duty Sit-Down Tractors. Fig. 7 shows some typical tractors of this class. All are four-wheel units with rear-wheel drive and front-wheel steer controlled by an automotive type hand wheel. All are mounted with solid, cushioned, or pneumatic tires. Locating the driver's seat at the forward end of the tractor provides excellent visibility and is particularly useful in indoor applications. Location of the seat in the rear of the tractor gives the driver visual control over coupling and uncoupling maneuvers. Some units, primarily for outdoor service, may be equipped with totally enclosed cabs for all-weather operations.

The **agricultural tractor,** here (Fig. 7) equipped with dual wheels for easier steering on rough terrain, is also capable of a wide range of industrial jobs. Wide front axle attachments are also available. Models represented are gasoline diesel or battery powered.

HEAVY-DUTY WHEELED TRACTORS. Fig. 8 shows various types of heavy duty industrial and construction type tractors. Those having four-wheel drive and four-wheel power steer may have all wheels of equal size as shown. The outsize pneumatic **traction cleat tires** permit outdoor operation over rough terrain.

The tractor shown is for shifting railroad cars and is equipped with an air brake system and railroad type car couplers on each side thus enabling it to straddle either rail to pull or shift a car from either end. Heavy duty four-wheel drive pneumatic-tired industrial tractors are used in heavy industry such as steel mills for moving of heavy-laden transfer cars and for hauling trailers with exceptionally heavy loads. These tractors are of exceptionally rugged design and will develop tremendous DBP.

The heavy duty **wheel type construction** tractor with load carrier is used mostly for **earth moving, grading,** and **excavating purposes** although its industrial application in **bulk handling** is increasing. The drive wheels in the rear carry part of the load to provide additional traction. The steer wheels in front are controlled by an automotive type wheel.

The "Sno-Buggy," designed for use in deep snow and over soft terrain, is supported on eight pneumatic tires which are approximately 10 ft. in diameter. It is powered with a 400 hp. diesel engine and electric generator with electric motor drive to all four wheels. All controls are located in the operator's cab where he steers by means of power control to all four dual wheels. This unit weighs approximately 23 tons.

CRAWLER TRACTORS. Fig. 9 illustrates basic types of crawler tractors. The small industrial tractor is available in various widths and clearances. This type of unit is used in both industrial and construction service. It is powered with a 20 hp. engine and will develop approximately 3,900 lb. DBP. A typical **medium duty** crawler tractor commonly used for both industrial and construction service is powered with a 40 hp. four-cycle diesel engine, is equipped with a selective gear transmission providing five speeds forward and one reverse, and will develop about 8,000 lb. DBP.

Frank G. Hough Co.

Tractor equipped with cab and couplers for moving railroad cars

Caterpillar

Rear drive front steer diesel tractor with load carrier

R. G. Le Tourneau, Inc.

Four-hundred horsepower Sno-buggy load carrier and tractor

Fig. 8. Four-wheeled heavy duty tractors.

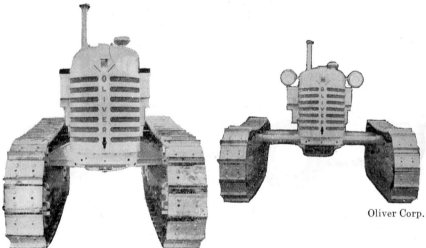

Oliver Corp.

Light tractors in three track widths

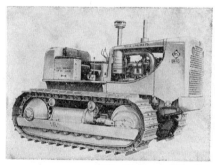

Allis-Chalmers Mfg. Co.   Euclid Div., General Motors Corp.
Diesel-powered crawler tractor with   Twin-engine heavy-duty tractor—365 hp.,
torque converter drive—204 hp.   54,000 lb.

Fig. 9. Industrial and construction crawler tractors.

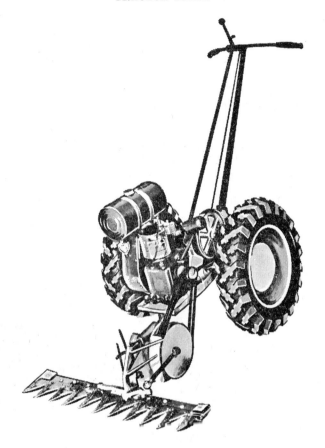

Eshelman

Two-wheeled walkie tractor with mower bar attachment

LeTourneau-Westinghouse

275-hp. two-wheeled tractor coupled to 35-ton load-carrying scraper

Fig. 10. Two-wheeled tractors.

The **heavy duty** tractors shown are also used in both industrial and construction applications. One unit is equipped with a 204 horsepower diesel engine and a hydraulic torque converter type transmission, and is rated at approximately 44,000 lb. DBP. The other is unique in that it is powered with twin diesel, two-cycle engines, which provide it with a total of 360 hp. Manufacturers' specifications rate it 54,000 lb. DBP.

TWO-WHEELED TRACTORS. Tractors of this type rely on the working attachment or load carrier for balance. They vary in size from the 1½ to 3 hp. walkie weighing 180 lb. to the 275 hp.–61,000 lb. unit shown in Fig. 10. As the two drive wheels are the only wheels, **steering** is accomplished by pivoting the unit around one wheel or the other. This is done manually in small walkie models and by varying the speed of the wheels in large power steer units. Because of the extremely small turning radius these tractors have high **maneuverability.** For example, the large unit illustrated has a minimum turning radius of 18 ft.

ATTACHMENTS. Fig. 11 illustrates some of the attachments commonly used on tractors. These illustrations cover but a few of the many attachments available for all types of tractors. Others include the crane booms and lifting forks described in other sections of this handbook, mower bars and other agricultural equipment, snowplow and bulldozer blades, and rollers and rotary brooms.

Oliver Corp.
Rear-mounted winch

LeTourneau-Westinghouse
Bulldozer and root rake

Oliver Corp.
Scoop loader

LeTourneau-Westinghouse
Bulldozer and logging winch

Fig. 11. Tractor attachments.

Equipment Selection

ANALYSIS OF THE SYSTEM. The most common error made in the application of the tractor and trailer system is the lack of a complete study of the problems involved. When all phases and conditions are not thoroughly analyzed and resolved, the ensuing result is an installation with overloaded equipment and high maintenance costs, or slow, inefficient operation. The fact that there are X tons to be moved from point A to point B is not enough. Why is a tractor trailer system being considered? Why not a cantilever or burden-bearing platform truck, or an overhead crane, monorail or conveyor system? These are all questions which must be explored before a definite decision as to a system best suited for the operation can be made. Tractor trailer systems have been a controversial subject for many years. Where does the fork or platform truck leave off and the tractor trailer begin? A thorough analysis should consider the following questions:

1. Is there enough material to be moved to necessitate large volume handling?
2. Will routing be such as to afford an efficient mode of dispatching?
3. Are hauls long enough to effect economies with this type of system?

Economic Distance. Generally speaking and on the basis of factual information from many industries, the **minimum distance** for tractor trailer haulage is from 150 to 200 ft. There is virtually no limit to the total length of haul as long as an efficient method of routing and dispatching has been developed and a sufficient amount of equipment supplied to complete the duty cycle. This is also true in the application of **construction and earth-moving tractors.** These were formerly in a field by themselves but in recent years a definite transition has taken place, interweaving the two types of equipment into one and the same pattern, predominantly from the construction into the industrial field. It is not an uncommon sight to see a construction type tractor in a large industrial plant hauling large heavy trailer loads over unimproved roadways or even performing hitherto unheard of duties. These tractors are of massive dimensions when compared to the usual industrial type and may be equipped with either pneumatic or crawler type running gear. When considering a piece of equipment of this type, the same basic factors must be taken into account as with the industrial type. This unit is extensively used in industry when equipped with a drag type scraper for **moving bulk materials** such as coal, building and construction materials, and iron ore.

Size and Capacity. Once having decided that the tractor trailer system is to be used, a further study must be made of the factors relative to the size, type, and capacity of a tractor suitable for the intended operation. The following is a list of factors which should be studied:

1. Size and type of material to be handled.
2. Length of haul (round trip).
3. Number of trailers efficiently and safely handled in one train.
4. Type and condition of roadways.
5. Indoor or outdoor operation, or both.
6. Width of aisles and intersecting aisles.
7. Grades, length, and percentage of grade and surfaces.
8. Clearances all along roadway.
9. Variations in kinds of roadway surfacing.

10. Turning radius of tractor trailer train.
11. Capacity of trailers in net weight.
12. Friction or antifriction bearing on trailers.
13. Caster or fifth-wheel type steer on trailers.
14. Quick hitch or pin type couplers.
15. Wood or steel deck construction.
16. Flat bed or stake type trailers.
17. Physical dimensions of trailer, i.e., length, width, and height.
18. Rubber-tired or steel-wheel trailer.
19. Double fifth-wheel with reversible draw bars.
20. Four-wheel steer trailers.
21. Tire rating in load capacity for maximum speed.
22. Duty cycle, number of tons to be moved in a given time.
23. Total number of trailers necesssary to complete cycle.
24. Door clearances.
25. Railroad crossings.
26. Use in conjunction with transfer cars.
27. Height of couplers (both tractors and trailers).
28. Type of couplers (general specifications).
29. Load capacity and clearances.
30. Floor loadings per sq. ft.
31. Used in inflammable or explosive areas.
32. Ventilated or nonventilated areas.
33. Safety factors used in conjunction with hot materials (acids, alkalis, explosives).
34. Head room.
35. Elevator capacity.
36. Engineering factors necessary to determine size and type of tractor suitable for intended operation. (See later subsection on engineering factors.)

MOTIVE POWER. Motive power, in tractor terminology, refers to the electrical or mechanical source of horsepower which is required to propel the equipment. There are seven different types of motive power units commonly used in modern tractors: straight gasoline, straight diesel, gasoline or diesel electric, gas engines (LP gas), gas electric (LP gas), and straight electric (storage battery power). These power sources have been treated in some detail in the section on powered industrial trucks.

POWER TRANSMISSION. The conventional **dry disc clutch** and **sliding gear transmission** are the most commonly used in the average medium size tractor. This type of transmission is available in various ratio combinations and will range as high as five or more speeds forward and two or more speeds reverse. In recent years the **fluid drive** type of clutch has come into existence and is extensively used in power transmission. This type of drive eliminates the direct connection with the engine necessary with the conventional clutch. It transmits its power hydraulically through the medium of the two sirroco-type fans totally submerged in a bath of hydraulic fluid. As one fan rotates a hydraulic pressure is developed causing the other to rotate in the same direction and thus transmitting torque to a selective gear transmission. A very recent type of transmission is the **hydraulic torque converter.** This unit embodies all the features of the fluid drive and the selective gear transmission in one unit, performs all its functions automatically, and has practically eliminated the high repair costs so commonly associated with clutch and transmission maintenance for many years. As a rule, the **electric motor-driven tractor** does not use a selective gear transmission or clutch. The torque is transmitted directly to the drive axle gearing from the armature shaft of the motor. Under special conditions electric tractors have

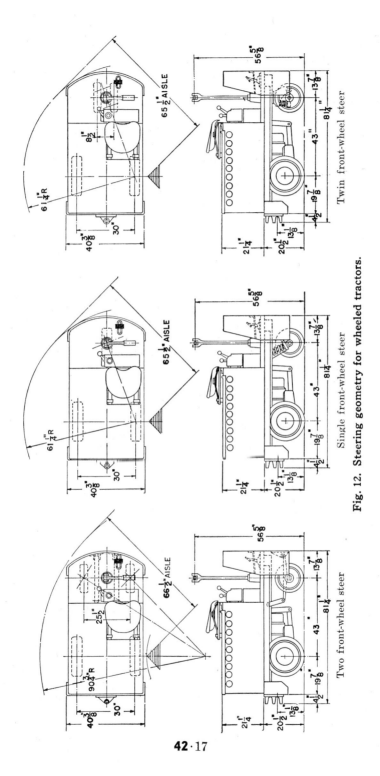

Fig. 12. Steering geometry for wheeled tractors.

Twin front-wheel steer

Single front-wheel steer

Two front-wheel steer

42·17

been supplied with two-speed selective gear transmissions between the motor and the drive axle gearing. This provides additional torque when negotiating exceptionally steep grades where speed is no factor. It is possible to deliver twice the amount of torque in pounds at one half the speed without increasing the available horsepower.

STEERING AND MANEUVERABILITY FACTORS. When selecting a tractor, it is important to be sure that the steering geometry affords a maximum flexibility. There are eight different **types of steer** available on tractors of modern design which are as follows:

1. Two front-wheel steer.
2. Two rear-wheel steer.
3. Single front-wheel steer.
4. Single rear-wheel steer.
5. Twin front-wheel steer.
6. Twin rear-wheel steer.
7. Four-wheel steer.
8. Crawler steer.

Wheel-Type Tractors. Each type of steer has some advantages over the other in so far as turning radii and intersecting aisles are concerned. While over-all length, width, and wheel base have a definite bearing on these factors, the location of the steered wheels is also important. Figs. 12, 13, and 14 show the various **turning radii, intersecting aisles** and **pivot points** of the various types of tractor. The **single front-wheel steer** tractor in Fig. 12 has a turning radius of 61¼ in., requires an intersecting aisle of 65½ in., and the pivot point directly on

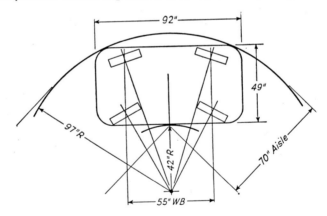

Fig. 13. Steering geometry for four-wheel drive, four-wheel steer.

a center point of the rear wheel closest to the inner turning radius. The same tractor with a **two front-wheel steer** has a turning radius of 90¾ in., and requires an intersecting aisle of 66½ in. The actual pivot point is approximately 30 in. below the inner turning radius circle. It should be noted that the pivot point in both instances is in a direct line with the center line of the drive axle. Note that the **two front steering wheels** pivot on steering knuckles while the **single and twin steering wheels** pivot on a caster fork with little or no lead. It should also be noted that the wheel base, over-all length, and over-all width of tractors illustrated are identical. Fig. 13 illustrates the steering geometry of a

four-wheel steer tractor. In comparing the two front-wheel steer and the four-wheel steer types shown, it will be seen that there is considerable difference in the over-all physical dimensions but not such a great difference in the turning radius and intersecting aisles. Actually, the tractor in Fig. 13 has a 12 in. greater wheel base and is 9 in. wider; however, it requires only a 6¼ in. greater turning radius and only a 3½ in. wider aisle. Fig. 12 shows **front-wheel steer tractors** in which

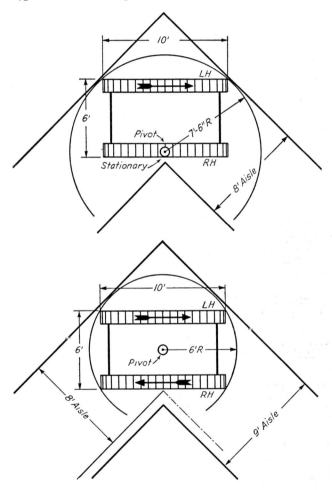

Fig. 14. Crawler tread steering geometry.

the driver faces the steering wheels. If the driver faces in the opposite direction, the tractor is termed a **rear-wheel steer.** Whether rear- or front-wheel steer, the steering geometry remains the same. The rear-wheel steer tractor has a tendency to cause the trailer train to weave because an immediate steering force is applied to the first trailer with every change of course of the tractor's steered wheels. This is not too important, except that it tends to make steering a little harder in manually steered units.

These maneuverability factors and values also hold true in the case of the small **walkie type tractors.**

Crawler-Type Tractors. The maneuverability values of the crawler-type tractor are somewhat different. The **pivot point** is in an entirely different location and its radius and intersecting aisle values are somewhat different. From Fig. 14 it can be seen that this type of unit can operate around two different pivot points. In one case the tractor will theoretically pivot around a point approximately at the dead center of the unit, providing the crawler tracks are moving in opposite directions at the same time and at the same rate of speed. A different pivot point is established when the right-hand track is stationary while the left-hand track is in motion. It should be noted that now the pivot point is on a center point of the stationary track. In the latter case the tractor turns in a 7 ft. 6 in. radius and can theoretically negotiate an 8 ft. intersecting aisle, while in the former it needs a 9 ft. aisle although turning in a 6 ft. radius. It is apparent that a direct relation between **turning radii** and **intersecting aisles** does not always exist.

While diagrams in Fig. 14 are drawn to scale, **scrubbing** has not been taken into consideration. When making layouts for this type of equipment sufficient space should be allowed for scrubbing and **side-slipping,** which is often an inherent characteristic of the crawler-type tractor.

STEERING MECHANISMS. There are four methods of applying steering force to a tractor: manual, mechanical, hydraulic, and electric. The **manual type** is most common on the smaller and lighter tractors. These are the automotive-type hand wheel, the horizontal lever or tiller type, the vertical lever or pump handle type, and the tee handle or handlebar as used on the small walkie tractors. Steering forces are applied manually by the operator or driver on this type of steer.

The mechanical, hydraulic, and electric types of steering are primarily used on heavier units where the weight of the tractor itself creates so much road friction that it is almost unsteerable by manual power. With the **mechanical type** used on most crawler tractors, steering is accomplished by two vertical levers each engaging a brake band on each drive shaft. Thus, when braking pressure is applied, differential action immediately stops the one track while the other continues its movement and pivots the tractor around its stationary track. On most larger tractors this same method is used, only the braking pressure is applied by hydraulic cylinders which actuate the brake bands. There are instances where steering is accomplished by hydraulically actuating the drive clutches themselves. The **hydraulic steer** is most popular on wheel tractors that have a hydraulic power unit. Steering forces are applied by two methods: the conventional double-acting hydraulic cylinder; and the hydraulic rotomation motor, which is in effect a hydraulic cylinder with a plunger traveling through an arc of about 280°. The actual steering force is applied through hydraulic pressure and is controlled by a hydraulic control valve. On most tractors this control valve is interlocked with the steering rods so that the control handle follows the travel of these rods and is at the same angle as the wheels. Thus the operator can tell the direction of the wheels without seeing the wheels themselves.

The **electric power steer** is most commonly used on electric-driven tractors such as storage battery, gas or gasoline electric, and diesel electric. The steering force is developed by an electric motor driving a reduction gear unit, which, in turn, actuates the steering rods. Usually this type steer also has the follow-through system where the control handle automatically aligns itself with the angle of the wheels. The electrical control in this instance consists of a master switch which actuates forward and reversing contactors. These, in turn, energize the motor for either direction of steer.

These types of steer are commonly termed **power steer** and should not be confused with another type known as **booster type steer**. This is often used on wheel tractors equipped with hydraulic units. It is a hydraulic steer system that augments or helps the manual steer. It consists of a double-acting hydraulic cylinder interlocked with the usual manual type steer and absorbs approximately 75 percent of the steering effort required. This system could quite properly be compared with the hydraulic power steer on our present-day automobiles. This steer has an added feature in that should the hydraulic mechanism fail it is still possible to steer the unit manually.

TIRES. Each type of tire has its own relative merits which should be carefully evaluated. For smooth, dry floor operation, **smooth tread solid rubber tires** will usually give the most satisfactory performance. However, if floor conditions are wet and smooth, then a solid rubber tire with a nonskid tread will usually give better performance, even though service life is not as long. The prime consideration is the amount of **traction** the tire can maintain. Where floors are slightly rough, **cushion or pneumatic tires** should be considered. These tires will develop less road shock and cause less damage to the floors. The pneumatic tires are also used very extensively for all kinds of outdoor or yard operations, where paved roadways are not always readily available. In cases where a tractor is strictly in outdoor or earth-moving operations, it can be equipped with pneumatic tires with **molded-on traction cleats.** These come in all sizes and capacities for use on all sizes of tractors. As a matter of fact most agricultural and construction wheel-type tractors come factory equipped with this traction type tire.

Plastic Tires. Smaller tractors, such as the walkie types, are sometimes equipped with plastic tires. These tires are made up of a masurated fabric impregnated with phenolic resin which makes it a very hard, durable, spark proof compound. As a rule, they are not just a tire but a completely **molded plastic wheel** complete with hubs and steel insert bushings for use in conjunction with nonfriction bearings. Their application has been limited to use on the small tractors. The wheels must of necessity be of an exceptionally small diameter to provide clearance for the load height of the semilive skids, while at the same time providing sufficient load-carrying capacity. Walkie tractors are sometimes provided with **steel wheels** on the trail end only, for the same reason as mentioned above.

Engineering Factors

SIZE AND CAPACITY DETERMINATION. When figuring the size and capacity of a tractor, the following factors are of prime importance:

1. Tractive effort—TE.
2. Tractive resistance—TR.
3. Acceleration resistance—AR.
4. Grade resistance—GR.

Two additional factors sometimes used in making tractor calculations are **drawbar pull** (DBP) and **curve and breaking resistance** (CBR). Generally speaking, the latter two factors are relatively unimportant, if the other four factors are worked out to a degree of accuracy.

Tractive Effort. Tractive effort (TE) is the motive force that must be exerted at the driving wheels in order to overcome **motion resistance** and is expressed in pounds.

Tractive Resistance. Tractive resistance is in effect **rolling friction.** Its values are expressed in pounds per ton of gross weight of the tractor plus the gross weight of the trailer train it must pull. These values vary with the condition of the roadway and the relative type of surface or paving. The following table is used when figuring TR for a tractor trailer operation. These values assume that all wheels of the tractor and trailer rotate on antifriction bearings.

Runway Surface	Tractive Resistance lb. per ton
Smooth concrete	30–50 lb.
Wood blocks	35–50
Smooth macadam or hard mastic	30–50
Granite paving blocks, poor brick, etc.	45–75
Hard packed gravel	60–80
Clay or sand	200–300

On well-maintained industrial floors 40 lb. per ton is an average figure that can be used with fair accuracy. If more accurate figures are desired the true values can be determined by pulling a load of known weight through a spring scale and noting the amount of force required to keep it in motion at a uniform speed. Thus, if a gross load of 1,000 lb. registers 20 lb. on the scale, the TR values would amount to $2 \times 20 = 40$ lb. per ton tractive resistance.

Acceleration Resistance. This factor is the **inertia** which must be overcome in starting the tractor. To accelerate 96.6 ft. per min. per sec. 100 lb. per ton of effort is required. An easy method of computing AR values is to figure 10 lb. per ton for each 10 ft. per min. of acceleration per sec. An average rate is 30 to 40 ft. per min. per sec., and thus 30 to 40 lb. per ton can safely be used in making AR calculations. AR is a very important factor in operations of short hauls with many starts and stops. It is, however, less important on long hauls.

Grade Resistance. This measure is the additional amount of TE required when negotiating a grade or ramp and amounts to 20 lb. per ton for each 1 percent of grade, or 1 ft. of vertical rise for each 100 ft. of horizontal length.

When going up grade, GR values must be added to other resistance values in order to provide sufficient TE. The GR values can be disregarded when going down grade.

Curve and Breaking Resistance. CBR values are commonly used in railroad engineering. These values, where the tractor is concerned, are small and of such relative unimportance that they may be disregarded.

Draw-Bar Pull. DBP is also commonly used in railroad engineering. The term is derived from the draw bar used to couple the locomotive to the train. In effect, DBP is the **motive force exerted externally** by the tractor when pulling or pushing any vehicle. The DBP of a tractor is the developed TE, less that consumed in overcoming its own resistance. Therefore, the DBP will vary when the resistance varies. While most tractor manufacturers include DBP ratings in their specifications, it is recommended that TE values be used when making tractor calculations of greater accuracy. For rough estimates DBP ratings are acceptable.

One important factor in developing DBP values is the **road friction percentage factors** tabulated below. The other is the **percentage of grade** to be encountered. For example, when operating on a smooth concrete floor up a 4 percent grade, the RFPF is 2.4 percent average. If a total gross load of 15,000 lb. is assumed:

$$DBP = 2.4\% \text{ RF} + 4\% \text{ grade} \times 15{,}000 \text{ lb.}$$
$$= 6.4\% \times 15{,}000 \text{ lb.}$$
$$= 960 \text{ lb.}$$

Road Friction Percentage Factors (RFPF)

Wood planking	2.0% to 3% of weight	Average	2.5%
Brick	2.0 to 2.9 "	"	2.5
Concrete	1.8 to 2.7 "	"	2.4
Macadam	2.5 to 3.2 "	"	2.9
Granite blocks	2.5 to 3.0 "	"	3.0
Gravel and cinders	3.0 to 5.0 "	"	4.0

COMPUTING FOR TRACTIVE EFFORT. The total amount of TE required for a tractor trailer operation is the sum of the TE's of each element of the operation. The following tractor trailer example will illustrate the method used.

A train of 6 trailers each carrying a load of 3,500 lb. is to be moved a distance of 1,200 ft. In the course of travel the trailer train must travel up a 2 percent grade 125 ft. long. The trailers are roller-bearing equipped, weigh 500 lb. each, and will travel over a smooth concrete road. To find TE values necessary to move both trailer train and tractor with a sufficient factor of safety first determine the **gross weight** to be moved. The train consists of 6 trailers each with a gross weight of 4,000 lb. Thus the gross weight of the train is:

$$4{,}000 \text{ lb.} \times 6 = \frac{24{,}000 \text{ lb.}}{2{,}000 \text{ per ton}} = 12 \text{ tons}$$

Then, since TR for travel on level floor equals 40 lb. per ton,

TE for travel on level floor = 12 × 40 lb. = 480 lb. TE

TR + AR for acceleration on level = 40 lb. + 30 lb. = 70 lb. TE

TE for acceleration on level = 12 × 70 lb. = 840 lb. TE

TR + GR up 2% grade = 20 lb.× 2 + 40 lb. = 80 lb. per ton

TE for travel up 2% grade = 12 × 80 lb. = 960 lb. TE

TR + AR + GR for acceleration up 2% grade =

40 lb. + 30 lb. + 40 lb. = 110 lb. per ton

TE for acceleration up 2% grade = 12 ton × 110 lb. = 1,320 lb. TE

Thus, 1,320 lb. TE is required to move the 12 ton trailer load over the worst conditions represented by a 2 percent grade. The TE required for the tractor itself is calculated as follows: If the tractor weighs 4,500 lbs. or 2¼ tons, that part of the TE developed by the tractor consumed in overcoming its own tractive resistance would not, in this case, exceed 110 lb. per ton or approximately 248 lb. This value added to the 1,320 lb. TE of the trailer train gives a total TE value of 1,568 lb. for the combined tractor trailer train.

To allow for acceleration of the trailer train on the level, 840 lb. TE is required at 70 lb. × 2¼ tons, or 158 lb. TE is needed. Thus 998 TE is required for level floor operation and 1,568 lb. TE for upgrade operation. Allowing a safety factor of .40 brings the total TE to 2,195 lb. From these calculations it will be seen that a tractor with a normal rating of 1,000 lb. TE and an ultimate of 2,500 lb. TE will perform this operation without being overloaded.

ENERGY CALCULATIONS FOR BATTERY-PROPELLED TRACTORS. When computing battery requirements for the electric tractor, the **duty cycle** should first be definitely established. Bearing in mind that the tractor will usually be required to perform more work than was originally anticipated, a reasonable **safety factor** should be allowed in the final calculations. These will vary with the time cycle involved. Experience has proven that a battery with

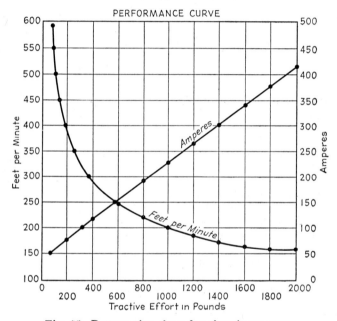

Fig. 15. Battery size chart for electric tractors.

greater capacity than the original duty cycle determination is often more economical in the long run. Because it does not work at full capacity it will have a longer life and keep operating costs at a low level. Moreover, the larger battery gives assurance of being able to perform extra duties when required, at no additional cost. The **duty cycle** of a battery is generally figured on the basis of an 8 hour day, although a 12 or even 16 hour day is often used. In the latter case, extra batteries must be provided to permit **recharging** in relays with a minimum of 8 hours allowed for recharging. See Fig. 15 for recommended battery sizes for various size electric tractors. These values are based on an 8 hour duty cycle for average tractor operation.

SECTION 43

HIGHWAY TRUCKS AND TRUCK-TRAILERS

CONTENTS

HIGHWAY TRUCKS AND TRUCK-TRAILERS

MOTOR TRUCKS. A motor truck is a single self-propelled motor vehicle carrying its load on its own wheels and primarily designed for the transportation of property, according to the Commercial-Vehicle Nomenclature of the Society of Automotive Engineers (SAE Handbook).

Basically, trucks are grouped by gross weight into three capacities as follows:

1. Light trucks—gross weight capacity less than 9,000 lb.
2. Medium trucks—gross weight capacity 9,000 to 16,000 lb.
3. Heavy trucks—gross weight capacity 16,000 lb. and over (AMA Motor Truck Facts).

Light Trucks. Light trucks are customarily used by the service trades, agriculture, and industry for all transportation needs where the weight and bulk of the commodities transported do not exceed 4,000 lb. or 300 cu. ft.

Medium Trucks. Medium trucks afford payload capacities up to approximately 5 tons. The great variety of body designs offers a wide range of cubic capacities which can best be considered under a more detailed description of special bodies. In very general terms, however, medium trucks with conventional cabs will accommodate bodies from 7 to 12 ft. in length and up to 14 ft. in length when cab-over-engine, i.e., COE, designs are used.

Heavy Trucks. Heavy trucks are usually designed for specialized transportation tasks and may, therefore, have an almost unlimited range of requirements. Gross weight capacities range up to 40,000 lb. for highway use and higher for off highway models. Cubic capacities are limited only by such practical considerations as turning radius, and by the legal restrictions of the state or states in which the truck will be used. Where cubic capacities indicate the need for a body exceeding 18 to 20 ft. in length, it becomes practical to consider the use of a truck-tractor and semitrailer.

The upper limit of current size and weight restrictions are shown in the chart of the Truck-Trailer Manufacturers Association, "State Size and Weight Restrictions for Trucks and Truck-Trailers," Fig. 1.

The varying size and weight limits of the different states present a difficult problem to truck-trailer manufacturers and to operators alike. Moreover, it is a problem which by its very nature will be with us for a long time. If we know the maximums, it will help us to live with the problem.

Fig. 1 on the following pages has been prepared to help trailer manufacturers, their salesmen, and their customers figure the applicable maximum limits in the various states.

EXPLANATORY REMARKS FOR FIG. 1, PP. 2–3.

Width limitations are not shown, since an 8-ft. limit is standard except in Connecticut, Rhode Island, and New Mexico on designated highways where 102 in. is permitted. In Arizona and Kansas 102 in. is permitted across the tires, but the

STATE SIZE AND WEIGHT RESTRICTIONS

State	Height	Length (B) Single Unit	Length (B) Tractor Semi-trailer	Length (B) Other Combinations	Maximum Axle Load in Pounds	Tandem Axles 4' Apart	Tractor Semitrailer Single Axle	Tractor Semitrailer Tandem	Combinations	Formulas** and Tables⊙
Alabama	12'6" A	35	50 T-5	N. P.	18,000 S	36,000	45,000	63,890***	N. P.	Table
Arizona	13'6"	40	65	65	18,000	32,000	45,000	68,000***	76,800 P	Table
Arkansas	13'6"	35 V	50 T-5	50 U	18,000	32,000	45,000	56,000****P	56,000 P	Table
California	13'6"	35 V	60 T	60 U	18,000	32,000	45,000	68,000***	76,800	Table
Colorado	12'6"	35 V	60 T-5	60	18,000	36,000	45,000	67,200***	75,200	800 (L + 40)
Connecticut	13'6" D	45	45	N. P.	22,400	36,000	50,000	60,000	N. P.	Table
Delaware	12'6" A	35	50	60	20,000 S-1	36,000	49,000	60,000	60,000	Table
Dist. of Col.	12'6"	35	50 T-5	50	22,000	38,000	53,000	63,890	65,400	Table
Florida	12'6" A	40 V	50 T-5	50 U-1	20,000	40,000	49,000	64,650	64,650	Table
Georgia	13'6"	39.55	48	48	20,340	40,680	63,280 D	63,280 D	63,280 D	
Idaho	14'	35	60 T-5	65	18,000 S-3	32,000	45,000	67,500***	76,800	Table
Illinois	13'6"	42 T-1	50	50	18,000 S-3	32,000 AA	45,000	59,000 AA	72,000 AA	
Indiana	13'6" A	36	50 T-5	50	18,000 M-3	32,000 M-3	45,000	72,000***	72,000	Table
Iowa	12'6" A	35 V	50 T-5	50	18,000 S-M-4	32,000	45,000	65,478 M-3	N. P.	Table
Kansas	12'6"	35 V	50	N. P.	18,000	32,000	45,000 M-3	63,890***	63,890	Table
Kentucky	12'6"	35	48 T-5	60	18,000 S-6	32,000	59,645 S-F	59,640 S-F	N. P.	
Louisiana	12'6" H	35 V	50 T-5	45 H-1	22,000 S	32,000	36,000 P	63,000***P	68,000 P	
Maine	12'6" A	45 H-1	45 H-1	55	22,400 S-3	40,000 I	50,000	50,000	50,000	Table
Maryland	N.R.	55	55 T-5	N.P.U.-2	22,400 S-1	36,000	53,800	65,000	65,000	
Massachusetts	12'6" A	35	45	55	22,400 S-3	36,000 J	60,000	60,000	N. P.	850 (L + 40)
Michigan	12'6" A	35 A-3	55	45	18,000 S-1	26,000 J	45,000	67,000***D	111,000 D	1,000 (L + 25)
Minnesota	12'6" A	40 A-4	45	45 U-1	18,000	28,000	45,000	65,000***	66,500	Table
Mississippi	12'6" A	35 V	45 U-1	45	18,000 S-4	32,000 D	45,000	55,980D	55,980 D	Table
Missouri	12'6"	35	45	45	18,000	32,000	45,000	60,010	60,010	Table
Montana	13'6"	35	60 T-5	60 U	18,000 S	32,000	45,000	76,000***	76,000	Table
Nebraska	12'6" A	35 V	60 T-5	50 U	18,000	33,600	45,000	63,890***	64,650	Table
Nevada	N.R.	N. R.	N. R.	N. R.	18,000	32,000	45,000	68,000***	76,800	Table
New Hampshire	13'6"	35	45	45	22,400	36,000	53,800	66,400	66,400	Table
New Jersey	13'6"	35	50	50	22,400 S-3	32,000	53,800	60,000	60,000	Table
New Mexico	13'6"	40	65 T-5	65	21,600 S	36,000	52,300	75,600***	86,400	Table

State										
New York	13'	35	50 T-5	50 U	22,400 S-3	36,000	53,800	65,000	65,000	34,000 + (Lx850)
North Carolina	12'6" A	35 V	48	48	18,000 M-2S	36,000	46,200	58,800	58,800	
North Dakota	13'6" A	35 V	50 T	50	18,000 S-2	30,000	45,000	63,000	63,000	750 (L + 40)
Ohio	12'6" A	35 V	50 T-5	60	19,000 S-5	24,000 W	47,000	72,000****W	78,000 W	38,000 + (Lx800)
Oklahoma	13'6"	35	50	50 C	18,000 S-5	32,000	45,000	60,000****W	60,000	Table
Oregon	13'6"	35	50 A-2	50	18,000 S-2	32,000	45,000	73,000****L	76,000	Table
Pennsylvania	12'6" A	35	50	50	22,400 S-3	36,000	50,000	60,000	62,000	Table
Rhode Island	12'6"	40	50	50	22,400 S-3	44,800	50,000	62,000	88,000 E	Table
South Carolina	12'6"	40 V	50	50	20,000	32,000	49,000 M-1	60,000 Z	68,350 M-1	Table
South Dakota	13'	35	50	45	18,000 S	32,000	45,000	88,000	73,280	Table
Tennessee	12'6"	35	45	50	18,000	32,000	45,000	63,890 M-1	55,980	
Texas	13'6"	35	50 T-5	60	18,000 S-5	32,000 R	45,000	64,650***	58,420	Table
Utah	14'	45	60	50	18,000	33,000	45,000	55,980 M-1	79,900	Table
Vermont	12'6"	50	50 T-5	60	N. S.-S.	N.S.S.	50,000	58,420	60,000	Table
Virginia	12'6" A	35	50 T-5	50	18,000	32,000	45,000	71,400***	56,800	
Washington	13'6" A	35	60 T	45	18,000 S-6	32,000	45,000	60,000	72,000	Table
West Virginia	12'6" A	35	45	50	18,000 M-4	32,000 M-4	45,000 M-4	56,800	73,280 L-1	Table
Wisconsin	12'6" A	35	50 T-5	50	19,500 S-3X	32,000 X	48,000 X	67,500***	68,000 X	Table
Wyoming	13'6"	40	60 T-5	60	18,000	36,000	45,000	63,840 M	73,950	Table

FOOTNOTES:

◎ —Tables may be obtained from state motor vehicle administrators.

* —Maximum Practical Gross (see third paragraph General Remarks).

** —Computation based on 6' overhang.

*** —3-axle tractor with tandem axle semitrailer.

A—Auto transporters allowed 13½'; A-1: 13'; A-2: 37½' length allowed auto transporter trailer; A-3: 40' length allowed auto transporters; A-4: 38" tolerance for length of auto transporters.

B—Semitrailer length controlled by single unit length except where footnote appears.

C—State Highway Department may permit 60'.

D—On designated highways.

E—3-axle truck with 3-axle trailer.

F—No tolerance allowed.

H—Height subject to 1'6" tolerance; H-1: 1% tolerance for length allowed.

I—36,000 lb. if axles spaced less than 48" apart.

J—On designated highways one tandem per combination permitted 32,000 lb.

L—Permit required for gross weight over 60,000 lb.; L-1: Permit required over 63,840 lb.

M—Includes 5% overload tolerance.

M-1—Plus 10% tolerance.

M-2—1,000-lb. tolerance on 1 axle; M-3—Plus 3% tolerance; M-4—Plus 5% tolerance.

N.P.—Not Permitted.

N.R.—No Restriction.

N.S.—Not Specified.

P—Plus weight on front axle.

R—36,000 lb. if axles do not have common point of suspension.

S—Subject to 600 lb. per inch tire requirements. S-1: 700 lb.; S-2: 550 lb.; S-3: 800 lb.; S-4 on tires 9:75 and larger; S-5: 650 lb.; S-6: 450 lb.

T—Semitrailer limited to 40'; T-1—Semitrailer limited to 42'; T-2—35'; T-5—Not restricted.

U—Full trailers limited to 35'; U-1—35' unless 3 axle, then 40'; U-2—33.

V—Vehicles over 35' must have 3 axles.

W—31,500 with tandem axles spaced more than 4' apart.

X—Includes 1,500 lb. tolerance single axle; tandem, 2,000 lb.

Y—With permit.

Z—Not less than 10:00 × 20 tires; not less than 25' between extreme axles.

AA—Double tandems 30,000 lbs. each, 68,000 lbs. total.

Truck-Trailer Manufacturers Association, Inc.

Fig. 1. State size and weight restrictions for trucks and truck-trailers.

body width may not exceed 96 in. In California and Oregon 100 in. is permitted across the tires.

In many states maximum gross weight depends on a formula or a table in which the controlling factor is either the wheel base of the individual vehicle or the over-all length from the center of the first axle to the center of the last axle, in the combination. In preparing a general chart based on tables or formulas, certain assumptions must be made. In this case, it has been assumed that the overhang front and rear totals 6 ft., i.e., approximately 3 ft. from the front bumper to the center line of the front axle and 3 ft. from the center of the rear axle to the rear of the body or body bumper. Many trucks and trailers have more overhang than this, especially in the rear. Tandem-axle trailers used with two-axle tractors have considerable overhang. Five-axle tractor semitrailers may readily come within the 6-ft. overhang allowance. Gross weights shown in this chart are maximum values under most favorable conditions. For vehicles of less than maximum wheelbase it is necessary to compute the gross weight by formula or read it from the table.

The laws of most states do not differentiate between front and rear axles in limiting maximum axle loads. It is, however, impractical to load the front axle beyond a certain point which, in the formula calculations for this chart, has been assumed to be 9,000 lb. For example, if the law allows 18,000 lb. per axle, the practical gross load on a two-axle truck-tractor and single-axle semitrailer would be 9,000 front axle, 18,000 rear tractor axle, and 18,000 on the trailer axle, or a total of 45,000 pounds.

In figuring the maximum gross for tandem-axle trailers (third column from right), the calculations are based on three-axle tractors and tandem-axle trailers wherever the greater total allowed by this arrangement of axles would be within the maximum gross allowable load. In calculating the total gross for tandem-axle trailers, it has been assumed that the practical maximum length of a tractor semitrailer is 50 ft. Thus, if the formula is $750 (L + 40) = W$, where L is the distance between the first and last axle, the value of L would be 44 ft. (i.e., 50 ft. less 6 ft. overhang) and the computation would be $750 \times 84 = 63,000$.

The second column from right shows the maximum gross load permitted on any full legal combination.

Types of Motor Trucks

CLASSIFICATION OF TRUCKS. It is best to consider trucks in relation to the various **body types** which enable them to serve the needs of industry and commerce in the most efficient manner. The following types of trucks are those which are in wide use in performing the important kinds of work for which motor trucks are employed.

Pickup and Express Trucks. The light truck with pickup or express body is widely used because this open type of body is adaptable to so many purposes. Frequently, it is used as a service truck and may be equipped with permanent or removable tool box or boxes. It may also be equipped with an air compressor when used to service a truck fleet, or as a road-service truck for a garage or service station. It is also widely used as a general utility vehicle on farms.

The typical pickup truck is built on a commercial chassis essentially similar to a passenger-car chassis. It is provided with a truck hood, cowl, and cab, usually with heavier springs than are used on a passenger-car chassis and frequently with a lower pinion ring gear ratio to afford more power but slightly lower top speed. It may have a larger radiator and a heavier clutch than a passenger car.

The **body** is essentially a steel or wood platform with permanent steel sides and front, and with a hinged back or tail gate. Customarily the upper 4 to 6 in. of the sides and front are flared outward at approximately a 45° angle. The body is approximately 48 to 50 in. wide inside, 78 in. long, and 14 to 20 in. high. The loading height of the floor, i.e., distance from the ground, is approximately

30 in. unloaded, 24 in. loaded. These bodies are customarily equipped with stake pockets and are sometimes offered with canopy tops.

When the job requirement indicates the need for a body similar to a pickup, except larger and designed for heavier service, it is customary to use a cab chassis with approximately a 9,000- to 10,000-lb. gross vehicle weight (GVW), equipped with an express body. The **express body** is similar to the pickup in design. The **dimensions** are approximately 54 in. in width, 90 to 96 in. in length, with sides 20 in. or more in height. The loading height of the floor body, i.e., distance from the ground, is approximately 35 in. when empty and 31 in. when loaded. Since the axle tread is approximately the same as the pickup, the clearance between the wheel housings is slightly less than 50 in. In some makes a **longer wheel-base model** is also offered to provide body lengths of 108 to 115 in.

Sedan Delivery Truck. A sedan delivery is a commercial type of closed body resembling a passenger car in style but equipped with a rear loading door and solid steel side panels with a window provided in the single rear door. The body loading space, back of the driver's seat, is approximately 73 to 78 in. in length, 55 to 60 in. in width, and 40 to 44 in. in height. The rear door opening is approximately 33 to 40 in. in width and 34 to 43 in. in height. The cubic capacity is approximately 92.5 cu. ft. The loading height of the body floor is approximately 26 in. when empty and 21 in. when loaded.

Panel Truck. The panel-body truck is a very popular vehicle for light delivery work when it is necessary to use a fully enclosed body. It has a larger cubic capacity than the sedan delivery and has the commercial car grille, hood, front fenders, cowl, and instrument panel.

Body dimensions of the panel delivery truck are approximately 78 to 92 in. in length, 55 to 63 in. in width, and 51 to 55 in. in height, with approximately 140 to 150 cu. ft. of **loading space.** The **loading height** of the body floor is approximately 28 in. when empty and 23 in. when loaded.

The body construction is all steel except for some makes which have wood floors with steel wearing strips. The double rear doors provide an opening of from 42 to 46 in., with one window in the top half of each door. This body type is practical only as a factory production unit.

Panel-type bodies are available on longer wheel-base chassis with higher **gross vehicle weight** (GVW) ratings for somewhat larger loads. **Body lengths** approximate 108 in. while other dimensions are the same as for the standard length panel bodies.

Multistop Truck. The multistop delivery truck is mounted on chassis of various gross vehicle weight (GVW) capacity from 5,000 to 10,000 lb. Some manufacturers who do not offer this type as a factory option provide a chassis designed for the mounting of a custom-built multistop body. The **advantages over the conventional panel** are ease of ingress and egress, increased loading space on the same length chassis, and greater headroom both for the convenience of the driver and for bulky or tall articles of merchandise. Driver controls are forward of the customary position, and the engine compartment is within the body structure, giving the driver better vision and more room in the driving compartment.

The approximate inside **dimensions of the loading space** in the three sizes generally available are: length, 7 to 7¾ ft., 9 to 9½ ft., and 12 to 12½ ft.; width, 70 to 72 in., with approximately 49 in. between the wheelhouses; and height, 70 to 72 in. If dual rear tires are used, the maximum distance between wheelhouses is reduced to 43 in. Cubic capacities range from approximately 235 to

250 cu. ft. for the 7-ft. body; 300 to 350 cu. ft. for the 9-ft. body; and 375 to 460 cu. ft. for the 12- to 12½-ft. body.

Floor heights range from 18 to 30 in. and the entrance step height from 14 to 20 in. above the street. **Rear door openings** range from approximately 38 to 60 in., depending on type of door. Customarily, bodies are of all-steel construction, lined on the interior, with double rear doors having windows.

Platform Truck—Light. Several manufacturers now offer a **light platform or open-rack body** with a wide, level loading space unencumbered by wheelhousings, on chassis of 5,000 to 9,000 or 10,000 lb. **gross vehicle weight** (GVW). The platform is approximately 94 in. in length and 77 in. in width, and the loading space with racks installed is about 88 in. in length and 70 to 78 in. in width. Racks are generally 28 to 30 in. in height. The loading height of the body floor is from 35 to 45 in. unloaded and 32 to 40 in. loaded, depending upon tire sizes used. Custom body builders can furnish special bodies.

Medium Trucks. The manufacturers of medium trucks customarily furnish only stake or rack bodies. The major portion of their production consists of cab and chassis trucks, flatfaced cowl chassis, and a few cowl and windshield chassis for school-bus bodies and custom bodies in which the driver's compartment is integral with the truck body.

Medium trucks, previously rated at 1½ tons capacity, range in **gross vehicle weight** (GVW) from 9,000 to 16,000 lb. They are offered in a wide range of wheel bases designed to provide satisfactory weight distribution, with **bodies** that vary in length from 8 to 14 ft., and even up to 28 ft. in school buses. Longer bodies can be accommodated on extended wheel-base chassis, which may be modified by a truck equipment or custom body manufacturer. **Weight distribution** is a factor which needs careful consideration to prevent hard steering. If the body is too long for the truck chassis, there will be partial loss of steering and braking control, unequal tire wear, and possible illegal rear axle weight. The truck manufacturer should be consulted as to the correct wheel base for any unusual body.

Most truck manufacturers are currently offering trucks with conventional cabs mounted back of a hood-enclosed engine compartment and some type of forward-mounted cab variously described as **cab-over-engine,** i.e., COE, **Cab-Forward,** and by other trade names. Where the cab is well out in front of the engine, the additional frame length is as much as 4 ft.

The shorter wheel base of a COE chassis suitable for any given length truck body provides a turning circle with a shorter diameter and makes the truck more maneuverable. The advantage in turning-circle diameter may be from 5½ ft. to 7 ft.

The relatively shorter over-all length of the COE is frequently an advantage in truck-tractors because it enables the operator to use a longer semitrailer within the same over-all combination length. Shorter over-all truck length is also an advantage in inside storage.

A recent development, especially in truck-tractors, has been the 102-in. wheelbase conventional cab truck in which the front axle is mounted as near as possible to the extreme front of the truck, thus enabling semitrailer operators to meet the over-all state length limit of 45 ft. (Fig. 1) and still operate 35-ft. trailers.

Heavy Trucks. Heavy trucks have a gross vehicle weight (GVW) rating of from 16,001 to 40,000 lb. Trucks rated over 40,000 lb. are usually referred to as off-highway trucks. The GVW is given on the truck identification plate affixed to the truck chassis. In this connection the Automobile Manufacturers Association has defined GVW thus:

The Maximum Gross Vehicle Weight Rating shall include the weight in pounds of the truck chassis with lubricants, water and full tank or tanks of fuel, plus the weights of the cab or driver's compartment, body, special chassis and body equipment and payload, as authorized by the chassis manufacturer. (Interpretation of Manufacturers' Maximum Gross Vehicle Weight Rating Recommended by the Motor Truck Division, Automobile Manufacturers Association.)

GRADE-ABILITY RATINGS. In the immediate postwar years, beginning in 1946, proposals were made by groups interested in size and weight legislation, that trucks be required to meet a minimum "grade-ability" requirement. The intent has been to bar from the highways underpowered or overloaded trucks that delay traffic on two-lane highways in hilly terrain. Generally these proposals have failed of enactment, the only exception being North Carolina, which adopted a requirement that trucks of over 40,000 lb. gross weight must have 300-cu.-in. motors. This requirement was eliminated, however, in the 1953 legislative session.

Currently there is a grade-ability requirement in Pennsylvania, and in addition there is a requirement that medium and heavy trucks have 1 sq. in. of brake lining for each 55 lb. of gross vehicle weight (GVW).

TRUCK CABS—CONVENTIONAL. The larger-volume truck manufacturers who build trucks in all sizes—light, medium, and heavy—design **one cab that is suitable for all sizes of trucks.** Thus they spread the tooling cost over larger production runs. Moreover, cab designs are not subject to yearly style change, but are generally changed only when significant improvements have been developed.

Cabs are customarily mounted on a subframe which, in turn, has either a three-point or four-point mounting on the truck chassis frame. The problem is

Autocar Div. White Motor Co.

Fig. 2. Cab-over-engine truck for delivery of fuel oil.

to obtain good support for the cab when the truck frame is subject to various distortions caused by overloading or riding over rough terrain.

Truck manufacturers now provide streamlined cabs through the use of more expensive dies, and by the use of passenger-car manufacturing methods, i.e., assembly of precision stampings on jigs, electric welding, smooth-filled joints, and attractive trim and paint combinations.

Customary accessories include adequate mirrors so placed as to enable the driver not only to watch overtaking traffic but also to maneuver when backing the truck into loading docks. Heaters and defrosters are required for winter operation in most areas, and air conditioning equipment of truck cabs may be offered in the near future.

TRUCK CABS: CAB-OVER-ENGINE. COE (cab-over-engine) cabs, such as shown in Fig. 2, are built in much the same manner as conventional cabs and generally a manufacturer building both conventional and COE trucks will use as many common components as possible.

The COE cab requires a specially designed subframe and specially engineered controls. More insulation and sound-deadening material may be required to protect the driver from the heat and noise of the engine.

Truck Bodies

PLATFORM, STAKE, OR RACK BODIES. On medium-sized trucks **three body lengths are available,** approximately 9, 12, and 14 ft. Body width for medium-sized trucks is usually 7 ft., or on some makes slightly more than 7 ft. Inside dimensions are 2 to 3 in. less.

Sectionalized racks are furnished on factory production trucks. Racks are customarily from 38 to 42 in. in height. They consist of steel upright stakes with approximately four wood cross-slats. Racks are tied together with metal fastenings and usually the center side sections are hinged so they can readily be opened for loading and unloading.

The loading height of medium trucks with platform, stake, or rack bodies varies with the tire sizes used, and will range from 44 to 50 in. unloaded and 40 to 45 in. when loaded. Heavy trucks with platform bodies may have loading heights ranging from 48 to 55 in., again depending on the tire size.

The solution to varying loading heights appears to be in **adjustable platforms, separate docks** for medium and heavy trucks or trailers, or in other mechanical means, because there is no practical way that truck floors can be of uniform height when tire sizes may range from 7.50 × 20 in. to 12.00 × 24 in.

Heavy trucks customarily use bodies 8 ft. in width because the over-all tire width is approximately 8 ft. when tire sizes are 9.00 × 20 in. and larger.

VAN BODIES. Basically, the distinction between a **panel truck body** and a **van truck body** is one of size, since both are fully enclosed bodies. For the purpose of this description, all fully enclosed bodies will be considered to be van bodies, except multistop truck bodies and bodies furnished as original factory installations by the motor truck manufacturers.

Van bodies are generally **box-shaped** and in fact have frequently been referred to as box panels, to distinguish them from factory panels with their more streamlined appearance. Customarily the van body is mounted in back of a factory-installed cab on a conventional truck, as in Fig. 3.

In recent years large-scale truck body manufacturers and most truck-trailer manufacturers have offered **all-steel, steel-and-aluminum, or all-aluminum van**

bodies. In these bodies, steel framing is used instead of wood. The framing is likely to be heavy gage metal formed into "Zee," "hat," "box," tubular, or other shapes.

In **steel bodies,** good specifications call for high-tensile corrosion-resisting metal of 12 to 13 gage, for body framing; 10 to 12 gage for cross sill, 14 to 16 gage for roof carlines, and 20 to 22 gage for side and roof panels. The **body framework** is generally either assembled on a jig and electrically welded, or prefabricated in main sections such as floors, roofs, sides, and front and rear frame and rear doors. These sections may be centrally manufactured and shipped in kits or sets for local assembly in branch or dealer shops.

Ford Motor Co.—Fruehauf Trailer Co.

Fig 3. **Special purpose panel-type delivery truck**

CORRUGATED STEEL VAN BODIES. Van bodies are customarily lined either part way or all the way to the roof, either with plywood or wood, or with metal slats above a lower course of plywood. Frequently, there is a specially reinforced section just above the floor to protect the walls and lining from hand trucks, lift trucks, or heavy or odd-shaped cargo.

The van body must be wired and equipped with necessary **marker lights** to meet either state or ICC requirements, depending upon the type of service in which it is used.

In recent years, many van bodies are being furnished with **insulation** in the roof, side walls, and sometimes under the floor. For ice cream and frozen foods generally a minimum of 6 in. of a high quality insulation is required. In addition, the body must be specially designed to eliminate metal-to-metal contacts that extend from the cargo compartment to the outside atmosphere. Avoidance of contacts is frequently accomplished by use of a wood strip applied between the body framework and the inner wall of the body.

Great care must be taken in installing the insulating material to insure that there are no voids which would become temperature leaks. Customarily, an extremely fine-gage fiber-glass insulation, formed into sheets or "batts" available in precut sections or rolls, is used. This insulation is installed between the body frame members, and the sections are cut sufficiently larger than the space to be filled so that the pieces are sprung or snapped into place. The insulation should not be compressed but it should fit so snugly that it will not sag or mat because of vibration and thus leave voids. A satisfactory insulating material is one which is as light as possible, does not disintegrate with age, and is fireproof and verminproof. It must be impervious to water, dry out fast, and not corrode or cause corrosion.

ALUMINUM VAN BODIES. In addition to steel van bodies with smooth sides, there are several makes of truck bodies, usually offered by truck-trailer manufacturers, that are of aluminum construction. These are usually of **two types.** One type consists of vertical panels or sheets of aluminum fastened together at the edges so as to form reinforcing ribs approximately one inch deep protruding out from the side of the truck body where the vertical panels are joined. This type of body requires no interior frame because the ribs add sufficient strength, especially when securely fastened to a conventional floor and roof.

OPEN-TOP VAN BODIES. In some instances, protection of the cargo is of relatively less importance than the ability to load **irregular objects,** which may be higher than would fit in a closed-top van body. There are also instances when it is desirable to be able to load and unload **heavy articles** with an overhead crane. In all such types of service, an open-type van body may be used rather than the more usual platform or rack body. An open-top van is one which has sides but no roof. It is different from a highrack because it has solid sides instead of slat or rack sides.

Standard truck body dimensions vary among manufacturers but are generally from 7 and 7½ ft. up to a full 8 ft. in width. The narrower 7- to 7½-ft. body is designed to fit the axle tread of medium-weight trucks which have tire sizes that range from 6.00 × 20 to 8.25 × 20 in. The 8-ft. body widths are for all heavy trucks which have tire sizes from 9.00 × 20 in. up.

Standard van bodies are available in **heights** ranging from approximately 72 to 78 in. and in some makes extra-high bodies are available at slightly higher costs. **Lengths** range all the way from 8 to 20 ft., depending entirely on the needs of the purchaser.

DUMP BODIES. The term "dump body" is defined in the Society of Automotive Engineers Commercial Vehicle Nomenclature (SAE Handbook) as "a body that can be tilted or otherwise manipulated to discharge its load by gravity."

Dump bodies are of steel construction and are usually mounted over a hydraulic hoist. They are generally referred to by cubic capacity in yards rather than by dimensions in feet and inches. Capacities range from 1 cu. yd. upward. The top limit on capacity will depend on the density of the material to be hauled, the GVW of the truck and perhaps, in the final analysis, on legal weight limits. **Medium trucks** normally accommodate from 1½- to 2½-yd. bodies in general contractors' service, hauling sand, gravel, earth, and other relatively dense materials. When coal, ashes, cinders, trash, rubbish, etc., are to be hauled, the cubic capacity may be anywhere from 4 to 10 cu. yd. A dump body truck for delivery of coal or other loose material is shown in Fig. 4.

Body dimensions for 1½- to 2½-cu.-yd. bodies are usually between 7 and 8 ft. in length by 6 ft. in width, and from 10 to 18 in. in height. Dump bodies generally have somewhat higher end sections than side sections, and these end sections are 2 in. wide and recessed to provide support for **side boards.** Side boards may be 2-in. × 6-in. or 2-in. × 8-in. planks, or special removable steel sections designed to fit into the end retainers. The use of side boards provides flexibility in loading capacity to adjust for density of material being hauled and nature of terrain to be traversed.

Dump bodies, at least those above 1½ cu. yd. capacity, designed for contractors' service, customarily have rub rails and vertical side braces to add strength or stiffness to the body. Frequently, dump bodies in contractor service have full or partial cab protectors. A cab protector is an upward and forward projection of the front end of the body, designed to prevent spillage from the bucket of the power shovel or other loading device, and to prevent the bucket itself from damaging the truck cab.

Fig. 4. Cable-reel-type dump trailer.

The **tail gate** of a dump body is usually removable and is customarily double-hinged so that the load may be dumped over or under. It is also supported by chains so that it may be lowered to a horizontal position and form an extension of the truck-body floor. The tail gate is released by a "dog" or catch, usually connected to a handle at the front of the body (see Fig. 4).

Dump bodies may have **fully removable sides,** but trucks of this type have only a limited market.

For heavy service, dump bodies are sometimes provided with double floors. In some instances wood planks are installed between the upper and lower steel floor plate. This type of reinforcing helps to protect the body from damage when rocks are loaded from a power shovel. Likewise, heavy-service rock bodies frequently have a raised rear section instead of a removable or hinged tail gate. This construction allows the load to be retained when the body is in the level position or readily dumped when the body is elevated.

Heavy-service dump bodies for use on heavy trucks are generally 4 to 10 cu. yd. in capacity and 6½, 7, or 8 ft. in width. The length of these bodies may range up to 10 or 12 ft. Off-highway mining, quarrying, or other types of trucks are built even larger and are usually specially engineered to meet the requirement of the particular kind of service in which they are to be used. Some of these heavy-service bodies are designed to be **side dumping** rather than rear dumping, and some are dumped by **hoisting or tripping equipment** at the predetermined unloading point rather than by a truck-mounted hoist.

DUMP-BODY HOISTS. Just as dump bodies come in a wide range of sizes and types to meet the requirements of different users and the many kinds of material that may be unloaded by gravity, dump-body hoists are also available in a range of capacities and types.

The most common type of hoist is the **underbody hydraulic hoist,** which consists of a subframe installed over the truck frame, and cylinder, piston, and connecting rod, so arranged that as the piston is forced rearward in the cylinder the connecting rod actuates a mechanism which causes the forward part of the body to rise. The dump body is hinged to the rear of the frame of the hoist. The hinge must be of sufficient strength to prevent twisting, bending, or shearing, even though the body is not resting on level terrain when elevated.

The piston is actuated by a **cab-controlled hydraulic pump** driven by a **power take-off** mounted to the transmission case of the truck. When the body is to be elevated the truck clutch is depressed, the power take-off shift lever is moved forward putting the power take-off (PTO) into gear with the idler gear of the truck. When the clutch is released, the pump commences to force oil into the hoist cylinder against the face of the piston. The truck motor should be run at a speed slightly above idling speed, or between 600 and 800 r.p.m. Overspeeding the truck engine will not only cause premature wear but also may damage the power take-off (PTO) or pump mechanism. It may also cause air to be drawn into the system, which will cause an airlock or a jerky motion when the hoist is operated.

It is important that the **manufacturers' directions** for care and servicing of the hoist be followed. The oil level in the cylinder should be maintained at the level prescribed by the manufacturer. Great care should be taken to use only clean oil of the prescribed type and viscosity and to keep it free from grit or other foreign substances.

Other types of hoists include **telescoping hoists,** i.e., one cylinder inside of another for greater length of stroke; and **double or twin hoists,** i.e., two cylinders mounted side by side with two connecting rods and vertical hoists mounted perpendicularly at the front of the body. This latter type is now seldom used, although it was frequently used on early-model dump trucks.

Although by definition a dump body cannot be used without a hoist, hoists are sometimes mounted under platform, stake, cargo, or other types of bodies. These bodies are then suitable for the normal service intended and may, in addition, be used to discharge cargo by dumping.

While nearly all hoists now being produced are operated by some kind of hydraulic cylinder and pump mechanism driven by the truck motor, there are some small-capacity bodies that are dumped by **manual devices.** These bodies are hinged slightly to the rear of the center and are elevated by a geared hand crank until the elevation of the forward section causes the center of gravity of the load to shift and the load itself completes the dumping action.

Another **special-purpose type of dump body** is a high-lift coal body. This is a regular steel coal body mounted on hinged arms which, in turn, are mounted on a framework. As the piston of the conventional hydraulic hoist elevates, the hinged side arms are brought into play by extreme leverage and further raise the body above the framework. The design is such that the body maintains a slanted position at all heights after being elevated from the truck bed.

This type of body is designed for delivering coal directly through chutes by gravity into the basement of a building, even though the truck must remain several feet away from the building. The truck body must never be elevated except when the truck is resting on a firm, level surface, because when the body is fully raised the center of gravity is so high that even a slight tilt will cause the truck and body to overturn.

TANK TRUCK BODIES. A tank body is a body designed for the transportation of fluid commodities in bulk, according to the SAE definition (SAE Handbook). This definition is intended to apply not only to those bodies used for transporting liquids but also to those intended for dry solids that will flow.

Indicative of the widespread use of truck and trailer tanks in industry and commerce is a list, Fig. 5, of more than 100 commodities commonly handled in tank trucks. (Paper by Frank Baird-Smith, President of the Refiners Transport and Terminal Corp., before the Central Committee on Automotive Transport of the American Petroleum Institute, Chicago, Ill., 1952.)

Mr. Baird-Smith does not claim that this is an all inclusive list but rather that it indicates the range of products suitable for truck or truck-trailer tank transportation. He points out the great care which must be taken to insure that the tank to be used be constructed of material not susceptible to chemical action by the corrosive or other types of liquids to be handled. Likewise, the tank must be built of material of sufficient thickness or gage to withstand the pressures of the materials to be transported.

Not only the tank but also all necessary fittings and loading and unloading equipment must be of a material and strength suitable for the type of commodity to be transported. In many instances truck and truck-trailer tanks must conform to **government specifications.** For example: all tank trucks hauling sulfuric acid or corrosive liquids must comply with the MC-310 Code of the Interstate Commerce Commission. The Commission has other codes for liquefied petroleum gas (LPG) tanks, for gasoline and fuel oil tanks, etc. There are also sanitary codes that apply to the transportation of various food products.

Many tanks, such as those handling liquefied petroleum gas (LPG) products, anhydrous ammonia, and other liquefied gases, must be capable of withstanding pressures of from 250 to 265 lb. per sq. in. All such requirements, and many more for other specialized purposes, must be met by manufacturers specializing in the truck and trailer tank field.

A manhole, or manholes, which can be securely sealed must be provided in the top of the tank. The **manhole cover** must afford not only a tight seal to prevent spillage, but also it must release any excessive pressure generated in the tank by temperature change or for other reasons.

The manner of **mounting** the tank on the truck chassis is important, because the tank must be supported to avoid stresses caused by distortion of the truck frame. Truck tanks have either various-size **compartments or built-in baffles or bulkheads,** to prevent surging of liquids. The bulkheads, and frequently the ends of the tank, are dished to afford greater strength.

SELECTED LIST OF COMMODITIES HAULED IN TANK TRUCKS

Acetic acid	Formaldehyde	Phosphoric acid
Acetone	Fuel oil	Phthalic anhydride
Acid	Gasoline	Pitch, tar
Alcohol, denatured	Glue	Plasticizers
Alcohol solvents	Glycerol	Potassium
Alkids	Grease, inedible	Red oil
Alum	Hydrogen peroxide	Resins, synthetic
Ammonium nitrate	Hydrol	Silicate soda waste
Aqua ammonia	Ink oil	Soap, liquid
Asphalt	Ink, printing	Sodium bichromate
Bardol	Insecticides	Spent sulfite
Benzene	Isopropyl ether	Sulfuric acid
Benzol still residue	Lacquer solvents	Tall oil
Blackstrap molasses	Lactic acid	Tallow
Brewers' slop	Latex	Tar
Butyl acetate	Lignin liquor	Tar acid
Calcium chloride	Liquid sugar	Tar acid oil
Caustic soda	Methanol	Toluol
Chemical oil, crude	Milk	Turpentine
Chlorobutadiene	Molasses	Ultrawet
Coal tar products	Motor fuel-anti-knock	Varsol
Coke oven tar, crude	compound	Vaseline
Creosote	Naphtha	Vegetable oils
Cresol	Naphtha solvent	Water
Dibutyl phthalate	Naphthalene	Water gas neutral oil
	Nitration benzene	
Disinfectant		Water gas tar
Distillers' slop	Nitric acid	Water works primer
Divinylbenzene	Ocuricury oil	solvent
Dizinyl	Oiticica oil	Wax
	Oleum	Wax distillate
Drain oil	Olive oil	Xylene
Drip oil		
Ester gum solution	Paint oil	Yeast, liquid
Ether	Palm oil	
Ethyl acetate	Parapoid	
Fatty acid	Paving tar	
	Phenol	

Fig. 5. Typical commodities transported in tank trucks.

Tanks are **unloaded by gravity or by pumps.** In the case of some chemicals or other products that solidify at normal temperatures, it is necessary to provide insulation, or even auxiliary heat, to be able to discharge the cargo.

Special Truck Bodies

TRUCK BODIES FOR PARTICULAR SERVICES. Among the special-purpose truck bodies that do not fit into any of the above classifications may be listed:

Aerial-tower bodies
Bakery bodies
Beverage or bottlers' bodies
Cement bodies or bulk cement "tanks"
Concrete mixers or ready-mix concrete trucks
Dairy or milk bodies, retail and wholesale routes
Fertilizer- or lime-spreader bodies
Fire apparatus trucks
Garbage or sanitary bodies (see also refuse bodies)
Grain bodies
Ice-delivery bodies
Line-construction or public utility bodies
Oilfield bodies
Oil-tank bodies
Plumbers' bodies (similar to a public utility body or service utility body)
Street sprinklers (a type of tank body for water distribution)

An **aerial-tower body** is one of the very many specially designed truck bodies available to the public utility, municipal, and general service trades. The aerial-tower body is a body equipped with an elevating platform or swivel-type ladder, the purpose of which is to enable a man to work on overhead equipment such as traffic lights, street lights, etc.

A **bakery body** is a closed-panel type body, frequently mounted on a multistop truck, especially fitted with drawers, shelves, etc., to serve the need of a retail route bakery driver-salesman.

A **concrete mixer** or ready-mix concrete truck body is a truck body designed to accept a charge of sand gravel, cement, and water, and to mix these materials in a power-operated rotating drum while in transit or on arrival at destination. This type of body can be manipulated so as to discharge the thoroughly mixed concrete. In some instances the truck motor rotates the mixing drum, while in other makes a separate power plant is provided. Bodies of this type require a relatively heavy-duty chassis, because of the weight of the equipment and the density of the materials transported. Moreover, ready-mix trucks are frequently required to traverse difficult terrain to deliver their cargo to a point where it can be discharged by gravity at a building or construction site. Bodies of this type are rated by their cubic capacity and those in most common use range from 1½ to 5 cu. yd. capacity.

A **dairy or milk body** may be a retail route delivery body or a wholesale route body. The former is customarily a panel-type body with a wide access door on each side of the driver's compartment.

A **fertilizer- or lime-spreader body** is an open-top metal body, quite frequently "V" or trough-shaped with a special spinning device at the rear to distribute the cargo evenly over a given area. The body may be fitted with hinged or removable metal covers for protection of cargo from blowing out while in transit. These bodies are usually equipped with a built-in conveyor at the bottom of the V to deliver the cargo to the discharge mechanism at the rear. In addition to the spinner type of spreader, there is also the conveyor type, with arms and belts extending out from each side at the rear of the truck.

Fire trucks are of concern mainly to city governments, and to large plants having extensive properties where apparatus must be immediately available.

A **garbage or sanitary body** is a body designed for the collection of garbage or refuse, with provision for easy loading and sometimes for compaction of the material as loaded. These are all-metal bodies, usually steel, equipped with an

underbody hoist for dumping. In some instances, they are conventional dump bodies of large cubic capacity fitted with removable steel covers in sections, usually hinged in place. Some of these are scow-end bodies, although this type has largely become obsolete as more and more users have changed over to specially designed refuse bodies. The advantage of the more modern equipment is the low loading provisions at the rear and the relatively greater capacity resulting from the compressing of the collected material.

A **grain body** is essentially a platform with tight, solid sides about 4 ft. high. Since these bodies are designed for the bulk transport of grain or similar material such as cottonseed, they must have a solid front end and sides with a provision for rear unloading.

A **line-construction or public utility body** is of a general type which may vary all the way from an installer's body, as used by the telephone company, to a rack- or van-type body mounted on a heavy-duty truck and equipped with a winch, together with power and hand tools sufficient to justify the term "mobile work shop." The former, or installer's body, type is an oversize tool box mounted on a 5,000-lb. GVW (gross vehicle weight) chassis.

An **oilfield body** is a special type of platform body of extremely heavy construction designed to serve the oilfield riggers and those in related trades. These bodies are customarily mounted on heavy trucks equipped with a heavy-duty winch. A variation of this type is one with a built-in fifth wheel for use inter-

Anthony Co.

Fig. 6. Elevating tail gate for motor trucks.

changeably as a truck-tractor or a truck. Most oilfield bodies are equipped with gin poles for improvising a derrick to load heavy objects. Customarily the winch is mounted in back of the cab, and it and the cab are protected by a strong framework of welded seamless tubing. Trucks equipped with oilfield bodies have a split-shaft power take-off, so that the full power or torque of the truck engine can be applied to the winch or other auxiliary equipment. Special features of oilfield bodies may include a rolling tail pipe to facilitate loading and unloading of heavy objects, auxiliary gas tanks, tool boxes, extra-strong bumpers and grille guards. Construction is heavy-gage welded steel, designed to withstand the most severe usage.

TRUCK AND TRUCK-TRACTOR AUXILIARIES AND COMPONENTS. Elevating tail gates are frequently specified when there is a need to load heavy and/or bulky objects from the street level and where power-operated equipment such as cranes, lift trucks, etc., are not available.

An elevating tail gate, such as shown in Fig. 6, is a tail gate which is constructed so that the truck drivers can raise or lower the tail gate in a vertical plane by mechanical power. In this respect the mechanism is also a type of positioning equipment. In many installations, the power is provided by a hydraulic pump driven by the power take-off of the truck. In some installations, the power is furnished by an electric motor powered by the truck battery.

Truck-Trailers

TYPES OF TRUCK-TRAILER EQUIPMENT. A truck-trailer is defined as a commercial motor vehicle with or without auxiliary motive power, designed to be drawn by a truck or truck-tractor (SAE Handbook). There are essentially two basic classes or groups of truck-trailer equipment: semitrailers and full trailers. This kind of equipment finds wide use in transportation.

Semitrailers. A semitrailer is a truck-trailer equipped with one or more axles and constructed so that a substantial part of its weight and load is carried by a truck-tractor (SAE Handbook). A typical semitrailer is shown in Fig. 7.

Highway Trailer Co.

Fig. 7. Typical semitrailer.

The SAE definitions of a truck-trailer and semitrailer show clearly that a semitrailer is a type of truck-trailer in which a substantial portion (in actual practice frequently as much as 50 percent) of the weight of the vehicle and payload rests on the truck-tractor, as would be the case with the truck-tractor equipment shown in Fig. 8.

Aluminum Company of America

Fig. 8. Semitrailer type of truck-trailer in which up to 50 percent of load rests on truck-tractor.

Full Trailers. A full trailer is a truck-trailer constructed so that practically all of its weight and load rests upon its own wheels (SAE Handbook). The principal difference between a semitrailer and a full trailer is that the latter has a front axle and is self-contained in the sense that it can be pulled by a truck which provides propulsion without providing additional weight-carrying capacity. Thus the truck may carry its own payload and in addition pull a full trailer with additional payload, as is shown in the last trailer in Fig. 9. A semitrailer, however, is pulled by a truck-tractor which normally does not carry any payload other than that contained in the semitrailer.

Fruehauf Trailer Co.

Fig. 9. Tractor pulling both a semitrailer and a full trailer.

Trailer Converter Dolly. A trailer converter dolly is a trailer chassis consisting of an auxiliary axle assembly equipped with a lower fifth wheel half, drawbar, and other necessary parts designed to convert a semitrailer to a full trailer (SAE Handbook).

Pole Trailer. A pole trailer is a truck-trailer without auxiliary motive power, designed to be drawn by a truck or truck-tractor and attached by means of a reach or pole, or by being "boomed" or otherwise secured to the drawing motor vehicle, and intended for transporting long or irregular shaped loads such as poles, logs, pipes, or structural members which are capable generally of sustaining themselves as beams between supporting bolsters.

Specially designed tires are required for **heavy-duty logging trailers** because of the extreme loads and also because the vehicles frequently are operated over rough terrain which would bruise and quickly destroy a highway-type tire.

Logging trailers designed to be used on public roads must conform to state size and weight limits (see Fig. 1) and so are frequently equipped with a built-in weighing device installed under the trailer bolster. The scale gives the approximate axle load, which shows the driver when the truck has been loaded to the full legal limit.

A recent development has been the introduction of a **short full trailer** with a steering front axle and a subframe and bolster used with a logging truck to haul maximum legal loads. The spacing of the two axles of the full trailer is at least 14 ft. and so each axle may carry 18,000 lb. instead of being held to the 32,000-lb. limit placed on tandem axles, the construction normally used in heavy-duty logging trailers. The manufacturer claims that through the use of a steering front axle on the full trailer, the entire vehicle can negotiate narrow, twisting roads where conventional trailers cannot be used.

The single-axle pole trailers commonly associated with logging operations in the eastern and southern states are much lighter in construction than the heavy-duty tandem logging trailers. In addition to transporting logs, these trailers are frequently used to haul telephone poles, lengths of pipe, and other long objects of a similar nature.

Military Truck-Trailers

SIMILARITY TO COMMERCIAL TRAILERS. Military truck-trailers are generally much heavier than comparable civilian types but, with the exception of some special-purpose trailers, are essentially similar in basic design. Military van trailers and semitrailers customarily have square corners although more recently the military services have been buying standard commercial models.

The military services have used a large number of **low-bed trailers,** both for moving construction machinery and as tank retrievers. Specially designed flat-bed trailers of 40 to 45 ft. in length have been used as aircraft retrievers.

USE OF COMMERCIAL-TYPE VEHICLES. Under a policy adopted by authority of the Secretary of the Army in 1952, the military services utilize commercial-type vehicles for administrative purposes and in support-type units, in the continental United States but not in overseas commands. The effect of this policy will be to increase the percentage of standard commercial vehicles.

Truck-Trailer Bodies

VAN TRUCK-TRAILERS AND SEMITRAILERS. Approximately half the truck-trailers produced in the United States are van type. Of these, nearly 90 percent are semitrailers, but since, through the use of a converter dolly, semitrailers may operate as full trailers, they are discussed as "trailers," meaning either semitrailers or full trailers.

Both prior to World War II and in the postwar period there has been available one make of van trailer built of **stainless steel.** The unusually high strength of the material in proportion to its weight has enabled the manufacturer to keep the weight competitive with that of **aluminum trailers.** Stainless steel is said to be even more resistant to weathering, oxidation, and corrosion than aluminum. Neither metal needs paint and, in fact, both are difficult to paint.

Van Trailer Floors. Van trailer floors are of wood, aluminum, magnesium, or steel. The woods used are oak, yellow pine, fir, and "hardwood"—a general specification which allows the manufacturers some latitude in selecting the best available flooring for the purpose. **Wood flooring** may be tongue and grooved, or of planks which in at least one make of trailer may be laid between "hat"-shaped steel reinforcing sections that provide wearing surfaces.

Aluminum floors are frequently made of extruded sections which lock together. Another type of aluminum floor is of either a smooth or a diamond-tread aluminum plate. This type of floor is of composite construction, the aluminum plate being installed over 5-ply waterproof plywood to give additional stiffness or rigidity. **Extruded aluminum floors** are sometimes furnished with inch-by-inch grooves for ventilation but, as in the case of wood floors of this type, the space available does not provide for sufficient air circulation under the load.

Doors. Van trailers customarily have **full-width double doors** in the rear. A right, and occasionally a left, side door is furnished where there is a requirement for **side loading or unloading.** These doors must be strong, although they are not subject to nearly so much abuse as rear doors. It is likewise important that the body side wall be adequately reinforced to compensate for the weakness caused by making a door opening.

The **rear door** should be protected by a solid rear bumper or cross-member at the conventional loading height or dock height. This member is often furnished with exposed rubber bumpers to absorb the shock which occurs when the trailer is backed into a loading dock.

The Interstate Commerce Commission has put into effect a **safety requirement for a rear bumper** to prevent passenger cars from running in under the rear of trailers (Motor Carrier Safety Regulations, Revision of 1952). The regulation states:

Rear-end protection. Every motor vehicle, except truck-tractors, pole trailers, and vehicles engaged in driveaway-towaway operations, the date of manufacture of which is subsequent to December 31, 1952, which is so constructed that the body or the chassis assembly if without a body has a clearance at the rear end of more than 30 in. from the ground when empty, shall be provided with bumpers or devices serving similar purposes which shall be so constructed and located that: (a) the clearance between the effective bottom of the bumpers or devices and the ground shall not exceed 30 in. with the vehicle empty; (b) the maximum distance between the closest points between bumpers or devices, if more than one is used, shall not exceed 24 in.; (c) the maximum transverse distance from the widest part of the motor vehicle at the rear to the bumper or device shall not exceed 18 in.; (d) the bumpers or devices shall be located not more than 24 in. forward of the extreme rear of the vehicle; and (e) the bumpers or devices shall be substantially constructed and firmly attached. Motor vehicles constructed and maintained so that the body chassis, or other parts of the vehicle afford the rear-end protection contemplated shall be deemed to be in compliance with this section.

Recently, several states have enacted requirements for **rear mudguards or splash protectors** on trucks and trailers. This type of equipment is being installed by a number of trailer manufacturers as a standard item for the good-will effect it will have on the motoring public.

Van trailers, as well as all other types of trailers, must have lighting equipment to comply with the requirements of either the local jurisdiction or the Interstate Commerce Commission, whichever is applicable in view of the type of operation contemplated.

Since ICC requirements are accepted in lieu of local requirements where they are not identical, most operators choose to meet ICC requirements even though it is not intended that the trailers shall be used in interstate commerce. Complete information on ICC requirements as to safety equipment, qualifications of drivers, driving of motor vehicles, reporting of accidents, hours of service of drivers, inspection and maintenance of vehicles, and other factors may all be found in Motor Carrier Safety Regulations, latest revision, copies of which are available from the Government Printing Office or from the Commission.

INSULATED AND REFRIGERATED TRUCK-TRAILERS. Insulated and refrigerated truck-trailers are van trailers especially designed and constructed for the protection of perishable commodities. There are essentially **three degrees of refrigeration** that are recognized, one of which provides a range of temperatures from approximately freezing, i.e., 32°F. to 45°F., one for temperature requirements of approximately 10°F., and 0° to −10°F. unit.

Normally, fresh produce such as green beans, lettuce, and all similar commodities are handled in the range of 33° to 35°F. Many frozen products, including meat, may be safely transported in the 10°F. range. Ice cream, frozen fruits, and other frozen products with a relatively high sugar content require 0°F., or below, temperatures.

Various types of **mechanical refrigeration equipment** are available, some designed for low-temperature requirements, and some for medium requirements. **Dry ice** is frequently used and is satisfactory when used with suitable equipment for obtaining air circulation and some degree of control over the rate at which the dry ice is consumed in absorbing heat. Without controlled application, dry ice will tend to overchill the cargo with which it is in contact and will leave heat unabsorbed in the more remote areas of the body

Water-ice and salt have been used for moderately low temperature requirements, but this method is not generally considered satisfactory because of the excessive corrosion induced by the action of the brine on metal parts of the vehicle. **Water-ice and air-circulating blowers** have proved satisfactory for the protection of fresh produce, especially those items that require a high humidity as well as a temperature just a degree or so above freezing.

Recent studies have tended to show that air circulation is one of the most important requirements for satisfactory service in the transportation of perishables. Accordingly, the use of **floor racks** affording a minimum of 2 in. free air space under the load is highly recommended. Such equipment is especially necessary in the transportation of such sensitive commodities as frozen citrus-juice concentrates.

When **water-ice** is used a separate bunker is usually provided in the front or "nose" of the trailer. Adequate drainage must also be provided, especially at the rear of the trailer, because water will run toward the rear as the trailer is propelled forward.

OPEN-TOP VAN TRAILERS. Open-top van trailers and semitrailers are essentially the same as closed van types except that most or all of the roof has been omitted. In many types of van-trailer construction, the roof, along with the side, contributes to the strength of the entire body, especially when the trailers are of "frameless" design.

It is necessary, therefore, in the design of an open-top trailer to provide additional strength in the side-wall construction and in the floor to compensate for the fact that the body is not a complete rectangle or "tube." Customarily, extra-strength framing is used at the top of the side walls.

Tarpaulin bows are also used for added strength, sometimes with a "ridge pole" running horizontally through the center of the top opening. Both bows and ridge pole are removable for top loading of bulky objects. A **header**, which may frequently be removable, is also used above the rear doors as a means of adding stability or stiffness to the trailer side walls.

PLATFORM TRUCK-TRAILERS. The Society of Automotive Engineers' definitions of **platform, stake, and rack bodies** are as follows (SAE Handbook):

1. A **platform body** is a body without raised sides or covering.
2. A **stake body** is a platform body with readily removable stakes which may be tied together with chains, slats, or panels.
3. A **rack body** is a platform body with slatted sides to contain the load.

From these identifications it is clear that a stake body and a rack body are each, essentially, a platform body with something added. In the one case, "stakes" are added, which may be tied together in any of several different ways. In the case of the rack body, sides are added, these sides often not being removable but rather constituting a permanent part of the body.

Platform trailers are widely used in hauling lumber and many other bulky or boxed commodities that do not need protection from the weather, and which, because of their bulk or awkward dimensions, may be loaded more readily on an open-type trailer than in a van.

An **oilfield float** is a special variety of platform trailer designed for front loading and for hauling heavy machinery and other objects too heavy to lift by conventional means. The oilfield float, together with the **winch-equipped truck-tractor** or the combination **oilfield truck body and fifth wheel,** is a surprisingly versatile piece of transportation equipment. The front of the trailer can be dropped to the ground to form a loading ramp and the truck is then moved into position so that the winch can pull the piece of machinery, or other object to be transported, up the ramp or slope of the body until it is far enough back over the rear wheels to take the weight off the front of the body. Rather than being raised by manually operated front trailer supports, the oilfield float then is "picked up" by the use of the cable and winch on the truck, and, once coupled to the truck, the object to be transported is moved forward until the correct weight distribution is obtained.

These trailers usually have a half-round or a rolling tail pipe, or tail board, at the rear for easier loading and unloading. Units of this type customarily have up to 2-in. oak floors for strength, easy sliding of heavy objects, and long wear under adverse conditions. A heavily reinforced bumper at the rear end of the frame and between the tires is another feature customarily provided on oilfield floats.

Stake trailers may be described as platform trailers with removable vertical "stakes" of wood or metal, used to retain the load on the trailer. In most instances, however, load binders are considered preferable to stakes. If the nature of the cargo is such that load binders, dunnage, or other forms of bracing are not considered practical, the operators usually prefer either a rack body or a grain body.

Rack trailers are used for cargo which does not require protection from the weather, and for livestock transportation. A conventional rack trailer is a platform with vertical and horizontal wood or metal posts and slats enclosing the loading space. In some cases, the racks are in sections which may be removed, but more frequently they are permanently installed as a part of the body. A ridge pole and cross-bows similar to those used on an open-top van are frequently supplied to provide support for a tarpaulin.

GRAIN-BODY TRAILERS. A grain-body trailer is a platform trailer with permanent side, front, and rear of tight construction suitable to contain loose material such as wheat, oats, cottonseed, etc. Besides handling bulk grain, bodies of this type are frequently used to transport citrus fruit in bulk from the groves to processing plants.

The **size** of grain-body truck trailers may depend upon the maximum gross weight limits permitted in the state or states in which they will operate, but customarily grain trailers are approximately 28 to 35 ft. in length, 8 ft. in width, and 4 ft. in height.

LOW-BED TRAILERS. Low-bed trailers, sometimes known as machinery trailers or "low boys," are defined by the Society of Automotive Engineers as "a truck-trailer with or without a platform body, constructed to provide a low loading height and designed for the transportation of extremely heavy or bulky property" (SAE Handbook).

As the various names and the SAE definitions imply, low-bed trailers are designed for a variety of purposes—all of which require **low loading height and/or ability to carry extreme weights.** Customarily, low-bed trailers have a floor or load-carrying platform no higher, and frequently lower, than the height of the rear tires. Frequently, the flooring is cut away or omitted over the tops of the tires so as to achieve low over-all height. Moreover, many types have drop-frame construction so as to provide a minimum loading height between the gooseneck and the rear wheels.

Low-bed trailers are constructed of steel beams, usually fabricated by the trailer manufacturer from plate steel. The web and flange shapes are cut out in the desired shape and then welded together, because it is generally impracticable to attempt to standardize dimensions sufficiently to permit efficient mill production. Low-bed trailers are usually semitrailers but are frequently used as full trailers, with the addition of a converter dolly, because the fifth-wheel weight would be too great for conventional truck-tractors.

Low-bed trailers customarily have floor planking laid crosswise rather than lengthwise as is usual on other types of trailers. Floor planks are usually of oak or other types of hardwood, 2 in. or more in thickness, and treated with a wood preservative. Floor planks are bolted to the frame of the trailer.

The **tonnage ratings** of low-bed trailers range from 10 tons up to 100 tons or more. The largest-known low-bed was designed to carry 600 tons on improved highways. It was equipped with 64 wheels. Low-bed trailers frequently require special permits to use the public highways because their weight, when loaded, exceeds the legal gross weight limit, or because their width exceeds the 8-ft. legal limit.

Among the more common **special types** are the removable gooseneck trailer, the tilt-bed, and the girder or I-beam trailer. The arched forward section, which extends forward over the truck frame or the dolly and supports the upper fifth-wheel plate and kingpin, is known as the **gooseneck.** In some models, this forward section may be disconnected, allowing the front of the platform to rest on the ground for front loading, in a manner somewhat similar to the oilfield float.

The gooseneck is supported and connected and disconnected by power obtained from the truck-tractor. This kind of trailer is known as the **removable gooseneck trailer.**

In the **tilt-bed trailer** a portion, if not all, of the floor is constructed on a hinged framework which can be raised up from its normal horizontal position until the rear of the body rests on the ground in back of the rear wheels. The movement of the body is generally controlled by one or more **hydraulic cylinders.** Bulldozers, road machinery, or other power-driven equipment may then be loaded on trailers by being driven up the ramp formed by the body.

Tilt-bed trailers can also be used to load tractors and other power-driven equipment onto the truck body itself, thus affording quick loading, transporting, and unloading of two pieces of equipment at the same time—one on the truck and one on the trailer.

A **girder-type, low-bed truck** is one in which two heavy steel girders, extending from the gooseneck back to the rear-axle assembly, provide support for a crawler crane with the treads straddling the girders. The advantage obtained is low load height, bringing the top of the crane down below the standard clearances under bridges and underpasses.

AUTO-TRANSPORT TRAILERS. These vehicles are steel semitrailers of light construction specially designed and equipped for the transportation of new or used automobiles or trucks. Since completed automobiles need not be protected from the weather, such trailers are not fully enclosed, although they do have partial sides. They are customarily 35 ft. in length and, when loaded, frequently are approximately 13 ft. in over-all height. To provide maximum inside clearance between the wheels, these trailers have tandem axles, each with a single rather than a dual-tired wheel.

TANK TRAILERS. As defined by the Society of Automotive Engineers, tank trailers are "truck-trailers designed for the transportation of fluid commodities in bulk." Essentially, tank trailers provide the same types of service as tank trucks, except that their greater carrying capacity makes them ideally suited for bulk and/or long-distance movement of all types of fluid commodities. (See Fig. 5 for a partial list of liquids transported in tank trucks or tank trailers.)

The difference between a **tank for truck mounting** and a **tank trailer** is that the former rests on a level truck frame, whereas the latter is generally frameless or self-supporting. As in the case of the modern van-type trailer, sufficient structural strength is engineered into the tank shell to obviate the need for a trailer frame. Instead, an upper fifth-wheel plate is installed under the front of the tank, and a subframe suitable to provide seats for the spring hangers is provided at the rear.

Tank trailers are **widely used for various chemicals** and, as in truck tanks, each requirement must be carefully studied to select the correct equipment for the use intended. Butane and propane have recently become widely accepted as **motor vehicle fuels,** and thus there is a need for their transportation over highways. Special liquefied petroleum gas (LPG) trailers with heavy steel plate tanks tested to 250 psi (lb. per sq. in.) have become quite common in this service.

DUMP TRAILERS. The Society of Automotive Engineers defines dump trailers as "truck-trailers provided with a body which can be tilted or otherwise manipulated to discharge its load by gravity" (SAE Handbook). Essentially similar to a dump truck, a dump trailer is a vehicle specially designed for the economical transportation of bulk materials such as sand, gravel, ore, coal, grain, or waste materials. The dump trailer, however, can provide both greater cubic capacity and greater payload capacity than the dump truck, especially in states that regulate weight by a formula or gross weight table based on axle spacing.

Most dump trailers are elevated and dumped by an **underbody hydraulic hoist** essentially similar to a heavy-duty truck hoist (see Fig. 10).

Fruehauf Trailer Co.

Fig. 10. Dump trailer.

Cable dump trailers, however, do not have an underbody hydraulic hoist but rather are elevated by two steel cables running from a winch mounted on the tractor back to the twin sheaves under the trailer. The sheaves are attached to supports which, in turn, are attached to the trailer frame, slightly forward of the trailer axle or tandem assembly. Tubular arms between the special fifth wheel and the trailer frame caused the trailer to elevate as it is pulled toward the truck.

TRUCK-TRAILER CHASSIS. Truck-trailer manufacturers provide the **complete vehicle, body, and chassis,** fully equipped ready to go into service. In many types of truck-trailers the separate chassis, as such, has disappeared entirely and the vehicle is now of integral construction. Vans, tanks, and some types of platform and rack bodies are examples of this type of construction. The structural strength formerly supplied by frame rails and cross members has been incorporated into the body framework.

Semitrailers were formerly built with one rear axle, but as operators' load requirements have increased and as state size and weight limits have been relaxed, there has been a requirement for an increasing number of **tandem-axle semitrailers.**

A tandem is an assembly of two axles for the support of the rear of a truck-trailer. It is distinguished from a "bogie" by the fact that a "tandem" is an assembly of axles for a trailer, and, as such, consists of two nondriving axles, while a "bogie" is an assembly of two rear axles, one or both of which are driven with a common transverse trunnion used on a three-axle truck or truck-tractor. A third axle is defined as an additional nondriving axle placed immediately behind, or in front of, the driving axle of a truck or truck tractor. Generally the five-axle combination of three-axle tractor and tandem trailer will best fit the state legal limits and provide the maximum legal payload.

TRAILER AUXILIARIES AND COMPONENTS. A principal component of truck-trailers as well as trucks is the elevating tail gate. The only difference between elevating tail gates on trucks and those on truck-trailers is the problem of obtaining a power supply. Generally, trailer elevating tail gates are powered by electric motors, drawing their supply of electricity from the truck battery. Other methods are to provide a rotating kingpin or hydraulic hose connections from a pump mounted on the tractor. These methods of power transmission have both already been discussed in connection with dump trailers.

SPECIAL TRUCK-TRAILERS NOT OTHERWISE CLASSIFIED. Among the many special types of truck-trailers not otherwise classified are **demountable trailer bodies,** usually van-type bodies, that serve as containers for package shipments, or as mobile refrigerators for perishable shipments. Among these bodies are milk tanks.

The procedure is to have a trailer body which can be readily dismounted from a special trailer chassis. The complete trailer body and chassis is loaded for shipment and hauled to either rail- or waterway terminal, where it is lifted or shifted from the trailer chassis and deposited on a rail flat car or a waterway barge. After completing the rail or water journey, the demountable body is lifted from the intermediate carrier, again placed on a trailer chassis, and is then ready to be hauled to final destination for delivery of the cargo.

In some cases the complete trailer is spotted on the rail flat car or barge. Neither of the above practices has as yet come into wide general use, but both are well established in actual operation. Both "piggyback" (the hauling of loaded trailers on rail flat cars) and "fishyback" (the overwater shipment of loaded trailers on specially designed trailer ships) are important recent developments in transportation. Both offer economies, principally in handling cost, by eliminating unloading and reloading.

Maintenance of Truck Bodies

METHODS FOR UPKEEP OF TRUCKS. One of the major independent manufacturers of motor truck bodies makes the following recommendations in a pamphlet on "The Care of Your Truck Body."

Body Mounting Bolts:
Tighten body **mounting bolts** after first 500 miles. Recheck these every 2,000 miles thereafter. Loose mounting bolts cause progressive fractures of truck and body frame members.

If body has wooden underframe, watch for excessive wear on wood sills. Add metal protectors to reduce wear.

If body has steel underframe, be sure **filler blocks or spaces** are provided within steel longitudinal sills. See that these are always in position at each mounting bolt.

Be sure **longitudinal sills** are spaced to match width of truck frame so that direct force of load is carried on vertical section of frame members.

Be sure mounting bolts are of correct size to prevent body from shifting, causing failures in equipment and severe accidents.

Body Assembly Bolts and Nuts:
Tighten all body assembly bolts, nuts, and screws after first 500 miles. Recheck these every 2,000 miles thereafter.

Be sure all grain sides or stock racks have hold-down fasteners to platform and keep these tight at all times. This helps to eliminate wear and increases safety factors when carrying capacity loads. The additional support in the body side walls adds strength to the platform.

Stakes and Stake Pockets:
Wooden stakes will wear rapidly in pockets if not provided with steel shoe. Pockets cut into wood framing or floor will wear rapidly if not metal lined. Tapered pockets and stakes are essential when made of wood. Wood stakes and wood around pockets will expand from moisture. This prevents removing sides. Keeping these points painted will help.

Expansion and Warpage of Wood:
Moisture will expand and warp lumber. Expansion is the most destructive of all. Apply hot oil to floor as soon as the first paint starts to wear off and at frequent intervals thereafter (crankcase drainings make a cheap protection for floors) keep remainder of body well painted.

Shrinkage and Warpage:
Seasoned kiln-dried lumber is less apt to shrink in seasons and climates of normal humidity. Unseasoned, air-dried lumber will shrink and warp without regard to seasons or climates. If constantly supplied with moisture this shrinking and warping may be minimized. Shrinkage of seasoned, kiln-dried lumber can be prevented only by the truck operator, by supplying moisture when needed, and protecting with paint and oil to "seal in" required moisture.

Bodies with Metal Sides:
All metal bodies dent very easily and are subject to "springing." Dented metal sides or bent upright members should be carefully straightened by experienced men in a body shop, where stretching of metal can be minimized to preserve the alignment of sides.

Hardware:
Check, tighten, and oil all hardware frequently. Loose hardware will shorten life of body and may cause loss of load.

Painting:
Body parts not painted before assembly will rust and deteriorate more rapidly. Close observation around joints and crevices will reveal whether manufacturer has taken this precaution. If not, joints and crevices should be sealed by forcing in extra quantities of paint before deterioration sets in. Repaint the entire body when paint begins to chip, peel, or slough off, exposing wood or metal surfaces. Use a good weatherproof paint.

TRAILER PREVENTIVE MAINTENANCE. The Trailer Maintenance Committee of the Truck-Trailer Manufacturers Association has developed an industry Trailer Preventive Maintenance Program. The purpose of the program is to set forth all of the procedures necessary to secure maximum life, satisfactory service, and safe operation, at minimum cost, from a piece of equipment, short of completely rebuilding or replacing it.

Records are few and easily maintained. Little follow-up is required. The trailer carries a visible, easily checked TPM Due Date Record, which is the heart of the program. However, simple as the program is, it is intended to be adequate to meet existing ICC requirements of inspection and maintenance (Part No. 196).

Many problems arise on leased and interchange units, and TPM with its uniform but simple and still flexible system of inspection and preventive maintenance is designed to handle them. ICC regulations (Part 196.2) state that when a trailer is accepted on lease or interchange, the party accepting it for operation is required to inspect the trailer to make sure it is in good condition, record the inspection, and continue a regular PM plan according to schedule.

RAILROAD FREIGHT CARS

CONTENTS

RAILROAD FREIGHT CARS

FUNCTIONS OF THE RAILROAD FREIGHT CAR. The railroad freight car is, basically, a platform on wheels. There are many variations in such platforms designed to make them good transportation media for the loads carried, easier for the railroads to handle, and easier to load and unload with current transportation facilities. But perhaps the most important fact from the railroad patron's point of view is the fact that there are cars available to fill practically all of the basic needs of shippers. Almost daily, a new device for application to freight cars comes on the market, or a new design of open or closed car appears for handling some new commodity or taking better care of an old one.

House Cars

BOXCARS. The house-type cars, such as boxcars and refrigerator cars, are extensively used, the boxcar being by far the most numerous of all the kinds of railroad cars and also the most versatile. Boxcars are constructed in a variety of lengths, widths, heights, and capacities, the usual inside lengths being 40 ft. 6 in. and 50 ft. 6 in., and the usual load capacity 100,000 lb. The dimensional capacity ranges from about 2,750 cu. ft. up to 5,000 cu. ft. **Doors** to the boxcar may be single or double on each car side, the single-door widths varying usually from 6 ft. to 8 ft. Some cars have 9-ft. doors. Double doors have a combined opening width of 12 ft. Another 60-ft. boxcar has two separate single doors on each side. There are some cars in use that have doors in the ends of the cars (see Fig. 1). The model shown is specially designed for transporting automobiles.

Many freight cars have a wide variety of **interior fittings** designed to hold loads in place and/or to make possible the best utilization of the cubic capacity of the cars. The variety of such fittings is gradually increasing (Railway Age, vol. 137), and there is no one descriptive source which covers them all. Many cars have been described in railway publications such as Railway Age, Railway Locomotives and Cars, and other predecessor publications—notably Car Builders' Cyclopedia, and, since 1946, Modern Railroads. The Official Railway Equipment Register lists all the kinds of revenue-service cars of the railroads in the United States, Canada and Mexico, but shows only car numbers, marked weight capacities, dimensions, and cubic capacities of such cars. It does give some other information in footnotes, many of which, however, state only general facts such as "equipped for handling automobile parts."

For **general service**—i.e., for handling a variety of commodities—the boxcar has been improved greatly in the last few years. Floors have been strengthened by the addition of more longitudinal stringers and the use of heavier flooring. To a great extent, increased use of the fork truck and other kinds of heavy materials handling equipment has helped bring about use of heavier flooring, and other measures for safety. Seven-, eight-, and even nine-foot doors are superseding the old standard six-foot doors (Car Builders' Cyclopedia, 19th edition, Box Cars Section).

44·1

Canadian National Railways

Fig. 1. Boxcar with end doors.

Boxcar Load-securing Devices. Cars are now being equipped with special devices, such as varieties of **lading anchors,** to which may be fastened the steel strapping or wire used with lumber for bracing cargo against in-transit shocks. One leading railroad, for example, has almost 1,200 boxcars equipped with the "Economy Safe-Load Device," which is a band of fixed lading anchors, extending lengthwise along the side walls of the car. In these cars there are six such bands, beginning 6 in. above the floor, with the top band almost 7 ft. from the floor. These strap-anchors are valuable in helping to brace loads, prevent damage to cargo, and cut bracing costs. They are particularly useful in the loading of a stop-off car, i.e., one whose load is to be delivered to several consignees at a number of different destinations.

A number of years ago the Pennsylvania Railroad introduced boxcars with a series of **gates**—the Steins gate-and-shelf device—which are used as load-retainers. Most of these cars are used only in the railroad's own L.C.L. (less-than-carload) freight service, and are not generally available to individual shippers. The cars have shelves attached to the gates. The gates divide the load vertically, and the shelves divide it horizontally. The load in the car may thus be double-decked and divided longitudinally into several sections. By so compartmentizing the load, the railroad eliminates many chances of damage to the freight.

There are many freight cars available to shippers that are fitted with flexible devices corresponding to the Steins gate-and-shelf system. These cars are known as **"D/F" (damage-free) cars,** and are equipped with Evans Products Co. load-dividers. Fig. 2 shows the interior of such a D/F car. The cross braces, shown on the floor, may be spaced as the shipper's needs dictate. The cross braces and the racks or deckboards standing at the rear of the car make it possible to divide the loads into decks as well as into longitudinal sections. These items, in addition to belt rails and doorway members, make the D/F car an extremely flexible device.

Atchison, Topeka and Santa Fe Railway Co.

Fig. 2. D/F (damage-free) boxcar.

The Pullman Standard **Compartmentizer** is another kind of load separator and retainer which to date, however, has not been so widely used as has the D/F car. The Compartmentizer gates, a pair of which are located in each end of the car, can be moved to almost any desired position, or they may be folded back against the wall and not used at all. The Compartmentizer, however, does not make double-decking of lading possible.

Metal Floor Protection. Most of the boxcars now being built—or rebuilt— have been equipped with metal floor-protectors in the doorway area, as in Fig. 2, or in some cases with complete **nailable steel floors**, as shown in Fig. 3, primarily because of the increased use of mechanical handling equipment in loading and unloading freight cars. Loaded fork trucks exert a heavy pressure on the floor at the car doors. The driver generally begins to turn his truck as soon as he gets the truck through the doorway of the freight car, thus causing excessive wear or damage to the flooring in the doorway area. Metal floor protectors should be used to reduce this damage to the boxcar floor, and possible injury to the truck driver if the car floor gives way.

Shippers should know which kinds and varieties of handling equipment are owned and used by the carrier or carriers serving their plant or plants, and should possess and be guided by the excellent information in the Railway Equipment Register, a copy of which should be in the shipping offices of all companies using railroad transportation facilities.

VENTILATED BOXCARS. There are still available on the railroads several thousand ventilated boxcars. These cars now are owned mainly by the

New York Central Railroad

Fig. 3. Boxcar with nailable steel flooring.

lines in the southeastern part of the United States. The **capacity** of these cars is seldom more than 80,000 lb., and nowadays they are used mainly by the owning lines for the transportation of L.C.L. freight and carloads of fruits and vegetables. Their usefulness seems to be about over, and it is likely that no more of them will be built. These cars have ventilating slats or screening in either the car ends or the side doors, or in both places. Some of these cars are insulated, either wholly or partially.

INSULATED BOXCARS. There are a number of insulated boxcars designed particularly to protect the lading against the injurious effects of heat or cold. Candy, for example, is shipped in such cars, as are potatoes.

UNIT-LOAD BOXCARS. One type of unit-load boxcar, shown in Fig. 4, is divided into compartments, each with rolling side doors and with area enough for four standard unit pallet loads. The inside width and height are, however, a few inches less than the A.A.R.-recommended standard dimensions.

REFRIGERATOR CARS. Many railroads now have refrigerator cars or so-called "reefers." Some of these cars are equipped with a variety of **mechanical temperature control units,** certain of which will produce only cold temperatures. Other cars are equipped with mechanical units which will produce either heat or cold, and control the temperature in the car at any preset figure. These mechanically refrigerated cars at present are used almost exclusively in the handling of frozen foods—frozen citrus juices in particular. The cars can maintain temperatures at 0° F. or lower, which frozen foods producers consider necessary if the foods are not to deteriorate.

Fig. 4. Unit-load compartmented car.

Other kinds of refrigerator cars are equipped for use in freight and/or passenger train service. The modern cars have a minimum of 4 in. of insulation and frequently are equipped with either floor-type or, better, overhead-type **fans** which circulate the cool or warm air through the load. Most "reefers" can be equipped with portable charcoal- or alcohol-burning heaters when the weather makes it necessary to apply heat instead of cold to the load.

There are refrigerator cars, known as **brine-tank cars,** which are used chiefly for shipping meat and packing-house products. The main difference between these cars and the ordinary "bunker"-type reefer is that ice (generally crushed) and salt are placed in a metal container. The metal container or brine tank may be located either in the spot where the bunker would be—overhead in a standard refrigerator car—or at the ends of the car, at floor level. Some of these brine-tank cars are equipped with meat rails from which quarters of meat are hung during transportation.

Today's refrigerator car, at first glance, may seem to be like its predecessor of 20 to 30 years ago. Closer inspection, however, will disclose that a number of changes have been made in this kind of car, especially over the past ten years. More and more cars are being equipped with **sliding doors**—now at least 6 ft. wide, and a foot or more higher than the doors of the older cars. This larger door has made possible the wider use of the fork-truck–pallet system in loading refrigerator cars. Sliding doors are being further perfected. Refrigerator cars with hinged 4-ft.-wide doors still, however, far outnumber those with the newer and wider sliding door.

It is highly unlikely that any newly-built reefers will have narrow doors, nor will they have wooden floor racks, because the wooden floor racks have tended to break under heavy concentrated loads. The metal racks in the newer cars stand up well under such loads.

STOCK CARS. One kind of house car with which almost everyone is familiar is the stock car, with its load of hogs, cattle, chickens, or other livestock. There are several different kinds of stock cars, ranging from 40-ft., 40-ton, single-deck cars for cattle to cars with adjustable decks and shelves for crates of poultry. These cars may or may not be equipped with feed and water troughs for the stock.

Tank Cars

TANK CAR CONSTRUCTION. Tank cars are most frequently used for bulk transportation of liquids. The load-container of the tank car may be built of metal or of wood. The tank may consist of one large container, or it may be compartmented. Tanks may be made of—or lined with—aluminum, rubber, glass, stainless steel, etc., depending upon the kind of commodity the car is designed to handle. Such cars may be insulated to protect the lading against extremes of temperature. The tank car also frequently is equipped with steam coils so that heat may be applied to the lading so as to simplify the unloading process if commodities have tended to congeal during transportation. Among cars in use are a 50-ton car with an 8,000-gal. corrosion-resistant aluminum tank and a 40-ton, 6,000-gal. general-purpose car with a three-compartment tank.

TANK CAR OPERATION. Of the roughly 150,000 tank cars in use on American railroads, only about 5 percent are owned by the railroads themselves. Most of the others are owned directly by the shippers, or are leased by them from private car lines such as, for example, General American Transportation Corp. General American alone owns and operates about 200 specialized types of tank cars.

Tank cars are usually **loaded** through domes at the top of the car, and **unloaded** through outlet valves projecting from the belly, or underside, of the tank. Unloading may be done either by gravity or by suction lines. Some commodities, however, such as liquefied gases, must be unloaded from the cars through **eduction pipes** which enter through the dome of the car.

Tank cars carry many **explosive or other dangerous commodities.** Hence their specifications are subject to the regulations of the Interstate Commerce Commission. Thus the ICC specifies the pressure to which tanks handling given ladings must be tested, as well as the settings for the safety valves located in the domes of most tank cars.

CARS FOR PORTABLE TANKS. There are a few so-called tank cars in existence—most if not all of them owned by the shippers themselves—which are more like flatcars than like conventional tankers in that the cars have floors. The floors of these cars are equipped with brackets or braces for holding in place a number of portable tanks. A salt manufacturer, for example, uses a number of these cars for transporting liquid chlorine. The Navy Department, on the other hand, uses cars in which multiple cylinders are an integral part of the car.

Hopper Cars

TYPES OF OPEN CARS. As common as the house car is the **open-type car,** i.e., a car, not roofed, with the lading exposed to the elements unless temporarily covered by paper, tarpaulins, boxes, etc., furnished by the shipper.

Most numerous and probably best known of all open-top equipment is the **open hopper car,** or as it is frequently called, the coal car. Next most numerous in the open-top field is the **gondola,** a car with sides and end walls and no roof. Finally, there are the **flatcar** and its modifications, the depressed-center car and the well-hole car.

HOPPER CAR DESIGN. The hopper car generally has from two to four hoppers, or pockets, with **gates** at the bottom so that the lading will flow from the car. These hoppers, or pockets, are sloped so that, under normal weather conditions, most of the lading will slide out of the gates with but a little help from vibrators, etc. Most of the newer hopper cars have a load capacity of 70 tons or more.

OPEN HOPPER CARS. Most open hopper cars have the hopper gates hinged crosswise of the car. Each of the hoppers is divided in two lengthwise at the bottom by the center sill of the car. Thus, when the car is standing, the larger part of the load is dumped so that it falls between the rails on which the car rests (see Fig. 5). The car shown has 4 hoppers. The usual car of this type is

Fig. 5. 70-ton quadruple hopper car; capacity, 2,736 cu. ft.

equipped with 2 or 3 hoppers. Some railroads have cars whose hopper doors are hinged lengthwise of the car (see Fig. 6). Some of these latter cars dump their loads outside the rails, some inside the rails, and some both inside and outside the rails. They are used chiefly on western and Canadian railroads. Most of the eastern carriers have such cars, but they are generally restricted to use in railroad ballast service. 70-ton quadruple hopper cars are also available with side discharge gates.

Fig. 6. 70-ton side-discharge hopper car; capacity, 2,075 cu. ft.

Some hopper cars are equipped with **coke racks.** Coke racks are (ordinarily) slatted frames which can be applied above the ends and side walls of the car, so that larger quantities of material, with a large volume and relatively little weight, may be placed in the car.

It is undoubtedly true that no other kind of railroad car takes the abuse that the hopper car does. In efforts to speed unloading, receivers—and sometimes the railroads themselves—use **car shakeouts** which, in time, may rattle the cars to pieces. In the winter, if the lading is frozen, heat may be applied to the hopper-slope sheets in an effort to thaw the lading so that it will run more freely. In so doing, the receiver sometimes damages the car in certain respects. Sledges are used to hammer the side sheets and slope sheets of these cars so as to shake the lading free, or to get it to flow faster. In the long run, of course, those who adopt such methods must pay for the damage done, even if only as an indirect expense.

Railroads handling large volumes of **iron-ore traffic** have some cars confined almost exclusively to this particular class of service. These cars generally have a low cubic capacity and high weight-bearing capacity. Most such cars now are built with one hopper which runs lengthwise of the car. Hopper doors, hinged lengthwise of the car, open so that practically all of the load in the car is dumped between the rails.

COVERED HOPPER CARS. The covered hopper car is basically a coal car with a roof. It is now used exclusively for the transportation of commodities which move in bulk (i.e., unpackaged) and are susceptible to weather damage. Originally, covered hoppers were designed for handling cement, but more recently their use in transporting sugar, flour, lamp black, chemicals, etc., has increased. There has been **increasing specialization** in the construction of these cars. The car builders, for example, have varied the angle or slope of the steel sheets of the hoppers in these cars, so that regardless of the flow characteristics of the commodities which the cars were designed to handle, the hoppers tend to be "self-clearing," aided only by gravity. The General American Transportation Corp., however, has built covered hoppers which can be unloaded by pneumatic conveying systems. This system, using air slides, is described and illustrated in the section on Pneumatic Conveyors. The same company also has built insulated covered hoppers for transporting refined sugar. It seems likely that the transportation field has seen only the beginning of specialization of the covered hopper car.

Covered hoppers are **loaded** through hatches in the "roof" and are **unloaded** through outlets on the underside of the car (see Fig. 7). The number of loading hatches and outlets may vary. Hatch covers and outlets are designed so that neither moisture nor dust from the outer air can get to the load. Most covered hoppers have a large load-bearing capacity.

Fig. 7. 70-ton covered hopper car with multiple hatches on roof.

Gondola Cars

TYPES OF GONDOLA CARS. A close relative of the hopper car is the gondola car. In fact, some gondolas are equipped with floor-doors so that loads of coal, coke, or other bulk materials may be discharged through the car bottom as shown in Fig. 8. This car, of 2,269 cu. ft. capacity, has 16 drop-bottom doors hinged at the center sill. Most gondolas today, however, have solid floors, made either of steel, lumber, or a combination of these two flooring materials, and fixed sides.

Fig. 8. 70-ton gondola car with drop-bottom doors.

Some gondolas have high sides (relatively) and many have low sides, say of slightly less than 4 ft. Gondolas are available with drop ends so that they may be loaded from the ends. Long loads of steel beams, for example, which require more than one car, may be placed on two such cars when the car-ends are lowered. Gondola cars range in length from about 40 ft. (inside) to about 70 ft., and load capacities are generally upward of 50 tons.

GONDOLA LOAD-SECURING DEVICES. Gondolas are sometimes equipped with **lading-band anchors** which are applied to the coping angles of the side walls. Also, some gondolas are built with devices on the floors or side walls of the cars to which strapping or wire used for tie-downs may be anchored.

At Grand Rapids, Michigan, a **modified gondola car** was developed to reduce blocking charges to a minimum for safe transportation of steel. The experimental car contained a cushioned steel platform which floated on H-type beams. It was equipped with movable partitions similar to those in a file drawer, and was found suitable for either coil or bundle steel. Fig. 9 shows the experimental gondola car with movable partitions, as designed by the Chesapeake & Ohio Railway.

In recent years the railroads have begun to apply Nailable Steel Flooring and Armco Freight Car Flooring to gondolas. Fig. 3 shows the **securing method** used with these floorings. Ordinary nails, driven into the grooves between nailable steel floor channels, are deformed by the bending action of the channel flanges and securely held. The proper size nails—16 penny and 20 penny in boxcars, 20 penny and 30 penny in gondolas—are easily driven, and readily removed with a clawbar. Nailing grooves are spaced 8 in. apart and permit the blocking of all types of freight with few modifications from conventional practice. These two floorings give the strength of steel to the floors, yet give the shipper something to which he may nail blocking so as to keep his load from moving all over the car, once it is en route to the receiver.

GONDOLA CONTAINER CARS. There are several **special types** of gondolas which are of importance. One is a gondola designed to handle demountable containers of several kinds. On eastern railroads, particularly, there are a number of these cars. Actually, most of them are little different from any

Fig. 9. Experimental gondola car with movable partitions.

other gondola, except that they may be equipped with **guides** and **cleats** for holding the containers in place (see Fig. 10). Some of these cars have side frames but no side sheets. Containers handled in such cars are usually loaded with bulk materials, such as cement. Other commodities, however, such as brick, also are handled in containers in this kind of car.

WELL-TYPE GONDOLA CAR. There is also a well-type gondola car. This car is one having large depressions in the floor which permit ladings to be lowered so as to clear overhead obstacles such as bridges crossing the railroad tracks.

COVERED GONDOLA CARS. In the last few years the railroads have designed several gondola cars with sliding covers. This experimentation was done at the behest of the steel companies who wished to obtain cheap weather protection for some steels shipped in open-top equipment. To date, no practical "covered" gondola has resulted from these experiments, although portable steel sectional covers have been used successfully. Developmental work, however, has not ceased.

Pennsylvania Railroad

Fig. 10. Gondola container car equipped with guides and spacers for 12 containers.

Flatcars

STANDARD TYPES. Flatcars come in a wide variety of lengths and capacities. Most such cars have two sets of standard four-wheel trucks under them, but some of the larger-capacity special flats are supported on as many as 32 wheels. For example, a 125-ton, 56-ft. flatcar rides on two 12-wheel trucks. These cars, however, might be called the superspecial flats, because some of them can handle loads of up to 250 tons.

Most standard flatcars have **wooden floors,** although of late some of them have been equipped with **nailable steel floors** (see previous references to the same devices applied to boxcars and gondolas). All the general-purpose cars have **stake-pockets** welded or bolted to the side sills. These stake-pockets can also be used as anchors in blocking, bracing, and tying down loads placed on the cars. One can readily understand why tying down loads on these cars is so important.

T.O.F.C. SERVICE. In the last few years, with the growth of the highway-trailer-on-flatcar movement as a revenue-producer for many railroads, the ordinary flatcar has been changed somewhat so as to accommodate this new traffic. The main visible changes have been:

1. **Low side rails,** to keep trailers on the car when they are being backed into position.
2. **Tie-down brackets** or U-bolts, to which are attached chains extending to the trailer to hold it in place when the car is in motion.
3. **Apron plates** which are carried in raised position when the car is in motion, but are lowered during the loading or unloading process to permit tractors and trailers to pass from one car to another.

RACK CARS. Probably the most frequently noticed of the special-type flats is the **rack** or **pulpwood car,** used especially in Canada and the southeastern

Fig. 11. 40-ton pulpwood car with end racks and sloping deck.

United States (see Fig. 11). Generally there are two major differences between the ordinary flatcar and the car for carrying pulpwood logs:

1. There are high **barricades** at each end of the pulpwood car.
2. The car is not really flat, since its floor gently V's in to the center of the car from the sides. This V'd flooring permits pulpwood to be loaded easily, and relieves the shipper from the necessity of tying down his load.

SPECIAL FLATCARS. The other two frequently-seen special kinds of flatcars are the depressed-center flat and the well-hole flat. These cars—but most generally the depressed-center cars—are the ones which take the heavy loads. The **depressed-center car** has that portion of the floor extending between trucks depressed, or lowered, so that high loads may be handled. Fig. 12 shows the world's largest railroad car, transporting a completely assembled 90,000 kw.

Fig. 12. 250-ton-capacity depressed-center flatcar, 124 ft. long over-all on 32 wheels.

Westinghouse turbogenerator for installation in the Houston Light & Power Company, in Texas. The railroad car is 124 ft. 3 in. long, weighs 495,000 lb., has 32 car-wheels and will carry a load of 500,000 pounds. Since most loads that require depressed-center flats to gain overhead clearance are very heavy, the cars usually have high weight-bearing capacity.

Well-hole cars generally serve a similar purpose. The well-hole car, however, instead of having its whole center depressed, is built with a hole in an otherwise regular flat floor. Because of the nature of the commodities shipped on well-hole flatcars (plate glass, etc.), the weight-bearing capacities of these cars are not generally quite so high as those of the average depressed-center car.

MILITARY RAILROAD EQUIPMENT. Many shippers today do a great deal of business with the Army, the Navy, and the Air Corps. Such persons should become familiar with the kinds of freight equipment owned and operated by these services. Upward of 9,000 freight cars are operated by the Army and Navy alone. This equipment includes boxcars, flatcars, tank cars, gondolas, and hoppers. Some of these cars—e.g., some of the Army flats—carry or contain special devices which are of aid in tying down or otherwise bracing freight which is to be transported.

There is a wide range of equipment available today to the shipper. For special purposes, railroad car-builders can design and build cars which carriers need to transport the almost limitless range of freight that they are called upon to transport. If a shipper has any considerable volume of traffic to offer to any railway freight agency, he is likely to obtain the service that he needs: perhaps not immediately, but almost always eventually.

MARINE CARRIERS

CONTENTS

MARINE CARRIERS

Ocean General Freight Carriers

MAIN KINDS OF MARINE CARRIERS. The important vessels that comprise the water-borne commercial fleet of the United States may be classified into the following groups: offshore ocean carriers, coastwise ocean carriers, Great Lakes carriers, and a host of smaller craft that make up the fleet of inland waterway and river carriers. To this large group—all mainly transporters of merchandise—may be added a large number of working craft, such as the dredge, that are engaged in moving materials of quite different kinds. Space does not permit a detailed discussion of each of the divisions and subdivisions into which these groups can be classified. The subdivisions presented here include the most important, and give a comprehensive picture of the classifications of boats and ships that make up the nation's merchant marine.

BASIC TYPES OF OCEAN CARRIERS. There are three basic divisions of ocean carriers:

1. The freighter.
2. The passenger ship.
3. The tanker.

The **freighter** is by far the most numerous. This type of ship is a carrier of dry merchandise or raw materials, at times with a small amount of liquid cargo in individual containers or small tanks on the ship. Ships that are operated on established trade routes, sail according to published schedules, and offer to carry the goods of any client are classified as **common carriers**. Ships operated by the owner to carry his own products mainly along fixed distribution routes are classified as **industrial carriers**. The majority of freighters are common carriers. All the major steamship companies operating over fixed international trade routes are operating common carriers. A typical example of the industrial carrier which is employed in transporting dry cargo is a ship of the Ore Steamship Company. This company operates large ore-carrying ships between South American ports and ports of the eastern United States seaboard, for its parent, the Bethlehem Steel Corporation.

About one-third of all ocean carriers operating under the United States flag are **tankers**. These ships are practically all industrial carriers, and are discussed later in this section. The **passenger ship**, with some details regarding its status as a marine carrier, is included here for the sake of completeness, but its importance is usually overestimated. An ocean-going carrier still in the development stage is the **roll-on–roll-off ship**—a kind of ship that promises revitalization of coastwise and intercoastal trade.

THE GENERAL DRY-CARGO CARRIER. All ships in this category are common carriers. They must be capable of accommodating all cargoes offered to them for transportation to the ports of call along their established routes. Hence they must be as flexible as possible in operation. Their cargo compartmentation and cargo-handling gear must be designed to this end.

CARGO COMPARTMENTATION. These ships must have most of their stowage volume devoted to large compartments suitable for the stowage of dry packaged or unit merchandise. The ships must, however, have some space allotted for carrying refrigerated items, bulk liquids, and perhaps bulk dry commodities. An example of the allocation of the total cubic capacity of a typical ocean freighter is found in the Mariner type of ship classified as the C4-S-1a:

Dry cargo .... 736,723 cu. ft.
Refrigerated cargo .... 30,254 cu. ft.
Tanks for bulk liquids .... 56,500 cu. ft.

The allocation for refrigerated cargo is probably low. A ship of this total cubic capacity would normally be able to use twice the amount of space provided for refrigerated cargo in the original plans of the Maritime Administration.

Dry Cargo Space. The spaces for dry cargo, in uncovered units or in packages, consist of **lower holds** ranging in depth from 15 to 20 ft., and an additional one to three compartments of less depth, known as **'tween decks.** The sides of these compartments of the interior of the ship's hull are bare except for 2-in. by 6-in. boards secured to the inside flanges of the ship's framing. These boards are spaced about 6 in. apart vertically, and run horizontally from one end of the hold to the other, and are called **sweat battens** or side battens (Fig. 1). They are placed in the ship to prevent the units of cargo from falling between the ship's frames and blocking the flow of air currents needed for adequate ventilation. They also prevent actual contact of the ship's structural parts with the cargo,

U.S. Maritime Administration

Fig. 1. Sweat or side battens in cargo hold.

thereby reducing moisture damage due to condensation on the ship's hull. These battens should be kept in good repair. They are vulnerable to breakage and misuse by longshoremen, and should be checked and, if damaged, replaced every time the ship is loaded or discharged.

The bottom of the lower hold is not the actual bottom of the ship. It is the top of a **double-bottom tank** about 4 ft. deep, on the average. This tank may be used to carry fuel oil or water. The plating must be protected from holes caused by rough handling of heavy metal cargoes. Permanent protection is afforded through the use of a wooden sheathing over the tank top directly below the opening of the hatch into the hold. This area is designated as the **square of the hatch.** Temporary protection is afforded by the use of dunnage wood under the first tier of cargo to be placed in position. This first tier has additional functions besides protection of the tank tops.

Because fuel oil is carried in these tanks, and cargo may be actually in the compartment directly over the tanks while fuel is received from ashore or a barge, it is extremely important to sound these tanks carefully as the fuel is received, to insure against overflow into the cargo compartment.

Drainage of the cargo compartments, is obtained through an athwartship sump, about 2 ft. deep, in the extreme after end of the hold, and running transversely between two consecutive floors for about 8 to 12 ft. Because of the trim of the ship aft, any liquids that may find their way into the hold will drain aft into this sump. At regular periods, this sump or drain well, must be sounded to determine whether the ship is making water from any cause, or if fuel oil or a liquid cargo has found its way into the hold. If a double-bottom tank is filled with fuel oil under very low pressure and the tank top is damaged and leaking, the oil will find its way into the cargo compartment. This may result in serious and costly damage to the cargo. An early indication of this potentially dangerous and costly situation is obtained by **sounding.** This check is a routine but highly important shipboard task. Unless the check is made often and carefully, the carrier company can be held liable for damage that could have been prevented by the proper inspection and precautions.

The overhead boundary of the dry cargo compartment is composed of the bare supporting beams and the deck plating of the next higher platform. No sheathing or battens of any kind are provided.

The best stowage is obtained in compartments that are shaped like cubes or wide parallelepipeds. The middle section of the ship provides the best possible stowage space. On many ships this space is allotted to the engine that propels the ship. From the standpoint of materials handling, the propelling machinery should be placed aft where the curvature is great, and the midship section should be reserved for the cargo.

The cargo spaces should be free from obstructions insofar as possible. All items of equipment that supplement the compartments in any way should be so located or set up as not to protrude into the areas used for actual stowage of the cargo. Proper ventilating ducts, equipment for opening and closing hatch covers, and safety equipment should be installed with this factor in mind.

The **'tween deck spaces** are similar to the lower hold spaces except that the decks are not tops of tanks. These areas also have less vertical clearance, 9 to 12 ft. being quite common. Drainage in these compartments is accomplished through a 2½ in. pipe leading from the after outboard corners of the compartment down to the drain well described above. Since the forward corners are not so equipped, it is obvious that a ship that is trimmed deeper forward than aft will have any liquids which are in her trapped in the forward corners of all compartments. This fact must be kept in mind when laying dunnage for drainage under certain conditions of operation.

REFRIGERATED COMPARTMENTS. The refrigerated compartments on the general cargo carrier are generally placed in the upper or lower 'tween deck spaces. The lower holds of a general cargo carrier are never converted to carry low-temperature cargoes.

The refrigerated compartments themselves are composed of **wings** and **ends** of the 'tween deck spaces. At times, the hatch squares are fitted with so-called **insulation plugs** and so also become compartments capable of carrying low-temperature commodities. The insulation plug is simply a removable insulated hatch-cover in the form of a pontoon made of lightweight, low-conductivity materials.

The conversion of an ordinary 'tween deck space to one capable of carrying products at −10° F. is accomplished by insulating all boundaries of the compartment and fitting it with a duct system capable of distributing cool air uniformly throughout the space. The **insulation** may be of pressed corkboard, glass wool, mineral wool, or some similar substance. This material is placed against the shell plating of the ship and held in place by a sheathing of tongue-and-groove fir, or a metal or plywood sheathing. The sheathing is nailed to wooden ground-pieces that are bolted to the frames or beams. The thickness of the insulation varies with the expected function of the compartment. Generally, the thickness is about 2 to 3 in. greater than the depth of flanges of the framing, running about 8 to 10 in. as a result. The insulation is subject to deterioration because of the infiltration of water vapor. This vapor is a major problem, and in recent years much research has gone into finding solutions. One very effective method of combating the gradual build-up of moisture on the cool side of the insulation is to circulate dry air through small-diameter passages cut into the insulation, running parallel to the face of the compartment and entirely around the perimeter.

In determining the optimum thickness of insulation, the goal is to adopt such a thickness that the sum of the cost of insulation and the cost of refrigeration machinery to remove heat from the compartment is at a minimum, with the final proviso that in no case must the insulation be so thin as to promote heavy condensation on surfaces outside the compartment. The **interior sheathing** of the refrigerated space is finished off with coved corners and chamfered edges, and is well varnished. This provides for a minimum accumulation of dirt and filth that might damage the commodities carried. Cleanliness is of major importance in these spaces.

Because of the probability of heavy condensation or drainage from some cargoes, these refrigerated compartments are equipped with four to six drain holes instead of only two. In addition, all such spaces have gratings of wood or light metal on which the cargo is stowed. This layout helps to provide for excellent drainage, but its primary purpose is to aid the circulation of air currents by which the actual refrigeration of the commodities is accomplished. The sides of the interior are protected by vertical battens which help to keep containers a few inches away from the bulkhead, for better air circulation.

Types of Refrigerated Spaces. There are only two basic kinds of refrigerated spaces, (1) the **wall-coil-cooled** space, and (2) the **air-cooled** space. Spaces cooled by wall coils have the coils secured to the side and end walls of the refrigerated spaces, and at times to the overhead structure. These coils are approximately 1½ to 2 in. in diameter and are generally thin-walled and of galvanized steel.

They are usually installed in two or three layers, to provide a greater surface area for heat transfer, and thus allow the cooling agent inside the coils to be maintained at a higher temperature than would otherwise be effective. This arrangement results in more economical operation. The cooling agent may be either a refrigerant that is actually evaporating within the coils, or a brine solution that has been cooled in a centrally located brine tank and then pumped into the coils. The former system is a **direct expansion system,** whereas the latter is known as a **secondary** or **indirect system.**

Coils in spaces of this kind are of the prime-surface type, not built with fins. The finned coil has the advantage of giving greater surface area per linear ft. of coil length, but has the disadvantage of frosting up very rapidly between the fins, if their temperature is below the freezing point of fresh water. Once a coating of frost has formed on the coil, the frost acts as an insulator and cuts down on the heat-transferring efficiency of the coil.

Hard-frozen, Chilled, and Cooled Cargo. Wall-coil-cooled spaces are most suitable for the carrying of **hard-frozen products.** They can, however, be adapted for the carrying of chilled or cooled cargoes. **Chilled cargo** may be defined as cargo that is carried at a temperature of 1 to 2 degrees above its freezing point. For example, chilled beef is carried at a temperature of 28½ to 29½° F.; the freezing point of beef is 27° F. **Cooled cargoes** are those that are carried at relatively high temperatures, but low enough to safely retard the ripening rate without causing damage, or to retard the growth of bacteria. A good example of a cooled cargo is the banana, which is carried at a temperature of 53° F. The freezing temperature of bananas is about 30° F., but if they are kept at that temperature they turn black rapidly after being removed from low-temperature storage.

Hard-frozen commodities stowed in wall-coil-cooled spaces should be stowed without voids, except on the sides and at the top and bottom. This space is necessary to allow the agitated air to flow around the cargo. With hard-frozen cargoes it is not mandatory to build air passageways between each tier. The air is agitated in such compartments to prevent some local spot in the periphery of the compartment from becoming sufficiently high in temperature to cause damage to the cargo.

Chilled and cooled cargoes in these spaces must be kept separated from the coils by at least 8 in. This spacing is desirable because the coils are several degrees lower in temperature than the average temperature maintained in the compartment. If the commodity is too close to the wall coil, it will become frozen, or at least chilled below the safe carrying limit. This spacing is obtained by stowing the containers away from the coils and using light dunnage to shore them up and act as distance pieces. In addition, air channels must be built into the cargo block vertically between the tiers, and horizontally between the rows. These complications are the reason why the wall coil type space is best suited for the stowage of hard-frozen commodities.

Cool Air Spaces. Approximately 90 percent of the ships that are capable of carrying refrigerated cargoes are equipped to cool their spaces by the **recirculation of a cool air current.** All vessels in the United States Merchant Marine that are completely refrigerated use the cool-air system.

The cool-air system utilizes an insulated space into which is blown a current of cool air. As this low-temperature air circulates through the cargo space passing over and around the cargo, it picks up heat from the cargo. It is discharged from the space after it has picked up its quota of heat units, but it does not pass out into the atmosphere. It is kept in a closed-circulation air stream, and the heat picked up from the cargo is, in turn, given up as the air passes over a bank of evaporator coils maintained at a suitably low temperature. The air is then again discharged into the refrigerated space to absorb more heat.

In some cases it is necessary to **introduce fresh outside air** into the recirculated air stream to prevent the percentage of carbon dioxide gas from rising too high for safety of the commodity. When part of the air in a refrigerated compartment is renewed, the air taken from the outside must always be adjusted thermally before being introduced into the air stream. This adjustment is usually downward, but there are times when such air must be heated. There is a need for some means of raising the temperature of new air when carrying cargoes maintained at temperatures above the winter temperatures along the vessel's route. All ships carrying bananas into northern waters during the winter time have **heating units** as well as cooling units in their recirculating systems.

The Cold-Air Bunker Room. The component parts of one cool-air system are essentially the same as those of any other, but there is a difference in types that leads to the use of two terms in describing them. In one kind of installation, the air stream passes over an evaporator coil installed in a compartment which may be adjacent to or remote from the space being cooled, but which is, in any case, definitely separated from such space. Such an arrangement is known as a cold-air bunker-room system and is used in the all-refrigerated ship.

Cold-Air Diffusers. Another type of installation, known as a cold-air diffuser, consists of cooling coils and fans, with appropriate controls, installed as a unit within the space to be refrigerated. These units may be quite small, such as the kind that is secured overhead in a small space, the air being circulated in the space by a fan behind the evaporator coils. Larger cold-air-diffuser units may take up as much as 10 percent of the available cubic volume. These units may utilize air ducts to distribute the cold air within the space. Fig. 2 shows a type of diffuser unit that is manufactured as a standard unit and may be installed in a properly insulated space. The recirculated air enters at the bottom, passes up the housing over the evaporator, and is blown into the space through the spouts shown at the top. This unit should incorporate only the evaporator and fans. The compressor, condenser, and receiver must be located outside the space.

Stowage in Cool-Air Space. When stowing cargo in any one of the cool-air spaces, the principal precaution to take is to allow adequate space between the tiers and rows. Adequate spacing is provided by using common building lath for dunnage. The possibility of improper stowage is greater when a **partial load** is stowed in such spaces. Partial loads in compartments using periphery ducts for air distribution purposes should be spread out over the deck area of the compartment, with good horizontal spacing between rows. The **air flow** in this case is from the duct slit in the upper boundary, downward to the deck, then under the gratings to the outlet. If the cargo is piled up in a block anywhere in the space, the air flow, in following the line of least resistance, passes over the cargo and then downward and to the outlet. Thus the air bypasses the cargo block, and the interior of the block is not properly refrigerated.

In a space equipped with a cold-air-diffuser unit but without ducts, the best way to stow a partial load is to build it up as high as feasible across the compartment in the end of the space where the outlet louver is located. If the cargo is stowed at the opposite end from the outlet louver, the air, again following the

Fig. 2. Diffuser unit for recirculating air.

line of least resistance, will drop to the lower portion of the compartment, after leaving the high outlet duct openings, and make its way directly back to the unit without permeating the cargo and picking up its quota of heat.

The general principle to be followed in all partial loadings of refrigerated spaces is to avoid stowing cargo so that the air flow will bypass the cargo and flow directly to the outlet rather than be forced through the cargo block. Obviously, there must be no deviation from good stowage principles that apply in general when meeting this special requirement (see section on Marine Terminal Handling).

DEEP-TANK SPACES. Every general cargo carrier is equipped with some deep-tank capacity. A deep tank may be defined as a tank made up of cubic space that ordinarily would constitute dry cargo space. In general, deep tanks are located aft of the forward collision bulkhead and forward of the after collision bulkhead. These tanks usually have a depth equal to approximately one-half the depth of a lower hold, or, when placed in the holds aft of the engine room, they are as deep as the shaft alley. Many operators have altered the original design of the ships they operate to include a deep tank in the lower hold of the hatch just forward or aft of the engine room.

Tanks that are located just forward of the forward-collision bulkhead and just aft of the after-collision bulkhead, are called **forepeak** and **afterpeak tanks,** respectively. These tanks are usually used only for salt-water ballast, to reduce the ship's gross and net tonnage, and are properly called not deep tanks, but rather **peak tanks.** These tanks are in an area of the ship subject to stresses that produce leaks; thus cargoes carried there would be in jeopardy.

Deep tanks do not extend down to the bottom of the ship. The lower boundary is, as with the lower holds, the double-bottom tank tops. Deep tanks do not have large hatchway openings, but are fitted with **single-leaf covers** that are hinged at one end, or with covers that must be completely raised up and moved to one side to allow access to the tank. These covers are secured by the use of dogs around the perimeter of the cover, and the cover itself has a gasket in a small channel that fits down over a rounded knife-edge to make the top of the tank secure from leakage. This kind of closure at the top is quite necessary when the tank is being used to carry a liquid that is topped off very near the top of the tank. The distance from the top of the tank down to the surface of the liquid in the tank is called the **ullage** or **outage.** The ullage must be carefully calculated to prevent overflow during the voyage. If the ullage is too small and the product contained in the deep tank expands because of heating, the tank will overflow through the venting pipe. These tanks must be vented, for if they are sealed off from the atmosphere entirely, the pressure in the tank may become high enough to cause structural damage to the ship.

Deep-Tank Fittings. When used to carry some liquid products, the ship's piping and pumps will be used to load and discharge the deep tanks. Cargoes so handled would be ordinary fuel oil being carried as cargo, most grades of vegetable oil, and molasses. To accomplish loading and discharging, the deep tank is equipped with a 6 or 8 in. pipe that can, by properly setting valves, be connected directly to a loading manifold opening on deck somewhere along the waist of the vessel. When **loading,** the liquid cargo flows along the pipe directly to the tank. The rate of flow, when only one tank is being loaded, must be controlled from the shoreside or barge pump. If the rate is reduced by closing down of valves on the ship, the pressure in the system may break the piping or the flexible rubber hose used to make the connection to the ship from the dock or barge.

When **discharging,** a cargo pump on the ship is lined up to take suction from the deep tank and discharge out through the same manifold as is used in loading. Some deep tanks are equipped with **drain wells,** similar to those described above for the lower holds. If drain wells exist, the liquid cargo will drain into this sump, and it becomes a relatively simple task to pump the tank dry. If no drain wells exist, the task of pumping out the very last bit of cargo requires care and skill. The task is called **stripping** the tank. This technique is discussed in connection with tankers further on.

Some cargoes carried in the deep tank will be extremely viscous when at sea temperature. Hence, deep tanks must be equipped with **steam coils** to heat such liquid cargo and reduce its viscosity for pumping. These steam coils usually run along the bottom of the tank and are prime-surface coils of about $1\frac{1}{2}$ or 2 in. in diam. Cargoes that require heating are black fuel oil, molasses, and vegetable oils with relatively high solidifying temperatures.

As mentioned above, deep tanks must be vented to prevent pressure developing within the tank. The kinds of cargoes carried in the deep tanks of general cargo carriers may be vented through gooseneck vent pipes, fitted with a ball check to prevent a flow-back of sea water into the tank. However, in many cases, these tanks are fitted with a pressure-vacuum relief valve such as is described later under "Tankers."

After carrying a liquid cargo, and in some cases just before, depending upon the condition of the tank, the tank may have to be cleaned by thoroughly washing it. Machines have been developed for quick and thorough tank cleansing. These machines—with some comments on the technique of using them—are also described under "Tankers."

Some liquid cargoes carried in the deep tanks are of such a nature that it is desirable to use pumps and lines that are entirely a part of the **shoreside equipment.** When **loading rubber latex,** for example, the tank must be exceptionally clean and must be coated with wax. All yellow-metal fittings in the tank, such as brass valve parts, must be removed. A hose connected directly to the shore tank is led down to within a few inches of the bottom of the deep tank. The latex flows into the tank, and the hose is gradually raised. When latex is discharged from deep tanks, centrifugal pumps are used. These pumps are portable and, as the depth of latex is lowered in the tank, the pumps are also lowered to prevent placing them under an excessive lift. Ship's lines and pumps used for this commodity would soon become inoperative. Another reason for not using the ship's pumps and lines for certain costly commodities is the danger of damage to the commodity. An example of this kind of commodity is palm oil.

Deep tanks do not extend uninterruptedly from one side of the ship to the other. They are divided along the ship's centerline by a **longitudinal bulkhead** to provide for completely separate port and starboard tanks. In some cases this bulkhead is fitted with a **crossover valve** which may be used to equalize the level of liquids being carried. When not being used to equalize the levels, these valves should be kept closed. Uncontrolled shifting of load between tanks may cause serious listing or even disaster.

Dry Cargo in Deep Tanks. Deep tanks may be converted to the carriage of dry cargo by thorough cleaning and the removal of heating coils, if they are present.

THE CARGO HANDLING GEAR. The general cargo carrier uses a set of booms equipped with electrical winches and cargo falls to load and discharge the cargo. On some ships the booms have been replaced by cranes, and there are indications that more cranes will be used in the future.

Ships' booms average 55 ft. in length, and the booms are usually rated as 5-ton or 10-ton capacity. Originally, the boom was swung in an arc between the ship and the dock, after picking up the load to transport it. Since late in the 19th century, however, booms have been used in pairs, with one boom fixed over the ship's hatch and the other over the dock. The cargo fall runs from the winch, through a heel-block, thence up to the head of the boom, and through a block at the head of each boom to a single hook. Thus the name sometimes used to designate this system is the **married fall system.** Before the two booms were used, it was the practice on some ships to marry the falls, but one fall passed through a block secured to a stay over the hatch, and the other fall passed through a block secured on the end of a yard, out over the dock. One fall was logically known as the stay-fall and the other as the yard-fall. Today, the two-boom and married-fall system is often called the **yard-and-stay rig.**

The boom is **positioned** by the use of a topping lift and guys. The **topping lift** positions the boom vertically; it runs from the head of the boom back to the mast or king post at an elevated position. It is often a double tackle, and the hauling part is led to a topping-lift winch, or simply to a cleat. The boom is positioned horizontally by **guys.** One guy is attached on the outboard side of the boom, the other on the inboard side. The outboard guy is known as the working guy because, as the load is picked up and transported between the boom heads, the greatest stress is placed on this guy. On many ships the two inboard guys are replaced by a light tackle running between the heads of the boom, and this arrangement is called a **midship or spanner guy.** The latter arrangement is safer, where it can be used, because it removes some of the confusing array of lines in the working area on deck.

Yard-and-Stay-Rig Operation. The operation of the yard-and-stay rig is simple. In a discharging operation, the hatch boom's fall picks the load up vertically out of the hold. At the proper height, this fall is stopped, and the fall on the dock boom is hauled on to move the load across the deck. To prevent raising the load too high and producing severe stresses in both falls, the hatch fall should be slacked at the same rate at which the dock fall is hauled in. When the load is under the dock boom's head and the hatch fall is slack, the load can be lowered to the dock by the dock fall. A skillful operator of this system can transport loads between ship and dock with considerable speed. The actual speed depends upon the mass of the load, and its volume and shape. If no difficulty is encountered under the hook at either end of the route, the cycle time with normal loads should not exceed 1 min.

Modifications of the Yard-and-Stay Rig. The basic idea of the yard-and-stay rig is being used today. There have been some slight improvements and modifications, however, to increase safety and/or the ease of handling the gear. Certain of these improvements are outlined below.

House Fall. This system simply uses a block attached to a structure on the pier-shed through which the dock fall is led, instead of using the dock boom, which is swung to one side out of the way. The advantages of this rig are that second-deck levels can be reached easily, that there is less danger of hanging up the dock boom when operating at narrow-apron piers, and finally, that when operating at piers with wide aprons, the load can be transported completely across the apron without having to work with a very low dock boom. If sufficient elevation is available on the dock shed, the ship can work into railroad cars or across railroad cars on second, or even third, sets of tracks along the apron.

Farrell Rig. This modification consists of placing posts outboard of the boom goosenecks on a line at right angles to the ship's centerline, with the upper ends of the posts at the same height as the goosenecks. The lower ends of the working guys are secured to these posts, called **vang posts or guy posts,** and the hauling part is secured as close to the end as possible. The midship guy is removed and the topping-lift lead block is secured aloft, very near to the ship's centerline.

With the guys rigged in this way, the boom gooseneck and the lower end of the guys become coaxial, and the booms can be topped or lowered without having to regulate the length of the guys. The placing of the topping lift inboard applies a **transverse component of force** to the boom when under load, which makes the midship or inboard guy unnecessary. With this rig equipped with topping-lift winches, it is possible to position the hatch boom between loads, so that one boom can supply two spots with loads to be handled by men in the hold. Hence, the same results are obtained with only one set of gear at a hatch as when the hatch is equipped with one set of conventional gear at each end.

Ebel Rig. This modification requires the installation of guy winches as well as topping-lift winches. Thus the gear is completely mechanized, and is almost as mobile as a crane. However, it is not intended for use in that manner. The changes consist of using a block down at the deck level, where the guy is usually made fast, and another block at the crosstree level far outboard. The guy runs from the crosstree, where the standing part is secured, out to the boom head, down to the block on deck, and outboard, back up to the block at the boom head, back to the block outboard on the crosstree, and down to the guy winch. The block for the guy on the boom must be a double block in this case. This is the rig for a 5-ton boom. If a 10-ton boom is used, a quadruple block is placed on the boom head, a double block on deck, and a double block and single block at the crosstrees. The topping lift is similar to the Farrell systems.

With this mechanical guy and mechanical topping lift, the booms can be raised by one man, with controls at the winch-operating position. The major advantage gained with this rig is its **safety of operation.** The regular yard-and-stay system places great stress on the guys under certain conditions. Certain loads are of a kind that cannot be handled even though they weigh less than the rated load of the boom. With the Ebel rig, and properly used doubling-up blocks, the 5- and 10-ton booms are able to load—by the yard-and-stay method—weights equal to the rated capacity of the booms.

SHIPBOARD CRANES. Cranes have been in use on ships for many years, but most installations have been on Swedish, Norwegian, and German ships. One United States-flag merchant ship has been operating with cranes in the packaged lumber trade for the past several years. This ship previously used the conventional yard-and-stay rig in the same trade, thus providing a good opportunity to compare the productivity of the two systems. The crane method proved to be much the faster. Some American companies have planned to install cranes on the ships which they operate in the general dry cargo trade.

Cranes may be placed on the ship in three areas. A crane with small scantlings may be placed for use near the end of the hatch and partway outboard. To equip one large hatch, a total of **four cranes** would be needed so that the ship could work with either side to the dock, and at both ends of the hold. Another method is to use athwartship tracks so that the crane can be moved from one side to the other. The crane is positioned to work at one point; it is not intended that it move athwartships with each load. Still another possibility is to install a crane of sufficient size to reach out over the dock from the ship's centerline. This plan, of course, requires the installation of a larger and heavier crane with a heavier supporting structure.

Some of the first complaints against the shipping crane concerned the tendency for the suspended load to swing, owing to tangential and radial forces caused by the circular motion as the crane was slewed with its load. Today, simple **damping devices** are often built right into the cranes of a ship to prevent swinging.

Among the important **advantages of the crane** are its simplicity of operation, and its safety about the decks of the ship. The crane cuts down on the number of parts of lines about the decks, and makes "housekeeping" easier.

As for **capacity,** the crane can be constructed to handle loads of the same weight as those transported by the yard-and-stay system, using booms. All present-day cranes are designed with the level luffing feature, which enables the operator to top up or lower the boom of the crane without having to adjust the height of the load.

Siporter. The siporter is a special kind of extensible boom fitted with a trolley, and is considered a type of crane. It has been used successfully to load and discharge cargo through **side ports.** The siporter is installed on the Constitution, the Independence, and some ships of the American President Lines. The boom can be extended out from the ship's side for about 15 ft. The trolley that travels on this boom carries the hook to which the load is attached. When the load is raised, the trolley transports the loaded hook transversely, and the operator lowers the load to the hold or to the dock.

Harrison Overhead Crane. An unsuccessful experimental prototype of this crane consisted of athwartship tracks that were extended out over the ship's side on jib booms. The tracks ran parallel to the hatch end-beams and supported a longitudinal girder that could be made to travel athwartships with the controls. To this girder a trolley was attached. The trolley could be made to travel longitudinally on the girder, and the trolley carried the hook. Although this crane was capable of carrying loads of up to 15 tons, and up to 30 tons with double trolleys, it was slower than the conventional rig with normal loads, required wide-apron piers, completely obstructed the deck run, and had other minor shortcomings. A **later design** eliminated the extending jib booms, making the rig operable at narrow-apron piers. This system operated faster than the conventional rig on loads above 4 tons and several times faster on loads over 15 tons. These facts indicate that the idea might have some application to container ships.

Heavy-Lift Booms. Two heavy-lift ships have been put into operation by the Military Sea Transportation Service. These ships are fitted with especially heavy-duty equipment and have booms capable of lifting a weight of 150 tons onto or off the ships. There are perhaps one or two other ships capable of carrying such weights with their own equipment, one being able to handle loads up to 200 tons. Such ships do not have the regular cargo gear, and are intended only for special duty.

The average general-cargo freighter is fitted with one, and sometimes two, booms capable of handling loads far in excess of the usual 1- to 3-ton lift. Generally, their limit of capacity ranges between 30 and 60 tons. On some ships, as on the Mariner type, the heavy-lift boom has two capacities: the lower lift limit, when the boom is rigged without preventer stays, and the upper limit, when the preventer stays are secured. The Mariner-type ships have a heavy-lift boom at the forward ends of No. 4 and No. 6 hatches, both of which have a capacity of 25 tons without the preventer stays rigged and 60 tons when these stays are rigged.

These booms are always **swinging booms or live booms.** They are positioned over the load, the load is picked up, then the boom and load are swung together, and finally the load is landed.

SOME OCEAN CARRIER DESIGNATIONS. A Victory ship bears the U. S. Maritime Administration classification of VC2-S-AP2. In this designation, the first group of letters and numbers refers to the **type of ship** and gives some indication of the ship's length. For example, the letter C means cargo ship, T means tanker, and P stands for passenger ship. The larger the number, the longer the ship. For example, the C-2 is a ship designed for carrying dry cargo and has a length of between 400 and 450 ft. A C-3 is a cargo ship between 450 and 500 ft. in length. These lengths are the lengths on the load waterline. The second group of letters and numbers refers to the **type of propulsion** and to the **number of screws.** S stands for steam turbine or reciprocating engines, SE for turbo-electric drive, and M for diesel propulsion. If the ship carries more than 16 passengers, she will have the number 1 after the second group of letters to indicate a single screw, the number 2 for a twin screw. If she carries less than 16 passengers she will have no number for a single screw, and the letter T will be added if she has twin screws. The last set of letters and figures indicates the **design** as established by the Maritime Administration.

During the heavy building activity of the war years, the United States built 531 Victory ships, designated as VC2's. All but one of these ships were steam-turbine-powered, the single exception being a diesel ship. Ninety-five C1-B's were built, 85 turbine-powered and 10 diesel-powered. Two hundred and sixty-two C2's were built of various designs, but almost the same throughout. Of these C2's, 22 were diesel-powered and all the rest were steam-turbine driven. One hundred and twenty-three C3's were built, of which four were diesel-powered and 119 were steam-turbine driven. The design most extensively built during the war years was the EC2-S-C1, known as the Liberty ship. There were about 2,600 of these ships built, large numbers of which are today kept in laid-up fleets maintained by the Maritime Administration.

CAPACITY DETERMINATION. A profile and the principal dimensions of the Victory ship, VC2-S-AP2, are given in Fig. 3. This ship has a foc'sle head extending aft of No. 1 hatch. Another feature of interest is her large deep-tank capacity. There are three such tanks under No. 4 and No. 5 holds, with the tops of the tanks at the approximate level of the shaft alley. The large double-bottom tanks under No. 1 hold could also be made into deep tanks. **Profile plans** give much information about a particular ship, and are usually used as part of **capacity plans.** Capacity plans state the length and capacity of the booms, the number of booms, and the location and size of tanks and cargo compartments, and also include a trim table with instructions for its use. Another very important item of information is the **deck-load capacity** of the ship.

The Stowage Factor. A ship is operated most economically when she runs with all her volume used and is down to her maximum legal draft. When in this condition she is known as **full and-down.** To be loaded in this manner, she must have one cargo that is of such a **density** as just to meet the required conditions, or a combination of cargoes the average density of which is optimum. The required density is not the term used in the industry to describe the desired cargo, but it is the specific volume stated in units of cu. ft. per 2,240 lb. (long ton). This value is called the stowage factor of the cargo.

To find the required stowage factor to fill a given ship full-and-down, it is necessary only to divide the bale cubic capacity of the ship by her **cargo deadweight carrying capacity.** The cargo deadweight is the difference between the ship's light and loaded displacements, minus the weight of the fuel, water, and stores that must be carried for the voyage. For example, if a C1-B type ship were employed on a route where she required 2,000 long tons of fuel, water, and stores, then she could carry 6,909 tons of cargo. Since she has a bale capacity of 433,975 cu. ft., the stowage factor needed to put her in a full-and-down condition is 63. This factor is slightly smaller that the average general cargo stowage factor, which is about 70, hence, if carrying average general cargo, she would be full before she was down to her marks. If carrying cargo with a stowage factor of less than 63, the ship would be down to her maximum legal draft before her holds were full.

Ships' Stores. Because of the considerable volume of ships' stores carried on modern ships, they are mentioned here. Items included are bos'ns stores, ammunition, dry stores, carpenter shop tools, linen, chests, etc. The table in Fig. 3 will give some measure of their significance.

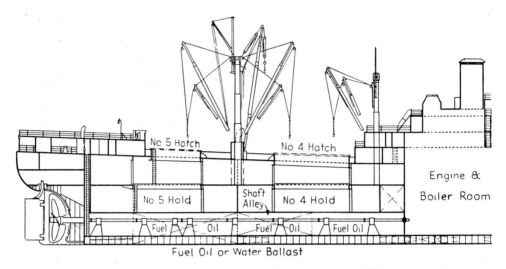

Principal Dimensions

Length over-all	455′3″
Length between perpendiculars	436′6″
Length at L.W.L. (designed)	444′0″
Breadth, extreme	62′1⅝″
Breadth, molded	62′0″
Depth, molded to main deck at side $\otimes$	38′0″
Draft, molded, to summer L.L. (scantling and subdivision)	28′6″
Designed load draft, molded	28′0″
Camber straight & level 9′6″ off ₵, 6″ drop in 21′6″ of outer dk.	
Sheer, main deck at F.P.	4′0″
Sheer, main deck aft end	6′2⅛″

Tonnages *	Gross Tonnage	Net Tonnage
U. S.	7612 tons	4555 tons
Panama	7742 tons	5239 tons
Suez	7792 tons	5638 tons

* Tonnages are averages for the class.

Dry Cargo

Space	Cubic Feet	
	Grain	Bale
Hold No. 1	86,300	73,740
Hold No. 2	89,370	76,760
Hold No. 3	158,000	136,190
Hold No. 4	113,080	100,300
Hold No. 5	81,575	69,535
Total dry cargo	528,325	456,525

Fig. 3. **VC2-AP2 Victory ship—profile with principal**

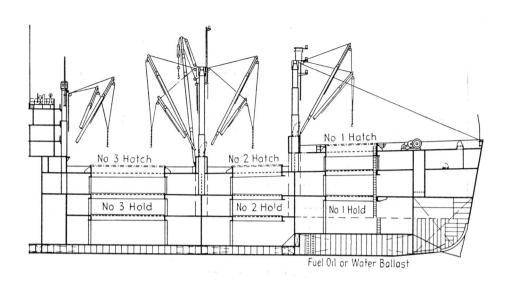

Ships Stores			
Space	Deck	Side	Bale Cu. Ft.
Paint locker	Foc'sle deck	Port	154
Lamp locker	Foc'sle deck	Stbd.	141
Bos'n stores	Main deck	℄	2,301
Bos'n stores in way of mast..........	Main deck	P ℄ S	325
Bos'n stores in way of mast..........	Main deck	P ℄ S	325
Bos'n stores	Second deck	℄	2,080
Dry stores	Second deck	Port	2,972
St'w'ds stores	Second deck	Port	1,314
Rope locker	Aft flat 35'6"	Stbd.	870
Eng'rs. stores	Mach'y flat	Port	1,080
Storeroom	Aft flat 35'6"	Stbd.	1,885
Storeroom	Aft flat 35'6"	Port	325
Total ships stores			13,772
Refrigerated Ships Stores			
Vegetable box	Second deck	Stbd.	2,004
Handling room	Second deck	Stbd.	604
Fish box	Second deck	Stbd.	269
Dairy box	Second deck	Stbd.	371
Meat box	Second deck	Stbd.	1,347
Total ships refrigerated stores ..			4,595

dimensions and capacities (continued on next page).

	Gallons	Barrels	Tons	S. W. Ballast Tons
Lubricating and diesel oil (oil 98% full)	5,296	125.5	18.4	
Fresh water (100% full)..............	79,454		294.9	
Fuel oil (98% full) and water ballast (100% full)				
Double bottom tanks..............	344,183	8,194.5	1,235.8	1,341.3
Deep tanks	422,901	10,069.0	1,518.6	1,648.2
Peak tanks				140.0
Settling tanks	35,711	850.0	128.2	
Total F. O. and S. W. ballast....	802,795	19,113.5	2,882.6	3,129.5

U.S. Maritime Administration

Fig. 3. (Concluded.)

HOMOGENEOUS-DRY-CARGO CARRIERS. A type of ship that has been growing in importance is the ship devoted to the carrying of products that are solid and dry, but are offered for transportation in the same form throughout.

The Refrigerated Ship. Of the many ships in the U.S. Merchant Marine capable of handling refrigerated products, only a few are designed as refrigerated ships throughout. The all-refrigerated ship is similar in general construction and in other details to the partially refrigerated ship, discussed earlier in this section. The all-refrigerated carrier does not have her hatch-square separated from the wings by a bulkhead. The entire 'tween-deck or lower-hold space comprises the compartment for stowage. In all such ships the decks are provided with gratings and the interior is sheathed. The cooling is always accomplished by the use of **recirculated cool air.** In the U. S. merchant fleet, most of the all-refrigerated ships are employed in the carrying of bananas. The remainder are used to carry meat and a variety of chilled or cooled products.

The all-refrigerated ship generally relies on a cold-air bunker room in one of the upper 'tween deck spaces for recirculating the cool air for the entire hold. In most cases, the refrigeration coils in the cold-air bunker room are indirect systems using brine as the coolant. The sides and ends of the space, the upper deck, and the tank tops are insulated, but the decks in between are not. The hatch opening on the top deck is fitted with insulation plugs, which are a form of pontoon filled with an insulating material. These plugs fit snugly and are caulked and covered with a mat. They are not constructed to add to the strength of the ship, but to create a heat barrier at this large opening.

The Lumber Carrier. The ideal lumber carrier is a single-deck ship with long hatches. If the **compartmentation** of the ship is kept to a minimum, the stowage space wasted will also be at a minimum. Moreover, compartmentation is not needed to protect lumber from the weight of superimposed cargo, nor to divide cargo by ports of discharge, which are usually few.

Since World War II, the **Liberty-type ship,** classified as the EC-2, has been accepted by many operators as a good lumber carrier. This ship has two decks, and her underwater shape is without great curvature. One operator has removed the bulkhead between No. 2 and 3 and No. 4 and 5 holds to give the ship less compartmentation. This change makes the ship better able to accommodate long lengths and to stow her cargo with less broken stowage.

The lumber carrier should be provided with **long booms.** The length of average booms is 55 to 60 ft., but on the lumber carrier they should be 70 ft. long, so as to assure safe handling of the long pieces. With short booms it sometimes becomes necessary to **tight-line the falls** to clear the ship's bulwark or hatch coaming, and this can cause guy failure, with serious injury, to personnel and to equipment.

The lumber cargo comes to the ship mostly in sawed shapes. There are two distinct categories. First, there are small structural pieces such as the 2 by 4's and 2 by 8's used in small house construction. These are often referred to as shipments of deals, battens, and boards. Second, there are heavier pieces used as supporting members in heavy construction or in mines, or for resawing at destination. These shipments consist of balks, squares, and flitches. The smaller items may be transported in strapped packages or loose. The large members are nearly always shipped as individual units. When lumber is shipped in package units, a certain percentage is left loose for stowage between the units so that broken stowage is kept at a minimum.

The Grain Carrier. In ocean transportation, ordinary general dry-cargo carriers are used to transport bulk grain cargoes. The only modification necessary is the building of a **temporary centerline bulkhead** in the deep lower holds, under certain conditions. These bulkheads are not required if the bulk grain does not consume more than one-third of the grain capacity of the hold.

In certain cases, tankers, discussed later in this section, have been used with success to transport full cargoes of bulk grain. The grain is loaded by allowing it to flow into the hold through long **telescopic chutes** from a grain elevator and discharged by the use of **high-capacity vacuum pumps.** Hence, the many obstructions in the tanks offer no great problem in the loading and discharging operations because, for all practical purposes, the cargo is a liquid. No additional bulkheads are required because the tank vessel is already equipped with three longitudinal compartments and shifting is impossible.

The Bulk Coal Carrier. Ships designed especially to carry bulk coal are called colliers. They are provided with quick-opening metal hatch covers and the holds do not have 'tween decks. The ship has deep double bottoms because it is desirable to bring the center of the weight up to prevent a stiff ship. The loss of cubic capacity is not important because the density of the cargo will put the ship down to her maximum legal draft without using the total volume of the underwater portion of the hull for cargo.

The **collier** is very similar to the bulk-ore carrier described below. She carries no cargo-handling gear because she is loaded by gravity flow and discharged at piers equipped with transporter-type cranes.

The Bulk Cement Carrier. A few ships have been equipped to carry bulk dry cement. Because cement has a very low angle of repose, the interior of the hull is compartmented like a tanker's. The cement flows aboard by gravity and is pumped ashore by large vacuum pumps. Perfectly dry cement that is slightly aerated flows readily along a large diameter pipe if accelerated by air pressure (see section on Pneumatic Conveyors).

The Bulk Raw Sugar Carrier. One shipping concern utilizes ordinary general dry-cargo carriers as bulk raw sugar carriers. In the trade that the ships operate, they are loaded with general cargo on the outbound voyage. They return to the home port loaded with bulk raw sugar, and with other commodities if conditions warrant. The bulk sugar is loaded by gravity into sheathed lower holds and 'tween-deck areas.

The cargo is discharged by a **vertical bucket conveyor** permanently installed at the port of discharge. It is lowered directly into the hold, and the buckets carry their loads vertically upward and deposit them on a conveyor belt that moves the sugar into a warehouse that is part of the sugar refinery. The equipment and operations involved are more fully described in the section on "Handling and Storage of Bulk Materials" and in sections dealing with specific equipment types.

The Bulk Ore Carrier. The ideas for design and methods of operating bulk ore carriers that are found on ocean carriers of this type were first developed for the Great Lakes ore carriers. The following description of the general principles involved will apply to both.

The ore carrier is a long vessel, with many hatches leading to four longitudinal compartments, and with no cargo gear of her own. The cargo is **loaded** by gravity at specially constructed piers from preloaded hoppers. When loading commences, large chutes are lowered into the holds and the ore is allowed to run directly into the ship. **Discharging** is done by the transporter-type crane with grab buckets capable of picking up 17 to 20 tons in one bite. On the Great Lakes, the Hulett unloader is often used.

Before World War II, one company operated five 20,000-ton-deadweight ore carriers between Chile and the southeast coast of the United States. After the war a large carrier, capable of loading 24,000 tons, was built for the same trade. For the trade between the United States and the rich Venezuelan ore deposits, ore carriers that rival the transatlantic liner in size were built. These are capable of carrying 60,000 tons deadweight, and displace 80,000 tons loaded. These large ore carriers have **four large holds.** The forward hold is served by four hatches, while the last three holds, aft of the midship house, have three hatches each. Like all ore carriers, the ships have very deep double-bottom tanks, which are in this case 22 ft. deep. The wing tanks on either side of the hold compartment extend inboard about 17 ft. These deep double-bottom and wing tanks are needed on these carriers to raise the load center and prevent a stiff ship when traveling loaded, and to carry ballast water when traveling empty.

Ore-and-Oil Carriers. These ore carriers have a large volume of tank capacity, as described above. This fact led to the development of ore-and-oil carriers. One ship of this kind, built for the trade between Liberia and the United States East Coast, carries about 24,000 tons deadweight in ore, or 21,000 tons in oil. The oil is carried in the double-bottom and wing-tanks. Such ships cannot carry both types of cargo simultaneously; they must carry one or the other, and conversion takes from 2 to 4 days.

These ships may be more economically employed in some trades where a payload of homogeneous solids may be carried on one leg of the voyage and a liquid cargo on the return leg. When the ore traffic is seasonal, combination vessels of this type can be used for oil in off seasons. The ore carrier per se usually makes one leg of its voyage unladen and may lie idle for long periods.

Ocean Tankers

A ship designed especially to carry liquids in bulk is known as a tanker. The great majority of tankers are employed in the carriage of bulk petroleum products, but these ships also are used to transport other products, such as certain chemicals, molasses, wine, and even beer.

OIL TANKER. The cargo-handling equipment on the tanker consists of a number of pumps; suitable pipelines on deck, in the tanks, and in the pump room; and a number of properly located and designed valves to control the route and rate of flow through the lines to and from the various tanks. The T-2 tanker, built in large numbers during World War II, displaces nearly 22,000 tons when loaded. Shortly after the end of the war, private operators began building so-called **supertankers** with loaded displacements of 28,000 tons. Tankers of 38,000-, 45,000-, and 58,000-tons loaded displacement followed, and there is reason to believe that a tanker approaching 100,000 tons loaded displacement may be built.

Typical Layout. Although the T-2 is only half as large as many tankers now being operated, the layout of her tanks and equipment is comparable. The only real difference lies in the **capacity of the tanks** and of her pumps. A modern tanker of 38,000 tons deadweight can be loaded or discharged in about 12 hr. The entire procedure is accomplished by the ship's regular crew without the help of longshoremen. This development constitutes one of the greatest economies in the marine transportation cycle.

Tables and profile in Fig. 4 give the principal dimensions, general layout, and capacities of the T-2 tanker. It should be noted that the tanker has no double-bottom tanks, and has no need for intermediate decks in the cargo carrying area. The engine room and most of the quarters for the crew are aft. The house over No. 4 and 5 tanks accommodates the deck officers, radio equipment, and the navigation bridge.

The cargo is carried in nine tanks. Even on the larger tankers the number of tanks does not exceed eleven. The hull is divided into three compartments by **twin longitudinal bulkheads.** These bulkheads are one-quarter of the beam inboard, thus forming two wing tanks whose width is one-quarter of the beam and a center tank whose width is one-half the beam.

Just aft of the last center tank on most tankers is a compartment containing all the **pumps** used to discharge the cargo. Shoreside pumps are not used for discharge. Main pumps are the high-capacity centrifugal type. When the last of the cargo is being discharged, smaller-capacity, positive-displacement pumps are needed. Each large pump is, therefore, paired with a rotary pump or reciprocating pump. The latter strip the tanks of the last few inches of oil from the bottom of the tanks. This is the delicate part of the operation and cannot be done safely and easily with the high-capacity centrifugal pumps. Cargo is discharged in such a way that the ship is kept trimmed slightly aft.

The pumps on the tanker are never used for loading cargo. Cargo is always received on board either from shoreside pumps or by the use of gravity flow. **Gravity loading** can be used when the shore tanks are located well above the ship. Connection between shoreside and ship's piping systems is made through a series of athwartship pipes located on deck somewhere just aft of the midship house. This system of pipes and valves is known as the **manifold.** From the manifold there are lines leading aft on deck. These deck-lines pass through the after-house bulkhead and down to the pumproom piping system, and connect with another set of pipes that run forward in the tanks. From this longitudinal tank line there are transverse lines that lead into each wing tank.

Loading Procedure. At dockside, 8-in. or 10-in. rubber hoses are connected to the tanker's manifold. These hoses generally are connected to shoreside pipe-

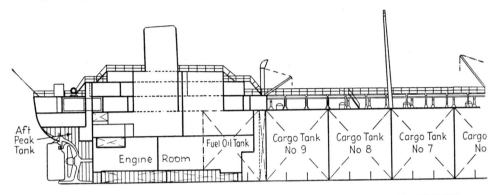

Principal Dimensions	
Length over-all	523′6″
Length between perpendiculars.................................	503′0″
Beam—molded	68′0″
Depth—molded to upper deck...................................	39′3″
Load draft—molded (design)....................................	29′11½″

Tonnages	Gross Tonnage	Net Tonnage
U.S. ....10,448..........................6,301		
Panama ....10,876..........................7,743		
Suez ....10,777..........................8,316		

Cargo Pumps	Capacity
Three main cargo pumps, motor-driven, horizontal centrifugal 100 lb.	2,000 G.P.M.
Two cargo stripping pumps, motor-driven, horizontal gear 100 lb.	400 G.P.M.
One cargo stripping pump, steam-driven, 14 × 14 × 12 vertical duplex	700 G.P.M.

Fig. 4. T-2 tanker—profile, with

lines leading back to the storage tanks. After the ship and dock personnel have checked all tanks on the ship and have made certain that she is ready to receive the cargo, the manifold valves are opened and the pumps ashore are started. By proper manipulation of valves, the oil is first routed to the tanks of the ship in such a way that she assumes a **fair trim,** then each tank is brought up to the required level and shut off. This **"topping off"** is done without slowing down the rate of loading, until the final tank is reached. Then the dock superintendent is notified that the ship is filling its last tank, and to stand by to slow down and stop the flow of oil. In this way the last tank is topped off.

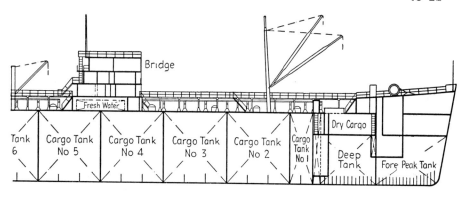

	Gallons	Barrels
Main cargo tanks (Nos. 1–9).....................	3,126,446.8	74,439.21
Side cargo tanks (Nos. 1–9 P & S)...............	2,802,193.1	66,719.10
Total Cargo	5,928,639.9	141,158.31
Dry cargo (second deck)..................................		15,203 cu. ft.

	Gallons	Barrels	Tons
Fuel oil (wing tank and deep tank).........	408,463.4	9,735.28	
Salt water ballast (ballast tanks and cofferdams).................			1,380.73
Fresh water, feed water tanks.................................			265.79
Drinking water tanks..			99.36
Total			365.15

U.S. Maritime Administration

principal dimensions and capacities.

Travel in Ballast. Tankers always have to make one leg of their total voyage in ballast. The ballast used is sea water. The master of the ship will load just enough ballast to put the propeller down in the water, obtain a desirable trim, cut down the vibration of the hull, and make the ship maneuverable. All these factors require the proper amount of ballast, depending upon the weather, hence the exact amount of ballast cannot be specified. The minimum amount on a T-2 tanker would be No. 3, 5, and 7 center tanks. If additional ballast is necessary, the wing tanks can be used.

Tank Washing. The cargo compartments of a tanker must be cleaned regularly. Five basic reasons for the washing of the tanks are:

1. Periodic maintenance cleaning.
2. Cleaning to accommodate clean ballast water.
3. Cleaning and gas freeing for tank inspection and/or repairs.
4. Cleaning and gas freeing for shipyard overhaul.
5. Cleaning for a change of product.

The cleaning process is always similar, the only variation being the length of time spent on the operations and, in some cases, a few added steps for thoroughness. The cleaning is done by a machine that consists of a two- or four-nozzle rotating sprinkler unit through which hot or cold salt water runs under a pressure of about 200 lb. per sq. in. Some products require a high temperature, and in such cases the water used is heated to 180° F. Other products are more easily cleaned out with cold water.

The machine is suspended in the tank through an opening about 12 in. in diam. in the ship's main deck. A saddle and clamp for holding the hose is placed over the opening to retain the heat and prevent the escape of the streams of water. The hose is marked in increments of 5 ft. and is lowered systematically so that the greatest area is washed. Two machines are used simultaneously in the large center tanks, and one is used in each of two wing tanks. During the washing procedure, it is important that all tanks be **stripped continuously** to prevent formation of sludge and bottom sediment deposits and to permit the stream of washing water to strike the bottom of the tank with full force.

After running the machine down a tank, the tank is well ventilated and then mucked out. **Mucking-out** is a process of cleaning out remaining bottom sediment and sludge after the washing is completed, and must be done by hand. The tank is then inspected and, if necessary, rewashed or spotted.

LIQUID CHEMICAL CARRIER. Although some ships had previously been fitted out to carry some chemicals, the first ship built especially for the transportation of liquid chemicals in bulk over ocean routes was the Marine Dow-Chem with a capacity of about 83,000 barrels of chemicals. In appearance she is much the same as all tankers. Her cargo tanks, however, are entirely isolated from the sea and from any sea water that may be used as ballast. This isolation is accomplished by using **double steel bulkheads** between every tank, and between any tank and the outside sea. The chemicals carried range from caustic soda to hydrochloric acid.

LIQUEFIED PETROLEUM GAS CARRIERS. There are about three ships employed in the transportation of full cargoes of **butane and propane.** These products require pressures of 200 lb. per sq. in. or more to remain in the liquid state at ordinary temperatures. The ships designed for this cargo have large **cylindrical tanks** installed in an upright position with their upper ends protruding above the main deck into the open air. As the connections for loading and discharging are made here leaking vapors do not become trapped in the hull interior. In the compartments below deck there is ample passage between the tanks to permit thorough inspection.

Since the cargo must be kept under pressure when loading and discharging, ordinary pumping systems cannot be used. The cargo is pushed rather than pumped into and out of the ship. To get the tanks completely empty, a vapor pump is used.

MISCELLANEOUS LIQUID BULK CARRIERS. Tank ships carry other cargoes besides those hitherto discussed. A small stainless-steel tank ship, operated on the inland waterways of Europe, carries about 250 barrels of beer. Another small tanker carries wine in bulk. Several large tankers carry full loads of molasses, which must be heated to about 105° F. before pumping. Tankers also carry cargoes that must be kept at very high temperatures all during the voyage. Liquefied sulfur is carried at about 270° F. and liquefied bitumen at 300° F. To maintain the high temperature at 300° F., the bitumen is carried only in the ship's center tanks, which are fitted with ample steam-heating coils.

Other Ocean Carriers

THE PASSENGER SHIP. The definition of a passenger ship must necessarily be a rather lengthy statement. To define it simply as a ship employed in the carriage of passengers is incorrect from the standpoint of the law, union regulations, and practicality. Under the law, a ship is a passenger ship if she carries more than 12 passengers, regardless of the cargo tonnage carried simultaneously. As such, she must add certain life-saving equipment, and be operated in ways that add to the total costs of running her. Also, union agreements require increased personnel, mainly in the steward's department, to care for the passengers. Hence, if passengers are to be carried, they should be sufficient in number to make it worth the trouble.

The ship that carries 100 or 200 passengers is definitely a passenger ship, and yet her cargo-carrying capacity may be so large that her itinerary, and much of her equipment, is shaped by her role as a cargo ship. This kind of vessel is really a **combination passenger-cargo** ship. The large passenger liners implied by the term **passenger ship** are few in number. The passenger ship carries very little cargo. Most of her volume is given to the accommodation of passengers or to facilities to care for them; she operates on a fast schedule and makes every effort to maintain it.

THE SEATRAIN. The seatrain is a special kind of carrier with no flexibility in operation. It is designed to carry one type of container, and must dock at a special type of dock built for its use exclusively. The cargo of this ship consists of **railroad boxcars.** The dock used to accommodate the seatrain is equipped with a railroad spur track serviced by a large transporter-type crane. The crane picks up each boxcar and sets it down on tracks within the ship. The **capacity** of one ship is about 100 cars on three decks, including the weather deck. Plans have been made for the construction of a pier and a ship that will enable the cars to roll onto and off the ship without reliance on a crane.

The seatrain is a very efficient cargo handling system. The shipper loads his cargo in the boxcar at his warehouse, and it is not rehandled until the car arrives at the consignee's warehouse. This system has operated successfully between the Gulf and East coasts of the United States and Cuba.

A typical ocean seatrain operation is that of the Seatrain Steamship Company, operating out of New York to ports along the southeast coast. A typical carrier is the Seatrain Georgia, 503 ft. long with a beam of 63½ ft. She is a lift-on, lift-off ship, and the operation is carried on through a large opening leading down to all decks, similar to a conventional ship's hatch. There are four cargo decks, including the main deck, each having four sets of tracks totaling about one mile in all. It can carry 100 railroad cars, and the complete loading and unloading cycle takes about 14 hours.

In loading, a railroad car is first spotted on a platform fitted with tracks, and clamped in place. The entire platform with the car then is lifted by a transporter crane with a capacity of 125 tons, and lowered through the opening, which is fitted with guides. On reaching the deck, the platform is secured, and the car is moved off the platform and along the track in the ship by a steam-driven car-hauling gear. When the deck is loaded, the last platform is left in place. Loading is started with the lowest deck.

To **secure the cars** for the voyage at sea, jacks relieve the weight of the car from the springs and wheel clamps hold the car in position. Chains fitted with turnbuckles are attached so that the cars may be drawn down tightly to the jack. This system secures the car rigidly and has proven successful in the rough seas encountered along the coast.

THE ROLL-ON, ROLL-OFF SHIP. One of the most promising concepts in the field of coastwise and intercoastal water transportation is that of a ship designed to transport **highway trailers,** with or without their powered trucks. Conventional ships could be used but not without prohibitive costs. The ship conceived for the express purpose of serving highway trailers was designed so that the trailers could be driven on and off with their own powered units, or with a special kind of industrial tractor. The **terminal** would be designed with ramps to accommodate the rapid transfer. One such operation uses a modified L.S.T.-type ship running between Savannah, Georgia and Puerto Rico. Modified L.S.T.'s have also been used with success on a run between New York and Albany on the Hudson River.

Designs for ship and terminal, and plans of the operation, allow for loading and discharging about 280 trailers in 4 hr. The **loss of cubic space** in carrying trailers so they can be rolled on and rolled off the ship is compensated for by rapid turnaround of the ship. It is expected that the sum total of cargo carried per year will exceed that for conventional ships of equal size packing cargo in the conventional manner. In one **cost comparison** the roll-on, roll-off system presented a total expense per ton of $5.37 against $17.41 per ton for a lift-in, lift-out system. This figure was computed assuming the roll-on, roll-off operation operating at 80 percent of capacity.

The **trades** in which this type of operation will succeed are those having short runs between ports where a good volume of highway traffic already exists and where longshoring labor costs are high. United States coastwise routes, and perhaps the intercoastal trade also, meet these conditions. Potential routes are from San Francisco to Los Angeles; from Portland and Seattle down to San Francisco and Los Angeles; from Brownsville (Tex.) to Mobile; from Jacksonville to New York and Providence; from Duluth to Buffalo; and similar routes.

THE CONTAINER SHIP. The idea of carrying cargo in a standard-size **unit container** of about 250 or 300 cu. ft. capacity has been exploited for a number of years in ocean transportation. The immediate **advantages** gained from such practice are reduction of pilferage and damage to the cargo. If the containers are loaded at the shipper's warehouse, delivered to the carrier's pier, and picked up by the consignee at the port of discharge, handling costs are likely to be reduced considerably. If the operation were properly organized, a container ship would be capable of handling the units rapidly and stowing them without dunnage or lashings in slots or other patented racks. While such coordination seems to be entirely possible along some coastwise or intercoastal routes, experimentation with various methods, equipment, and procedures is necessary.

Today, the majority of the cargo arrives at the pier in units, which are placed in the containers by longshoremen, for loading on the ship. At the port of discharge, the unit containers are unpacked and the individual packages removed to other carriers for delivery to the consignee's warehouse. The **high cost** of collecting, coordinating, and redistributing cargo has been the principal drawback to container-ship development.

The container ship has the same disadvantage as the trailer ship in that much cubic space is consumed for the amount of cargo carried. In the same way, it compensates by giving rapid ship turnaround, and a reduction in the cost for longshore labor in loading and discharging.

Unitization. The pressure of economics may ultimately force all ships to carry cargoes in units of some kind. The unit container is not the only answer. Cartons of merchandise can be placed on expendable **pallets,** or built up without pallets, into units capable of being handled mechanically on the pier and in the ship. In time, operators may be forced to work out systems utilizing such methods.

The Alaska Steamship Co. carries a great majority of its cargo in one of three unitized forms. This is a coastwise operation; and it is logical that coastwise operators should be the first to show initiative in this area. The United States coastwise and intercoastal shipping business has dwindled down to a mere fraction of its pre-World War II volume. The disappearance of this segment of the United States merchant fleet can be attributed to the inability or failure of the operators to meet extraordinary increases in the costs of loading and discharging the ships. As a consequence, the railroads and the trucks have captured the trade. The only hope of the water carrier is to meet this competition by operating methods based on **sound economics,** taking into consideration the reality of high labor costs.

Great Lakes Carriers

The Great Lakes have carried a diversified trade since early in the 19th century. Canals and a set of locks make it possible for large steamers to ply between Buffalo, Duluth, and Chicago. Small ocean-going steamers with drafts not exceeding 14 ft. can pass from Montreal up the St. Lawrence River and its canals, the Welland Ship Canal, and about 28 locks, to reach the Great Lakes and Buffalo. With the completion of the St. Lawrence Seaway, ships drawing 27 ft. will be able to navigate between the open sea and the Great Lakes.

THE BULK ORE CARRIER. The kind of ship, described earlier under "The Bulk Ore Carrier" had its beginning on the Great Lakes. The ore carrier on the Lakes has four large **compartments,** with a total of 18 hatches. The double-bottom tanks are deep, and wing tanks are used to further raise the cargo-carrying compartment, and to provide ample ballasting space. The major difference between the lake and the ocean ore carrier is the location of the **bridge.** On the Lakes, the bridge is placed forward of the first hatch, on the forecastle head of the ship. On the ocean-going ore carrier, the bridge is placed aft of the third or fourth hatch to afford more protection in the heavy weather experienced at times on the open sea. The **loading and discharging procedures** are almost identical, the operators of the ocean-going carriers having adopted the basic ideas used for years by the Great Lakes carriers. These procedures are described in the discussion of the ocean-going carriers.

THE BULK GRAIN CARRIER. The ore ships may at times be used to carry grain in bulk. Because of their construction, there is no need to erect centerline shifting boards. The only special preparation that must take place is the thorough cleaning up of the cargo spaces.

THE CAR FERRY. The car ferry, or train ferry, is mentioned under the heading of Great Lakes carriers because this kind of ship has found its greatest development in this area. However, the car- or train-ferry concept has also been exploited on ocean routes for many years.

There are two kinds of car ferries. One receives and discharges its railroad cars via a ramp with tracks that connect with the ship's tracks. The railroad cars roll onto and off the ship. The other kind is the **lift-on, lift-off type** described under "The Seatrain." The **roll-on, roll-off ship** has one deck for stowage of the cars. A typical ship of this kind is the S.S. Spartan, which has a capacity of 32 railroad cars, or 150 automobiles, on her car deck. This ship runs between Ludington, Michigan and Milwaukee, Wisconsin and also carries passengers.

No longshore labor is needed for loading or discharging the Spartan. The car-deck has four tracks, each of which holds eight 40-ft. freight cars weighing up to 80 tons each. At the same time, the car deck can accommodate an additional load of 25 automobiles. The railroad cars are secured for the voyage by blocking all wheels, then lifting the load off the springs of the car by powerful jacks operating at an angle of about 45°. The cars are then clamped to the jacks and the rails. In bad weather, cars may be further secured with chain passed over the top.

When the cars roll onto the ship, the forward car connects to a spring buffer which receives and holds the car's coupling. All following cars remain coupled together. The complete turn-around time, including unloading and loading and taking on coal bunkers, is as low as 1½ hr.

Inland Waterway Carriers

CLASSIFICATION. Inland waterway carriers may be classified as barges, scows, lighters, and carfloats; towboats and tugboats which propel the non-self-propelled group; and a few self-propelled carriers. An example of a **self-propelled** unit is the automobile carrier Commercial Clipper built by the St. Louis Shipbuilding and Steel Co. (Fig. 5). The Commercial Clipper has a capacty of 600 automobiles. This kind of carrier must not be confused with the **carfloat**. The carfloat is a flush-decked craft with tracks on its deck to receive railroad freight

St. Louis Shipbuilding and Steel Co.

Fig. 5. Self-propelled automobile carrier of three integrated barge units.

cars. Some of the carfloats have lengths of 300 ft. and a beam of 40 ft., and are capable of carrying 20 cars. Loading platforms may be erected between tracks.

TOWBOATS. The terms towboat, tugboat, and tug generally refer to vessels of small tonnage used for pulling, pushing, or securing alongside of, a barge or similar craft, to assist or propel it from one terminal to another. Fig. 6 illustrates a kind of towboat with squared-off bow and towing knees, designed to face into a tow and to handle it as a unit by pushing. This kind of boat may be called a **push-boat** in some localities. It is widely used on the inland waterways of the United States, being first developed on the Mississippi River and its tributaries. The towboat illustrated is the Gene C. Hutchinson, with twin screws developing 3,200 hp. Some towboats are in operation with 5,400 hp. and bigger ones are being planned.

St. Louis Shipbuilding and Steel Co.

Fig. 6. Towboat with squared-off bow and towing knees.

The term **tug** or **tugboat**, as used in the ocean harbors, refers to crafts with 250 to 4000 hp. used to assist ships into and from their berths along the waterfront. At times they pull large barges along the sea lanes of the coastal waters, but in the crowded waters of harbors, they secure alongside of the craft they are assisting. In the rivers the tug pulls with a line over the stern for short hauls, and may even assist the towboat in making up the tow.

BARGES, SCOWS, AND LIGHTERS. The meaning of the words barge, scow, and lighter is not easy to set forth. The meaning may vary with locality, and the distinctive features are not clearly discernible. A flat-bottomed craft with sloping ends, without a change in beam from end to end, and with an open hold, is a **scow**. If the craft has a separate hold inside the framing of the hull with a coaming, without or with sliding covers, it is called a **hopper or covered barge** (Fig. 7). If the craft has no hold and the load is carried entirely above the deck, it is known as a **lighter** if used for transferring freight in harbor and terminal use (Fig. 8). Lighters with deck structures to give cargo protection from the weather are called **covered lighters.** Lighters may also have derricks or cargo booms for transferring freight to and from their decks. Vessels designed

Dravo Corp.

Fig. 7. 195 ft. × 35 ft. jumbo semi-integrated hopper barge.

Fig. 8. Harbor deck lighter.

Fig. 9. Sand and gravel box-type deck barge.

Fig. 10. 290 ft. × 50 ft. tank barge.

for use as **carfloats** are described above. If the craft has no hold and has an open deck box for carrying bulk materials such as sand and gravel, it is called a **deck barge** or **sand and gravel barge** (Fig. 9). If the hold is divided into tanks for carrying liquid cargoes, the craft is known as a **tank barge** (Fig. 10).

The barge is generally used for long hauls, while the lighter is commonly considered suitable only for short transfers of goods, as from a dock out to a vessel working in the stream, or across a harbor from one terminal to another.

Barges used on the inland waterways of the United States, for the most part, are of relatively shallow draft and are approximately square ended with a long bow rake and a shorter stern rake. For use in integrated tows, barges have one square end without rake so that two barges with the square ends together offer a surface to the water equivalent to one continuous hull. In long tows, intermediate barges with both ends square are sometimes used.

Although barges used on the inland waterways cover a wide **range of sizes,** the hopper and dry cargo covered barges are largely standardized into three sizes— the small "Pittsburgh" barge, 175 feet long by 26 feet wide; the "Jumbo" barge, 195 feet long by 35 feet wide; and the large barge, 240 feet long by 40 to 50 feet wide. These barges fit efficiently in the standard river lock, 110 feet wide by 600 feet long—four, three and two abreast respectively. Various types of **harbor and sea going barges** usually are of deeper draft than river barges and have blunt bow and stern figurations approximately those of deep water vessels.

A recent count showed the **inland waterways commercial fleet** to include approximately 18,400 towboats, tugs, barges, scows, lighters, and carfloats. This figure includes all such craft operating on the rivers and canals of the U. S., and in the harbors of the Great Lakes and the coastal seaports. This figure does not include fishing boats, nor the large bulk carriers of the Great Lakes. The number of craft may be subdivided into 4,000 towing and self-propelled vessels; 12,000 barges, scows, and other non-self-propelling shallow-draft carriers; 2,000 tank barges; and about 400 carfloats.

AIR CARRIERS

CONTENTS

AIR CARRIERS

Types of Aircraft and Cargo

CLASSES AND TYPES OF AIR TRANSPORTS. The following section deals with air transports, and the means they offer for carrying cargo and passengers. Particular emphasis is given to the **cargo-carrying features** of the various kinds of aircraft herein described, since passenger handling techniques form a field of their own and are outside the main scope of this discussion. Fixed-wing aircraft treated in detail herein are of two basic types: **all-cargo** aircraft and **passenger-cargo** aircraft. A section is also devoted to **helicopters,** which form a distinct and rapidly growing segment of the air transport industry. Gliders—a war time military expedient—no longer form an important means of air transport and are therefore not included.

Four **other general types** of aircraft are in common use:

1. Military combat aircraft.
2. Private or military trainers and sport aircraft.
3. Corporation and general-purpose airplanes.
4. Special-purpose aircraft.

No detailed discussion of these types is included in this section, since their uses are of a specialized nature and are beyond the scope of the handbook. However, since these four classes of aircraft constitute thousands of airplanes, a brief description of their nature and capabilities is in order.

Military Combat Aircraft. This general classification includes all airplanes used by the military services for actual combat purposes. They constitute the fighters, bombers, patrol aircraft, and other types with which readers are generally familiar. Detailed specifications and performance are of a classified nature and will not be dealt with herein. Cargo airplanes, when used in assault missions, might be classified as a combat aircraft, but, for purposes of this handbook, will be considered as all-cargo airplanes, and, therefore, will be described under that category up to the limits of military security.

Trainers and Sport Aircraft. Trainers, both military and commercial types, and sport aircraft form one of the largest groups of airplanes, if not the largest. In size they range from the popular Piper Cubs up to the Lockheed T-33 two-place jet trainer and the Convair T-29, a navigational trainer which is a military version of the popular CV-240 airliner. In many cases, the same general types are used by both commercial and military services. Other types are exclusively military in character. Some, such as the Piper Cubs or the Ryan Navions may be used either for training or sport, depending upon the owner.

Corporation and General-Purpose Aircraft. The past years have brought about a large increase in the number of airplanes owned and operated by private corporations, primarily for executive transportation. Types used range from small single-engine airplanes, such as those manufactured by Piper, Beech, or Cessna, to converted bombers, such as the North American B-25's and Douglas

B-26's, or transport types, primarily Lockheed Lodestars or Douglas DC-3's. Some large corporations operate fleets of 4-engine aircraft composed of Douglas DC-4's and DC-6's to transport company personnel to out-of-the-way places around the globe. The number of aircraft so used is constantly growing and various manufacturers are giving serious thought to a special type of airplane designed expressly for corporation use. The speed and mobility of the airplane has been put to good use by corporation executives, and indications are that this specialized use will continue to grow.

Special-Purpose Airplanes. Airplanes, like trucks and automobiles, are growing highly specialized in nature, and aircraft modified or designed for one particular purpose are becoming more and more commonplace. Crop dusters and photographic airplanes are two examples of highly specialized types in commercial use. They have proved their value beyond all doubt and have brought huge savings and efficiencies into their particular fields. Additional types are sure to follow.

THREE BASIC TYPES OF AIR CARGO. Air cargo is a generic term and covers three basic types of revenue material moving by air, namely: **Air Mail** (which includes Air Parcel Post), **Air Express,** and **Air Freight.** Passengers' baggage may also be considered a form of air cargo, but since individual pieces are usually small in size, no particular handling problems are involved as far as loading is concerned. It is the airlines' responsibility to provide sufficient space to accommodate a passenger's baggage on the same plane on which the passenger travels. It may therefore become a limiting factor for the amount of revenue cargo that can be loaded aboard a passenger-cargo airplane. Generally speaking Air Mail and Air Express, while constituting an important revenue source for the airlines, are like passengers' baggage, composed of relatively small pieces and therefore do not present a difficult materials handling problem.

Air Freight. This newest member of the air-cargo family is also the largest, both in the size of the pieces handled and in its over-all volume. Its commercial development since the end of World War II has been phenomenal. The first all air cargo service by a common carrier was inaugurated by American Airlines in the spring of 1934, with air cargo moving under a special tariff filed by that airline. The service was not successful and was abandoned after a few months. During World War II, however, the military services took to the air, and the exploits of the Air Transport Command, and the Naval Air Transport Service proved beyond a doubt that air cargo transport was here to stay. The Services established methods and standards of operation still in effect, introducing to the air transport scene aircraft and materials handling techniques never previously used (see section on Air Terminal Handling). Today the Military Air Transport Service, the Fleet Logistic Air Wings, the Troop Carrier Command, and other specialized military transport services continue the traditions of A.T.C. and N.A.T.S. Equipment and techniques used generally parallel those of commercial operations. Since such military information is of a restricted nature, data in this section regarding military operations is, of necessity, limited.

Air freight is the primary reason for the existence of the all-cargo airplanes and airlines in operation today. Special materials handling techniques and equipment have been—and are being—developed to handle the ever increasing volume of air freight. Special air freight terminals, many with specialized materials handling facilities, have made their appearance at the larger airports. They foreshadow further increases in air cargo transport.

Standard Aircraft Specifications

BASIC DIVISIONS OF CARGO AIRCRAFT. There are three over-all classifications of cargo aircraft: all-cargo aircraft, passenger-cargo aircraft, and helicopters. Specifications for helicopters will be given under the heading "Helicopters"; specifications for all-cargo aircraft and passenger-cargo aircraft are given in Figs. 1, 2, 3, 10, and 11. The data are confined to United States aircraft generally used in the transportation of cargo and passengers by both domestic and foreign airlines. Military aircraft are included by types whenever data are available and not classified.

ALL-CARGO AIRCRAFT. Principal types of all-cargo aircraft now in service are listed in Figs. 1 and 2. These tables, taken from a study prepared for the Air Cargo Advisory Committee of the National Security Industrial Association, give air transport data for each airplane listed.

Air Transport Dimensional and Loading Data. In compiling this material, certain generalizations were necessarily made because the interior arrangements, floor structure, or operating limits of the same type of aircraft may vary among the commercial airlines and between military and commercial users. This is particularly true in the case of passenger-cargo airplanes (Fig. 10), but also holds for all-cargo airplanes, especially the older types, such as the DC-4/C-54 and the C-46. Door sizes—their locations or other external details—are, for all practical purposes, the same for all users of the same type of aircraft. Interiors, however, will vary as already noted. Critical loads or maximum package sizes, when intended for transportation by a particular aircraft, should therefore be considered with caution. It is recommended that local airline representatives be consulted whenever maximum limits are in question.

Aircraft Performance Data. The following general definitions of aircraft performance nomenclature are useful when comparing the various aircraft types. They refer particularly to the more modern airplanes and are used in connection with Fig. 3

1. **Operating weight empty** is derived from manufacturer's weight empty, plus systems (unusable) fuel and oil, plus crew and crew equipment, plus operating equipment (cargo tie-down equipment, life rafts, passengers' food, etc.) plus total consumable oil and A.D.I. fluid. NOTE: Inclusion of consumable oil and A.D.I. fluid in operating weight will vary according to the various manufacturers or users. All data in this handbook include consumable oil and A.D.I. fluid in operating weight empty.
2. **Payload** equals the revenue-paying load carried, in pounds of cargo or number of passengers.
3. **Zero fuel weight** equals the maximum weight in pounds to which an aircraft may be loaded with no usable or reserve fuel aboard. Zero fuel weight minus operating weight empty equals maximum permissible payload in pounds. In some cases, because of undumpable fuel required by C.A.A. regulations for emergency operations, the zero fuel weight at which an aircraft is actually operated will be less than the maximum structural zero fuel weight. In such cases the lower figure (operational zero fuel weight) is used herein.
4. **Maximum landing weight** is the maximum weight at which an aircraft may be landed. The difference between zero fuel weight and maximum landing weight equals the normal reserve fuel weight incorporated in the design of the aircraft. If more reserve fuel is required, payload must be reduced.
5. **Gross take-off weight** represents the maximum permissible take-off weight of the aircraft. The weight difference between maximum take-off and maxi-

AIRCRAFT TYPE	CARGO COMPT. DIMENSIONS & VOLUME					CARGO FLOOR DATA				TIE DOWN CAPACITY LBS.			TIE DOWN LIMITATIONS & REMARKS Angularity Restrictions, Screw Or Ring Type, Swiveling or Fixed, Grid Pattern, Etc.
	Length	Width	Height	Volume Cu. Ft.	Floor Area Sq. Ft.	Floor Loading Lbs. Sq. Ft.	Floor Loading Lbs. Lineal Ft.	Floor Slope	Floor Material	Regular Floor Fittings	Engine Floor Fittings	Wall Fittings	
BOEING C-97 (A THRU G) "STRATOFREIGHTER" Main Cargo Compartment	63' 8"	10' 6"	7' 5"	4,320	567	200	1800	2°	All metal (24 ST)	Main compt. 10,000 within 30° 1,250 vertical 500 horizontal	10,000 All directions	1. 25,000 @ 0° 3,400 @ 90° 2. 10,000 @ 0° 2,100 @ 90°	Main cargo comp. has concentrated Load Cap. of 200 lbs./sq. in. Tie down data shown for main compt. with 20" grid. Lower compts. equipped with 200 lb. floor fittings good in all directions. No wall fittings, 10,000 lb. overhead monorail fittings.
Forward Lower Cargo Compartment	21' 1"	6' 10"	5' 11"	839	108	100	730	2°					
Aft Lower Cargo Compartment	17' 1"	9' 2"	5' 11"	639	94	100	730	2°					
Stowage Compartment	17' 0"	7' 6"	3' 4"	340	40	50	--	14°					
Total				6,138	809								
FAIRCHILD C-123B Main Cargo Compartment	36' 8"	9' 2"	8' 2"	3,570	450	Not Available	Not Available	level	Not Available	10,000 ultimate	Not Available	Not Available	20" floor grid pattern
Total				3,570	450								
CURTISS WRIGHT C-46 "COMMANDO" Main Cargo Compartment	48' 0"	9' 10"	6' 8"	2,300	384	185 *	Not Available	inclined 9.5°	watertight plywood	200	11,000	200	No angularity factors in tie down pattern 21" grid pattern Original C-46 Floor stressed for 70# per square foot. Modified by carriers to value shown.
Forward Cargo Compartment	12' 4"	3' 8"		250									
Aft Lower Cargo Compartment	11' 10"	3' 8"		276									
Total				2,826									
DOUGLAS DC-3 (Cargo Version) Main Cargo Compartment	27' 9"	6' 10"	6' 5"	1,120	191	40	Not Available	inclined	plywood	200	None	None	Very few now in service
Forward Cargo Compartment				68		75 - 100							
Aft Cargo Compartment	4' 2"	6' 10"	6' 5"	103		75 - 100							
Total				1,291									
DOUGLAS C-47 "SKYTRAIN" Main Cargo Compartment	30' 0"	6' 10"	6' 5"	1,245	211	125	Not Available	inclined	metal	500	1,500	200	Engine tie down fittings in center row of floor
Forward Cargo Compartment	9' 3"	6' 10"	6' 5"	102	18								
Total				1,347	229								
DOUGLAS R4D-8 (Super DC-3) Main Cargo Compartment	36' 7"	6' 10"	6' 5"	1,500	256	125-250	Not Available	inclined	composition	550	Not Available	180	
DOUGLAS C-54 (DC-4) "SKYMASTER" Main Cargo Compartment	57' 3"	9' 10"	7' 9"	3,583	450	200	360-960	level	wood or composition	200-830	2105-2550	300	Volumes shown are for American Airlines version. Will vary slightly with airlines.
Forward Lower Cargo Compartment	12' 5"		2' 7"	130	31								
Aft Lower Cargo Compartment	14' 8"		2' 7"	150	31								
Total				3,863									
DOUGLAS DC-6A "LIFTMASTER" Main Cargo Compartment	67' 11"	9' 11"	7' 9"	4,433	584	200 main cabin	960 main cabin	level	composition	4000 - 5000	10,000	1150 - 10,000	Floor and wall fittings allowable loads vary with angularity Engine fittings good in any direction
Forward Lower Cargo Compartment	21' 0"	6' 0"	2' 6"	267	142								
Aft Lower Cargo Compartment	28' 2"	6' 2"	2' 7"	300	189								
Total				5,000	915								

* Flying Tiger Line modifying fleet with Lockheed extruded magnesium floor with loading capacity of 400 Lbs / Sq. Ft.

Fig. 1. Dimensional and loading data for military and commercial cargo transports (continued on next page).

AIRCRAFT TYPE	CARGO COMPT. DIMENSIONS & VOLUME				CARGO FLOOR DATA					TIE DOWN CAPACITY LBS.			TIE DOWN LIMITATIONS & REMARKS Angularity Restrictions, Screw Or Ring Type, Swiveling or Fixed Grid Pattern, Etc.
	Length	Width	Height	Volume Cu. Ft.	Floor Area Sq. Ft.	Floor Loading Lbs. Sq. Ft.	Floor Loading Lbs. Lineal Ft.	Floor Slope	Floor Material	Regular Floor Fittings	Engine Floor Fittings	Wall Fittings	
DOUGLAS R6D-1 Main Cargo Compartment	67' 11"	9' 11"	7' 9"	4,160	551	200 main cabin	960 main cabin	level	composition	4000 – 5000	10,000	1150 – 10,000	Floor and wall fitting allowable loads vary with angularity 5,000 & 10,000 lbs. floor fittings good in any direction
Forward Lower Cargo Compartment	21' 0"	6' 0"	2' 6"	217	137								
Aft Lower Cargo Compartment	28' 2"	6' 2"	2' 7"	300	149								
Total				4,677	837								
DOUGLAS C-74 "GLOBEMASTER" Main Cargo Compartment	75' 0"	11' 6"	7' 10"	6,658	850	200	720–1200	level	aluminum over magnesium beams	1250	2,700 – 10,000	Not Available	20" grid pattern Allowable loads on engine fittings vary with angularity
Forward Lower Cargo Compartment	11' 8"												
Center Lower Cargo Compartment	8' 4"												
Center Wing Cargo Compartment	9' 11"			816									
Aft Lower Cargo Compartment	6' 9"												
Total				7,474									
DOUGLAS C-124A "GLOBEMASTER II" Main Cargo Compartment	77' 0"	12' 6"	12' 10"	11,390	900	4320–7200	4500–40,000 lbs. per 100 in. compartment	level and 17° slope fwd.	plywood over aluminum web on mag. beams	5000 & 15,000 ultimate	20,000 – 50,000 ultimate	None	Angularity factors govern engine fitting strength. No angularity factors for regular floor fittings.
Auxiliary Upper Deck	46' 8"	13' 0"			53*								
Lower Compartments		12' 9"		773	9"								
Total				12,163	1,53-								
FAIRCHILD C-82 PACKET Main Cargo Compartment (Cargo Hold)	38' 6"	8' 8"	8' 5"	2,312	306	200	720	none	plywood with skid strips	1250 – 5000	Not Available	Not Available	20" grid pattern
FAIRCHILD C-119 (A THRU G) PACKET Main Cargo Compartment (Cargo Hold)	36' 11"	Floor 9' 2" 15" above floor 9' 10"	8' 5"	2,700	353	200	Not Available	none	plywood with skid strips	5,000 to 10,000 ultimate	7,000 – 12,000 ultimate	Not Available	Angularity factors govern fitting strength
FAIRCHILD C-120 (Pack Plane) Main Cargo Compartment (Cargo Hold)	36' 11"	Floor 9' 2" 15" above floor 9' 10"	8' 0"	2,704	338	Not Available	Not Available	level	plywood with skid strips	Not Available	Not Available	Not Available	

Fig. 1. (Continued on next page.)

AIRCRAFT TYPE	CARGO COMPT. DIMENSIONS & VOLUME				CARGO FLOOR DATA					TIE DOWN CAPACITY LBS.			TIE DOWN LIMITATIONS & REMARKS Angularity Restrictions, Screw Or Ring Type, Swiveling or Fixed, Grid Pattern, Etc.
	Length	Width	Height	Volume Cu. Ft.	Floor Area Sq. Ft.	Floor Loading Lbs. Sq. Ft.	Floor Loading Lbs. Lineal Ft.	Floor Slope	Floor Material	Regular Floor Fittings	Engine Floor Fittings	Wall Fittings	
LOCKHEED C-121A ALL-CARGO CONSTELLATION													
Main Cargo Compartment	64' 1"	10' 9"	7' 0"	3,750	561	125–250	400–900	level	plywood	1,400 ultimate	yes	Not Available	20" grid pattern in floor Cabin volume shown with relief crew quarters and buffet removed
Forward Lower Cargo Compartment	14' 7"	6' 2"	2' 10"	141	70								
Aft Lower Cargo Compartment	24' 9"	6' 9"	2' 11"	223	124								
Total				4,114	755								
LOCKHEED 1049D/R7V-1 ALL CARGO 1049H/C-121C SUPER CONSTELLATION													
Main Cargo Compartment	84' 0"	10' 10"	7' 0"	4,875	744	150–300	500–1000	1° 53'	extruded magnesium 1049H— extruded aluminum	4,000 ultimate	1049D/R7V-1 10,500 13,500	4,500 lbs. ultimate	No angularity factor on floor fittings. Wall Fittings rated for 60° cone normal to center line.
Forward Lower Cargo Compartment	25' 4"	6' 2"	2' 10"	269	112								
Aft Lower Cargo Compartment	32' 5"	7' 0"	2' 11"	424	176								
Total				5,568	1,032								
LOCKHEED C-130A MEDIUM CARGO TRANSPORT													
Main Cargo Compartment	41' 5"	13' 8" 10' 3" *	9' 1"	4,500	512	500 1080	1000 & 3000	level	aluminum alloy	10,000 lb. ultimate (5,000 lb. ultimate on ramp)	25,000 lb. ultimate	5,000 lbs. ultimate	No angularity factor on any of fittings. 20" grid

*(at wheel well area)

NOTE:
1. Under "Cargo Compartment Dimensions & Volume", the figures given are maximum lengths, widths and heights, as the fuselage configurations in many instances are elliptical or cylindrical, the width and height will naturally not be constant throughout. In the tabular form as presented here it is not practical to show tapering dimensions.

2. Asterisks denote figures which are either estimates or approximates, and their accuracy has not been verified.

3. Where spaces are blank, information was not available.

Fig. 1. (Concluded.)

AIRCRAFT TYPE	GENERAL AIRPLANE DIMENSIONS			DOOR DIMENSIONS & HEIGHTS			MISCELLANEOUS DATA			REMARKS
	Wing Span	Overall Length	Overall Height	Height Door Sill Above Ground	Height or Breadth	Width or Length	Mechanical Material Handling Devices		Pressurization	
							Overhead	Floor		
BOEING C-97 (A thru G) "STRATOFREIGHTER"	141' 3"	110' 4"	38' 2.8" (26' 7")				Hoist 5,000 Lb. Traverse 10,000 Lb.	Horizontal Towing Force of Hoist 7,500 Lb. From Monorail	5,500 @ 25,000 Alt. 6.55 Lb./Sq. In. Differential	Self contained power operated ramps at rear main opening. Aerial delivery system - 25,000 Lb. Cargo ejected for drop in 15 Sec. Heating 70° F. in cabin, @ - 66° outside.
Main Cargo Openings - (Rear)				8' 10"	8' 7" - 6' 0"	13' 3"				
Forward Upper Cargo Door				11' 5"	6' 6"	6' 8"				
Forward Lower Cargo Compartment Door				4' 9"	4' 4"	2' 11"				
Rear Lower Cargo Compartment Door				4' 2"	4' 2"	2' 11"				
FAIRCHILD C-123B	110' 0"	76'3"	34' 1"				None	Pulling Cable Tunnel in Nose	None	Rear ramp loading
Main Cargo Opening (Ramp)				2' 8"	8' 4"	9' 2"				
CURTISS WRIGHT C-46 "COMMANDO"	108' 0"	76' 4"	22' 0"				None	None	None	Ram air ventilation 2 - 100,000 B.T.U./hr. heaters
Main Cargo Door				7' 6"	6' 6" - 5' 7"	8' 0"				
Forward Belly Compartment Cargo Door				8' 4"	2' 8"	3' 5"				
Rear Belly Compartment Cargo Door				4' 9"	2' 8"	3' 5"				
DOUGLAS DC-3	94' 7"	64' 5"	16' 11"				None	None	None	Very few now in all cargo service. Ram air ventilation and heat
Main Cargo Door				4' 8"	4' 11"	2' 2-1/2"				
Forward Cargo Door					3' 2"	1' 10"				
Rear Cargo Door					1' 11"	2' 4"				
DOUGLAS C-47 "SKYTRAIN"	94' 7"	64' 5"	16' 11"				None	None	None	Ram air ventilation + heat
Main Cargo Door				4' 11"	5' 9" - 4' 10"	7' 1/2"				
Forward Cargo Door					3' 2"	1' 10"				
DOUGLAS R4D-8 (SUPER DC-3)	90' 0"	67'8-1/2"	18' 3"				None	None	None	Ram Air ventilation and heat
Main Cargo Door				4' 4"	5' 9" - 4' 10"	7' 1/2"				
Forward Cargo Door					3' 2"	1' 10"				
DOUGLAS C-54 (DC-4) "SKYMASTER"	117' 6"	93' 11"	27' 6"				None	None	None	Some C-54's equipped with winch and hoisting boom. Not standard equipment. Ram ventilation 2 - 100,000 B.T.U./hr. heaters.
Main Cargo Door				8' 11"	5' 7"	7' 11"				
Forward Belly Compartment Cargo Door				6' 6"	2' 6"	3' 0"				
Rear Belly Compartment Cargo Door				6' 0"	2' 6"	3' 0"				
DOUGLAS DC-6A "LIFTMASTER"	117' 6"	105' 7"	28' 8"				None	None	8000' @ 20,000 alt.	Heating and refrigeration systems available. Portable power winches and door hoists available as extra equipment.
Main Cargo Door				8' 10"	6' 6"	10' 4"				
Forward Cargo Door				8' 10"	5' 7"	7' 7"				
Forward Belly Compartment Cargo Door				6' 6"	3' 9"	3' 1"				
Rear Belly Compartment Cargo Door				6' 0"	3' 9"	3' 1"				

Fig. 2. Additional dimensional and loading data for military and commercial cargo transports listed in Fig. 1 (continued on next page).

AIRCRAFT TYPE	GENERAL AIRPLANE DIMENSIONS			DOOR DIMENSIONS & HEIGHTS			MISCELLANEOUS DATA			REMARKS
	Wing Span	Overall Length	Overall Height	Height Door Sill Above Ground	Height or Breadth	Width or Length	Mechanical Material Handling Devices Overhead	Floor	Pressurization	
DOUGLAS R6D-1/C-118A Main Cargo Door Forward Cargo Door Forward Lower Cargo Door Aft Lower Cargo Door	117' 6"	106' 7"	28' 8"	8' 10" 8' 10" 6' 6" 6' 0"	6' 6" 5' 7" 3' 9" 3' 9"	10' 4" 7' 7" 3' 1" 3' 1"	NONE	NONE	8000' @ 20,000 alt.	Heating and refrigeration systems available. Portable power winches and door hoists available as extra equipment.
DOUGLAS C-74 "GLOBEMASTER" Main Cargo Elevator Opening Forward Main Cargo Door	173' 3"	124' 2"	43' 9"	12' 11" 12' 11"	11' 8" 7' 1"	11' 4" 11' 0"	Dual traveling cranes 8000 lbs. capacity ea.	NONE	NONE	Side cargo hoist of 4,500 pound capacity and rear cargo elevator
DOUGLAS C-124 A Main Cargo Door Elevator Opening	174' 2"	130' 0"	48' 4"	8' 2" 12' 0"	11' 8" 7' 8"	11' 4" 13' 4"	Dual traveling cranes 8000 lbs. capacity ea.	NONE	NONE	Self contained power operated loading ramps in nose. 9,300 pound elevator in rear Winching pulleys 30,000 lb. capacity
FAIRCHILD C-82 PACKET Main Cargo Door Forward Cargo Door	106' 6"	77' 1"	26' 4"	4' 0" 4' 0"	8' 0" 6' 3"	8' 0" 3' 3-1/2"	Monorail	NONE	NONE	Built in loading ramp supports at rear
FAIRCHILD C-119 (A thru G) PACKET Main Cargo Door Forward Cargo Door	109' 3"	86' 6"	26' 8"	4' 0" 4' 0"	8' 0" 5' 10-3/4"	9' 2" 3' 1/2"	Monorail	NONE	NONE	Built in loading ramp supports at rear
FAIRCHILD C-120 "PACK PLANE" Main Cargo Doors (Front and Rear) Fwd. Side Door	109' 3"	83' 0"	24' 10"	3' 7" * 2' 8" ** 3' 7" * 2' 8" **	8' 0" 6' 1"	9' 2" 3' 2"	NONE	NONE	NONE	Built in loading ramp support at Fwd. and Rear Cargo Door
LOCKHEED C-121A ALL-CARGO CONSTELLATION Main Cargo Door Forward Belly Compartment Cargo Door Aft Belly Compartment Cargo Door	123' 0"	95' 3"	23' 0"	9' 9" 7' 11" 6' 8"	6' 0" 1' 10" 2' 6"	9' 1" 3' 5" 3' 4"	NONE	NONE	8000' @ 20,000' alt.	Complete heating and refrigeration system.
LOCKHEED 1049D/R7V-1 CARGO 1049H/C-121C SUPER CONSTELLATION Main Cargo Door Forward Cargo Door Forward Belly Compartment Cargo Door Aft Belly Compartment Cargo Door	123' 0"	113' 7" 116' 2"	24' 9"	9' 4-1/2" 11' 1-1/2" 7' 11" 6' 8"	6' 2-1/2" 6' 4-3/4" 2' 6" 2' 6"	9' 4.5" 5' 1.5" 3' 4" 3' 4"	NONE	Aero-Trusty Floor Conveyor R7V-1	8000' @ 22,800' alt.	Complete heating and cooling system. Conveyor has 4000 Lb. chain pull capacity. R7V-1 only

* Pack attached to carrier
** Pack on ground

Fig. 2. (Continued on next page.)

AIRCRAFT TYPE	GENERAL AIRPLANE DIMENSIONS			DOOR DIMENSIONS & HEIGHTS			MISCELLANEOUS DATA			REMARKS
							Mechanical Material Handling Devices			
	Wing Span	Overall Length	Overall Height	Height Door Sill Above Ground	Height or Breadth	Width or Length	Overhead	Floor	Pressurization	
LOCKHEED C-130A MEDIUM CARGO TRANSPORT Forward Cargo Door Rear Ramp Door	132' 7"	95'2"	38' 3"	3'5" 3'5"	6'1" 9'0"	7'4" 10'0"	NONE	Snatch Blocks	8000' @ 35,000' alt. 7.5 Lb./Sq.In.	Complete heating and refrigeration for cargo compartment and flight station. Rear ramp positioned horizontally permits direct one level loading from trucks – lowered to ground it permits direct entry of wheeled items.

NOTE: 1. Asterisks denote figures which are other estimates or approximates, and their accuracy has not been verified.

2. Where spaces are blank, information was not available.

Fig. 2. (Concluded.)

mum landing weights represents the consumable fuel that may be carried with maximum payload and reserve fuel aboard. Increased fuel loads will require a reduction in payload and/or in reserve fuel.

6. **In commercial operations, aircraft may never exceed gross take-off weights or maximum landing weights.** They may, however, operate below these values at the convenience of the operator, or because of airport or other restrictions. Military services at times require operations under overload conditions, in which case gross take-off and maximum landing weights will be exceeded.

Basis of Comparison. Performance and other aircraft data contained in Fig. 3 were obtained through the cooperation of the various manufacturers. Insofar as possible performance figures were compiled on the basis of the following "ground rules" so that a uniform basis of comparison would be available:

1. **Gross weights** are the standard, C.A.A.-approved, manufacturers' gross take-off weights and do not include military overload gross weights.

2. Where different **fuel tank configurations** are available in the same basic type of aircraft, the most commonly used tankage is assumed to be the standard.

3. **Normal operating weights empty** for 4-engine cargo planes, except the DC-4/C-54, include a crew of three @ 175 lb. each plus 25 lb. of baggage for each crew member, in addition to all normal operating equipment, and consumable oil carried aboard the airplane. The DC-4/C-54 crew consists of two members.

4. For 2-engine all-cargo airplanes, a **crew** of two is assumed, other items being as listed in paragraph 3 above.

5. The **operating weights** of the 4-engine passenger airplanes, except the DC-4/C-54, include a crew of five, plus normal passenger service equipment.

6. **Crew complements** of 2-engine passenger airplanes vary. The more commonly used crews for each type of aircraft were assumed in arriving at the operating weights shown.

7. When a commercial and a military version of the same airplane are in use and data are included herein, the **commercial values** for operating weights, payloads, ranges, etc., are shown. Examples of this type may be seen in the Lockheed 1049D or R7V-1 and the Douglas DC-6A or R6D-1 airplanes.

8. **Maximum and cruising speeds** for the various airplanes are given at the maximum landing weights whenever possible.

9. **Performance** herein is generally based on zero winds and normal reserve fuel. Reserves will vary slightly depending on manufacturers but usually are for $2\frac{1}{2}$ to 3 hr. of flight, or 300 miles to an alternate airport plus 1 hr. of flight.

10. **Door sizes,** height and length, are given in feet and inches, or in inches only for the smaller doors. Two dimensions for the length or height indicate doors of different sizes.

11. **Military airplanes** convertible to cargo, passengers, or litter patients are listed in the cargo version only. No confidential military data are included in the tabulations that follow. Data shown are either unrestricted or were obtained from public sources. Their accuracy, therefore, may in some instances be open to question.

12. **Cabin volume and areas** shown for passenger-cargo airplanes refer to cargo space only, since passenger areas are not generally available for cargo purposes.

13. **Payloads** given for passenger-cargo airplanes are based on the number of passengers carried and cargo and baggage space available, and are usually space-limited unless otherwise noted. Data given are based on a standard passenger weight of 160 lb. plus an allowance of 40 lb. of baggage, for a total of 200 lb. Baggage and cargo are considered as weighing 13 lb. per cu. ft.

14. **Passenger capacities** are based on standard seat arrangements. No coach or high-density configurations are shown or considered unless specifically noted.

	Gross Take-off Weight (lb.)	Max. Landing Weight (lb.)	Zero Fuel Weight (lb.)	Operating Weight Empty (lb.)	Maximum Payload Total (lb.)	Cargo (lb.)	Maximum Speed (M.P.H.) @ Alt. in ft.	Normal Cruising Speed (M.P.H.) @ Alt. in ft.	Range-Max. Payload (mi.) @ Alt. in ft.
Boeing B-377 C-97 (Air Force)	153,000	135,500	128,000	81,306	47,000	47,000	375/30,000	300/25,000	1,440/25,000
Curtiss Wright Commando C-46 (Air Force)	48,000	46,800	45,168	30,000	15,168	15,168	265/13,000	223/15,000	400/10,000
Douglas DC-3 C-47 (Air Force) R4D-1 (Navy)	26,900	26,900	–	17,702	6,698	6,698	232/7,500	205/10,000	525/10,000
Douglas DC-4 C-54G (Air Force) R5D (Navy)	73,000	63,500	59,900	40,400	19,500	19,500	307/20,000	229/10,000	1,550/10,000
Douglas DC-6A C-118A (Air Force) R6D-1 (Navy)	107,000	88,200	84,540	54,949	29,591	29,591	371/19,400	315/22,400	2,400/10,000
Douglas C-124A Globemaster II (Air Force)	194,500	160,300	N.A.	96,444	50,000	50,000	300	255	N.A.
Fairchild C82A (Air Force)	50,000	47,200	N.A.	32,500	21,500	21,500	248/17,500	218/10,000	1,000*
Fairchild C-123B (Air Force)	54,000	N.A.	N.A.	30,000	22,694	22,694	245	215	1,325
Fairchild C-119F (Air Force)	72,800	72,500	72,800	42,522	28,000	28,000	250/10,000	205/10,000	2,000*
Lockheed 749A C-121 (Air Force)	107,000	89,500	87,000	63,414	23,586	23,586	346/20,000	322/20,000	1,944/10,000
Lockheed 1049D C-121C Air Force R7V-1 (Navy)	133,000	110,000	105,000	70,530	34,500	34,500	372/20,000	330/22,600	2,460/10,000
Lockheed 1049H	140,000	113,000	108,000	72,547	35,400	35,400	370/20,000	329/22,600	2,760/10,000
Lockheed YC-121F (Air Force) R7V-2 (Navy) Prop-jet	150,000	113,000	104,800	69,850	34,950	34,950	440/18,000	420/23,000	2,315/25,000
Lockheed C130-A (Air Force) Prop-jet	124,200	110,000	99,100	59,800	39,300	39,300	362/20,000	322/20,000	–

Distances and speeds in statute miles. Ranges with max. payloads based on long-range cruise powers.

* 15,000 lb. payload.

Fig. 3. Performance data for all-cargo aircraft.

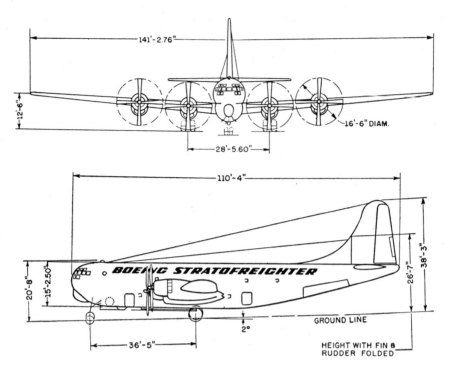

REAR LOADING DOOR—30° RAMP

Inches

	6	12	18	24	30	36	42	48	54	60	66	72	78	84
6	730	730	730	730	730	730	730	730	730	730	730	730	730	730
12	730	730	730	730	730	730	730	730	730	730	730	730	730	730
18	730	730	730	730	730	730	730	730	730	730	730	730	730	730
24	730	730	730	730	730	730	730	730	730	730	730	730	730	730
30	730	730	730	730	730	730	730	730	730	730	730	730	730	730
36	730	730	730	730	730	630	630	620	620	610	594	578	569	545
42	730	730	730	730	730	630	500	495	494	485	472	455	440	350
48	730	730	730	730	730	620	495	408	402	394	382	371	359	263
54	730	730	730	730	730	620	494	402	339	331	323	313	303	206
60	730	730	730	730	730	610	485	394	331	287	280	271	239	157
66	730	730	730	730	730	594	472	382	323	280	245	237	185	123
72	730	730	730	730	730	578	455	371	313	271	237	200	151	100
78	730	730	730	730	730	569	440	359	303	239	185	151	100	
84	730	730	730	730	730	545	350	263	206	157	123	100		
90	730	730	730	730	500	300	196	150	106					
96	730	730	712	270	166	100								

Boeing Airplane Co.

Fig. 4. Boeing Stratofreighter (military C-97) with package-size chart.

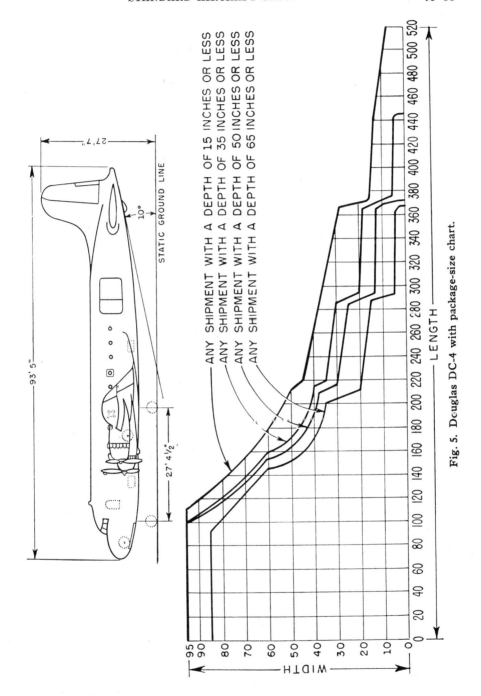

Fig. 5. Douglas DC-4 with package-size chart.

PACKAGE-SIZE DETERMINATION. While cargo space within all-cargo aircraft may be considerable, the size and shape of each unit of cargo is limited by the dimensions and location of the access doorway. Fig. 4 shows a Boeing Stratofreighter (military C-97) with a package-size chart for the rear loading door. The dimensions in this chart allow for a minimum of 1 in. clearance between the cargo and airplane structure. Special loading techniques and a decrease in clearance dimensions will allow larger items to pass through the cargo opening.

The all-cargo Douglas DC-4 (military C-54) has its cargo door located in the side of the airplane. Packages may be passed through this doorway within the limitations shown in Fig. 5. This opening is 66 in. high, 94 in. long, and has a corner radius of 8¼ in. To determine whether a shipment can be loaded through it, find the width and length of the package on the chart. If the lines for these two figures meet within the curve denoting maximum depth, the package can be loaded.

Another type of package-size chart is shown with the Lockheed Super Constellation Model 1049D C-121C (Air Force) R 7V-1 (Navy) in Fig. 6.

LOADING POSITION. The on-the-ground position of the airplane and the resulting floor slope of the cargo compartment are important considerations in materials handling. Floor slopes for all-cargo aircraft are tabulated in Fig. 1. The typical level position of aircraft equipped with nose wheels is illustrated by the Boeing Stratofreighter, the Douglas DC-4, and the Lockheed Super Constellation in Figs. 4, 5, and 6. The Douglas Super DC-3 in Fig. 7 illustrates the sloped static position.

CONDITION	A	B	C	D*
1	11' 1.4"	9' 4.5"	6' 2.8"	831.3"
2	11' 0.8"	12' 5.3"	7' 8.5"	240.3"
3	12' 5.3"	7' 9.1"	4' 11.1"	931.3"

*"D" VARIES WITH AIRPLANE ATTITUDE

EMPTY WEIGHT FLOOR ANGLES
FWD. COMPARTMENT SLOPES DOWN 0°9' REARWARD
AFT. COMPARTMENT SLOPES DOWN 1°53' REARWARD

CONDITION
1. STATIC (133,000 lb. AT 29% M.A.C.)
2. NOSE DOWN (MAIN GEAR EXTENDED NOSE STRUT COMPR. & TIRE FLAT)
3. NOSE UP (NOSE GEAR EXTENDED MAIN STRUT COMPR. & TIRE FLAT)

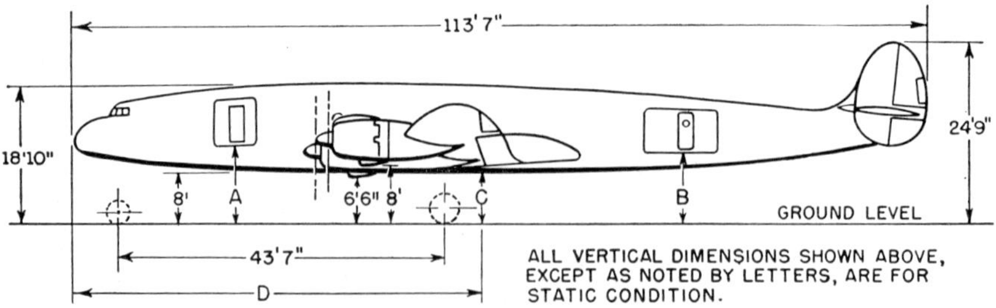

ALL VERTICAL DIMENSIONS SHOWN ABOVE, EXCEPT AS NOTED BY LETTERS, ARE FOR STATIC CONDITION.

Lockheed Aircraft Corp.

Fig. 6. Lockheed Super (1049D) Constellation with package-size chart (continued on next page).

DOOR LOCATION. This factor has already been mentioned. Door position as well as size may determine the dimensions of the package that can be loaded. This factor will also help determine the handling methods that may be used. Typical of aircraft with cargo doors placed in the afterside of the fuselage are the DC-4, the Lockheed Super Constellation, and the DC-3 (Figs. 5, 6, and 7). The Boeing Stratofreighter is equipped with a rear cargo door (Fig. 4).

There is a continuing effort to develop aircraft designs that will permit easier loading and unloading of the cargo compartment. The Air Force's Fairchild C-119F (Fig. 8) is designed to bring the cargo floor close to the ground. It has a large cargo compartment with double rear doors that open almost to the full

Height	49	54	60	66	72	74	Height	49	54	60	66	72	74
L	W	W	W	W	W	W	L	W	W	W	W	W	W
73	10	6½					40	25½	22	17½	11		
72	10¾	7					39	26	22¾	18	11½	3¼	
71	11¼	7¾					38	26¾	23½	18½	12¼	4	
70	12	8¼	3½				37	27½	24¼	19¼	13	4¾	
69	12¼	9	4				36	28¼	25	20	13¾	5¼	
68	12¾	9½	4¾				35	29	25¾	20¾	14¼	6	
67	13¼	10	5¼				34	29¾	26½	21¾	15	6¾	
66	13¾	10½	5¾				33	30½	27½	22¾	16	7½	
65	14¼	11	6¼				32	31½	28¼	23¾	16¾	8¼	3
64	14¾	11½	7				31	32½	29¼	24½	17¾	9	3½
63	15	12	7¼				30	33½	30¼	25½	18¾	10	4½
62	15½	12½	7¾				29	34¾	31¼	26½	19¾	11	5¾
61	16	12¾	8¼				28	36	32½	27¾	20¾	12	6¾
60	16¼	13¼	8¾				27	37½	33¾	29	22	13¼	8
59	16½	13½	9				26	39	35¼	30¼	23¼	14½	9¼
58	17	14	9½	3¼			25	40½	37	32	24¾	15¾	10¼
57	17¼	14¼	10	3½			24	42¼	38¾	33½	26¼	17¼	11½
56	17½	14¾	10¼	4			23	44	40½	35	27¾	19	13
55	18	15	10½	4¼			22	46	42½	37	29¾	20½	14¾
54	18¼	15¼	11	4½			21	48	45	39½	31¾	22½	16½
53	18¾	15¾	11¼	5			20	50½	47½	41½	33¾	24½	18½
52	19	16	11½	5¼			19	53	50	44	36	26½	20¾
51	19½	16½	12	5½			18	56	52½	46½	38½	29	23
50	20	17	12¼	6			17	59	55½	49½	41¼	31¼	25¾
49	20½	17½	12¾	6½			16	62¼	58½	52½	44	34¼	28½
48	21	18	13	7			15	66	62	56	47½	37½	31½
47	21¼	18¼	13½	7½			14	69¾	66	60	51	41	34¼
46	22	18¾	14	8			13	74	70½	64	54¾	44¼	37¾
45	22½	19¼	14½	8½			12	79	75	68¾	59½	48¼	41¾
44	23	19¾	15	9			11	84¾	80½	74	64¾	53	46
43	23½	20¼	15½	9½			10	91¼	87¼	80¾	71	58	51
42	24	21	16	10			9	99	96	89	78	64	56
41	24¾	21½	16½	10½			8	106½					62

L = Length in feet   W = Width in inches   H = Height in inches

To use:
  Read length in feet under "L"
  Read across columns to proper height in inches
  Read width in inches at intersection of vertical and horizontal columns
  Interpolate for heights and widths falling between those listed in table

Fig. 6. (Concluded.)

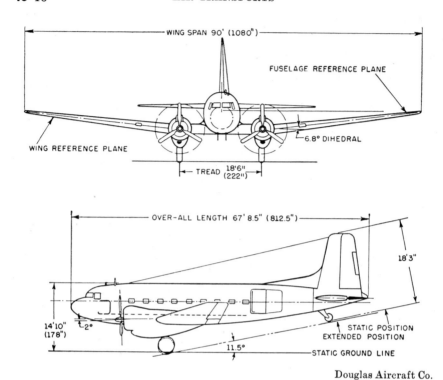

Douglas Aircraft Co.

Fig. 7. Douglas commercial Super DC-3 R4D-8

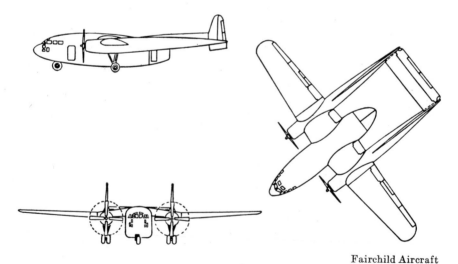

Fairchild Aircraft

Fig. 8. Fairchild C-119F (Air Force).

extent of the fuselage circumference. An experimental Air Force model is the Fairchild XC-120 (Fig. 9). The cargo compartment is in the form of a detachable pod.

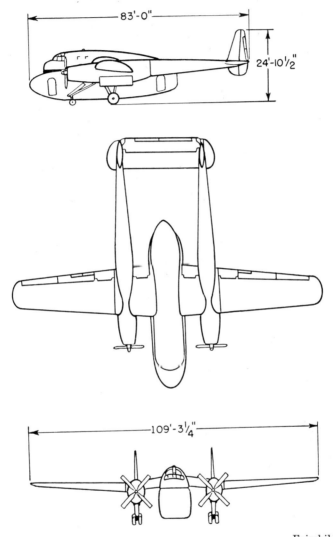

Fairchild Aircraft

Fig. 9. Experimental model, military XC-120, Fairchild.

PASSENGER-CARGO AIRCRAFT. Fig. 10 lists the principal aircraft now in use in this category and gives cargo capacities and loading data. This table also gives general dimensions of each aircraft. Fig. 11 gives operational data for passenger-cargo airplanes and provides comparisons on the bases specified under the headings "Aircraft Performance Data" and "Basis for Comparison" earlier in this section. Package-size charts similar to those described earlier in this

AIRCRAFT TYPE	GENERAL AIRPLANE DIMENSIONS			DOOR DIMENSIONS & HT			MAXIMUM COMPARTMENT DIMENSIONS & VOLUMES					CARGO COMPT FLOOR DATA	TIE-DOWN CAPACITY POUNDS		PRESSUR-IZATION	HEATING SYSTEM	
	Wing Span	Overall Length	Overall Height	Height Sill Above Ground	Height or Breadth	Width or Length	Length	Width	Height	Usable Volume Cu. Ft.	Area Sq. Ft.	Allowable Loading Lbs/Sq.Ft.	Floor Fittings	Wall Fittings		Upper Cabin	Lower Compts
BOEING 377 STRATOCRUISER	141' 3"	110' 4"	38' 2.8" (26' 6")												Yes 5000' Cabin @25,000'	Heating · 70@-65° Cooling 10° Below Ambient	Heating · 70°@-65° Cooling 10° Below Ambient
Main Passenger Cabin				10' 0"	5' 11"	2' 6"	79' 3"	10' 4"	7' 0"	845	148	100	500	600			
Forward Cargo Compartment				4' 9"	4' 4"	2' 11"	21' 1"	6' 10"	5' 11"				500	600			
Aft Cargo Compartment				4' 2"	4' 2"	2' 11"	17' 0"	7' 6"	3' 4"								
CONVAIR LINER 240	91' 9"	74' 8"	26' 11"											Web net Restraint	Web net Restraint	Yes 8000' @17,500'	Heating and Cooling	Heating and Cooling
Main Passenger Cabin				7' 7"	6' 4.8"	3' 0"	36' 6"	8' 10"	6' 6"	336.7	55.9	150					
Upper Cargo Compartment				7' 7"	4' 0"	2' 6"				83.	51.4	65					
Lower Cargo Compartment				5' 3"	3' 0"	3' 2"				419.7	107.3						
Total																	
CONVAIR LINER 340	105' 4"	79' 2"	28' 1.6"											Web Net Restraint	Web Net Restraint	Yes 8000' @20,000'	Heating and Cooling	Heating and Cooling
Main Passenger Cabin				7' 3"	6' 4.8"	3' 0.5"	40'	8' 10"	6' 7"	237.4	40.1	150					
Upper Forward Cargo Compartment				7' 3"	4' 2"	3' 0.5"	9' 4"	2' 9"	6' 4"	199.4	33.5	150					
Upper Rear Cargo Compartment				8' 1.9"	4' 2"	2' 6"	6' 10"	7' 0"	6' 4"	77.8	47.4	65					
Lower Cargo Compartment				4' 8.8"	2' 11"	3' 2"	10' 8"	4' 0"	1' 4"	514.6	121.0						
Total																	
DOUGLAS DC-3	95'	64' 5"	16' 11"											Light Fittings Web Nets	NONE	NONE	Heating	No Lower Compts
Main Passenger Cabin				4' 8"	4' 8"	2' 1"	30'	6' 10"	6' 5"	131.4	28.36	75					
Forward Cargo Compartment				9' 10"	2' 11"	1' 10"	44"	46"	72"	156.	12.	80					
Rear Cargo Compartment				4' 0"	1' 11"	2' 4"				287.4	40.36						
Total																	
DOUGLAS DC-4	117' 6"	93' 11"	27' 6"											Web Nets	Web Nets	NONE	2-100,000 B.T.U. Heaters	NONE
Main Passenger Cabin				8' 11"	6' 0"	3' 0"	49' 9.5"	9' 10"	7' 9"	275	47	70-120					
Forward Cargo Compartments				8' 11"	4' 8"	2' 4"	7' 0"	3' 10"	6' 4"	130		31					
Lower Forward Compartment				6' 6"	2' 6"	3' 0"	12' 6"	6' 0"	2' 6"	150		31					
Lower Aft Compartment				6' 6"	2' 6"	3' 0"	14' 8"	6' 2"	2' 7"	555							
Total																	

Fig. 10. Dimensional and loading data for passenger-cargo transports (continued on next page).

AIRCRAFT TYPE	Wing Span	Overall Length	Overall Height	Door Height Above Ground Sill	Door Height or Breadth	Door Width or Length	Max Length	Max Width	Max Height	Usable Volume Cu. Ft.	Area Sq. Ft.	Allowable Loading Lbs/Sq.Ft.	Floor Fittings	Wall Fittings	PRESSURIZATION	Upper Cabin	Lower Compts
DOUGLAS DC-6	117' 6"	100' 7"	28' 5"														
Main Passenger Cabin				8' 10"	6' 0"	3' 0"	61' 9"	9' 11"	7' 9"	168	30	150	Tie-Downs And Web Nets	Tie-Downs And Web Nets	Cabin 8000' at 20,000	200,000 B.T.U. Heater	NONE
Forward Cargo Compartments				8' 10"	5' 0"	3' 6"	4' 5"	3' 8"	3' 0"	203	199	75					
Lower Forward Compartment				6' 6"	3' 9"	3' 1"	15' 11"	6' 2"	2' 7.5"	170		75					
Total				6' 6"	3' 9"	3' 1"	13' 4"	6' 2"	2' 7.5"	541	229						
DOUGLAS DC-6B	117' 6"	105' 7"	28' 8"														
Main Passenger Cabin				8' 10"	6' 0"	3' 0"	61' 9"	9' 11"	7' 9"	377	53	150	Tie-Downs And Web Nets	Tie-Downs And Web Nets	Cabin 8000' at 20,000	Yes	NONE
Forward Cargo Compartment*				8' 10"	5' 0"	3' 7"	9' 5"	3' 8"	6' 0"	267	142	75					
Lower Forward Compartment				6' 6"	3' 9"	3' 1"	21' 0"	6' 0"	2' 6"	242	141	75					
Lower Aft Compartment				6' 0"	3' 9"	3' 1"	20' 3"	6' 2"	2' 7"	886	336						
DOUGLAS DC-7	117' 6"	108' 11"	28' 7"														
Main Passenger Cabin				8' 10"	6' 0"	3' 0"	71' 4"	9' 11"	7' 9"	137	25.2	150	Tie-Downs And Web Nets	Tie-Downs And Web Nets	Cabin 8000' at 25,000	Heating 75° at -50° Freon Cooling System	NONE
Forward Cargo Compartment				8' 10"	5' 0"	3' 7"				267	142	75					
Lower Forward Compartment				6' 6"	3' 9"	3' 1"	21' 0"	6' 0"	2' 6"	323	205	75					
Lower Aft Compartment (With Freon System)				6' 0"	3' 9"	3' 1"	30' 9"	6' 2"	2' 7"	727	372.2						
LOCKHEED LODESTAR 18	65' 6"	49' 10"	17' 10.5												NONE	Hot Air System	
Main Passenger Cabin				6' 11"	5' 3"	2' 7"	29' 0"	6' 5"	6' 3"	82	12	125					
Nose Cargo Compartment					3' 0"	2' 5"	4' 10"	3' 11"	5' 6"	42	18.3	45					
Intermediate Compartment				5' 2"	1' 10"	2' 9"	4' 7"	4' 0"	2' 6"	66	39.5						
Lower Compartments				3' 7"	1' 6"	2' 4"	5' 0"	5' 0"	1' 7"	190	69.8						
LOCKHEED 049 - 149	123' 0"	95' 2"	22' 5"										Tie-Downs And Web Nets	Tie-Downs And Web Nets	Cabin 8000' at 20,000	Heating 75°F at -60°F Cool 80°F at +90° F	Heating 32° F at 0°F
Main Passenger Cabin				10' 0"	5' 5"	2' 8"	65' 7"	10' 9"	7' 0"	180	83	70					
Lower Forward Compartment				7' 11"	2' 2"	3' 5"	14' 7"	6' 9"	2' 10"	265	118	70					
Lower Aft Compartment**				6' 8"	2' 6"	3' 1"	24' 9"	6' 9"	2' 11"								
Total										445	201						

* Total volume 25 cu. ft. when forward cabin converted to passengers.   ** 35 cu. ft. deducted from gross volume for door clearance.   ‡ Total volume 549 cu. ft. when forward passenger cabin converted to cargo.

Fig. 10. (Continued on next page.)

AIRCRAFT TYPE	GENERAL AIRPLANE DIMENSIONS			DOOR DIMENSIONS & HT			MAXIMUM COMPARTMENT DIMENSIONS & VOLUMES				CARGO COMPT FLOOR DATA		TIE-DOWN CAPACITY POUNDS		PRESSUR-IZATION	HEATING SYSTEM	
	Wing Span	Overall Length	Overall Height	Height Sill Above Ground	Height or Breadth	Width or Length	Length	Width	Height	Useable Volume Cu. Ft.	Area Sq. Ft.	Allowable Loading Lbs/Sq.Ft.	Floor Fittings	Wall Fittings		Upper Cabin	Lower Compts
LOCKHEED 649 – 749	123' 0"	95' 2"	22' 5"												Cabin 8000' at 20,000'	Heating 75°F at –60°F Cooling 80°F at +99°F	Heating 32°F at 0°F
Main Passenger Cabin				10' 0"	5' 5"	2' 3"	65' 7"	10' 9"	7' 0"	154	74	70	Tie-Downs And Web Nets				
Lower Forward Compartment				7' 11"	2' 2"	3' 5"	14' 7"	6' 9"	2' 10"	280	124	70					
Lower Aft Compartment*				6' 8"	2' 6"	3' 4"	24' 9"	6' 9"	2' 11"	434	298						
Total																	
LOCKHEED 1049	123' 0"	113' 7"	24' 9"												Cabin 8000' at 22,800'	Heating 70°F at –50°F Cooling 88°F at +99°F	Heating 32°F at 0°F
Main Passenger Cabin				9' 6"	5' 5"	2' 3"	84' 0"	10' 9"	7' 0"	305	112	70	300 – 700 Lbs & Web Nets	NONE			
Lower Forward Compartment				7' 6"	2' 2"	3' 5"	25' 4"	6' 3"	2' 10"	410	176	70					
Lower Aft Compartment*				6' 6"	2' 6"	3' 4"	32' 5"	6' 11"	3' 2"	714	288						
Total																	
LOCKHEED 1049C–E AND G	123' 0"	113' 9"	24' 9"												Cabin 8000' at 22,800'	Heating 70°F at –50°F Cooling 80°F at +99°F	Heating 32°F at 0°F
Main Passenger Cabin				9' 6"	6' 0"	2' 3"	84' 0"	10'8.5"	6' 6"	620	82	150	300 – 700 Lbs	NONE			
Optional Upper Cargo Compartment				11' 3"	5' 5"	3' 4"	17'3.5"	3' 6"	6' 6"	304	112	70					
Lower Forward Compartment				7' 6"	2' 6"	3' 4"	25' 4"	6' 3"	2' 10"	424	176	70					
Lower Aft Compartment*				6' 6"	2' 6"	3' 4"	32' 5"	6' 11"	3' 2"								
MARTIN 202	93'3"	71' 4"	28' 7"												NONE	Heating 75°F at –40°F No Cooling	NONE
Main Passenger Cabin				7' 11"	6' 2"	3' 0"	34' 8"	9' 0"	6' 7"	217		50	Floor and Wall Rings				
Upper Cargo Compartment				7' 11"	2' 0"	3' 2"				38		100					
Total				5' 8"						245							
MARTIN 202-A	93' 3"	71' 4"	28' 7"												NONE	Heating 75°F at –40°F No Cooling	NONE
Main Passenger Cabin				7' 11"	6' 2"	3' 0"	34' 8"	9' 0"	6' 7"	192		50	Floor and Wall Rings				
Upper Compartment				7' 11"	2' 0"	2' 0"				83		100					
Lower Cargo Compartments				5' 8"						275							
Total																	

* 35 cu. ft. deducted from gross volume for door clearance

Fig. 10. (Continued on next page.)

AIRCRAFT TYPE	GENERAL AIRPLANE DIMENSIONS			DOOR DIMENSIONS & HT			MAXIMUM COMPARTMENT DIMENSIONS & VOLUMES				CARGO COMPT FLOOR DATA		TIE-DOWN CAPACITY POUNDS		PRESSURIZATION	HEATING SYSTEM	
	Wing Span	Overall Length	Overall Height	Height Sill Above Ground	Height or Breadth	Width or Length	Length	Width	Height	Useable Volume Cu. Ft.	Area Sq. Ft.	Allowable Loading Lbs./Sq.Ft.	Floor Fittings	Wall Fittings		Upper Cabin	Lower Compts
MARTIN 404	93'3-3/8	74'7"	28'5-3/8				34'7"	9'0"	6'7"						Cabin 8000' at 16,000'	Heating 75°F at −40°F Cooling 87°F at +100°F	Heating 32°F at −40°F
Main Passenger Cabin				7'11"	5'0"	2'8"				150			150 Each	Web Nets			
Upper Forward Compartment				Load Thru Passenger Door						64		150					
Upper Aft Compartment				5'8"	1'8"	2'4"				107			150 Each				
Lower Cargo Compartments												100					
Total										321							

Fig. 10. (Concluded.)

GENERAL NOTES:

1. Under "Maximum Compartment Dimensions & Volumes" the figures given are maximum lengths, widths and volumes. As the fuselage configurations in many instances are elliptical or cylindrical, the width or height will not be constant throughout. In tabular form, it is not practical to show tapering dimensions.

2. Where spaces are blank, information was not available.

Aircraft	Gross Take-off Weight (lb.)	Max. Landing Weight (lb.)	Zero Fuel Weight (lb.)	Operating Weight Empty (lb.)	Maximum Payload (lb.)	Cargo (lb.)	Passengers* (No.)	Maximum Speed (M.P.H.) @ Alt. in ft.	Normal Cruising Speed (M.P.H.) @ Alt. in ft.	Range-Max. Payload (mi.) @ Alt. in ft.
Boeing Stratocruiser B377	145,800	132,500	115,625	83,485	23,359	8,359	75	375/30,000	300/25,000	1,415/10,000
Convair CV 240	41,790	39,800	38,900	28,745	10,155	2,155	40	337/15,000	274/15,000	760/16,000
Convair CV 340	47,000	46,500	45,000	31,259	13,741	4,941	44	315/15,000	260/16,000	1,329/15,000
Douglas DC-3	26,200	26,000	—	18,350	5,000	800	21	232/ 7,500	205/10,000	525/10,000
Douglas DC-4	73,000	63,500	59,000	41,740	14,078	5,278	44	307/20,000	227/10,000	2,250/10,000
Douglas DC-6	97,200	80,000	74,000	57,600	15,613	5,213	52	346/19,400	310/19,400	3,000/10,000
Douglas DC-6B	107,000	88,200	83,200	60,076	16,514	4,914	58	371/19,400	315/22,400	3,400/10,000
Douglas DC-7	122,200	97,000	91,630	70,926	19,345	7,345	60	410/22,000	350/20,000	3,150/10,000
Lockheed Lodestar	18,500	17,500	—	13,713	3,200	400	14	275/16,500	234/10,000	390/ 5,000
Lockheed Constellation 049D	96,000	83,000	79,964	59,200	15,196	3,796	57	341/18,000	313/20,000	2,500/10,000
Lockheed Constellation 749A	107,000	89,500	86,464	65,074	14,415	3,015	57	354/20,000	322/20,000	3,060/10,000
Lockheed Super Constellation 1049E	133,000	110,000	100,000	77,300	20,189	7,189	65	372/20,000	330/22,600	3,340/10,000
Lockheed Super Constellation 1049G	137,500	113,000	103,500	78,300	20,189	7,189	65	370/20,000	329/22,600	3,660/10,000
Martin 202A	43,000	41,000	36,500	28,870	7,630	430	36	291	270	1,135
Martin 404	44,900	43,000	42,500	32,340	10,161	2,161	40	297/ 8,500	256/10,000	780/10,000

* Not including lounge seating.

Distances and speeds in statute miles. Ranges with max. payloads based on long-range cruise powers.

Fig. 11. Performance data for passenger-cargo aircraft.

section have been developed for determining maximum package sizes that can be accommodated by the cargo holds of these airplanes.

Helicopters

ADVENT OF THE HELICOPTER. During the latter part of 1940, Igor Sikorsky developed the helicopter, and in so doing reached a goal that had been sought by aircraft designers since man first dreamed of flight. The helicopter can rise and descend vertically; it can fly forward, backward and sidewise. It has developed into a sound flying machine, has created its own place in the field of

Manufacturer	Model Com'l. Military	Total Seats	Engine Type and Horsepower	Speed M.P.H. @ S.L.		Normal Range (mi.)	Gross Weight (lb.)	Empty Weight (lb.)
				Max.	Cr.			
Bell Aircraft Corp. Fort Worth, Texas	47-G H-13G	3	1-Franklin 6V-200-C32 200 H.P.	99	78	247	2,350	1,435
	61 XHSL-1	4	1-Pratt & Whitney R-2800-50 1900 H.P.	132				
	204 XH-40	6	1-Lycoming XT-53 825 H.P.	152	115	202	5,194	3,344
Doman Helicopters, Inc. Danbury, Conn.	L25-1 YH-31	8	1-Lycoming SO-580-D 400 H.P.	98	86	350	5,200	3,400
Gyrodyne Co. of America, Inc. Long Island, N.Y.	GCA-41 XRON-1	1	1 Nelson 40 H.P.				500	250
Hiller Helicopters, Inc. Palo Alto, Calif.	UH-12D H-23D	3	1-Franklin 6V4-200-C33 200 H.P.	94	83	190	2,600	1,720
	HJ-1 YH-32	2	2-Hiller Ram Jet 8RJ2B	68		31	1,080	544
Kamen Aircraft Corp. Windsor Locks, Conn.	K-240 HTK-1	3	1-Lycoming 0435 250 H.P.	86		120	3,100	2,300
	K-600 HOK-1	4	1 Pratt & Whitney R-1340-48 600 H.P.	110@ 8000'		220	5,800	4,040
Sikorsky Aircraft Div. United Aircraft Corp. Bridgeport, Conn.	S-52 YH-18	4	1-Franklin 6U6-25-B16F 245 H.P.	111	91	306	2,700	1,825
	S-55C H-19A H04S	9-12	1-Pratt & Whitney R-1340-S1H2 600 H.P.	101	85	405	7,200	4,888
	S-56 HR2S H-37	26-28	2-Pratt & Whitney R-2800 1900 H.P. ea.	162		200	28,500	
	S-58 H-34A H-SS1	14-20	1-Wright R-1820-84 1525 H.P.	132	103		12,700	7,560
Vertol Aircraft Corp. Morton, Pa.	PD-18 H-25A HUP-3	6	1-Continental R-975-46 550 H.P.	108	80	490	5,750	3,928
	H-21B H-21C	22	1-Wright R-1820-103 1425 H.P.	140+		300+	13,300	8,600
	YH-16	43-44	2-Pratt & Whitney R-2180-11 1650 H.P. ea.	125		200	30,000+	

Note: All data obtained from public sources and not from the manufacturers of the equipment described. Data are, therefore, subject to change and/or variations.

Fig. 12. U. S. military and commercial helicopters.

aviation, and has proved its usefulness beyond all question of doubt in peacetime and wartime operations.

APPLICATIONS OF THE HELICOPTER. The helicopter is a special-purpose machine, still essentially a short-range, slower vehicle and limited in payload capacity. Development-wise the largest units have been compared to the early fixed-wing transports, such as the Douglas DC-3. Basic problems, such as rotor control, rotor configuration, and construction have, in a large measure, been solved, and design refinement and enlargement have followed. Progress has been made in increasing the size of helicopters and developing a more distinct specialization into various types for transport, ambulance and air rescue, executive service, survey, and other uses to which the helicopter is particularly suited. Because of its special nature and possibilities the helicopter should not be compared with fixed-wing aircraft either on the basis of performance or as to operating cost. It can perform services that no other kinds of aircraft can supply, and therefore it should be judged on its own merits, particularly when it is used in its peculiar sphere of operations.

During the past few years there has been a very rapid increase in the number and kinds of helicopters in military and commercial use, particularly the former. All the cargo types, however, even in the military services, have generally been small in size, and a great many of the cargo loads have been carried externally, slung beneath the machine in nets. Large helicopters, such as the Piasecki YH-16, now have brought the helicopter into the heavy transport field.

Commercial Uses. Commercially, helicopters are being used on numerous local air-mail routes, and increasingly to carry passengers and moderate-sized express and freight packages. Commercial types used in mail and passenger service have generally been the Bell 47G, the Sikorsky S-52, S-55, and the S-58—a fourteen to twenty place machine for mail, passenger transportation, and cargo. Future developments will make new and larger military planes available in commercial versions.

Fig. 12 lists the over-all characteristics of representative military and commercial types of helicopters. As their dependability increases and their operating costs decrease, the use of such planes should widen considerably.

PALLETS AND CONTAINERS

CONTENTS

CONTENTS (*Continued*)

PALLETS AND CONTAINERS

Pallets and Skid Platforms

TYPES AND CONSTRUCTION FEATURES OF PALLETS. Pallets are classified in two ways: first, by construction features, and second, by the materials of which they are made. This grouping permits a distinction to be drawn between the individual kinds of pallets. Under construction features, pallets are classed by:

1. Number of **faces.**
2. Number of **ways of entry.**
3. Whether **wing or flush-stringer type.**

The materials of which pallets are made include wood, cardboard, and metals such as steel, aluminum, and wire mesh.

SELECTING TYPES OF PALLETS. Regardless of what materials are used in pallet construction—wood, metal, corrugated cardboard, plastics, or other material—the **designs, shapes, sizes, proportions, and methods for pickup and stacking** are the same. Therefore the user can choose his material according to the applications and service features he desires and the required durability of the pallets, and can handle the pallets by fork truck or other methods with equal facility.

Pallet Sizes. Sizes for wood, paperboard, and metal pallets can vary almost infinitely, and special pallets have been made up to 6, 8, or 10 ft. in length, but the normal sizes used in manufacturing plants and warehouses have dimensions in the range of 32, 36, 40 and 48 in. Among the most common sizes are the 32 by 40, the 40 by 48, and the 48 by 48 in. Pallet sizes have a direct relationship to pallet patterns. The number of sizes should be held to a minimum.

WOODEN PALLET NOMENCLATURE. Minimum standard specifications are published by the National Wooden Pallet Manufacturers' Association, as a guide to the construction of general-purpose pallets. These specifications include the following definitions:

Deckboards are the boards which make up the faces of a pallet, and which either carry or rest upon the goods packed thereon.
Stringers are the wooden runners to which the deckboards are fastened, and which serve as spacers between the top and bottom decks to permit the entry of mechanical handling devices.
Stringer boards are boards used over blocks below the deckboards on the four-way block-type pallet.
Blocks are square or rectangular wooden parts employed on some four-way pallets in place of stringers, and serve the same purpose.
In speaking of pallet sizes, **dimensions** shall always be stated in inches, and the **length** shall always be designated first before the width. The **width** shall always be the dimension parallel to the top of the deckboards.

WOODEN PALLET STYLES. Generally speaking, it is advantageous to use as few pallet sizes as possible in any plant or warehouse so as to standardize the handling procedure. From the various designs and constructions given below, the pallet or pallets most suitable to the handling facilities and requirements of the specific situation can be selected.

Single-faced Pallets. Single-faced pallets (Fig. 1), also known as "open-faced" pallets, have only one deck or platform. The deck can be solid or it can have any desired amount of space between the successive deckboards. Although the single-faced pallet resembles a skid, it cannot be handled with the usual skid-handling equipment because of its lower stringer height. Also, the pallet usually has a center stringer. The low stringer height gives the pallet a **space-saving advantage in stacking or storage.** This single-faced construction is often used with expendable nonreturnable pallets.

Double-faced Pallets. Double-faced pallets are in common use, particularly those of wooden construction. The bottom deck adds strength and makes the pallets more stable when loaded and stacked. It also provides more bearing surface for superimposed loads.

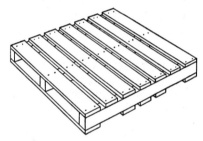

Fig. 1. Standard single-deck wooden pallet.

Fig. 2. Double-faced nonreversible pallet for pallet truck handling.

If the upper and lower decks of a pallet are identical, the pallet is said to be **reversible**; it can be used either side up. Double-faced pallets, however, are most often **nonreversible**, because they are used not only with fork trucks but also with hand lift trucks, which are constructed to lift the pallets clear of the floor.

For this purpose, the prongs of the hand lift truck are equipped at their outer ends with wheels which will collapse upward into the prongs of the forks and allow the forks to go into the pallet between its upper and lower decks. The wheels are then dropped down to raise the load clear of the floor for transportation. So that it will be possible to use the fork truck at either end of the pallet, two bottom boards of the pallet are omitted as shown in Fig. 2. A slight variation of this type of pallet is of notched-runner construction, the cutout extending up into the runner itself for a short distance.

Two-Way, Four-Way, and Eight-Way Pallets. When pallets can be entered from either end, they are called "two-way" pallets. "Four-way" pallets are those of such construction that the forks of a lift truck can pick them up from any of the four sides (Fig. 3). If the forks can also enter diagonally at the corners of the pallet, it is called an "eight-way" pallet. Four-way pallets offer the following advantages:

1. In **loading freight cars** (or working in other confined areas), a fork truck may put a unit load in the doorway and then return for another load while a hand

pallet truck already in the car approaches the load from a 90° angle and positions the load at the end of the car. This can be done only with four-way pallets.

2. With one very common pallet size—the 40 by 48 in. pallet—four-way pallets may be **stacked two abreast** on the short dimension in motor trucks. With two-way pallets it is impossible to enter the pallets along both the 40- and 48-in. dimensions, since stringers are on two opposite sides.

3. Four-way pallets with **block-leg construction** may be nested in storage when empty, thus conserving space.

4. With four-way types, a fork-truck operator can always **utilize the smaller dimension** when carrying loads through narrow aisles.

5. **Materials stored in blocks** bounded by intersecting aisles may be picked up from either aisle.

6. **Stake-body highway trucks** can be loaded from both rear and side with equal facility.

7. **Steel strapping** can be applied in either direction when securing a unit load.

Four-way pallets are of either the **notched-stringer** type or the **block-leg** type. The block-leg type is four-way for fork trucks and pallet trucks, while the notched-stringer type is four-way for fork trucks only.

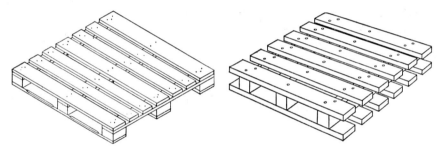

Fig. 3. Four-way block-leg pallet.   Fig. 4. Double-wing-type (stevedore) pallet.

Wing-Type Pallets. Wing-type pallets have their outside runners or stringers set in so that the deckboards project to form the "wings." The double-wing type (Fig. 4) is sometimes called a "stevedore" pallet because it is commonly used for shiploading purposes. In use, a bar sling is placed under the wings to lift the pallet. In the single-wing type, the bottom deck is cut off flush with the stringers, and is designed for use with straddle-type lift trucks, where the truck outrigger must run in astride the bottom pallet in a tier. Wing pallets, in general, have the disadvantage of structural weakness. Unless reinforced by cleats or by some other structural member, the wings are often the first point of pallet failure.

Expendable Shipping Pallets. In answer to demands for a lightweight shipping pallet of reduced weight and cost that could be discarded after initial use, if desired, expendable pallets have been developed. This type of pallet, shown in Fig. 5, permits four-way entry, but because of the method of construction it is, in effect, an eight-way pallet. It is made in a three-board and a five-board construction. Typical sizes are 32 by 40 in. and 48 by 40 in. A single-wing six-board expendable shipping pallet, similarly blocked inboard for support, is also available for stevedoring.

Stack-Type Pallets. In certain cases it is desirable to combine the advantages of palletization with stacking or tiering. Standard-size pallets have been devised

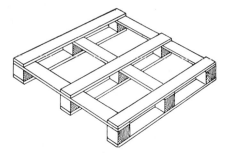

Fig. 5. Three-board single-deck expendable shipping pallet.

for stacking and are in regular use. They are fitted with **sockets in the four corners** into which removable pipe supports can be set so as to mount one pallet above another. Each set of pipe supports extends down through its pallet and is cone-shaped on the underside so as to fit into a fixture on the top of the pipe support immediately below. The construction is shown in Fig. 6. Empty pallets can be disassembled and stored. This equipment is strong and rigid and permits stacking pallets one on the other, commensurate with the weights involved and the ceiling height of the storage area.

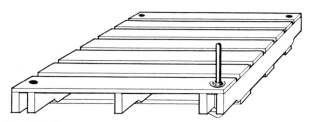

Double-deck type to accommodate hand trucks—two-way entry

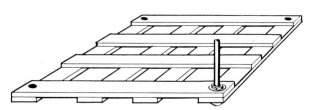

Single-deck type—light duty

Fig. 6. Stackable wooden pallets equipped with special corner fittings for loading and stacking.

Another variety of these pallets consists of a pair of tiering horses which can be assembled on any standard three-stringer pallet. Posts fit into socket assemblies and the crossbars slip-fit over the tops of the posts. Angles on top of the crossbar help center the stringers on the bar and prevent superimposed pallets from shifting or sliding.

Many varieties of stacking pallets are available for various handling operations.

Take-It-Or-Leave-It Pallets. For rapid transfer of loads of material from pallets into storage or to manufacturing operations, in cases where the material can be handled on the forks of a truck as well as on a pallet, the "take-it-or-leave-it" pallet has come into use. By means of such a pallet (Fig. 7), the fork-truck operator can pick up the loaded pallet by running the truck fork into the pallet between top and bottom boards and moving the material to a storage or operating area. At this point he can deposit the pallet on the floor, withdraw the forks, run them under the material itself, and deliver it into storage or to a processing operation.

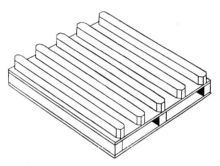

Fig. 7. Typical take-it-or-leave-it wooden pallet.

WOODEN PALLET CONSTRUCTION. Pallets are made of wood, metal, cardboard, and a few have been made of plastic. The pallets already illustrated in Figs. 1–6 are all of wood, and wooden construction is by far the most common. Both hardwoods and softwoods are used, but hardwoods predominate. **Softwoods** tend to wear or chew, but have the advantage of lighter weight and less warping and splitting than hardwoods. To some extent the selection of the proper type of wood will depend on the kind and amount of lumber available in the geographical area concerned.

Properties of Woods. The Forest Products Laboratory of the Department of Agriculture at Madison, Wis., has prepared the data given in Fig. 8 showing the strength properties of commercial woods commonly employed for pallets.

According to the National Wooden Pallet Manufacturers' Association, it is recommended for good, general-purpose pallet construction that **sound, fairly dry lumber** from Group III or IV (Fig. 8) be used. No one piece should have defects that might weaken the whole pallet. If lumber from Group III or IV is not readily available, it is recommended that at least the edge boards of the top and bottom deck be made from such wood. Where Group I or Group II wood is used, increases in the thickness of the pieces can help to make up for the lack of strength. Lumber from any group must be free from decay and should not have knots with an average diameter greater than one-third the width of the board.

Proportions of Pallets. The Association further recommends that for loads up to 2,000 lb., **deckboards** (from Group III to IV lumber) should not be less than ⅝ in. thick. For loads up to 3,500 lb., the thickness should not be less than ²⁵⁄₃₂ in. Edge deckboards should have a minimum width of 5½ to 6 in. Other deckboards should be not less than 4 in. and not more than 9 in. wide, but may be of random widths within these limits. Spacing between boards depends on the merchandise to be palletized. Pallets required to handle more than 3,500 lb. should

STRENGTH PROPERTIES OF COMMERCIAL WOODS EMPLOYED FOR PALLETS

(Figures shown are for 12% moisture content.)

Species	STATIC BENDING Fiber Stress at Proportional Limit (lb. per sq. in.)	COMPRESSION Perpendicular to Grain (lb. per sq. in.)
GROUP IV		
Oak, red	8,400	1,260
Oak, white	7,900	1,410
Maple, sugar	9,500	1,810
Beech	8,700	1,250
Birch	10,100	1,250
Hickory, true	10,900	2,310
Ash, white	8,900	1,510
Pecan	9,100	2,040
GROUP III		
Ash, black	7,200	940
Gum, black	7,300	1,150
Maple, silver	6,200	910
Gum, red	8,100	860
Sycamore	6,400	860
Tupelo	7,200	1,070
Elm, white	7,600	850
GROUP II		
Douglas fir	7,400	950
Hemlock, western	6,800	680
Larch (Tamarack)	8,000	990
N. C. pine	7,700	1,000
Southern yellow pine (Longleaf)	9,300	1,190
GROUP I		
Aspen	5,600	460
Cottonwood	5,700	470
Cypress	7,200	900
Redwood	6,900	860
Spruce	6,700	710
Sugar pine	5,700	590
Ponderosa pine	6,300	740
White fir	6,300	610
White pine (Northern)	6,300	550
White pine (Western)	6,200	540
Yellow poplar	6,100	580

Forest Products Laboratory, Madison, Wis.

Fig. 8. Bending and compression strains of woods used for pallets.

be considered special-purpose pallets and should be designed for the particular load. The Association also recommends that:

1. **Stringers** should be 1¾ in. thick by 3¾ in. wide after surfacing. Stringers must be either surfaced or smooth-sawn, at least on the top and bottom dimensions; outside stringers should also be surfaced on the outside surfaces. All pallets should have not less than the number of stringers or blocks shown below:

	Number of	
Deckboard Length	Stringers	Blocks
Not exceeding 24″	2	6
25″ to 48″ inclusive	3	9
Over 48″ *	3	9

* If load exceeds 2,000 pounds on deckboards over 48 in., a special-purpose pallet is indicated.

2. The outside edges of the bottom **deckboards** should be chamfered. The chamfer should be at least 12 in. long, with the two chamfers on each board spaced to accommodate the forks of a truck.
3. **Tolerances** of the over-all width and length of the pallet should be within plus or minus ¼ in. Where it is necessary to specify a minimum measurement, only plus tolerances should be accepted.

Standards of the National Wooden Pallet Manufacturers' Association establish two grades of moisture content:

1. **Grade AA.** Deckboard wood should have a maximum moisture content of 25% for Group IV woods and 20% for Group I, II, and III woods. Wood for stringers or blocks may be of any degree of seasoning.
2. **Grade A.** Wood with any degree of moisture content may be used for deckboards, stringers, and blocks.

Preservatives. Wood preservatives are widely used on pallets. Their main purpose is to retard dimensional instability caused by too rapid drying. When lumber shrinks or warps, nailheads protrude and snag the merchandise loaded on the pallet, or injure workmen's hands. All the **standard preservatives** give some protection against rapid drying, but many of them have the disadvantage of being toxic, and, therefore, may constitute a hazard and a possible contaminating agent if food products are handled on the pallet. Certain **nontoxic preservatives** eliminate this objection.

Fastenings for Wooden Pallets. The fastenings are the most vulnerable parts of a wooden pallet. It is for this reason that special drive-screw nails, cement-coated nails, carriage bolts, glue-and-dowel construction, and a multiple of other fastenings have been developed. Fig. 9 shows five representative **types of nails** used in pallets.

Standard nails must be of either the cement-coated or the chemically etched box type. Fig. 10 shows the sizes of box nails which should be used for the stated deckboard thickness and lumber class. All nails should be staggered and should be countersunk about ¹⁄₃₂ in. Standard nails give the least holding power, but they are also the least expensive. **Annular-threaded (fettering) nails** and **drive-screw nails** are widely used. The recommended number of nails of either of these types to be used at all bearing points is the same as that for standard nails, given in Fig. 11. When Class III or IV lumber is used, the outside edges of the deckboards should be predrilled with a drill about ¹⁄₃₂ in. smaller than the nail shank. Nails should be staggered and countersunk.

A: Plain-shank nail.
B: Cement-coated, plain-shank nail.
C: Helically groved Screwtite nail.
D: Annularly grooved Stronghold nail.
E: Plain-shank, low-carbon, steel-wire nail.
Nails A–D are 2″ × 0.135″; nail E is 2½″ × 0.135″.

Fig. 9. Representative types of nails used in pallets.

Deck Thickness	Lumber Class I or II	Lumber Class III or IV
⅝ in.	7d	6d
25⁄32 in.	8d	8d

National Wooden Pallet Manufacturers' Assn.

Fig. 10. Sizes of box nails for stated deckboard thickness and lumber class.

Width of Deckboard	Number of Nails (Either Type)
3½″ to 5⅝″	2
5½″ to 7⅜″	3
7½″ to 9″	4

National Wooden Pallet Manufacturers' Assn.

Fig. 11. Recommended nailing for pallets.

A **clinched-nail** construction imported from Sweden, and now widely adopted in the United States, uses either standard or drive-screw nails, but clinches them inside the stringer, as shown in Fig. 12, by a special process. After the nails are clinched, the hole in the stringer is plugged with a wooden dowel to prevent the nails from unclinching. This clinched-nail construction provides exceptional resistance to withdrawal and thus tends to solve the most basic wooden pallet weakness at a comparatively low cost. For **bolted construction of wooden pallets,** standard steel carriage bolts or car bolts can be used in any of three styles—

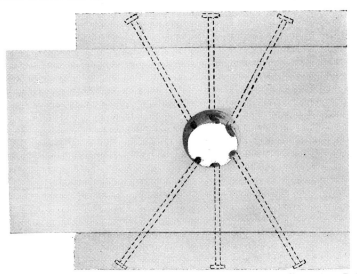

Clinch-Tite Pallet Co.

Fig. 12. Clinched-nail pallet construction.

standard, slotted, or large-head. The coarse-thread series, Class 2, free fit, is sufficient. With ordinary commercial **carriage bolts,** flat washers should be ⅛ in. larger in diameter than the bolt, and holes in the stringer should be 1/16 in. larger. Square or hex nuts may be used. "Teenuts" or "HY-C" nuts are also recommended by the National Wooden Pallet Manufacturers' Association. Outside deckboards should have at least two bolts at each end, and inside boards should have one bolt at each bearing point. **Glued construction** may also be used for pallets, but such use has not become widespread.

METAL SKID PLATFORMS AND PALLETS. Metal skid platforms and pallets are made of corrugated steel, pressed steel, expanded metal, steel wire, aluminum, and magnesium, and in a combination of wood and metal. Their main advantages lie in strength and durability, and, in some cases, light weight. Metal skid platforms are used for a variety of handling purposes in manufacturing plants. They are simply constructed and readily transported by platform lift trucks or fork trucks, either manually operated or power operated. **Pressed-steel pallets** are widely used and can be light in weight as well as strong. One manufacturer's product weighs 69 lb., is 40 by 48 in. in size and is recommended for a single load of 2,500 lb. or a tiered load of 15,000 lb. Pressed steel pallets are usually made of 12- to 18-gage sheet steel and sometimes have a crimped, rather than welded, construction. Certain types of **corrugated steel pallets** are quite heavy and are placed in service where durability is more important than weight-saving. They are commonly used in foundries and for similar heavy-duty processes.

Types of Steel Pallets and Skid Platforms. Fig. 13 illustrates an **extra corrugated deck skid platform,** recommended where materials handled are heavy, rough, abrasive, and/or hot (900° F. or more). Corrugations run opposite to the skid deck for the purpose of air circulation.

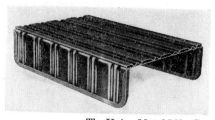

The Union Metal Mfg. Co.

Fig. 13. Skid platform with extra-corrugated deck.

Powell Pressed Steel Corp.

Fig. 14. Bumper channel-runner type of skid platform with fork pockets.

The reinforced-bumper, channel-runner type of pallet (Fig. 14) with **side fork pockets** increases the versatility in storage areas because it can be picked up by a fork truck from any of the four sides.

In Fig. 15 is shown an all-metal, welded pallet with **stake pockets.** It is made of heavy corrugated steel and is reinforced on all four sides. The stake pockets have removable steel uprights so that the truck can handle high loads with complete safety. The pallet is designed for use by power trucks only.

Palmer-Shile Co.

Fig. 15. Metal pallet with stake pockets for high loads.

Fig. 16 shows a heavy, **single-deck,** all-steel, single-faced pallet supported on three metal runners. It is designed to handle heavy loads such as kegs, drums, and other weighty containers. Two-way **double-decked** steel pallets are also available.

The pallet shown in Fig. 17 is of table-top construction with **bound-in flanges** to permit safe hand-moving of the pallet when it is not loaded. Recessed side channels enable the pallet to be handled by crane grabs, or by crane-sling operation if the corner reinforcement is omitted.

Powell Pressed Steel Corp.
Fig. 16. All-steel single-faced pallet.

Powell Pressed Steel Corp.
Fig. 17. Table-top-constructed pallet with side channels for crane grab.

A pallet specially designed to handle **bagged materials** is shown in Fig. 18. It has been designed to eliminate sharp edges or corners which might tear the bags. The pallet is completely reversible, having identical top and bottom decks, and, for greater strength, is corrugated on the sides as well as on the top and bottom.

The Union Metal Mfg. Co.
Fig. 18. Double-faced reversible steel pallet for handling bagged materials.

The pallet illustrated in Fig. 19 is of four-way, all-metal construction and can be picked up by hand-operated trucks as well as by fork trucks. It has **beveled pads** to permit easy entry of fork truck wheels. Sometimes the nature, shape, and

Palmer-Shile Co.
Fig. 19. Four-way all-metal pallet.

volume of materials moved regularly in large quantities may make the use of special-dimension pallets more economical than the use of standard-size pallets.

Where large quantities of materials are continually handled and a large number of sturdy pallets are in use, the problem arises of convenient storing of pallets to conserve room. This problem is solved by the use of **nesting pallets,** whereby a far larger number of pallets can be handled or stored at one time in one place. The Nesteel type of pallet is shown in Fig. 20. It is of corrugated construction for strength and rigidity, and allows many pallets to be stacked—one pallet on another—in a very small area. The fork holes in the nested pallets allow the pallets to be picked up by fork truck from the side without disturbing the load. Pickup from the front is made by running the forks of a truck into the spaces between the corrugations.

Powell Pressed Steel Corp.

Fig. 20. Pallets nested to save storage space.

In industry and transportation, much material that is handled is most cheaply and conveniently moved and stored in unit loads. The unit loads are often standardized in quantity and so handled. For space conservation and convenience in handling, these loads are often stacked one on another. Equipment has been devised which considerably facilitates and makes flexible the storing of these palletized loads and permits desired loads to be obtained readily and quickly. Such equipment has been described under "Wooden Stack-Type Pallets" but is also available in steel.

This pallet consists of all-metal frameworks of standard dimensions corresponding to the usual dimensions of palletized loads. In each of the four corners of this framework a **socket fitting** is welded. The fitting is pointed on the bottom to fit into the socket top of another mating fitting on which the pallet framework of the first pallet may be set by a fork truck. In this manner the loads are tiered to reasonable height, and are stackable and reclaimable by fork trucks.

Where small or boxed items are being stored, the frameworks may be covered by standard **sheet-metal cover plates** to hold the loads in place.

Types of Wire-Mesh Pallets. Along with the more recent use of wire-mesh containers for industrial and shipping operations, there has come about a corresponding development of wire-mesh pallets with metal framework bases. Such types of pallets are illustrated in Fig. 21. Characteristics of such pallets are durability and light weight. They are used in shipments over distances such that pallets may be collected and returned in carload lots without excessive cost. There is some risk of damage to the pallets if roughly treated by irresponsible persons at delivery points, and railroads and motor trucking companies should be warned to take proper precautions in handling them.

Tri-State Engineering Co.

Fig. 21. Wire-mesh pallet with metal framework base.

Wire-mesh pallets have a galvanized or painted **finish** and give good service handling heavy loads. An average 40-by-48-in. pallet weighs 70 to 80 lb., and will take a single-unit load up to 4,000 lb. and a tiered load up to about 16,000 lb.

Aluminum and Magnesium Pallets. Pallets and skid platforms of these lighter metals evoke interest because of their weight savings. Aluminum pallets weigh about one-half as much as steel, and magnesium weighs about one-third as much as steel; and this saving in weight becomes important for some applications. Also, galvanizing and painting are unnecessary.

COMPOSITE WOOD AND METAL SKID PLATFORMS AND PALLETS. Other kinds of pallets and skid platforms made up of a combination of wood and metal are made by a number of manufacturers who claim that such units have the advantage of somewhat lighter weight and still are very durable. As in Figs. 22 and 23, **legs** and **frame** are of steel, with wooden **deckboards**

Powell Pressed Steel Corp.

Fig. 22. Composite wood and metal pallet.

bolted to the steel frames. If well adapted to the services to which they are put, these pallets and skid platforms may have economies and sufficient durability to answer certain needs not well provided for by the usual types of pallet equipment.

Weco

Fig. 23. Composite wood and metal skid platform.

PAPERBOARD PALLETS. Paperboard expendable pallets have the advantages of light weight and low cost. Some of them weigh under 10 lb. They will take relatively heavy loads, since the entire weight of the load rests on the nine or more posts or supports and not on the paperboard deck, which merely serves as a firm spacer for the supports. A static load of up to 27,000 lb. can be supported on some paper pallets.

Paper pallets may be grouped according to the post construction, with the main classifications being:

1. Expendable pallets with **spiral-wound chipboard tube posts.** For moisture-proofing, this type of post can be immersed to any given depth of paraffin or a similar waterproofing material. (Figs. 24 and 25.)
2. Pallets with **wound corrugated posts,** in both square-wound and round-wound types (Fig. 26).
3. Pallets with **built-up fiberboard supports,** which consist of several pieces of fiberboard glued together to form individual posts or stringers.
4. Fiberboard pallets with wooden block legs and fiberboard decks.

Paper pallets are usually considered **expendable,** although they may often be re-used. Re-use depends not only on the particular construction, but also on the types of use to which the pallets are subjected. They are employed almost entirely for shipping purposes, any storage use being mainly in connection with the shipping of palletized loads.

It is the accepted standard commercial practice that when paperboard pallets are used, the load must be secured to the deck with either palletizing adhesive or steel strapping. In this way, the expendable pallet simply supports the cube

Addison-Semmes Co.

Fig. 24. Expendable pallet with disk-based spiral-wound chipboard tube posts.

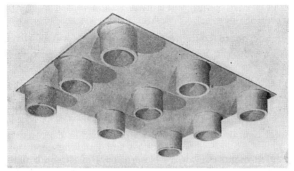

Signode Steel Strapping Co.

Fig. 25. Bottom view of pallet with chipboard tube posts.

Addison-Semmes Co.

Fig. 26. Pallet with round-wound corrugated posts.

form by the above methods. The latest development is the manufacture of king-sized containers on which are secured the paperboard posts making what is termed an **all corrugated unit load.** These king-sized containers replace a given quantity of smaller containers on a separate pallet. The usual result is lower packaging costs.

DEVELOPMENTS IN PLASTIC PALLETS. For a considerable period experiments have been carried on to develop plastic pallets with the construction features, strength, and durability which would make them feasible and commercially applicable. Government research, in combination with explorations by plastics producers, has finally resulted in pallets which have been successfully manufactured, but as yet at a cost, and of characteristics as to durability and resistance to shocks, that make them commercially uncertain. Sample pallets are now under test which will reveal the points of strength as well as weakness. There is a likelihood that eventually a plastic compound will be developed which will have the breaking, crushing, bending, chipping, and other resilience and resistance features necessary to provide a long-life pallet that may overcome many of the unavoidable defects in current equipment.

Industrial Containers

MATERIALS FROM WHICH CONTAINERS ARE CONSTRUCTED. There are five basic kinds of materials from which containers are constructed: (1) paper and fiberboard, (2) wood, (3) metal—solid, expanded, or wire mesh, (4) plastic, and (5) canvas. Each material has particular characteristics warranting its use:

1. **Paper or fiberboard containers,** usually in the form of sliver cans, wheeled trucks, treated tote boxes, etc., are used for specific handling operations such as in textile manufacturing where only lightweight construction and a relatively small capital investment are necessary.

2. **Wooden containers,** both solid and wirebound types, are designed for relatively long life but cannot withstand excessive abuse, long outdoor storage, and weathering. Where low tare weight is a factor in the handling, wooden containers are substituted for metal.

3. **Solid metal containers** are designed for heavy loads, rough abuse, long life and use under adverse outside storage and handling conditions. **Wire mesh and expanded-metal containers** have nearly the strength of solid containers, but are lighter, and are usually adaptable to easy knockdown for empty storage. Wire containers or baskets serve in the dual capacity of in-transit containers and in-process containers for operations such as cleaning, dipping, and spraying.

4. **Plastic containers,** as well as recently developed rubber containers, are applicable when dealing with bulk liquids, where prevention of contamination is important, where color coding is required, and under special conditions of quality and appearance requirements. Reinforced plastic is light and extremely durable, and is used successfully for tote pans and open shop containers. A plastic carboy is shown in Fig. 27.

5. **Canvas containers** are light in weight and where the operation calls for manual movement, are easily handled and easily cleaned.

Plax Corp.

Fig. 27. Carboy made of Alathon—a lightweight container.

Into each of the basic material classes, one or more features common to all can be incorporated to serve a wide variety of special requirements. For example, where a durable container is a prerequisite, yet the quality of the material handled may be impaired by contamination, rough wood surfaces, or other factors, a low-cost plastic sheet or filming or corrugated board liner can be used to overcome the quality objections, while serving as an economical method of handling. In other instances, paper, canvas, and even wood containers best satisfy the intended purpose when the basic structure is reinforced with metal, such as stainless steel. The combination of the materials to provide the most satisfactory container are best established by controlled tests and practical experience, the only limiting factor being one of economics.

WIDE VARIETY OF CONTAINERS. In manufacturing and assembly plants wide varieties of industrial containers are used to carry the vast flow of **in-process and finished parts** going through all the particular phases of production, packaging, and shipping. Whatever his particular field, the packaging engineer should be thoroughly familiar with metal, fiber, and glass shipping containers—their present and future possibilities, their limitations, and all regulations governing their use. They are, at least, part of his professional "stock in trade."

DESIGN FEATURES. After deciding upon the combination of basic materials from which the container is to be constructed, the **specific design** of the container may be worked out. The aim in design, of course, is to provide maximum flexibility at a predetermined allowable cost, and to build in as many features to

General Box Co.

Fig. 28. Collapsible wooden container.

meet the principles of container design as is economically feasible. Certain important factors enter into the decision.

Collapsible Containers. Considerable use is being made of collapsible containers, which have certain advantages, especially in industries having wide fluctuations of in-process and storage items, through savings in valuable storage space. Also collapsible containers are used for interplant shipping, and may be shipped back to the supplier in full truckloads of knocked-down units. Wirebound wood (Fig. 28), wire-mesh, canvas-reinforced, and rubber-ballooning containers can be designed with this feature.

Material Accessibility. Design features which permit quick accessibility to the contents are especially important when a container is used in machining and assembly operations. The **drop front,** used with rigid containers, gives storage and in-transit protection and orderly arrangement to the unit load. Wing nuts, hinges, hooks and eyes, etc., allow the drop front or panel to be opened, making selection of material easy. The hopper boxes shown in Fig. 29 are illustrative of

Powell Pressed Steel Corp.

Fig. 29. Drop-front steel hopper boxes.

this feature. Similar to this arrangement is the **bottom drop,** most generally used with permanent-type metal containers for bulk movement of small parts to machining operations, and subsequent controlled gravity feed for parts-positioning. In well-engineered container systems **pegboard containers,** pin racks to segregate parts or assemblies for easy identification and procurement, are coming into increasing use in parts assembly work. Like units on the pegboard container are positioned according to principles of work simplification, around a work station, minimizing the reach, search, and identification in selecting a part. In other instances, a complete assembly is mounted on the pegboard container from central storage and moved for purpose of assembly and test at the work station.

To simplify that portion of materials handling often referred to as "positioning" in the selection of parts to be processed, **hydraulic and spring-lift devices** are incorporated in some container supports. As items are removed, the spring base elevates the lower layers, thereby permitting the reach element to be constant for all parts in the container. Waste motion is eliminated, fatigue from bending and lifting is minimized, and the entire cycle is consequently speeded up with increased utilization of machine run and production time (see section on Work Positioning).

Handling Considerations in Container Design. As the unit load principle becomes more universally adopted, the container, of course, serves not only in a storage capacity but also in a processing capacity. This means that planned handling and container design must receive proper consideration. The container, regardless of basic material, can be equipped with a **permanent or semi-permanent pallet** or skid base adaptable to manual and powered materials

The Union Metal Mfg. Co.

Fig. 30. Box truck with tiering channels.

handling equipment, as well as to gravity and powered conveyors. Attachments, mounted on or built into the container, will provide for suspension from overhead monorail systems, bridge cranes, and other handling systems. For purposes of pinpointing, positioning, or making short-distance moves between adjacent operations, containers are frequently equipped with **casters,** allowing for manual movement where mechanical means cannot be justified economically. The castered box truck in Fig. 30 is also equipped with tiering channels for storage.

Stock and Inventory Control. The **unit load principle,** where constant tare weight is anticipated, assists materially in the establishment of a company's inventory position. Small parts not easily counted can be weighed and, where a perpetual inventory is not in effect, the parts remaining in stock at time of physical inventory are weighed and the quantity on hand is thereby ascertained. In other instances, where the item stored is of regular pattern and greater bulk, so many items per standard container are easily viewed by use of the **open-type container**—either expanded-mesh basket or open-design wirebound wood container. The open-type container is of further importance in certain operations such as yarn-conditioning, heat-treating, and wool-degreasing, in that it permits access of the cleansing or conditioning agent to the contained material. Several types designed for **intermixed stacking** are shown in Fig. 31.

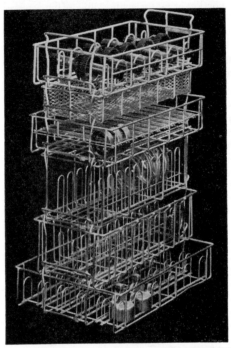

Mid-West Wire Products Co., Inc.

Fig. 31. Wire tote baskets.

Storage Effects of Design. Quantity processing and storing, under modern storage operations, requires full use of the assembly cube. It is important, therefore, that the containers selected be suitable for high stacking without the installation of expensive racks, unless a high degree of selectivity is also required. In turn, fluctuations in the manufacturing cycle may at times cancel the need for all the containers on hand. In the interest of space-saving and proper storage space utilization, excess containers should be stored in the minimum space. The **knock-down features** of metal and wirebound containers have previously been discussed. Where the container and its function does not permit knocking down, **nesting** has been successfully employed to hold a number of containers in slightly more than the cube of an individual container. This procedure is exemplified by steel tote boxes, plastic containers, and even the rigid bulk container having **sloping sides.** Tote boxes in Fig. 32 are designed for stacking and nesting.

Quality and Protection Considerations. Aside from completely enclosed and sealed containers such as carboys, all containers can be equipped with covers for long-term storage of materials, or to guard against contamination, etc. The cover does not necessarily become an integral part of the container, especially if it is employed in only isolated instances. Where fragile items are unitized, the dunnage or dividers are designed so as not only to provide segregation but also to provide protection to polished surfaces and easily damaged precision parts.

DEVELOPMENT OF FIBER CONTAINERS. A widespread, continuous, and effective program of research has been carried on to develop and improve loaded containers which can be safely transported by truck, railroad, ship, or airplane. Probably the greatest change has been brought about by the wide acceptance of fiber drums over the last 45 years. In the fiber-drum industry an aggressive program has developed many new diversified and far more efficient containers than were formerly available. The fiber drum lends itself admirably to

The U. S. Rubber Co.

Fig. 32. Plastic tote boxes for stacking and nesting.

a tailor-made package because of the many methods of construction and the linings and treatments now available in the standard constructions. New or improved inner linings have made possible the handling of a great number of products which previously had to be shipped in heavy and expensive containers. Fiber drums have now been developed to carry up to 400 lb. of liquids, and temporary permits have been secured under the Uniform Freight Classification (U.F.C.) to use such drums. For example, a fiber drum with a dispenser head has proved to be a very satisfactory form of cylindrical container. Fiber drums are available which will carry 487 lb. of gross weight consisting of small loose metal parts.

FIBER DRUMS. Fiber drum containers, as defined in the Modern Packaging Encyclopedia, are "straight-sided cylindrical shipping containers for either domestic or export" use. Capacities are listed from ¾ gal. up to 75 gal.

The U.F.C. (Rule 41, Sec. 12) provides a table showing **maximum weight ranges** of 30 to 400 lb. and corresponding maximum capacities of 15 to 75 gal. for dry or solid articles. Side-wall bursting test requirements range from 250 lb. to 900 lb. per sq. in. Ply thickness and construction details are fully specified. Minimum requirements for various types of tops and bottoms are also specified. For semiliquid articles the fiber drums must be treated or proofed to prevent any absorption of contents by side-walls, tops, or bottoms. Side-wall bursting test requirements are considerably higher than for similar capacities of dry or solid articles. Fiber drums for liquids are limited to 5 gal., and the requirements are considerably higher than for similar capacity of semiliquids. The test for liquid-container drums is specified as two drops from a height of 2 ft., one on bottom chime, and one flat on top, on a solid concrete floor. Tested drum must stand for 24 hr. on each end in turn without leakage.

The U.F.C. requires the drums to bear the **certificate of the maker**, showing that they conform to the construction requirements and specifications. The certificate must be of specified form, size, type, and wording. In addition to the maker's name and address and the type of container, space is provided for the results of sidewall tests in pounds per square inch and net weight limit in pounds.

TM-28-230 covering preservation, packaging and packing of military materials, supplies and equipment lists **two types** of fiber drums. Type 1, for powdered, granular, or flaked materials, is divided into Class A, without liners, and Class B, with liners. Type 2, for hot-poured materials which solidify on cooling is divided into Class A for contents having a minimum melting point of 120° F., and Class B for contents having a minimum melting point of 160° F. Tables are shown giving construction specifications for side walls and heads having capacity ranges from 20 to 55 gal. Manufacturer's certification is required. No provision is made for shipping liquids or semiliquids. Tests are very rigid, including 4-ft. drops, ply separation on wetting, and compression.

Construction of Fiber Drums. The great **advantage of fiber drums** lies in the wide variety of sizes and styles available. Other advantages are their relative economy and lightness. The ability of fiberboard to take printing and stenciling inks makes labeling easy. Fiberboard containers are easy to clean, in many cases, and can be used over and over. Dispensing devices can be incorporated into the construction of the heads. The construction permits convenient stacking and tiering.

The usual construction method is a **convolute winding** to produce a laminated or multiple-fiber side wall. The fiberboard itself is tough, pliable, and water-resistant. It may be manufactured from whatever raw material is most economical, while at the same time it can be made into a finished board meeting the required specifications. Frequently the product to be packaged must be thoroughly analyzed, and the kind of fiberboard stock, construction lining, and closure chosen to fit the requirements of the particular commodity. Many drums have an **inner or outer coating,** or both, which adds protective qualities to the container. The outer lining may be merely paints or lacquers applied for decoration or may be synthetic resin coatings which increase drum resistance to weather and physical damage and scuffing.

Inner linings can be **transparent films**—cellophane, glassine, polyethylene, cellulose acetate, Saran, or pliofilm. Kraft paper, wax coatings, metal foils, resins, or any of a number of other chemical solutions offer protection against moisture-vapor transmissions, retard grease and oil penetration, reduce porosity, and prevent contamination. They are now being used in conjunction with the volatile corrosion inhibitors (VCI).

Fiber-drum manufacture is unique in that each producer has his own patent, with no two making their drums alike. Bottoms are applied by several methods, and closures differ radically in most cases. There are three **general classes** of fiber-drum construction:

1. All fiber.
2. Fiber side walls and wood headings.
3. Fiber side walls and metal headings.

The Modern Packing Encyclopedia illustrates some **typical top and bottom construction combinations** as follows:

1. Exterior metal rolling band on bottom.
2. Metal top and bottom.
3. Metal cover with locking band.
4. Wood top and bottom with triple metal seal.
5. Metal hoops at top and bottom with metal clip closure.
6. Recessed fiber ends.
7. Metal top and bottom with slip, clip, or friction cover.

There are five general kinds of **closures:**

1. Friction-type or telescopic slip-on covers, secured by gummed or pressure-sensitive tape.
2. Lever-actuated locking band or other types of bands.
3. Expanding or crimped lids.
4. Nails.
5. Metal lugs or clips.

Types of Fiber Drums and Their Uses. There are several general kinds of drums, each one slightly different from the others in construction details. One is a slip-cover type in which the cover and body form a smooth butt joint, accomplished by the inclusion of a cylinder liner. This type has the advantage of being easily sealed by tape.

Other kinds of fiber drums are the **wooden-head** or **plug type,** the **metal-end type** with lever-locking ring, the **slip-cover type** with locking clips, the **all-fiber type** with recessed heads; and there are several other varieties. Each supplier has several styles, and most of them are good. Transportation agencies class drums as fiber drums wherever the side walls are fiber. Sizes range from about ¾ gal. to 75 gal. Dimensions vary from 8 in. to 23 in. in diameter and 3 in. to 42 in. in height.

Unless special authorization has been obtained, the contents-weight maximum of 400 lb. applies. **Octagonal or hexagonal fiber containers are** classed as boxes, not drums, and are subject to box rules. Specifications, weight limits, and construction minimums are set up by the Consolidated Freight Classification (C.F.C.) and the Interstate Commerce Commission (ICC). The ICC controls packages for dangerous articles, the C.F.C. all nondangerous articles. Both agencies specify full convolute winding or solid fiberboard side walls for containers. In no case is spiral winding permissible in a fiber drum. C.F.C. requirements are covered by Rule 41, ICC by Sec. 21A and 21B, Armed Forces export by JAN-D-111, and domestic by Fed. Specification UU-D-723.

Though much progress has been made in supplying linings and treatments, no completely satisfactory drum has been found for the **shipment of liquids.** A drum with inner bag and boot is being used for a liquid, but this kind of container is still in the experimental stages. One company has conducted field tests on a fiber drum without a bag, but the drum has not yet been made available for general use. Another company has had considerable success in shipping semiliquids and semisolids in particular kinds of containers. In any case, it is necessary to obtain special permits to ship liquids. These permits are temporary and are for experimental use only. Compliance with certain specified performance tests is required.

There has been considerable advance in the **decoration of fiber drums.** In most cases printing is done by the silk-screen method. This process has its limitations, but with the introduction of new techniques the field has been broadened and several colors can now be applied to a drum. Close register work is difficult because the drums must be printed after they are made up. Some manufacturers have gone far in this development, but the demand for decoration has caused all users of drums to offer more colors.

Cans made of fiber are one of the commoner types of **internal containers** in current use. Products such as scouring powder, insecticides, grass seed, and tooth powder, are packaged in this kind of container. There are three basic types of fiber cans: the round can, which can be either spiral- or convolute-wound, the rectangular can, either spiral- or convolute-wound, and the metal-strip can, which is almost universally a convolute-wound container. The item is known as a fiber can as long as the side walls are of fiberboard. Wall thickness can be varied by changing either the number of plies or the thickness of the individual plies. Perhaps the greatest variation occurs in the end pieces with which these fiber bodies are fitted.

When fiber cans are purchased a **label** must either be supplied by the purchaser or printed up by the manufacturer and must conform to certain specifications for size and layout established by the supplier. The number of bodies which are run together as a unit is dependent upon the production schedule. The cans may be produced in groupings of 2, 3, 4, or 5 and up, depending on size and quantities ordered. Each kind of can requires a slightly different label layout.

Another novel kind of fiber can is known as the **string-tear type.** It is used by the General Motors Diesel Division for packing the company's fuel-injector unit.

The uses to which spiral- or convolute-wound tubing can be put are almost unlimited. A slip-over spiral-wound paper tube is used to protect threads on metal parts. A spiral-wound paper tube is also used as the core of a reel. These reels can be used for many kinds of material.

The extremely small-size fiber can is particularly adaptable for **one-shot applications of powder,** such as flux used in the welding of steel rails. With items of a nature not considered dangerous, experience is the only guide to minimum specifications. Where dangerous commodities, such as insecticides and poisons, are packaged in fiber cans, however, certain maximum-size limitations and other restrictions are applied in the regulations published by the Bureau of Explosives.

Fiber cans are ordered according to inside diameter or inside length and width, wall thickness, and over-all height (outside). Specifications should call for convolute- or spiral-wound construction and specific types of ends. Many kinds of barriers can be incorporated in the side walls, if desired.

CARBOYS AND BOTTLES. Glass shipping containers include carboys. Bottles can be made of earthenware, clay, or stoneware; glass is the commonest material used. Bottles are protected by cushioning material and are inserted in wooden boxes. Corrosive liquids of various kinds are the chief commodity carried. The term "carboy" includes bottle, cushioning, and box. The two standard sizes are 6½ and 13 gal. The top of the box is usually open for visibility. The U.F.C. (Rule 40, Sec. 9) declares that carboys must be so cushioned with packing material that the glass will not come into contact with the box. The 6½-gal. size can also be enclosed in a wooden drum meeting the requirements of Rule 40, Sec. 7. Necks of bottles may project through an aperture in box or drum, with or without protection. If carboys are completely enclosed, the box or drum must be marked on top: "Top Load, This Side Up." The **13-gal. bottle** is hand-blown in cast-iron molds. The **6½-gal. bottle** is now being blown on automatic machines.

Internal pressures make necessary the use of vent-type closures for acid bottles. The 13-gal. bottle is usually closed with a porous clay stopper. Two complete winds of asbestos rope around the flange of the stopper provide the seal. Stoppers are fastened to bottles by soft steel wire. **Cushioning materials** used include mineral wool, cork blocks, molded ground cork with an asphalt binder, and special rubber.

The Interstate Commerce Commission classes containers of 5 to 13 gal. as **carboys.** The 13-gal. carboys must contain at least 21 lb. of glass. Glass in the side wall must be well distributed and at least $\frac{1}{16}$ in. thick. The outer box must completely enclose the body or the body and neck of the carboy. The weight includes four vertical corner posts, two cleats for shoes, and two carrying cleats.

Each container must be marked with letters and figures at least $\frac{3}{4}$ in. high, applied by a hot branding iron or in black printing ink with high-pressure dies, indicating maker, year of manufacture, applicable specifications, such as ICC 1A, thus insuring compliance with all requirements. Tests are rigid, including ten swing tests from 55 in.

TIN CANS. One of the major kinds of miscellaneous containers is the tin can. In 1949, 3,276,925 tons of steel were used to make cans. If all this steel were to be made into No. 2 cans, it would produce about 30 billion of them.

Cans are generally divided into two groups: the **food-packers' cans** and the **general line.** A number of important factors must be considered in the selection of a can for a product. First there is **outage,** the dead air space above the product in the can. This factor must be given serious consideration where vapor pressures are present, but there again with some items, such as paint, the tendency to skin dictates that this internal space be kept practically to an absolute minimum. Some products will attack the **seam dope** used in the can, therefore tests must be made on any doped cans to protect them from leaking. Where it is practical, the side seam is usually soldered. However, under the M-25 tin restriction order, many of the cans must be made of black plate, which introduces a soldering problem. Recent developments indicate that this problem is just about solved, although there may be some delay in getting the new methods into production.

Another consideration is the **shape of the can.** Round cans lend themselves to automatic labeling and conveying much more readily than rectangular cans. A rectangular can, however, consumes less metal, but owing to manufacturing techniques it is a more expensive container. Regardless of the shape of a can, the kind of closure must be decided upon. Therefore consideration must be given to how the product affects the reclosing. Also, the size of the closure enters into the question, because this factor affects filling speeds. **Can-lining materials** must also be taken into account. The bright yellow color of the interior of a can of corn is due to a special lining to resist the attack of the contents. There are hundreds of variations of can linings, each one made specially for a certain product or a small group of products.

The possible use of **lithographed cans** must be considered. Is the quantity of product sufficiently large to justify the plate cost? If it is, the canning company will probably save money by lithographing rather than paper-labeling the cans. Lithographed cans, however, reduce flexibility and bring about problems of stacking.

Selection of a can must also take into consideration the type of closing equipment available and the effect of a particular can on the speed of filling and closing. Another important consideration is the weight of metal used in the can. In the case of certain products a high vacuum must exist; with other products a pressure somewhat above atmospheric is maintained; still other products are sealed at atmospheric pressure. All these considerations affect the choice of metal for the can. Certainly customer convenience should be considered when selecting a can for any product. In most cases ICC regulations exert little influence on the selection of the can; however, Specification 2A covers the limitations of an inside container. It must not be over 10 gal. in capacity and must be of at least 28-gage metal, or in terms of the can-maker, 135-lb. plate for all sizes over 1 gal. For 1 gal. and smaller the regulation calls for adequate thickness. Details concerning various kinds of can metals are covered in the Steel Products Manual (American Iron and Steel Institute).

METAL PAILS. Typical metal pails may be defined as circular vessels having wire hoops or "bails" for handles. The U. S. Department of Commerce defines them as "single-walled shipping containers, with a range of capacity from 1 to 12 gal., constructed of steel heavier than 29 gage."

There is some overlapping of standards among industries, the Uniform Freight Classification, and the military forces. The U.F.C. has established specifications for all kinds of freight containers. Railway Express and Motor Carrier standards are much the same as those of the U.F.C. **Typical specifications** for metal pails, for example, may be as follows:

Made in 5-gal. size only. Available in 24-, 26-, and 28-gage steel. Bottoms are double-seamed and compounded. Side seams are welded. Body beaded and curled. Ears riveted to body. Bail handles with wooden grips. Sixteen lug covers with flowed-in gaskets. Body is necked in to allow for stacking in storage.

Under a federal government specification—RR-P-45 for Pails, Steel, ICC Type 37-D, 5-Gal. Single-Trip Container—three classes are listed for domestic shipment: lug cover, ring-seal or band-seal cover, and bottled-ring or locking-lever-ring cover. For these classes 24-gage steel is required. The pails must bear the embossed initials STC (at least 2 in. high) to signify that they are single-trip containers and not to be used again as shipping containers for the original product after the contents have been removed following initial shipment.

The Uniform Freight Classification (Rule 40, Sec. 5) terms pails as "containers of less than 5 gallons capacity, with bails." A minimum steel thickness of 28 gage for dry or solid articles and 26 gage for other than dry or solid articles is specified. **Single-trip pails** may be used as shipping containers for dry or solid articles without regard for metal gage. They must bear the initials STC.

All pails other than single trip must bear a symbol indicating metal gage, capacity, and year of manufacture, in the order given. Thus 26–5–56 would indicate 26-gage metal, a 5-gal. container, manufactured in 1956. The manufacturer's name or trademark must also be shown. This marking is also required under federal and ICC specifications.

For military requirements there is an Army technical manual (TM-38-230) for the **packing of military supplies.** Under Type VI Container, Round, Open-Top Metal Pail or Drum, with Full Removable Bolted-Ring or Lug Cover, capacities of 5, 10, 25, and 35 lb. and 5 gal. are listed. Sizes range from a 5⅝-in. to an 11¼-in. diam. and from a 5⅞-in. to a 13⅝-in. body height. Side seams must be welded and bottom seams compound-lined and attached to the body by double seaming. Bail ears must be welded or riveted. Bails for 25-lb., 35-lb. and 5-gal. sizes have 8-gage handles with hand grips. **Metal thicknesses** are set up for bodies, bottoms, and tops. The cover is to be provided with a gasket. The 5-gal.-size lug type requires 16 lugs. Lugs must be closed by special tools: hammers and pliers will not do. TM-38-230 covers several other details, many with informative illustrations, for both metal pails and drums.

As to the **marking** of metal pails, the usual good practices should be followed. Old markings should be effaced. If possible, all standard markings should be put on by the supplier. Lithography is used to some extent. Stenciling or glued labels are simple and generally satisfactory. If tags are used, the U.F.C. specifies that they be of cloth, leather, metal, or patch-reinforced tagboard and be securely attached with strong cord, wire, or blunt-wire tag fasteners.

Metal pails are used for such products as greases, waxes, cements, pastes, granular materials, paints, enamels, lacquers, and oils of many types. Another use is for finished metal products such as instruments and aircraft parts. Metal pails can be injected with an inert gas or dehydrated with silica gel to make a Method-II pack, sturdy, moisture-vaporproof, thus eliminating the need for preservation and depreservation of the item. The 5-gal. 24-gage pail is the container most in demand, there being perhaps some thirty to forty million pails of this capacity now being sold annually.

It is well to work with the supplier in developing specifications for metal pails. A knowledge of Uniform Freight Classification and Interstate Commerce Commission regulations is essential. Personal considerations include compatibility of the product with the pail lining, filling and handling problems, palletizing, storing, and carloading requirements.

Under U.F.C. Rule 5, Sec. 4, a 20 percent **additional freight charge** can be made on less-than-carload shipments and 10 percent on carload shipments if the containers do not conform to regulations. Damage-claim collection can also be adversely affected.

There are two regulations affecting the steel container. Rule 40 of the Consolidated Freight Classification applies if a material is in the nondangerous group. However, if the material is classified as dangerous, the regulation of the Bureau of Explosives applies. In this class there are two kinds of containers: single-trip containers, which are covered by ICC Regulations 17, for drums, or 37, for pails; and returnable containers, covered by Reg. ICC 5 or 6. For single-trip containers the regulation requires that the manufacturer's name or registered symbol, the gage of the metal, the capacity, and the date of manufacture, be embossed in the head of the drum.

In the 18-gage 55-gal. size, over one million containers per month are used for the nonregulated liquids. As mentioned above, this class is covered in Rule 40, Sec. 5C. Regulations governing the dangerous items are specifically covered in Sec. 17C, 17E, 17F, and 17X of the ICC regulations. Many **light-gage drums** are used in the shipment of items which solidify upon loss of heat, such as asphalt and resins. The use of the pail, covered by Rule 40 and ICC 37, depends on the product. Well over three million of these pails are used per month. In addition to the regulations, there are many items to be considered in the specification of a drum or pail. The following is a list of some of these items:

1. Outage required by the product.
2. Number of rolling hoops.
3. Type of interior lining.
4. Agitators, if required.
5. Location of bung openings.
6. Whether the drum should be of open-head or tight-head construction.
7. The exterior finish. (Consideration should be given to lithographed drums.)
8. Type of gasket necessary to hold the contained material.

In the case of certain liquid chemicals, aluminum drums or stainless-steel drums of a returnable type should be considered. In the case of solids, light-gage materials should be considered.

TYPES AND CONSTRUCTION OF METAL DRUMS. The U. S. Department of Commerce defines metal drums as "single-walled cylindrical- or bilge-shaped shipping containers, with a range of capacity from 12 to 132 gal., constructed of steel." The Uniform Freight Classification covers "containers of 5-gal. capacity or over, with or without bails. Drums exceeding 165-gal. capacity will not be accepted as freight shipping containers." Drums are further defined as "straight-sided cylindrical containers without bilge, with ends of equal diameter." The Army defines metal drums as "cylindrical metal containers of 10 gal. capacity or greater, including single-trip and returnable containers" (TM-38-230).

Metal-drum specifications vary. The U. S. Department of Commerce distinguishes between two types:

1. **Heavy**—19 gage or heavier (with slight exceptions) divided into single-trip and returnable containers. Heavy returnable drums are usually constructed from 12- to 16-gage steel.
2. **Light**—20 gage and lighter (with slight exceptions). This classification is subdivided into Tight-Head Drums, equipped with two screw-thread openings, and Full-Open-Head Drums. On the latter the heads are usually secured to the bodies by lever-locking or bolted rings, which are drawn tight to give a leak-proof closure.

In the U.F.C. (Rule 40, Sec. 5) eight groups are listed, ranging in capacity from 5 to 165 gal. For **returnable containers,** the minimum thickness of the steel ranges from 28 gage to 18 gage for dry or solid articles and from 26 to 12 gage for other than dry or solid articles, descending as the capacity increases. Side seams must be welded. No thickness of metal is prescribed for **single-trip drums,** but they must conform to the minimum and maximum capacities given. Also, they must bear the embossed STC. All drums must bear the code for metal gage, capacity, and year of manufacture, as well as the manufacturer's name and/or trademark. Shipments of some liquids listed in ICC Regulations for the Transportation of Explosives and Other Dangerous Commodities must be in single-trip containers.

Under **closures,** the U.F.C. says: "Caps, covers, plugs, or tops must be securely fastened and be proof against leakage or sifting."

Again turning to TM-38-230, the first of several steel drums listed is the **55-gal. Type 5,** for inflammable or poisonous liquids. According to ICC Regulations, the Type-5 drum is approved for a long list of such kinds of commodities as arsenic acid, alcohol, benzine, motor fuel, naphtha and paint. It is also suitable for other inflammable liquids having a vapor pressure of less than 40 lb. per sq. in. at 100° F. It is likewise satisfactory for nondangerous liquids.

Most **55-gal. drums** are of a 33.03-in. inside height and a 22.35-in. inside diameter. Nominal sheet-steel thickness is 0.0598, and the weight is 40 oz. plus or minus 2 oz. per sq. ft. Workmanship and finish details are carefully specified. Capacity is to be not less than rated capacity plus 2 percent or greater than the rated capacity plus 2 percent plus 1 qt. This capacity signifies a range of from 56.1 to 56.35 gal. Body seams are welded. Heads are joined to the body by brazing, welding, double-seaming, or a seamless chime. **Riveting is not permitted** in any part of the drum. No extension of a plug, or the head inside the chime, can be less than 3/8 in. from a plane surface in contact with the end of the drum.

There are two styles of **rolling hoops.** Style 1 consists of two corrugations swaged into the body of the drum, equidistant from each end, to protect the drum and chime rings when rolling. Step 2 consists of two hoops made of steel

I-section, attached to the body of the drum. Spacing is the same as for Style 1. Hoops are attached either by deforming the body of the drum outward to form continuous beads on each side of the hoop or by attaching substantial metal lugs to the body on each side of each hoop. Lugs are equally spaced and welded to the body.

Rolling hoops (or beads) in the body of the drum not only increase the strength, rigidity, and ease of handling the container but also provide a means for anchoring internal dunnage through the use of split, expanding steel rings which fit inside the grooves. Diameters of upper and lower chimes are such as to permit stacking, the bottom fitting inside the cover. Inside diameters range from about 10 to 15 in., and inside heights from 13 to 24 in. Special cup-type drilled mounts have been devised to which generators, etc., can be bolted. Crate-type inserts are also available. These containers can be used for **Method II** packs with a dehydrating agent.

Closures and Coatings. Bung and vent closures must be adequate to **prevent leakage and breathing.** Welded or grazed flanges are preferable (heavy wrenches often weaken the joints in rolled or pressed-in flanges). There are three or more complete threads in each closure and a minimum of five when a flat-type gasket is used.

Bung and vent **plugs** are made of the same material as the flanges or of a suitable die-cast material. The bung has an indented top, so designed for ease of opening with a rectangular steel bar. The vent plug is similar in design to the bung, except that it has a hexagonal head and is removable with an ordinary wrench. Each plug has a gasket which may be made of synthetic rubber, lead, vulcanized fiber, or leather. It must not affect, nor be affected by, the product to be contained.

The two commonest kinds of **coatings** used on Type 5 drums are zinc and black asphaltum. Black-asphaltum varnish is used only as an exterior coating. Zinc is preferable unless emergency conditions apply.

Tamperproof **cap seals** are usually furnished for the bung and vent, with the same coating as the drum. Cap seals and extra gaskets are sent in a separate box by the drum supplier with each shipment, and with a 5 percent overage, according to standard practice. Empty drums are shipped with gaskets in place and bung and vent plugs only hand tightened.

Tests and Uses of Drums. Tests for Type 5 drums include air- and hydrostatic-pressure tests and a drop test, wherein the drum is filled to 98 percent capacity with water and dropped from a height of 4 ft. onto solid concrete, striking diagonally on a chime or other circumferential seam.

The Type 5A, 55-gal. steel drum is for **acids and other dangerous materials.** By ICC regulation, steel drums are required for such commodities as liquid carbolic acid, sulfuric acid, carbon tetrachloride, electrolyte, caustic potash, and potassium cyanide—to name but a few. Inflammable and poisonous liquids approved for Type 5 drums can also be shipped in 5A drums if Type 5 drums are not available. Drums for certain chemicals, such as sulfuric acid, may have only one opening, which must be located in the body of the drum.

The principal **differences** in the 5A drum (from the Type 5) are:

1. Slightly heavier sheet steel and slightly different dimensions.
2. Body seams welded. Head seams limited to welding or seamless.
3. Style 2 hoops must be used (somewhat heavier than for Type 5).

4. Closure flanges must be welded around entire circumference, five or more threads per flange.
5. Gaskets must be of asbestos or other suitable acid-resisting material. Special inner linings must be used, including on surfaces of flanges and plugs.
6. Hydrostatic tests are more severe.

The Type 5C, 55-gal. drum is for **nitric acid.** The principal feature is the use of sheet steel, alloyed, for resistance to this acid, and a special acid-resisting test is added.

The Type 5D, 55-gal. drum is for **hydrochloric and similar acids.** Here the inside of the drum must be completely lined with rubber, attached by cement or other suitable means. Plugs are also rubber lined. The interior is treated with black asphaltum. A special test with an electrical circuit is required to prove that the rubber lining is continuous and complete.

Type 5B is for **liquid petroleum products.** Here the chimes must be welded or double-seamed, and Style 1 rolling hoops are required. Special gaskets are specified. Coating requirements are strict, particularly in regard to cleaning before application. Special tests are required for the coating, including a salt-spray test.

Type 6C is for **inflammable solids or oxidizing materials** and is required for such items as barium, potassium, and sodium compounds. The construction is similar to Type 5 except for special closures, and Style 1 rolling hoops only are used. Tests are similar to those for Type 5 except that additional drop tests are applied, the drums being filled with powder.

Type 37D, 55-gal. is a **single-trip container for inflammable solids,** such as oxidizing material, and other commodities, such as chromic acid and ammonium compounds. It is similar to Type 5 except that the openings are somewhat like those of Type 6C. It includes some drums which can be stripped away from the product contained in them.

Style 1 rolling hoops are used (except on strippable drums). Authorized gross weights range from 80 to 880 lb. The applicable approved sheet gage ranges from 24 for 80 lb. to 18 gage for the 880 pounder. No official tests are prescribed, but standard practice is to fill the container to the authorized gross weight and then so drop it 4 ft. onto solid concrete as to have it strike diagonally on the top chime. Somewhat less than 2 oz. of the material is allowed to fall out when the drum is stood on one end and then on the other, and rolled two complete revolutions on the floor.

The same **marking and specification** considerations apply as for pails, except that tags are hardly practical.

Re-usable Drums. Re-usable drums are sturdy and built for long and repeated service. The full-open-head drum is intended especially for heavy liquids, shortenings, greases, and other products hard to pour or pump from tight-head drums. The **light-type** drum is used primarily for solid or dry materials, such as asphalt, grease, lime, and powdered or granular materials requiring a strong yet inexpensive container. Steel gage usually runs from 20 to 28, and the bodies are corrugated for strength. Steel drums provide leakproof protection for fluids, withstand rough handling, have ready portability, and can be inventoried easily. Recent cumulative sales of the 18-gage 55-gal. drum for a 7-mo. period amounted to about 9,500,000 units, compared with approximately 8,500,000 for the same period during the preceding year. This kind of container is the leading seller of the drum industry. Total sales of all drums for the 7-mo. period numbered about

20,000,000 units, compared with approximately 20,000,000 during the entire preceding year.

The Army (TM-38-230) has a series of **exterior re-usable metal containers** ranging in capacity from approximately 5 to 20 gal., covered by Specification MIL-C-6054. Designed for the preservation and packaging of metal parts and accessories, the construction features include 18- to 22-gage steel, full removable covers with gasket, and bolted-ring closure. A standard nut and bolt locks the ends of the locking ring.

VARIETIES OF RACKS. While not strictly within the scope of containers, the several basic types of racks become integral parts of the container system where the nature of the product does not permit either direct container-stacking or bulk-container-moving to processing points. Racks fall naturally into three groupings according to the services performed:

1. A **conventional rack** employed to support unit containers in instances where direct stacking cannot be conveniently accomplished.
2. **Portable racks** containing not only a quantity of items but also a variety of items moving to assembly operations.
3. **Permanent racks** specially designed to contain large parts, in-process parts, or parts kept in reserve storage.

Conventional Racks. Where permanent cubicle-type racks are used, selectivity of the unit container, either by item or by stage of completion, becomes a controlling factor. Both aging and turnover are important factors in the selection of racks. Selection of the proper kind of rack will materially speed handling to— and from—in-process storage.

Portable Racks. Portable racks usually will be found in use at in-process storage points, such as between successive machining operations, or in reserve storage areas, to be moved to parts assemblies areas. The decision as to **rack construction and size** will usually be governed by machine runs and economy of machine loadings, adjusted to some extent by considerations of scheduling.

The plan usually followed is to supply a definite quantity of large parts on mobile shelving, and a proportionate number of smaller parts to keep production equipment busy. This plan permits portable storage of many kinds of units in an orderly and space-saving manner. The plan can be further modified through the use of individual tote bins and other types of shop boxes. The shelving is adjustable so that it can be adapted to many kinds of work. Where short moves occur, castered trucks are provided in place of skid or pallet racks. Rotary bins are in general use where large quantities of small parts are stored or at assembly operations where a number of parts must be within operator reach and quickly available. Gravity feed racks have come into considerable use, in both permanent or portable design, having rear loading and gravity feed of either units or small containers, to a central dispatch point, or to the assembly point.

Permanent Racks. The third panel type of rack is usually of permanent construction and designed to hold a specific product such as carpet rolls, reels, bar stock, and large dies. Each kind of article is retained in one predetermined type of cubicle. The cubicles, if necessary, can be vertically adjusted to accommodate changes in the size and/or design of the kind of item stored. The racks may be of the roller-bed type, the christmas-tree type, etc. Where necessary, the cubicles are equipped with flooring, which may be either permanent or removable.

Shipping Containers

ORIGIN OF CONTAINERIZATION. Containerization of cargo for shipping purposes is not a new venture. The idea was first expressed in England in 1801 by Dr. James Anderson, before steam locomotives were introduced.

Objectives of Containerization. From its earliest advent to the present day, containerization has met with varying degrees of success throughout the world. The basic objectives which brought about its conception are as sound today as they were in 1801. They can be generalized as follows:

1. Elimination of multiple handlings of individual packages.
2. Increased protection to ladings through the elimination of manual handling.
3. Reduction in packaging and crating costs.
4. Reduction in pilferage.

In recent years efforts along these lines have vastly increased. The ever rising costs of the elements involved in the movement of cargo from consignor to consignee, particularly in the export trades, have brought about redoubled efforts to reduce shipping expenditures. Costs of labor, materials, and shipping space, coupled with high pilferage resulting in shortages and the relative high value of most merchandise today, have brought about increasing use of containers. It is estimated that there are in service today, in one form or another throughout the world, well over 250,000 re-usable cargo containers.

Savings Possible Through Containerization. Specific savings which can be effected through the use of re-usable cargo containers in place of conventional containers depend to a large measure on a number of factors. These factors will become evident as this section progresses. However, general indications of dollars and man-hours saved can be had from a typical report of a test shipment and results obtained from a commercial user. A toilet goods manufacturer using cargo containers for export shipments reports:

1. An average savings of $120 per container, obtained through the use of domestic-type internal packaging, thus eliminating expensive packing materials.
2. Approximately 36 man-hr. per container saved in packaging, marking, weighing, and handling operations in making export shipments.
3. A 75% reduction in breakage.
4. A 100% reduction in pilferage.
5. A 50% reduction in insurance rates.

RE-USABLE SHIPPING CONTAINERS. Re-usable cargo containers may be described as self-contained units for the transportation of freight in fractional carload packages. They are generally closed and weathertight and are designed for movement on, or in, railroad cars, highway vehicles, or marine vessels. There are many types and classes of containers currently in use. Categorically there are five main groups:

1. Bulk freight containers.
2. Refrigerated freight containers.
3. Pallet containers.
4. General cargo (merchandise) containers.
5. Van containers.

BULK FREIGHT CONTAINERS. Bulk freight containers and liquid containers provide a unit for the transportation of bulk commodities and afford a means for eliminating costly handling operations incident to bagging, losses through spillage, the need for elevators, chutes, etc. In addition, they provide flexibility and economy.

Four Types of Bulk Freight Containers. Bulk cargo containers are further divided into four types as follows:

1. **Containers that are not weathertight:** for rough freight, i.e., rough brick, crushed stone, ores, gravel and other aggregates. They are normally provided with a means for handling by overhead crane, with drop bottoms for quick discharge, and with or without doors in the top for loading. In application, unloading from the railroad car is accomplished by an overhead crane, with the car being released in less than one hour. The loaded container may be dumped into an overhead hopper adjacent to the tracks or into a highway truck for delivery, or the container itself may be loaded into the truck for movement to point of use. Fig. 33 shows such a unit constructed of steel and having a capacity of 12,000 lb. or 100 cu. ft.

The L. C. L. Corp.

Fig. 33. Drop-bottom bulk container.

2. **Weather-sealed containers:** for such commodities as dolomite, lime, cement, flour, malt, etc. This type of container is provided with weathertight hatches at the top for loading, drop bottoms for discharging contents, and loops at the top for handling by overhead crane. Fig. 34 illustrates this type of container with a **controlled-discharge gate.** The smaller sizes ordinarily have one hopper discharge gate and the large containers two gates, usually of the slide type. The rubber container in Fig. 35 comes in sizes of 70, 300, and 370 cu. ft. Larger units are handled by crane by a lifting eye, while small ones can be handled in boxcars and vans by a fork truck with crane bracket. These containers are collapsible and are well adapted for handling bulk material under certain circumstances.

The L. C. L. Corp.

Fig. 34. Controlled-discharge bulk container.

The U. S. Rubber Co.

Fig. 35. Rubber bulk container.

3. **Containers for bulk commodities requiring careful handling,** such as face bricks, hollow tile, glazed brick, are equipped with hooks or loops at the top for overhead handling. They have no doors; the top and one side are open. Cargo is loaded by fork lift trucks, as it is packed at the kiln. This type of container, shown in Fig. 36, has a 1,500-lb. capacity and can be carried on conventional highway trucks or on railroad gondola cars.

4. **Air-activated containers:** for cement, lime, soda ash, fly ash, salt, and other pulverulent materials in bulk (Fig. 37). This is a steel cylindrical container with a dome-shaped top, in which an 18-in. opening is provided for loading. It is available in capacities of 240 and 258 cu. ft. The cover is bolted fast, making the container weathertight and airtight to withstand a pressure of 30 lb. per sq. in.

A 15-in. opening is provided in the center of the sloping floor, from which extends a 4-in. discharge pipe to the outer circumference of the container. The contents of the container is fluffed by mixing it with air under pressure. Air is

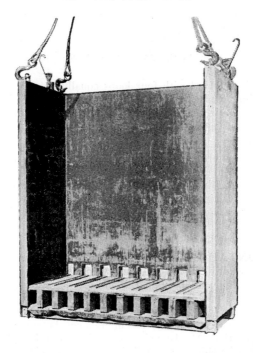

The L. C. L. Corp.

Fig. 36. Container for bulk commodities requiring careful handling.

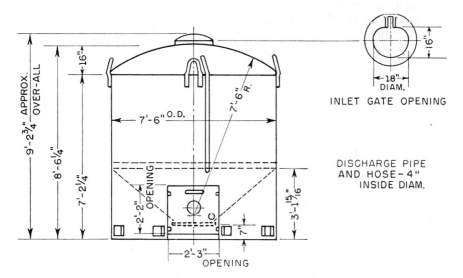

Fig. 37. Air-activated container: dimensions and specifications.

also used to force the contents out through the discharge pipe. The air is introduced into the container through two pipes extending inward from the outer circumference, one through the bottom and one at the top just below the 18-in. opening. A reducing valve in the line automatically prevents air pressure from exceeding 30 lb. per sq. in.

The container is provided with four loops equally spaced around the top for **overhead handling.** Unloading is accomplished by ejecting the contents by air directly from the container while mounted on a railroad car or trucking unit. All discharging operations require an air compressor.

REFRIGERATED CONTAINERS. Considerable experimentation has been conducted with refrigerated containers both in the United States and in foreign countries. Containers for chilled and frozen foods have been designed and tested. These containers employ various refrigerants, bunker arrangements, temperature controls, air circulation systems, and insulation materials. Many valuable data have been gathered. No design has been generally accepted as yet, but the widespread interest evidenced in such containers assures their ultimate adoption.

PALLET CONTAINERS. Pallet sizes are discussed under the heading of Pallets. Hall (Standard Sizes of Shipping Containers for Carrier Interchange, ASME) recommends, in addition to the 40-in. × 32-in. and the 48-in. × 40-in. sizes, standard pallets—the 32-in. × 24-in. size for handling high density material and the 72-in. × 48-in. size for use in stevedoring. These four sizes meet most shipping requirements and are suitable for interchange between highway, railroad, marine, and air carriers. As he points out, sizes that include a dimension of 48 in. or 32 in. can be efficiently handled two or three abreast in standard railroad boxcars and those with a 40-in. dimension can be stowed two abreast in highway vans. With the adoption of the 48-in. × 40-in. standard pallet, various stacking patterns, discussed in the section on palletization, were developed for making up unit loads of cartons, packages, bags, and other containers.

A pallet container is a rigid unit that can be loaded satisfactorily into boxcars or vans with only enough clearance for convenient loading. As pallet containers vary widely in type and construction, the desirable working clearance in loading varies. According to Hall,

Using optimum pallet containers of maximum outside dimensions with smooth side walls, preferably with scuff plates near the top and bottom, two units 54 in. or three units 36 in. wide can be easily loaded in a 110-in.-wide boxcar, provided the lining of the car is smooth so that the containers can be slid into place. Similarly, two containers 44 in. wide or three containers 29 in. wide with smooth side walls can be easily loaded into a van with a minimum inside width of 90 in., providing the van has a smooth lining or guide rails.

Recommended sizes for pallet containers are 36-in. × 29-in., 44-in. × 36-in., 54-in. × 44-in., and 78-in. × 54-in.

Types of Pallet Containers. Many types of pallet containers are now in use for intra-factory and inter-plant transfer. These include pallet boxes, baskets, racks, bins or hoppers, crates and carton containers. Construction design may vary, including containers with open tops, top covers, or side or end doors. Also, the container may be made collapsible or may be expendable. The pallet container may have various **mountings,** such as four casters, four legs, skid runners, or two casters and two legs for use with a hand or power lift jack. Typical examples are shown in Fig. 38.

Missouri Pacific Lines

International Paper Co.

Fig. 38. Typical pallet containers.

Pallet box containers with smooth inside walls and side doors can be used for holding unit loads of fragile or costly merchandise packaged to fit standard pallets because the inside dimension of such box containers provides sufficient clearance. Such unit loads can be removed intact if on paper or fiber pallet sheets or expendable pallets.

Pallet containers can be made from a **variety of materials.** Depending on weight, strength and cost factors, steel, aluminum, plywood, wood, fiberboard or corrugated paper can be used alone or in combination.

Hall holds that optimum heights of pallet containers for stacking in either standard boxcars 10½ ft. high or vans 88 in. high could be 28 in., 40 in., 60 in., and 84 in. This means that three 28-in. containers would stack to a height of 84 in. in a van and four to a height of 112 in. in a boxcar. Two 40-in. containers would stack to a height of 80 in. in a van and three to a height of 120 in. in a boxcar. The 60-in. container, stacked two high in a boxcar would also give a height of 120 in. and the 84-in. container would be a good fit one high in a van. In most cases, pallet containers arranged for tiering will nest from 1 in. to 2 in. These tiered heights would, in such cases, be adjusted by this amount.

Jumbo Pallet Containers. Hall describes a larger container, which is about double the size of the large pallet container and fits broadside into a van, that is coming into use. This container, with optimum outside dimensions of 88 in. long × 44 in. wide, can be mounted on legs, skid runners, casters, or with flat-bottom and can be handled by cranes, by fork or straddle trucks, or on rollers. This type of container (Fig. 39) can be rolled either endwise or broadside into a van on its own casters, with either side guides or channels attached to the floor of the van to guide the casters. The flat-bottom or end-runner type (Fig. 40) can be handled by fork or straddle truck or rolled into a trailer body on rollers. With

Fig. 39. Castered jumbo basket pallet container.

Ford Motor Co.

Fig. 40. Steel shop containers with end runners on rollers in van secured with cross braces.

the arrangement shown here, a set of rollers would be permanently attached to the floor of the van. Similar rollers on a slight slope would be mounted on the shipping dock, and a short hinged connecting section of rollers would permit loading an entire truckload of these jumbo pallet containers into the van body at one time. By means of perforated angle securement rails on the side wall of the van and cross braces, the entire load can be secured against fore and aft movement. These jumbo pallet containers can be furnished with covers or side doors or removable panels. Recommended heights for use with vans are 28 in. (triple tiering), 42 in. (double tiering), 63 in., and 84 in.

Some jumbo pallet containers, sometimes referred to as **truck liners,** are just high enough to enter the door of the van and are in varying lengths, sometimes the full length of the van body. Such units sometimes have a structural metal frame with wire mesh sides and ends and are loaded in the shipping room with small packages, such as parcel post or small commodities, so that the van can be quickly loaded by rolling the entire unit into the truck in a matter of seconds.

CARGO CONTAINERS. Containers for general cargo or merchandise are used extensively throughout the world. This type of container is the one for which there is the greatest demand. Developed after much experimentation and testing, and with considerable emphasis on standardization, it is receiving broader acceptance. The cargo container is usually larger, more rigid, and of stronger construction than the pallet container to withstand rough handling and outside storage.

CLASSES OF CARGO CONTAINERS. General cargo containers are capable of handling varied types of commodities without extensive pre-packaging at the place of origin, thus eliminating delays otherwise incurred by consolidation procedures. They are divided into two major classes and five types.

Class A comprises **collapsible cargo containers,** which have sides, ends, and roof capable of being collapsed onto the base for shipment empty. All components make up into a compact integral package with a minimum cube, secured to the base without loose parts. However, they are used mainly for one-direction flow of traffic, because, while they have all the normal advantages attributable to containers, the cost of returning them to their point of origin may often be more than the cost of the containers. Other **disadvantages** of collapsible con-

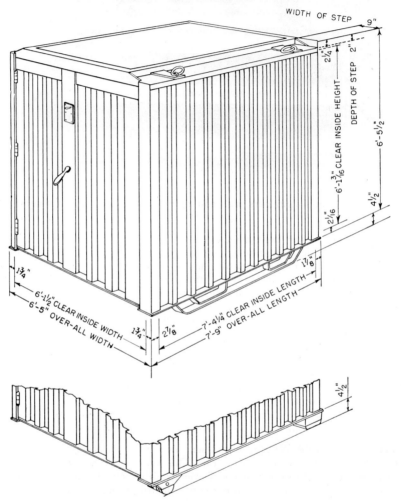

Fig. 41. Corrugated steel cargo container.

tainers are: high initial cost, the difficulty of making them weatherproof, and lack of structural strength, particularly in interlocking fittings. Class B comprises the **noncollapsible** rigid cargo containers of welded, riveted, or bolted construction, provided with one or more doors through which cargo is loaded and unloaded (Fig. 41).

Types of Cargo Containers. The containers are grouped into five types according to the handling mounts provided. Several of these features are shown in Fig. 41.

Type 1. Lift-off. A flush-base type provided with loops or hooks at the top for handling by crane and spreader with slings to facilitate transfer operations.

Type 2. Roll-off. Provided with retractable wheels or rollers in the base, thereby incorporating as an integral unit mechanisms required for transfer. During the transportation phase, with wheels or rollers retracted, the container rests directly on the floor of the car or truck, simplifying securing devices. The principal deterrents to wider acceptance of such containers are: high initial capital investment, maintenance costs, and excessive platform surface stresses, injurious to warehouse or carrier floors.

Type 3. Leg-type. Provided with legs at the base for transfer by platform lift truck. This type is limited in application because of the variations in platform heights of the lift trucks used to move these containers.

Type 4. Skid-type. Provided with skids or runners incorporated within the frame of the unit at the base. These runners add very little to the cost or weight of the unit. Transfer operations are accomplished by fork lift truck or sliding, the power in the latter case being provided by winch or tractor.

Type 5. Combined lift-off and wheel, leg skid. Both such provisions for transfer operations are incorporated. This type affords the greatest flexibility and is the most economical and practical of all types.

VAN CONTAINERS. The van container is equivalent to a truck or trailer body, but built so that it can be mounted on a flat-frame highway truck, trailer, or special railroad container flatcar or gondola car. These van containers vary in length from the short unit, which can be carried crosswise in a gondola car, to the 35-ft. unit, which is the longest legal single-vehicle length permitted in all states. The cross sections of all sizes of van containers correspond in outside and inside width and height dimensions to a standard highway truck and trailer high volume body.

Among its many advantages over the trailer-on-flatcar (T.O.F.C., piggy-back) method, the van container on a container car is less costly to load and can be handled with the same flexibility as a boxcar. It requires no expensive flatcars with special hold-down gear.

Recommended Sizes. Hall (Standard Sizes of Shipping Containers for Carrier Interchange, ASME) recommends five sizes of van containers as most practical. These are 8 ft., 11 ft., 17 ft., and 34 ft. lengths considering the statutory limitations for highway vehicles (see section on Highway Trucks and Truck Trailers), sizes of truck and trailer beds, and size of railroad cars.

Construction and Design. The construction of the van container will have to be more rugged than that of a corresponding highway trailer body, since these units must be able to stand the rigors of handling in railroad transfer and classification yards. The container car, of course, would be provided with suitable **shock-absorbing accessory equipment;** but in addition to this, the van container should be provided with facilities for securing its cargo very similar to the securing equipment used in damage-free boxcars (see sections on Railroad Freight Cars and Railroad Terminal Handling).

Van containers are designed to be suitable for handling general freight or pallet containers. To properly secure several tiers of pallet containers or other unitized loads, perforated **securement rails** must be incorporated in the construction of the sides of the van container, as shown in Fig. 42. Thus the van container is in itself a damage-free unit.

All sizes of van containers should be provided with **side sills,** probably of channel construction, which permit use of crane grabs for transferring the van container. They should also be provided with **lifting eyes** for crane spreader

Fig. 42. Cross braces and deck over open pallet containers in van container or DF boxcar.

Fig. 43. Special devices to transfer body from truck to flatcar.

slings and should be strong enough for, and arranged for, tiering in a ship's hold or in yard storage. **Pockets** for the use of fork trucks should also be provided.

Demountable Truck Body. There have been a number of demountable truck body installations designed for transfer between truck chassis and flatcar. These, in many cases, have been designed to meet special conditions and are not universal in their application or always well adapted to general trucking and railroad practices. Fig. 43 shows a special arrangement for transferring demountable truck bodies between a frame bed truck and special flatcar.

Container Design

OPTIMUM SIZE FOR A CONTAINER. A principal governing factor in container usage is container size. The optimum size for a container can be determined through an evaluation of the pertinent elements.

Factors for the Designer To Determine. The designer must make a number of basic determinations consistent with the traffic pattern flow with which he is concerned. These are:

1. **Use.** Whether the container is to be used for a specific commodity or group of commodities, i.e., general cargo.
2. **Density.** The density of cargo to be transported in lb. per cu. ft. Experience indicates that for general (merchandise) cargo 35 lb. per cu. ft. is average. For bulk cargo 110 lb. per cu. ft. is average.
3. **Size limitation.** Limiting dimensions as imposed by rail, highway, or water carriers normally used, e.g., in export trades the 'tween-deck clearance of approximately 7 ft. can be considered a limiting dimension; the widths of rail cars or motor vehicles may be other limiting dimensions.
4. **Weight limitation.** The lifting capacity of transfer equipment at terminals and transfer points, or of ships' gear, determines the weight limitation.
5. **Quantity limitation.** Where containers are to be used for a specific commodity, the desirable maximum weight of that cargo to be moved as a unit must be determined.

Computing Optimum Size. Assume, for example, that it is required to compute the optimum size for a container to satisfy the following conditions:

1. General cargo.
2. 35 lb. per cu. ft.
3. Height, 7 ft.
4. 11,200 lb. gross. (When container is concerned with a specific commodity and a known quantity, this factor is reached by a quantity density determination.)

Having established basic limitations, a **planned gross volume** for the unit, including allowances for the container itself, must be computed. This factor is used in finding the over-all dimensions of the container. To assist in this process, experience provides the following guides:

1. The **weight of re-usable containers** of conventional construction materials averages 5.5 lb. per cu. ft. of usable space (interior cube). Where lightweight or unconventional materials are used (aluminum, plastics, etc.), standard conversion factors can be applied to convert the weights to this average.
2. The difference between the **net volume** (interior) and **gross volume** (exterior) averages approximately 16.5 percent of the interior volume. This increase is due to unusable space required for skids, framing, doors, and other construction.

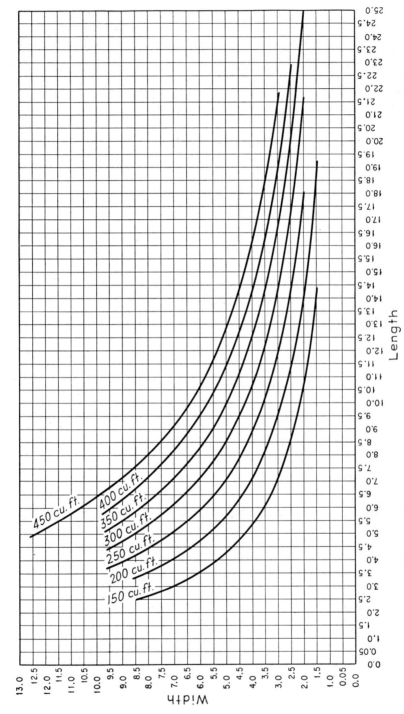

Fig. 44. Chart to determine length and width dimensions (optimum) when limiting height dimension of 7 ft. is known.

3. The following formula is used:

$$Y = (0.165 + 1)\frac{a}{b + c}$$

or

$$Y = \frac{0.165a}{b + c} + \frac{a}{b + c}$$

where Y = planned gross volume (cu. ft.)
a = weight limitation
b = density (lb. per cu. ft.)
c = average density of re-usable container materials, 5.5 lb. per cu. ft.

Applying these guides to the conditions assumed in the example above, planned gross volume is 312.5 cu. ft.

Having established a planned gross volume and one dimensional limitation, one can establish the remaining optimum dimensions from the chart shown in Fig. 44. This chart assumes the limiting dimension to be a height of 7 ft. Where the limiting dimension differs, a similar chart can be prepared as follows:

$$\text{Dimension } A \times \text{dimension } B = \frac{\text{gross volume}}{\text{limiting dimension}}$$

A curve may be plotted, by progressive increments, through any desired dimension. The next and final step is the **reconciliation of optimum dimensions** to afford maximum utilization of the principal transportation media to be used.

A tabulation of sizes of flatcars and gondola cars of 14 major railroads is shown in Fig. 45. Typical length and width dimensions of highway vehicles, by capacity, are shown in Fig. 46. Except for height and weight limitations, containers sized for efficient highway and rail transportation present no problems in marine transport.

The ideal in sizing of a container is compatability with, and maximum utilization of, space available in the transportation media. Thus, where a unit is to be transported solely by rail, one dimension should be equal to the width of the car while the other should be such that the sum total thereof will be equal to the length of the car. However, should the container require transportation by rail and highway, dimensions must be compatible with the length and width of trucks. As a **general rule**, the long dimension (width of rail cars) should be such

	No. in Service *	Length	Width
Flatcars			
	4,100	40 ft. 10 in.	9 ft. 4 in.
	1,730	49 ft. 3 in.	9 ft. 3 in.
	7,377	53 ft. 6 in.	10 ft. 4 in.
	3,020	53 ft. 6 in.	10 ft. 6 in.
Gondola Cars			
	32,925	52 ft. 6 in.	9 ft. 6 in.
	17,160	41 ft. 6 in.	9 ft. 4 in.
	13,460	40 ft. 6 in.	9 ft. 6 in.

* 14 major railroad companies.

Fig. 45. **Dimensions of flatcars and gondola cars on fourteen railroads.**

Type	Rated Capacity (tons)	Body Length (in.)	Body Width (in.)
Pick-up	1½ to 1	$\begin{cases}78\\96\end{cases}$	
	1 to 1½	$\begin{cases}78\\96\end{cases}$	48½
	1½ to 2½	$\begin{cases}78\\110\end{cases}$	
Stake and platform	½ to 1½	92	80
	1½ to 7½	$\begin{cases}102\frac{3}{4}\\144\end{cases}$	80 / 86
	2½ to 7½	168	86
Platform	1½ to 7½	$\begin{cases}8\text{ ft.-}\\16\text{ ft.}\end{cases}$	90 / 95½
Trailer	to 20 tons	$\begin{cases}17\text{ ft.-}\\35\text{ ft.}\end{cases}$	96

Fig. 46. Dimensions of typical highway vehicles.

as to equal, as a single unit or multiple units, the length of the truck bed, while the short dimension (sum of which equals the length of railroad cars) should be the equivalent of the width of the truck bed.

Assuming that a container is to be transported by rail, thence by truck in door-to-door delivery service, the truck having approximate body dimensions of $L = 10$ ft., $W = 6$ ft. 8 in., a container the size of which is 9 ft. 4 in. × 6 ft. 6 in. would be the most efficient. Another possible size combination would be 6 ft. 6 in. × 4 ft. 8 in. The latter must be considered in the light of other factors previously discussed.

In the above assumption, should the truck movement be a long haul by tractor-trailer, width 8 ft., other combinations of dimensions are possible. In the last analysis, the final determination of dimensions is dependent on the type of service in which the container is to be placed and on the transportation media to be used.

SELECTING CONTAINER MATERIALS. The selection of a particular material for the construction of a container is based on five major considerations, namely:

1. **Weight** should be as light as possible, consistent with usage, desired design life, safety factors, and a minimum of maintenance.
2. **Strength** must be adequate to withstand the stresses and strains which may be imposed by the type of traffic anticipated.
3. Consistent with other factors, the initial **capital investment** must be amortized over a reasonable period of time.
4. The material must be **available** (noncritical), and require only minimal or no special production facilities or techniques.
5. The material must be **compatible** with the type of cargo to be carried in the container.

A number of different materials are used in the construction of containers, each having a particular desirability. The principal types have been tabulated in Fig. 47 together with such pertinent characteristics as apply to containers.

	Sheet Steel	Corrugated Steel	Sheet Aluminum	Corrugated Aluminum	Plywood
Principal use	Bulk materials	General cargo	General cargo	General cargo	General cargo
Structural strength	Good	Good	Good	Good	Good
Type constr.	Welded or riveted	Welded	Welded or riveted	Welded	Stressed wood or steel frame
Longevity	Good	Good	Fair	Fair	Poor
Maintenance	Low	Low	High	Low	High
Resistance to puncture	High	High	Low	Low	Low
Resistance to bending	Low	High	Low	High	High
Tare weight	High	Medium	Low	Low	High
Reinforcing required	Vertical in sides and ends; horizontal in roof and floor.	Floor sections generally.	Same as sheet steel.	Same as corrugated steel.	Wood framing generally provides reinforcement. Where steel frame is used, same as sheet steel.
Cost	Medium	Medium	High	High	Low
General		Rectangular, "U," and "V" corrugations are available. Internal bracing easy to apply. Corrugations provide recesses for handles, etc.	Semicritical. Limited production.	Same as sheet aluminum.	Weatherproof plywood required. Difficult to provide security. High difference between in and out cube.

Fig. 47. Container materials and their general characteristics.

FUNCTIONAL REQUIREMENTS. In general, designs for general cargo containers must be such as to withstand the stresses and strains imposed by the roll and pitch of vessels at sea, the rough handling they will receive at docks, piers, or freight terminals, the shock and vibrations of rail transport—including the humping of cars, and the tension and compression loads imposed by lifting and tiering. Structurally, containers should be designed with a **safety factor** of 4 to 1 (yield) to compensate for dynamic loadings such as imposed sudden accelerations and decelerations in shiploading operations.

Elements in Structural Design. Specifically, structural design must consider the following elements:

1. **Terminal handling devices.** For handling by overhead crane, a standard, simple means of attaching the slings or chains of the hoisting gear must be provided as a permanent part of the unit. The attachments should be located at the top corners wtih openings of not less than 2 in. in diam. and they should be designed to withstand, without permanent deformation, strains due to an angle of 45° between the lifting cables hooked to the four corners, and the horizontal. For handling by lift truck or fork truck, legs or skids with appropriate openings should be provided at the base of the unit. Skids should be placed at the outer sides of the unit (parallel to the long axis of the unit) approximately 4 to 6 in. from the ends.

2. **Tiering and nesting.** In many operations of storage and shiploading, it becomes necessary to tier containers two or more high. To facilitate these operations, the provisions made for lifting should be combined with self-nesting features to eliminate or minimize the need for dunnage and blocking. By this means, the weights of superimposed loads are carried by vertical frame members to the base and skid sections.

3. **Understowage.** When understowed on shipboard, loads of 100 lb. per sq. ft. of roof area, concentrated, can be anticipated. When tiered, or when dunnaged over (distributed load), 400 lb. per sq. ft. of roof area, distributed to vertical members, is the average weight carried.

4. **Light weight.** Many of the transportation charges encountered are on the basis of gross weight, therefore the tare weight of the container must be as small as possible consistent with its use and the materials of which it is constructed. Full advantage must be taken of shaped, pressed, or formed sheet-stock for frame and load-carrying members. The ratio of tare to net weight averages 5.5 lb. per cu. ft. for general cargo containers and 21 lb. per cu. ft. for bulk cargo. Since the container provides the mechanical protection, thus eliminating the need for over-packing of commodities, the allowable tare weight of the container should not exceed the weight of the packing and crating material thus eliminated.

5. **Security.** Since much of the otherwise extensive packing and crating is normally eliminated in container shipments, it is imperative that adequate security provisions be made. These are best accomplished by using concealed-type or nonremovable pin-type door hinges. Locking must be positive, with the opening of either the right- or the left-hand door contingent on the prior opening of the other. Padlocks, combination locks or other types of locks may be used. If twisted wire or numbered wire seals are used, a slot of not less than 7/16 in. must be provided. All security devices are designed to deter the pilferer, and to simplify detection of tampering.

6. **Weather protection.** Protection from the weather must be an inherent feature of the container. Continuous welding at joints, sealing with waterproofing compounds, and provision of run-offs at low points, are general practices. Doors

are the most likely places for moisture to gain access. Gasketing is one method of waterproofing doors. Gaskets, however, should be used with caution because tight fittings tend to cause permanent damage to the doors or the container if deformation or distortion has occurred. A better method of waterproofing doors is the use of labyrinthed framing around doors, with runoff holes at the bottom. This method allows limited distortion of the container to occur without damage to doors.

7. **Condensation.** Temperature differentials encountered in the movement of cargo can cause severe conditions of condensation within the container, with resulting damage to the contents. The design of the unit must be such as to provide maximum ventilation of the contents while maintaining protection against the weather. Ventilating arrangements must also prevent the entrance of vermin and free water. Unless the structure of the container itself assures adequate ventilation, appliances must be provided for this purpose.

8. **Doors.** Doors should be provided at one end of the container, or at both ends if the container is large. These doors may be of the single or the double type, the latter being preferable. They should open to the widest possible extent. To facilitate loading and unloading, door openings should be kept clear and unobstructed with no step-up, step-down, or step-over at the threshold.

9. **Bulkheading, Interior Blocking, and Bracing.** Normally, re-usable containers are block-loaded to their maximum interior capacity with cargo consigned to a single destination. In these instances, little or no extra interior blocking is required. Delicate or fragile items, requiring protection from shock which may be transmitted through sides or ends, can be protected by use of conventional

Washington Quartermaster Depot

Fig. 48. Transporter with partial load secured by bulkhead.

cushioning materials and practices. Free spaces, particularly longitudinal and horizontal voids, must be filled with cushioning materials to prevent excessive shifting of cargo within the unit. When it becomes necessary or desirable to partition sections of the interior, the following procedures can be applied: For **smooth-walled interiors,** a wood-frame-type bulkhead, sized to the interior width and length dimensions minus ½ in., may be positioned at the desired location and locked in place with wood wedges inserted between the sides and roof and the bulkhead. For **corrugated-type containers,** bulkheading may be accomplished by use of wood planks, 1 in. × 6 or 8 in. nominal size, cut to a length approximately equal to the interior width of the container (inside corrugations). These bulkheads are wedged from side to side against the corrugations. Where found necessary, additional vertical members, wedged between floor and roof, can be nailed to the cross bulkheads, as shown in Fig. 48.

INDEX

(Boldface numbers, followed by a dot, refer to sections; lightface numbers following are the pages of the section.)

1

Industrial Trucks (*Continued*)
Flat stock handled by, **12**·19–23
For handling pieces and unit loads, **18**·34
Fork trucks, **40**·6–15 (See also "Fork Lift Trucks")
Form for analyzing manufacturers' specifications, **40**·2
Gas-electric power units, **40**·31–32
Hand, **41**·1–25 (See also "Hand Trucks")
Lift trucks
  Inboard pallet, **40**·4–6
  Inboard platform, **40**·4
  Outboard, **40**·6–15
  Pallet lift trucks, **40**·4–6
Powered, **40**·1–32
  Characteristics, **40**·21–24
  Determining aisle width for, **18**·10–11
  Determining storage space for palletized goods stored by, **18**·5–8
  For yard storage, **18**·32
  Fork lift, **40**·17
  High-lift pallet outrigger-type, **40**·17
  High-lift platform, **40**·17, **40**·18
  Low-lift platform, **40**·17, **40**·18
  Maintenance equipment, **18**·15
  Motorized, **40**·15
  Motorized wheelbarrows, **40**·16
  Pallet low-lift, **40**·17
  Selection of, **40**·1
  Special industrial, **40**·17
  Steering, **40**·23–24
  Straddle carrier, **40**·11, **40**·12
  Test for operators, **9**·35–37
  Tires, **40**·21
  Transmissions, **40**·22–23
  Underwriters' ratings, **40**·21–22
  Used to position work, **39**·3
  Walkie trucks, **40**·15–20
Rider-type trucks, **40**·1–15
Industrial Vehicles
Agricultural vehicles and attachments, **1**·11
Bulk materials handling equipment, **1**·11
Classification of, **1**·10–11
Hand trucks, **1**·10 (See also "Hand Trucks")
Industrial cars, **1**·10–11
Industrial tractors and locomotives, **1**·11
Industrial trailers, **1**·10
Powered-industrial trucks, **1**·10
Special military vehicles, **1**·11
Special vehicles and attachments, **1**·11
Industries
Materials handling applied to, **1**·3–4
  Processing, **1**·4
Uses of containers in, **15**·1–16
Inertia Forces, Belt conveyors, **23**·31–37
Ingots
Ingot-casting conveyor, **25**·7
Ingot-mold tongs, **38**·8–9
Marine cargo loading of, **21**·17
Insect Infestation, Protective packaging to prevent, **16**·20
Inspection, **3**·11
Checking packaging materials against general specifications, **16**·9
Containers, **15**·14–16
Fiberboard corrugated, **16**·6–8
Damaged cargo, **21**·14
Department, **7**·17
  Adjustments with vendors, **7**·17
  Methods, **7**·17
Electronic beverage-inspection device on bottle turret conveyor, **5**·14
Gaging and sorting mechanisms, **5**·13–14

Installation
Live-roll package conveyors, **31**·20
Materials handling equipment, **31**·18–20
Insulating Materials, Used in packaging, **16**·19–20
Insulation
Boxcars, **44**·4
For van-type truck bodies, **43**·9–10
Truck-trailers, **43**·21
Integrated Materials Handling, 4·10
Interceptors, Pneumatic conveyors, **30**·21–22
Intercommunication Systems, 7·12, **8**·3–8 (See also "Communication Systems")
Advantages of, **8**·7
Truck terminals, **19**·19–20
Uses of, **8**·6
Interlocks
High-pressure pneumatic conveyors, **30**·24
Safety device used on elevators, **36**·22
Interplant Shipments
Break-even charts, expendable pallets, **17**·24–25
Break-even point
  Lightweight metal pallets, **17**·22
  Using standard wooden pallets, **17**·19, **17**·21
Cost of lightweight metal pallets for, **17**·22–23
Cost of palletized loads, **17**·18–19
Cost of using wooden pallets, **17**·20–21
Inventories
Control
  Containers designed to assist in stock and, **47**·19–20
  Production control and, **7**·10
Determining storage space requirements, **18**·1, **18**·5
  Finished goods, **18**·1–3
  In-process goods, **18**·3
  Plant supplies, **18**·4–5
  Raw materials and packing materials, **18**·3–4
  Usage rates, **18**·3–4, **18**·5
Materials handling influence on plant, **4**·4
Recording and transcribing equipment for taking, **8**·13–14
  Method of procedure, **8**·13
Reducing time for, **6**·28
Type of container can simplify taking of, **15**·9
Iron
Cast-iron borings, transported by pneumatic conveyors, **30**·17–18
Packaging paper to inhibit corrosion, **6**·33
VCI papers for protective packaging, **16**·19
Iron and Steel Scrap, 14·1, **14**·10–13
Basic grades, **14**·10–12
Briquetting installations, **14**·23
Chip handling installations, **14**·20–28 (See also "Chip Handling Installations")
Disposal of, **14**·2
Electric furnace and foundry grades, **14**·12–13
Materials handling equipment, **14**·20
Stainless steel scrap, **14**·12
"Iron-Hand" Mechanized Grab Device, 5·12–13
Iron Ore
Blending procedures, **11**·5
Gantry bridges used in handling, **10**·15–16
Hopper cars carry, **44**·8
Marine terminal handling, **21**·21–23
Ore pockets for storing, **10**·4
Transported by conveyor belt, **21**·23
Trunk-line stocking-out conveyor and traveling gantry bridge, **10**·12

J

Jacks, Self-locking lift jack for platform trucks, **41**·14

Slat Conveyors, 25·13–16
Applications, 25·13
Chain attachments 25·15–16
Conveyor width, 25·14
Definition, 25·13
Maximum length between centers, 25·14
Ramp conveyor, 25·14
Selection of components, 25·16
Slats, 25·14–15
Special fixtures, 25·14
Typical construction, 25·16
Used in sugar mills, 25·7–8
Slider-Belt Conveyors, For packages, 31·1–2
Slides
For conveying packages, 31·16–17
For handling box shapes, 12·1
Slings
Canvas, 21·16
Choker slings used to handle sugar, 21·24
Manila or wire-rope, 21·16
Marine terminal handling, 21·16, 21·17
Platform, for handling bags and sacks, 12·32–33
Simple, 38·2
Used in handling long stock, 12·16
Slips, Marine terminals, 21·4
Small Craft, Classification of, 1·14
Snub Rolls, Live-roll conveyors, 31·20
Snubbed Load Method, Of loading rail cars, 20·43
Snubbing Drum (See "Capstans")
Solid Materials
Characteristics of, 3·3–5
Flow-resistant solids, 10·21
Forms of, 3·4
Free-flowing, 10·20–21
Handling and storage of bulk, 10·1–21 (See also "Bulk Handling and Storage")
Solvents, Salvage value of, 14·8
Sorting Shipments, 20·2–3 (See also "Assorting Methods")
Mechanisms, 5·13–14
Space-Control, Two-way radio for, 8·10
Spaced-Bucket Centrifugal-Discharge Elevators, 24·1–3
Spans, For track of trolley conveyors, 26·11
Spear Pins, To protect against overloads, 24·38
Special-Order Plant
Analysis of materials handling problems, 13·39–45
Evaluating the data, 13·41–45
Finding out what is needed, 13·40
Gathering the necessary data, 13·40–41
Assembly chart, 13·42–43
Basic principles of materials handling, 13·32–34
Definition of, 13·31–32
Economic analysis of alternative materials handling equipment, 13·46
Integrated materials handling system recommended, 13·33
Major factors in materials handling operations, 13·34–35
Operation process chart, 13·43–45
Plant layout, 13·45
Reporting findings to plant executives, 13·46–47
Selecting materials handling equipment, 13·32–33
Staff vs. individual management, 13·35–39
Work-flow analysis, 13·45
Speed, Movement of Materials, 3·12
Determining average rate of, 4·25
Multiple-speed transmissions, 37·9
Of belt conveyors, 23·22

Speed, Movement of Materials (*Continued*)
Speed load curves, for analysis of crane control mechanisms, 34·21, 34·22
Synchronism, 3·12
Speedpaks, For cargo airplanes, 22·30–32
Spiral Chutes
For bins, 10·3
Grades for, 31·17
Used to lower packages, 31·17–18
Splicing Belts, 23·5–6, 24·13
Sponson, To hold cargo being unloaded, 21·6
Spotting Trucks and Railroad Cars
Car-spot utilization chart, 20·28
Dumpers, 39·20
Railway freight terminals, 20·27–28 (See also "Railroad Terminal Handling")
Truck terminals handling, 19·21–22
Sprockets
Conventional style, 25·34
Drives, trolley conveyors, 26·18–19
Selecting size and style, 25·34
Shear, on trolley conveyors, 26·22
Wildcat, 37·1
Stackers, 23·14
Booms for, 10·12–14
Flat-belt conveyors, 32·7–8
For handling box shapes, 12·3
Luffing booms, 10·12–13
Radial conveyor, 10·13–14
For handling bulk materials, 18·33
Revolving, 10·13–14, 10·18
Single- and double-boom, 10·12–13
Traveling, 10·11
Used for stockpiling, 10·12–15
Stacking
And nesting containers, 47·20, 47·21
Clear stacking height in warehouses, 18·12
Oil drums, 6·38
Stacks
Pallets, 18·6–8
Right-angle stacking into storage from the aisle, 18·11
Truck terminal handling, 19·2
Yard storage, 18·27, 18·32
Stairs, For passing traffic through belt-conveyor lines, 31·9
Stake Truck Bodies, 43·6, 43·8
Maintenance, 43·27
Platform truck-trailers, 43·22
Standards
Application in analysis, 2·61–75
Evaluation of average pallet travel, 2·65–68
Plant layout, 2·61–64
Comparison of standard time data with conventional time study, 2·74–75
Development of basic time data, 2·61
Evaluation of variables, 2·68–75
Manual, 2·58–61
Methods-Time Measurement, 2·58–61
Standard deviation scale, 11·10
Standard time data for 21 basic fork truck motions, 2·61–64
Using predetermined standards in analysis, 2·58–75
Statistical Analysis
Accuracy measurement, 11·38
Queuing or "waiting-line" theory, 2·75
Sampling techniques, 2·75
Steam, Multiple-drum winches, 37·7
Steam-Pneumatic Ash Conveyors, 30·24–36
Additional equipment, 30·26
Air washers, 30·25, 30·26
Ash hoppers, 30·31–32

LIST OF SECTIONS

Alphabetical